Diesel Engine Service Guide

by Christopher Rogers

The Haynes Manual for servicing the Diesel engines fitted to: *(3286 - 360)*

Austin/Rover, Citroën, Fiat, Ford, Land Rover, Mercedes-Benz,

Peugeot, Renault, Vauxhall/Opel and Volkswagen cars and light vans

ABCDE
FGHIJ
KLMN

Printed in the USA

A book in the **Haynes Service and Repair Manual Series**

ISBN 1 85960 286 X

British Library Cataloguing in Publication Data
A catalogue record for this book is available from the British Library

Haynes Publishing
Sparkford, Nr Yeovil, Somerset BA22 7JJ, England

Haynes North America, Inc
861 Lawrence Drive, Newbury Park, California 91320, USA

Editions Haynes S.A.
Tour Aurore - IBC, 18 Place des Reflets,
92975 Paris La Défense 2, Cedex, France

Haynes Publishing Nordiska AB
Box 1504, 751 45 Uppsala, Sverige

Contents

Introduction

Chapter 1 The Diesel engine

Chapter 2 Austin/Rover engines

Chapter 3 Citroën engines

Chapter 4 Fiat engines

Contents

Contents

The aim of this Manual is to provide the experienced technician with all the information needed to service the most popular types of Diesel engines, in particular the Routine Maintenance tasks specified by each vehicle manufacturer and all information needed to service the fuel system components attached to each engine.

It is assumed that the technician is fully conversant with the maintenance of petrol engines and is able to apply that knowledge to the Diesel engine when renewing components which are common to both engine types, for example, the cylinder head, crankshaft, etc.

The following list provides a guide to the engine types covered in this Manual and their vehicle application. For more detailed information, such as the Manufacturer's engine codes, refer to the Specifications Section at the beginning of Part A of each Chapter.

Vehicle type	***Year***	***Engine capacity***
Austin/Rover Maestro and Montego	1986 to 1993	1994cc
Citroën AX	1987 to 1994	1360cc and 1527cc
Citroën BX/Visa/C15	1984 to 1996	1769cc and 1905cc
Citroën ZX	1991 to 1993	1769cc and 1905cc
Citroën Xantia	1993 to 1995	1905cc
Fiat Punto	1994 to 1996	1698cc
Ford Fiesta, Escort, Orion	1984 to 1996	1608cc
Ford Fiesta, Escort, Orion and Mondeo	1984 to 1996	1753cc
Ford Transit	1986 to 1995	2496cc
Land Rover Series IIA & III, 90, 110 and Defender	1958 to 1995	2286cc
Land Rover Discovery, 90, 110 and Defender	1983 to 1995	2495cc
Mercedes-Benz 200D 123 Series	1976 to 1985	1988cc
Mercedes-Benz 200 124 Series	1985 to 1993	1997cc
Mercedes-Benz 240D & TD 123 Series	1976 to 1985	2399cc
Mercedes-Benz 240D 123 Series	1976 to 1985	2404cc
Mercedes-Benz 250 124 Series	1985 to 1993	2497cc
Mercedes-Benz 300 124 Series	1985 to 1993	2996cc
Mercedes-Benz 300D & TD 123 Series	1976 to 1985	2998cc
Peugeot 106	1991 to 1996	1360cc and 1527cc
Peugeot 205, 305, 306, 309, 405	1982 to 1996	1769cc
Peugeot 305, 306, 309, 405	1982 to 1996	1905cc
Renault Clio and 19	1989 to 1996	1870cc
Renault Espace	1985 to 1996	2068cc
Renault Laguna	1994 to 1996	2188cc
Vauxhall/Opel Nova, Corsa and Combi van	1982 to 1996	1488cc
Vauxhall/Opel Astra, Belmont, Cavalier and Bedford equivalents	1982 to 1996	1598cc
Vauxhall/Opel Astra and Cavalier	1982 to 1996	1686cc
Vauxhall/Opel Astra, Belmont and Cavalier	1982 to 1996	1699cc
Volkswagen Golf and Vento	1992 to 1996	1896cc

Buying spare parts

Only buy spare parts supplied by the engine manufacturer or equivalent quality parts of reputable make. "Pirate" parts, often of unknown origin, may not meet the manufacturer's standards either dimensionally or in material quality.

Large items or sub-assemblies (eg. cylinder heads, starter motors, injection pumps) may be available on an "exchange" basis. Consult a dealer for availability and conditions. Dismantled or badly damaged units may not be accepted in exchange.

When buying engine parts, be prepared to quote the engine number. This is stamped into the engine block, its exact position depending on engine type.

Working on your car can be dangerous. This page shows just some of the potential risks and hazards, with the aim of creating a safety-conscious attitude.

General hazards

Scalding

- Don't remove the radiator or expansion tank cap while the engine is hot.
- Engine oil, automatic transmission fluid or power steering fluid may also be dangerously hot if the engine has recently been running.

Burning

- Beware of burns from the exhaust system and from any part of the engine. Brake discs and drums can also be extremely hot immediately after use.

Crushing

- When working under or near a raised vehicle, always supplement the jack with axle stands, or use drive-on ramps. ***Never venture under a car which is only supported by a jack.***

- Take care if loosening or tightening high-torque nuts when the vehicle is on stands. Initial loosening and final tightening should be done with the wheels on the ground.

Fire

- Fuel is highly flammable; fuel vapour is explosive.
- Don't let fuel spill onto a hot engine.
- Do not smoke or allow naked lights (including pilot lights) anywhere near a vehicle being worked on. Also beware of creating sparks (electrically or by use of tools).
- Fuel vapour is heavier than air, so don't work on the fuel system with the vehicle over an inspection pit.
- Another cause of fire is an electrical overload or short-circuit. Take care when repairing or modifying the vehicle wiring.
- Keep a fire extinguisher handy, of a type suitable for use on fuel and electrical fires.

Electric shock

- Ignition HT voltage can be dangerous, especially to people with heart problems or a pacemaker. Don't work on or near the ignition system with the engine running or the ignition switched on.

- Mains voltage is also dangerous. Make sure that any mains-operated equipment is correctly earthed. Mains power points should be protected by a residual current device (RCD) circuit breaker.

Fume or gas intoxication

- Exhaust fumes are poisonous; they often contain carbon monoxide, which is rapidly fatal if inhaled. Never run the engine in a confined space such as a garage with the doors shut.

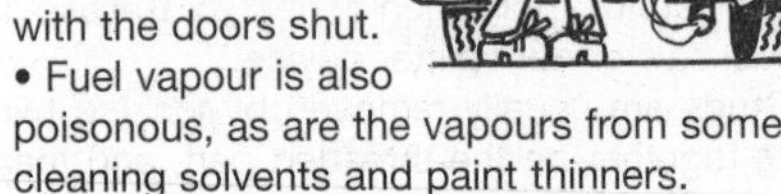

- Fuel vapour is also poisonous, as are the vapours from some cleaning solvents and paint thinners.

Poisonous or irritant substances

- Avoid skin contact with battery acid and with any fuel, fluid or lubricant, especially antifreeze, brake hydraulic fluid and Diesel fuel. Don't syphon them by mouth. If such a substance is swallowed or gets into the eyes, seek medical advice.
- Prolonged contact with used engine oil can cause skin cancer. Wear gloves or use a barrier cream if necessary. Change out of oil-soaked clothes and do not keep oily rags in your pocket.
- Air conditioning refrigerant forms a poisonous gas if exposed to a naked flame (including a cigarette). It can also cause skin burns on contact.

Asbestos

- Asbestos dust can cause cancer if inhaled or swallowed. Asbestos may be found in gaskets and in brake and clutch linings. When dealing with such components it is safest to assume that they contain asbestos.

Special hazards

Hydrofluoric acid

- This extremely corrosive acid is formed when certain types of synthetic rubber, found in some O-rings, oil seals, fuel hoses etc, are exposed to temperatures above 400°C. The rubber changes into a charred or sticky substance containing the acid. *Once formed, the acid remains dangerous for years. If it gets onto the skin, it may be necessary to amputate the limb concerned.*
- When dealing with a vehicle which has suffered a fire, or with components salvaged from such a vehicle, wear protective gloves and discard them after use.

The battery

- Batteries contain sulphuric acid, which attacks clothing, eyes and skin. Take care when topping-up or carrying the battery.
- The hydrogen gas given off by the battery is highly explosive. Never cause a spark or allow a naked light nearby. Be careful when connecting and disconnecting battery chargers or jump leads.

Air bags

- Air bags can cause injury if they go off accidentally. Take care when removing the steering wheel and/or facia. Special storage instructions may apply.

Diesel injection equipment

- Diesel injection pumps supply fuel at very high pressure. Take care when working on the fuel injectors and fuel pipes.

Warning: Never expose the hands, face or any other part of the body to injector spray; the fuel can penetrate the skin with potentially fatal results.

Remember...

DO

- Do use eye protection when using power tools, and when working under the vehicle.
- Do wear gloves or use barrier cream to protect your hands when necessary.
- Do get someone to check periodically that all is well when working alone on the vehicle.
- Do keep loose clothing and long hair well out of the way of moving mechanical parts.
- Do remove rings, wristwatch etc, before working on the vehicle – especially the electrical system.
- Do ensure that any lifting or jacking equipment has a safe working load rating adequate for the job.

DON'T

- Don't attempt to lift a heavy component which may be beyond your capability – get assistance.
- Don't rush to finish a job, or take unverified short cuts.
- Don't use ill-fitting tools which may slip and cause injury.
- Don't leave tools or parts lying around where someone can trip over them. Mop up oil and fuel spills at once.
- Don't allow children or pets to play in or near a vehicle being worked on.

Whenever servicing, repair or overhaul work is carried out on the car or its components, observe the following procedures and instructions. This will assist in carrying out the operation efficiently and to a professional standard of workmanship.

Joint mating faces and gaskets

When separating components at their mating faces, never insert screwdrivers or similar implements into the joint between the faces in order to prise them apart. This can cause severe damage which results in oil leaks, coolant leaks, etc upon reassembly. Separation is usually achieved by tapping along the joint with a soft-faced hammer in order to break the seal. However, note that this method may not be suitable where dowels are used for component location.

Where a gasket is used between the mating faces of two components, a new one must be fitted on reassembly; fit it dry unless otherwise stated in the repair procedure. Make sure that the mating faces are clean and dry, with all traces of old gasket removed. When cleaning a joint face, use a tool which is unlikely to score or damage the face, and remove any burrs or nicks with an oilstone or fine file.

Make sure that tapped holes are cleaned with a pipe cleaner, and keep them free of jointing compound, if this is being used, unless specifically instructed otherwise.

Ensure that all orifices, channels or pipes are clear, and blow through them, preferably using compressed air.

Oil seals

Oil seals can be removed by levering them out with a wide flat-bladed screwdriver or similar implement. Alternatively, a number of self-tapping screws may be screwed into the seal, and these used as a purchase for pliers or some similar device in order to pull the seal free.

Whenever an oil seal is removed from its working location, either individually or as part of an assembly, it should be renewed.

The very fine sealing lip of the seal is easily damaged, and will not seal if the surface it contacts is not completely clean and free from scratches, nicks or grooves. If the original sealing surface of the component cannot be restored, and the manufacturer has not made provision for slight relocation of the seal relative to the sealing surface, the component should be renewed.

Protect the lips of the seal from any surface which may damage them in the course of fitting. Use tape or a conical sleeve where possible. Lubricate the seal lips with oil before fitting and, on dual-lipped seals, fill the space between the lips with grease.

Unless otherwise stated, oil seals must be fitted with their sealing lips toward the lubricant to be sealed.

Use a tubular drift or block of wood of the appropriate size to install the seal and, if the seal housing is shouldered, drive the seal down to the shoulder. If the seal housing is unshouldered, the seal should be fitted with its face flush with the housing top face (unless otherwise instructed).

Screw threads and fastenings

Seized nuts, bolts and screws are quite a common occurrence where corrosion has set in, and the use of penetrating oil or releasing fluid will often overcome this problem if the offending item is soaked for a while before attempting to release it. The use of an impact driver may also provide a means of releasing such stubborn fastening devices, when used in conjunction with the appropriate screwdriver bit or socket. If none of these methods works, it may be necessary to resort to the careful application of heat, or the use of a hacksaw or nut splitter device.

Studs are usually removed by locking two nuts together on the threaded part, and then using a spanner on the lower nut to unscrew the stud. Studs or bolts which have broken off below the surface of the component in which they are mounted can sometimes be removed using a stud extractor. Always ensure that a blind tapped hole is completely free from oil, grease, water or other fluid before installing the bolt or stud. Failure to do this could cause the housing to crack due to the hydraulic action of the bolt or stud as it is screwed in.

When tightening a castellated nut to accept a split pin, tighten the nut to the specified torque, where applicable, and then tighten further to the next split pin hole. Never slacken the nut to align the split pin hole, unless stated in the repair procedure.

When checking or retightening a nut or bolt to a specified torque setting, slacken the nut or bolt by a quarter of a turn, and then retighten to the specified setting. However, this should not be attempted where angular tightening has been used.

For some screw fastenings, notably cylinder head bolts or nuts, torque wrench settings are no longer specified for the latter stages of tightening, "angle-tightening" being called up instead. Typically, a fairly low torque wrench setting will be applied to the bolts/nuts in the correct sequence, followed by one or more stages of tightening through specified angles.

Locknuts, locktabs and washers

Any fastening which will rotate against a component or housing during tightening should always have a washer between it and the relevant component or housing.

Spring or split washers should always be renewed when they are used to lock a critical component such as a big-end bearing retaining bolt or nut. Locktabs which are folded over to retain a nut or bolt should always be renewed.

Self-locking nuts can be re-used in non-critical areas, providing resistance can be felt when the locking portion passes over the bolt or stud thread. However, it should be noted that self-locking stiffnuts tend to lose their effectiveness after long periods of use, and should then be renewed as a matter of course.

Split pins must always be replaced with new ones of the correct size for the hole.

When thread-locking compound is found on the threads of a fastener which is to be re-used, it should be cleaned off with a wire brush and solvent, and fresh compound applied on reassembly.

Special tools

Some repair procedures in this manual entail the use of special tools such as a press, two or three-legged pullers, spring compressors, etc. Wherever possible, suitable readily-available alternatives to the manufacturer's special tools are described, and are shown in use. In some instances, where no alternative is possible, it has been necessary to resort to the use of a manufacturer's tool, and this has been done for reasons of safety as well as the efficient completion of the repair operation. Unless you are highly-skilled and have a thorough understanding of the procedures described, never attempt to bypass the use of any special tool when the procedure described specifies its use. Not only is there a very great risk of personal injury, but expensive damage could be caused to the components involved.

Environmental considerations

When disposing of used engine oil, brake fluid, antifreeze, etc, give due consideration to any detrimental environmental effects. Do not, for instance, pour any of the above liquids down drains into the general sewage system, or onto the ground to soak away. Many local council refuse tips provide a facility for waste oil disposal, as do some garages. If none of these facilities are available, consult your local Environmental Health Department, or the National Rivers Authority, for further advice.

With the universal tightening-up of legislation regarding the emission of environmentally-harmful substances from motor vehicles, most vehicles have tamperproof devices fitted to the main adjustment points of the fuel system. These devices are primarily designed to prevent unqualified persons from adjusting the fuel/air mixture, with the chance of a consequent increase in toxic emissions. If such devices are found during servicing or overhaul, they should, wherever possible, be renewed or refitted in accordance with the manufacturer's requirements or current legislation.

Note: It is antisocial and illegal to dump oil down the drain. To find the location of your local oil recycling bank, call this number free.

Conversion factors

Length (distance)

Inches (in)	x 25.4	= Millimetres (mm)	x 0.0394	= Inches (in)
Feet (ft)	x 0.305	= Metres (m)	x 3.281	= Feet (ft)
Miles	x 1.609	= Kilometres (km)	x 0.621	= Miles

Volume (capacity)

Cubic inches (cu in; in^3)	x 16.387	= Cubic centimetres (cc; cm^3)	x 0.061	= Cubic inches (cu in; in^3)
Imperial pints (Imp pt)	x 0.568	= Litres (l)	x 1.76	= Imperial pints (Imp pt)
Imperial quarts (Imp qt)	x 1.137	= Litres (l)	x 0.88	= Imperial quarts (Imp qt)
Imperial quarts (Imp qt)	x 1.201	= US quarts (US qt)	x 0.833	= Imperial quarts (Imp qt)
US quarts (US qt)	x 0.946	= Litres (l)	x 1.057	= US quarts (US qt)
Imperial gallons (Imp gal)	x 4.546	= Litres (l)	x 0.22	= Imperial gallons (Imp gal)
Imperial gallons (Imp gal)	x 1.201	= US gallons (US gal)	x 0.833	= Imperial gallons (Imp gal)
US gallons (US gal)	x 3.785	= Litres (l)	x 0.264	= US gallons (US gal)

Mass (weight)

Ounces (oz)	x 28.35	= Grams (g)	x 0.035	= Ounces (oz)
Pounds (lb)	x 0.454	= Kilograms (kg)	x 2.205	= Pounds (lb)

Force

Ounces-force (ozf; oz)	x 0.278	= Newtons (N)	x 3.6	= Ounces-force (ozf; oz)
Pounds-force (lbf; lb)	x 4.448	= Newtons (N)	x 0.225	= Pounds-force (lbf; lb)
Newtons (N)	x 0.1	= Kilograms-force (kgf; kg)	x 9.81	= Newtons (N)

Pressure

Pounds-force per square inch (psi; lbf/in^2; lb/in^2)	x 0.070	= Kilograms-force per square centimetre (kgf/cm^2; kg/cm^2)	x 14.223	= Pounds-force per square inch (psi; lbf/in^2; lb/in^2)
Pounds-force per square inch (psi; lbf/in^2; lb/in^2)	x 0.068	= Atmospheres (atm)	x 14.696	= Pounds-force per square inch (psi; lbf/in^2; lb/in^2)
Pounds-force per square inch (psi; lbf/in^2; lb/in^2)	x 0.069	= Bars	x 14.5	= Pounds-force per square inch (psi; lbf/in^2; lb/in^2)
Pounds-force per square inch (psi; lbf/in^2; lb/in^2)	x 6.895	= Kilopascals (kPa)	x 0.145	= Pounds-force per square inch (psi; lbf/in^2; lb/in^2)
Kilopascals (kPa)	x 0.01	= Kilograms-force per square centimetre (kgf/cm^2; kg/cm^2)	x 98.1	= Kilopascals (kPa)
Millibar (mbar)	x 100	= Pascals (Pa)	x 0.01	= Millibar (mbar)
Millibar (mbar)	x 0.0145	= Pounds-force per square inch (psi; lbf/in^2; lb/in^2)	x 68.947	= Millibar (mbar)
Millibar (mbar)	x 0.75	= Millimetres of mercury (mmHg)	x 1.333	= Millibar (mbar)
Millibar (mbar)	x 0.401	= Inches of water (inH_2O)	x 2.491	= Millibar (mbar)
Millimetres of mercury (mmHg)	x 0.535	= Inches of water (inH_2O)	x 1.868	= Millimetres of mercury (mmHg)
Inches of water (inH_2O)	x 0.036	= Pounds-force per square inch (psi; lbf/in^2; lb/in^2)	x 27.68	= Inches of water (inH_2O)

Torque (moment of force)

Pounds-force inches (lbf in; lb in)	x 1.152	= Kilograms-force centimetre (kgf cm; kg cm)	x 0.868	= Pounds-force inches (lbf in; lb in)
Pounds-force inches (lbf in; lb in)	x 0.113	= Newton metres (Nm)	x 8.85	= Pounds-force inches (lbf in; lb in)
Pounds-force inches (lbf in; lb in)	x 0.083	= Pounds-force feet (lbf ft; lb ft)	x 12	= Pounds-force inches (lbf in; lb in)
Pounds-force feet (lbf ft; lb ft)	x 0.138	= Kilograms-force metres (kgf m; kg m)	x 7.233	= Pounds-force feet (lbf ft; lb ft)
Pounds-force feet (lbf ft; lb ft)	x 1.356	= Newton metres (Nm)	x 0.738	= Pounds-force feet (lbf ft; lb ft)
Newton metres (Nm)	x 0.102	= Kilograms-force metres (kgf m; kg m)	x 9.804	= Newton metres (Nm)

Power

Horsepower (hp)	x 745.7	= Watts (W)	x 0.0013	= Horsepower (hp)

Velocity (speed)

Miles per hour (miles/hr; mph)	x 1.609	= Kilometres per hour (km/hr; kph)	x 0.621	= Miles per hour (miles/hr; mph)

Fuel consumption*

Miles per gallon (mpg)	x 0.354	= Kilometres per litre (km/l)	x 2.825	= Miles per gallon (mpg)

Temperature

Degrees Fahrenheit = (°C x 1.8) + 32

Degrees Celsius (Degrees Centigrade; °C) = (°F - 32) x 0.56

** It is common practice to convert from miles per gallon (mpg) to litres/100 kilometres (l/100km), where mpg x l/100 km = 282*

Chapter 1
The Diesel engine

Contents

1 History

Rudolf Diesel invented the first commercially successful compression ignition engine at the end of the 19th century. Compared with the spark ignition engine, the Diesel had the advantages of lower fuel consumption, the ability to use cheaper fuel and the potential for much higher power outputs. Over the following two or three decades, such engines were widely adopted for stationary and marine applications but the fuel injection systems used were not capable of high-speed operation. This speed limitation, and the considerable weight of the air compressor needed to operate the injection equipment, made the first Diesel engines unsuitable for use in road-going vehicles.

In the 1920s the German engineer Robert Bosch developed the in-line injection pump, a device which is still in extensive use today. The use of hydraulic systems to pressurize and inject the fuel did away with the need for a separate air compressor and made possible much higher operating speeds. The so-called high-speed Diesel engine became increasingly popular as a power source for goods and public transport vehicles, but for a number of reasons (including specific power output, flexibility and cheapness of manufacture) the spark ignition engine continued to dominate the passenger car and light commercial market.

In the 1950s and 60s, Diesel engines became increasingly popular for use in taxis and vans, but it was not until the sharp rises in oil prices in the 1970s that serious attention was paid to the small passenger car market.

Subsequent years have seen the growing popularity of the small Diesel engine in cars and light commercial vehicles, not only for reasons of fuel economy and longevity but also for environmental reasons. Every major European car manufacturer now offers at least one Diesel-engined model. The Diesel's penetration of the UK market has been relatively slow, due in part to the lack of the considerable fuel price differential in favour of Diesel which exists in other parts of Europe, but it has now gained widespread acceptance and this trend looks set to continue.

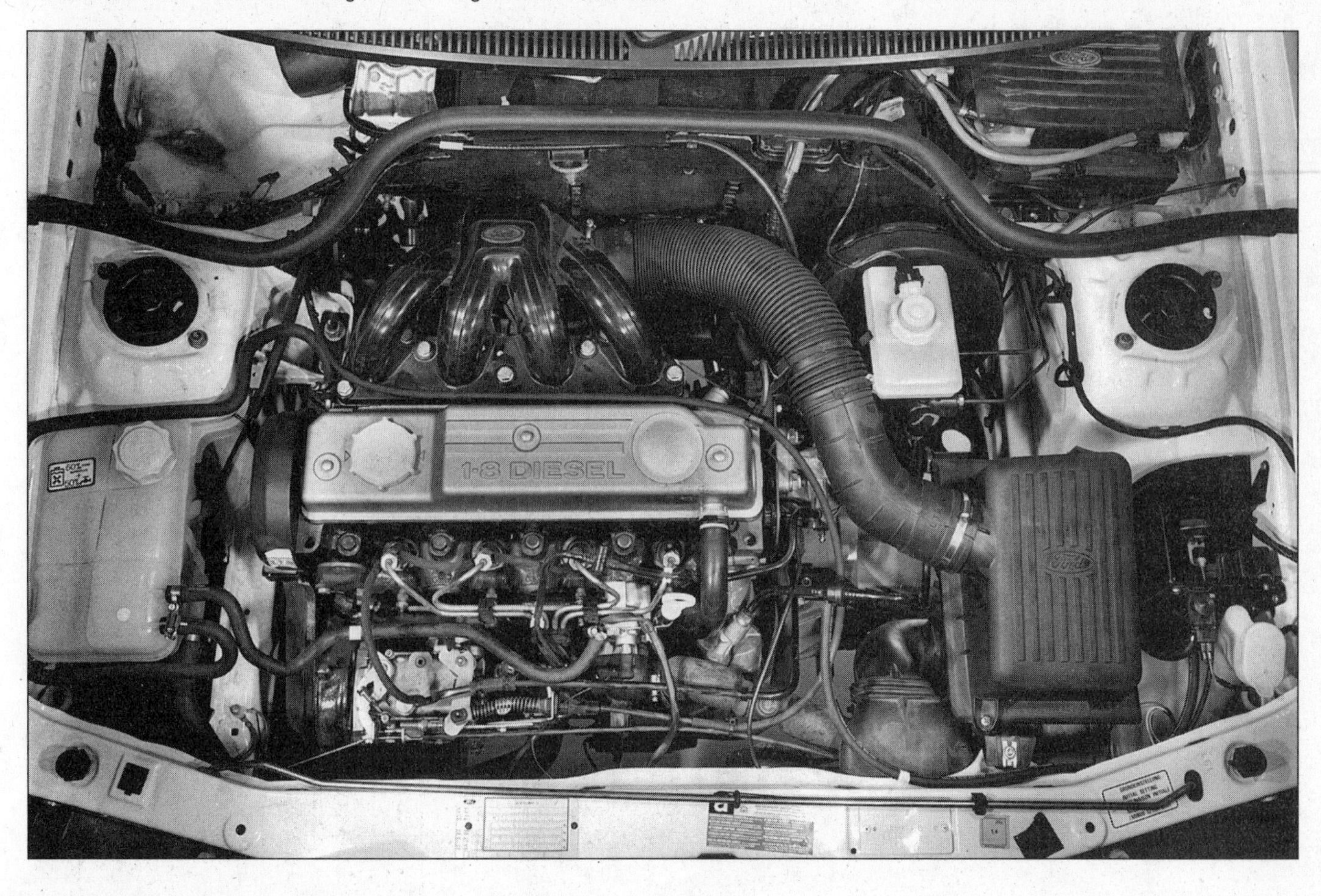

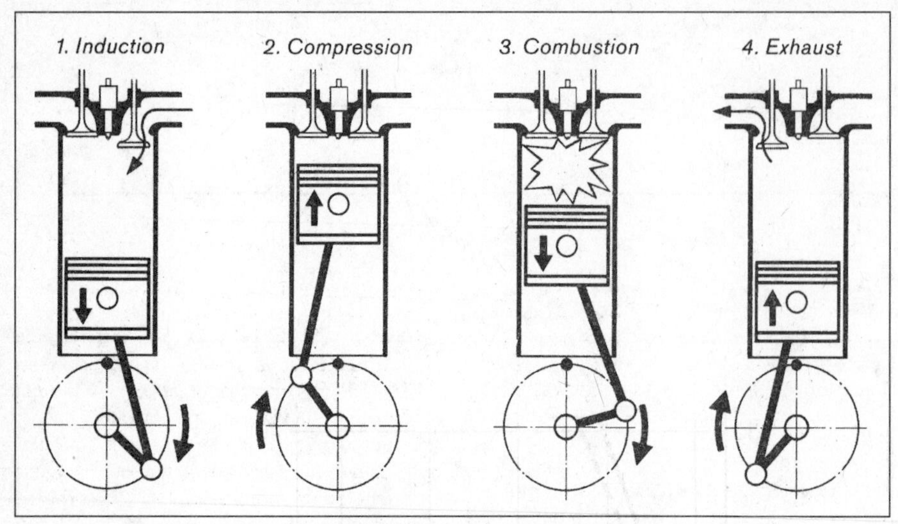

2.1 Four-stroke diesel cycle
© Robert Bosch Limited

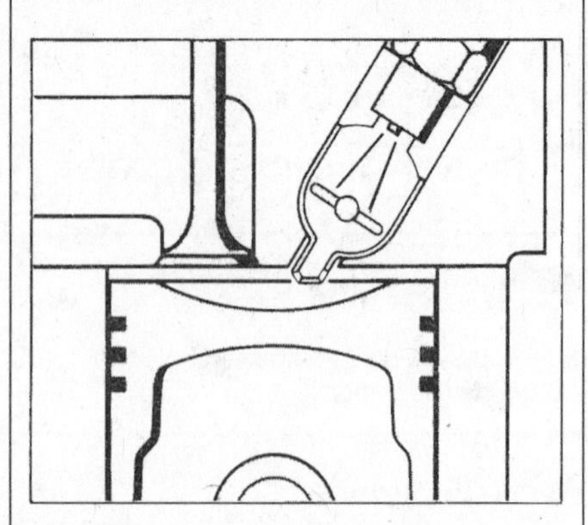

Injection into pre-chamber.

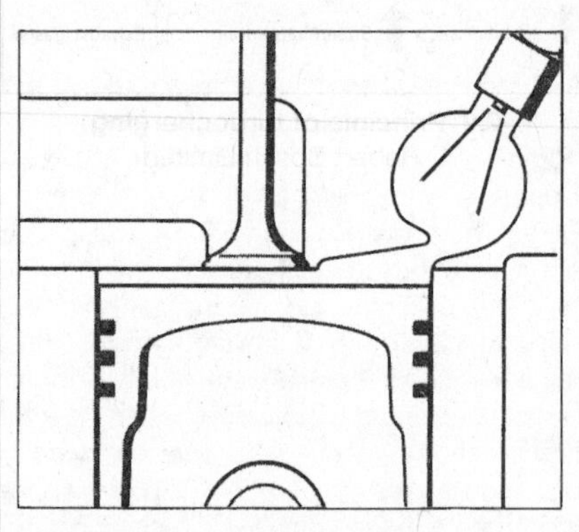

Injection into turbulence chamber.

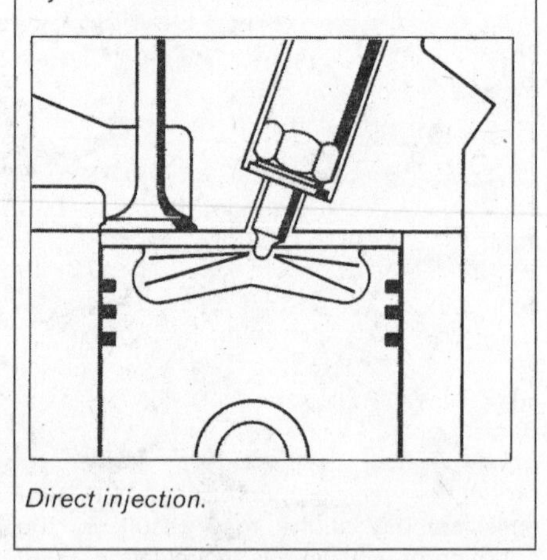

Direct injection.

2.6 Direct and indirect injection
© Robert Bosch Limited

2 Principles of operation

1 All the Diesel engines covered in this book operate on the familiar four-stroke cycle of induction, compression, power and exhaust **(see illustration)**. Two-stroke Diesels do exist, and may in future become important, but they are not used in light vehicles at present. Most have four cylinders, some larger engines have six, and five- and three-cylinder engines also exist.

Induction and ignition

2 The main difference between Diesel and petrol engines is in the means by which the fuel/air mixture is introduced into the cylinder and then ignited. In the petrol engine the fuel is mixed with the incoming air before it enters the cylinder, and the mixture is then ignited at the appropriate moment by a spark plug. At all conditions except full throttle, the throttle butterfly restricts the airflow and cylinder filling is incomplete.

3 In the Diesel engine, air alone is drawn into the cylinder and then compressed. Because of the Diesel's high compression ratio (typically 20 : 1) the air gets very hot when compressed - up to 750°C (1382°F). As the piston approaches the end of the compression stroke, fuel is injected into the combustion chamber under very high pressure in the form of a finely atomised spray. The temperature of the air is high enough to ignite the injected fuel as it mixes with the air. The mixture then burns and provides the energy which drives the piston downwards on the power stroke.

4 When starting the engine from cold, the temperature of the compressed air in the cylinders may not be high enough to ignite the fuel. The preheating system overcomes this problem. The engines in this book have automatically-controlled preheating systems, using electric heater plugs (glow plugs) which heat the air in the combustion chamber just before and during start-up.

5 On most Diesel engines there is no throttle valve in the inlet tract. Exceptions to this are those few engines which use a pneumatic governor, which depends on a manifold depression being created. Even more rarely a throttle valve may be used to create manifold depression for the operation of a brake servo, though it is more usual for a separate vacuum pump to be fitted for this purpose.

Direct and indirect injection

6 In practice, it is difficult to achieve smooth combustion in a small-displacement engine by injecting the fuel directly into the combustion chamber. To get around this problem the technique of indirect injection is widely used. With indirect injection, the fuel is injected into a pre-combustion or swirl chamber in the cylinder head, alongside the main combustion chamber **(see illustration)**.

7 Indirect injection engines are less efficient than direct injection ones and also require more preheating when starting from cold, but these disadvantages are offset by smoother and quieter operation.

Mechanical construction

8 The pistons, crankshaft and bearings of a Diesel engine are generally of more robust construction than in a petrol engine of comparable size, because of the greater loads imposed by the higher compression ratio and the nature of the combustion process. This is one reason for the Diesel engine's longer life. Other reasons include the lubricating qualities of Diesel fuel on the cylinder bores, and the fact that the Diesel engine is generally lower-revving than its petrol counterpart, having much better low-speed torque characteristics and a lower maximum speed.

Turbocharging

9 Turbochargers have long been used on large Diesel engines and are becoming common on small ones. The turbocharger uses the energy of the escaping exhaust gas to drive a turbine which pressurizes the air in the inlet manifold. The air is forced into the cylinders instead of being simply sucked in. If more air is present, more fuel can be burnt and more power developed from the same size engine **(see illustration)**.

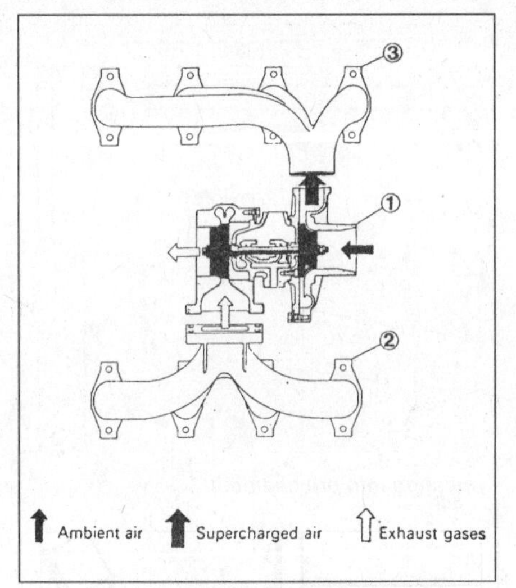

2.9 Principle of turbocharging
© Robert Bosch Limited

1 Turbocharger
2 Exhaust manifold
3 Inlet manifold

10 Greater benefit can be gained from turbocharging if the pressurized air is cooled before it enters the engine. This is done using an air-to-air heat exchanger called an intercooler or charge air cooler (CAC). The cooled air is denser and contains more oxygen in a given volume than warm air straight from the turbocharger **(see illustrations)**.

Exhaust emissions

11 Because combustion in the correctly functioning Diesel engine nearly always occurs in conditions of excess oxygen, there is little or no carbon monoxide (CO) in the exhaust gas. A further environmental benefit is that there is no added lead in Diesel fuel.

12 At the time of writing there is no need for complicated emission control systems on the Diesel engine, though simple catalytic converters are beginning to appear on production vehicles. Increasingly stringent emission regulations may result in the adoption of exhaust gas recirculation (EGR) systems and carbon particle traps **(see illustration)**.

Knock and smoke

13 The image of the Diesel engine for many years was of a noisy, smoky machine, and to some extent this was justified. It is worth examining the causes of knock and smoke, both to see how they have been reduced in modern engines and to understand what causes them to get worse.

14 There is inevitably a small delay (typically 0.001 to 0.002 sec) between the start of fuel injection and the beginning of proper combustion. This delay, known as ignition lag, is greatest when the engine is cold and idling.

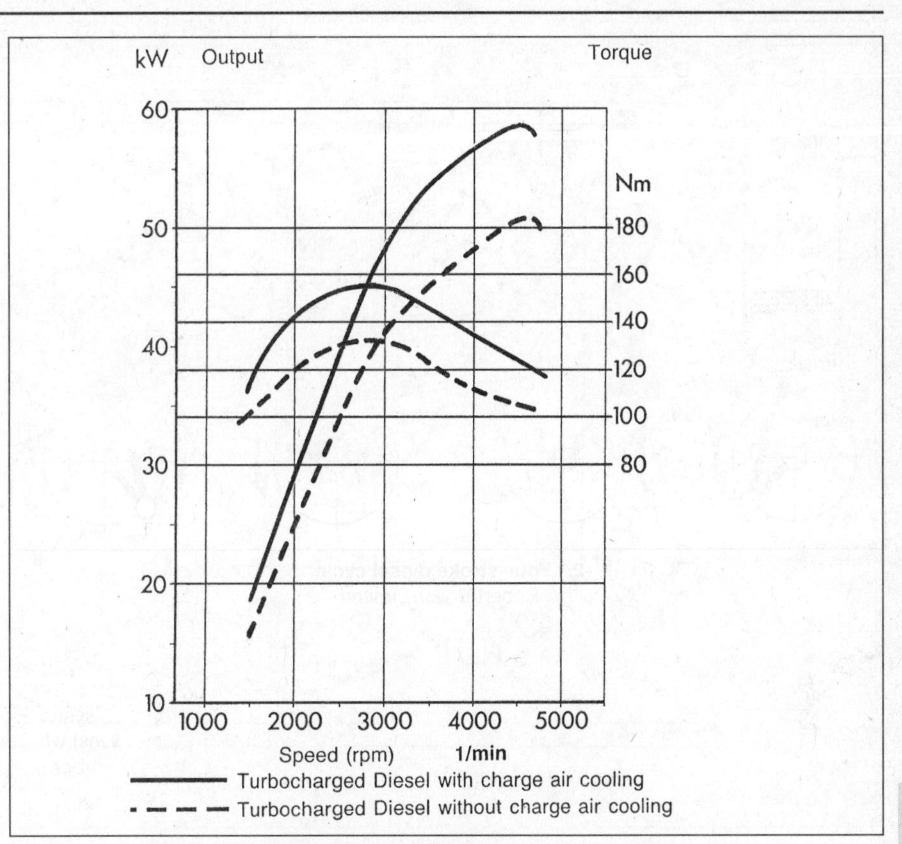

2.10a Power and torque outputs from a turbocharged engine with and without charge air cooling

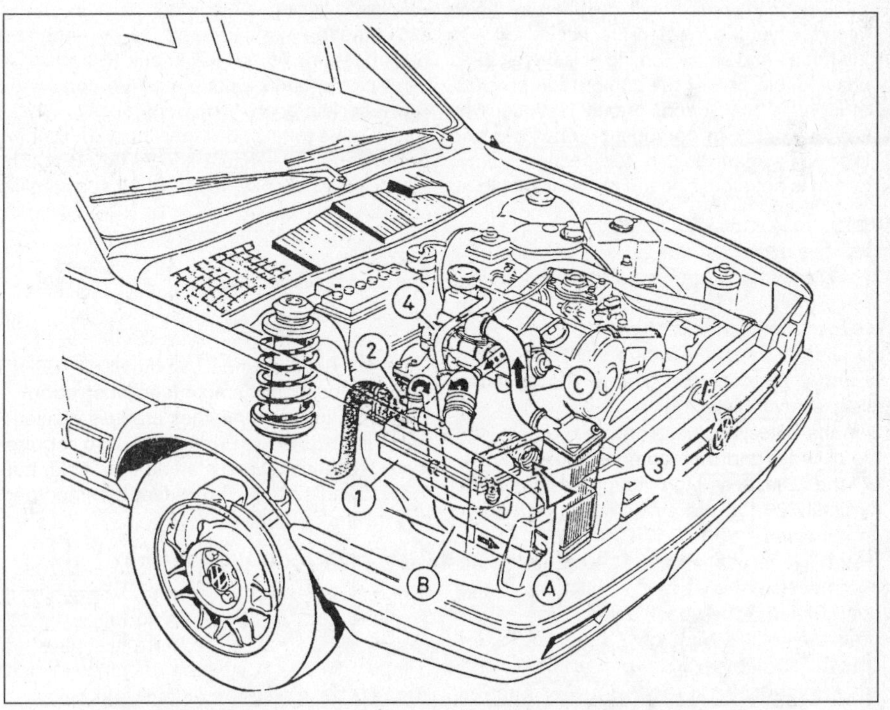

2.10b Induction airflow in a turbocharged engine with charge air cooling

1 Air cleaner
2 Turbocharger
3 Intercooler
4 Inlet manifold
A Inducted air
B Compressed air before cooling
C Compressed air after cooling

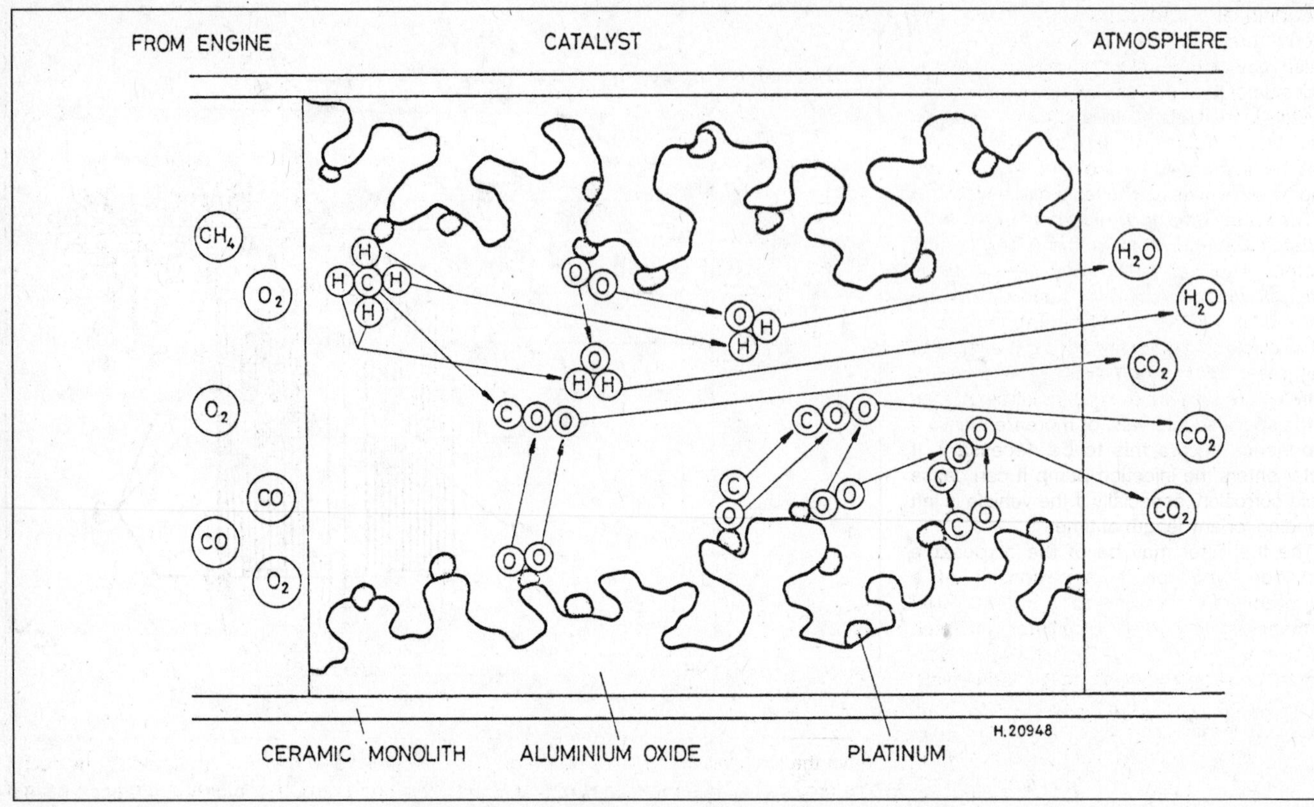

2.12 Chemical reactions in an oxidation catalytic converter

The characteristic Diesel knock is caused by the sudden increase in cylinder pressure which occurs when the injected fuel has mixed with the hot air and starts burning. It is therefore an unavoidable part of the combustion process, though it has been greatly reduced by improvements in combustion chamber and injection system design. A defective injector (which is not atomising the fuel as it should for optimum combustion) will also cause the engine to knock.

15 Smoke is caused by incorrect combustion, but unlike knock it is more or less preventable. During start-up and warm-up a certain amount of white or blue smoke may be seen, but under normal running conditions the exhaust should be clean. The thick black smoke which is all too familiar from old or badly-maintained vehicles is caused by a lack of air for combustion, either because the air intake is restricted (clogged air cleaner) or because too much fuel is being injected (defective injectors or pump). Causes of smoke are examined in more detail in Chapter 12.

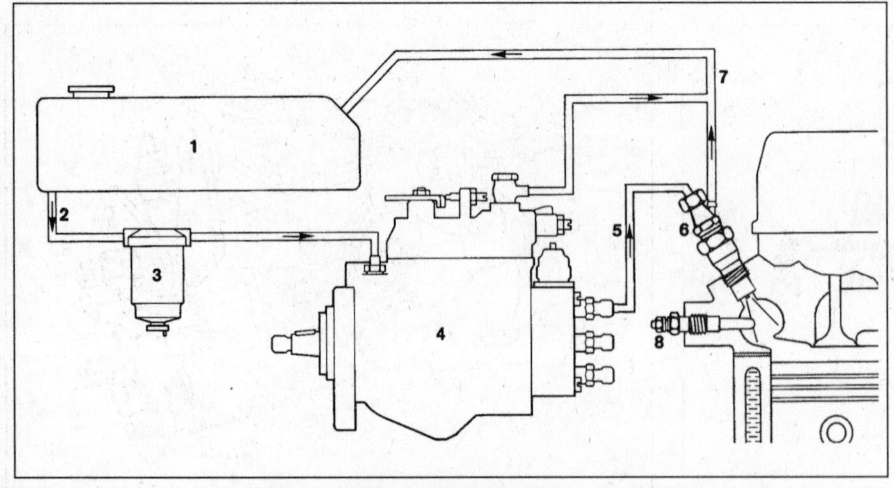

3.1 Fuel circulation - typical passenger car system
© Robert Bosch Limited

1 Fuel tank
2 Fuel feed line
3 Fuel filter / water trap
4 Injection pump with integral supply pump
5 Injector pipe
6 Injector
7 Fuel return (leak-off) line
8 Glow plug

3 Fuel supply and injection systems

Fuel supply

1 The fuel supply system is concerned with delivering clean fuel, free of air, water or other contaminants, to the injection pump. It always includes a fuel tank, a water trap and a fuel filter (which may be combined in one unit), and the associated pipework. Some arrangement must also be made for returning fuel leaked from the injection pump and injectors to the tank **(see illustration)**.

2 A fuel lift pump is fitted between the tank and the filter on vehicles which use an in-line injection pump, or where the fuel tank outlet is significantly lower than the injection pump. When a distributor injection pump is fitted and the tank outlet is at about the same level as the injection pump (as is the case with many passenger cars), a separate fuel lift pump is not fitted. In this case a hand priming pump is often provided for use when bleeding the fuel system.

3 Additional refinements may be encountered. These include a fuel heater, which may be integral with the filter or on the tank side of it, to prevent the formation of wax crystals in the fuel in cold weather. A "water in fuel" warning light on the instrument panel may be illuminated by a device in the water trap when the water reaches a certain level.

4 The water trap and fuel filter are vital for satisfactory operation of the fuel injection system. The water trap may have a glass bowl, in which case water build-up can be seen, or it may as already mentioned have some electrical device for alerting the driver to the presence of water. Whether or not these features are present, the trap must be drained at the specified intervals, or more frequently if experience shows this to be necessary. If water enters the injection pump it can cause rapid corrosion, especially if the vehicle is left standing for any length of time.

5 The fuel filter may be of the disposable cartridge type, or it may consist of a renewable element inside a metal bowl. Sometimes a coarser pre-filter is fitted upstream of the main filter. Whatever the type, it must be renewed at the specified intervals. Considering the damage which can be caused to the injection equipment by the entry of even small particles of dirt, it is not worth using cheap replacement filters, which may not be of the same quality as those of reputable manufacture **(see illustration)**.

3.5 Sectional view of a typical fuel filter

1 *Hand priming plunger*
2 *Fuel bleed screw (on outlet union)*
3 *Seals*
4 *Water drain tap*
5 *Through-bolt*
6 *Through-bolt seal*
7 *Filter element*
8 *Air bleed screw (on inlet union)*

Fuel injection pump

6 The pump is a mechanical device attached to the engine **(see illustrations)**. Its function is to supply fuel to the injectors at the correct pressure, at the correct moment in the combustion cycle and for the length of time necessary to ensure efficient combustion. The pump responds to depression of the accelerator pedal by increasing fuel delivery, within the limits allowed by the governor. It is also provided with some means of cutting off fuel delivery when it is wished to stop the engine.

7 Some kind of governor is associated with the injection pump, either integral with it or attached to it. All vehicle engine governors regulate fuel delivery to control idle speed and maximum speed; the variable-speed governor also regulates intermediate speeds. Operation of the governor may be mechanical or hydraulic, or it may be controlled by manifold depression.

8 Other devices in or attached to the pump include cold start injection advance or fast idle units, turbo boost pressure sensors and anti-stall mechanisms.

9 Fuel injection pumps are normally very reliable. If they are not damaged by dirt, water or unskilled adjustment they may well outlast the engine to which they are fitted.

Fuel injectors

10 One fuel injector is fitted to each cylinder. The function of the injector is to spray an evenly atomised quantity of fuel into the

3.6a Bosch PE in-line injection pump and associated components
© Robert Bosch Limited

1 *Pump*
2 *Governor housing*
3 *Lift pump*
4 *Drivegear and advance mechanism*

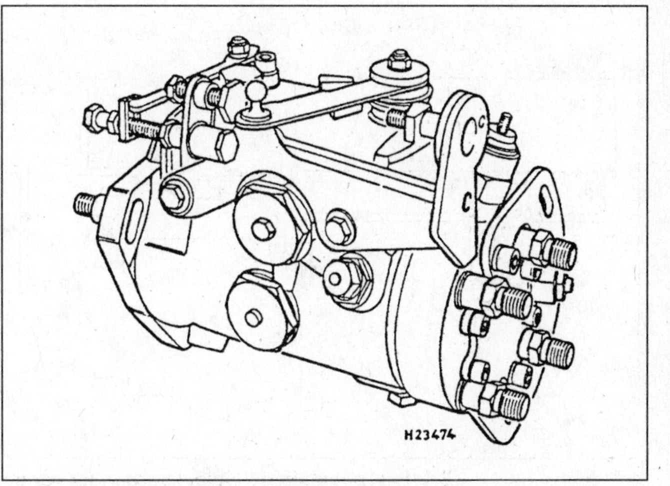

3.6b Lucas / CAV distributor injection pump type DPC

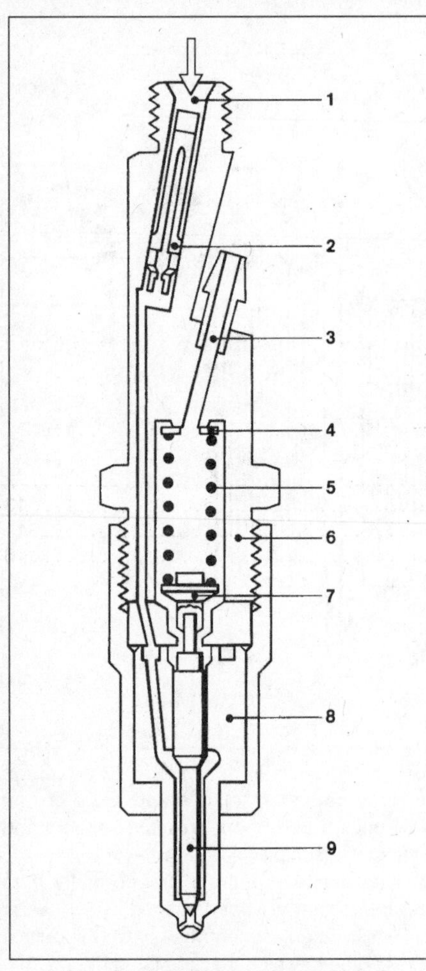

3.11a Sectional view of a multi-hole injector
© Robert Bosch Limited

1	*Fuel inlet*	5	*Spring*
2	*Integral filter*	6	*Body*
3	*Fuel return*	7	*Spindle*
4	*Pressure adjusting shim*	8	*Nozzle body*
		9	*Nozzle needle*

combustion or pre-combustion chamber when the fuel pressure exceeds a certain value, and to stop the flow of fuel cleanly when the pressure drops. Atomisation is achieved by a spring-loaded needle which vibrates rapidly against its seat when fuel under pressure passes it. The needle and seat assembly together are known as the injector nozzle.

11 Injectors in direct injection engines are usually of the multi-hole type **(see illustration)**, while those in indirect engines are of the pintle type **(see illustration)**. The "throttled pintle" injector gives a progressive build-up of injection, which is valuable in achieving smooth combustion.

12 The injector tips are exposed to the temperatures and pressures of combustion, so not surprisingly they will in time suffer from carbon deposits and ultimately from erosion and burning. Service life will vary according to factors such as fuel quality and operating conditions, but typically one could expect to clean and recalibrate a set of injectors after about 50 000 miles, and perhaps to renew them or have them reconditioned after 100 000 miles.

Injector pipes

13 The injector pipes are an important part of the system and must not be overlooked. The dimensions of the pipes are important and it should not be assumed that just because the end fittings are the same, a pipe from a different engine can be used as a replacement. Securing clips must be kept tight and the engine should not be run without them, as damage from vibration or fuel cavitation may result.

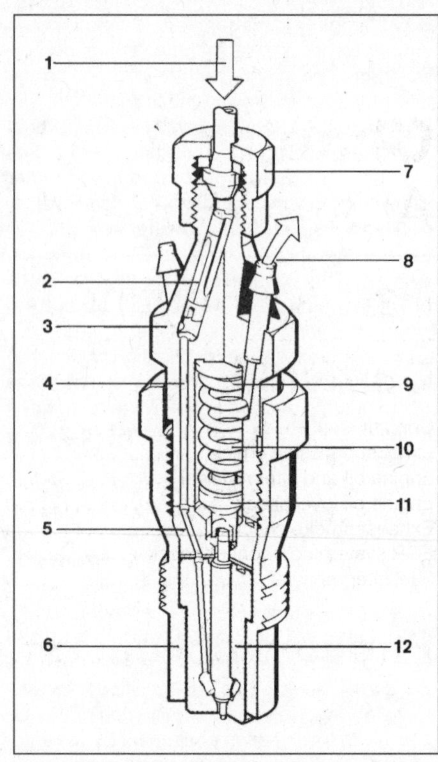

3.11b Cutaway view of a pintle injector
© Robert Bosch Limited

1	*Fuel inlet*	7	*Union nut*
2	*Integral filter*	8	*Fuel return*
3	*Body*	9	*Pressure adjusting shim*
4	*Pressure passage*	10	*Spring*
5	*Sleeve*	11	*Spindle*
6	*Nozzle retainer*	12	*Nozzle*

4 Future developments

1 Development of the Diesel engine, and particularly the fuel injection system, has been relatively slow compared with the advances which have been made in petrol engine fuel injection and management systems. However, new systems such as 'EPIC' (Electronically Programmed Injection Control) by Lucas and EDC (Electronic Diesel Control) by Bosch are already in production or in an advanced stage of development. These systems will provide further improvements in smoothness, economy and reduced exhaust emissions.

2 There can be no doubt that the current combination of high fuel prices and increased environmental awareness will provide the necessary stimuli for further improvements in the near future.

Chapter 2
Austin/Rover 1994cc engine

Part A: Routine maintenance and servicing

Contents

Engine application

1994cc (Perkins Prima) engine .... Austin/Rover Maestro and Montego - 1986 to 1993

Servicing Specifications

Oil filter

Type .... Champion B103

Valve clearances (cold)

Inlet:
- Checking .... 0.20 to 0.40 mm
- Adjusting .... 0.25 to 0.35 mm

Exhaust:
- Checking .... 0.30 to 0.50 mm
- Adjusting .... 0.35 to 0.45 mm

Timing belt

Type .... Toothed belt

Tension (measured with Rover tool KM 4088 AR - midway between camshaft gear and fuel injection pump gear):
- Used belt .... 6 gauge units
- New belt .... 6.5 to 7.5 gauge units

Camshaft

Maximum endfloat .... 0.51 mm

Auxiliary drivebelts

Type .... V-belt

Deflection:
- Coolant pump/alternator .... 7.0 to 12.0 mm - Midway between crankshaft and alternator pulleys, under load of 44 N
- Power steering pump .... 7.0 to 12.0 mm - Midway between pump and camshaft pulleys. Nominal value

Air filter

Type .... Champion W227

Fuel filter

Type .... Champion L111

Glow plugs

Type .... Champion CH88 or CH137

Torque wrench settings	Nm	lbf ft
Camshaft cover	22	16
Camshaft gear centre bolt	85	63
Camshaft gear hub bolts	22	16
Timing belt tensioner	43	32
Sump drain plug	30	22
Timing belt cover bolts:		
M5	3	2.2
M6	6	4.4
M8	10	7
Fuel filter banjo bolt	30	22
Fuel injector high pressure pipe union nuts	22	16
Glow plugs	20	15
Alternator adjusting link	22	16
Alternator mounting/pivot bolt	27	20
EGR valve to pipe screws	22	16
EGR valve to inlet manifold screws	22	16

Lubricants, fluids and capacities

Component or system	Lubricant or fluid	Capacity
Engine	Multigrade engine oil, viscosity range SAE 10W/40 to 15W/50, to specification API SG/CD	5.25 litres - With filter
Cooling system	Ethylene glycol based antifreeze. 50% volume with water	7.5 litres
Fuel system	Commercial Diesel fuel for road vehicles (DERV)	50 litres - Except van 54 litres - Van

Austin/Rover diesel engine - maintenance schedule

The maintenance schedules which follow are basically those recommended by the manufacturer. Servicing intervals are determined by mileage or time elapsed - this is because fluids and systems deteriorate with age as well as with use. Follow the time intervals if the appropriate mileage is not covered within the specified period.

Vehicles operating under adverse conditions may need more frequent maintenance. Adverse conditions include climatic extremes, full-time towing or taxi work, driving on unmade roads, and a high proportion of short journeys. The use of inferior fuel can cause early degradation of the engine oil. Consult an Austin/Rover dealer for advice on these points.

Every 250 miles (400 km), weekly, or before a long journey

- ☐ Check engine oil level and top up if necessary (Section 3)
- ☐ Check coolant level and top up if necessary (Section 4)
- ☐ Check exhaust smoke (Section 5)
- ☐ Check operation of glow plug warning light (Section 6)

Every 12 000 miles (20 000 km) or 12 months, whichever comes first

- ☐ Renew engine oil and oil filter (Section 7)
- ☐ Check condition and tension of auxiliary drivebelts
- ☐ Check coolant strength
- ☐ Check cooling system hoses for condition and security
- ☐ Check EGR system components (Section 8)
- ☐ Renew fuel filter (Section 9)
- ☐ Check fuel system hoses and pipes for condition and security
- ☐ Check exhaust emissions (Section 10)
- ☐ Check pressure sensing hoses and vacuum pipes for condition and security

Every 24 000 miles (40 000 km) or 2 years

- ☐ Check crankcase vent hoses for condition and security
- ☐ Check engine breather PCV valve
- ☐ Renew engine coolant
- ☐ Renew air filter element

Every 36 000 miles (60 000 km) or 3 years

- ☐ Check valve clearances (Section 11)

Every 48 000 miles (80 000 km) or 4 years

- ☐ Clean fuel lift pump strainer (Section 12)

Every 72 000 miles (120 000 km) or 6 years

- ☐ Renew timing belt (Section 13)

Underbonnet view of 1992 Maestro Turbo Diesel engine

1 *Speedometer cable*
2 *Brake fluid reservoir*
3 *Thermostat housing*
4 *Fuel lift pump*
5 *Self-adjusting clutch cable*
6 *EGR valve*
7 *Brake vacuum pump*
8 *Fuel filter and housing*
9 *Windscreen washer fluid reservoir*
10 *EGR modulator valve*
11 *Air cleaner and housing*
12 *Battery*
13 *Air inlet hose*
14 *Accelerator cable*
15 *Engine oil filler cap*
16 *Crankcase ventilation PCV valve*
17 *Engine oil level dipstick*
18 *Fuel injection pump*
19 *Throttle potentiometer*
20 *Fast idle solenoid*
21 *Radiator top hose*
22 *Timing belt cover*
23 *Cooling system expansion tank*
24 *Right-hand engine mounting*
25 *Front suspension top mounting*

Maintenance procedures

1 Introduction

1 This Chapter is designed to help the home mechanic maintain his/her engine for economy, long life and peak performance.

2 The Chapter contains a master maintenance schedule, followed by Sections dealing specifically with each task in the schedule. Visual checks, adjustments, component renewal and other helpful items are included. Refer to the engine compartment illustration for the locations of the various components.

3 Servicing your engine in accordance with the mileage/time maintenance schedule and the following Sections will provide a planned maintenance programme, which should result in a long and reliable service life. This is a comprehensive plan, so maintaining some items but not others at the specified service intervals, will not produce the same results.

4 As you service your engine, you will discover that many of the procedures can, and should, be grouped together, because of the particular procedure being performed, or because of the close proximity of two otherwise-unrelated components to one another.

5 The first step in this maintenance programme is to prepare yourself before the actual work begins. Read through all the Sections relevant to the work to be carried out, then make a list and gather together all the parts and tools required. If a problem is encountered, seek advice from a parts specialist or dealer service department.

2 Intensive maintenance

1 If from the time the engine is new, the routine maintenance schedule is followed closely and frequent checks are made of fluid levels and high-wear items, then the engine will be kept in relatively good running condition and the need for additional work will be minimised.

2 It is possible that there will be times when the engine is running poorly due to the lack of regular maintenance. This is even more likely if a used vehicle, which has not received regular and frequent maintenance checks, is purchased. In such cases, additional work may need to be carried out, outside of the regular maintenance intervals.

3 If engine wear is suspected, a compression test will provide valuable information regarding the overall performance of the main internal components. Such a test can be used as a basis to decide on the extent of the work to be carried out. If, for example, a compression test indicates serious internal engine wear, conventional maintenance as described in this Chapter will not greatly improve the performance of the engine and may prove a waste of time and money, unless extensive overhaul work is carried out first.

4 The following series of operations are those most often required to improve the performance of a generally poor-running engine:

Primary operations

a) Clean, inspect and test the battery
b) Check all the engine-related fluids
c) Check the condition and tension of the auxiliary drivebelt
d) Check the condition of the air cleaner filter element, and renew if necessary
e) Check the fuel filter
f) Check the condition of all hoses, and check for fluid leaks
g) Check the idle speed settings

5 If the above operations do not prove fully effective, carry out the following secondary operations:

Secondary operations

a) Check the charging system
b) Check the preheating system
c) Check the fuel system

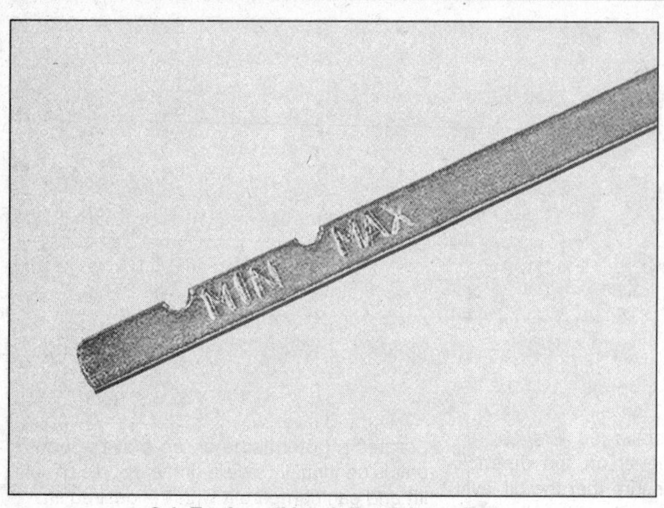

3.4 Engine oil level dipstick markings

3.5 Topping-up engine oil

250 mile (400 km) Service

3 Engine oil level check

1 Ensure that the vehicle is on level ground. Check the oil level before the vehicle is driven, or at least 5 minutes after the engine has been switched off.
2 Refer to the underbonnet illustration for location of the dipstick and oil filler cap.
3 Withdraw the dipstick and using a clean rag or paper towel, wipe all oil from its end. Insert the clean dipstick into the tube as far as it will go, then withdraw it again.
4 Note the oil level on the end of the dipstick, which should be between the upper MAX mark and the lower MIN mark **(see illustration)**.
5 Oil is added through the filler cap. A funnel may help to reduce spillage. Add the oil slowly, checking the level on the dipstick often. Do not overfill **(see illustration)**.

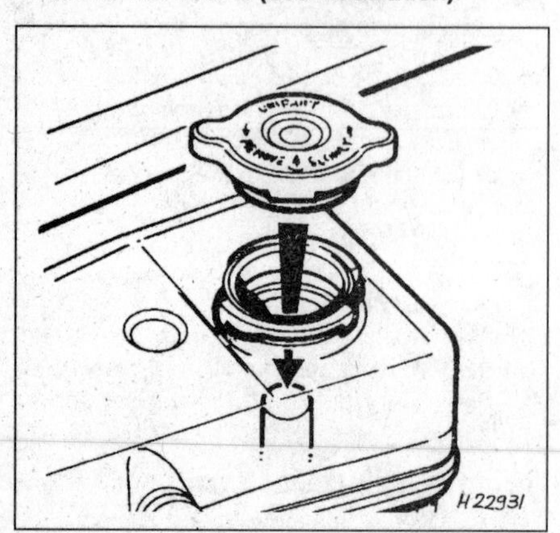

4.3 Coolant level indicator post (arrowed)

4 Coolant level check

1 Check the coolant level by inspecting the expansion tank. Refer to the underbonnet illustration for location of the expansion tank.
2 Take great care to avoid scalding if the system is hot. Place a thick cloth over the expansion tank cap and turn the cap slowly anti-clockwise, waiting for any pressure to be released. Turn the cap further anti-clockwise and remove it completely.
3 Look into the tank and check that the coolant is just covering the indicator post **(see illustration)**.
4 If necessary, top up the tank using antifreeze mixture of the correct type and concentration **(see illustration)**. In an emergency, plain water may be used but this will dilute the antifreeze remaining in the system. Do not add cold water to an over-heated engine or damage may result.

4.4 Topping-up engine coolant

5 Refit the expansion tank cap when the level is correct. Check for leaks if frequent topping-up is required. Normally loss from this type of system is minimal.

5 Exhaust smoke check

1 Start the engine and visually check the exhaust emissions. Any smoke in the emissions will indicate one of the following faults:

White smoke in exhaust

a) Injection timing incorrect
b) Low compression
c) Coolant entering cylinders

Black smoke in exhaust

a) Air cleaner blocked
b) Injector(s) defective

Blue smoke in exhaust

a) Engine oil entering cylinders
b) Injector(s) defective

2 If any fault is indicated then take action immediately.

6 Warning light check

1 The glow plug warning light in the instrument console should extinguish approximately 5 seconds after the ignition is switched on. If it does not do so, then suspect a fault in the circuit or one of the plugs and take the appropriate action.

12 000 mile (20 000 km) Service

7 Engine oil and filter renewal

Oil draining

1 The engine oil should be drained just after a run, when the contaminants which it carries are still in suspension.

2 Park the vehicle on level ground. Position a drain pan of adequate capacity beneath the sump. Wipe clean around the sump drain plug, then remove it. Be careful to avoid scalding if the oil is very hot. Do not lose the drain plug washer (where fitted).

3 Remove the oil filler cap to speed up the draining process. Allow the oil to drain for at least 15 minutes. Inspect the drain plug washer and renew it if necessary.

4 When draining is complete, refit the drain plug with washer and tighten it to the specified torque. Before refilling the engine with oil, renew the oil filter as follows.

Filter renewal

5 Position the drain pan underneath the oil filter. Unscrew the filter and remove it. A chain or strap wrench will probably be needed to undo the filter **(see illustration)**. Failing this, a screwdriver can be driven through the filter and used as a lever to unscrew it. Be prepared for considerable oil spillage in this case. Some spillage is inevitable as the filter is withdrawn.

6 Wipe clean around the filter seat on the engine and check that no sealing rings have been left behind. Smear the sealing ring on the new filter with engine oil or grease, then screw the filter into position. Unless instructed otherwise by the filter maker, tighten the filter by hand only. Usually, tightening by two-thirds of a turn beyond the point where the sealing ring contacts the seat is sufficient.

Oil refilling and engine checks

7 Refill the engine with new oil of the specified type through the filler cap. A funnel may help to reduce spillage. Add the oil slowly, checking the level on the dipstick often. Do not overfill. Ensure that the oil level is at least up to the MIN mark on the dipstick.

8 Refit the filler cap, then start the engine. The oil pressure warning light will take a few seconds to go out as the filter fills with oil. Do not rev the engine until the light has gone out.

9 With the engine running, check for leaks around the filter base and the drain plug. Tighten further if necessary. Stop the engine and check again for leaks.

10 Allow a couple of minutes for the oil to return to the sump, then recheck the level on the dipstick and top up if necessary to the MAX mark. The new filter will absorb approximately 0.5 litre of oil.

11 Put the old oil into a sealed container and dispose of it safely.

8 EGR system component check

1 The exhaust gas recirculation (EGR) control unit is supplied with engine speed, engine load and EGR valve lift information. From this, it determines the signal to send to the vacuum modulator, which in turn controls the amount of vacuum applied to the EGR valve. Engine speed information is taken from the alternator and throttle position is monitored by a potentiometer. The EGR valve incorporates a potentiometer, so that the control unit is continually aware of the degree of valve lift and can compare it with the desired lift.

2 Check that each system component is clean and securely mounted.

3 Inspect the system wiring for damage and deterioration and ensure that it is correctly routed, clear of any hot or moving parts. Disconnect the battery earth lead and disconnect each component wiring connection. Inspect each connection for signs of dirt or corrosion and clean if necessary **(see illustrations)**.

4 Inspect each system vacuum hose for splitting, damage and deterioration. Ensure each hose is correctly routed, clear of any hot or moving parts. Replace any suspect hose immediately.

5 The EGR valve should now be removed for cleaning. Proceed as follows:

6 Disconnect the battery earth (negative) lead.

7 Carefully disconnect the multi-plug from the top of the valve.

8 Disconnect the vacuum hose from the top of the valve.

9 Unscrew and remove the bolts securing the recirculation pipe to the EGR valve **(see illustration)**.

10 Remove the bolts securing the EGR valve to the inlet manifold.

11 Withdraw the EGR valve from the inlet manifold and recirculation pipe, recovering the gaskets **(see illustration)**.

7.5 Using a chain wrench to loosen the oil filter

8.3a EGR control unit multi-plug (arrowed)

8.3b EGR modulator valve multi-plug

8.9 Removing the recirculation pipe-to-EGR valve bolts

8.11 Removing the EGR valve

9.2a Removing the fuel filter

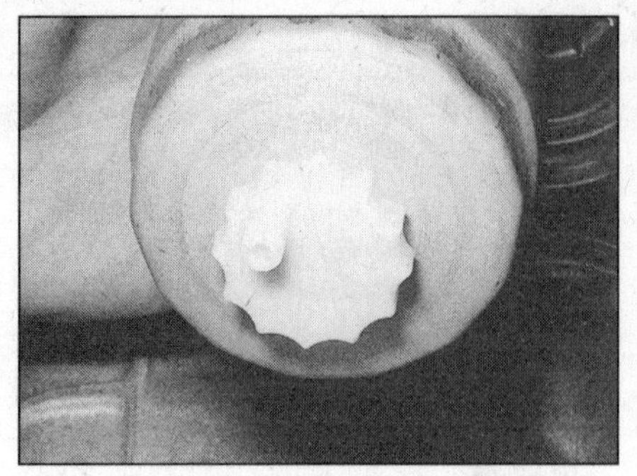
9.2b Fuel filter drain tap at base of filter

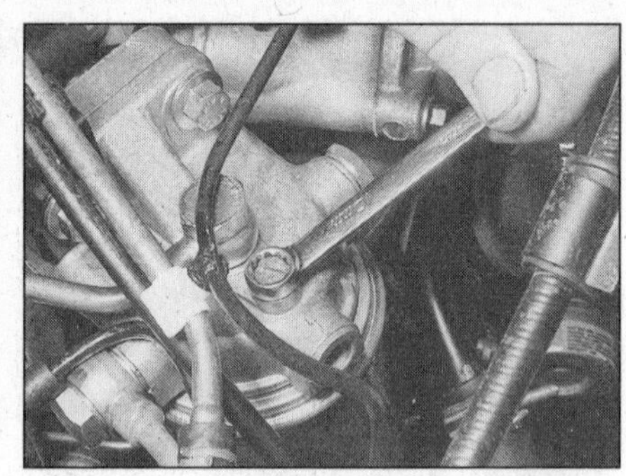
9.6 Loosening bleed screw on fuel filter head

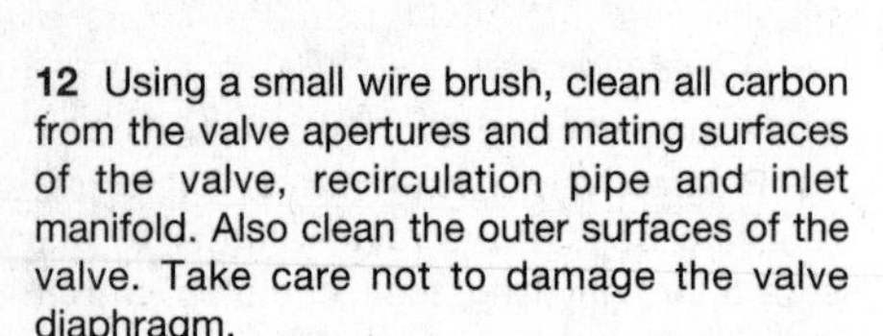

12 Using a small wire brush, clean all carbon from the valve apertures and mating surfaces of the valve, recirculation pipe and inlet manifold. Also clean the outer surfaces of the valve. Take care not to damage the valve diaphragm.

13 Using a screwdriver, depress the valve against its diaphragm and check the valve seating for deposits of carbon.

14 To check the diaphragm, apply vacuum to the port and ensure that the valve moves away from, and back onto, its seat correctly.

15 Refitting the EGR valve is a reversal of the removal procedure. Use new gaskets and tighten all bolts to the specified torque.

9 Fuel filter renewal

Warning: Do not attempt to bleed the fuel system by towing the vehicle. The injection pump will be seriously damaged if it is turned without fuel in it.

1 Wipe clean the area around the fuel filter head.

2 Position rags beneath the filter to absorb spilt fuel, then unscrew the filter from the head using a chain or strap wrench. Keeping the filter upright, withdraw it from the head then drain the fuel into a suitable container **(see illustrations)**.

3 Smear the seal on the new filter with clean fuel. If sufficient fuel is readily available, fill the new filter with fuel. Fit the filter and tighten it by hand only.

4 Bleed the fuel system as follows:

Fuel system priming and bleeding

5 Check that the hand-priming plunger on the fuel lift pump can be moved through its full stroke. If not, turn the crankshaft through one complete turn by using a socket on the crankshaft pulley bolt. This will reposition the fuel pump lever on its operating cam, thus allowing the plunger to move through its full stroke.

6 Using a screwdriver or spanner, loosen the bleed screw on the fuel filter head **(see illustration)**.

7 Operate the hand-priming plunger on the fuel lift pump **(see illustration)**. When fuel that is free of air bubbles emerges from the bleed screw, tighten the screw.

8 Loosen the feed pipe union bolt on the injection pump, then continue to operate the hand-priming plunger until fuel that is free of air bubbles emerges. Tighten the union bolt securely.

9 Loosen all of the high-pressure union nuts at the injectors, sufficiently enough to allow fuel to escape.

10 Fully depress the accelerator pedal, then spin the engine on the starter motor until fuel

9.7 Operating fuel lift pump hand-priming plunger

that is free of air bubbles emerges from the high-pressure unions.

11 Tighten the union nuts to the specified torque then mop up all spilt fuel with rags.

12 Start the engine and let it run until it is firing on all cylinders.

10 Exhaust emission check

1 This check should include an inspection of all "pollution-relevant" components, including the exhaust gas recirculation (EGR) system and catalytic converter, where fitted. Because of the specialist equipment required, inspection should therefore be carried out by a dealer.

36 000 mile (60 000 km) Service

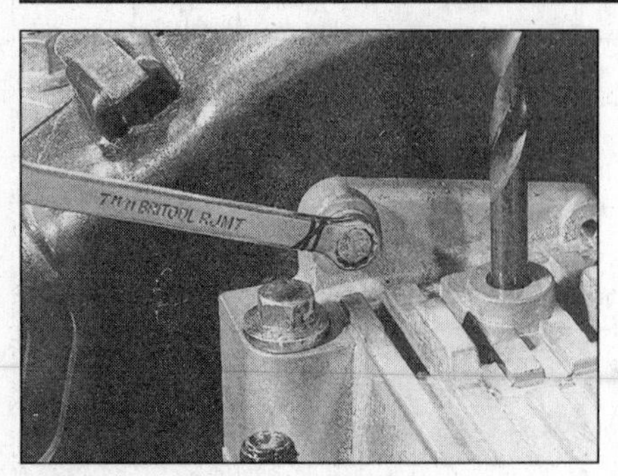
11.3 Unscrewing timing belt inner cover to camshaft cover screw

11 Valve clearance check

Note: *Timing pins (or 6.75 mm diameter drills), camshaft holding clamps, and on models not fitted with power steering, a camshaft retaining tool, are required for this operation.*

Valve clearance check

1 The valve clearances should be checked and adjusted with the engine cold. First disconnect the battery earth (negative) lead.

2 Refer to Section 13 and remove the timing belt cover.

3 Remove the screw securing the timing belt inner cover to the camshaft cover **(see illustration)**.

4 Unscrew the blanking screw from the top of the camshaft cover, then turn the crankshaft using a socket on the crankshaft pulley bolt until the timing hole in the camshaft is aligned with the hole in the camshaft cover (this is the TDC position for No 1 piston). Insert timing pins (or 6.75 mm diameter drills) in the camshaft and also in the flywheel through the timing hole in the cylinder block (see illustrations - Section 13).

11.5 Unbolting the camshaft rear cover

11.7a Home-made camshaft retaining tool fitted over camshaft

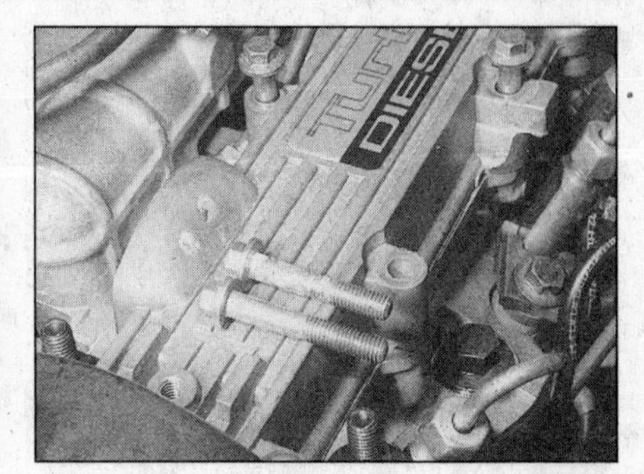

11.11a Two different lengths of camshaft cover retaining bolt

5 On pre 1989 models and on models not fitted with power steering, unbolt and remove the camshaft rear cover **(see illustration)**.

6 Unscrew the nut securing the accelerator cable support bracket to the camshaft cover and move the bracket to one side.

7 On pre 1989 models and on models not fitted with power steering, fit a camshaft retainer tool to hold the rear end of the camshaft down while the camshaft cover is being removed. Rover supply tool no. 18G 1548 for this purpose. A similar tool may be made out of flat metal bar to do the same job **(see illustrations)**.

8 Unscrew the nut securing the front cable support bracket to the cylinder head, release the bracket from the cylinder head and speedometer cable, then move the bracket to one side.

9 On power steering models from 1989 on, unscrew the screw holding the power steering pump drivebelt inner cover to the camshaft cover.

10 Unbolt and remove the fuel lift pump and brake vacuum pump from the camshaft cover.

11 Progressively unscrew the camshaft cover retaining bolts in the reverse order to that shown for tightening, then lift the cover from the cylinder head. Note the positions of the bolts as they are of different lengths **(see illustration)**. If the cover is stuck, use a soft-faced mallet to tap it free **(see illustration)**. Make sure that the semi-circular thrustwasher remains in the cover.

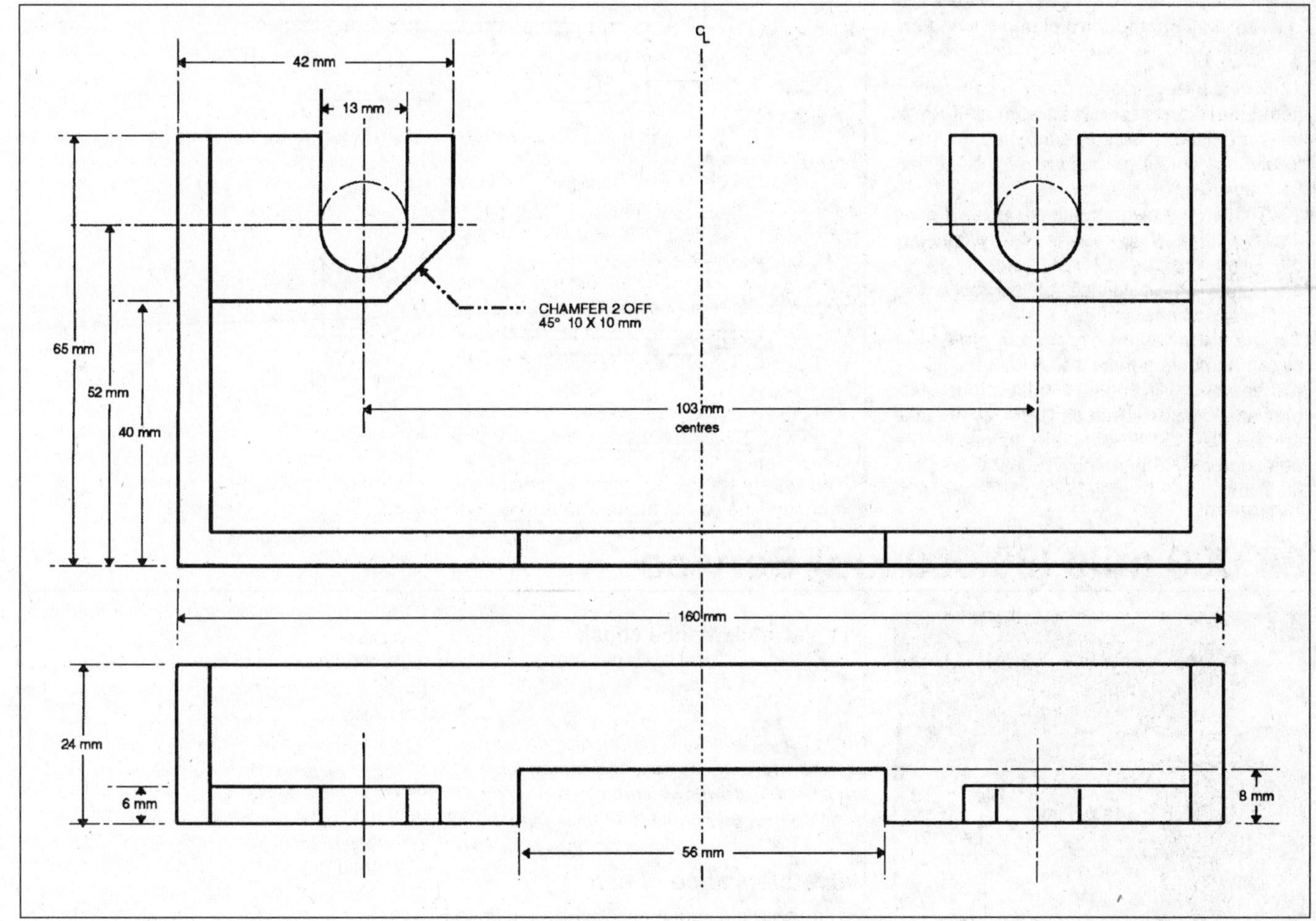

11.7b Home-made camshaft retaining tool dimensions

11.11b Lifting camshaft cover from cylinder head

11.12a Camshaft centre clamp in position

12 Fit the three camshaft clamps or alternative home-made tools **(see illustrations)**. If Rover tools are used, ensure that the pressure pads follow the contour of the journals and are fully unscrewed.

13 Tighten the clamp bolts or pressure pads until the camshaft journals are lightly seated in the cylinder head.

14 Remove the camshaft retainer tool where this has been fitted.

15 Draw the valve positions on a piece of paper, numbering them 1 to 8 from the timing belt end of the engine **(see illustration)**. Mark the valve positions with an "I" if they are inlet or with an "E" if they are exhaust. The positions of the inlet and exhaust valves are as follows:

1	2	3	4	5	6	7	8
Ex	*In*	*In*	*Ex*	*Ex*	*In*	*In*	*Ex*

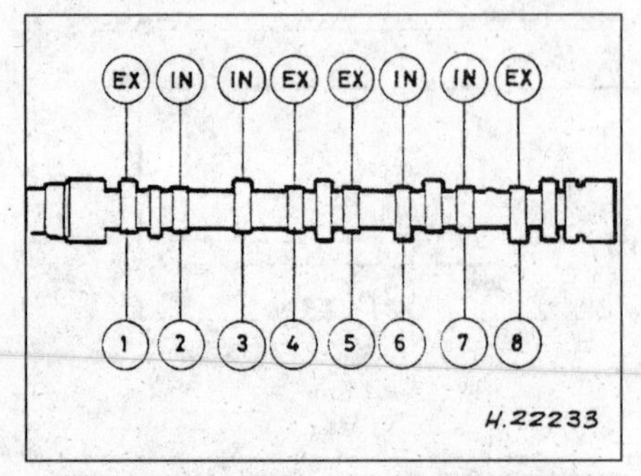

11.15 Valve sequence - numbered from timing end of camshaft

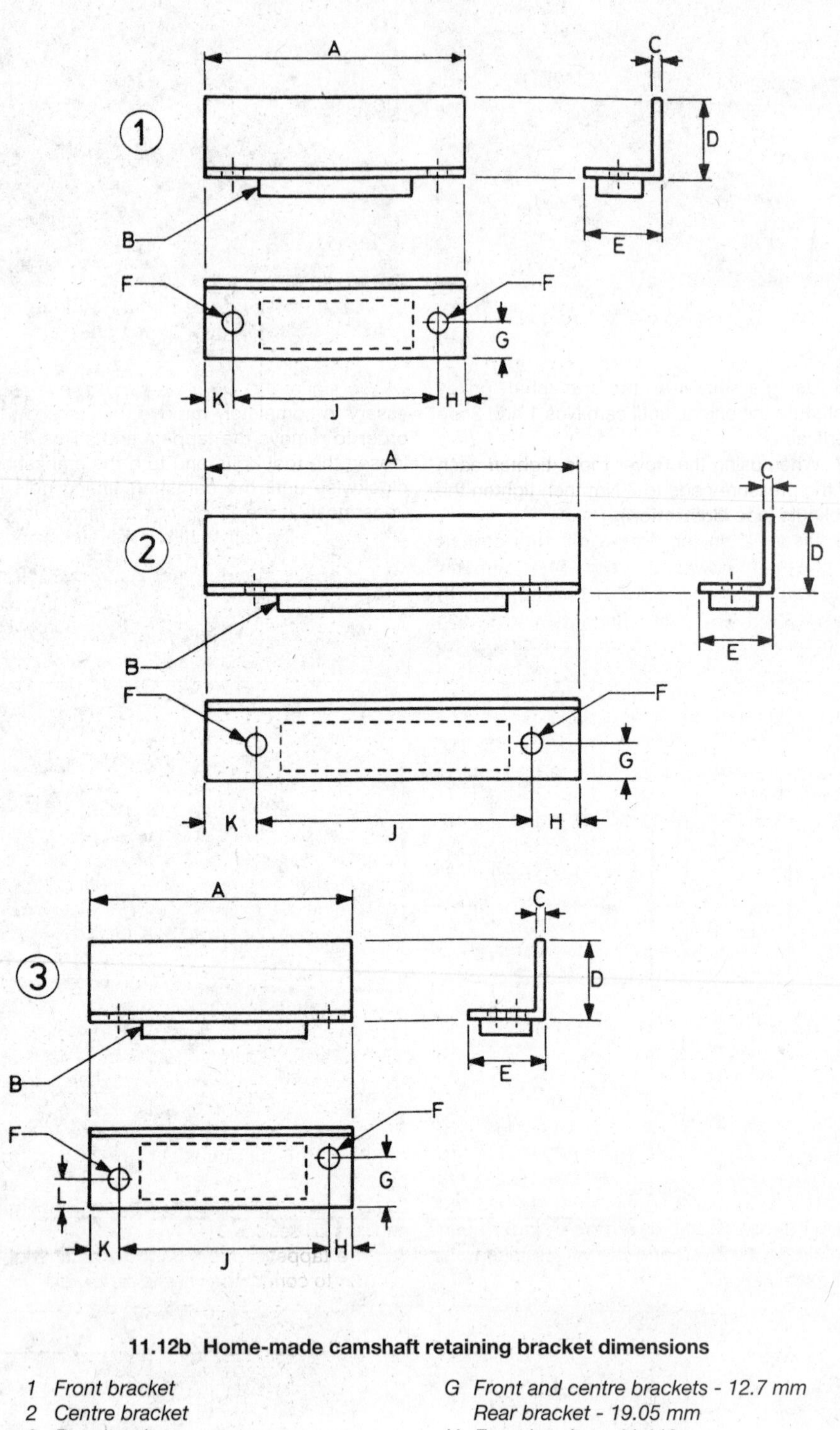

11.12b Home-made camshaft retaining bracket dimensions

1 Front bracket
2 Centre bracket
3 Rear bracket
A Front and rear bracket - 101.6 mm
Centre bracket - 146.05 mm
B Plywood or other soft material positioned centrally on base of bracket
C 3.175 mm
D 30.162 mm
E 30.162 mm
F 7.937 mm
G Front and centre brackets - 12.7 mm
Rear bracket - 19.05 mm
H Front bracket - 11.112 mm
Centre bracket - 19.05 mm
Rear bracket - 9.525 mm
J Front and rear bracket - 79.37 mm
Centre bracket - 107.95 mm
K Front bracket - 11.112 mm
Centre bracket - 19.05 mm
Rear bracket - 12.7 mm
L 11.112 mm

11.17 Tightening clamp tool locknuts

11.18 Using cranked feeler gauge to check valve clearances

11.29a Unscrewing camshaft gear/hub centre bolt

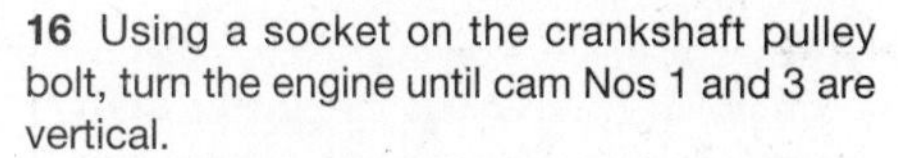

16 Using a socket on the crankshaft pulley bolt, turn the engine until cam Nos 1 and 3 are vertical.

17 When using the Rover tools, tighten each of the pressure pads to 7 Nm then tighten the locknuts **(see illustration)**.

18 Insert a feeler gauge of the correct specified thickness between No 1 cam and No 1 valve stem and check that it is a firm sliding fit. If not, insert different feeler gauges until the fit is correct. Record the clearance. Note that a cranked feeler gauge will make the checking easier, due to the raised camshaft cover sealing face **(see illustration)**.

19 Without moving the camshaft, check the clearance of No 3 valve in the same manner and record it.

20 Loosen the pressure pad bolts on the Rover tool, or slightly loosen the bolts holding the home-made tool to the cylinder head.

21 Turn the crankshaft until Nos 4 and 7 cams are vertical. Tighten the tool bolts so that the camshaft journals are seated in the cylinder head. Record the clearances for Nos 4 and 7 valves.

22 Repeat the procedure for Nos 6 and 8, then Nos 2 and 5 valves.

Valve clearance adjustment

23 If the valve clearances have reduced by more than 0.11 mm below the standard setting, damage may have occurred to the valve seats, valves, camshaft cams and tappet faces. In this case, the cylinder head should be removed and the valves taken out for examination.

24 To adjust the valve clearances, it is necessary to completely remove the camshaft in order to remove the tappets and shims. First loosen the tool bolts and turn the crankshaft clockwise until the camshaft timing hole is uppermost (at the 12 o'clock position). Unbolt and remove the camshaft retainer and clamps.

25 Remove the camshaft as follows:

26 Remove the timing belt, see Section 13.

27 Remove the camshaft gear as follows.

28 Where the camshaft gear is taper-mounted, hold the gear stationary using a tool similar to that used for the hub-mounted gear, then unscrew and remove the centre bolt. Withdraw the gear from the taper on the end of the camshaft. There is no dowel in the end of the camshaft as fitted to the hub-mounted type.

29 Where the camshaft gear is hub-mounted, mark the hub, gear and timing cover in relation to each other. Hold the gear stationary using a suitable holding tool, then unscrew and remove the centre bolt securing the hub to the camshaft **(see illustration)**. Do not rely on the timing pin to hold the camshaft stationary. Withdraw the gear and hub from the camshaft. Note the location dowel in the camshaft end **(see illustration)**.

30 On power steering models from 1989 on, remove the power steering drivebelt pulley and remove the drivebelt inner cover.

31 Using vernier calipers, note the fitted depth of the oil seals at each end of the camshaft.

32 Lift out the camshaft and remove the front and rear oil seals.

33 The tappet shims must now be changed in order to correct the valve clearances.

11.29b Location dowel (arrowed) in camshaft end

34 Working on the first valve, remove the tappet from the cylinder head and extract the shim from the tappet using a small screwdriver **(see illustrations)**. Measure the thickness of the shim using a micrometer. Select the new shim using the following formula:

A + B - C = Shim thickness required
Where A = Valve clearance measured with feeler gauge
B = Thickness of shim removed
C = Correct valve clearance required

35 Locate the new shim in the tappet, then oil the tappet and locate it in the cylinder head.

36 Change the remaining shims in the same manner as above.

37 With all valve clearances thus adjusted, refit the camshaft as follows:

38 Lubricate the camshaft journals and cams with clean engine oil, then lower the camshaft into the cylinder head with the timing hole at the 12 o'clock position **(see illustration)**.

11.34a Remove each tappet . . .

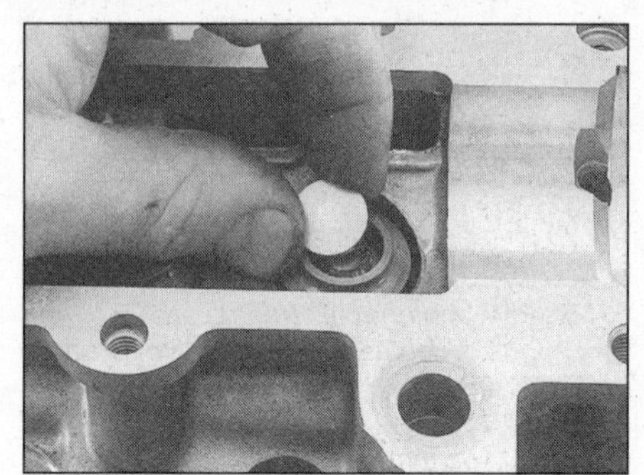

11.34b . . . and shim

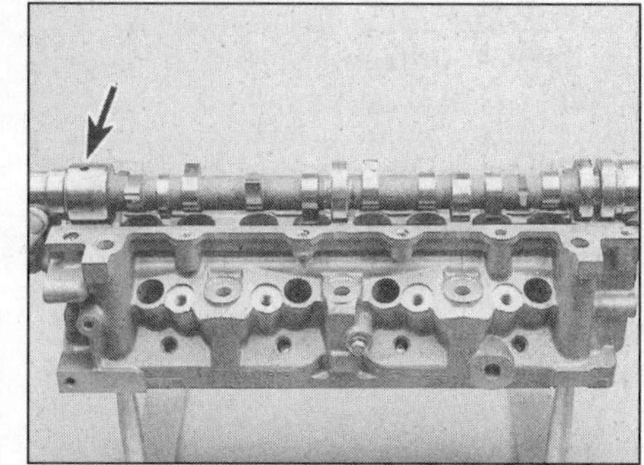

11.38 Lowering camshaft into cylinder head (timing hole arrowed)

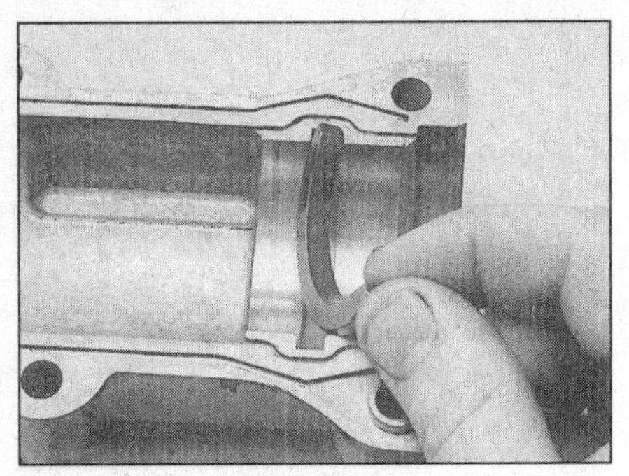

11.41a Fitting camshaft cover thrustwasher

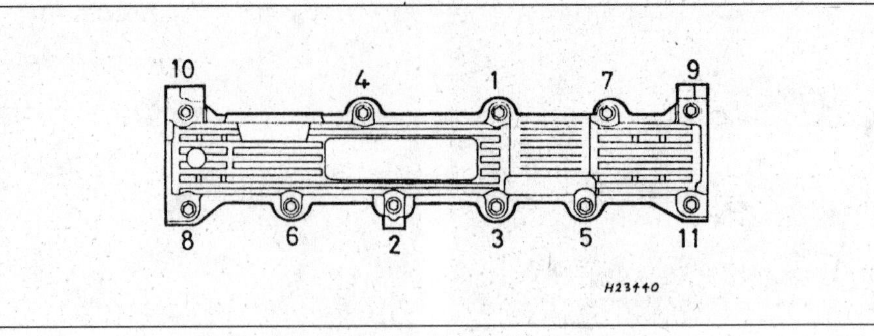

11.41b Camshaft cover bolt tightening sequence

39 Ensure No 1 piston is at TDC with the flywheel timing pin or drill fitted.

40 Clean all old sealant from the camshaft cover and cylinder head mating surfaces. Ensure that all sealant is removed from the grooves in the cover.

41 Refit the camshaft cover (together with the semi-circular thrustwasher) without applying any sealant at this stage. Insert and tighten the bolts progressively to the specified torque and in the sequence shown **(see illustrations)**.

42 Attach a dial test indicator to the end of the cylinder head, with the probe touching the end of the camshaft. Move the camshaft fully to the timing cover end of the cylinder head and zero the dial test indicator. Now move the camshaft fully in the opposite direction and measure the amount of endfloat.

43 If the endfloat recorded is in excess of the maximum specified, a new thrustwasher must be fitted.

44 Remove the camshaft cover and apply a bead of suitable silicone sealant to its grooves and outer mating surface **(see illustration)**. Immediately refit the cover to the cylinder head. Progressively tighten the bolts to the specified torque, in the correct sequence.

45 Insert the timing pin (or drill) through the camshaft cover and into the camshaft.

46 Clean the oil seal seating surfaces at the front and rear of the camshaft. Smear a little clean oil on the sealing lip of each new oil seal. Locate each seal over the camshaft and drive it into position using a socket or metal tube of suitable diameter, until located at the previously-noted depth **(see illustrations)**.

47 On all models not fitted with power steering and all models manufactured before 1989, refit the camshaft rear cover to the cylinder head and tighten the bolts.

48 On power steering models from 1989 on, refit the drivebelt inner cover and tighten the bolts. With the timing pin (or drill) in position, refit the hub and pulley to the end of the camshaft and tighten the bolts. Refit the power steering drivebelt.

49 Insert and tighten the upper bolt securing the timing cover to the camshaft cover.

50 Refit the camshaft gear.

51 On taper-mounted gears, insert the centre bolt finger-tight. The bolt is fully tightened during timing belt refitting and adjustment.

52 On hub-mounted gears, locate the hub on the camshaft, ensuring that the locating pin is correctly inserted. Locate the gear on the hub, making sure that the previously made alignment marks are in line. Insert the centre bolt and bolts securing the hub to the camshaft and tighten them sufficiently to hold the gear and hub firm. Counterhold the gear using the special tool used in timing belt removal, then fully tighten the centre bolt to the specified torque. If necessary, re-align the marks on the hub and gear and tighten the bolts finger-tight. The bolts are fully tightened during the timing belt refitting and adjustment procedure.

53 Refit the timing belt and cover as described in Section 13.

54 Refit the brake vacuum pump and fuel lift pump to the camshaft cover.

55 Bleed the fuel system as described in Section 9.

56 Refit the front cable support bracket to the cylinder head.

57 Refit the accelerator cable support bracket to the camshaft cover.

58 Reconnect the battery earth (negative) lead.

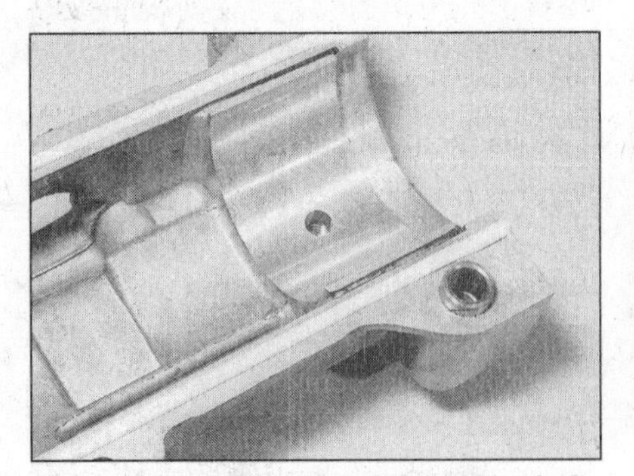

11.44 Apply silicone sealant to camshaft cover

11.46a Using socket and camshaft gear retaining bolt to fit new front (RH) oil seal

11.46b Driving in a new camshaft rear (LH) oil seal

12.1 Removing the fuel lift pump cover retaining screw

12.2 Removing the fuel lift pump strainer

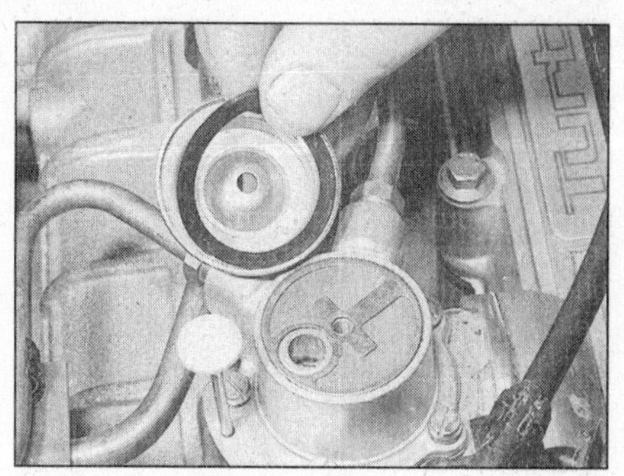
12.5 Renewing the fuel lift pump cover seal

48 000 mile (80 000 km) Service

12 Fuel lift pump strainer check

1 Unscrew the retaining screw and remove the fuel lift pump cover. Be prepared for some fuel spillage **(see illustration)**.
2 Remove and clean the fuel strainer **(see illustration)**.
3 Also clean the sediment chamber.
4 Refit the fuel strainer.
5 Refit the lift pump cover, using a new sealing washer if necessary **(see illustration)**.
6 Bleed the fuel system at the filter head with reference to Section 9.

72 000 mile (120 000 km) Service

13 Timing belt renewal

Note: *Timing pins (or 6.74 mm diameter drills) and a tension gauge (Rover tool KM 4088 AR) are required for this operation.*

13.7 Removing the timing belt access cover

Timing belt cover removal

Pre 1989 non-Turbo models

1 Apply the handbrake, then jack up the front of the vehicle and support it on axle stands. Remove the right-hand roadwheel.
2 Remove the plastic panel from under the wheel arch for access.
3 Remove the coolant pump/alternator drivebelt.
4 Unbolt the pulley from the coolant pump drive flange.
5 Remove the access cover from the top of the timing belt cover, carefully prising it outwards to disengage the retaining lugs and lifting upwards.
6 Unscrew the retaining screws, release the spring clips (where fitted) and remove the timing belt cover.

Turbo and 1989 models on

Upper cover
7 Remove the access cover from the top of the timing belt cover, carefully prising it outwards to disengage the retaining lugs and lifting upwards **(see illustration)**.
8 Unscrew the retaining screw located below the access cover aperture, release the spring clips and remove the upper cover **(see illustrations)**.

Lower cover
9 Remove the upper cover.
10 Apply the handbrake, then jack up the front of the vehicle and support it on axle stands. Remove the right-hand roadwheel.
11 Remove the plastic panel from under the wheel arch for access.
12 Remove the coolant pump/alternator drivebelt.
13 Unbolt the pulley from the coolant pump drive flange.
14 Undo the retaining bolts and screws, release the spring clips and remove the lower cover **(see illustrations)**.

Timing belt removal

15 Disconnect the battery earth (negative) lead.

2A

13.8a Remove the retaining screw . . .

13.8b . . . release the spring clips . . .

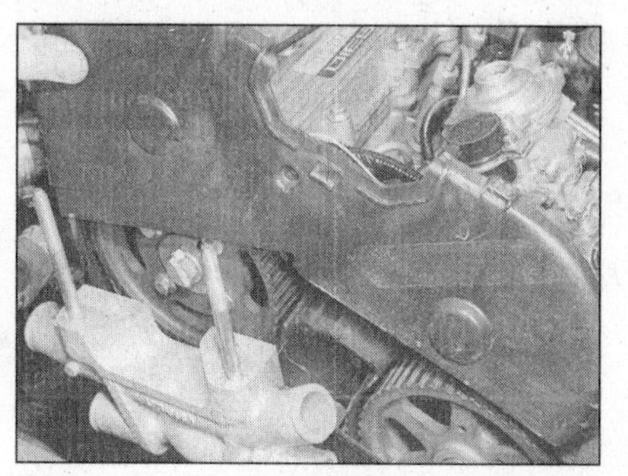
13.8c . . . and remove the timing belt upper cover

13.14a Remove the lower bolt . . .

13.14b . . . the two lower screws (arrowed) . . .

13.14c . . . and withdraw the timing belt lower cover

16 Drain the cooling system.

17 Remove the coolant hoses from the coolant pump.

Turbo and 1989 models on

18 Remove the cooling system expansion tank.

19 Support the weight of the engine on a trolley jack and piece of wood located under the right-hand end of the sump.

20 Unscrew the bolts securing the right-hand engine mounting bracket to the wheelarch and body panel.

21 Unscrew the two bolts and two nuts securing the right-hand engine mounting to the top of the coolant pump and remove the complete right-hand engine mounting assembly **(see illustration)**.

22 Hold the crankshaft stationary, then unscrew and remove the crankshaft pulley centre bolt. Where the pulley incorporates holes, a home-made scissor-type tool made from two lengths of metal bar with long bolts at one end can be used to hold the crankshaft pulley **(see illustration)**. If there are no holes in the pulley, one alternative method is to remove the starter motor and use a wide-bladed screwdriver engaged with the starter ring gear. The Rover tool for holding the crankshaft is bolted to the pulley using the existing four bolt holes. If required, a similar tool may be made.

23 Using an Allen key, unscrew the bolts securing the pulley to the crankshaft gear and withdraw the pulley **(see illustration)**.

All models

24 Unscrew the blanking plug from the right-hand end of the camshaft cover **(see illustration)**, then turn the crankshaft in a clockwise direction until the timing pin hole in the camshaft is aligned with the hole in the cover. In this position, No 1 piston (nearest the timing belt end of the engine) will be at Top Dead Centre (TDC) on compression.

25 Insert the timing pin (or 6.75 mm diameter drill) through the hole in the camshaft cover, so that it engages in the hole in the camshaft **(see illustration)**.

26 Using two suitable bolts, lock the injection pump gear by tightening the bolts into the injection pump mounting bracket through two diagonally-opposite unthreaded holes (the threaded holes are for pulling off the gear). Note also that the timing marks on the gear and mounting bracket are aligned with each other **(see illustrations)**.

27 Where the camshaft gear is taper-mounted, hold the camshaft gear stationary and loosen the camshaft gear retaining bolt one or two turns.

28 Where the camshaft gear is hub-mounted,

13.21 Removing complete right-hand engine mounting assembly

13.22 Loosening crankshaft pulley centre bolt

13.23 Removing crankshaft pulley to gear retaining bolts

13.24 Removing camshaft cover blanking plug

13.25 Using 6.75 mm diameter drill to lock camshaft in position

13.26a Two bolts inserted through injection pump gear into mounting bracket

13.26b Timing mark (arrowed) on injection pump gear (Turbo model shown)

13.28 Loosen four bolts securing hub-mounted camshaft gear to hub

13.29 6.75 mm drill inserted through gearbox adapter plate at rear of cylinder block into flywheel timing hole

13.31a Unscrew multi-splined tensioner lockbolt (arrowed) . . .

13.31b . . . and remove tensioner

hold the camshaft gear stationary and loosen the four bolts securing the gear to the hub one turn each. The camshaft gear can be held against rotation using a home-made scissor type tool **(see illustration)**. Do not rely on the timing pin alone to hold the camshaft.

29 Insert a timing pin (or 6.75 mm drill) through the gearbox adapter plate at the rear of the cylinder block and into the timing hole in the flywheel **(see illustration)**. Do not turn the crankshaft with the timing belt removed and the cylinder head in position, otherwise the pistons will collide with the valves.

30 Check if the timing belt is marked with the normal direction of rotation. If necessary, mark it with chalk.

31 Unscrew the multi-splined tensioner lockbolt and remove the timing belt tensioner pulley **(see illustrations)**.

32 On Turbo and 1989 models on, unbolt and remove the idler pulley **(see illustration)**.

33 Ease the timing belt progressively off the gears and remove it.

34 Where the camshaft gear is taper-mounted, finger-tighten the centre bolt if a new timing belt is not being fitted immediately.

35 Clean all the gears, the oil pump casing and the timing covers, wiping them dry.

Timing belt refitting

36 Check that the timing marks on the injection pump are still correctly aligned and that the timing pins are still in position.

37 On Turbo and 1989 models on, refit the idler pulley and tighten the bolt.

38 Locate the timing belt around the crankshaft and idler pulleys, making sure that the direction of rotation marks are facing the correct way. Locate the belt on the injection pump and camshaft gears and centralise it midway on the gear teeth.

13.32 Removing timing belt idler pulley

39 Fit the tensioner pulley, then unscrew the bolts holding the injection pump gear.

40 On Turbo and 1989 models on, refit the crankshaft pulley and tighten the bolts.

41 Adjust the timing belt tension as follows:

42 The only accurate method of determining timing belt tension is with a Rover tension gauge. If no gauge is available, an approximate method of checking tension is to twist the belt using moderate finger and thumb pressure. It should be possible to twist the belt through 45° **(see illustration)**.

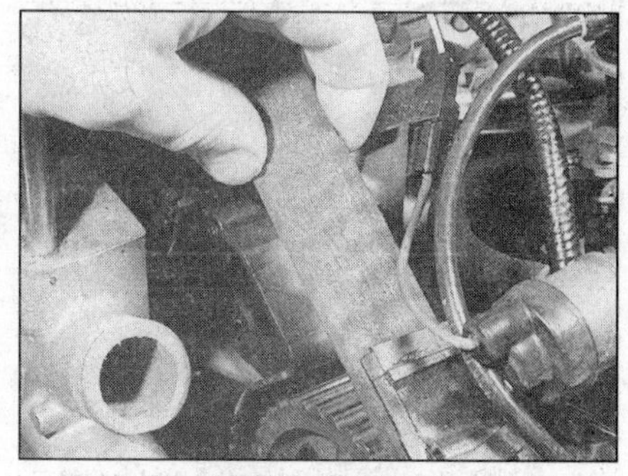

13.42 Checking timing belt tension by twisting it through 45°

43 Fit the tension gauge midway between the camshaft gear and fuel injection pump gear **(see illustration)**.

44 Loosen the tensioner retaining bolt, then use an Allen key to turn the tensioner until the specified tension is obtained. Turn the tensioner clockwise to tension the belt.

45 Tighten the retaining bolt. If the tensioner rotates over-centre, unscrew the tensioner bolt and insert it in the innermost of the two retaining holes.

46 Remove the tension gauge.

47 Hold the camshaft gear stationary and tighten the camshaft gear retaining bolt (taper-mounted gear) or hub bolts (hub-mounted gear) to the specified torque.

48 Check that the timing pins are still fully inserted (proving that the timing is still correct), then remove them. Refit the camshaft cover blanking plug.

49 Using a socket on the crankshaft pulley bolt, turn the crankshaft through two complete revolutions in order to check that there is no obstruction.

50 Check and if necessary, adjust the fuel injection pump timing.

51 On Turbo and 1989 models on, refit the right-hand engine mounting and the cooling system expansion tank. Lower the trolley jack from under the engine.

52 Refit the timing belt cover, using a reversal of the removal procedure. Refit and tension the coolant pump/alternator drivebelt the specified amount.

53 Refit the coolant hoses to the coolant pump.

54 Refill the cooling system and reconnect the battery.

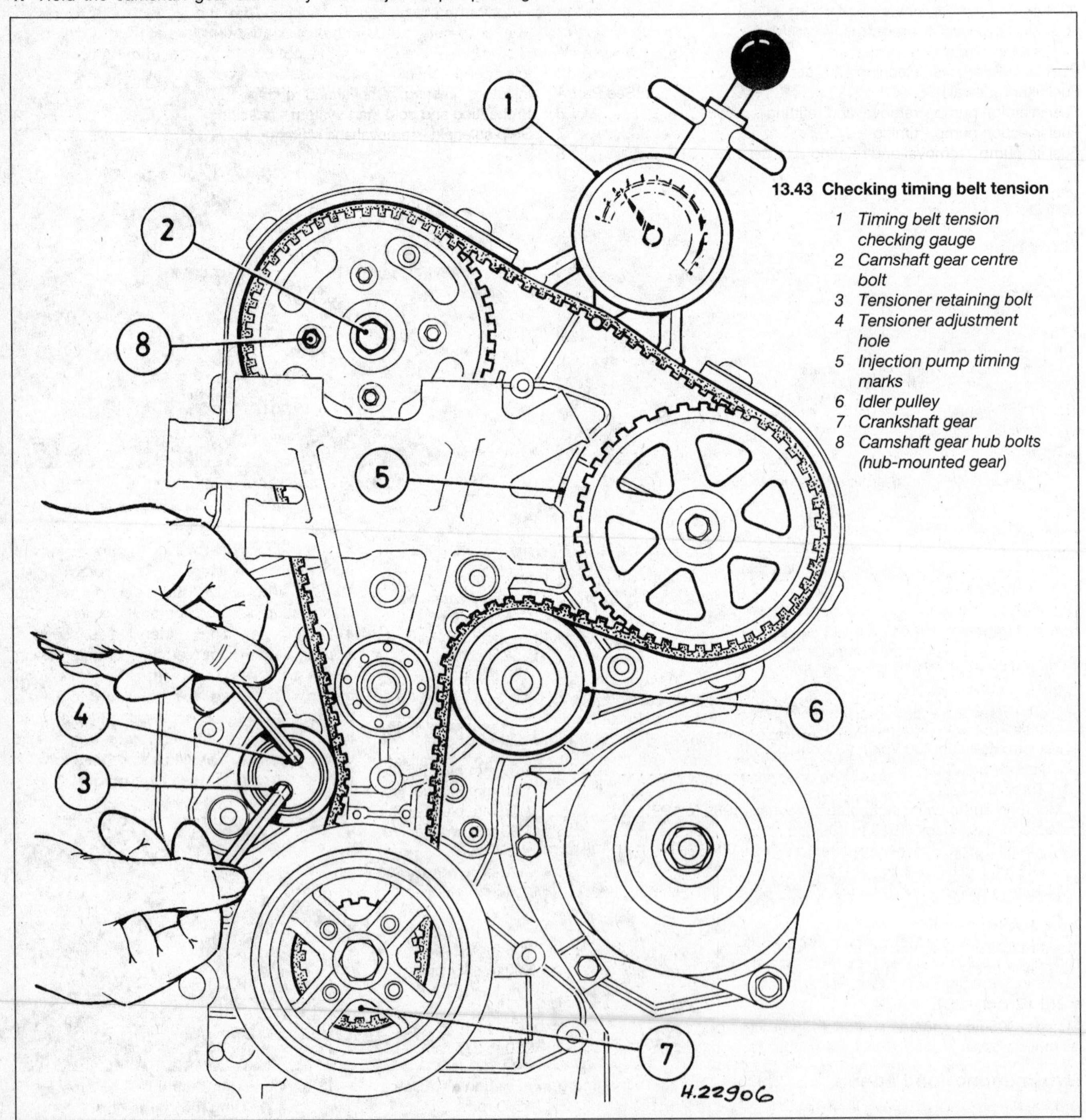

13.43 Checking timing belt tension

1 *Timing belt tension checking gauge*
2 *Camshaft gear centre bolt*
3 *Tensioner retaining bolt*
4 *Tensioner adjustment hole*
5 *Injection pump timing marks*
6 *Idler pulley*
7 *Crankshaft gear*
8 *Camshaft gear hub bolts (hub-mounted gear)*

Chapter 2
Austin/Rover 1994cc engine

Part B: Fuel system servicing

Contents

Specifications

Glow plugs

Type	Champion CH88 or CH137
Tip starts to glow	5 seconds
Initial current draw	25 amps
Current draw after 20 seconds	12 amps
Nominal operating voltage	11 volts

Injectors

Maestro 500 and 700 Van (1986 to 1988)	CAV 4-hole
Maestro 500 and 700 Van (1989 on):	
Non-turbo	CAV 4-hole
Turbo	CAV 5-hole
Montego Turbo (1989 to 1991)	CAV 5-hole
Maestro Hatchback (1990 to 1992)	CAV 4-hole, 2-stage
Montego Turbo (from VIN 606579 RHD, VIN 606709 LHD) (1991 on)	Bosch 4-hole, 2-stage
Maestro Turbo and Montego (from VIN 635617) (1992 on)	Bosch 5-hole, 2-stage

Fuel lift pump

Type	AC/YD
Static pressure (no delivery)	41 to 69 kPa (6 to 10 lbf/in^2)

Fuel injection pump

Type	Bosch EPVE
Static timing (No 1 piston at TDC on compression):	
Maestro 500 and 700 Van (1986 to 1988)	1.37 mm plunger lift
Maestro 500 and 700 Van (1989-on):	
Non-turbo	1.37 mm plunger lift
Turbo	1.00 mm plunger lift
Montego Turbo with single-stage injectors (1989 to 1991)	1.00 mm plunger lift
Maestro Hatchback (1990 to 1992).	1.00 mm plunger lift
Montego Turbo with 2-stage injectors (from VIN 606579 RHD, VIN 606709 LHD) (1991-on)	1.20 mm plunger lift
Maestro Turbo and Montego (from VIN 635617) (1992 on)	1.20 mm plunger lift

Idle speed

Maestro 500 and 700 Van (1986 to 1988)	900 to 950 rpm
All other models	800 to 850 rpm

Fast idle speed

Maestro 500 and 700 Van (1986 to 1988)	1050 to 1075 rpm
All other models	950 to 975 rpm

Maximum no-load speed

All models	4500 rpm

Torque wrench settings

	Nm	lbf ft
EGR pipe to exhaust manifold nuts	22	16
EGR valve to EGR pipe screws	22	16
EGR valve to inlet manifold screws	22	16
Fuel lift pump	22	16
Glow plugs	20	15
Injection pump gear/pulley nut	60	44
Injector clamp bolts	43	32
Injector high-pressure pipe union nuts	22	16

1 Accelerator cable - adjustment

1 With the accelerator pedal fully released, adjust cable tension by means of the two locknuts **(see illustration)**, until side movement of the cable inner at a point midway between the injection pump control lever and the outer cable is between 8.0 and 10.0 mm. Tighten the locknuts on completion.

2 Have an assistant depress the accelerator pedal fully, then check that the control lever contacts the maximum speed screw. Check that, with the accelerator pedal fully released, the control lever is in contact with the idle speed adjusting screw.

2 Idle speed - checking and adjustment

1 The type of tachometer (rev counter) which senses ignition system HT pulses via an inductive pick-up cannot be used on diesel engines, unless a device such as the Sykes-Pickavant timing light adapter is available, see Chapter 13. Alternatively, an optical or pulse-sensitive tachometer may be used.

2 The optical tachometer registers the passage of a paint mark or (more usually) a strip of reflective foil placed on the crankshaft pulley. It is not as convenient to use as the electronic or pulse-sensitive types, since it has to be held so that it can see the pulley. It does, however, have the advantage that it can be used on any engine, petrol or diesel, with or without a diagnostic socket.

3 The pulse-sensitive tachometer uses a transducer similar to that needed for a timing light. The transducer converts hydraulic or mechanical impulses in an injector pipe into electrical signals, which are displayed on the tachometer as engine speed.

4 Some dynamic timing equipment for diesel engines incorporates a means of displaying engine speed. If this equipment is available, a separate tachometer will not be required.

5 The owner-mechanic who only wishes to check the idle speed of one engine occasionally may well feel that the purchase of a special tachometer is not justified. Assuming that mains electric light is available, the use of a stroboscopic disc is a cheap alternative. The principle will be familiar to anyone who has used such a disc to check the speed of a record-player turntable.

6 A disc must be constructed of stiff paper or card to fit onto the crankshaft pulley (or camshaft pulley, if appropriate - but remember that this rotates at half speed). The disc should be white or light-coloured and divided using a protractor into regular segments with heavy black lines, see Chapter 13. The number of segments required will depend on the desired idle speed and the frequency of the alternating current supply. For the 50 Hz supply used in the UK and most of Europe, the figures are as follows:

Speed (rpm)	No of segments	Angle per segment
706	*17*	*21° 11'*
750	*16*	*22° 30'*
800	*15*	*24°*
857	*14*	*25° 43'*
923	*13*	*27° 42'*

7 Remove the right-hand roadwheel and inner wheelarch access panel. Attach the disc to the crankshaft pulley and position the vehicle so that the disc can be viewed using only artificial light. A fluorescent tube is best but failing this, a low-wattage incandescent bulb will give better results than a high-wattage one.

8 The disc is observed with the engine running at idling speed. If the engine speed corresponds to the calculated disc speed, the disc segments will appear to be stationary. If the speed is different, the segments will appear to drift in the direction of engine rotation (too fast) or against it (too slow). The segments will also appear to be stationary at multiples or sub-multiples of the calculated speed - twice or half the speed, and so on - so some common sense must be used.

9 Bring the engine to normal operating temperature and connect a tachometer (or suitable alternative) to it. The cooling fan must have operated at least once. Do not run the engine in a confined space without some means of extracting the exhaust fumes.

10 Disconnect the wiring lead from the fast idle speed solenoid.

11 Allow the engine to idle and check the speed against that specified.

12 If adjustment is necessary, slacken the locknut and turn the idle speed adjusting screw **(see illustration)**. Tighten the locknut when adjustment is correct.

13 Check adjustment of the fast idle solenoid as follows. Connect a 12-volt supply to the solenoid. Accelerate the engine slightly to allow the solenoid plunger to extend, then release the accelerator and check that the fast idle speed is as specified. If adjustment is required, screw the plunger adjuster in or out. Disconnect the 12-volt supply and check that idle speed returns to normal.

14 Stop the engine and reconnect the wiring lead to the fast idle speed solenoid. Disconnect the tachometer.

1.1 Adjusting accelerator cable tension at locknuts

2.12 Idle speed adjusting screw (1) and maximum no-load speed screw (2)

3 Stop solenoid - removal and refitting

Removal

1 Unbolt and remove the fuel injection pump rear support plate to improve access.

2 Make sure that the ignition is switched off, then unscrew the solenoid terminal nut and disconnect the wire **(see illustration)**.

3.2 Stop solenoid (arrowed)

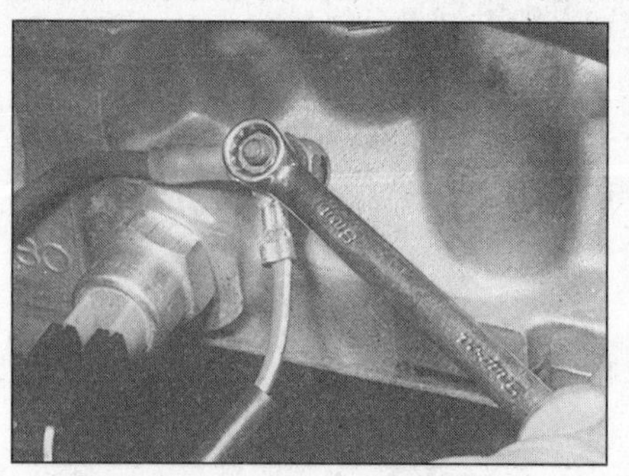

4.2 Removing main supply wire retaining nut from No 4 glow plug

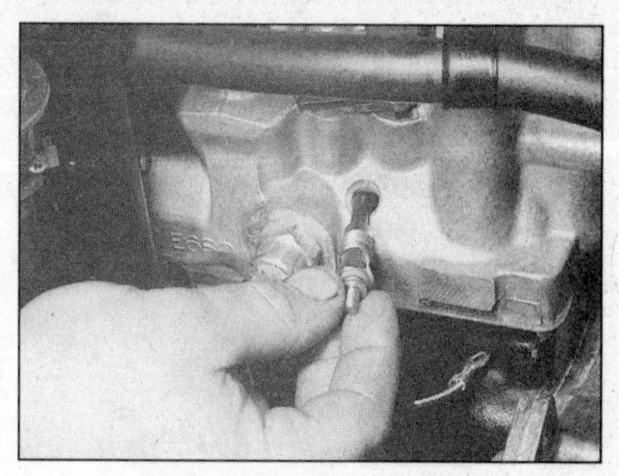

4.4 Removing a glow plug

3 Clean around the solenoid. Unscrew it from the pump and recover the sealing washer. Operate the hand-priming plunger on the fuel lift pump as the solenoid is removed, to flush away any dirt.

Refitting

4 Refitting is a reversal of the removal procedure.

4 Glow plugs - removal and refitting

Warning: If the glow plugs have just been operated in the engine, or if the engine has just been running, they may be very hot.

Removal

1 Make sure that the ignition is switched off.

2 Unscrew the retaining nut and disconnect the current feed wire from each glow plug **(see illustration)**. Note that the main supply wire is also fitted to No 4 glow plug. Recover any terminal nut washers.

3 Brush or blow away any debris from around the glow plugs.

4 Unscrew and remove the glow plugs from the cylinder head, using a deep socket **(see illustration)**.

5 If the glow plugs are not to be refitted immediately, plug or cover the openings in the cylinder head.

Refitting

6 Commence refitting by applying a smear of copper-based anti-seize compound to the threads of each glow plug.

7 If the openings in the cylinder head were plugged while the glow plugs were removed, unplug the holes and check that the glow plug seats are clean.

8 Insert the glow plugs into their holes, tightening them by hand initially.

9 Now tighten to the specified torque. Beware of overtightening, which as well as stripping the thread, can damage the glow plug by reducing the gap between the element and its surround.

10 Reconnect and secure the current feed wires.

5 Injectors - testing, removal and refitting

Warning: Never expose the hands, face or any other part of the body to injector spray, since the high working pressure can cause the fuel to penetrate the skin, with potentially-fatal results.

Testing

1 A faulty injector which is causing knocking noises can be identified as follows.

2 Clean around the injector fuel pipe unions. Run the engine at a fast idle so that the knock can be heard. Using a suitable split ring spanner, slacken and retighten each injector union in turn. Cover the union with a piece of rag to absorb any spilt fuel.

3 When the union supplying the defective injector is slackened, the knock will disappear. Stop the engine and remove the injector for inspection.

4 The balance between injectors can be checked in a similar way, provided an accurate tachometer is available. With the engine idling, each union is slackened in turn and the drop in rpm noted. Any injector which produces a much larger or smaller drop in rpm when its union is slackened should be viewed with suspicion.

5 With equipment such as Dieseltune's Injector Tester, it is possible to check injector opening pressures and leakage without removing the injectors from the engine. This is obviously a time-saving measure if it is simply wished to verify that pressures are correct, or to locate one defective injector.

6 Testing the spray pattern by cranking or running the engine with an injector out of its hole and connected to its fuel pipe, should not be attempted. It is tempting to use this method because it is quick and requires no special equipment but the risks of fire and blood poisoning from the injector spray mean that it cannot be recommended.

Removal

7 To remove the injectors, first disconnect the battery earth (negative) lead.

8 Unscrew and remove the banjo bolts securing the leak-off pipes to the injectors **(see illustration)**. Recover the sealing washers. Note that when removing No 2 or No 3 injector, the leak-off pipe must be removed from both injectors.

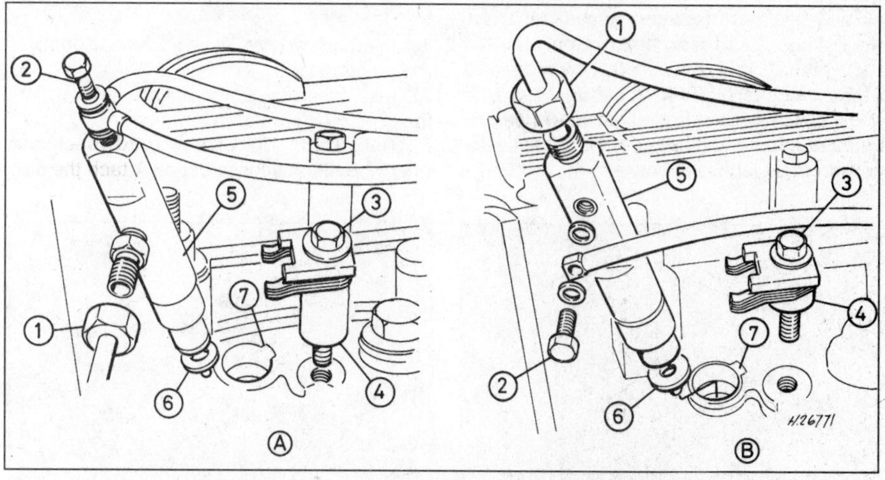

5.8 Single-stage (A) and two-stage (B) injectors

1 Injector pipe union
2 Leak-off (return) pipe banjo union bolt
3 Clamp bolt assembly
4 Pedestal
5 Injector
6 Seat washer
7 Locating ring

5.11 Removing injector clamp and pedestal components

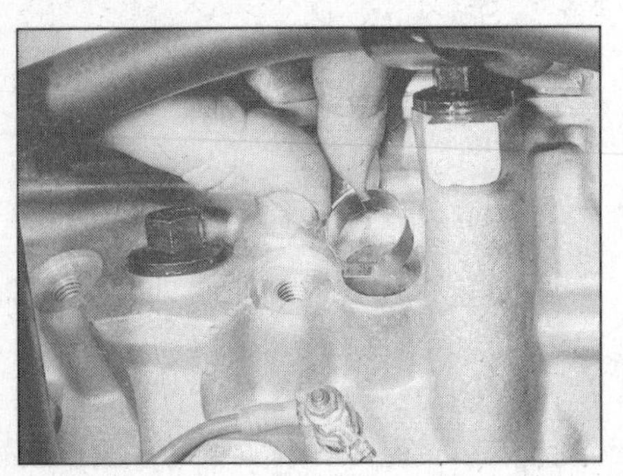
5.13a Removing an injector locating ring . . .

9 Counterhold the delivery valves on the injection pump and loosen the high-pressure pipe unions. Note that the delivery valves will be distorted if they are not counterheld when loosening the unions. Also take care not to bend the pipes.

10 Unscrew the unions at the injectors and remove the high-pressure pipes.

11 Note the fitted position of the injector clamps and pedestals, then unscrew the bolts and remove the clamps and pedestals **(see illustration)**.

12 Brush or blow away any debris from around the injectors, then remove them from the cylinder head **(see illustration)**. Carbon deposits can cause an injector to stick in its recess. In this case, an injector puller or a small slide hammer **(see illustration)** can be used, or it may be possible to free the injector by careful levering. Do not attempt to free a

5.12a Removing an injector

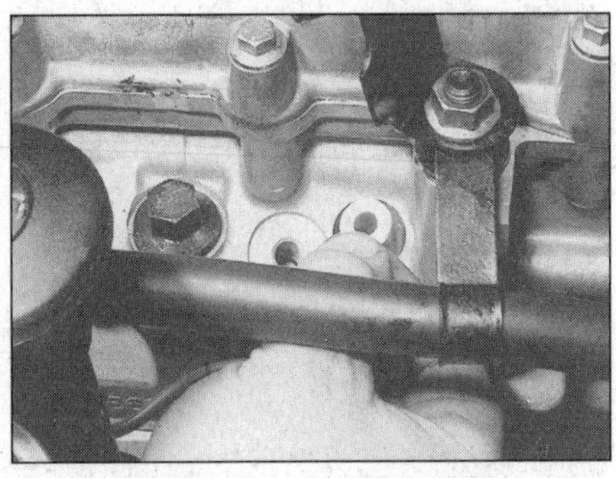
5.13b . . . and seat washer

sticking injector by cranking the engine, as it could be ejected with enough force to cause damage or serious injury.

13 Prise out the locating rings and seat washers from the bottom of the injector hole **(see illustrations)**.

14 Examine the clamps for damage, in particular the retaining arms. If any one of these is damaged, then the clamp must be renewed.

15 Wipe clean the injector seatings in the cylinder head.

Refitting

16 Locate new seat washers in the bottom of the injector holes.

17 Insert the new locating rings, then locate the injectors in the cylinder head.

18 Refit the injector clamps and pedestals in their previously-noted positions. Finger-

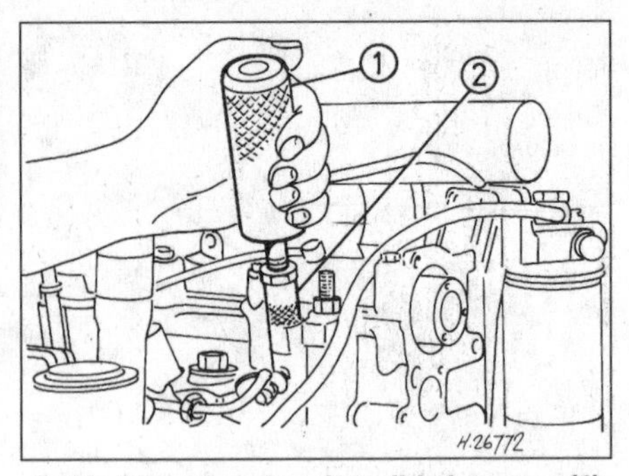

5.12b Injector-removing slide hammer (1) and adapter (2)

tighten the bolts at this stage. Make sure that the clamp arms are located squarely on the injector shoulders.

19 Refit the high-pressure pipes and tighten the unions at the injection pump to the specified torque. Ensure that the delivery valves are counterheld. Leave the unions at the injector ends loose at this stage.

20 Tighten the clamp bolts to the specified torque.

21 Bleed the fuel system as described in Part A of this Chapter.

22 Refit the leak-off pipes to the injectors using new sealing washers, then tighten the banjo bolts securely.

23 Reconnect the battery earth (negative) lead.

24 Start the engine and check for fuel leaks.

6 Fuel injection pump - removal and refitting

Removal

1 Disconnect the battery earth (negative) lead.

2 Remove the timing belt as described in Part A of this Chapter. If preferred, it is not essential to completely remove the belt, in which case do not drain the cooling system or remove the crankshaft pulley.

3 Disconnect the accelerator cable from the injection pump.

4 Disconnect the wiring leads from the stop solenoid, the fast idle solenoid and the automatic advance unit **(see illustrations)**.

5 Disconnect the wiring lead from the throttle potentiometer (where fitted). Where applicable, unscrew the union bolt and disconnect the manifold pressure line from the compensator on the top of the injection pump **(see illustrations)**.

6 Place rags beneath the fuel injection pump, then unscrew the fuel inlet hose union bolt and recover the sealing washers. Alternatively, loosen the clip and disconnect the fuel inlet hose from the union adapter on the injection pump. Plug the hose to prevent loss of fuel.

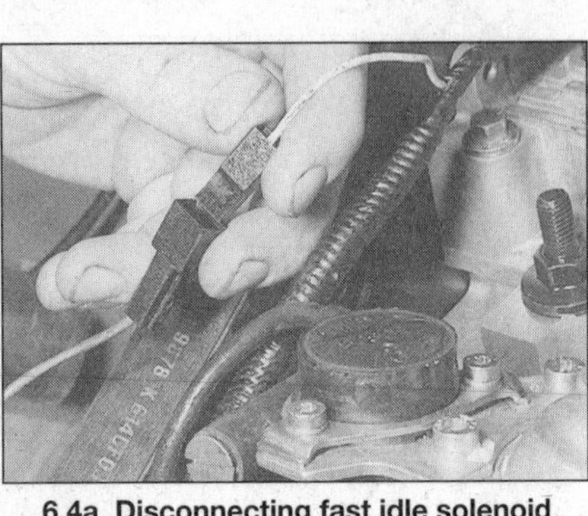
6.4a Disconnecting fast idle solenoid wiring

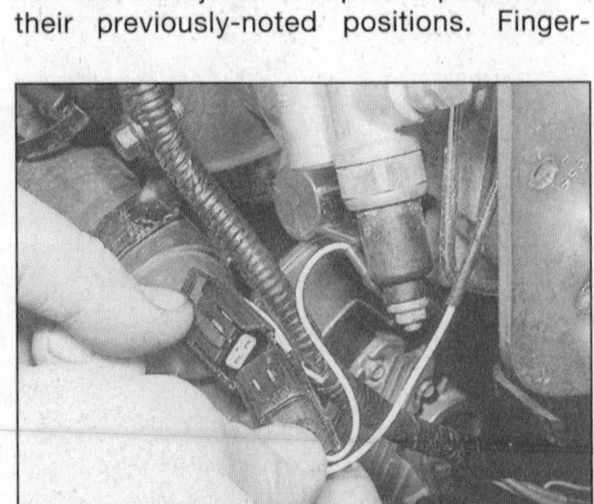
6.4b Disconnecting automatic advance unit and stop solenoid wiring

6.5a Disconnecting throttle potentiometer wiring

6.5b Disconnecting manifold pressure line from compensator

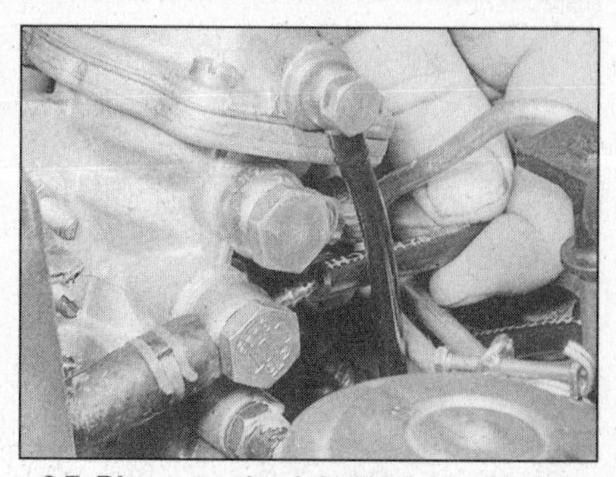
6.7 Disconnecting injector leak-off pipe from union adapter

7 Note the routing of the fuel main leak-off pipe to ensure correct refitting (routing varies between turbo and non turbo models), then disconnect the injector leak-off pipe from the union adapter **(see illustration)**.

8 Unscrew the fuel leak-off banjo union bolt while holding the adapter stationary. Move the hose to one side and recover the sealing washers. Alternatively, disconnect the leak-off hose at the rear of the injection pump and plug the hose **(see illustration)**.

9 Identify the high-pressure pipes for location, then unscrew the high-pressure pipe union nuts and remove the pipes from the injection pump and injectors. Always counterhold the delivery valves when loosening the high-pressure pipe unions at the injection pump **(see illustration)**.

10 Plug or cover the openings in the injection pump, to prevent the ingress of dust and dirt.

11 If the same injection pump is to be refitted, lock its timing as follows. Unscrew the locking bolt and remove the arrow-shaped spacer. Ensure that the pump gear timing marks are correctly aligned, then refit and tighten the locking bolt to lock the injection pump shaft **(see illustrations)**.

12 Counterhold the injection pump pulley gear **(see illustration)** then unscrew the nut and remove the washer.

13 Unscrew and remove the two timing bolts securing the gear to the injection pump mounting bracket.

14 Using a suitable puller, pull the gear/pulley off the injection pump driveshaft. The Rover tool consists of a circular block of metal bolted to the gear, through which a central bolt is screwed. The bolt bears against the driveshaft and forces the gear off. An alternative puller may be made out of 9 mm thick metal bar to the dimensions shown **(see illustration)**. Two 8 mm diameter (M8) bolts are then screwed into the holes in the gear and a 12 mm diameter (M12) bolt in the centre hole pulls the gear off **(see illustration)**.

15 If necessary, remove the location key from the driveshaft.

16 Mark the injection pump flange and the mounting bracket in relation to each other, as a reference for refitting the pump.

17 If the same injection pump is to be refitted, unscrew and remove the two mounting bolts securing the small rear mounting bracket to the main mounting bracket. The bolts are

6.8 Disconnecting fuel leak-off hose at rear of injection pump

6.9 Unscrewing high-pressure pipe union nuts . . .

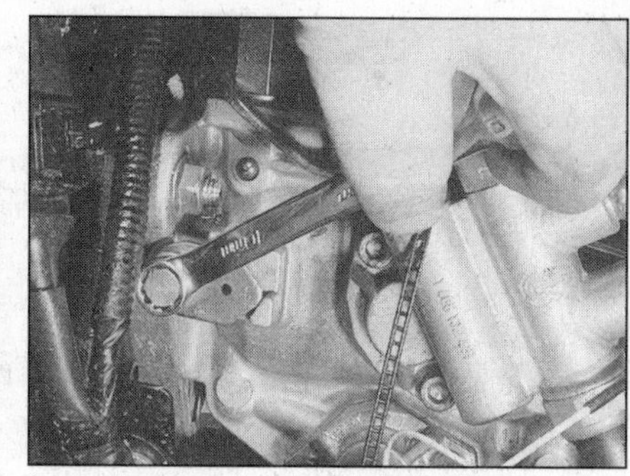
6.11a Unscrew locking bolt . . .

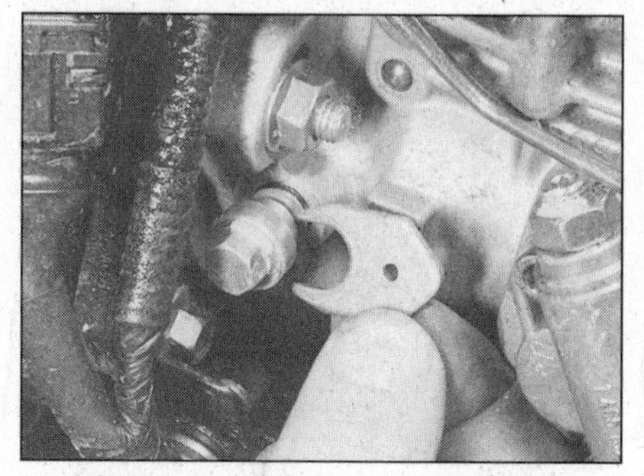
6.11b . . . and remove arrow-shaped spacer from injection pump

6.11c Injection pump gear timing marks (arrowed)

6.12 Removing injection pump pulley gear retaining nut

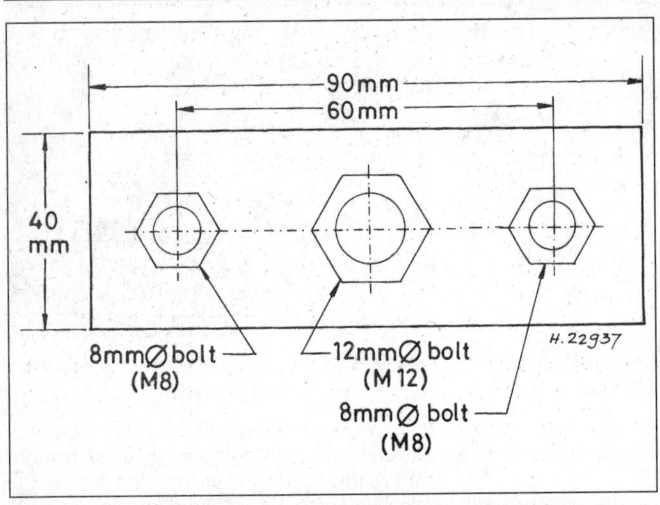

6.14a Injection pump gear/pulley puller dimensions

6.14b Using home-made puller to release injection pump gear/pulley from driveshaft

6.17 Unscrew these bolts if same injection pump is to be refitted

slightly concealed but by removing these bolts instead of the rear support plate bolts, the pump timing will be maintained for the refitting procedure **(see illustration)**.

18 If a different injection pump is being fitted, unscrew the two lower bolts securing the rear support plate to the small bracket. The bolts are located just below the high-pressure delivery valves.

19 Unscrew the nuts securing the pump flange to the mounting bracket, then withdraw the injection pump and remove it from the engine compartment **(see illustrations)**.

20 If a new injection pump is being fitted, transfer the rear support plate to the new pump and tighten its retaining bolts securely. Also transfer the stop solenoid to the new pump.

21 If necessary, unbolt the injection pump mounting bracket from the cylinder block and unbolt the small bracket from the main bracket.

Refitting

22 Start by refitting the main mounting bracket to the cylinder block (if removed) and tighten the bolts.

23 Where applicable, attach the small bracket to the main mounting bracket and finger-tighten the bolts.

24 Locate the injection pump in the mounting bracket. Where applicable, position it in the mid-range of the travel allowed by the slots and finger-tighten the nuts at this stage. Insert the rear mounting bolts and finger-tighten as well **(see illustration)**.

25 Fully tighten the two bolts securing the small bracket to the main bracket.

26 If removed, refit the location key in the injection pump driveshaft groove.

27 Locate the gear/pulley on the injection pump driveshaft with the correct timing marks aligned, then refit the washer and nut. Ensure that the gear/pulley engages correctly with the key and does not push it out of its groove. Hold the gear/pulley stationary using the special tool, then tighten the nut to the specified torque. Refit the two temporary timing bolts.

28 Make sure that the camshaft and flywheel timing pins are still in position, then check that the injection pump timing marks are aligned.

29 Unscrew the timing locking screw on the side of the injection pump, refit the arrow-shaped spacer, then tighten the screw to the specified torque.

30 Refit the timing belt and adjust its tension as described in Part A of this Chapter. Do not attempt to turn the engine until after the timing pins and injection pump gear holding bolts have been removed.

31 Check and adjust the injection pump timing, then fully tighten the pump flange nuts and the two rear support plate bolts. Where the original pump is being refitted, align the previously-made marks as a starting point.

32 Reconnect the high-pressure pipes to the injection pump and injectors **(see illustration)**. Counterhold the delivery valves and tighten the high-pressure pipe unions at the injector pump to the specified torque. Do

6.19a Unscrew flange nuts . . .

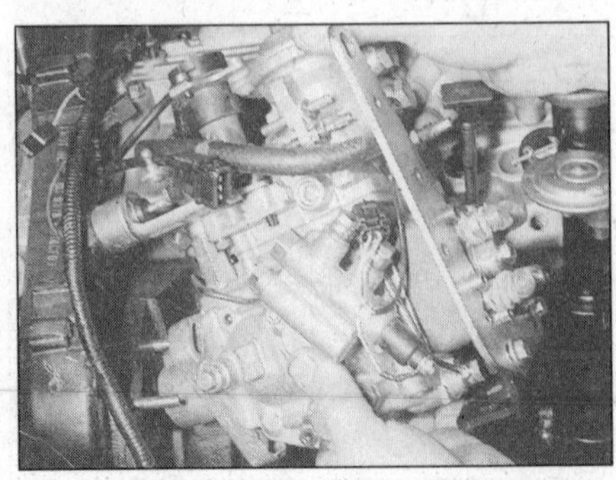
6.19b . . . and remove fuel injection pump

6.24 Slots (arrowed) in injection pump mounting flange

not overtighten the unions as the delivery valves can be distorted. Leave the unions at the injector ends loose at this stage.

33 Refit and tighten the leak-off banjo union bolt and the injector leak-off pipe (ensure that the union bolt with OUT stamped on it is used). Renew the aluminium sealing washers if necessary and ensure that the pipe is routed correctly. If the hose at the rear of the pump was disconnected on removal, reconnect the hose and fit the clip **(see illustration)**.

34 Refit the fuel inlet hose or union (as removed). Renew the copper union sealing washers if necessary. Note that the inlet union bolt is identified by having three large holes in it.

35 Reconnect the wiring lead to the throttle potentiometer where fitted.

36 Reconnect the wiring leads to the automatic advance unit, fast idle solenoid and stop solenoid.

37 Refit the accelerator cable to the injection pump and adjust it.

38 Reconnect the battery.

39 Bleed the fuel system as described in Part A of this Chapter

40 Finally, tighten the high-pressure pipe unions at the injectors to the specified torque.

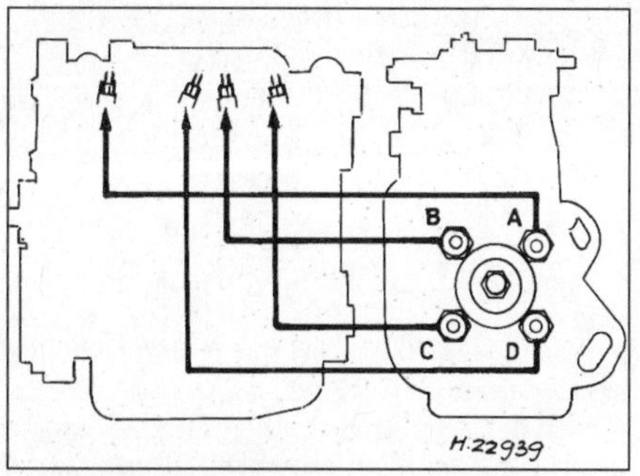

6.32 High-pressure pipe connections to injectors and fuel injection pump

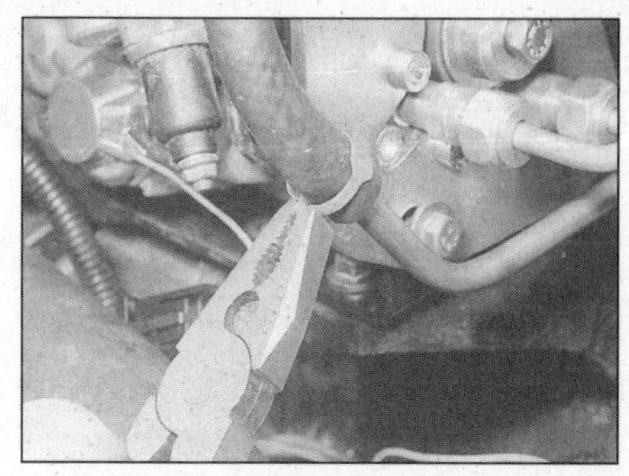

6.33 Tightening leak-off hose at rear of injection pump

7 Fuel injection pump - timing

Note: *A dial test indicator will be required for this work.*

1 For optimum engine performance, a finely-controlled amount of fuel must be supplied by the fuel injection pump to the injector of each cylinder, so that fuel is injected when the piston reaches a predetermined point before TDC on the compression stroke. If the timing is incorrect, the engine will exhibit various symptoms such as emission of smoke, lack of power, knocking noises, etc. It follows, therefore, that whenever the fuel injection pump has been removed, or if any of the timing components are renewed, the timing should be checked and if necessary, reset.

2 For the home mechanic, injection timing is checked statically. Some garages may have special equipment for checking the timing dynamically. At the time of writing, neither Rover nor Perkins provide dynamic timing values.

3 Start by disconnecting the battery earth (negative) lead.

4 Unscrew the blanking screw from the right-hand end of the camshaft cover, then have an assistant turn the engine slowly clockwise using a socket on the crankshaft pulley bolt, while you look through the hole in the camshaft cover. When the timing hole in the camshaft appears, align it with the cover and insert a timing pin (or 6.75 mm drill) to lock it. Access to the crankshaft pulley bolt may be improved if the front right-hand side of the vehicle is jacked up and the roadwheel and inner wheelarch cover removed. Refer to the illustrations in Part A of this Chapter (timing belt renewal).

5 Insert another timing pin through the adapter plate into the flywheel. If this pin will not enter, then it will be necessary to remove the timing belt cover and loosen the camshaft gear mounting centre bolt (taper-mounted gear) or the camshaft gear hub mounting bolts (hub-mounted gear), so that the crankshaft may be moved slightly to the TDC position. Tighten the centre bolt or hub bolts, using a suitable tool to counterhold the camshaft gear.

6 Remove the timing cover and check that the timing mark on the injection pump gear is aligned with the mark on the timing belt inner cover. Note that there are two timing marks, on opposite sides of the gear. The A mark is for non turbo models and the B mark for Turbo models.

7 Wipe clean the rear of the injection pump. Unscrew the blanking screw **(see illustration)** and remove the washer from the rear of the injection pump. Be prepared for some spillage of fuel. Do not allow any dust or foreign matter to enter the injection pump.

8 Fit a dial test indicator (DTI), adapter and probe, so that the probe enters the access hole and the DTI displays movement of the pump plunger **(see illustrations)**. Temporarily preload the DTI by 2.0 mm.

9 Remove both timing pins, then slowly turn the crankshaft anti-clockwise until the DTI pointer reaches its lowest reading (pump plunger at BDC). Zero the DTI at this point.

10 Slowly turn the crankshaft clockwise until the timing pin can be inserted in the flywheel timing hole.

11 Note the plunger movement on the DTI and compare it with the specified value. If the movement is not within 0.03 mm of the specified value, then the timing must be adjusted as follows.

12 Loosen the high-pressure pipe unions at the injectors. Counterhold the delivery valves, then unscrew the high-pressure pipe unions at the pump and disconnect the pipes.

13 Loosen the two lower bolts securing the rear support plate to the small bracket. The bolts are located just below the high-pressure delivery valves.

14 Loosen the nuts securing the pump flange to the mounting bracket.

15 If plunger movement is too low, move the top of the injection pump body towards the engine (ie. clockwise viewed from the left-hand, or flywheel, side of the engine) until the

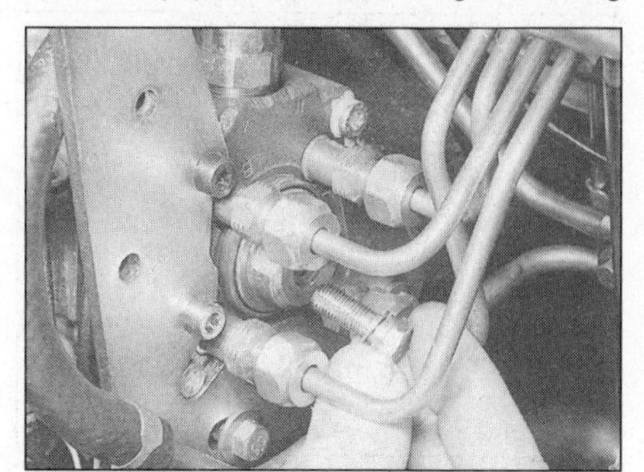

7.7 Removing blanking screw from rear of injection pump

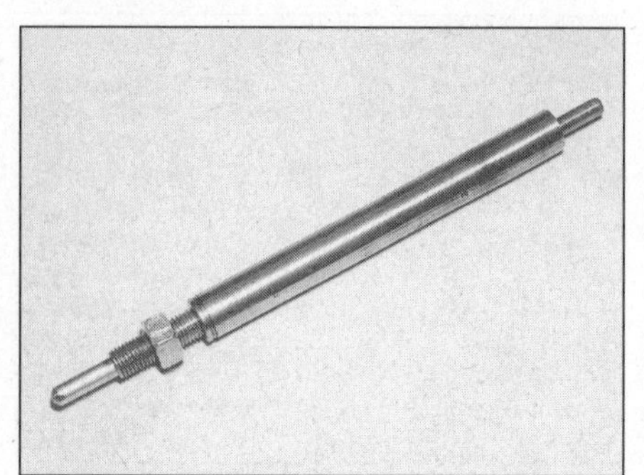

7.8a Home-made probe for fitting to rear of injector pump

7.8b Dial test indicator and probe located on rear of injection pump

8.3 Loosen union nut and disconnect fuel lift pump outlet pipe

reading is correct. Note that left-hand and right-hand are always as seen from the driver's seat.

16 If plunger movement is too high, move the top of the injection pump body away from the engine (ie. anti-clockwise viewed from the left-hand, or flywheel, side of the engine) until the reading is correct.

17 With the plunger movement correct, tighten the pump flange nuts and the rear support plate bolts.

18 Remove the timing pin from the flywheel and turn the crankshaft a quarter-turn anti-clockwise. Now turn the crankshaft clockwise until the timing pin can be inserted in the camshaft timing hole.

19 Check that the plunger movement is as specified. If not, check the timing belt tension and recheck the injection pump timing again.

20 Remove the timing pin and refit the blanking screw to the right-hand end of the camshaft cover.

21 Remove the dial test indicator and adapter, then refit the blanking screw and washer. Tighten the screw securely.

22 Reconnect the high-pressure pipes and tighten the unions at the injection pump ends. Do not forget to counterhold the delivery valves. Leave the high-pressure pipe unions at the injectors loose at this stage.

23 Reconnect the battery.

24 Bleed the fuel system as described in Part A of this Chapter.

25 Finally, tighten the high-pressure pipe unions at the injectors to the specified torque.

8 Fuel lift pump - removal and refitting

Removal

1 Disconnect the battery earth (negative) lead.

2 Unscrew and remove the timing blanking screw from the right-hand end of the camshaft cover housing, then turn the engine using a socket on the crankshaft pulley bolt until the TDC timing hole in the camshaft is aligned with the hole in the cover. This procedure is necessary to position the eccentric on the camshaft away from the fuel lift pump. Refit and tighten the timing screw.

3 Unscrew the union nuts and disconnect the inlet and outlet pipes from the pump **(see illustration)**. A little fuel will escape as the pipes are disconnected, so position a rag beneath them first. Plug the ends of the pipes, to prevent dust and dirt entering the fuel system.

4 Unscrew the mounting bolts and withdraw the fuel lift pump from the camshaft cover housing. Recover the gasket **(see illustrations)**.

Refitting

5 Clean the mounting faces of the pump and camshaft cover housing.

6 Locate the fuel lift pump on the camshaft cover housing, making sure that the operating lever locates on the camshaft eccentric correctly.

7 Apply a little locking fluid to the threads of the mounting bolts.

8 Hold the fuel lift pump square to the camshaft cover housing face with a new gasket in position, then insert the mounting bolts and tighten them progressively to the specified torque.

9 Reconnect the fuel inlet and outlet pipes, then tighten the union nuts.

10 Loosen the bleed screw on the fuel filter, then operate the plunger on the fuel pump until fuel emerges free from air bubbles. Tighten the bleed screw.

11 Reconnect the battery.

8.4a Unscrew mounting bolts . . .

8.4b . . . and remove fuel lift pump

9 Preheating and cold start system - checking

1 The minimum equipment required for this operation is a 12-volt test lamp. More detailed testing will require a multi-meter with the appropriate voltage and current ranges. For a comprehensive test of the glow plugs, they should be taken to a Rover dealer or diesel specialist who will check them in a glow plug tester.

Voltage supply checks with a test lamp or voltmeter

2 Connect the test lamp or voltmeter between the glow plug supply wire and a suitable earth **(see illustration)**. Do not let the live side connections touch earth. Have an assistant energise the preheating system. The test lamp should light brightly, or the voltmeter should read at least 10 volts.

3 If there is no voltage at all, this suggests a fault such as a blown fuse, a disconnected wire, a defective relay or a defective switch. A blown fuse may only be a pointer to some underlying fault, such as a short-circuit in the wiring or a glow plug which has failed so as to cause a short.

4 If the voltage is low and the battery OK, this suggests a bad connection somewhere in the wiring, or possibly a faulty relay.

Glow plug checks with a test lamp or multi-meter

5 A simple continuity check can be made by disconnecting the wires from the glow plugs (ignition switched off!), then connecting the test lamp between the battery positive terminal and each glow plug terminal in turn **(see illustration)**. Alternatively, measure the resistance between each glow plug terminal and earth. The lamp should light brightly, or the meter read a very low resistance (typically 1 ohm or less).

6 If the lamp does not light or the meter shows a high resistance, the glow plug has failed open-circuit and must be renewed.

7 The above is only a rough test and will not detect a glow plug which has failed so as to cause a short-circuit, or one which is no longer heating properly even though its resistance is still more or less correct. More accurate testing requires the use of an ammeter, of range 0 to 25 or 0 to 30 amps. It should incorporate some kind of overload protection, either in the instrument itself or by means of a fuse in its lead.

8 Connect the ammeter between the battery positive terminal and one of the glow plugs (the glow plugs must still be disconnected from each other). Note the current draw over a period of 20 seconds. Typically, an initial surge of 25 amps or more will fall over 20 seconds to a steady draw of 12 amps. A very high draw shows a short-circuit, whereas zero amps shows an open-circuit.

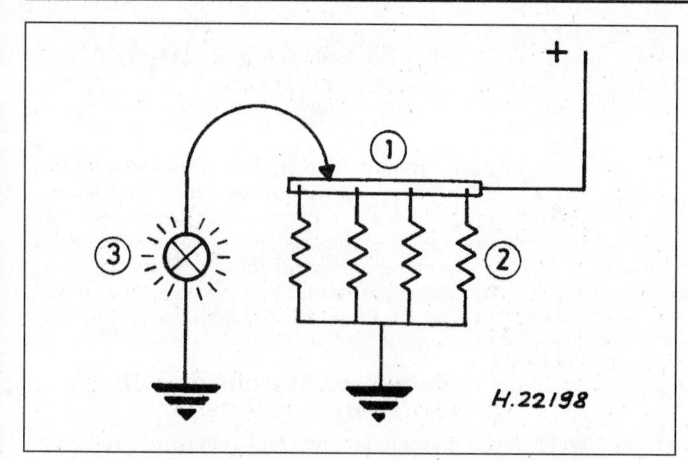

9.2 Checking glow plug supply voltage with test lamp

1 Glow plug supply wire
2 Glow plugs
3 Test lamp

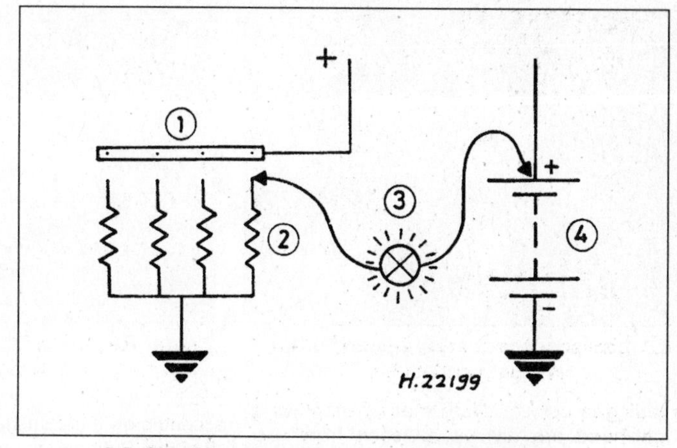

9.5 Checking glow plug continuity with test lamp

1 Glow plug supply wire (disconnected)
2 Glow plugs
3 Test lamp
4 Battery

9 Repeat the current draw check on the other glow plugs and compare the results. Obvious differences will not be hard to spot. A difference in the rate at which the current falls off is also significant and may indicate that the glow plug in question is no longer heating at the tip first.

10 The physical condition of the glow plugs is also important. To establish this, they must be removed and inspected for burning or erosion. Damage can be caused by a fault resulting in too long a post-heating time but it is more often due to an injector fault. If damaged glow plugs are found, the injectors in the cylinders in question should be removed and checked. Take them to a Rover dealer or fuel system specialist, who will have the necessary equipment to test the spray pattern and calibration.

11 As a final check, the glow plugs can be energised while they are out of the engine and inspected to see that they heat evenly, with the tip glowing first and no local hot or cold spots. Some means of supporting the plug while it is being tested must be devised and the power supply lead should be fused, or should incorporate some other overload protection. Ideally, a purpose-made glow plug tester with a hot test chamber should be used.

12 Any glow plug which takes much longer than specified for its tip to glow red, or which shows uneven heating, should be renewed.

Control circuitry checks

13 The preheating control unit (and on single-stage injection, the resistor) are located on the left-hand inner wing, behind the battery.

14 The system continues to apply voltage to the glow plugs (via the resistor, when fitted) for up to 90 seconds after a cold start.

15 Component checking is by substitution with a known serviceable item. Alternatively, have the system circuitry checked by a Rover dealer.

Cold idle and cold start devices

16 With the engine cold, switch on the ignition and depress the accelerator pedal once, then check that the fast idle solenoid has moved the control lever on the injection pump to the fast idle position **(see illustration)**. If not, connect a 12-volt supply to the solenoid. If there is still no movement, check that there is a 12-volt supply at the temperature switch located on the thermostat housing. If there is voltage at the temperature switch input terminal but not at the output terminal, then the switch is faulty and should be renewed. If there is no voltage at the switch, check all of the associated wiring.

17 If the engine is warm and the coolant temperature above 30°C, the fast idle solenoid will not be energised.

18 The automatic advance unit located on the front of the injection pump **(see illustration)** can only be accurately tested using special equipment. A fault in the unit may be indicated if the engine is difficult to start from cold, or if there is excessive white smoke from the exhaust when it does start. In this case, the unit may not have changed the timing position for a cold start. If the engine is noisy when warm or low on power, the unit may not have returned the timing to normal after the cold start.

19 To check the electrical supply to the automatic advance unit, connect a 12-volt test lamp between the unit and its disconnected wire. With the engine cold and the ignition switched on, the lamp should remain off. With the engine warm, the lamp should be lit. If either of these conditions is incorrect, check the temperature switch, located on the front-facing side of the cylinder head by the oil filler tube. If necessary, disconnect the wiring and unscrew the switch from the head **(see illustration)**.

9.16 Fast idle solenoid

9.18 Automatic advance unit located on front of injection pump

9.19 Removing temperature switch for automatic advance unit from cylinder head

10.2 Fuel vapour separator and hoses

10 Fuel vapour separator - removal and refitting

Note: *The fuel vapour separator is not fitted to all models.*

Removal

1 Unscrew the mounting bolt and lift the EGR modulator valve and bracket from the left-hand side of the engine compartment, leaving all the wiring and vacuum hoses still attached.

2 Identify the hoses for position, then loosen the clips and disconnect them from the fuel vapour separator **(see illustration)**.

3 Unscrew the mounting bolts and withdraw the unit.

Refitting

4 Refitting is a reversal of the removal procedure.

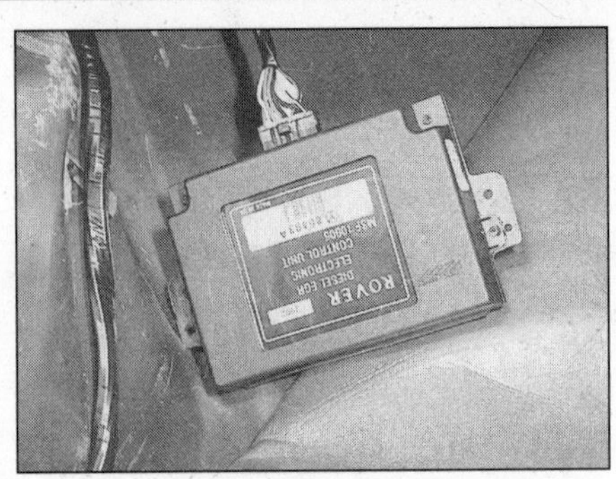

11.4 Removing EGR control unit from bulkhead

11 EGR control unit - removal and refitting

Removal

1 Disconnect the battery earth (negative) lead.

2 With the left-hand passenger door open, pull the carpet from the bulkhead to reveal the EGR control unit.

3 Carefully disconnect the multi-plug from the bottom of the unit.

4 Unscrew the two cross-head mounting screws and withdraw the control unit from the bulkhead **(see illustration)**.

Refitting

5 Refitting is a reversal of the removal procedure.

12 EGR valve - removal, cleaning and refitting

1 Refer to Part A of this Chapter, Section 8, paragraphs 5 to 15 inclusive.

13 EGR modulator valve - removal and refitting

Removal

1 Disconnect the battery earth (negative) lead.

2 Disconnect the multi-plug from the side of the valve **(see illustration)**.

3 Identify the hose positions then disconnect them from the modulator valve.

4 Unscrew the mounting screws and remove the modulator valve from the mounting on the side of the front suspension turret.

Refitting

5 Refitting is a reversal of the removal procedure.

13.2 Disconnecting multi-plug from side of EGR modulator valve

Chapter 3
Citroën 1360cc, 1527cc, 1769cc and 1905cc engines

Part A: Routine maintenance and servicing

Contents

Engine application

1360cc and 1527cc engines	Citroën AX - 1987 to 1994
1769cc and 1905cc engines	Citroën BX/Visa/C15 - 1984 to 1996
1769cc and 1905cc engines	Citroën ZX - 1991 to 1993
1905cc engine	Citroën Xantia - 1993 to 1995

Manufacturer's engine codes

Citroën AX	
1360cc	K9A
1527cc	VJZ and VJY
Citroën BX/Visa/C15	
1765cc non-turbo (Visa, BX and C15)	XUD7 (161A)
1765cc turbo (BX)	XUD7TE/L (A8A)
1905cc non-turbo (BX)	XUD9 (162B) or XUD 9A/L (D9B)
Citroën ZX	
1769cc non-turbo	XUD7 (A9A)
1905cc non-turbo, non-catalyst (Pre 1993)	XUD9A (D9B)
1905cc non-turbo, non-catalyst (1993 on)	XUD9A/L (D9B)
1905cc non-turbo, catalyst	XUD9/Y (DJZ)
1905cc turbo, non-catalyst	XUD9TE/L (D8A)
1905cc turbo, catalyst	XUD9TE/Y (DHY or DHZ)
Citroën Xantia	
1905cc non-turbo	XUD9 A/L (D9B)
1905cc turbo	XUD9 TF/L (D8B)
1905cc turbo	XUD9 TF/Y (DHX)

Servicing Specifications

Oil filter

All engines	Champion F104

Valve clearances (cold)

	Inlet	Exhaust
Citroën AX	0.15 ± 0.075	0.30 ± 0.075 mm
Citroën BX/Visa/C15:		
1765 cc non turbo	0.10 to 0.25 mm	0.25 to 0.40 mm
1765 cc turbo	0.15 ± 0.08 mm	0.30 ± 0.08 mm
1905 cc non turbo	0.15 to 0.25 mm	0.35 to 0.45 mm
Citroën ZX	0.15 ± 0.05 mm	0.30 ± 0.05 mm
Citroën Xantia	0.15 ± 0.08 mm	0.30 ± 0.08 mm

Timing belt

Type	Toothed belt
Tension:	
AX	25 units on Citroën special tool
All other engines	Automatic sprung tensioner

Auxiliary drivebelt tension

AX, BX, Visa and C15:	
With or without air conditioning	5.0 mm deflection, midway between pulleys on longest run
ZX and Xantia:	
Without power steering or air conditioning	5.0 mm deflection, midway between pulleys on longest run
With power steering or air conditioning	90° rotational movement, midway between pulleys
With power steering and air conditioning	By automatic tensioner

Air filter

Citroën AX:	
1360cc engine	Champion U543/W117
1527cc engine	Champion V414
Citroën BX/Visa/C15:	
BX (pre mid 1987 - round type)	Champion W117
BX (post mid 1987 - square type)	Champion U543
Visa and C15	Champion W117
Citroën ZX:	
Non turbo	Champion W233
Turbo	Champion V433
Citroën Xantia	Champion U543

Fuel filter

Citroën AX	Champion L113
Citroën BX and C15:	
Roto-diesel	Champion L132
Bosch	Champion L135
Citroën Visa:	
Roto-diesel	Champion L131 or L137
Bosch	Champion L136
Citroën ZX and Xantia	Champion L141

Glow plugs

Citroën AX	Champion CH147
Citroën BX/Visa/C15	Champion CH68
Citroën ZX and Xantia:	
Non turbo	Champion CH68
Turbo	Champion CH163

Idle speed

Citroën AX

All models	775 ± 25 rpm

Citroën BX/Visa/C15

Roto-diesel injection pump:	
BX	775 ± 25 rpm
Visa	750 rpm
C15	800 ± 50 rpm
Bosch injection pump:	
Automatic transmission	825 ± 25 rpm
Manual transmission	775 ± 25 rpm

Idle speed (continued)

Citroën ZX

Manual transmission:
- Without air conditioning .... 800 + 50 rpm
- With air conditioning .... 850 + 50 rpm

Automatic transmission:
- Without air conditioning .... 850 + 50 rpm
- With air conditioning .... 900 + 50 rpm

Citroën Xantia

Without air conditioning .... 800 +0 -50 rpm
With air conditioning .... 850 +0 -50 rpm

Fast idle speed

Citroën AX

Roto-Diesel injection pump .... 950 ± 50 rpm
Bosch injection pump .... 850 to 900 rpm

Citroën BX/Visa/C15

Bosch injection pump:
- Pre 1987 - automatic transmission .... 1150 to 1250 rpm
- BX - post early 1993 .... 900 to 1000 rpm
- C15 - post early 1993 .... 950 ± 50 rpm

Lucas injection pump:
- C15 - post early 1993 .... 950 ± 50 rpm

Citroën ZX

1769cc engine .... 1050 ± 50 rpm
1905cc engines .... 950 ± 50 rpm

Citroën Xantia

1905cc engines .... 950 ± 50 rpm

Anti-stall speed

Citroën AX

With 1.0 mm shim/feeler blade inserted .... 1600 ± 50 rpm

Citroën BX/Visa/C15

Lucas/Roto-Diesel injection pump:
- With 3.0 mm shim/feeler blade inserted .... 900 ± 100 rpm

Bosch injection pump:
- With 1.0 mm shim/feeler blade inserted:
  - Automatic transmission .... 875 ± 25 rpm
  - Manual transmission .... 825 ± 25 rpm

Citroën ZX

Lucas fuel injection pump:
- XUD7 (A9A) and XUD9A (D9B) engines with 4.0 mm shim .... 1500 ± 100 rpm
- XUD9A/L (D9B) engine with 3.0 mm shim .... 900 ± 100 rpm

Bosch fuel injection pump:
- XUD7 (A9A), XUD9A (D9B), XUD9Y (DJZ), XUD9TE/L (D8A) and XUD9TE/Y (DHY and DHZ) engines with 1.0 mm shim .... 800 + 20 to 50 rpm
- XUD9A/L (D9B) engine with 3.0 mm shim .... 1250 ± 100 rpm

Citroën Xantia

Speed .... 1500 ±100 rpm

Shim thickness:
- Lucas .... 4.0 mm
- Bosch .... 3.0 mm

Torque wrench settings

Citroën AX	Nm	lbf ft
Crankshaft pulley-to-sprocket	16	12
Timing belt cover bolts:		
Except upper cover-to-cylinder head cover	8	6
Upper cover-to-cylinder head cover	5	5
Timing belt tensioner pulley nut	23	17

3A

Torque wrench settings (continued)	Nm	lbf ft
Citroën BX/Visa/C15		
Crankshaft pulley bolt:		
Stage 1	40	30
Stage 2	Tighten through a further 60°	
Timing belt tensioner	18	13
Timing belt cover, lower	12	9
Sump oil drain	3	2.2
Engine mounting bracket, right-hand lower	18	13
Engine mounting bracket, right-hand upper:		
To engine	35	26
To mounting rubber	28	21
Fuel filter through-bolt	10	7
Citroën ZX and Xantia		
Crankshaft pulley bolt*:		
Stage 1	40	30
Stage 2	Tighten through a further 50°	
Timing belt cover bolts	8	6
Timing belt tensioner adjustment bolt	18	13
Timing belt tensioner pivot nut	18	13

** A new bolt must be used on refitting*

Lubricants, fluids and capacities

Component or system	Lubricant or fluid	Capacity
Citroën AX		
Engine	Multigrade engine oil, viscosity range SAE 10W/40, 15W/40 or 15W/50, to specification API SG/CD	3.5 litres - 1360cc engine without filter 4.5 litres - 1527cc engine without filter
Cooling system	Ethylene glycol based antifreeze. 50% volume with water	4.8 litres
Fuel system	Commercial Diesel fuel for road vehicles (DERV)	43.0 litres
Citroën BX/Visa/C15		
Engine	Multigrade engine oil, viscosity range SAE 15W/40, to specification API SG/CD	5.0 litres - with filter
Vacuum pump - Visa only	Multigrade oil, viscosity range SAE 10W/30	N/A
Cooling system	Ethylene glycol based antifreeze. 50% volume with water	7.0 litres - BX non turbo 6.5 litres - BX turbo 7.5 litres - Visa/C15
Fuel system	Commercial Diesel fuel for road vehicles (DERV)	52.0 litres - BX pre early 1993 except turbo and TZD non turbo 60.0 litres - BX TZD non turbo 66.0 litres - BX post early 1993, and all turbo 43.0 litres - Visa 47.0 litres - C15
Citroën ZX		
Engine	Multigrade engine oil, viscosity range SAE 10W/40 to 15W/50, to specification API SG/CD	4.5 litres - Non turbo without filter 4.8 litres - Turbo without filter
Cooling system	Ethylene glycol based antifreeze. 50% volume with water	8.5 litres - Non turbo, manual transmission 9.0 litres - Non turbo, automatic transmission 9.0 litres - Turbo
Fuel system	Commercial Diesel fuel for road vehicles (DERV)	56.0 litres
Citroën Xantia		
Engine	Multigrade engine oil, viscosity range SAE 10W/40 to 15W/50, to specification API SG/CD	4.8 litres - without filter
Cooling system	Ethylene glycol based antifreeze. 50% volume with water	7.5 litres - Non turbo, without air conditioning 8.5 litres - Non turbo, with air conditioning 9.0 litres - Turbo
Fuel system	Commercial Diesel fuel for road vehicles (DERV)	65.0 litres

Citroën diesel engine - maintenance schedule

The maintenance schedules which follow are basically those recommended by the manufacturer. Servicing intervals are determined by mileage or time elapsed - this is because fluids and systems deteriorate with age as well as with use. Follow the time intervals if the appropriate mileage is not covered within the specified period.

Vehicles operating under adverse conditions may need more frequent maintenance. Adverse conditions include climatic extremes, full-time towing or taxi work, driving on unmade roads, and a high proportion of short journeys. The use of inferior fuel can cause early degradation of the engine oil. Consult a Citroën dealer for advice on these points.

Every 250 miles (400 km), weekly, or before a long journey - All models

- ☐ Check engine oil level and top up if necessary (Section 3)
- ☐ Check coolant level and top up if necessary (Section 4)
- ☐ Check exhaust emission (Section 5)
- ☐ Check operation of glow plug warning light (Section 6)

Every 6000 miles (10 000 km) or 12 months - Citroën AX

- ☐ Renew engine oil and filter (Section 7)
- ☐ Drain water from fuel filter (Section 8)
- ☐ Check engine compartment hoses for security and leaks

Citroën specify that the fuel filter should be renewed at the first 6000 mile service. After that, they recommend filter renewal at 12 000 mile intervals, with water being drained from the filter at the intermediate 6000-mile service interval.

Every 6000 miles (10 000 km) or 6 months - Citroën BX/Visa/C15

- ☐ Renew engine oil and filter (Section 9)
- ☐ Clean engine oil filler cap (Section 10)
- ☐ Drain water from fuel filter (Section 11)
- ☐ Check engine compartment hoses for security and leaks

The maintenance interval for pre 1989 models is 5000 miles (7500 km). The time interval remaining at 6 months.

Every 6000 miles (10 000 km) or 6 months - Citroën ZX

- ☐ Renew engine oil and filter (Section 12)
- ☐ Drain water from fuel filter (Section 13)
- ☐ Check engine compartment hoses for security and leaks

Every 6000 miles (10 000 km) or 12 months - Citroën Xantia

- ☐ Renew engine oil and filter (Section 14)
- ☐ Drain water from fuel filter (Section 15)
- ☐ Check engine compartment hoses for security and leaks
- ☐ Check auto-diagnostic memories (Section 16)

Every 12 000 miles (20 000 km) - Citroën AX

- ☐ Check engine idle speed and anti-stall speed (Section 17)
- ☐ Check emission control system (Section 18)
- ☐ Renew fuel filter (Section 19)
- ☐ Check condition and tension of auxiliary drivebelt

Every 12 000 miles (20 000 km) - Citroën BX/Visa/C15

- ☐ Check engine idle speed and anti-stall speed (Section 20)
- ☐ Renew fuel filter (Section 21)
- ☐ Check condition and tension of auxiliary drivebelt
- ☐ Check vacuum pump - Visa only (Section 22)

The maintenance interval for pre 1989 models is 10 000 miles (15 000 km). The time interval being 12 months.

Every 12 000 miles (20 000 km) - Citroën ZX and Xantia

- ☐ Check engine idle speed and anti-stall speed (Sections 23 and 24)
- ☐ Check emission control system (Section 25)
- ☐ Check condition and tension of auxiliary drivebelt

Every 18 000 miles (30 000 km) or 18 months - Citroën ZX

- ☐ Renew air filter element
- ☐ Renew fuel filter (Section 26)

Citroën diesel engine - maintenance schedule (continued)

Every 18 000 miles (30 000 km) - Citroën Xantia

- [ ] Renew fuel filter (Section 27)

Every 24 000 miles (40 000 km) - Citroën AX

- [ ] Renew air filter element

Every 24 000 miles (40 000 km) - Citroën BX/Visa/C15

- [ ] Renew air filter element

The maintenance interval for pre 1989 models is 20 000 miles (30 000 km). The time interval being 2 years.

Every 30 000 miles (45 000 km) - Citroën BX/Visa/C15

- [ ] Renew engine coolant

Every 36 000 miles (60 000 km) - Citroën AX

- [ ] Renew timing belt (Section 28)

Citroën recommend renewal of the timing belt at 72 000 mile (120 000 km) intervals. It is strongly recommended that this interval is halved on vehicles which are subjected to intensive use, ie. mainly short journeys or a lot of stop-start driving. The actual belt renewal interval is therefore very much up to the individual owner but bear in mind that severe engine damage will result if the belt breaks.

Every 36 000 miles (60 000 km) - Citroën Xantia

- [ ] Renew auxiliary drivebelt - manually adjusted belt
- [ ] Renew air filter element
- [ ] Renew timing belt (Section 29)

Citroën recommend renewal of the timing belt at 72 000 mile (120 000 km) intervals. It is strongly recommended that this interval is halved on vehicles which are subjected to intensive use, ie. mainly short journeys or a lot of stop-start driving. The actual belt renewal interval is therefore very much up to the individual owner but bear in mind that severe engine damage will result if the belt breaks.

Every 40 000 miles (60 000 km) or 2 years - Citroën ZX

- [ ] Renew engine coolant

Every 48 000 miles (80 000 km) - Citroën BX/Visa/C15

- [ ] Renew timing belt (Section 30)

Every 48 000 miles (80 000 km) - Citroën ZX

- [ ] Renew timing belt (Section 31)

Every 72 000 miles (120 000 km) - Citroën Xantia

- [ ] Renew auxiliary drivebelt - automatically adjusted belt

Every 2 years (regardless of mileage) - Citroën Xantia

- [ ] Renew engine coolant

Underbonnet view of 1360 cc Diesel engine in Citroën AX

1 Engine oil filler cap
2 Engine oil dipstick
3 Battery earth (negative) terminal
4 Master cylinder/brake fluid reservoir
5 Auxiliary fusebox
6 Fuel injection pump
7 Radiator filler cap
8 Braking system vacuum pump
9 Washer fluid reservoir filler cap
10 Braking system vacuum servo unit
11 Preheating control unit
12 Relay box
13 Suspension strut upper mounting
14 Air cleaner housing
15 Fuel system priming bulb

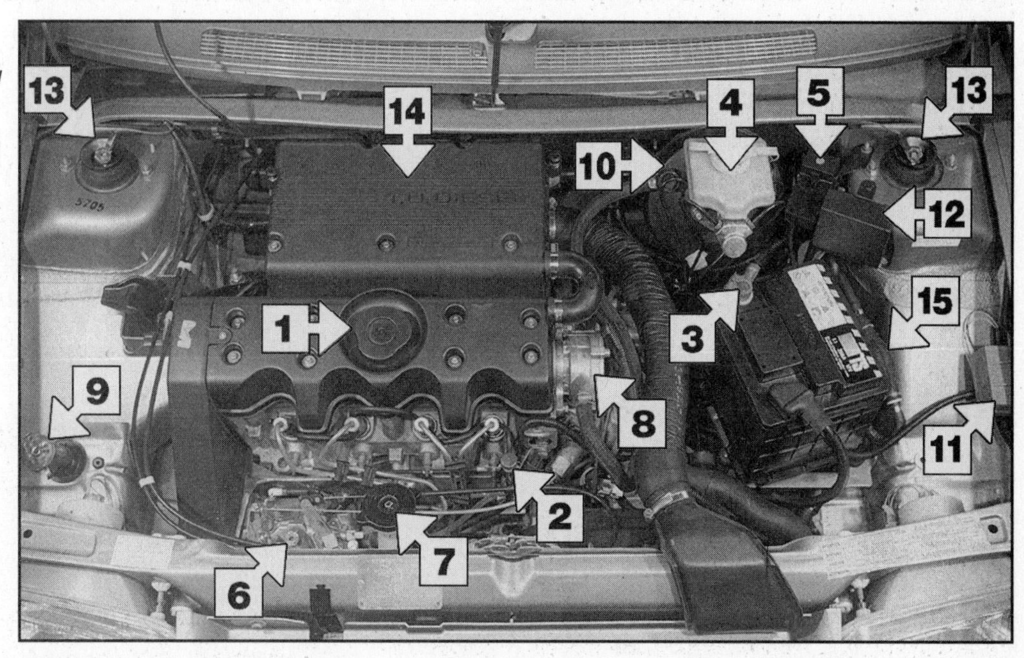

Underbonnet view of 1527 cc Diesel engine in Citroën AX

1 Engine oil filler cap
2 Engine oil dipstick
3 Battery earth (negative) terminal
4 Master cylinder/brake fluid reservoir
5 Auxiliary fusebox
6 Fuel injection pump
7 Expansion tank filler cap
8 Braking system vacuum pump
9 Washer fluid reservoir filler cap
10 Braking system vacuum servo unit
11 Relay box
12 Suspension strut upper mounting
13 Air cleaner housing
14 Fuel system priming bulb

Underbonnet view of Diesel engine in Citroën BX - air cleaner removed for clarity

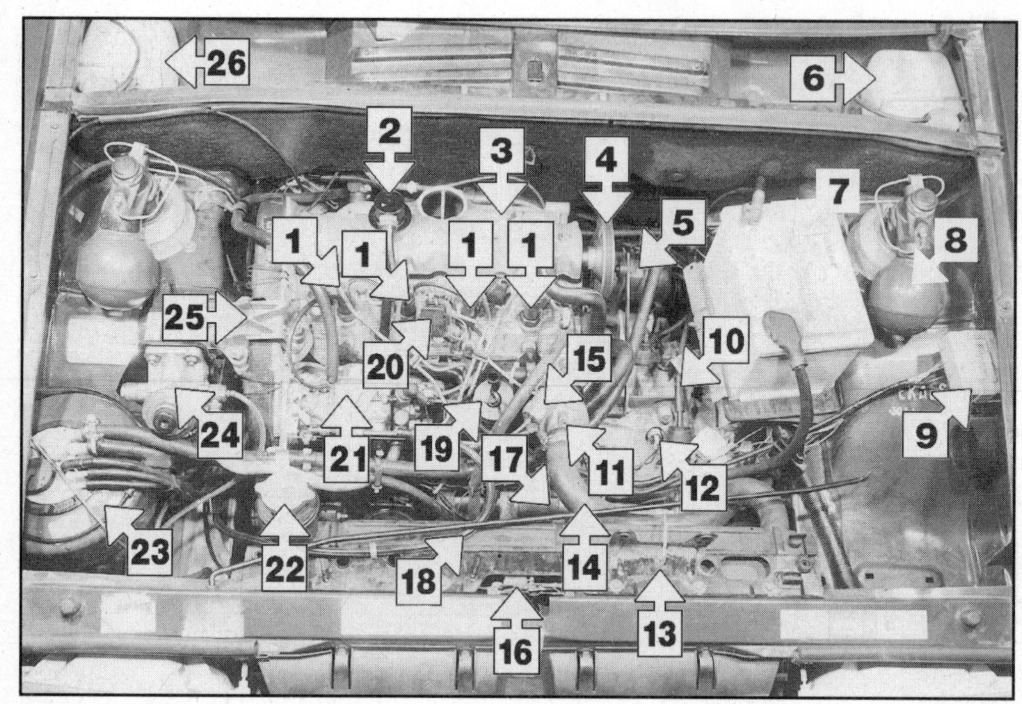

1 Injectors
2 Oil filler cap and ventilation hose
3 Valve cover
4 HP pump drivebelt
5 HP pump
6 Washer reservoir
7 Battery
8 Front suspension hydraulic unit
9 Heater plug relay
10 Clutch cable
11 Thermostat cover
12 Reversing lamp switch
13 Radiator
14 Top hose
15 Fast idle thermo unit
16 Bonnet lock
17 Starter motor
18 Accelerator cable
19 Engine oil dipstick
20 Diagnostic socket
21 Injection pump (Roto-diesel)
22 Coolant filler cap
23 Hydraulic system reservoir
24 Fuel filter
25 Right hand engine mounting
26 Washer reservoir

Underbonnet view of Turbo Diesel engine in Citroën BX - intercooler removed for clarity

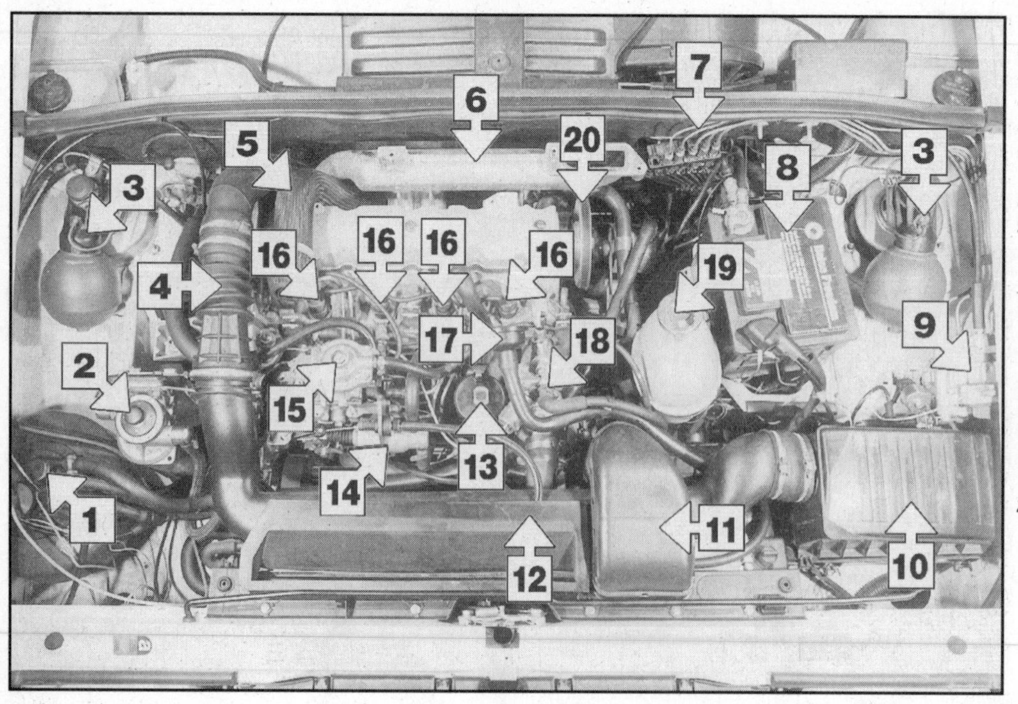

1 LHM fluid reservoir
2 Fuel filter
3 Suspension units
4 Air cleaner to turbo trunking
5 Turbo to intercooler trunking
6 Inlet manifold
7 Brake pipe unions
8 Battery
9 ABS control block
10 Air cleaner
11 Air intake
12 Intercooler air inlet duct
13 Engine oil filler/dipstick
14 Cold start accelerator
15 Richness limiter
16 Fuel injectors
17 Crankcase ventilation oil trap
18 Thermostat housing
19 Expansion tank cap
20 Hydraulic pump drive pulley

Underbonnet view of Diesel engine in Citroën Visa - air cleaner removed for clarity

1 *Coolant filler cap and expansion tank*
2 *Injectors*
3 *Accelerator cable*
4 *Brake vacuum pump*
5 *Fusebox*
6 *Servo unit*
7 *Speedometer cable*
8 *Brake fluid reservoir*
9 *Washer pump*
10 *Washer reservoir*
11 *Front suspension upper mounting*
12 *Brake master cylinder*
13 *Battery*
14 *Heater plug relay*
15 *Clutch cable*
16 *Reversing light switch*
17 *Top hose*
18 *Radiator*
19 *Fast idle thermo unit*
20 *Engine oil dipstick and filler cap*
21 *Starter motor*
22 *Oil filler*
23 *Injection pump (Bosch)*
24 *Alternator*
25 *Fuel filter*
26 *Right hand engine mounting*

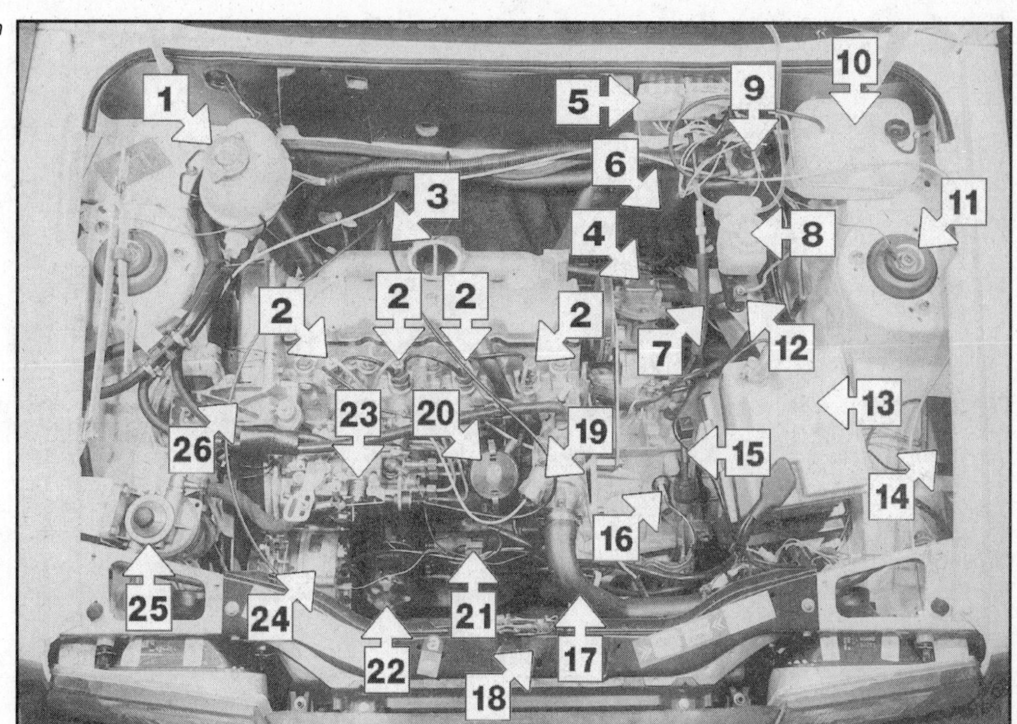

Underbonnet view of 1905 cc Turbo Diesel engine in Citroën ZX

1 *Washer fluid reservoir filler cap*
2 *Suspension strut top mounting*
3 *Fuel system priming bulb*
4 *Brake fluid reservoir*
5 *Intercooler*
6 *Battery negative terminal*
7 *Junction box*
8 *Radiator top hose*
9 *Fuel filter housing*
10 *Thermostat housing*
11 *Fuel system water drain hose*
12 *Accelerator cable*
13 *Oil level dipstick and oil filler cap*
14 *Oil filter*
15 *Fuel injection pump*
16 *Alternator*
17 *Cooling system (expansion tank) filler cap*
18 *VIN plate*
19 *Power steering fluid reservoir*
20 *Right-hand engine mounting*

Underbonnet view of 1905 cc Turbo Diesel engine in Citroën Xantia

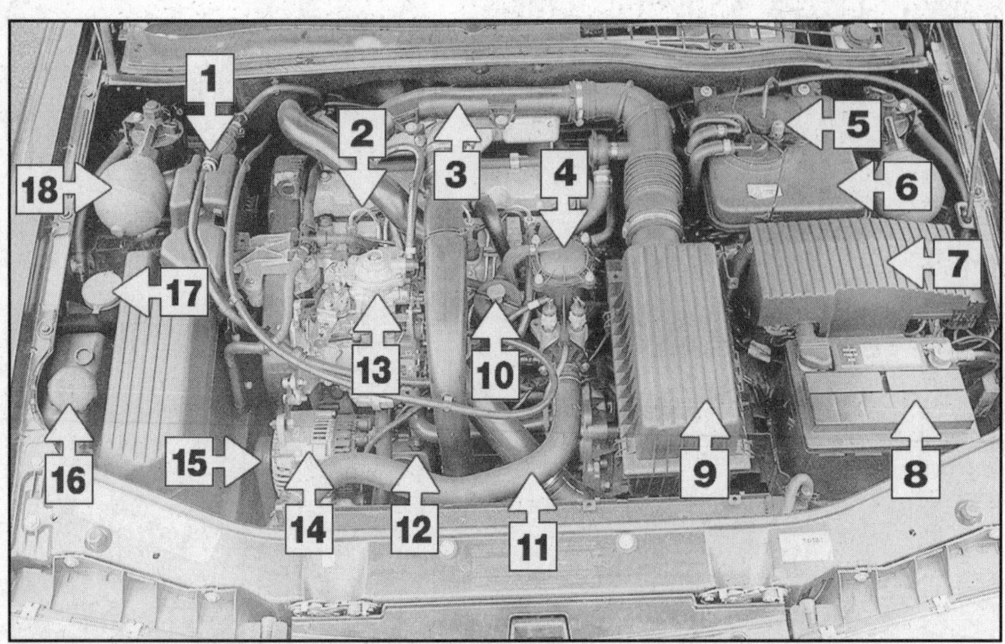

1 Fuel system priming pump
2 Injector pipe
3 Air duct to the Turbocharger
4 Fuel filter housing
5 LHM Hydraulic fluid level indicator
6 LHM Hydraulic fluid reservoir
7 Fuse/relay cover
8 Battery
9 Air cleaner housing
10 Engine oil filler cap/dipstick
11 Coolant top hose
12 Engine oil cooler and filter
13 Fuel injection pump
14 Alternator
15 Auxiliary drivebelt
16 Coolant expansion tank filler cap
17 Windscreen/tailgate washer fluid reservoir filler cap
18 LHM Hydraulic Fluid reservoir bulb

Maintenance procedures

1 Introduction

Refer to Chapter 2, Part A, Section 1.

2 Intensive maintenance

Refer to Chapter 2, Part A, Section 2.

250 mile (400 km) Service - All models

3 Engine oil level check

1 Refer to Chapter 2, Part A, Section 3 **(see illustrations)**.

4 Coolant level check

1 Refer to Chapter 2, Part A, Section 4, whilst noting the following.

2 On Visa models, the coolant should be up to the level plate visible through the expansion tank filler neck **(see illustration)**.

3 On BX models, withdraw the black plastic tube from the radiator filler neck and check that the coolant level is on the upper limit of the threaded section **(see illustration)**.

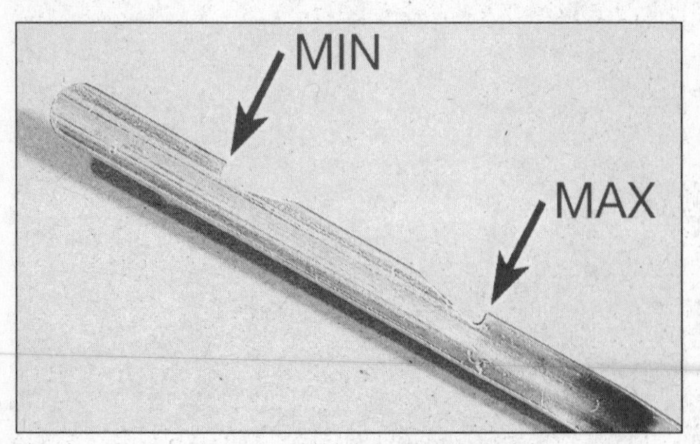

3.1a Engine oil level dipstick markings - Xantia shown, others similar

3.1b Topping-up engine oil - Citroën ZX shown

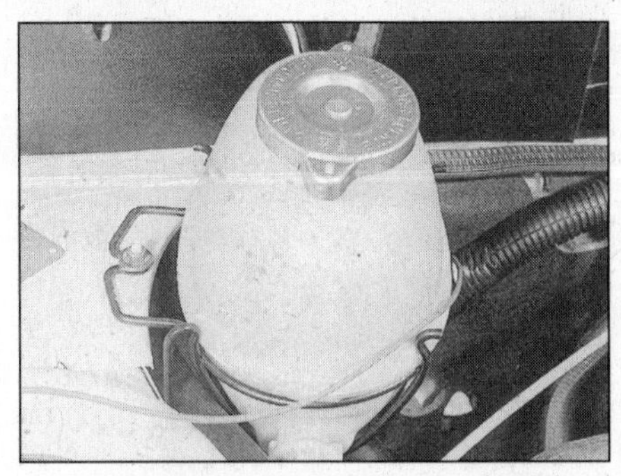

4.2 Cooling system expansion tank - Citroën Visa

4.3 Withdrawing coolant level tube - Citroën BX

4.4a Coolant level MIN and MAX marks - Citroën ZX

4 On all other models, the expansion tank is translucent, so the coolant level can be verified without removing the filler cap. Depending on model year, the tank may be either incorporated in the right-hand side of the radiator or a separate unit located within the engine compartment. The coolant level should be between the MAX (HOT) and MIN (COLD) marks embossed on the side of the tank. If it is below the MIN mark, remove the cap and top up with coolant to the MAX mark **(see illustrations)**.

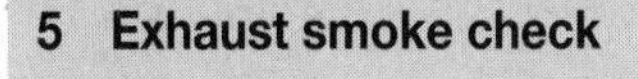

5 Exhaust smoke check

1 Refer to Chapter 2, Part A, Section 5.

6 Warning light check

1 Refer to Chapter 2, Part A, Section 6.

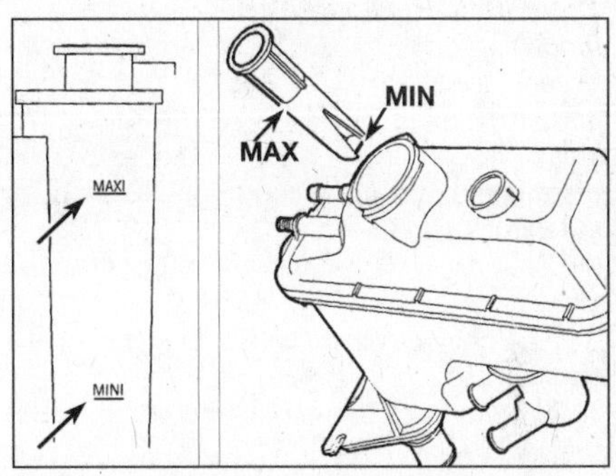

4.4b Coolant level MIN and MAX marks - Citroën Xantia

6000 mile (10 000 km) Service - Citroën AX

7 Engine oil and filter renewal

1 Refer to Chapter 2, Part A, Section 7 **(see illustrations)**.

8 Fuel filter water draining

1 Follow the procedure given in Section 13 whilst noting the following:

a) The priming pump rubber bulb is located on the left-hand suspension strut turret or near the battery.

b) Unlike the automatic bleed valve fitted to the Citroën ZX, a bleed screw is located on top of the fuel filter/thermostat housing. This screw must be loosened to facilitate bleeding of the fuel system.

c) Where no bleed screw is fitted, loosen the outlet union, either at the filter/thermostat housing or at the fuel injection pump.

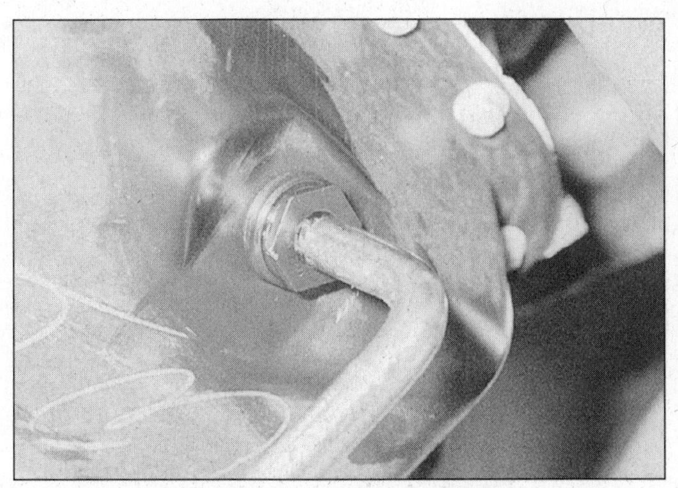

7.1a Removing engine oil drain plug

7.1b Removing engine oil filter

6000 mile (10 000 km) Service - Citroën BX/Visa/C15

9 Engine oil and filter renewal

1 Refer to Chapter 2, Part A, Section 7.

10 Engine oil filler cap cleaning

Note: *This procedure is only applicable to models with the oil filler cap fitted to the valve cover.*

1 Pull the oil filler cap from the top of the valve cover then loosen the clip and disconnect the crankcase ventilation hose **(see illustration)**.

2 Clean the wire mesh filter in paraffin and allow to dry.

3 If the cap is blocked with sludge, renew the cap complete.

4 Refit the hose to the cap and fit the cap to the valve cover.

11 Fuel filter water draining

1 Position a small container beneath the fuel filter.

2 Loosen the bleed screw on the bottom of the filter and allow any water to drain into the container. Where fitted, also loosen the air bleed screw on the filter head or inlet union bolt **(see illustration)**.

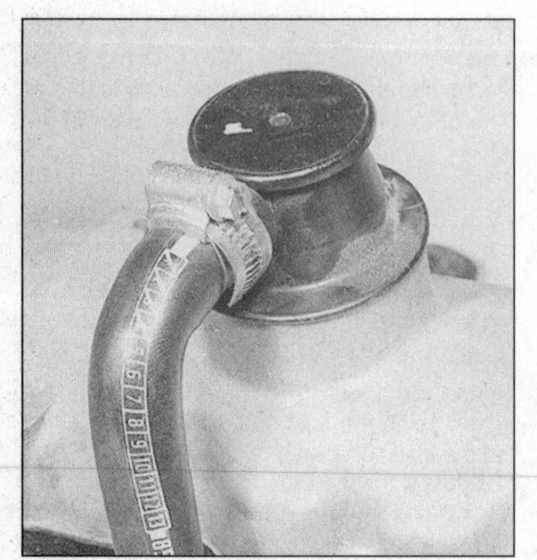

10.1 Oil filler cap and ventilation hose - Citroën BX

3 Tighten the lower bleed screw when fuel which is free of water flows. Retighten the air bleed screw, where fitted.

4 Prime the fuel injection system, according to model type, as follows:

Fuel system priming and bleeding

Early models

5 Loosen the bleed screw on the fuel filter head two or three turns. On the Roto-diesel type of filter, a plastic drain tube may be fitted to the bleed screw.

6 Actuate the plunger until fuel which is free from air bubbles flows from the bleed screw. On some Roto-diesel filter heads, the plunger must first be unscrewed and with this type, the plunger may become detached from the internal piston. If this happens, unscrew the housing and press the piston back onto the plunger. Refit the housing and operate the plunger slowly.

7 Tighten the bleed screw.

8 Turn on the ignition so that the stop solenoid is energised then activate the plunger until resistance is felt.

9 Where applicable on Roto-diesel filters, retighten the plunger.

10 Turn the ignition switch to position M and wait for the preheater warning light to go out.

11 Fully depress the accelerator pedal and start the engine. Additional cranking may be necessary to finally bleed the fuel system before the engine starts.

Later models

12 Later models are provided with a rubber hand-operated priming bulb, located on the right-hand side of the engine compartment. When this bulb is squeezed, fuel is forced into the fuel filter housing and then through a double valve. The valve forces fuel initially in the direction of the fuel injection pump, then any excess, along with fuel returned from the injectors, is returned to the fuel tank.

13 To prime the fuel lines, depress the priming bulb several times to force any trapped air back to the fuel tank.

14 Purging of air from the injection pump itself and the injectors is carried out when the engine is turned by the starter motor. However this process may be accelerated by temporarily slightly loosening each pipe in turn at the injector end until fuel emerges as the engine is being turned. Note that the fuel may spurt out under considerable pressure when doing this and precautions should be taken to prevent personal injury.

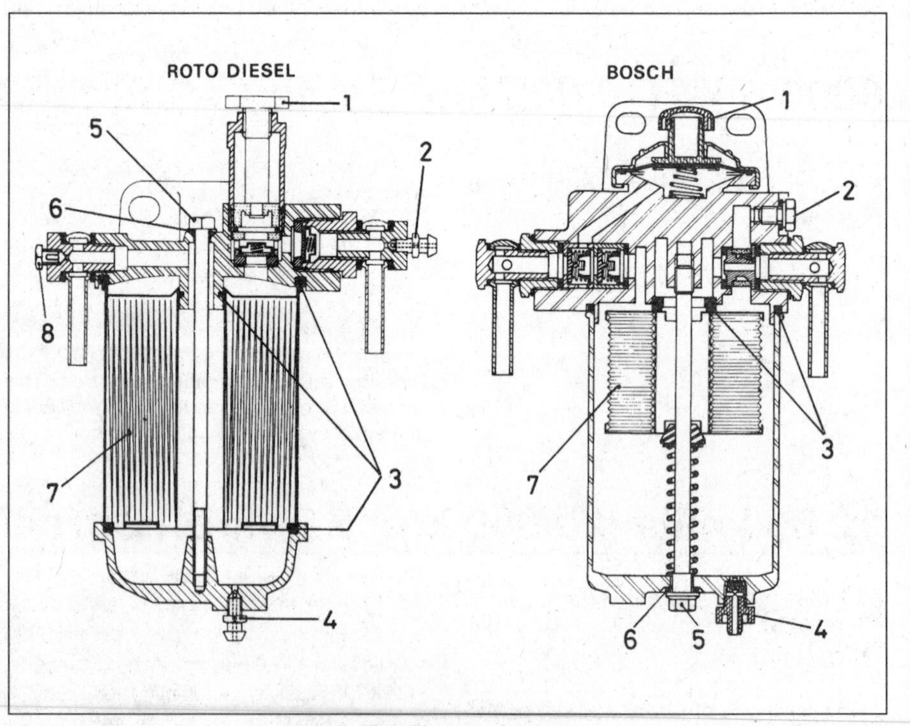

11.2 Fuel filter components

1 Priming plunger
2 Fuel bleed screw
3 Seals
4 Water bleed screw
5 Through bolt
6 Through bolt seal
7 Cartridge/element
8 Air bleed screw

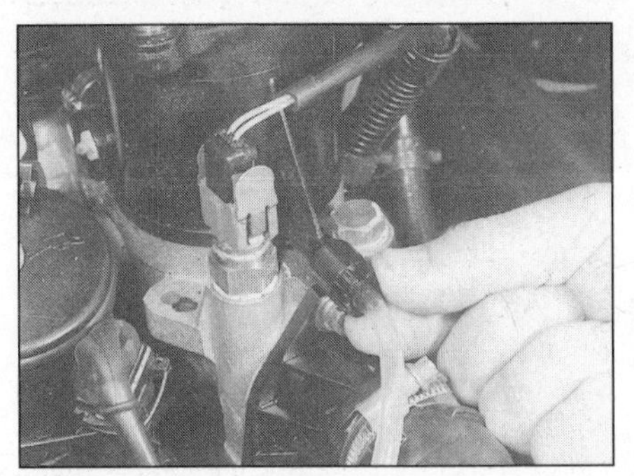

13.3 Opening fuel filter water drain plug

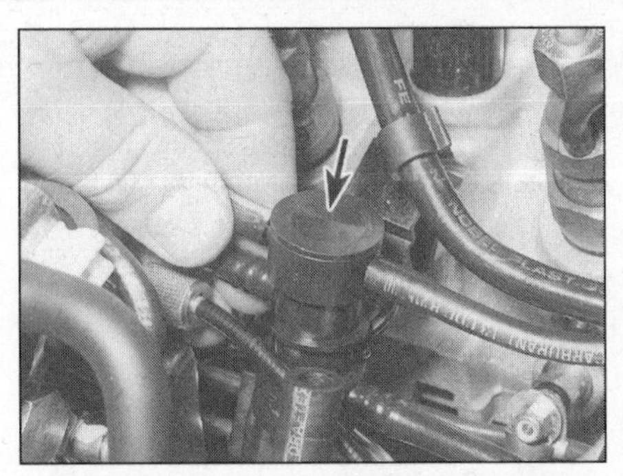

13.7 Automatic fuel system bleed valve (arrowed)

13.8 Fuel system priming pump

6000 mile (10 000 km) Service - Citroën ZX

12 Engine oil and filter renewal

1 Refer to Chapter 2, Part A, Section 7.

13 Fuel filter water draining

1 A drain plug and tube are provided at the base of the fuel filter housing.
2 Place a suitable container beneath the drain tube and cover the clutch bellhousing.
3 Open the drain plug by turning it anti-clockwise. Allow fuel and water to drain until fuel which is free from water emerges from the end of the tube **(see illustration)**. Close the drain plug.
4 Dispose of the drained fuel safely.
5 Start the engine. If difficulty is experienced, bleed the fuel system as follows:

Fuel system priming and bleeding

6 A hand-operated priming pump is fitted, comprising a rubber bulb located on the right-hand side of the engine compartment.
7 An automatic bleed valve is fitted, which bleeds air from the low-pressure fuel circuit when it is primed **(see illustration)**.
8 To prime the system, switch on the ignition so that the stop solenoid is energised. Pump the rubber bulb until resistance is felt, indicating that air has been expelled from the fuel injection pump **(see illustration)**. It should be possible to hear the fuel circulating through the pump when the all the air has been expelled.
9 If air has reached the injectors, the high-pressure circuit must be bled as follows:
10 Place wads of clean rag around the fuel pipe unions at the injectors to absorb spilt fuel, then slacken the fuel pipe unions.
11 Crank the engine on the starter motor until fuel emerges from the unions, then stop cranking the engine and tighten the unions. Mop up any spilt fuel.
12 Start the engine with the accelerator pedal fully depressed. Additional cranking may be necessary to finally bleed the system before the engine starts.

6000 mile (10 000 km) Service - Citroën Xantia

14 Engine oil and filter renewal

1 Refer to Chapter 2, Part A, Section 7.

15 Fuel filter water draining

1 Follow the procedure given in Section 13. When bleeding the fuel system, note that unlike the automatic bleed valve fitted to the Citroën ZX, a bleed screw is fitted in the injection pump inlet pipe union bolt. This screw must be loosened to facilitate bleeding of the fuel system.

16 Auto-diagnostic memory check

1 This check can only be carried out by a Citroën dealer using special diagnostic equipment. The check will reveal any fault codes stored in the engine management ECU. The codes indicate the exact location of any fault.

12 000 mile (20 000 km) Service - Citroën AX

17 Idle speed and anti-stall speed check

1 The usual type of tachometer (rev counter) which works from ignition system pulses, cannot be used on Diesel engines. A diagnostic socket is provided for the use of Citroën test equipment but this will not normally be available to the home mechanic. If it is not felt that adjusting idle speed by ear is satisfactory. It will be necessary to purchase or hire an appropriate tachometer, or leave the task to a Citroën dealer.
2 Before making adjustments, warm up the engine to normal operating temperature and ensure that the accelerator cable is correctly adjusted.

Idle speed

3 Check that the engine idles at the specified speed. If necessary, adjustments can be made using the idle speed adjustment screw on the injection pump.
4 Loosen the locknut, then adjust the screw (as necessary) until a position is found where the engine is idling at the specified speed **(see illustrations)**. Once the screw is correctly positioned, securely tighten the locknut.

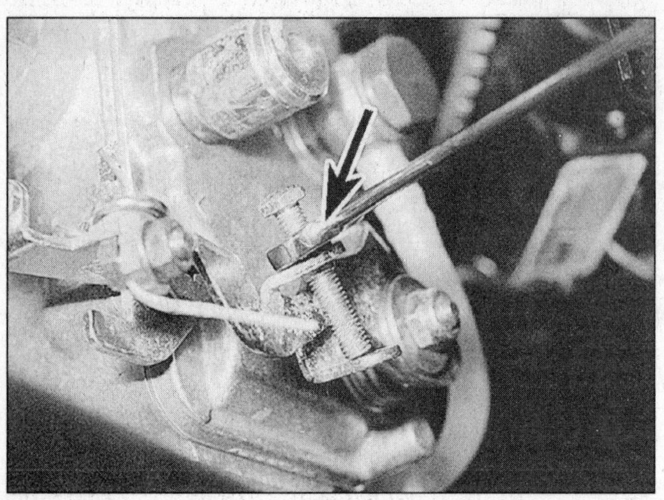

17.4a On Lucas/CAV injection pump, slacken locknut (arrowed) . . .

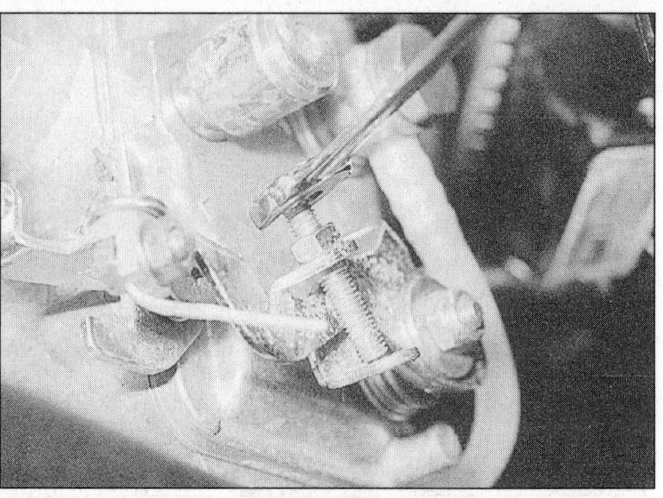

17.4b . . . then turn idle speed screw

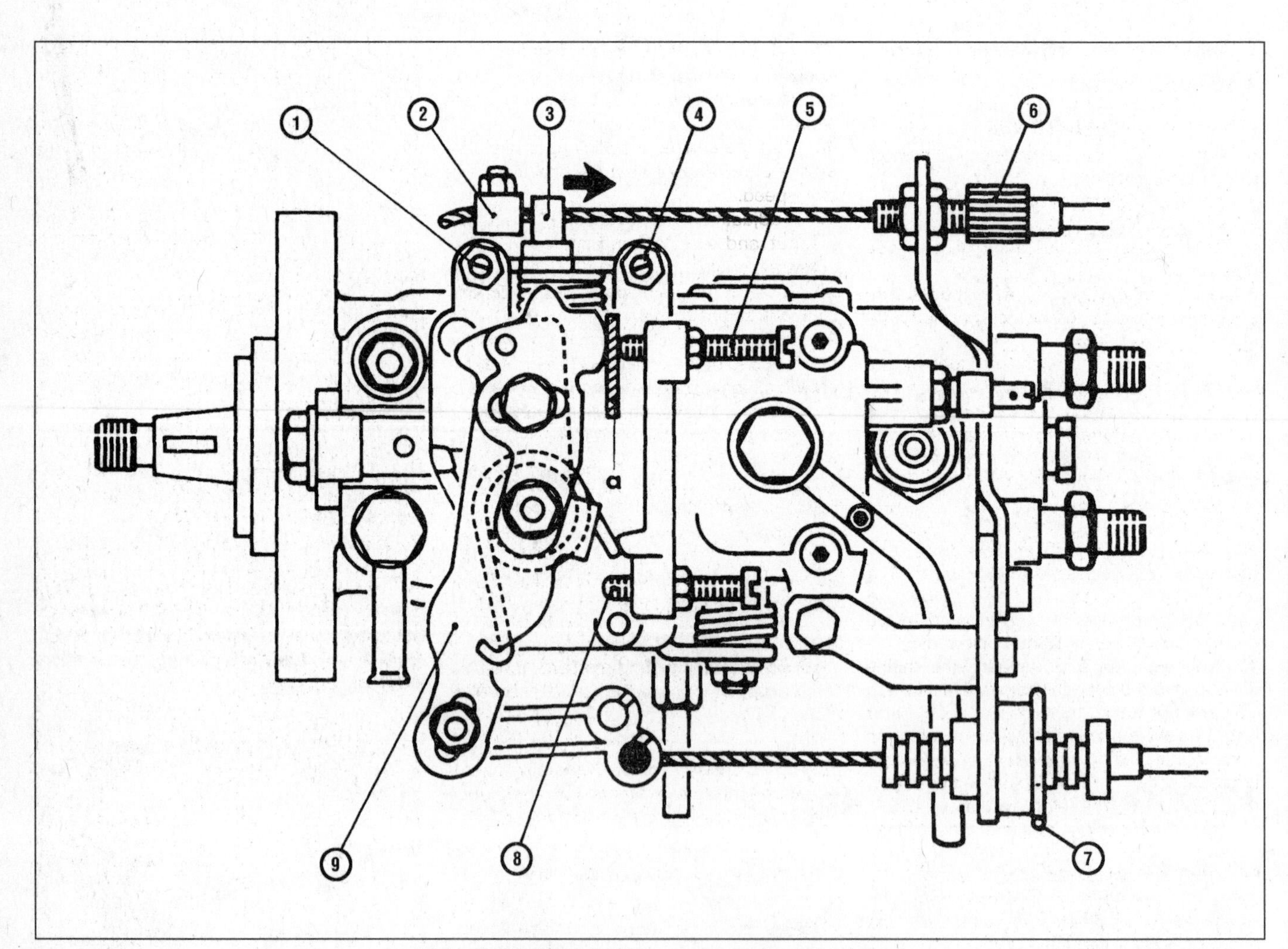

17.4c Bosch fuel injection pump adjustment points

1 Fast idle adjustment screw
2 Cable end fitting
3 Fast idle lever
4 Idle speed adjustment screw
5 Anti-stall adjustment screw
6 Fast idle cable adjustment ferrule
7 Accelerator cable adjustment ferrule
8 Maximum speed adjustment screw
9 Control (accelerator) lever
a Shim for anti-stall adjustment

17.7 On Lucas/CAV injection pump, insert feeler blade (arrowed) between anti-stall adjustment screw and accelerator lever . . .

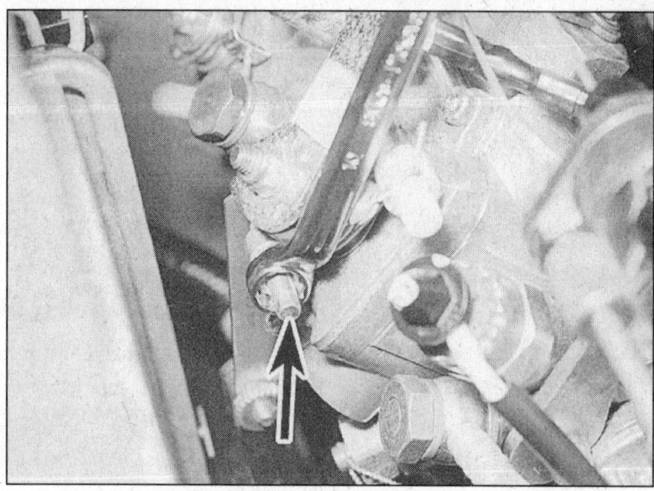

17.9 . . . then slacken locknut and turn screw (arrowed) to set anti-stall speed

5 Check the anti-stall adjustment as follows:

Anti-stall speed

Lucas/CAV injection pump

6 With the idle speed correctly adjusted, switch off the engine.

7 Insert a shim or feeler blade of the specified thickness between the pump accelerator lever and the anti-stall adjustment screw **(see illustration)**.

8 Start the engine and allow it to idle. The engine should now run at the specified anti-stall speed.

9 If adjustment is necessary, loosen the locknut and turn the anti-stall adjustment screw as required, until the anti-stall speed is correct **(see illustration)**. Hold the screw in this position and securely tighten the locknut.

10 Remove the shim or feeler blade then recheck the idle speed.

11 Move the accelerator lever to increase the engine speed to approximately 3000 rpm, then quickly release the lever. The deceleration period should be between 2.5 and 3.5 seconds and the engine speed should drop to approximately 50 rpm below idle.

12 If deceleration is too fast and the engine stalls, screw the anti-stall adjustment screw in a quarter of a turn towards the accelerator lever. If deceleration is too slow, resulting in poor engine braking, unscrew it a quarter of a turn away from the lever. Adjust as necessary, then securely retighten the locknut.

13 Recheck the idle speed and, if necessary, adjust.

14 With the engine idling, check the operation of the manual stop control by turning the stop lever anti-clockwise. The engine must stop instantly.

15 Where applicable, disconnect the tachometer on completion.

Bosch injection pump

16 Adjust the idle speed, then switch off the engine.

17 Insert a shim or feeler blade of the specified thickness between the pump accelerator lever and the anti-stall adjustment screw.

18 Start the engine and allow it to idle. The engine should now run at the specified anti-stall speed.

19 If adjustment is necessary, loosen the locknut and turn the anti-stall adjustment screw as required. Retighten the locknut.

20 Remove the shim or feeler blade and allow the engine to idle.

21 Move the fast idle lever fully towards the flywheel end of the engine and check that the engine speed increases to the fast idle speed. If necessary, loosen the locknut and turn the fast idle adjusting screw as required, then retighten the locknut.

22 With the engine idling, check the operation of the manual stop control by turning the stop lever. The engine must stop instantly.

23 Where applicable, disconnect the tachometer on completion.

18 Emission control system check

1 Detailed checking of the evaporative and/or exhaust emission systems (as applicable) should be entrusted to a Citroën dealer.

19 Fuel filter renewal

1 The fuel filter is screwed onto the underside of the filter/thermostat housing on the left-hand end of the cylinder head. To improve access to the filter, remove the battery and any inlet ducting.

2 Cover the clutch bellhousing with a piece of plastic sheeting, to protect the clutch from fuel spillage.

3 Position a suitable container under the end of the fuel filter drain hose. Open the drain screw on the base of the filter and allow the fuel to drain completely.

4 With the filter drained, close the bleed screw and unscrew the filter by using a suitable strap or chain wrench **(see illustration)**.

5 Remove the filter and dispose of it safely. Ensure that the sealing ring comes away with the filter and does not stick to the filter/thermostat housing mating surface.

6 Apply a smear of clean diesel oil to the filter sealing ring and wipe clean the housing mating surface. Screw the filter on until its sealing ring lightly contacts the housing mating surface, then tighten it through a further three-quarters of a turn.

7 Prime the fuel system as described in Section 13.

8 Open the drain screw until clean fuel flows from the hose, then close the drain screw and withdraw the container from under the hose.

9 Refit the battery and ducting, then start the engine.

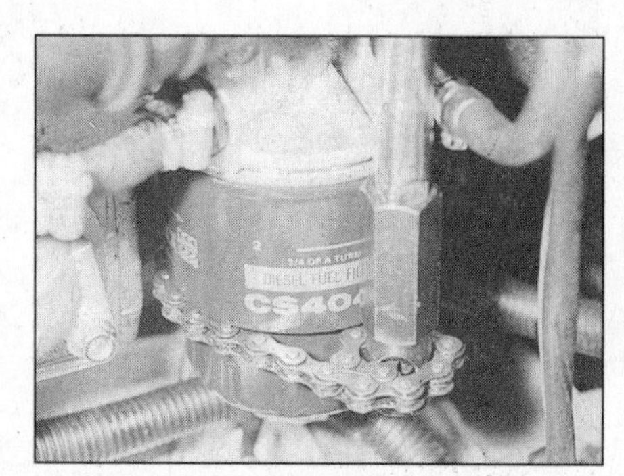

19.4 Using chain wrench to unscrew fuel filter

12 000 mile (20 000 km) Service - Citroën BX/Visa/C15

20 Idle speed and anti-stall speed check

Idle speed

1 The usual type of tachometer (rev counter) which works from ignition system pulses, cannot be used on diesel engines. A diagnostic socket is provided for use of Citroën test equipment but this will not normally be available to the home mechanic. If it is not felt that adjusting idle speed by ear is satisfactory, use one of the following alternatives:

a) Purchase or hire of an appropriate tachometer
b) Delegation of the job to a Citroën dealer or other specialist
c) Timing light (strobe) operated by a petrol engine running at the desired speed. If the timing light is pointed at a mark on the camshaft pump pulley, the mark will appear stationary when the two engines are running at the same speed (or multiples of that speed). The pulley will be rotating at half crankshaft speed but this will not affect adjustment. In practice, it was found impossible to use this method on the crankshaft pulley due to the acute viewing angle

2 Warm up the engine to normal operating temperature and check that the engine is idling at the specified speed.

Roto-diesel injection pump

3 If adjustment is necessary, loosen the locknut on the fast idle lever then turn the adjustment screw as required and retighten the locknut **(see illustration)**. Adjust the anti-stall setting.

Bosch injection pump

4 If adjustment is necessary, first loosen the locknut and unscrew the anti-stall adjustment screw until it is clear of the accelerator lever. Loosen the locknut and turn the idle speed adjustment screw as required then retighten the locknut - see illustration 17.4c. Adjust the anti-stall setting.

Anti-stall speed

Roto-diesel injection pump

5 Run the engine to normal operating temperature then switch it off.

6 Insert a 3.0 mm shim or feeler blade between the accelerator lever and the anti-stall adjustment screw.

7 Turn the stop lever clockwise until it is clear of the hole in the fast idle lever then insert a 3.0 mm dowel rod or twist drill **(see illustration)**.

8 Start the engine and allow it to idle. The engine speed should be as specified.

9 If adjustment is necessary, loosen the locknut, turn the anti-stall adjustment screw as required, then tighten the locknut.

10 Remove the feeler blade and twist drill and readjust the idling speed.

11 Turn the accelerator lever to increase engine speed to 3000 rpm then quickly release the lever. If deceleration is too fast and the engine stalls, turn the anti-stall adjustment screw one quarter turn anti-clockwise (viewed from flywheel end of engine). If deceleration is too slow, resulting in poor engine braking, turn the screw one quarter turn clockwise.

12 Retighten the locknut after making an adjustment then recheck the idling speed.

13 With the engine idling, check the operation of the manual stop control by turning the stop lever clockwise. The engine must stop instantly.

14 Stop the engine and disconnect any instruments.

Bosch injection pump

15 Run the engine to normal operating temperature. Note the exact idling speed then switch off the engine.

16 Insert a 1.0 mm shim or feeler blade between the accelerator lever and the anti-stall adjustment screw - see illustration 17.4c.

17 Start the engine and allow it to idle. The engine speed should be as specified.

18 If adjustment is necessary, loosen the locknut and turn the anti-stall adjustment screw as required. Retighten the locknut.

19 Remove the feeler blade and allow the engine to idle.

20 Move the fast idle lever fully towards the flywheel end of the engine and check that the engine speed increases to 950 ± 50 rpm. If necessary, loosen the locknut and turn the stop adjusting screw as required, then retighten the locknut.

21 With the engine idling, check the operation of the manual stop control by turning the stop lever. The engine must stop instantly.

22 Stop the engine and disconnect any instruments.

21 Fuel filter renewal

Note: *Although not essential, it is always beneficial to change the fuel filter just before winter, regardless of mileage.*

Except C15

Removal

1 This job may be carried out leaving the filter head in situ. However, due to limited access and the possibility of spilling fuel over the

20.3 Idle speed adjustment screw (arrowed) - Roto-diesel injection pump

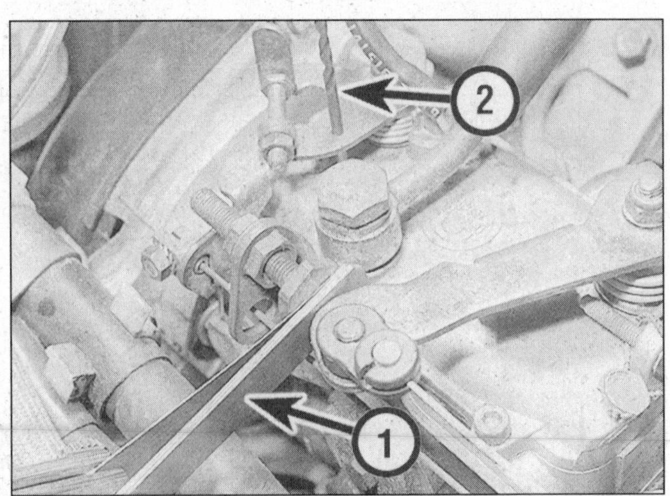

20.7 Anti-stall adjustment. Feeler blade (1) and twist drill (2) - Roto-diesel injection pump

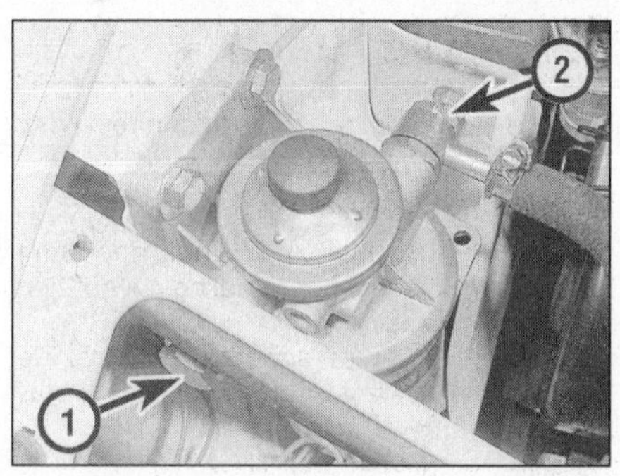

21.2 Inlet (1) and outlet (2) unions - Bosch fuel filter

21.3 Removing Roto-diesel filter head and cartridge

21.4 Unscrew through bolt . . .

engine, it is recommended that the filter head is removed, together with the cartridge.

2 Unscrew the union bolts and disconnect the inlet and outlet fuel unions from the filter head **(see illustration)**. Recover the union washers.

3 Unbolt the filter head from the bracket and withdraw it, together with the cartridge **(see illustration)**.

4 With the assembly in a container to catch spilled fuel, unscrew the through-bolt **(see illustration)**.

5 On the Roto-diesel filter, this will release the end cap and enable the cartridge and seals to be removed **(see illustration)**.

6 On the Bosch filter, remove the chamber followed by the element and seals. The Purflux filter fitted to some models is similar to the Bosch filter.

Refitting

7 Clean the filter head and end cap or chamber.

8 Locate the new seals in position, then fit the new cartridge or element using a reversal of the removal procedures.

9 Prime the fuel injection system as described in Section 11.

Citroën C15

Note: *If fuel is allowed to escape from the filter housing onto the engine, it will find its way into the clutch and possibly damage the linings.*

Removal

10 From early 1993, the fuel filter is modified. The coolant-heated filter base is no longer fitted. The fuel filter is relocated in a housing on the cylinder head, above the thermostat and cylinder head coolant outlet housing. The new housing has a water detector and a water drain plug in its base. There is an external hand-priming bulb and a double valve return system.

11 To remove the filter, first drain the housing by loosening the drain plug. A plastic tube should be attached to the drain plug, so that the fuel can be directed into a suitable container **(see illustration)**.

12 With the fuel drained, unscrew the cover bolts, remove the cover and lift out the filter **(see illustrations)**.

13 Removal of the water detector is straightforward **(see illustrations)**.

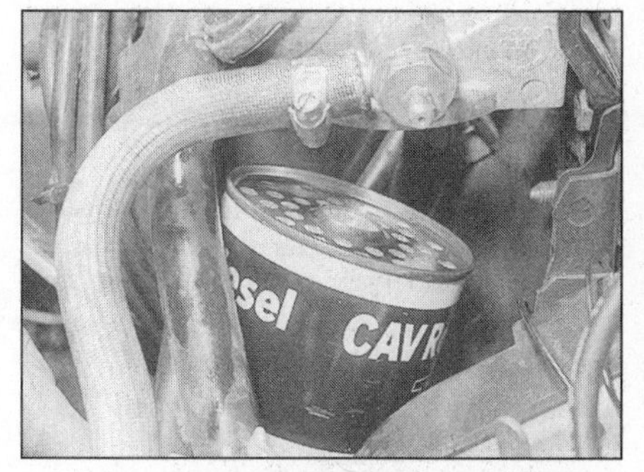

21.5 . . . and remove Roto-diesel filter cartridge

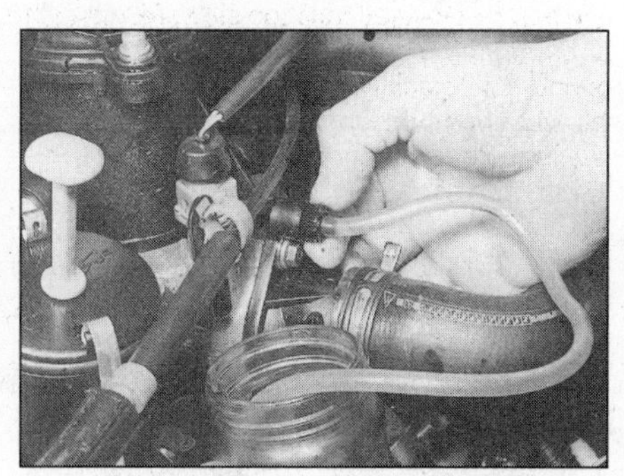

21.11 Draining fuel from filter housing

21.12a Unscrew cover bolts . . .

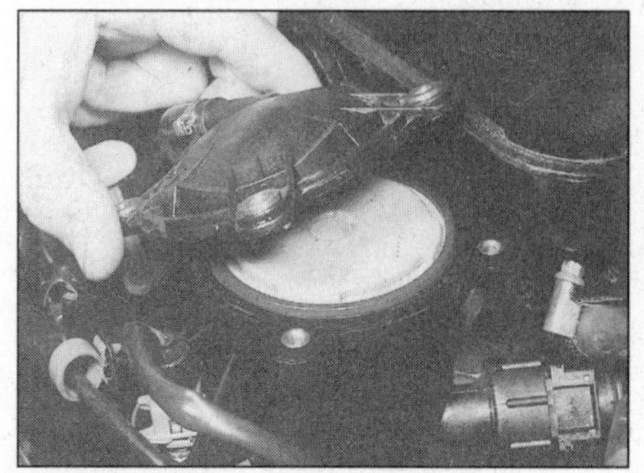

21.12b . . . remove cover . . .

21.12c . . . and remove filter

21.13a Disconnecting wiring plug . . .

21.13b . . . and removing water detector (arrowed)

Refitting

14 Check the sealing rubber before reversing the removal procedure to fit the filter **(see illustration)**.

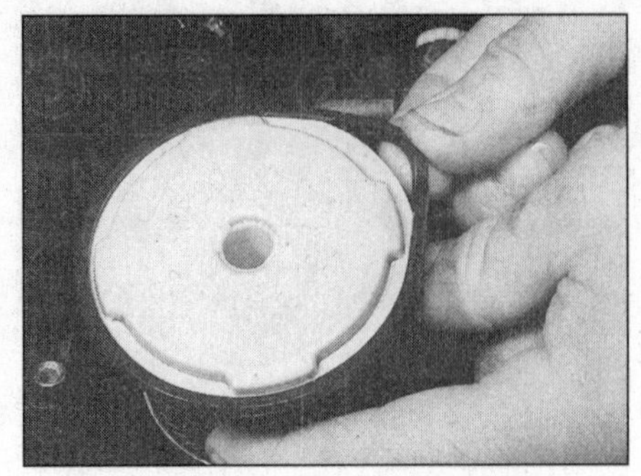
21.14 Checking the sealing rubber

22 Vacuum pump check - Visa only

Oil level

1 With the vehicle on level ground, unscrew the vacuum pump filler/level plug and check that the oil level is up to the bottom of the plug hole **(see illustration)**. If not, top-up with the correct grade of oil then refit and tighten the plug.

22.1 Vacuum pump filler/level plug (arrowed)

Drivebelt

2 Depress the drivebelt midway between the pulleys. If the deflection is not as specified, loosen the pivot and adjustment bolts, reposition the vacuum pump, then tighten the bolts.

12 000 mile (20 000 km) Service - Citroën ZX and Xantia

23 Idle speed and anti-stall speed check - Citroën ZX

1 The usual type of tachometer (rev counter), which works from ignition system pulses, cannot be used on diesel engines. A diagnostic socket is provided for the use of Citroën test equipment but this will not normally be available to the home mechanic. If it is not felt that adjusting the idle speed by ear is satisfactory, one of the following alternatives may be used:

a) Purchase or hire of an appropriate tachometer.
b) Delegation of the job to a Citroën dealer or other specialist.
c) Timing light (strobe) operated by a petrol engine running at the desired speed. If the timing light is pointed at a mark on the camshaft pump pulley, the mark will appear stationary when the two engines are running at the same speed (or multiples of that speed). The pulley will be rotating at half the crankshaft speed but this will not affect adjustment. In practice, it was found impossible to use this method on the crankshaft pulley, due to the acute viewing angle.

2 Before making any adjustment, warm-up the engine to normal operating temperature. Ensure that the accelerator cable is correctly adjusted.

Idle speed

3 Check that the engine idles at the specified speed. If necessary, adjust as follows.

Lucas CAV/Roto-Diesel fuel injection pump

4 Loosen the locknut on the idle speed adjustment screw. Turn the screw as required and retighten the locknut **(see illustration)**.

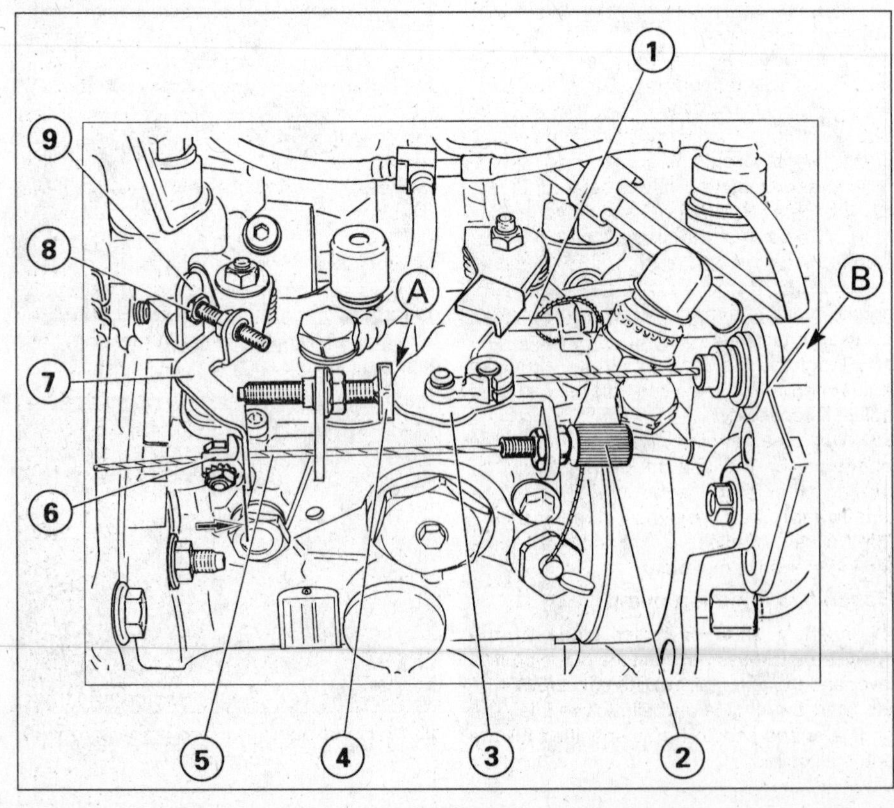

23.4 Lucas fuel injection pump adjustment points

1 Maximum speed adjustment screw
2 Fast idle cable adjustment ferrule
3 Pump control lever
4 Anti-stall adjustment screw
5 Fast idle cable
6 Fast idle cable end fitting
7 Fast idle lever
8 Idle speed adjustment screw
9 Manual stop lever
A Anti-stall adjustment shim location
B Accelerator cable adjustment ferrule

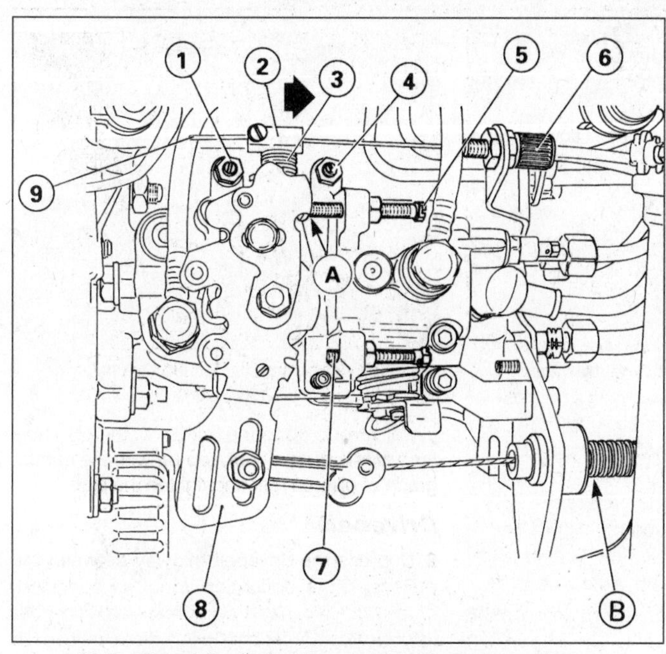

23.7a Bosch fuel injection pump adjustment points - non turbo engines

1 Fast idle lever stop screw
2 Fast idle cable end fitting
3 Fast idle lever
4 Idle speed adjustment screw
5 Anti-stall speed adjustment screw
6 Fast idle cable adjustment ferrule
7 Maximum speed adjustment screw
8 Pump control lever
9 Fast idle cable
A Anti-stall adjustment shim location
B Accelerator cable adjustment ferrule

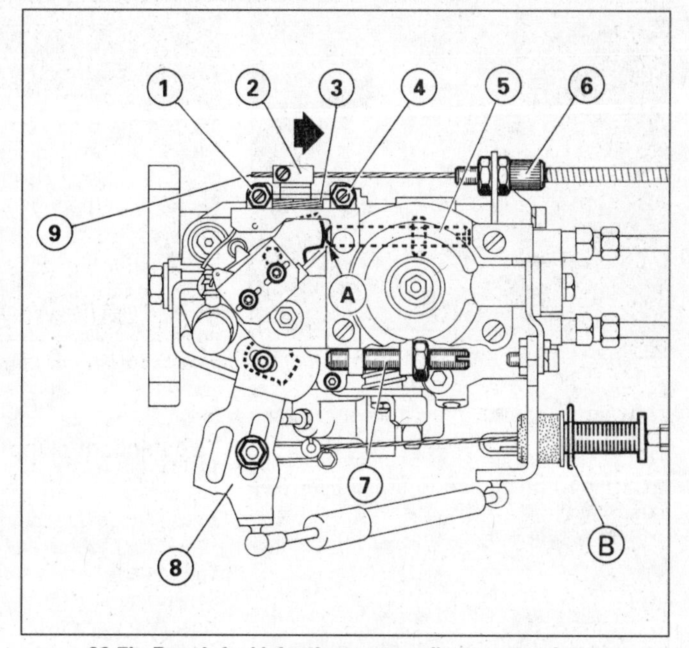

23.7b Bosch fuel injection pump adjustment points - Turbo engines

1 Fast idle lever stop screw
2 Fast idle lever cable end fitting
3 Fast idle lever
4 Idle speed adjustment screw
5 Anti-stall speed adjustment screw
6 Fast idle cable adjustment ferrule
7 Maximum speed adjustment screw
8 Pump control lever
9 Fast idle cable
A Anti-stall adjustment shim location
B Accelerator cable adjustment ferrule

5 Check the anti-stall speed adjustment.
6 Stop the engine and disconnect the tachometer, where applicable.

Bosch fuel injection pump

7 Loosen the locknut and unscrew the anti-stall adjustment screw until it is clear of the pump control lever **(see illustrations)**.
8 Loosen the locknut and turn the idle speed adjustment screw as required, then retighten the locknut.
9 Check the anti-stall speed adjustment.
10 Stop the engine and disconnect the tachometer, where applicable.

Anti-stall speed

11 Ensure that the engine is at normal operating temperature, then note the idle speed and switch off.

Lucas CAV/Roto-Diesel fuel injection pump

12 Insert a shim or feeler blade of the specified thickness between the pump control lever and the anti-stall adjustment screw.
13 Start the engine and allow it to idle. The engine speed should be as specified for the anti-stall speed.
14 If adjustment is necessary, loosen the locknut, turn the anti-stall adjustment screw as required, then tighten the locknut.
15 Remove the shim or feeler blade and check the idle speed.
16 Move the pump control lever to increase the engine speed to approximately 3000 rpm, then quickly release the lever. The deceleration period should be between 2.5 and 3.5 seconds and the engine speed should drop to approximately 50 rpm below idle.
17 If deceleration is too fast and the engine stalls, unscrew the anti-stall adjustment screw a quarter-turn towards the control lever. If deceleration is too slow, resulting in poor engine braking, turn the screw a quarter-turn away from the lever.
18 Retighten the locknut after making an adjustment. Recheck the idle speed and adjust if necessary.
19 With the engine idling, check the operation of the manual stop control by turning the stop lever clockwise **(see illustration)**. The engine must stop instantly.
20 Where applicable, disconnect the tachometer on completion.

Bosch fuel injection pump

21 Insert a shim or feeler blade of the specified thickness between the pump control lever and the anti-stall adjustment screw.
22 Start the engine and allow it to idle. The engine speed should be as specified for the anti-stall speed.
23 If adjustment is necessary, loosen the locknut and turn the anti-stall adjustment screw as required. Retighten the locknut.
24 Remove the shim or feeler blade and allow the engine to idle.
25 Move the fast idle lever fully towards the flywheel end of the engine and check that the engine speed increases to the specified fast idle speed. If necessary, loosen the locknut and turn the fast idle adjusting screw as required, then retighten the locknut.
26 With the engine idling, check the operation of the manual stop control by turning the stop lever **(see illustration)**. The engine must stop instantly.

23.19 Hand-operated stop lever (arrowed) - Lucas pump

23.26 Hand-operated stop lever (arrowed) - Bosch pump

27 Where applicable, disconnect the tachometer on completion.

24 Idle speed and anti-stall speed check - Citroën Xantia

1 The usual type of tachometer (rev counter) which works from ignition system pulses cannot be used on Diesel engines. A diagnostic socket is provided for the use of Citroën test equipment but this will not normally be available to the home mechanic. If it is not felt that adjusting idle speed by ear is satisfactory. It will be necessary either to purchase or hire an appropriate tachometer, or to leave the task to a Citroën dealer or other suitably equipped specialist.

2 Before making any adjustment, run the engine until it reaches normal operating temperature and ensure that the accelerator cable and fast idle cables are correctly adjusted.

Lucas fuel injection pump

3 Place a shim of specified thickness between the pump control lever and the anti-stall adjustment screw - see illustration 23.4.

4 Push the manual stop lever back against its stop and hold it in position by inserting a 3 mm diameter rod/drill through the hole in the fast idle lever.

5 The engine speed should be as specified for the anti-stall speed.

6 If adjustment is necessary, loosen the locknut, turn the anti-stall adjustment screw as required, then tighten the locknut.

7 Remove the rod/drill and the shim and check that the engine is idling at the specified speed.

8 If adjustment is necessary, loosen the locknut on the idle speed adjustment screw. Turn the screw as required and retighten the locknut.

9 Move the pump control lever to increase the engine speed to approximately 3000 rpm, then quickly release the lever. The deceleration period should be between 2.5 and 3.5 seconds, and the engine speed should drop to approximately 50 rpm below idle.

10 If the deceleration is too fast and the engine stalls, unscrew the anti-stall adjustment screw a quarter-turn towards the control lever. If the deceleration is too slow, resulting in poor engine braking, turn the screw a quarter-turn away from the lever.

11 Retighten the locknut after making an adjustment. Recheck the idle speed and adjust if necessary as described previously.

12 With the engine idling, check the operation of the manual stop control by turning the stop lever clockwise. The engine must stop instantly.

13 Where applicable, disconnect the tachometer on completion.

Bosch fuel injection pump

Non turbo models

14 Loosen the locknut and unscrew the anti-stall adjustment screw until it is clear of the pump control lever - see illustrations 23.7a and 23.7b.

15 Loosen the locknut and turn the idle speed adjustment screw as required, then retighten the locknut.

16 Insert a shim or feeler blade of the correct thickness between the pump control lever and the anti-stall adjustment screw.

17 Start the engine and allow it to idle. The engine speed should be as specified for the anti-stall speed.

18 If adjustment is necessary, loosen the locknut and turn the anti-stall adjustment screw as required. Retighten the locknut.

19 Remove the shim or feeler blade and allow the engine to idle.

20 Move the fast idle lever fully towards the flywheel end of the engine and check that the engine speed increases to the specified fast idle speed. If necessary, loosen the locknut and turn the fast idle adjusting screw as required, then retighten the locknut.

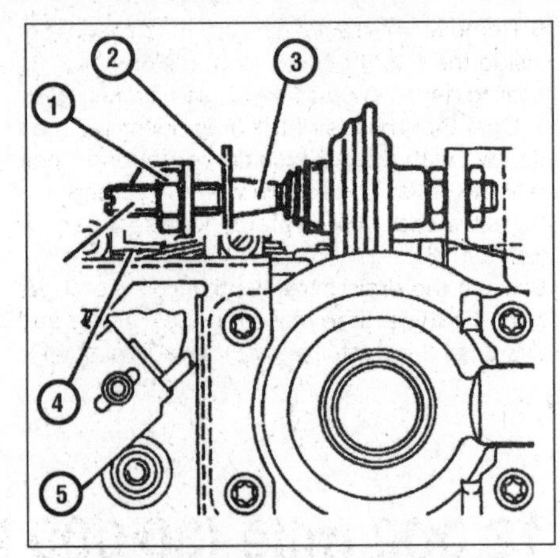

24.24 Fuel injection pump damper adjustment - Turbo engines

1 Locknut
2 Shim
3 Damper rod
4 Adjustment screw
5 Pump control lever

21 With the engine idling, check the operation of the manual stop control by turning the stop lever. The engine must stop instantly.

22 Where applicable, disconnect the tachometer on completion.

Turbo models

23 Carry out the operations described above in paragraphs 14 to 19.

24 Slacken the locknut and unscrew the control lever damper adjustment screw, located on the rear of the lever, and insert the shim or feeler blade between the damper rod and adjustment screw **(see illustration)**. Ensure the pump control lever is in the idle position then position the adjustment screw so that the feeler blade/shim is a light, sliding fit between the screw and damper rod. Hold the screw in this position and securely tighten its locknut.

25 Carry out the operations described in paragraphs 19 to 22.

25 Emission control system check

1 Where applicable, detailed checking of the exhaust gas recirculation system and/or atmospheric pressure correction system should be entrusted to a Citroën dealer.

18 000 mile (30 000 km) Service - Citroën ZX

26 Fuel filter renewal

1 The fuel filter is located in a plastic housing at the front of the engine.

2 Where applicable, cover the clutch bellhousing with a piece of plastic sheeting to protect the clutch from fuel spillage.

3 Position a suitable container under the end of the fuel filter drain hose. Open the drain screw on the front of the filter housing and allow the fuel to drain completely.

4 Securely tighten the drain screw, then undo the filter housing cover retaining screws and lift off the cover **(see illustration)**.

5 Lift the filter from the housing **(see illustration)**. Ensure that the rubber sealing ring comes away with the filter, and does not stick to the housing/lid.

6 Remove all traces of dirt or debris from inside the filter housing then, making sure its sealing ring is in position, fit the new fuel filter.
7 Coat the threads of the filter cover securing screws with thread-locking compound, then refit the cover and secure with the screws.
8 Prime the fuel system as described in Section 13.
9 Open the drain screw until clean fuel flows from the hose, then close the drain screw and withdraw the container from under the hose.

26.4 Lift off fuel filter cover . . .

26.5 . . . then lift filter from housing

18 000 mile (30 000 km) Service - Citroën Xantia

27 Fuel filter renewal

Refer to Section 26.

36 000 mile (60 000 km) Service - Citroën AX

28 Timing belt renewal

Note: *At the time of writing, only limited information was available on the cast-iron block Diesel engine introduced in July 1994, therefore the following information refers only to the aluminium block engine. Whenever renewing the timing belt, it is a wise precaution to check the coolant pump for signs of coolant leakage at the same time. This may avoid the need to remove the timing belt again at a later stage, should the coolant pump fail.*

28.5 Removing timing belt upper cover

Removal

1 Disconnect the battery negative terminal.
2 For improved access, remove the right-hand headlight.
3 Three 8 mm diameter bolts and one 6 mm diameter rod or drill will be required to lock the crankshaft and the camshaft and fuel injection pump sprockets in position.
4 For the purpose of timing this engine, TDC refers to the position of No 4 piston at the end of its compression stroke. No 4 piston is at the timing belt end of the engine.
5 Remove the timing belt upper cover by removing its retaining bolts and lifting the cover from the cylinder head **(see illustration)**.
6 Remove the timing belt centre cover by first turning the wheels onto full right-hand lock, then prising out the rubber plug from underneath the right-hand front wheel arch. Unscrew the cover bolt which is accessible through the hole in the wing valance. Unscrew the other retaining bolt from the centre of the cover, then manoeuvre the cover out of position **(see illustrations)**.
7 The crankshaft must now be turned until the three bolt holes in the camshaft and injection pump sprockets (one hole in the camshaft sprocket, two holes in the injection pump sprocket) are aligned with the corresponding holes in the cylinder head and injection pump mounting bracket. The crankshaft can be turned by using a spanner on the pulley bolt, after having removed the glow plugs to facilitate easier turning of the engine. Improved access to the pulley bolt can be obtained by jacking up the front right-hand corner of the vehicle and removing the roadwheel and wheel arch covers.

28.6a Remove rubber plug . . .

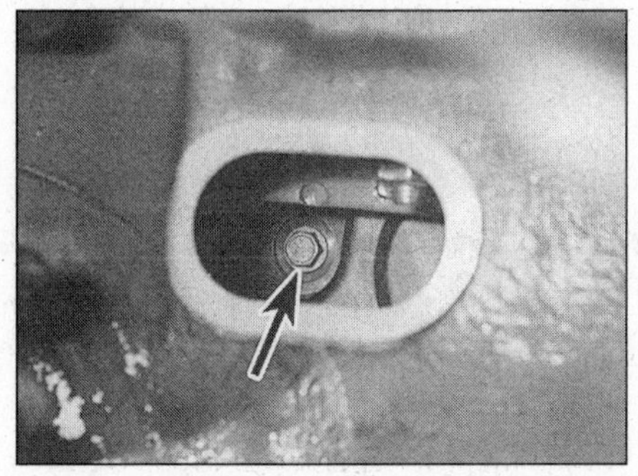

28.6b . . . to gain access to the timing belt cover bolt (arrowed)

28.6c Unscrew remaining bolt (arrowed) and remove centre cover

28.8 Insert 6 mm bolt (arrowed) through hole in cylinder block flange and into flywheel timing hole

28.9a Insert 8 mm bolt (arrowed) through camshaft sprocket timing hole and into cylinder head . . .

8 Insert a 6 mm diameter rod or drill through the hole in the left-hand flange of the cylinder block (just above the TDC sensor position). If necessary, carefully turn the crankshaft either way until the rod enters the TDC hole in the flywheel **(see illustration)**.

9 Insert three M8 bolts through the holes in the camshaft and fuel injection pump sprockets, then screw them into the engine finger-tight **(see illustrations)**.

10 The crankshaft, camshaft and injection pump are now locked in position with No 4 piston at TDC.

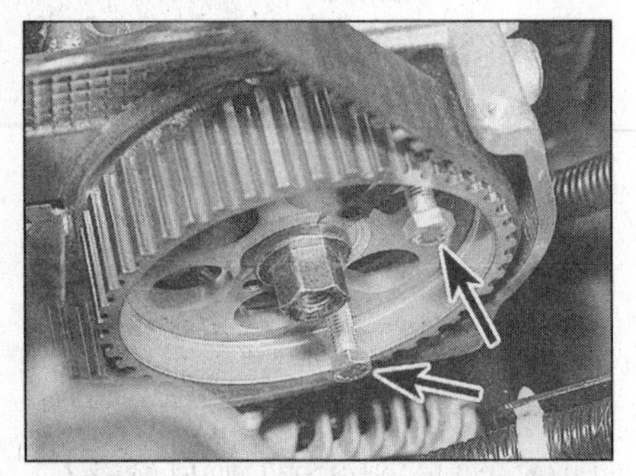

28.9b . . . then insert two 8 mm bolts (arrowed) into injection pump sprocket holes and into mounting bracket

11 Loosen the timing belt tensioner pulley retaining nut. Pivot the pulley in a clockwise direction, using a square-section key fitted to the hole in the pulley hub, then retighten the retaining nut.

12 Slip the belt off the sprockets, idler and tensioner.

Fitting and tensioning

13 Thoroughly clean the timing belt sprockets. Check that the tensioner pulley rotates freely, without any sign of roughness. If necessary, renew the tensioner pulley. Ensure that the locking tools are still in place.

14 Manoeuvre the new belt into position, ensuring that the arrows on the belt are pointing in the direction of rotation (clockwise when viewed from the right-hand end of the engine) **(see illustration)**.

15 Do not twist the belt sharply while refitting it. First locate the belt over the crankshaft sprocket, then feed it over the coolant pump sprocket, idler and injection pump sprocket, making sure that it is kept taut **(see illustration)**. Locate the back of the belt under the tensioner roller, then engage it with the camshaft sprocket. Ensure that the belt teeth are seated centrally in the sprockets.

16 Loosen the tensioner pulley retaining nut. Pivot the pulley anti-clockwise to remove all free play from the timing belt, then retighten the nut **(see illustration)**.

17 Citroën dealers use one of two special tools to tension the timing belt. One of these tools is fitted on the belt between the injection pump and camshaft sprockets and the belt is tensioned until the tool reads 25 units.

18 The second tool consists of a bar and weight applied to the tensioner pulley **(see illustration)**. A similar tool may be fabricated using a suitable square-section bar attached to an arm. A hole should be drilled in the arm at a distance of 80 mm from the centre of the square-section bar. Fit the tool to the hole in the tensioner pulley, keeping the tool arm as close to the horizontal as possible, and hang a 2.0 kg weight from the hole in the tool. In the absence of an object of the specified weight, a spring balance can be used to exert the required force, ensuring that the spring balance is held at 90° to the tool arm **(see illustration)**. Slacken the pulley retaining nut, allowing the weight or force exerted (as applicable) to push the tensioner pulley against the belt, then retighten the pulley nut.

19 Remove the locking tools from the camshaft sprocket and injection pump sprocket, and from the flywheel.

20 Using a suitable socket and extension bar on the crankshaft sprocket bolt, rotate the crankshaft through ten complete rotations in a

28.14 Direction of rotation arrows on timing belt

28.15 Engaging timing belt with sprockets

28.16 Remove all free play from belt, then securely tighten tensioner pulley retaining nut

28.18a Using Citroën special tool to tension timing belt

1 *Tensioner roller*
2 *Pulley retaining nut*
3 *Special tool fitted to tensioner roller*

clockwise direction (viewed from the right-hand end of the engine). Do not at any time rotate the crankshaft anti-clockwise.

21 Slacken the tensioner pulley nut, re-tension the belt using the method just described, then tighten the tensioner pulley nut to the specified torque.

22 Rotate the crankshaft through a further two turns clockwise and recheck that both the camshaft sprocket and flywheel timing holes are correctly aligned.

23 If all is well, refit the timing belt covers, using a reversal of the removal procedure.

24 Reconnect the battery negative terminal.

25 If removed, refit the right-hand headlight.

28.18b Using home-made tool and spring balance to tension timing belt

36 000 mile (60 000 km) Service - Citroën Xantia

29 Timing belt renewal

1 Refer to Section 31 whilst noting that there may be some variation in timing belt cover removal, due to model year.

48 000 mile (80 000 km) Service - Citroën BX/Visa/C15

30 Timing belt renewal

Removal

1 On Visa models apply the handbrake.

2 On BX models, chock the rear wheels and release the handbrake. The handbrake operates on the front wheels.

3 On manual transmission models, jack up the front right-hand corner of the vehicle until the wheel is just clear of the ground. Support the vehicle on an axle stand and engage 4th or 5th gear. This will enable the engine to be turned easily by turning the right-hand wheel.

4 On automatic transmission models, use an open-ended spanner on the crankshaft pulley bolt.

5 Remove the engine splash guard from under the right-hand front wheel arch.

6 Disconnect the battery negative lead.

7 Loosen the alternator pivot and adjustment bolts then unscrew the tension bolt until it is possible to slip the drivebelt from the pulleys.

8 With 4th or 5th gear selected on manual transmission models, have an assistant depress the footbrake pedal, then unscrew the crankshaft pulley bolt. On BX models, the handbrake may be applied instead of the footbrake pedal to hold the crankshaft stationary. On automatic transmission models, unbolt the transmission cover and lock the starter ring gear. Note that the bolt is extremely tight.

9 Slide the pulley from the front of the crankshaft. Unbolt the bottom timing cover.

10 Support the weight of the engine using a hoist or trolley jack.

11 Unscrew the nuts and remove the right-hand engine mounting bracket **(see illustration)**.

12 Pull up the front clip (early models), release the spring clips and withdraw the two timing cover sections **(see illustrations).** Note that the spring clip is not fitted to later models, which have a modified cover and fastenings.

13 Turn the engine by means of the front right-hand wheel or crankshaft pulley bolt until the three bolt holes in the camshaft and injection pump sprockets are aligned with the corresponding holes in the engine front plate.

14 Insert an 8.0 mm diameter metal dowel rod or drill through the special hole in the left-hand rear flange of the cylinder block by the starter motor. Then carefully turn the engine either way until the rod enters the TDC hole in the flywheel.

30.11 Engine right-hand mounting bracket

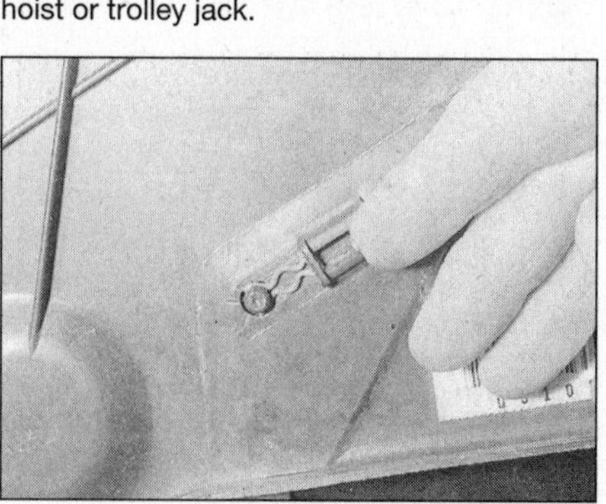

30.12a Timing cover front clip (early models) . . .

30.12b . . . and spring clips

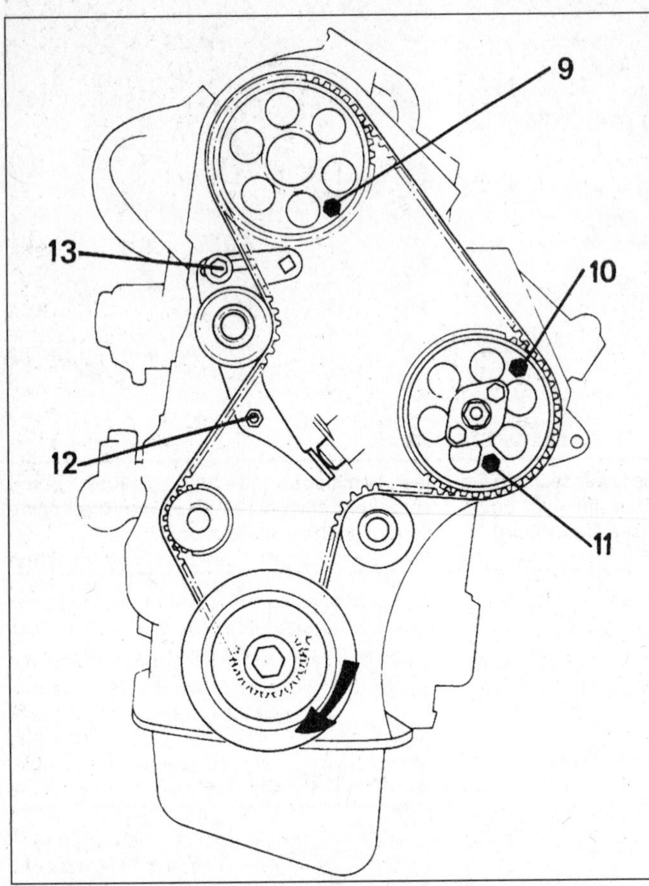

30.15 Holding camshaft and injection pump sprockets in position using M8 bolts

9, 10 and 11 M8 bolts
12 Tensioner pivot nut
13 Tensioner adjustment bolt

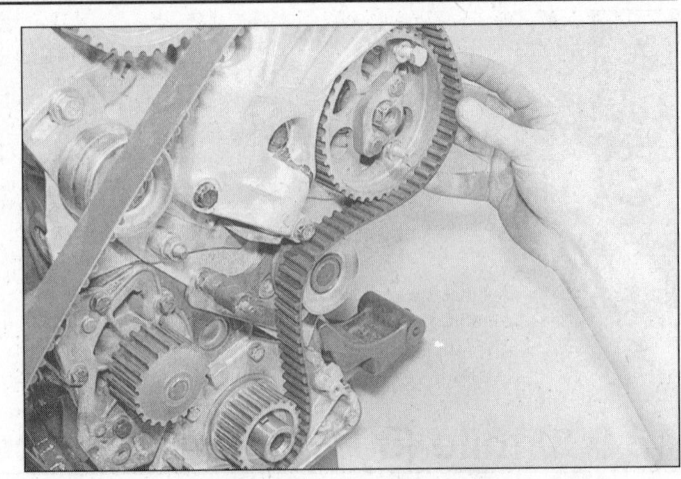

30.19a Fitting timing belt over injection pump sprocket . . .

30.19b . . . camshaft sprocket . . .

15 Insert three M8 bolts through the holes in the camshaft and injection pump sprockets and screw them into the engine front plate finger-tight **(see illustration)**.

16 Loosen the timing belt tensioner pivot nut and adjustment bolt, then turn the bracket anti-clockwise to release the tension and retighten the adjustment bolt to hold the tensioner in the released position. If available use a 3/8 inch square drive extension in the hole provided to turn the bracket against the spring tension.

30.19c . . . and coolant pump sprocket

17 Remove the timing belt from the camshaft, injection pump, coolant pump and crankshaft sprockets.

Refitting and tensioning

18 Locate the new belt on the crankshaft sprocket, ensuring that the rotation arrow is facing the correct way.

19 Hold the belt engaged with the crankshaft sprocket then feed it over the roller and onto the injection pump, camshaft and coolant pump sprockets and over the tensioner roller. To ensure correct engagement, locate only a half width on the injection pump sprocket before feeding the timing belt onto the camshaft sprocket, keeping the belt taut and fully engaged with the crankshaft sprocket. Locate the timing belt fully onto the sprockets **(see illustrations)**.

20 With the pivot nut loose, slacken the tensioner adjustment bolt while holding the bracket against the spring tension. Slowly release the bracket until the roller presses against the timing belt. Retighten the adjustment bolt.

21 Remove the bolts from the camshaft and injection pump sprockets. Remove the metal dowel rod from the cylinder block.

22 Rotate the engine two complete turns in its normal direction. Do not rotate the engine backwards as the timing belt must be kept tight between the crankshaft, injection pump and camshaft sprockets.

23 Loosen the tensioner adjustment bolt to allow the tensioner spring to push the roller against the timing belt, then tighten both the adjustment bolt and pivot nut.

24 Recheck the engine timing then remove the metal dowel rod.

25 Refit the three timing cover sections and secure with the special clip and spring clips.

26 Refit the right-hand engine mounting bracket and tighten the nuts.

27 Remove the trolley jack or hoist.

28 Slide the pulley onto the front of the crankshaft.

29 Apply three drops of locking fluid on the threads of the crankshaft pulley bolt then insert it and tighten to the specified torque while holding the crankshaft stationary.

30 Refit and tension the alternator drivebelt.

31 Reconnect the battery negative lead.

32 Refit the engine splash-guard under the right-hand front wheel arch.

33 Lower the vehicle to the ground.

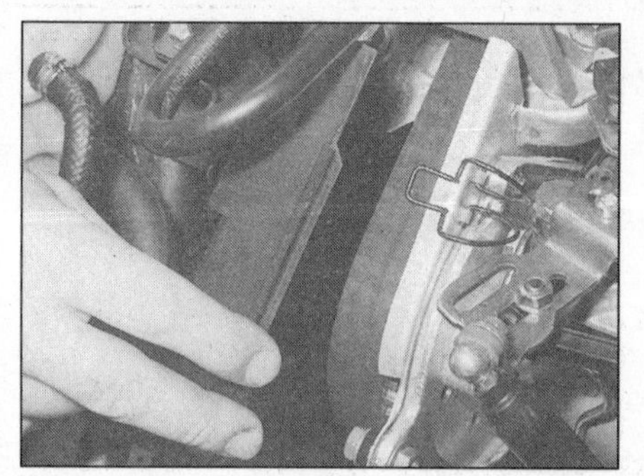
31.3 Removing right-hand timing belt cover

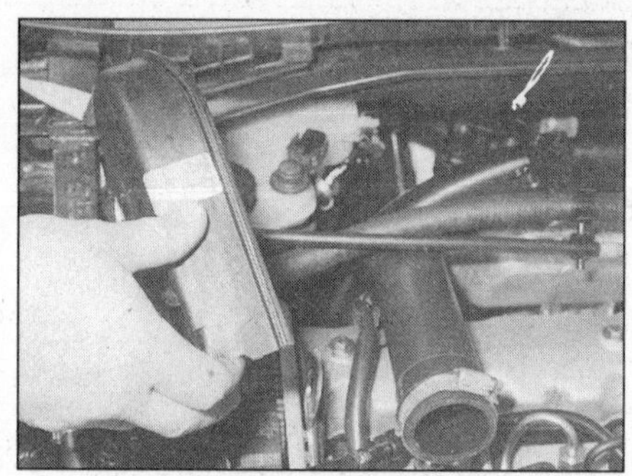
31.4 Removing left-hand timing belt cover

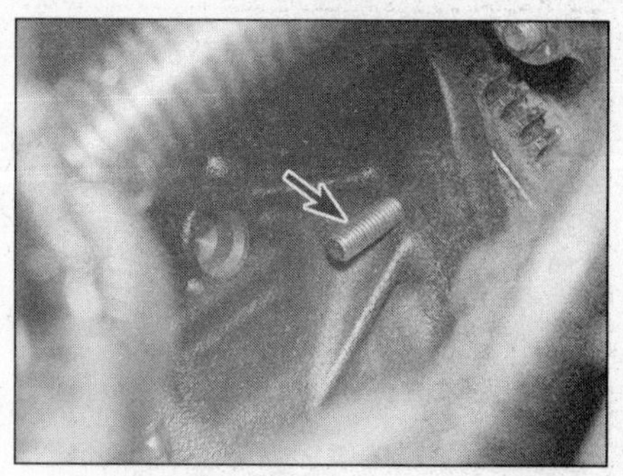
31.6 Rod (arrowed) inserted through cylinder block into TDC hole in flywheel

48 000 mile (80 000 km) Service - Citroën ZX

31 Timing belt renewal

Note: *Whenever renewing the timing belt, it is a wise precaution to check the coolant pump for signs of coolant leakage at the same time. This may avoid the need to remove the timing belt again at a later stage, should the coolant pump fail.*

Removal

1 Note that three 8 mm diameter bolts and one 8 mm diameter rod or drill will be required to lock the crankshaft, camshaft and fuel injection pump sprockets, in position.

2 For the purpose of timing the engine, TDC refers to the position of No 1 piston at the end of its compression stroke. No 1 piston is at the flywheel/driveplate end of the engine.

3 Remove the right-hand upper timing belt cover by first removing the right-hand engine mounting-to-body bracket. This will greatly improve access. Release the upper spring clip from the cover. Release the lower securing lug using a screwdriver, then lift the cover upwards from the engine **(see illustration)**.

4 Remove the left-hand upper timing belt cover by releasing the two securing clips, manipulating the cover over the studs on the front of the engine, then withdrawing the cover upwards **(see illustration)**. Clearance is limited and if desired, access can be improved by removing the engine mounting bracket.

5 The crankshaft must now be turned until the three bolt holes in the camshaft and injection pump sprockets (one hole in the camshaft sprocket, two holes in the injection pump sprocket) are aligned with the corresponding holes in the engine front plate. The crankshaft can be turned by using a spanner on the pulley bolt.

6 Insert an 8 mm diameter rod or drill through the hole in the left-hand flange of the cylinder block by the starter motor. If necessary, carefully turn the crankshaft either way until the rod enters the TDC hole in the flywheel **(see illustration)**.

7 Insert three M8 bolts through the holes in the camshaft and fuel injection pump sprockets, then screw them into the engine finger-tight **(see illustrations)**.

8 The crankshaft, camshaft and injection pump are now locked in position with No 1 piston at TDC.

9 Remove the crankshaft pulley.

10 Loosen the timing belt tensioner pivot nut and adjustment bolt, then turn the tensioner bracket anti-clockwise to release the tension. Retighten the adjustment bolt to hold the tensioner in the released position. If available, use a 10 mm square drive extension in the hole provided, to turn the tensioner bracket against the spring tension **(see illustration)**.

11 Remove the timing belt from the sprockets.

Fitting and tensioning

12 Commence fitting by ensuring that the M8 bolts are still fitted to the camshaft and fuel injection pump sprockets, and that the rod or drill is positioned in the TDC hole in the flywheel.

13 Locate the new belt on the crankshaft sprocket, ensuring that the direction of rotation arrow is facing the correct way.

31.7a M8 bolt (arrowed) inserted through TDC hole in camshaft sprocket

31.7b M8 bolts (arrowed) inserted through TDC holes in fuel injection pump sprocket

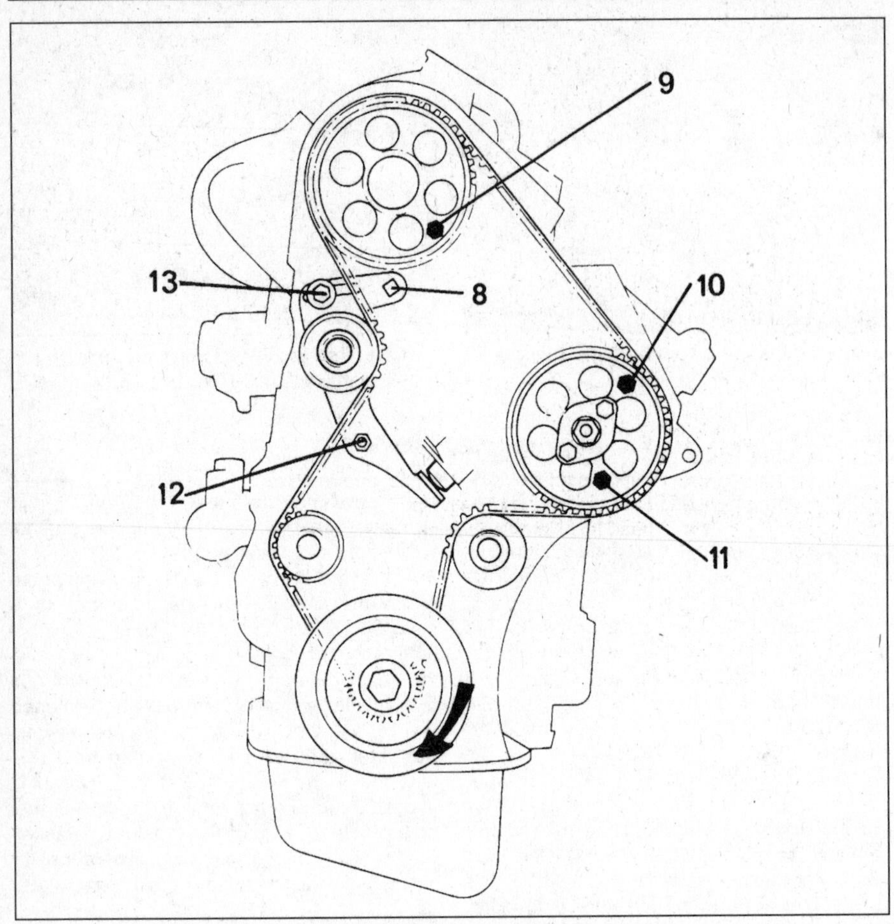

31.10 Removing timing belt

8 Square hole
9, 10 and 11 M8 bolts
12 Tensioner pivot nut
13 Adjustment bolt

31.15 Half-width of timing belt correctly engaged with camshaft sprocket

14 Engage the belt with the crankshaft sprocket. Hold it in position, then feed the belt over the othere sprockets in the following order:

a) Idler roller.
b) Fuel injection pump.
c) Camshaft.
d) Tensioner roller.
e) Coolant pump.

15 Be careful not to kink or twist the belt. To ensure correct engagement, locate only a half-width on the injection pump sprocket before feeding the belt onto the camshaft sprocket, keeping the belt taut and fully engaged with the crankshaft sprocket. Locate the belt fully onto the sprockets **(see illustration)**.

16 Remove the bolts from the camshaft and fuel injection pump sprockets. Remove the rod or drill from the TDC hole in the flywheel.

17 With the pivot nut loose, slacken the tensioner adjustment bolt while holding the bracket against the spring tension. Slowly release the bracket until the roller presses against the timing belt. Retighten the adjustment bolt and the pivot nut.

18 Rotate the crankshaft through two complete turns in the normal running direction (clockwise). Do not rotate the crankshaft backwards, as the timing belt must be kept tight between the crankshaft, fuel injection pump and camshaft sprockets.

19 Loosen the tensioner adjustment bolt and the pivot nut to allow the tensioner spring to push the roller against the timing belt, then tighten both the adjustment bolt and pivot nut to the specified torque.

20 Check that No 1 piston is at TDC by reinserting the sprocket locking bolts and the rod or drill in the flywheel TDC hole. If No 1 piston is not at TDC, then the timing belt has been incorrectly fitted (possibly one tooth out on one of the sprockets). In this case, repeat the fitting procedure from the beginning.

21 Refit the timing belt covers. Do not lower the vehicle to the ground until the engine mounting-to-body bracket has been refitted. On completion, refit the crankshaft pulley then refit and tension the auxiliary drivebelt.

Chapter 3
Citroën 1360cc, 1527cc, 1769cc & 1905cc engines
Part B: Fuel system servicing

Contents

Specifications

Glow plugs

Citroën AX	Champion CH147
Citroën BX/Visa/C15	Champion CH68
Citroën ZX and Xantia:	
Non turbo	Champion CH68
Turbo	Champion CH163

Injectors

Type (all models)	Pintle
Opening pressure:	
Citroën AX and Visa:	
Roto-Diesel	115 ± 5 bar
Bosch	130 bar
Citroën C15:	
Post early 1993 Lucas injection pump:	
Green collar	138 to 143 bar
Green collar and green spot	142 to 147 bar
All other models	130 bar
Citroën BX:	
Post early 1993 Lucas injection pump:	
161-A XUD7/L 052 - R8444 - B030A	118 ± 5 bar
A8A XUD7TE/L 056 - R8443 - B941A	143 ± 5 bar
All other models	130 bar
Citroën ZX:	
Lucas CAV/Roto-Diesel injection pump:	
No mark on injector body	113 to 118 bar
Green mark on injector body	117 to 122 bar
Pink mark on injector body	123 to 128 bar
Pink and green marks on injector body	127 to 132 bar
Bosch injection pump:	
All non turbo engines	130 bar
Turbo engines	175 bar
Citroën Xantia:	
Lucas fuel injection pump:	
Pink mark on injector body	123 to 128 bar
Green/pink mark on injector body	127 to 132 bar
Bosch fuel injection pump (Turbos) Blue mark on injector body	175 bar

Fuel injection pump

Direction of rotation (all models) .... Clockwise from sprocket end

Citroën AX

Type:
- 1360 cc engine .... Roto-Diesel or Bosch
- 1527 cc engine .... Roto-Diesel/Lucas

Static timing:
- Setting:
  - Engine position .... No 4 piston at TDC
  - Pump position:
    - Roto-Diesel .... Value shown on pump
    - Bosch .... 0.80 mm (ABDC on pump)
- Equivalent static advance:
  - 1360 cc engine .... 11° 30' BTDC
  - 1527 cc engine .... 14° BTDC

Dynamic timing at normal operating temperature:
- 1360 cc engine .... 12° BTDC
- 1527 cc engine .... Not available

Citroën BX - Post early 1993 Bosch type

Type	D9B XUD9A/L BVM XUD201 - R425/1	D9B XUD9A/L BVA XUD201 - R425/3
Static timing (pump ABDC)	1.07 mm	0.98 mm

Citroën BX - Post early 1993 Lucas type

Type	161-A XUD7/L 052 R8444 - B030A	A8A XUD7TE/L 056 R8443 - B941A
Static timing	X dimension marked on pump	X dimension marked on pump
Dynamic timing	14° ± 1°	-

Citroën BX and Visa - Roto-Diesel type

Static advance .... 2.26 ± 0.05 mm BTDC (equivalent to 16° BTDC)

Dynamic advance:
- Visa and BX17 .... 14 ± 1° BTDC at 800 rpm
- BX19 with injection pump code DPCR 844 3161 A .... 17 ± 1° BTDC at idle speed
- BX19 with injection pump code DPCR 844 3261 C .... 14 ± 1° BTDC at idle speed

Citroën BX and Visa - Pre 1987 Bosch type	Static advance	Dynamic advance
Visa	0.72 ± 0.03 mm BTDC	14 ± 1° BTDC at 800 rpm
BX17	0.80 ± 0.03 mm BTDC	14 ± 1° BTDC at 800 rpm
BX19	0.57 ± 0.03 mm BTDC	13 to 14° BTDC at idle speed

Citroën BX and Visa - Post 1987 Bosch type

Timing values at TDC (refer to text):

Engine code	Pump code	Timing value
XUD 7 (Oct. 1987 on)	VER 171-1	0.90 mm
XUD 7 (Early 1993 on)	VER R171-3	0.89 mm
XUD 9A (April 1987 to April 1988)	VER 272-1	0.83 mm
XUD 9A (April 1988 on)	VER 272-2	0.90 mm
XUD 7TE	-	0.80 mm

Citroën C15:	Type	Static timing
Post early 1993 Bosch type	523 (R171-3)	(pump ABDC) 0.89 mm
Post early 1993 Lucas type	047 (R 8443B 930 A)	X dimension marked on pump

Citroën ZX - Lucas CAV/Roto-Diesel type

Static timing:
- Engine position .... No 4 piston at TDC
- Pump position .... Value shown on pump

Dynamic timing at idle:
- XUD7 (A9A) engine .... 12° ± 1°
- XUD9A (D9B) engine .... 14.5° ± 1°
- XUD9A/L (D9B) engine .... 12.5° ± 1°

Citroën ZX - Bosch type

Static timing

Engine position .... No 4 piston at TDC

Pump position:
- XUD7 (A9A) engine .... 0.90 mm ABDC
- XUD9A (D9B) and XUD9A/L (D9B) engines .... 1.07 mm ABDC
- XUD9Y (DJZ) engine .... 0.77 mm ABDC
- XUD9TE/L (D8A) and XUD9TE/Y (DHY and DHZ) engines .... 0.66 mm ABDC

Citroën ZX - Bosch type (continued)

Dynamic timing at idle	
XUD7 (A9A) engine	15.5° ± 1°
XUD9A (D9B) and XUD9A/L (D9B) engines	17.5° ± 1°
XUD9Y (DJZ) engine	14° ± 1°
XUD9TE/L (D8A) and XUD9TE/Y (DHY and DHZ) engines	12.5° ± 1°

Citroën Xantia - Lucas type, D9B engine

Static timing:	
Engine position	No 4 piston at TDC
Pump position	Value shown on pump
Dynamic timing at idle	12° ± 1°

Citroën Xantia - Bosch type, D8B engine

Static timing:	
Engine position	No 4 piston at TDC
Pump timing measurement	0.66° 0.02 mm
Dynamic timing at idle	12.5° ± 1°

Fast idle speed

See Chapter 3A Specifications

Maximum speed

Citroën AX

Maximum no-load speed:	
1360 cc engine	5500 rpm
1527 cc engine	5450 rpm

Citroën BX - Post early 1993 Bosch injection pump

Maximum loaded speed	4600 rpm

Citroën BX - Post early 1993 Lucas injection pump

Maximum loaded speed:	
161-A XUD7/L 052 - R8444 - B030A	4600 rpm
A8A XUD7TE/L 056 - R8443 - B941A	4300 rpm

Citroën BX - All other models

Maximum no-load speed	5100 ± 100 rpm

Citroën C15 and Visa

Maximum no-load speed	5100 ± 100 rpm

Citroën ZX

No-load:	
1.7 litre engine	5100 ± 125 rpm
1.9 litre non turbo engines	5150 ± 125 rpm
1.9 litre Turbo engines	5050 ± 125 rpm
Full-load:	
All non turbo engines	4600 ± 80 rpm
Turbo engines	4500 ± 80 rpm

Citroën Xantia

D9B non-turbo engines	5150 ± 125 rpm
D8B Turbo engines	5100 ± 80 rpm

Torque wrench settings

	Nm	lbf ft
Citroën AX		
Glow plugs	22	16
Injection pump:		
Feed and return hose union bolts	25	18
Front mounting nuts	18	12
Rear mounting bolt	23	17
Injector pipe union nuts	20	15
Injectors	70	52
Citroën BX/Visa/C15		
Cylinder head blanking plug	30	22
Glow plugs	22	16
Injection pump:		
Mounting nuts	18	13
Blanking plug (Bosch)	20	15
Sprocket nut	50	37

Torque wrench settings (continued)

	Nm	lbf ft
Citroën BX/Visa/C15 (continued)		
Injector pipe union nuts	20	15
Injectors:		
Bosch	90	66
Roto-diesel	130	96
Citroën ZX and Xantia		
Fuel pipe union nuts	20	15
Glow plugs	22	16
Injection pump:		
Sprocket nut	50	37
Sprocket puller bolts	10	7
Mounting nuts/bolts	20	15
Timing hole blanking plug:		
Lucas	6	4
Bosch	15	11
Injectors to cylinder head	90	66
No 4 cylinder TDC blanking plug	30	22
Stop solenoid:		
Lucas	15	11
Bosch	20	15

1 Accelerator cable - adjustment

1 Remove the spring clip from the accelerator cable outer **(see illustration)**. Ensuring that the control lever is against its stop, gently pull the cable out of its grommet until all free play is removed from the cable inner.

2 With the cable held in this position, refit the spring clip to the last exposed cable outer groove in front of the rubber grommet and washer. When the clip is refitted and the cable outer released, there should be only a small amount of free play in the cable inner.

3 Have an assistant depress the accelerator pedal and check that the control lever opens fully and returns smoothly to its stop.

2 Maximum speed - checking and adjustment

Caution: The maximum speed adjustment screw is sealed by the manufacturers at the factory, using paint or locking wire and a lead seal. Do not disturb the screw if the vehicle is still within the warranty period, otherwise the warranty will be invalidated. Adjustment requires the use of a tachometer.

1 Run the engine to normal operating temperature.

2 If the vehicle does not have a tachometer (rev counter), connect a suitable instrument in accordance with its manufacturer's instructions.

3 Have an assistant fully depress the accelerator pedal and check that the maximum engine speed is as specified. Do not keep the engine at maximum speed for more than two or three seconds.

4 If adjustment is necessary, stop the engine then loosen the locknut, turn the maximum speed adjustment screw as necessary and retighten the locknut **(see illustrations)**.

5 Repeat the procedure in paragraph 3 to check adjustment.

6 Stop the engine and disconnect the tachometer, where applicable.

3 Fast idle control - removal, refitting and adjustment

Note: *A new sealing washer must be used when refitting the thermostatic sensor.*

Removal

1 Disconnect the battery negative terminal.

2 Partially drain the cooling system.

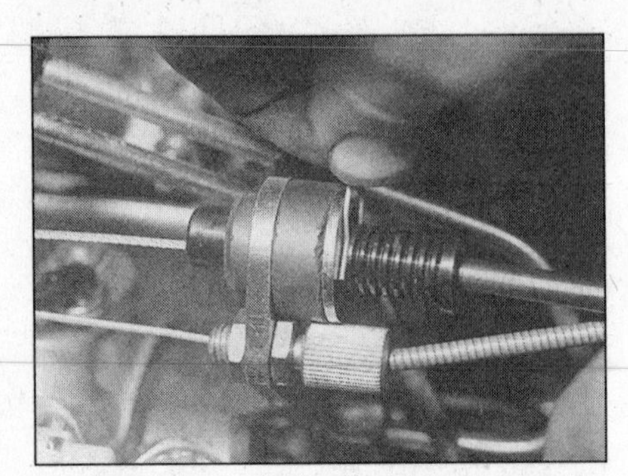

1.1 Removing spring clip from accelerator cable

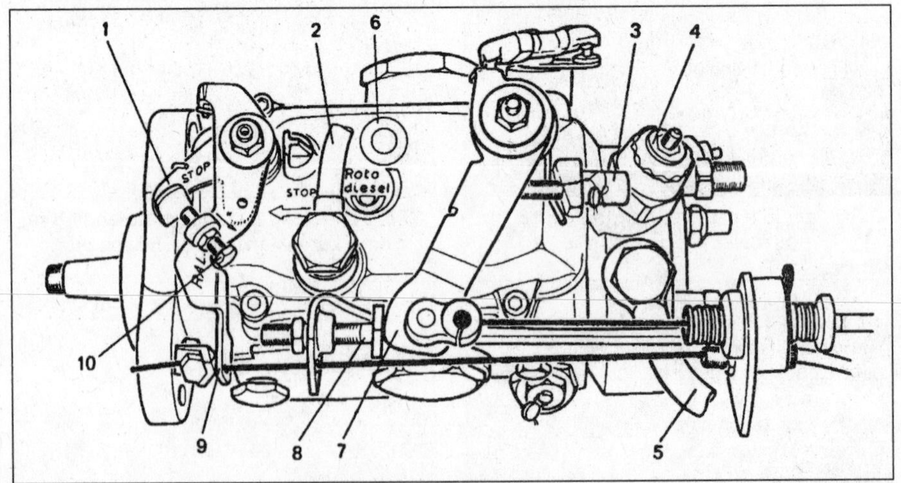

2.4a Lucas fuel injection pump adjustment points

1 Manual stop lever
2 Fuel return pipe
3 Maximum speed adjustment screw
4 Stop solenoid
5 Fuel inlet
6 Timing access plug
7 Control (accelerator) lever
8 Anti-stall adjustment screw
9 Fast idle lever
10 Idle speed adjustment screw

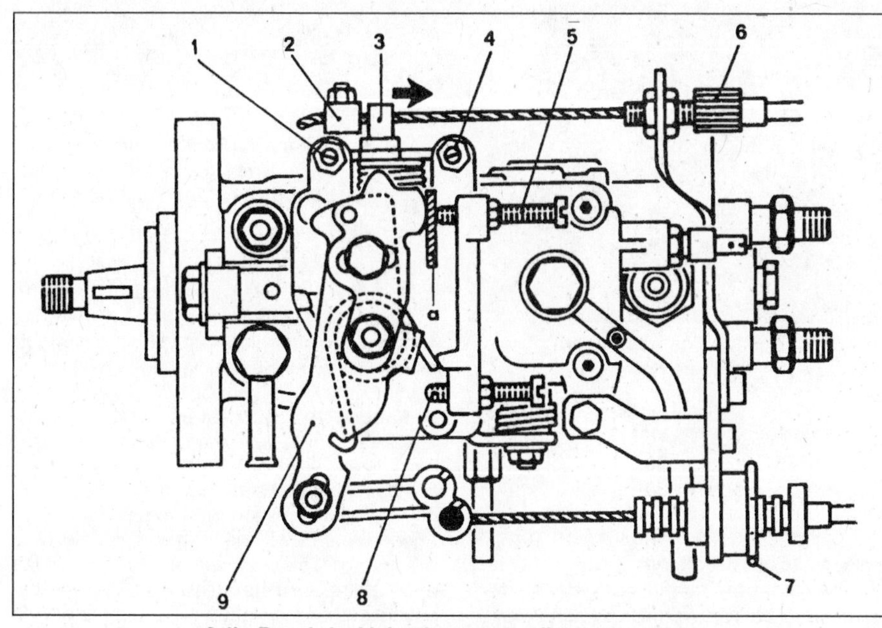

2.4b Bosch fuel injection pump adjustment points

1 *Fast idle adjustment screw*
2 *Cable end fitting*
3 *Fast idle lever*
4 *Idle speed adjustment screw*
5 *Anti-stall adjustment screw*
6 *Fast idle cable adjustment screw*
7 *Accelerator cable adjustment screw*
8 *Maximum speed adjustment screw*
9 *Control (accelerator) lever*
a *Shim for anti-stall adjustmen*

3 Loosen the clamp screw or nut and remove the end fitting from the cable inner at the fuel injection pump fast idle lever **(see illustrations)**.

4 Unscrew the locknut and remove the adjustment ferrule and cable outer from the bracket on the injection pump **(see illustrations)**.

5 Unscrew the thermostatic sensor from its housing and recover the sealing washer **(see illustrations)**.

Refitting

6 If sealing compound was originally used to fit the sensor in place of a washer, thoroughly clean all traces of old sealing compound from the sensor and housing. Ensure that no traces of sealant are left in the internal coolant passages of the housing.

7 Fit the sensor, using suitable sealing compound or a new washer as applicable, and tighten it.

8 Insert the adjustment ferrule into the bracket on the fuel injection pump and screw on the locknut, finger-tight.

9 Insert the cable inner through the fast idle lever and position the end fitting on the cable but do not tighten the clamp screw or nut (as applicable).

10 Adjust the cable as follows.

Adjustment

Citroën AX

11 With the engine cold, push the fast idle lever fully to the end of its travel (towards the rear of the pump). Hold it in this position and slide the cable end fitting along the cable until its abuts the fast idle lever or bracket (as applicable) then securely tighten its clamp nut **(see illustration)**.

12 Start the engine and warm it up to its normal operating temperature. As the engine warms up, the fast idle cable should extend so that the fast idle lever returns to is stop.

3B

3.3a Fast idle cable end fitting clamp nut (arrowed) - Lucas pump

3.3b Loosening fast idle cable end fitting clamp screw (arrowed) - Bosch pump

3.4a Fast idle cable adjustment ferrule - Roto-diesel pump

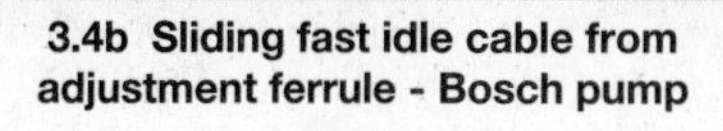

3.4b Sliding fast idle cable from adjustment ferrule - Bosch pump

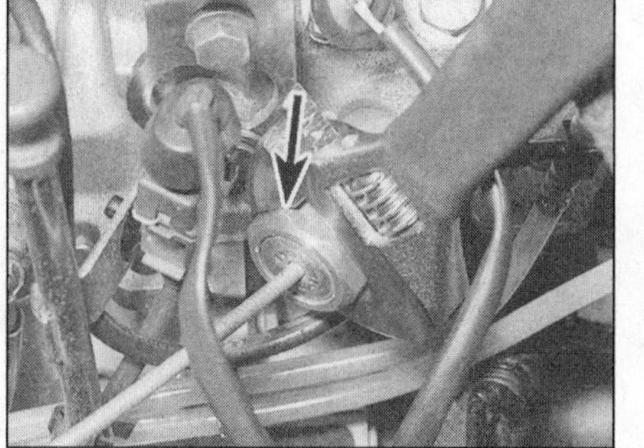

3.5a Unscrew fast idle valve (arrowed) from cylinder head . . .

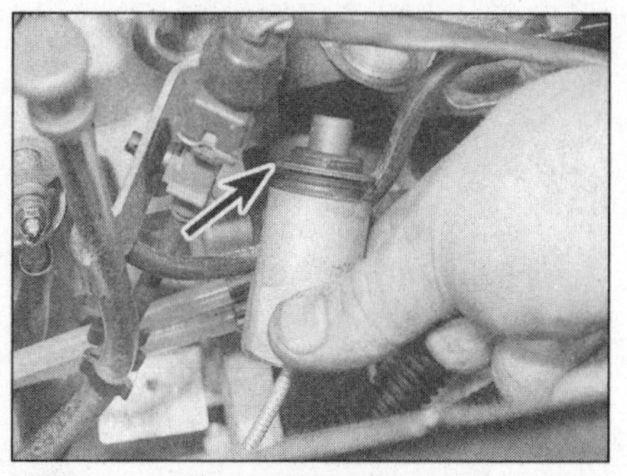

3.5b . . . and remove it along with sealing washer (arrowed)

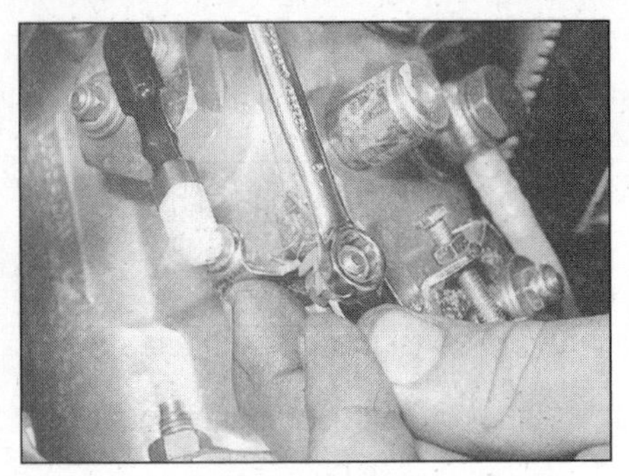
3.11 Adjusting fast idle cable

3.13 Making fine adjustment of fast idle cable

13 Once the cooling fan has cut in, switch off the engine and measure the clearance between the fast idle lever and the cable end fitting. There should be a gap of approximately 0.5 to 1 mm. If not, slacken the clamp nut, move the end fitting to the correct position, then securely retighten the screw or nut. Note that fine adjustment of the cable can be made using the adjuster ferrule on the mounting bracket **(see illustration)**..
14 With the cable correctly adjusted, allow the engine to cool. As it cools, the fast idle cable should be drawn back into the valve, moving the fast idle lever back against its stop.

All other models

15 With the engine cold, push the fast idle lever fully towards the flywheel end of the engine. Tighten the clamp screw or nut with the cable end fitting touching the lever.
16 Adjust the ferrule to ensure that the fast idle lever is touching its stop, then tighten the ferrule locknut.
17 Measure the exposed length of cable inner.
18 Refill the cooling system and run the engine to its normal operating temperature.
19 Check that the fast idle cable is slack. If not, it is likely that the sensor is faulty.
20 With the engine hot, check that the exposed length of the inner cable has increased by at least 6.0 mm, indicating that the thermostatic sensor is functioning correctly.
21 Check that the engine speed increases when the fast idle lever is pushed towards the flywheel end of the engine. With the lever against its stop, the fast idle speed should be as specified, see Part A of this Chapter.
22 Stop the engine.

4 Stop solenoid - removal and refitting

Warning: Do not allow dirt to enter the fuel injection pump during the following procedure.

Removal

1 Disconnect the battery negative lead.
2 On Citroën ZX and Xantia models fitted with a Bosch fuel injection pump, it may be necessary to unbolt the fast idle cable support bracket from the side of the pump, to improve access.
3 Withdraw the rubber boot (where applicable), then unscrew the terminal nut and disconnect the wire from the top of the solenoid **(see illustrations)**.
4 Carefully clean around the solenoid, then unscrew and withdraw the solenoid and recover the sealing washer or O-ring (as applicable) **(see illustration)**. Recover the solenoid plunger and spring if they remain in the pump **(see illustration)**. Operate the hand-priming pump as the solenoid is removed, to flush away any dirt.

Refitting

5 Refitting is a reversal of removal, using a new sealing washer or O-ring.
6 If the fast idle cable was disconnected, reconnect it with reference to Section 3.

5 Load lever position switch (Bosch injection pump, BX/Visa/C15) - adjustment

Note: *This information applies to later Bosch fuel injection pumps only.*
1 Mark the accelerator cable inner 11.0 mm from the end of the cable outer **(see illustration)**.
2 Move the load lever until the mark on the cable inner coincides with the end of the cable outer. Hold the lever in this position.
3 Loosen the switch mounting screws, then turn the switch until the internal contacts click open **(see illustration)**.
4 Tighten the mounting screws with the switch in this position, then release the lever.

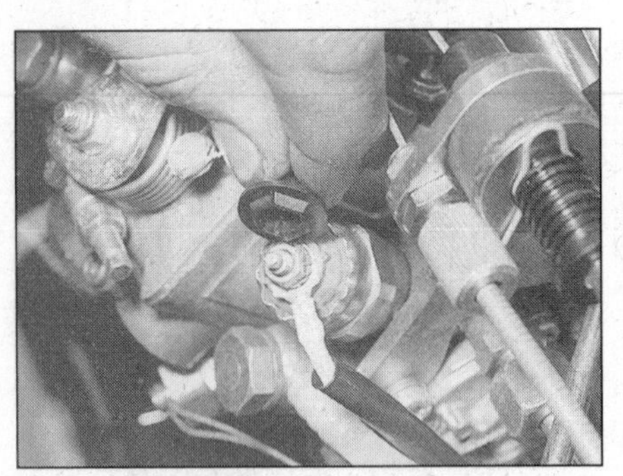
4.3a Remove rubber cover . . .

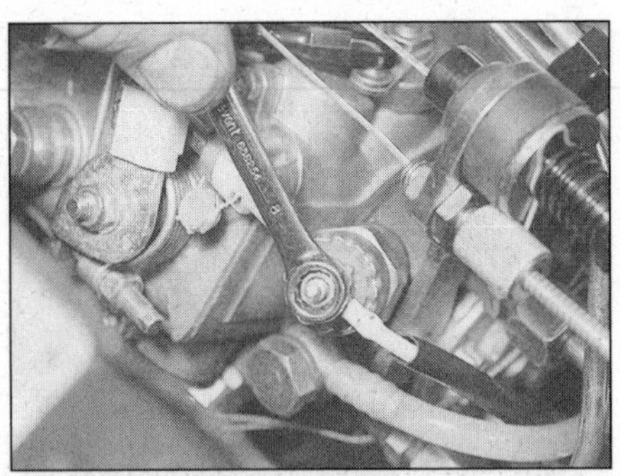
4.3b . . . then unscrew retaining nut and disconnect stop solenoid wiring connector

4.4a Unscrew stop solenoid from pump and recover O-ring (arrowed)

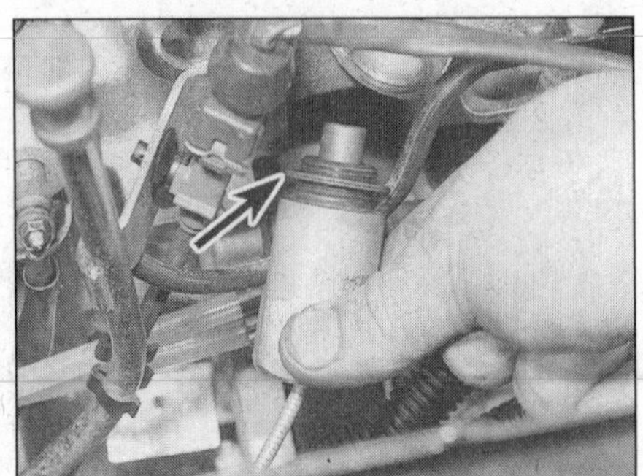
4.4b Remove solenoid and withdraw plunger and spring (arrowed)

5.1 Marking accelerator cable inner 11.0 mm from end of cable outer

5.3 Load lever position switch

5 Move the lever again and check that the switch contacts operate when the mark on the cable inner reaches the end of the cable outer.

6 Glow plugs - removal, inspection and refitting

Caution: If the preheating system has just been energised, or if the engine has been running, the glow plugs may be very hot.

Citroën ZX

Removal

1 Disconnect the battery negative lead.

2 For improved access, remove the intercooler (Turbo engines) or the air distribution housing (XUD9/A - D9B engine), where applicable. Similarly, disconnect the air hose which connects the air cleaner assembly to the top of the inlet manifold, where applicable.

3 Unscrew the nuts from the glow plug terminals and recover the washers. Note that the main supply cable is connected to one of the glow plugs (normally No 2 or 3 cylinder) and is secured by a Nyloc nut. Remove the interconnecting wire from the top of the glow plugs **(see illustrations)**.

4 Carefully move any obstructing pipes or wires to one side, to gain access to the glow plugs.

5 Unscrew the glow plugs and remove them from the cylinder head **(see illustration)**. Note that on certain models, access to No 4 cylinder glow plug is extremely limited and the plug is most easily removed using a cranked spanner. Alternatively, it may be possible to remove the plug after it has been initially slackened by using two screwdrivers acting on opposing flats of the plug.

Inspection

6 Inspect the glow plugs for physical damage. Burnt or eroded glow plug tips can be caused by a bad injector spray pattern. Have the injectors checked if this sort of damage is found.

7 If the glow plugs are in good physical condition, check them electrically using a 12-volt test lamp or continuity tester, as described in Section 15.

8 The glow plugs can be energised by applying 12 volts to them, to verify that they heat up evenly and in the required time. Observe the following precautions:

a) Support the glow plug by clamping it carefully in a vice or self-locking pliers. Remember, the plug will become red-hot.
b) Ensure that the power supply or test lead incorporates a fuse or overload trip, to protect against damage from a short-circuit.
c) After testing, allow the glow plug to cool for several minutes before attempting to handle it.

9 A glow plug in good condition will start to glow red at the tip after drawing current for 5 seconds or so. Any plug which takes much longer to start glowing, or which starts glowing in the middle, instead of at the tip, is defective.

Refitting

10 Refit by reversing the removal operations. Apply a smear of copper-based anti-seize compound to the threads and tighten the glow plugs to the specified torque. Do not over-tighten, as this can damage the glow plug element.

Citroën AX

11 Carry out the procedures given for the Citroën ZX whilst noting the following:

a) Ignore all specific references to improving access to the glow plugs but, where applicable, carefully move any obstructing pipes or wires to one side so as to gain access to the relevant plug.
b) Note that the main supply cable is connected to No 1 cylinder glow plug and an interconnecting wire is fitted between the four plugs.

Citroën BX/Visa/C15

12 Carry out the procedures given for the Citroën ZX whilst noting the following:

a) Ignore all specific references to improving access to the glow plugs but to improve access on BX models, remove the air duct between the air cleaner and inlet manifold.
*b) Prise off the plastic clips to allow removal of the glow plug terminal nuts **(see illustration)**.*
c) Note that the main supply cable is connected to No 1 cylinder glow plug (flywheel end) on Visa models.
d) Note that the main supply cable is connected to No 2 cylinder glow plug on BX models.

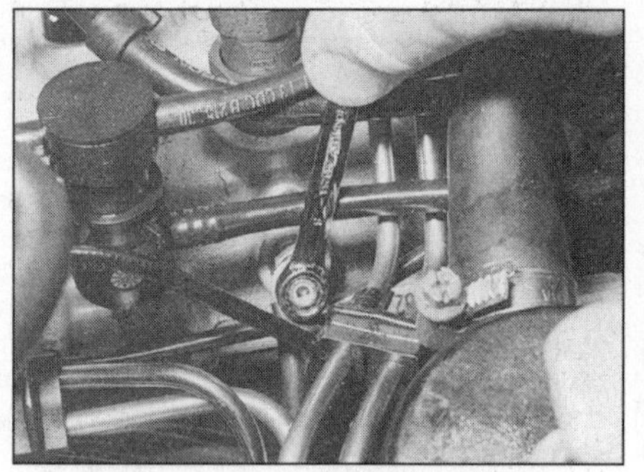

6.3a Unscrew retaining nut . . .

6.3b . . . and disconnect the main supply cable . . .

6.3c . . . and interconnecting wire from glow plug

6.5 Removing a glow plug

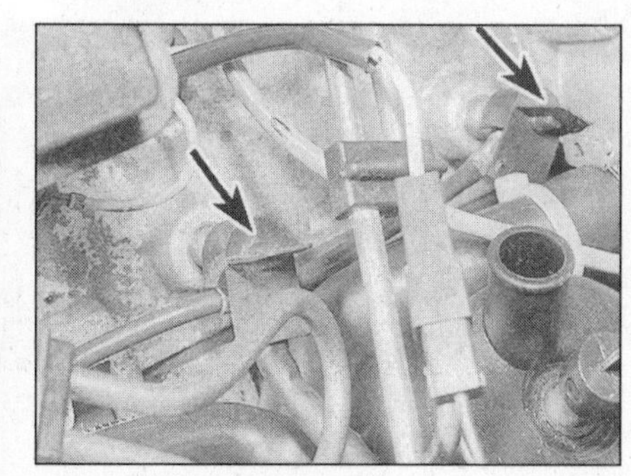

6.12 Plastic clips (arrowed) on glow plug terminals

7.5 Pulling a leak-off pipe from a fuel injector

7.7 Unscrewing an injector pipe union nut

7.8 Removing injector from cylinder head

Citroën Xantia

13 Carry out the procedures given for the Citroën ZX whilst noting the following:

a) *To improve access to the glow plugs, remove the air distribution housing. If necessary, also remove the inlet duct and disconnect the breather hose from the engine oil filler tube.*

b) *Note that the main supply cable is connected to No 1 cylinder glow plug and an interconnecting wire is fitted between the four plugs.*

7 Injectors - testing, removal and refitting

Warning: Exercise extreme caution when working on fuel injectors. Never expose the hands or any part of the body to injector spray, as the high working pressure can cause fuel to penetrate the skin, with possibly fatal results. You are strongly advised to have any work which involves testing the injectors under pressure carried out by a dealer or fuel injection specialist.

Note: *Take great care not to allow dirt into the injectors or fuel pipes during this procedure. Do not drop the injectors or allow the needles at their tips to become damaged. Injectors are precision-made to fine limits and must not be handled roughly. Do not mount them in a bench vice.*

7.9a Removing fuel injector copper washer . . .

Citroën ZX

Testing

1 Injectors do deteriorate with prolonged use and it is reasonable to expect them to need reconditioning or renewal after 60 000 miles (90 000 km) or so. Accurate testing, overhaul and calibration of the injectors must be left to a specialist. A defective injector which is causing knocking or smoking can be located without dismantling as follows.

2 Run the engine at a fast idle. Slacken each injector union in turn, placing rag around the union to catch spilt fuel and being careful not to expose the skin to any spray. When the union on the defective injector is slackened, the knocking or smoking will stop.

Removal

3 For improved access, remove the intercooler (Turbo engines) or the air distribution housing (XUD9/A - D9B engine), where applicable. Similarly, disconnect the air hose from the top of the inlet manifold, where applicable.

4 Carefully clean around the injectors and injector pipe union nuts.

5 Pull the leak-off pipes from the injectors **(see illustration)**.

6 Unscrew the union nuts securing the injector pipes to the fuel injection pump. Counterhold the unions on the pump when unscrewing the nuts. Cover open unions to keep dirt out.

7 Unscrew the union nuts and disconnect the pipes from the injectors **(see illustration)**. If necessary, the injector pipes may be completely removed. Note carefully the locations of the pipe clamps, for use when refitting. Cover the ends of the injectors, to prevent dirt ingress.

8 Unscrew the injectors using a deep socket or box spanner (27 mm across-flats) and remove them from the cylinder head **(see illustration)**.

9 Recover the copper washers and fire seal washers from the cylinder head. Also recover the sleeves if they are loose **(see illustrations)**.

Refitting

10 Obtain new copper washers and fire seal washers. Also renew the sleeves, if they are damaged.

11 Commence refitting by inserting the sleeves (if removed) into the cylinder head, followed by the fire seal washers (convex face uppermost) and copper washers **(see illustration)**.

7.9b . . . fire seal washer . . .

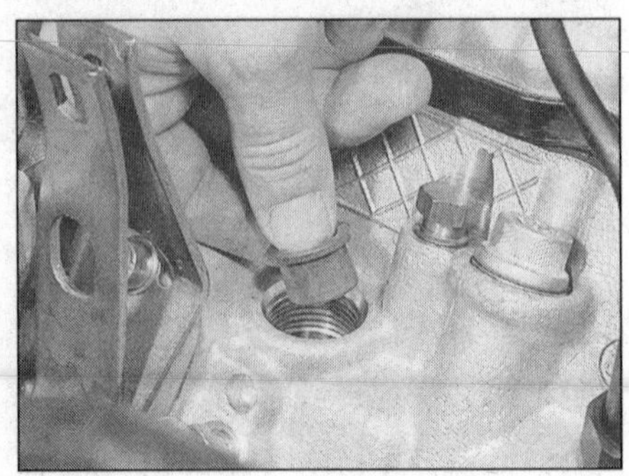

7.9c . . . and sleeve

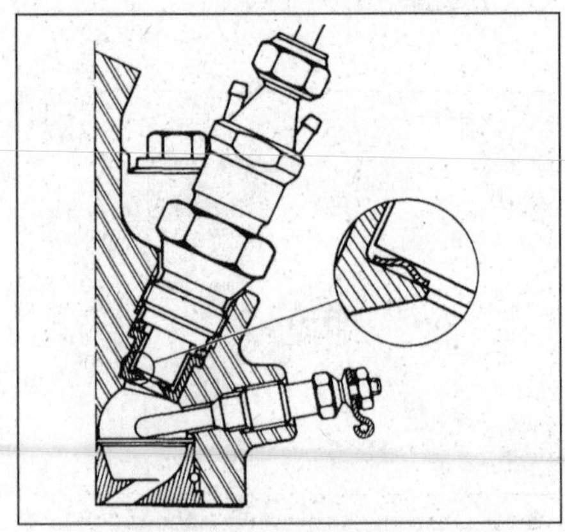

7.11 Ensure convex side of fire seal washer is facing towards injector

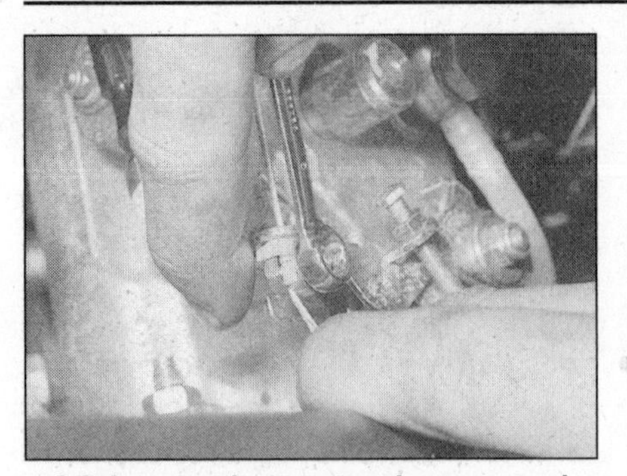
8.6 Loosen clamp nut and remove end fitting from fast idle cable

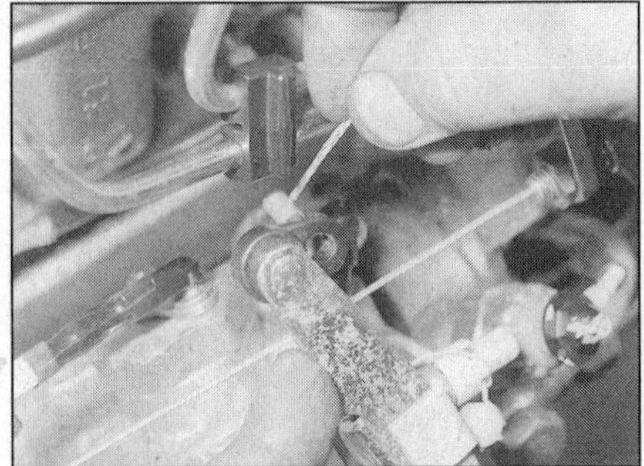
8.7a Free accelerator cable inner from pump lever . . .

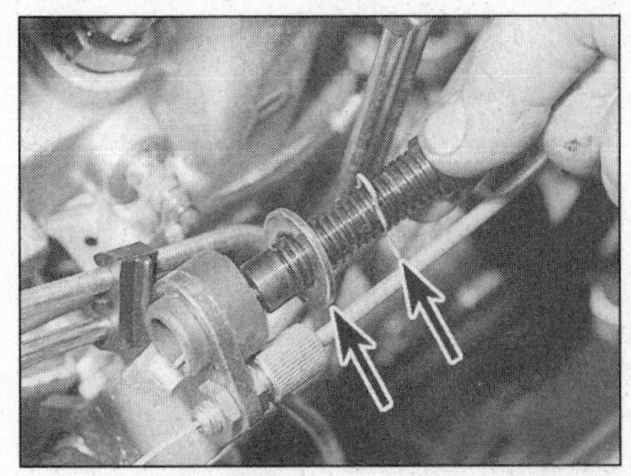
8.7b . . . then withdraw cable outer from mounting bracket, recovering washer and spring clip (arrowed)

12 Insert the injectors and tighten them to the specified torque.
13 Refit the injector pipes and tighten the union nuts to the specified torque. Ensure the pipe clamps are in their previously-noted positions. If the clamps are wrongly positioned or missing, problems may be experienced with pipes breaking or splitting.
14 Reconnect the leak-off pipes.
15 Refit the intercooler or air distribution housing, where applicable.
16 Start the engine. If difficulty is experienced, bleed the fuel system as described in Part A of this Chapter.

Citroën AX

17 Carry out the procedures given for the Citroën ZX whilst noting the following:
- *a) Ignore all specific references to improving access to the injectors.*
- *b) Cover the alternator to protect it from spilt fuel.*
- *c) Completely remove the injector pipes from the engine.*

Citroën BX/Visa/C15

18 Carry out the procedures given for the Citroën ZX whilst noting the following:
- *a) Ignore all specific references to improving access to the injectors but to improve access on BX models, remove the air duct between the air cleaner and inlet manifold.*

Citroën Xantia

19 Carry out the procedures given for the Citroën ZX. For improved access to the injectors, carry out the following:
- *a) On Turbo models, remove the air distribution housing.*
- *b) If necessary, also remove the inlet duct and disconnect the breather hose from the engine oil filler tube.*

8 Fuel injection pump (Citroën AX) - removal and refitting

Note: *Be careful not to allow dirt into the fuel injection pump or injector pipes during this procedure.*

Removal

1 Disconnect the battery negative terminal.
2 Remove the right-hand headlight unit to provide additional working room.
3 Remove the timing belt covers as described in Part A of this Chapter.
4 Align the engine TDC timing holes as described in Part A of this Chapter (timing belt renewal) and lock the crankshaft, camshaft sprocket and injection pump sprocket in position. Do not attempt to rotate the engine whilst the locking tools are in position.
5 Remove the injection pump sprocket.

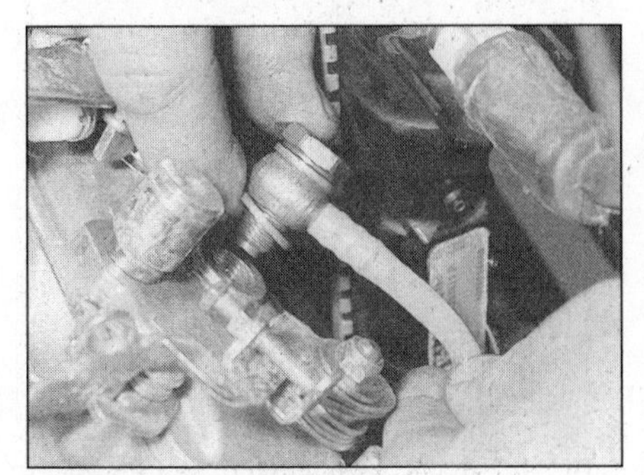
8.10 Unscrew fuel return hose union bolt and recover sealing washer from each side of hose union

8.11 Removing injector pipes from pump whilst retaining pump adapters

6 Loosen the clamp nut and disconnect the fast idle cable end fitting from the injection pump end of the cable inner **(see illustration)**. Free the fast idle cable from the bracket or lever (as applicable) on the fuel injection pump.
7 Free the accelerator cable inner from the pump lever, then pull the cable outer out from its mounting bracket rubber grommet. Slide the flat washer off the end of the cable and remove the spring clip **(see illustrations)**.
8 Wipe clean the fuel feed and return unions on the injection pump. Cover the alternator to protect it from fuel spillage.
9 Slacken and remove the fuel feed hose union bolt from the pump. Recover the sealing washer from each side of the hose union and position the hose clear of the pump. Screw the union bolt back into position on the pump for safe-keeping and cover both the hose end and union bolt to prevent the ingress of dirt into the fuel system.
10 Detach the fuel return hose from the pump, as described in the previous paragraph **(see illustration)**. Note that the injection pump feed and return hose union bolts are not interchangeable.
11 Wipe clean the pipe unions, then slacken the union nut securing the injector pipes to the top of each injector and the four union nuts securing the pipes to the rear of the injection pump. As each pump union nut is slackened, retain the adapter with a suitable open-ended spanner, to prevent it being unscrewed from the pump. With all the union nuts undone, remove the injector pipes from the engine (the pipes are removed in pairs) **(see illustration)**.
12 Remove the rubber cover (where fitted) then undo the retaining nut and disconnect the wiring from the injection pump stop solenoid.
13 Using a scriber or suitable marker pen, make alignment marks between the injection pump front flange and the front mounting bracket. These marks can then be used to ensure that the pump is correctly positioned on refitting. To improve access to the pump, undo the two screws and remove the cover panel (where fitted) from the right-hand side of the radiator.

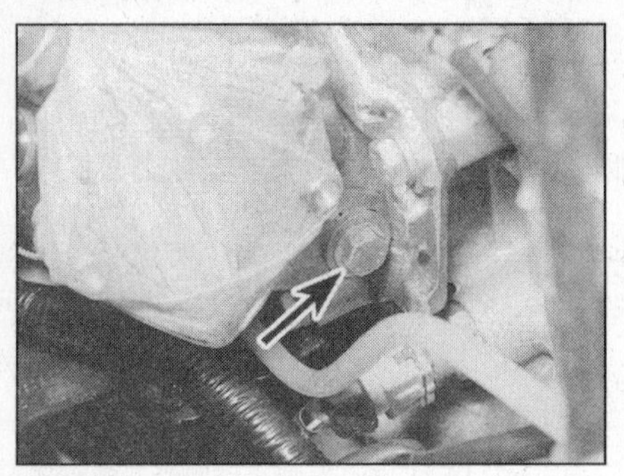
8.14 Unscrew rear mounting bracket bolt (arrowed) . . .

8.15a . . . then unscrew front mounting nuts and washer . . .

8.15b . . . and remove injection pump from the engine

14 Unscrew the bolt securing the rear of the injection pump to its mounting bracket on the cylinder block **(see illustration)**.

15 Slacken and remove the three nuts and washers securing the pump to its front mounting bracket, then manoeuvre the pump away from the bracket and out of the engine compartment **(see illustrations)**.

Refitting

16 If a new pump is being fitted, transfer the alignment mark from the original pump onto the mounting flange of the new pump.

17 Manoeuvre the pump into position then refit its three front washers and mounting nuts, and the rear mounting bolt. Align the marks made prior to removal, then securely tighten the retaining nuts and bolt.

18 Refit the injection pump sprocket. Align the sprocket timing holes with those in the mounting plate and lock the sprocket in position with the two locking tools.

19 Check the crankshaft, camshaft and injection pump sprockets are all correctly positioned, then engage the timing belt and tension it as described in Part A of this Chapter. With the timing belt correctly fitted, remove the locking tools from the sprockets.

20 Set the injection pump timing as described in Section 11.

21 With the pump timing correctly set, reconnect the wiring to the stop solenoid and securely tighten its retaining nut. Refit the rubber boot.

22 Reconnect the fuel feed and return hose unions to the pump, not forgetting to fit the filter to the feed hose union. Position a new sealing washer on each side of both unions and tighten the union bolts to the specified torque setting.

23 Refit the injector pipes and tighten their union nuts to the specified torque setting.

24 Mop up any spilt fuel, then remove any materials used to cover the alternator.

25 Reconnect and adjust the accelerator cable.

26 Reconnect and adjust the fast idle valve cable.

27 Refit the right-hand headlight unit.

28 Reconnect the battery negative lead.

29 Bleed the fuel system as described in Part A of this Chapter.

30 On completion, start the engine and adjust the idle speed and anti-stall speed, as described in Part A of this Chapter.

9 Fuel injection pump (Citroën BX/Visa/C15) - removal and refitting

Note: *Be careful not to allow dirt into the fuel injection pump or injector pipes during this procedure.*

Non turbo engines

Removal

1 Disconnect the battery negative lead.

2 Cover the alternator as a precaution against spillage of diesel fuel.

3 On Visa models apply the handbrake. On BX models chock the rear wheels and release the handbrake.

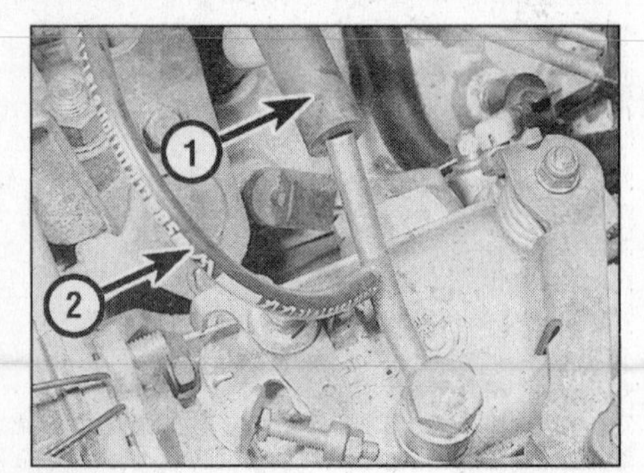

9.9 Main fuel return pipe (1) and injector leak off return pipe (2) - Roto-diesel pump

9.11 Injector pipe union nuts on Roto-diesel pump

4 On manual transmission models, jack up the front right-hand corner of the vehicle until the wheel is just clear of the ground. Support the vehicle on an axle stand and engage 4th or 5th gear. This will enable the engine to be turned easily by turning the roadwheel. On automatic models, the engine must be turned by using a spanner on the crankshaft pulley bolt. It may be advantageous to remove the glow plugs.

5 Remove the timing belt covers as described in Part A of this Chapter.

6 Open the accelerator lever on the injection pump and disconnect the cable by passing it through the special slot. Disconnect the cable adjustment ferrule from the bracket.

7 Note the position of the end stop on the fast idle cable then loosen the screw and disconnect the inner cable. Unscrew the adjustment locknut and remove the cable and ferrule from the bracket.

8 Loosen the clip and disconnect the fuel supply hose.

9 Disconnect the main fuel return pipe and the injector leak off return pipe from the union tube **(see illustration)**.

10 Disconnect the wire from the stop solenoid.

11 Unscrew the union nuts securing the injector pipes to the injection pump **(see illustration)**.

12 On BX models, remove the clip securing the hydraulic pipes to the engine front plate.

13 Turn the engine until the two bolt holes in the injection pump sprocket are aligned with the corresponding holes in the engine front plate.

14 Insert two M8 bolts through the holes and hand tighten them. The bolts must retain the sprocket while the injection pump is removed, thereby making it unnecessary to remove the timing belt.

15 Mark the injection pump in relation to the mounting bracket using a scriber or felt tip pen **(see illustration)**. This will ensure the correct timing when refitting. If a new pump is being fitted, transfer the mark from the old pump to give an approximate setting.

16 Unscrew the three mounting nuts and remove the plates. Unscrew and remove the rear mounting bolt and support the injection pump on a block of wood **(see illustrations)**.

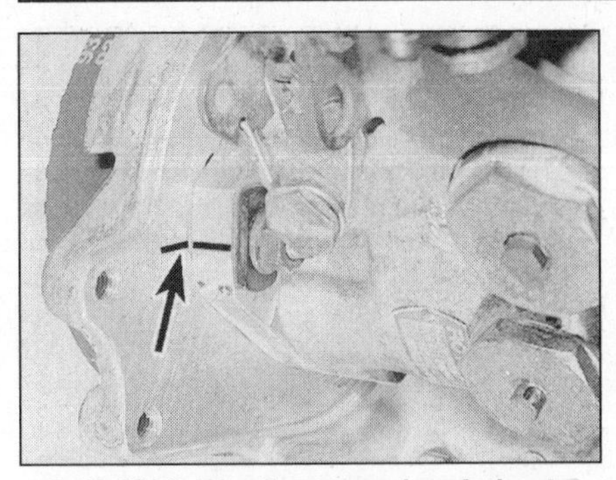

9.15 Mark injection pump in relation to mounting bracket (arrowed)

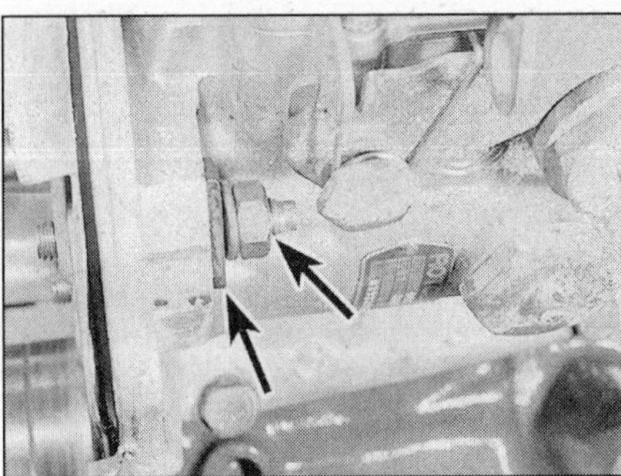

9.16a Injection pump mounting nut and plate (arrowed)

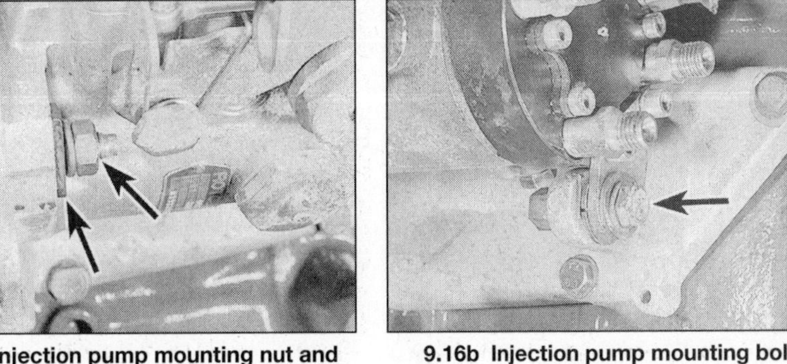

9.16b Injection pump mounting bolt (arrowed)

17 Unscrew the sprocket nut until the taper is released from the sprocket. The nut acts as a puller, together with the plate bolted to the sprocket. From late 1992, the fuel injection pump sprocket bolt no longer incorporates a puller. To free the sprocket from the taper on the injection pump shaft, a flange must be bolted to the sprocket before unscrewing the bolt. Ideally, a flange should be removed from an old sprocket and used to remove the new-type sprocket. Alternatively, a flange can be made up from steel plate.

18 Continue to unscrew the sprocket nut and withdraw the injection pump from the mounting bracket. Recover the Woodruff key from the shaft groove if it is loose.

Refitting

19 Refit the Woodruff key to the shaft groove (if removed).

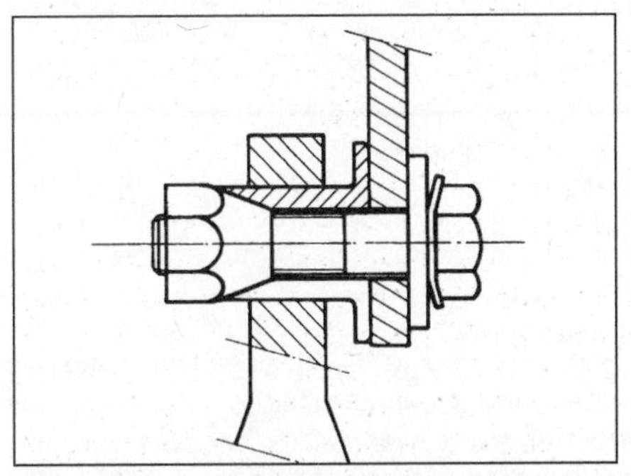

9.26 Cross-section of injection pump rear mounting

20 Unbolt the puller plate from the injection pump sprocket.

21 Insert the injection pump from behind the sprocket, making sure that the shaft key enters the groove in the sprocket. Screw on the nut and hand-tighten it.

22 Fit the mounting nuts together with their plates, then hand-tighten the nuts.

23 Tighten the sprocket nut to the specified torque then refit the puller plate and tighten the bolts.

24 Unscrew and remove the two bolts from the injection pump sprocket.

25 If the original injection pump is being refitted, align the scribed marks and tighten the mounting nuts. If fitting a new pump, the timing must be set as described in Section 12.

26 Refit the rear mounting bolt and special nut, tightening the nut slowly to allow the bush to align itself as shown **(see illustration)**.

27 On BX models, refit the clip securing the hydraulic pipes.

28 Refit the injector pipes to the injection pump and tighten the union nuts.

29 Reconnect the wire to the stop solenoid.

30 Refit the fuel supply and return pipes.

31 Refit the fast idle cable and accelerator cable, then adjust them.

32 Refit the timing belt covers.

33 Lower the vehicle to the ground and apply the handbrake (BX models).

34 Uncover the alternator and reconnect the battery negative lead.

35 Prime the fuel circuit by first switching on the ignition to energise the stop solenoid, then actuating the pump on the fuel filter until resistance is felt. On early models fitted with a Roto-diesel filter, the pump plunger must first be unscrewed then retightened after priming.

36 Turn the ignition key to position M and wait for the preheating warning light to go out. Start the engine and adjust the idle speed, referring to Part A of this Chapter.

Turbo engines

37 The injection pump fitted to Turbo engines is similar to that fitted to non turbo engines but incorporates the following additional features:

Lucas CAV/Roto-diesel pump

*a) An over-fuelling device varies the quantity of fuel injected in response to turbo boost pressure. Pressure is sensed through a hose connected to the inlet manifold **(see illustration)**.*

*b) An electromagnetic timing system advances injection timing when the engine is cold. The system is switched off by a contact activated by movement of the fast idle control lever **(see illustrations)**.*

c) These additional devices cannot be checked or adjusted by the home mechanic.

Bosch pump

*a) A richness limiter replaces the over-fuelling device just described and a cold start accelerator replaces the electromagnetic timing system **(see illustrations)**.*

9.37a Overfuelling device - Lucas CAV/Rotor-diesel pump

9.37b Electromagnetic timing device (arrowed) - Lucas CAV/Roto-diesel pump

9.37c Electromagnetic timing contact on fast idle lever

9.37d Richness limiter - Bosch pump

9.37e Cold start accelerator - Bosch pump

b) The cold start accelerator receives its own coolant feed. Because it is a mechanical device, it must be disconnected when timing the pump.

Removal

38 Proceed as described for non turbo engines but additionally, disconnect the boost pressure hose from the over-fuelling device or richness limiter.

39 On the Bosch pump, the coolant hoses must be disconnected from the cold start accelerator. If the cooling system is first depressurised by removing the expansion tank cap (system cold), and preparations made to plug the disconnected hoses, coolant loss can be kept to a minimum.

Refitting

40 Refit by reversing the removal operations. If necessary, check the pump timing and top-up the coolant level.

10 Fuel injection pump (Citroën ZX and Xantia) - removal and refitting

Note: *Be careful not to allow dirt into the fuel injection pump or injector pipes during this procedure. New sealing rings should be used on the fuel pipe banjo unions when refitting.*

Citroën ZX

Removal

1 Disconnect the battery negative lead.

2 Cover the alternator with a plastic bag, as a precaution against spillage of diesel fuel.

3 For improved access, remove the intercooler (Turbo engines) or the air distribution box (XUD9/A - D9B engine), where applicable. Similarly, disconnect the air hose from the top of the inlet manifold, where applicable.

4 On manual transmission models, jack up the front right-hand corner of the vehicle until the wheel is just clear of the ground. Support the vehicle on an axle stand and engage 4th or 5th gear. This will enable the engine to be turned easily by turning the right-hand wheel. On automatic transmission models, turn the engine using a spanner on the crankshaft pulley bolt. It will be easier to turn the engine if the glow plugs are removed.

5 Remove the upper timing belt covers, with reference to Part A of this Chapter.

6 On XUD9/Y (DJZ) engines, disconnect the hoses from the vacuum converter on the end of the fuel injection pump.

7 Disconnect the accelerator cable from the fuel injection pump. On models with automatic transmission, also disconnect the kickdown cable.

8 Disconnect the fast idle cable from the fuel injection pump.

9 Loosen the clip or undo the banjo union and disconnect the fuel supply hose. Recover the sealing washers from the banjo union, where applicable. Cover the open end of the hose and refit and cover the banjo bolt to keep dirt out **(see illustrations)**.

10 Disconnect the main fuel return pipe and the injector leak-off return pipe banjo union **(see illustration)**. Recover the sealing washers from the banjo union. Again, cover the open end of the hose and the banjo bolt to keep dirt out. Take care not to get the inlet and outlet banjo unions mixed up.

11 Disconnect all relevant wiring from the pump. Note that on certain Bosch pumps, this can be achieved by simply disconnecting the wiring connectors at the brackets on the pump **(see illustration)**. On some pumps, it will be necessary to disconnect the wiring from the individual components (some connections may be protected by rubber covers).

12 Unscrew the union nuts securing the injector pipes to the fuel injection pump and injectors. Counterhold the unions on the pump while unscrewing the pipe-to-pump union nuts. Remove the pipes as a set. Cover open unions to keep dirt out **(see illustration)**.

10.9a Disconnecting fuel pump supply banjo union. Note sealing washers (arrowed) - Bosch pump

10.9b Refitting fuel supply banjo bolt with small section of fuel hose (arrowed) to prevent dirt ingress

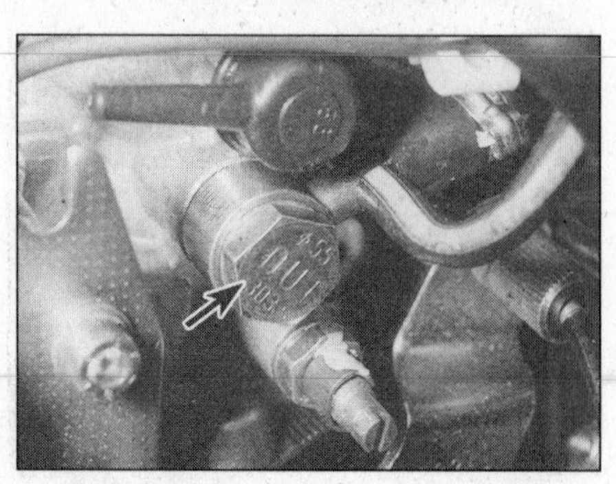
10.10 Injection pump fuel return pipe banjo union (arrowed) - Bosch pump

10.11 Disconnecting fuel injection pump wiring plug - Bosch pump

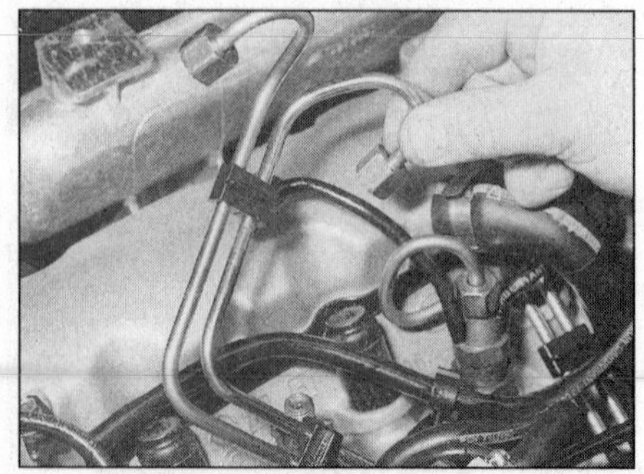
10.12 Removing a fuel pipe assembly

10.14 M8 bolts inserted through timing holes in injection pump sprocket

10.15 Mark injection pump in relation to mounting bracket (arrowed)

10.16a Unscrewing an injection pump front mounting nut - Bosch pump

13 Turn the crankshaft until the two bolt holes in the fuel injection pump sprocket are aligned with the corresponding holes in the engine front plate.

14 Insert two M8 bolts through the holes and hand-tighten them. Note that the bolts must retain the sprocket while the fuel injection pump is removed, thereby making it unnecessary to remove the timing belt **(see illustration)**.

15 Mark the fuel injection pump in relation to the mounting bracket, using a scriber or felt tip pen **(see illustration)**. This will ensure the correct pump timing is retained when refitting.

16 Unscrew the three front mounting nuts and recover the washers. Unscrew and remove the rear mounting nut and bolt, noting the locations of the washers, and support the injection pump on a block of wood **(see illustrations)**.

17 Release the injection pump sprocket from the pump shaft. Note that the sprocket can be left engaged with the timing belt as the pump is withdrawn from its mounting bracket. Refit the M8 bolts to retain the sprocket in position while the pump is removed.

18 Carefully withdraw the pump. Recover the Woodruff key from the end of the pump shaft if it is loose and then recover the bush from the rear of the mounting bracket **(see illustrations)**.

Refitting

19 Fit the Woodruff key to the shaft groove (if removed).

20 Offer the pump to the mounting bracket and support on a block of wood, as during removal.

21 Engage the pump shaft with the sprocket and refit the sprocket. Ensure that the Woodruff key does not fall out of the shaft as the sprocket is engaged.

22 Align the marks made on the pump and mounting bracket before removal. If a new pump is being fitted, transfer the mark from the old pump to give an approximate setting.

23 Refit and lightly tighten the pump mounting nuts and bolt.

24 Set up the injection timing.

25 Refit and reconnect the injector fuel pipes.

26 Reconnect all relevant wiring to the pump.

27 Reconnect the fuel supply and return hoses, and tighten the unions, as applicable. Use new sealing washers on the banjo unions.

28 Reconnect the fast idle cable and adjust it, as described in Section 3.

29 Reconnect and adjust the accelerator cable with reference to Section 1. Also reconnect the kickdown cable, where applicable.

30 On XUD9/Y (DJZ) engines, reconnect the hoses to the vacuum converter.

31 Refit the upper timing belt covers.

32 Lower the vehicle to the ground.

33 Where applicable, refit the intercooler or the air distribution housing.

34 Remove the plastic bag used to cover the alternator.

35 Reconnect the battery negative lead.

36 Bleed the fuel system, as described in Part A of this Chapter.

37 Start the engine and check the idle and anti-stall speed adjustments as described in Part A of this Chapter.

Citroën Xantia

38 Carry out the procedures given for the Citroën ZX. For improved access to the fuel injection pump, carry out the following:

a) *On models with air conditioning, remove the alternator and mounting bracket. Also remove the auxiliary drivebelt tensioner.*
b) *Remove the air distribution housing.*
c) *If necessary, also remove the inlet duct and disconnect the breather hose from the engine oil filler tube.*

11 Fuel injection pump (Citroën AX) - timing

Note: *Some fuel injection pump setting and access plugs are sealed by the manufacturer, with locking wire and lead seals. Do not disturb these seals if the vehicle is still within the warranty period, otherwise the warranty will be invalidated.*

Note: *The following procedure describes checking the injection timing using the special Citroën tools and mounting brackets (Citroën tool no. 4093-T for Lucas/CAV pumps and tool no. 7010-T and 2438-T for Bosch pumps). Without access to this equipment (or similar accurate tooling designed specifically for the injection pump being worked on), injection pump timing should be entrusted to a Citroën dealer.*

1 Refer to Section 13, paragraphs 1 to 3 inclusive.

2 If using dynamic timing equipment, the

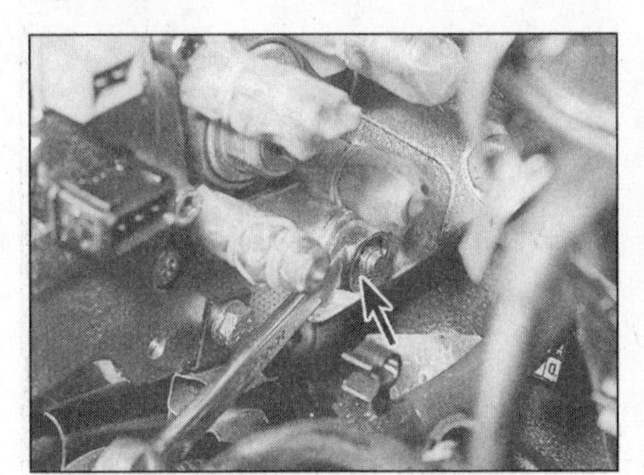

10.16b Unscrewing an injection pump rear mounting nut (arrowed) - Bosch pump

10.18a Removing a Bosch injection pump

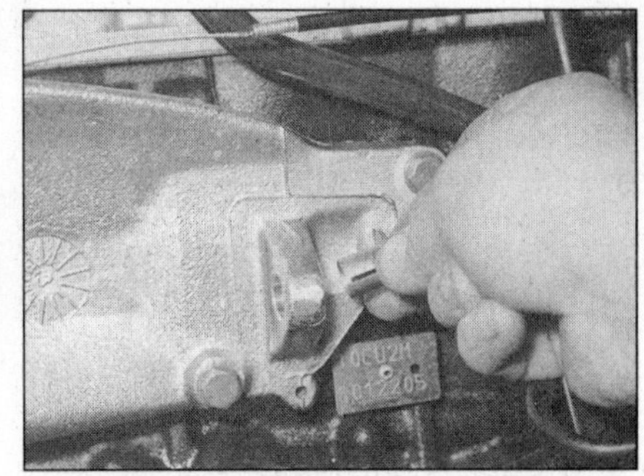

10.18b Recover bush from rear of pump mounting bracket

11.7 Injection pump timing access plug (arrowed)

engine should be at normal operating temperature to ensure that it is running at the correct idle speed. On the Bosch injection pump, running at normal operating temperature will also ensure that the cold advance system is not functioning.

3 Static timing is as follows.

4 If injection timing is being checked with the pump in position on the engine, rather than as part of the pump refitting procedure, disconnect the battery negative lead and cover the alternator to protect it from any spilt fuel.

5 Remove the injector pipes.

6 Referring to Part A of this Chapter (timing belt renewal), align the engine TDC timing holes then lock the crankshaft by inserting the locking tool into the flywheel. Do not insert the camshaft and injection pump locking tools. Remove the locking tool, then turn the crankshaft backwards (anti-clockwise) approximately a quarter of a turn. Turning the engine will be much easier if the glow plugs are removed.

7 On Lucas/CAV pumps, unscrew the access plug from the guide on the top of the pump body and recover the sealing washer **(see illustration)**. On Bosch pumps, unscrew the blanking plug from the end of the pump (between the injector pipe connections) and recover the sealing washer.

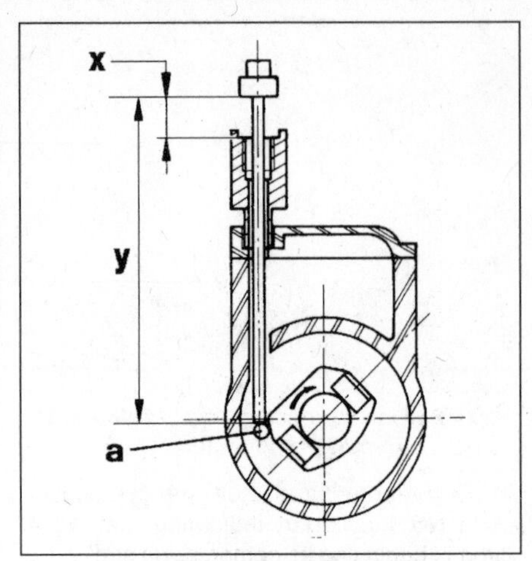

11.8a Lucas/CAV injection pump timing tool

a Timing piece
x Timing value (on disc or label)
y 95.5 ± 0.1 mm
Probe diameter = 7.0 mm

8 Clean the tool guide and the contact surface on the pump, then locate the dial gauge and bracket on the pump. On the Lucas/CAV pump, ensure that the probe is correctly seated against the guide sealing washer surface **(see illustrations)**. The timing probe must be seated against the guide sealing washer surface and not the upper lip of the guide, for the measurement to be accurate.

9 Position the dial gauge so that its plunger is at the mid-point of its travel, then zero the gauge.

10 Rotate the crankshaft slowly in the correct direction of rotation (clockwise) until the crankshaft locking tool can be re-inserted.

11 With the crankshaft locked in position, read the dial gauge. The reading should correspond to the value marked on the pump (there is a tolerance of ± 0.04 mm) or with the information given in Specifications. The timing value may be marked on a plastic disc attached to the front of the pump, or alternatively, on a tag attached to the accelerator pump lever **(see illustration)**.

12 If adjustment is necessary, slacken the pump front mounting nuts and the rear mounting bolt, then slowly rotate the pump body until the point is found where the specified reading is obtained on the dial gauge. When the pump is correctly positioned, tighten both its front mounting nuts and rear bolt to their specified torque settings. To improve access to the pump nuts, undo the two screws and remove the cover panel (where fitted) from the side of the radiator, if not already done.

13 Remove the crankshaft locking tool. On the Lucas/CAV pump, withdraw the timing probe so that it is positioned clear of the pump rotor dowel. Rotate the crankshaft through one and three-quarter rotations in the normal direction of rotation.

14 Slide the timing probe back into position (ensuring that it is correctly seated against the guide sealing washer surface, not the upper lip on the Lucas/CAV pump), then zero the dial gauge.

15 Rotate the crankshaft slowly in the correct direction of rotation until the crankshaft locking tool can be re-inserted. Recheck the timing measurement.

16 If adjustment is necessary, slacken the pump mounting nuts and bolt and repeat the timing operations.

17 When the pump timing is correctly set, remove the dial gauge and mounting bracket and withdraw the timing probe.

18 Refit the access plug and sealing washer, tightening it securely.

19 If the procedure is being carried out as part of the pump refitting sequence, proceed as described in Section 8.

20 If the procedure is being carried out with the pump fitted to the engine, refit the injector

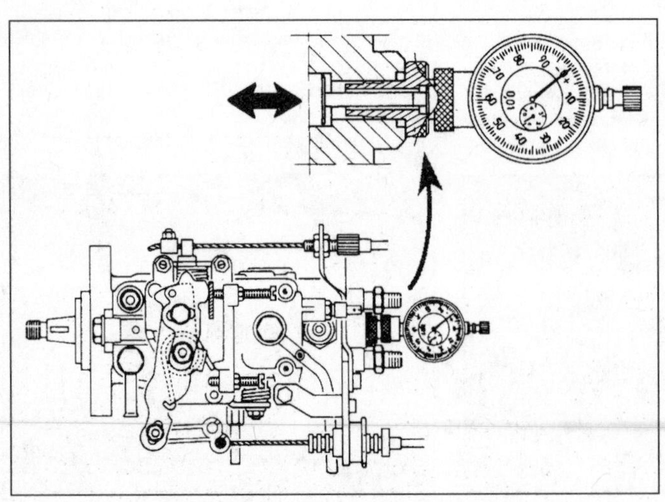
11.8b Bosch injection pump timing tool

11.11 Injection pump timing value tag attached to pump accelerator lever

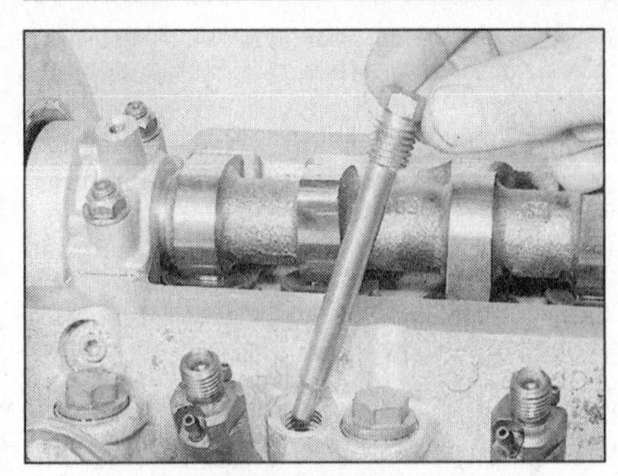

12.7 Removing blanking plug from No 4 cylinder

12.9 Setting No 4 piston timing position with dial test indicator

12.12 Roto-diesel injection pump with timing plug removed

pipes, tightening their union nuts to the specified torque setting.

21 Reconnect the battery, then bleed the fuel system as described in Part A of this Chapter.

22 Start the engine and adjust the idle speed and anti-stall speed as described in Part A of this Chapter.

12 Fuel injection pump (Citroën BX/Visa/C15) - timing

Note: *Some fuel injection pump setting and access plugs are sealed by the manufacturer, with locking wire and lead seals. Do not disturb these seals if the vehicle is still within the warranty period, otherwise the warranty will be invalidated.*

1 Refer to Section 13, paragraphs 1 to 3 inclusive.

Roto-Diesel pump

Pre mid-1987

2 Disconnect the battery negative lead and cover the alternator as a precaution against fuel spillage.

3 On Visa models, apply the handbrake. On BX models, chock the rear wheels and release the handbrake.

4 On manual transmission models, jack up the front right-hand corner of the vehicle until the wheel is just clear of the ground. Support the vehicle on an axle stand and engage 4th or 5th gear. This will enable the engine to be turned easily by turning the roadwheel. On automatic transmission models, use an open-ended spanner on the crankshaft pulley bolt.

5 Disconnect the wire and unscrew the glow plug from No 4 cylinder (timing belt end). Note that the engine is timed with No 4 piston at TDC compression (ie No 1 piston at TDC with valves rocking).

6 Two dial test indicators (DTIs) are now necessary for checking the positions of No 4 piston and the injection pump. Magnetic type stands will be found helpful or alternatively brackets may be made for fitting to appropriate positions on the engine.

7 Unscrew and remove the blanking plug from the cylinder head next to No 4 injector **(see illustration)**.

8 Turn the engine forwards until pressure is felt in No 4 cylinder, indicating that No 4 piston is beginning its compression stroke.

9 Position the DTI over the blanking hole and fit the probe **(see illustration)**.

10 Turn the engine forwards until the maximum lift of piston No 4 is registered on the DTI. Turn the engine slightly back and forth to determine the exact point of maximum lift then zero the indicator.

11 On BX models, remove the clip securing the hydraulic pipes to the engine front plate and move the pipes to one side.

12 Loosen the lower of the two large side plugs on the side of the injection pump. Position a small container beneath the plug then remove the plug and catch the escaping fuel in the container **(see illustration)**.

13 Inside the plug aperture there is a probe guide. Insert the probe and connect it to the DTI directly over the hole **(see illustration)**. Note that the end of the probe must be pointed in order to fully engage the groove in the pump rotor **(see illustration)**.

14 Turn the engine backwards approximately one eighth of a turn or until No 4 piston has moved 4.0 mm down the cylinder. Now turn the engine slowly forwards while watching the DTI on the injection pump. After the probe has reached the bottom of the timing groove then risen by 0.01 to 0.02 mm, check that the upper DTI reads 2.26 ± 0.05 mm before TDC. If the timing is incorrect continue as follows.

15 Check the zero setting of the upper DTI by repeating the procedure given in paragraph 10.

16 Turn the engine backwards approximately one eighth of a turn or until No 4 piston has moved 4.0 mm down the cylinder. Now turn the engine slowly forwards until No 4 piston is 2.26 ± 0.05 mm before TDC.

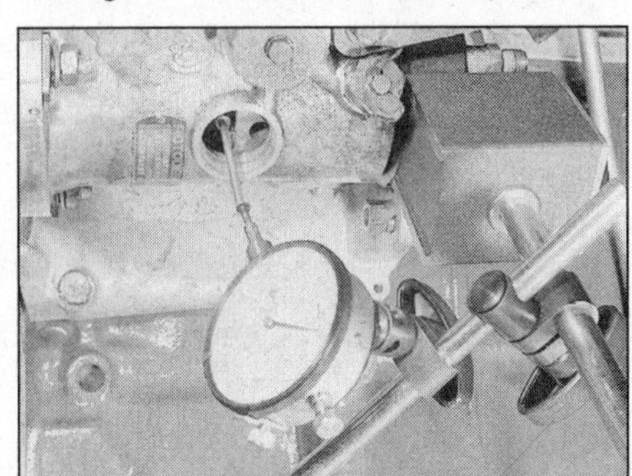

12.13a Timing Roto-diesel injection pump with dial test indicator

17 Unscrew the union nuts and disconnect the injector pipes from the injection pump. Loosen the injection pump mounting nuts and bolt.

18 Turn the pump body until the probe is at the bottom of the timing groove in the rotor. Zero the DTI. Now turn the pump clockwise (from the injector pipe end) until the probe has risen by 0.01 to 0.02 mm.

19 Tighten the mounting nuts and bolts, ensuring that there is no movement on the DTI.

20 Recheck the timing as described in paragraph 14.

21 Remove the DTIs and refit the plugs. Reconnect the injector pipes and tighten the union nuts.

22 Refit the hydraulic pipe clip on BX models

23 Refit the glow plug and connect the wire.

24 Lower the vehicle to the ground and reconnect the battery negative lead. Uncover the alternator.

25 Prime the fuel system as described in Part A of this Chapter.

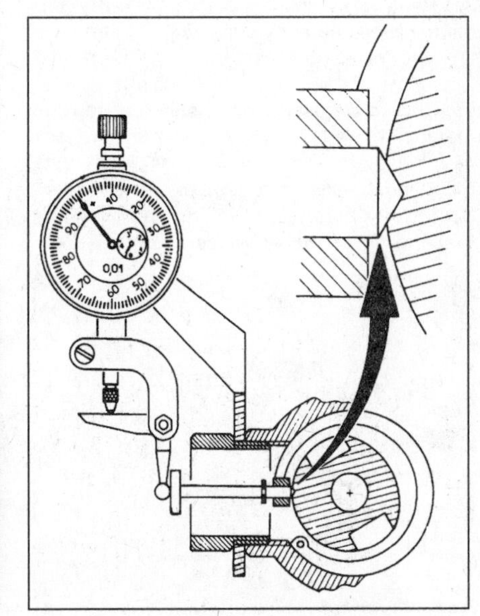

12.13b Checking timing on Roto-diesel fuel injection pump

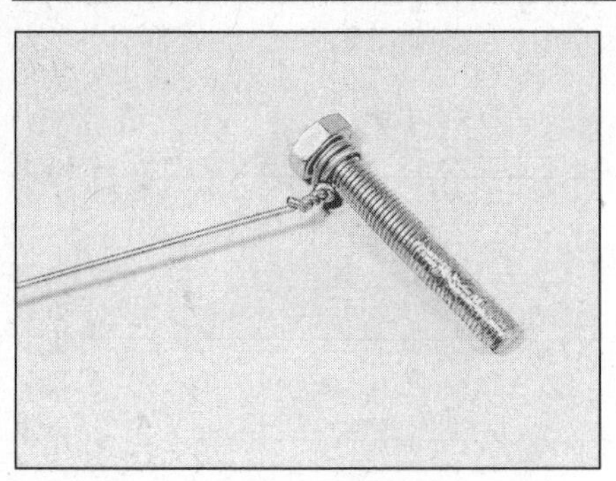

12.27 Home-made TDC setting tool

Post mid-1987

26 From mid 1987, a modified pump is fitted. The pump can be recognised by the presence of a white or blue plastic disc on its front face. A timing value is engraved on the disc - see illustration 13.16a.

27 Pump timing is now carried out at TDC. Only one dial test indicator (DTI) is needed but it will be necessary to make up a bent rod (8.0 mm diameter) or similar tool to enter the TDC setting hole. The tool made up in the workshop consisted of an M8 bolt with the threads filed away, attached to a piece of welding rod **(see illustration)**.

28 Prepare the engine as described in paragraphs 2 to 4.

29 Turn the engine to bring No 4 cylinder (timing belt end) to TDC on compression. To establish which cylinder is on compression, either remove No 4 cylinder glow plug and feel for pressure, or remove the valve cover and observe when No 1 cylinder valves are rocking (inlet opening and exhaust closing).

30 Insert the TDC setting tool into the hole and turn the engine back and forth slightly until the tool enters the hole in the flywheel. Leave the tool in position.

31 Remove the inspection plug from the top of the pump **(see illustration)**. Position the DTI so that it can read the movement of a probe inserted into the hole. If a magnetic stand is to be used, the absence of ferrous metal in the vicinity poses a problem. A piece of steel plate can be bolted to the engine mounting or valve cover to carry the stand.

32 Insert a probe into the inspection hole so that the tip of the probe rests on the rotor timing piece. Position the DTI so that it reads the movement of the probe.

12.31 Removing injection pump inspection plug

33 Remove the TDC setting tool. Turn the engine approximately a quarter-turn backwards. Zero the DTI.

34 Turn the engine forwards slowly until the TDC setting tool can be re-inserted. Read the DTI. The reading should correspond to the value engraved on the pump disc (± 0.04 mm).

35 If the reading is not as specified, continue as follows.

36 Disconnect the injector pipes from the pump. Slacken the pump mounting nuts and bolts, then swing the pump away from the engine. Zero the DTI.

37 With the engine still at TDC, slowly swing the pump back towards the engine until the DTI displays the value engraved on the pump disc. In this position, tighten the pump mountings, then remove the TDC setting tool and recheck the timing as just described.

38 When the timing is correct, reconnect the injector pipes, remove the DTI and the TDC setting tool and refit the inspection plug.

39 Refit any other disturbed components, uncover the alternator and lower the vehicle to the ground.

Bosch pump

Pre October 1987

40 Proceed as described in paragraphs 2 to 10.

41 Unscrew the union nuts and disconnect the injector pipes for cylinders 1 and 2 from the injection pump.

42 Unscrew the blanking plug from the end of the injection pump between the injector pipe connections. Be prepared for the loss of some fuel.

43 Insert the probe and connect it to the DTI positioned directly over the hole. The fixture used by Citroën technicians is shown in illustration 11.8b.

44 Turn the engine backwards approximately one eighth of a turn or until No 4 piston has moved 4.0 mm down the cylinder.

45 Zero the DTI on the injection pump.

46 Turn the engine slowly forwards until the DTI on the injection pump reads 0.30 mm, then check that the upper DTI reads as follows:

0.72 ± 0.03 mm BTDC for Visa models
0.80 ± 0.03 mm BTDC for BX17 models
0.57 ± 0.03 mm BTDC for BX19 models

47 If the timing is incorrect, check the zero setting of the upper DTI by repeating the procedure given in paragraph 10.

48 Turn the engine backwards approximately one eighth of a turn or until No 4 piston had moved 4.0 mm down the cylinder. Now turn the engine slowly forwards until the upper DTI reads as specified in paragraph 46.

49 Unscrew the union nuts and disconnect the remaining injector pipes from the injection pump. Loosen the injection pump mounting nuts and bolt.

50 Turn the pump body anti-clockwise (from the injector pipe end) and check that the DTI is zeroed. Now turn the pump body slowly clockwise until the DTI reads 0.30 mm.

51 Tighten the mounting nuts and bolts, making sure that there is no movement on the DTI.

52 Recheck the timing as described in paragraphs 44 to 46.

53 Remove the DTIs and refit the plugs. Reconnect the injector pipes and tighten the union nuts.

54 Refit the glow plug and connect the wire.

55 Lower the vehicle to the ground and reconnect the battery negative lead. Uncover the alternator.

56 Prime the fuel system as described in Part A of this Chapter.

Post October 1987

57 Later Bosch pumps are timed at TDC. Refer to Specifications for pump identification and timing values. Only one dial test indicator (DTI) is needed but it will be necessary to make up a TDC setting tool as described for the Roto-diesel pump.

58 Prepare the engine as described in paragraphs 2 to 4. On Turbo models, disconnect the cold start accelerator.

59 Bring the engine to TDC with No 4 cylinder on compression and insert the TDC setting tool, referring to paragraphs 29 and 30.

60 Fit the DTI to the rear of the pump as described in paragraphs 41 to 43.

61 Remove the TDC setting tool. Turn the engine approximately a quarter-turn backwards and zero the DTI.

62 Turn the engine forwards slowly until the TDC setting tool can be re-inserted. Read the DTI. The value should correspond to that specified.

63 If the reading is not as specified, continue as follows.

64 Disconnect the remaining injector pipes from the pump. Slacken the pump mounting nuts and bolts, then swing the pump away from the engine. Zero the DTI.

65 With the engine still at TDC, slowly swing the pump back towards the engine until the DTI displays the desired value. In this position, tighten the pump mountings then remove the TDC setting tool and recheck the timing as just described.

66 When the timing is correct, remove the DTI and the TDC setting tool. Reconnect the injector pipes.

67 Refit any other disturbed components, uncover the alternator and lower the vehicle to the ground.

13 Fuel injection pump (Citroën ZX) - timing

Note: *Some fuel injection pump setting and access plugs are sealed by the manufacturer, with locking wire and lead seals. Do not disturb these seals if the vehicle is still within the warranty period, otherwise the warranty will be invalidated. Also, do not attempt the timing procedure unless accurate instrument-*

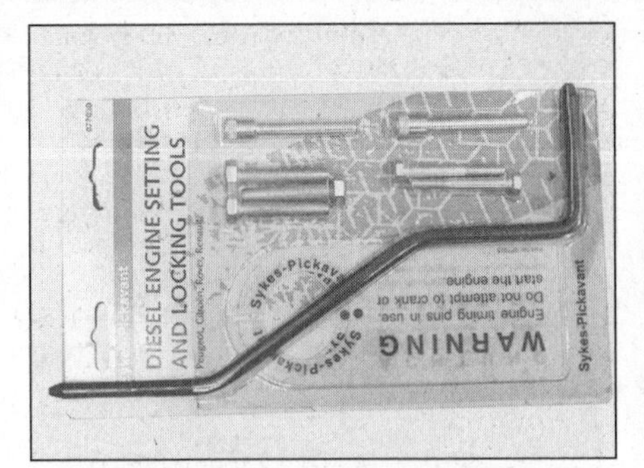

13.3 TDC setting and locking tools for setting injection timing on Citroën diesel engines

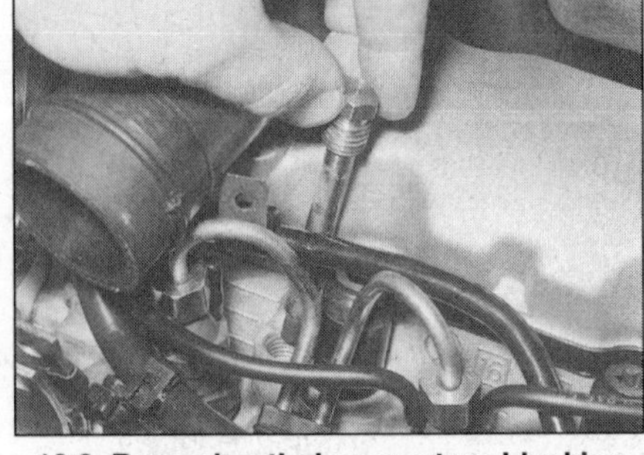

13.9 Removing timing aperture blanking plug from cylinder head

13.11 Inserting suitable cranked rod into flywheel TDC hole

ation is available. Suitable special tools for carrying out pump timing are available from motor factors. A dial test indicator (DTI) will be required, regardless of the method used.

1 Checking the injection timing is only necessary after the fuel injection pump has been disturbed.

2 Dynamic timing equipment does exist but it is unlikely to be available to the home mechanic. If such equipment is available, use it in accordance with the manufacturer's instructions.

3 Static timing, as described in this Section, gives good results if carried out carefully. A dial test indicator (DTI) will be needed, with probes and adapters appropriate to the type of injection pump **(see illustration)**. Read through the following procedure before starting work, to find out what is involved.

Lucas CAV/Roto-Diesel pump

4 Disconnect the battery negative lead.

5 Cover the alternator with a plastic bag, as a precaution against spillage of diesel fuel.

6 On manual transmission models, jack up the front right-hand corner of the vehicle until the wheel is just clear of the ground. Support the vehicle on an axle stand and engage 4th or 5th gear. This will enable the engine to be turned easily by turning the right-hand wheel.

7 On automatic transmission models, use an open-ended spanner on the crankshaft pulley bolt.

8 For improved access, remove the intercooler (Turbo engines) or the air distribution housing (XUD9/A - D9B engine), where applicable. Similarly, disconnect the air hose from the top of the inlet manifold, where applicable.

9 Note that the engine is timed with No 4 piston at TDC on the compression stroke. Disconnect the feed wire and unscrew the glow plug from cylinder No 4 (timing belt end). Alternatively, the blanking plug can be removed from the top of the cylinder head (located above No 4 cylinder, next to the cylinder head bolt) **(see illustration)**.

10 Pump timing is now carried out at TDC. Turn the engine to bring No 4 cylinder to TDC on compression. To determine whether the cylinder is on compression, if the glow plug has been removed, place a finger over the glow plug hole. It should be possible to feel pressure building up as the piston approaches TDC on the compression stroke. Alternatively, if the blanking plug has been removed from the cylinder head, probe the hole revealed by removing the blanking plug, using a long rod. By resting the rod on the top of the piston, it should be possible to determine when the piston is approaching TDC at the upper limit of its travel.

11 Insert an 8 mm diameter rod or drill through the hole in the left-hand flange of the cylinder block by the starter motor. If necessary, carefully turn the crankshaft either way until the rod enters the TDC hole in the flywheel **(see illustration)**.

12 A dial test indicator (DTI) will now be required and if a suitable special probe (designed specifically for the Lucas pump and available from motor factors) is not available, an alternative should be made up to the dimensions shown in illustration 11.8a.

13 Remove the inspection plug from the top of the pump. Position the DTI so that it can read the movement of the probe inserted into the hole. Note that a gauge mounted anywhere other than on the pump will also measure pump movement.

14 Insert the probe into the inspection hole, so that the tip of the probe rests on the rotor timing piece. Position the DTI to read the movement of the probe **(see illustration)**.

15 Remove the TDC locking rod or drill from the flywheel. Turn the engine approximately a quarter-turn backwards. Zero the DTI.

16 Turn the engine forwards slowly until the TDC locking tool can be re-inserted. Read the DTI. The reading should correspond to the value marked on the pump. The timing value may be marked on a plastic disc on the front of the pump, or alternatively may appear on a label attached to the top of the pump, or a tag attached to the accelerator pump lever **(see illustrations)**.

17 If the reading is not as specified, proceed as follows.

18 Unscrew the union nuts securing the injector pipes to the fuel injection pump. Counterhold the unions on the pump when unscrewing the nuts. Cover all open unions to keep dirt out.

13.14 Dial test indicator positioned to read injection pump timing - Lucas pump

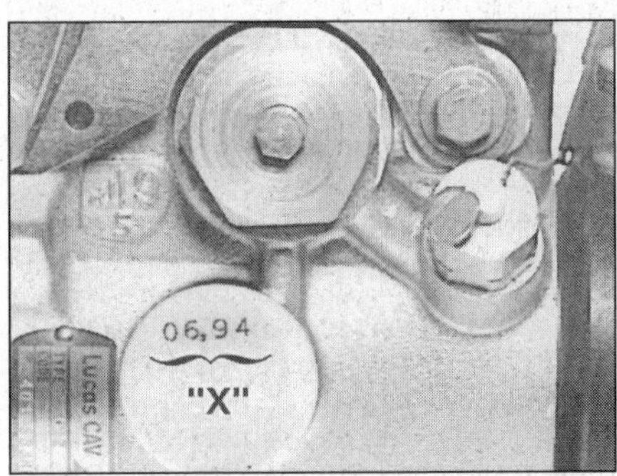

13.16a Pump timing value (x) marked on plastic disc - Lucas pump

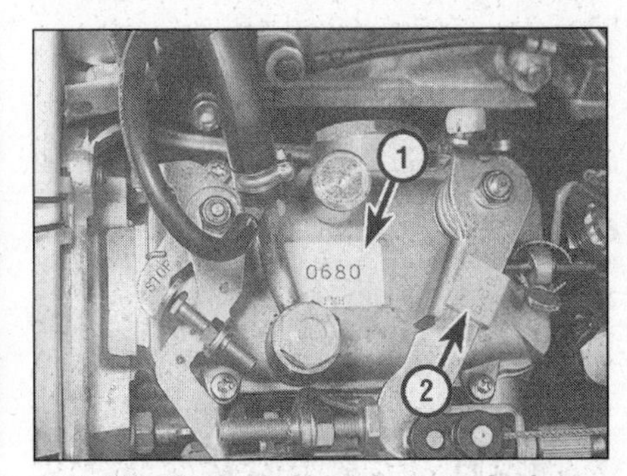

13.16b Pump timing values marked on label (1) and tag (2) - Lucas pump

13.34 Dial test indicator positioned to read injection pump timing - Bosch pump

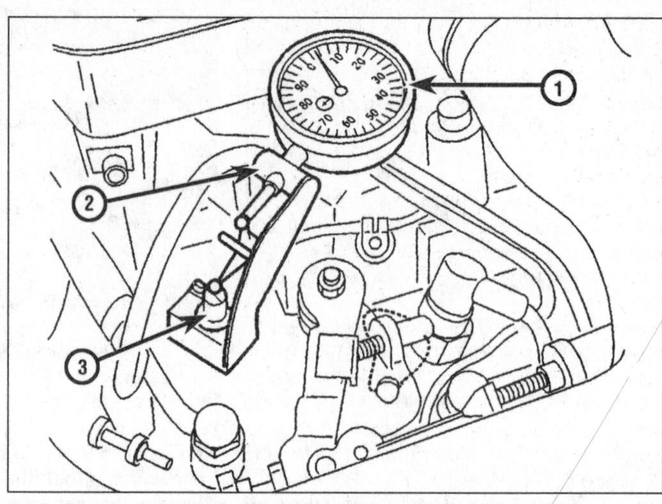

14.6 Citroën injection pump timing gauge (1) mounting bracket (2) and setting rod (3) in position on pump

19 Slacken the four pump mounting nuts (three front and one rear) and swing the pump away from the engine. Zero the DTI.

20 With the engine still at TDC, slowly swing the pump back towards the engine until the DTI displays the value marked on the front face of the pump. In this position, tighten the pump mountings (the reading on the DTI should not change as the pump mountings are tightened), then remove the TDC locking tool and recheck the timing as just described.

21 When the timing is correct, reconnect the injector fuel pipes and remove the DTI. Remove the probe from the inspection hole and refit the inspection plug. Remove the TDC locking tool from the flywheel.

22 Refit the glow plug and connect the wire, or refit the blanking plug to the top of the cylinder head, as applicable.

23 Refit the intercooler or the air distribution housing, where applicable.

24 Lower the vehicle to the ground and reconnect the battery negative lead. Remove the plastic bag used to cover the alternator.

25 Bleed the fuel system as described in Part A of this Chapter.

26 Check and if necessary, adjust the idle speed and anti-stall speed as described in Part A of this Chapter.

Bosch pump

27 Carry out the procedures given in paragraphs 4 to 11 inclusive.

28 A dial test indicator (DTI) will now be required, along with a suitable special probe and adapter to screw into the hole in the rear of the pump (designed specifically for the Bosch pump and available from motor factors) - see illustration 11.8b.

29 On XUD9/Y (DJZ) engines, disconnect the vacuum hoses from the vacuum converter on the top of the fuel injection pump.

30 Unscrew the union nuts securing the injector pipes to the fuel injection pump. Counterhold the unions on the pump while unscrewing the nuts. Cover all open unions to keep dirt out.

31 Unscrew the blanking plug from the end of the injection pump between the injector pipe connections. Be prepared for the loss of some fuel.

32 Insert the probe and connect it to the DTI positioned directly over the hole.

33 Remove the TDC locking tool from the flywheel, and turn the engine approximately a quarter-turn backwards until the needle on the DTI no longer moves. Zero the DTI.

34 Turn the engine forwards slowly until the TDC locking tool can be re-inserted into the flywheel. Read the DTI. The value should correspond to that specified **(see illustration)**.

35 If the reading is not as specified, proceed as follows.

36 Slacken the four pump mounting nuts (three front and one rear) and swing the pump away from the engine. Zero the DTI.

37 With the engine still at TDC, slowly swing the pump back towards the engine until the DTI displays the value specified. In this position, tighten the pump mountings (the reading on the DTI should not change as the pump mountings are tightened), then remove the TDC locking tool and recheck the timing as just described.

38 When the timing is correct, remove the DTI and the probe and adapter, then reconnect the injector fuel pipes.

39 Refit the blanking plug to the end of the pump and remove the TDC locking tool from the flywheel.

40 Refit the glow plug and connect the wire, or refit the blanking plug to the top of the cylinder head, as applicable.

41 Where applicable, reconnect the hoses to the vacuum converter on the top of the injection pump.

42 Refit the intercooler or the air distribution housing, where applicable.

43 Lower the vehicle to the ground and reconnect the battery negative lead. Remove the plastic bag used to cover the alternator.

44 Bleed the fuel system as described in Part A of this Chapter.

45 Check and if necessary, adjust the idle speed and anti-stall speed as described in Part A of this Chapter.

14 Fuel injection pump (Citroën Xantia) - timing

Note: *Some fuel injection pump setting and access plugs are sealed by the manufacturer, with locking wire and lead seals. Do not disturb these seals if the vehicle is still within the warranty period, otherwise the warranty will be invalidated.*

1 Refer to Section 13, paragraphs 1 to 3 inclusive.

Lucas pump

2 To check the injection pump timing, a special timing probe and mounting bracket (Citroën tool No. 4093-TJ) is required. Without access to this piece of equipment, injection pump timing should be entrusted to a Citroën dealer or other suitably equipped specialist.

3 If the timing is being checked with the pump in position on the engine, rather than as part of the pump refitting procedure, disconnect the battery negative lead and cover the alternator to prevent the possibility of fuel being spilt onto it. Remove the injector pipes.

4 Refer to Part A of this Chapter (timing belt renewal) and lock the crankshaft in position. Remove the crankshaft locking tool, then turn the crankshaft backwards (anti-clockwise) approximately a quarter of a turn.

5 Unscrew the access plug from the guide on the top of the pump body and recover the sealing washer - see illustration 12.31. Insert the special timing probe into the guide, making sure it is correctly seated against the guide sealing washer surface. The timing probe must be seated against the guide sealing washer surface and not the upper lip of the guide for the measurement to be accurate.

6 Mount the bracket on the pump guide (Citroën tool No. 4093-TJ) and securely mount the dial test indicator (DTI) in the bracket so that its tip is in contact with the bracket linkage **(see illustration)**. Position the DTI so that its plunger is at the mid-point of its travel and zero the gauge.
7 Rotate the crankshaft slowly in the correct direction of rotation (clockwise) until the crankshaft locking tool can be re-inserted.
8 With the crankshaft locked in position, read the dial gauge. The reading should correspond to the value marked on the pump (there is a tolerance of ± 0.04 mm). The timing value may be marked on a plastic disc attached to the front of the pump, or alternatively on a tag attached to the pump control lever - see illustrations 13.16a and 13.16b.
9 If adjustment is necessary, slacken the front pump mounting nuts and the rear mounting bolt, then slowly rotate the pump body until the point is found where the specified reading is obtained on the dial gauge. When the pump is correctly positioned, tighten both its front mounting nuts and the rear bolt to their specified torque settings. To improve access to the pump nuts, undo the two screws and remove the cover panel from the side of the radiator.
10 Withdraw the timing probe slightly, so that it is positioned clear of the pump rotor dowel, then remove the crankshaft locking pin. Rotate the crankshaft through one and three quarter rotations in the normal direction of rotation.
11 Slide the timing probe back into position, ensuring that it is correctly seated against the guide sealing washer surface, not the upper lip, then zero the dial gauge.
12 Rotate the crankshaft slowly in the correct direction of rotation until the crankshaft locking tool can be re-inserted. Recheck the timing measurement.
13 If adjustment is necessary, slacken the pump mounting nuts and bolt and repeat the operations in paragraphs 9 to 12.
14 When the pump timing is correctly set, remove the DTI and mounting bracket and withdraw the timing probe.
15 Refit the screw and sealing washer to the guide and tighten it securely.
16 If the procedure is being carried out as part of the pump refitting sequence, proceed as described in Section 10.
17 If the procedure is being carried out with the pump fitted to the engine, refit the injector pipes, tightening their union nuts to the specified torque setting.
18 Reconnect the battery, then bleed the fuel system as described in Part A of this Chapter.
19 Start the engine and adjust the idle speed and anti-stall speeds as described in Part A of this Chapter.

Bosch pump

20 To check the injection pump timing, a special adapter (Citroën tool No. 4123-T) is required. Without access to this piece of equipment, injection pump timing should be entrusted to a Citroën dealer or other suitably equipped specialist.
21 If the injection timing is being checked with the pump in position on the engine, rather than as part of the pump refitting procedure, then disconnect the battery negative lead and cover the alternator to prevent the possibility of fuel being spilt onto it. Remove the injector pipes.
22 If not already done, slacken the clamp screw and/or nut (as applicable) and slide the fast idle cable end fitting arrangement along the cable so that it is no longer in contact with the pump fast idle lever (ie. so the fast idle lever returns to its stop).
23 Refer to Part A of this Chapter (timing belt renewal) and lock the crankshaft in position. Remove the crankshaft locking tool, then turn the crankshaft backwards (anti-clockwise) approximately a quarter of a turn.
24 Unscrew the access screw, situated in the centre of the four injector pipe unions, from the rear of the injection pump. As the screw is removed, position a suitable container beneath the pump to catch any escaping fuel. Mop up any spilt fuel with a clean cloth.
25 Screw the special adapter into the rear of the injection pump and mount the dial test indicator (DTI) in the adapter - see illustration 11.8b. Position the DTI so that its plunger is at the mid-point of its travel and securely tighten the adapter locknut.
26 Slowly rotate the crankshaft back and forth whilst observing the dial gauge, to determine when the injection pump piston is at the bottom of its travel (BDC). When the piston is correctly positioned, zero the dial gauge.
27 Rotate the crankshaft slowly in the correct direction until the crankshaft locking tool can be re-inserted.
28 The reading obtained on the dial gauge should be equal to the specified pump timing measurement. If adjustment is necessary, slacken the front and rear pump mounting nuts and bolts and slowly rotate the pump body until the point is found where the specified reading is obtained. When the pump is correctly positioned, tighten both its front and rear mounting nuts and bolts securely.
29 Rotate the crankshaft through one and three quarter rotations in the normal direction of rotation. Find the injection pump piston BDC and zero the dial gauge.
30 Rotate the crankshaft slowly in the correct direction of rotation until the crankshaft locking tool can be re-inserted (bringing the engine back to TDC). Recheck the timing measurement.
31 If adjustment is necessary, slacken the pump mounting nuts and bolts and repeat the operations in paragraphs 28 to 30.
32 When the pump timing is correctly set, unscrew the adapter and remove the dial gauge.
33 Refit the screw and sealing washer to the pump and tighten it securely.
34 If the procedure is being carried out as part of the pump refitting sequence, proceed as described in Section 10.
35 If the procedure is being carried out with the pump fitted to the engine, refit the injector pipes, tightening their union nuts to the specified torque setting.
36 Reconnect the battery, then bleed the fuel system as described in Part A of this Chapter.
37 Start the engine and adjust the idle speed and anti-stall speeds as described in Part A of this Chapter.
38 Adjust the fast idle cable as described in Section 3.

15 Preheating system - testing, component removal and refitting

System testing

1 If the preheating system malfunctions, testing is ultimately by substitution of known good units but some preliminary checks may be made as follows.
2 Connect a voltmeter or 12-volt test lamp between the glow plug supply cable and earth (engine or vehicle metal). Ensure that the live connection is kept clear of the engine and bodywork.
3 Have an assistant switch on the ignition and check that voltage is applied to the glow plugs. Note the time for which the warning light is lit and the total time for which voltage is applied before the system cuts out. Switch off the ignition.
4 At an under-bonnet temperature of 20°C, typical times noted should be 5 or 6 seconds for warning light operation, followed by a further 10 seconds supply after the light goes out. Warning light time will increase with lower temperatures and decrease with higher temperatures.
5 If there is no supply at all, the relay or associated wiring is at fault.
6 To locate a defective glow plug, disconnect the main supply cable and the interconnecting wire or strap from the top of the glow plugs. Be careful not to drop the nuts and washers. For access to the glow plugs on ZX and Xantia models, first remove the intercooler (Turbo engines) or the air distribution housing (XUD9/A - D9B engine), where applicable. If necessary, also remove the inlet duct then disconnect the breather hose from the engine oil filler tube and the air hose from the top of the inlet manifold, where applicable.
7 Use a continuity tester, or a 12-volt test lamp connected to the battery positive terminal, to check for continuity between each glow plug terminal and earth. The resistance of a glow plug in good condition is very low (less than 1 ohm), so if the test lamp does not light or the continuity tester shows a high resistance, the glow plug is certainly defective.

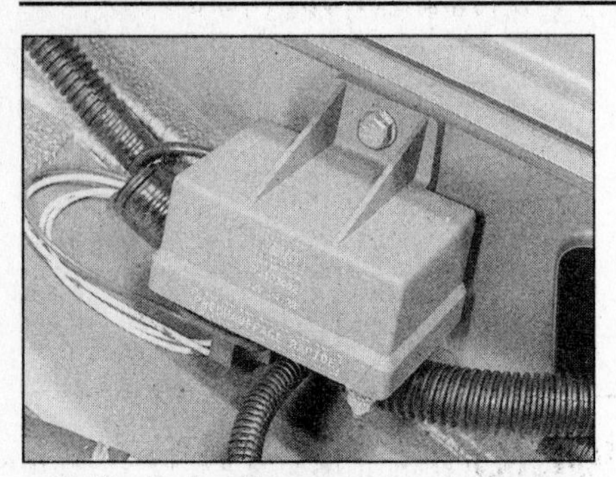

15.10a Preheating system control unit - Citroën AX

15.10b Glow plug control relay on Citroën BX . . .

8 If an ammeter is available, the current draw of each glow plug can be checked. After an initial surge of 15 to 20 amps, each plug should draw 12 amps. Any plug which draws much more or less than this is probably defective.

9 As a final check, the glow plugs can be removed and inspected as described in Section 6.

Control unit

Location

10 This unit is located as follows, according to model type:

*Citroën AX - On the left-hand side of the engine compartment, on the inner wing panel **(see illustration)**.*

*Citroën BX/Visa/C15 - On the left-hand side of the engine compartment, near the battery **(see illustrations)**.*

*Citroën ZX - On the front of the relay/junction box, at the front left-hand corner of the engine compartment **(see illustration)**.*

Citroën Xantia - On the left-hand side of the engine compartment, beneath a plastic cover behind the battery.

Removal

11 Disconnect the battery negative lead.

12 Unscrew the retaining bolt/nut(s) and remove the unit.

13 Note the location of the wiring, then disconnect it from the unit.

14 Remove the unit from the engine compartment.

Refitting

15 Refitting is a reversal of removal, ensuring that all wiring is securely connected to its original location, as noted on removal.

16 Exhaust gas recirculation system - testing and component renewal

System testing

1 Testing of the exhaust gas recirculation (EGR) system must be entrusted to a Citroën dealer.

Component renewal

2 At the time of writing, no specific information was available regarding removal and refitting of the system components.

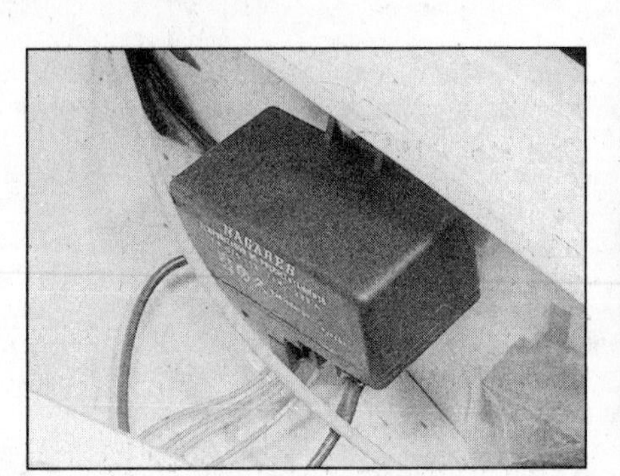

15.10c . . . and Citroën Visa

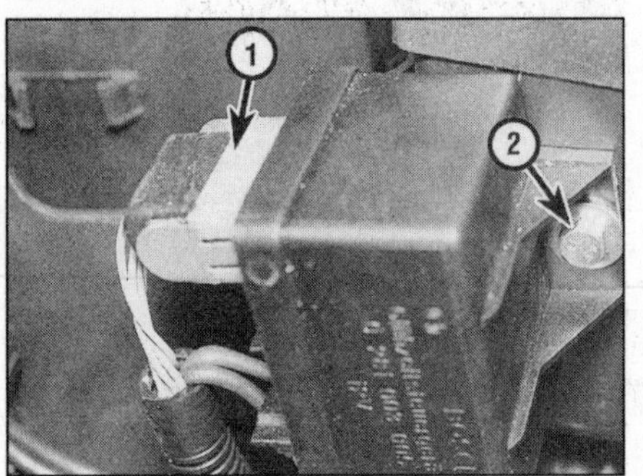

15.10d Preheating system relay/timer unit wiring plug (1) and securing bolt (2) - Citroën ZX

Chapter 4
Fiat 1698cc engine

Part A: Routine maintenance and servicing

Contents

Engine application

1698cc engine	Fiat Punto - 1994 to 1996

Servicing specifications

Oil filter

Type	Champion C112

Valve clearances (cold)

Inlet	0.30 ± 0.05 mm
Exhaust	0.35 ± 0.05 mm

Timing belt

Type	Toothed belt
Tension	See text

Auxiliary drivebelt

Type	Multi-ribbed
Tension	5.0 mm deflection midway between pulleys

Air filter

Type:	
Bosch injection	Champion U579
Lucas/CAV injection	Champion U611

Fuel filter

Type	Champion L111

Glow plugs

Type	Champion CH163

Idle speed

Bosch and Lucas/CAV injection	880 to 920 rpm

Torque wrench settings	Nm	lbf ft
Crankshaft pulley bolt	190	140
Fuel filter bracket to body	18	13
Fuel filter to bracket	24	18
Glow plugs	15	11
Timing belt tensioner and idler	44	33

4A

Lubricants, fluids and capacities

Component or system	Lubricant or fluid	Capacity
Engine	Multigrade engine oil, viscosity range SAE 15W/40 to specification API SG/CD	4.95 litres - Non turbo with filter 4.84 litres -Turbo with filter
Cooling system	Ethylene glycol based antifreeze. 50% volume with water	7.2 litres
Fuel system	Commercial Diesel fuel for road vehicles (DERV)	47 litres

Fiat diesel engine - maintenance schedule

The maintenance schedules which follow are basically those recommended by the manufacturer. Servicing intervals are determined by mileage or time elapsed - this is because fluids and systems deteriorate with age as well as with use. Follow the time intervals if the appropriate mileage is not covered within the specified period.

Vehicles operating under adverse conditions may need more frequent maintenance. Adverse conditions include climatic extremes, full-time towing or taxi work, driving on unmade roads, and a high proportion of short journeys. The use of inferior fuel can cause early degradation of the engine oil. Consult a Fiat dealer for advice on these points.

Every 250 miles (400 km), weekly, or before a long journey

- ☐ Check engine oil level and top up if necessary (Section 3)
- ☐ Check coolant level and top up if necessary (Section 4)
- ☐ Check exhaust emission (Section 5)
- ☐ Check operation of glow plug warning light (Section 6)

Every 5000 miles (7500 km) or 6 months, whichever comes first

- ☐ Renew engine oil and filter (Section 7)

Every 10 000 miles (15 000 km) or 12 months

- ☐ Renew air filter element
- ☐ Check and adjust idle speed (Section 8)
- ☐ Check pipes and hoses for condition and security
- ☐ Check for engine fluid leakage
- ☐ Check condition of exhaust system and mountings
- ☐ Renew fuel filter (Section 9)

Every 20 000 miles (30 000 km) or 2 years

- ☐ Check condition and tension of auxiliary drivebelt(s)
- ☐ Check valve clearances (Section 10)
- ☐ Check engine management system (Section 11)

Every 40 000 miles (60 000 km) or 3 years

- ☐ Renew engine coolant
- ☐ Check condition and tension of timing belt (Section 12)

Every 60 000 miles (90 000 km) or 6 years

- ☐ Check condition and operation of crankcase emission control system (Section 13)

Every 70 000 miles (105 000 km)

- ☐ Renew timing belt (Section 14)

Maintenance procedures

1 Introduction

Refer to Chapter 2, Part A, Section 1.

2 Intensive maintenance

Refer to Chapter 2, Part A, Section 2.

Underbonnet view of FIAT Punto Turbo Diesel engine

1 *Engine oil filler cap*
2 *Engine oil dipstick*
3 *Oil filter*
4 *Brake/clutch fluid reservoir*
5 *Air cleaner cover*
6 *Power steering pump*
7 *Coolant expansion tank*
8 *Windscreen washer fluid reservoir*
9 *Front suspension strut upper mounting*
10 *Fuel filter/heater housing*
11 *Fuel injection pump*
12 *Battery*
13 *Power steering fluid reservoir*

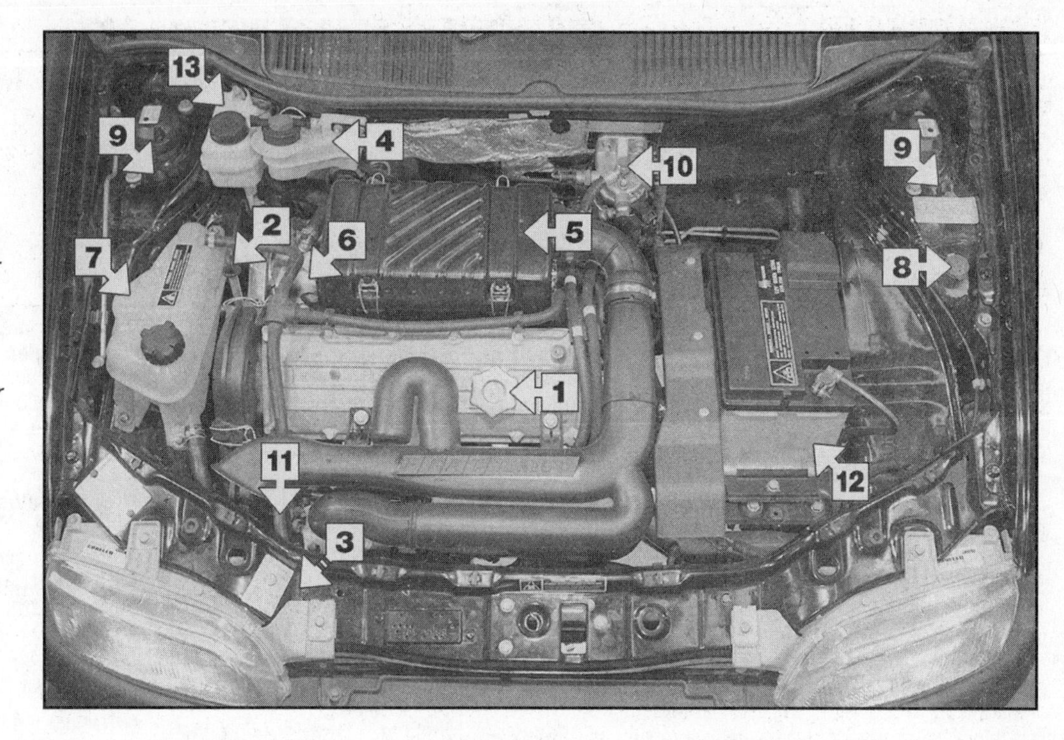

250 mile (400 km) Service

3 Engine oil level check

1 Refer to Chapter 2, Part A, Section 3 **(see illustrations)**.

4 Coolant level check

1 Refer to Chapter 2, Part A, Section 4. Note that the tank is translucent, so the coolant level can be verified without removing the cap. The level should be between the MAX (HOT) and MIN (COLD) marks embossed on the side of the tank. If it is below the MIN mark, remove the cap and top up with coolant to the MAX mark **(see illustration)**.

5 Exhaust smoke check

1 Refer to Chapter 2, Part A, Section 5.

6 Warning light check

1 Refer to Chapter 2, Part A, Section 6.

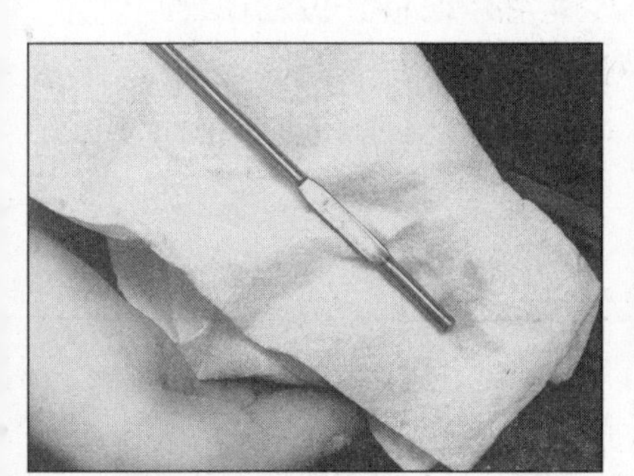

3.1a Wipe clean oil level dipstick markings

3.1b Topping-up engine oil

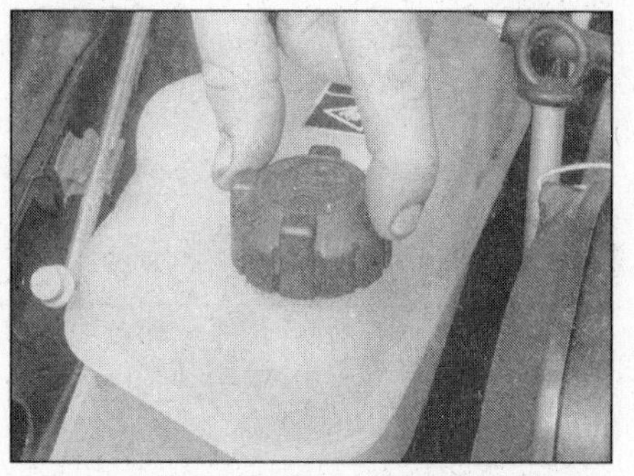

4.1 Coolant level MIN and MAX marks are on tank side nearest engine

5000 mile (7500 km) Service

7 Engine oil and filter renewal

1 Refer to Chapter 2, Part A, Section 7 **(see illustrations)**.

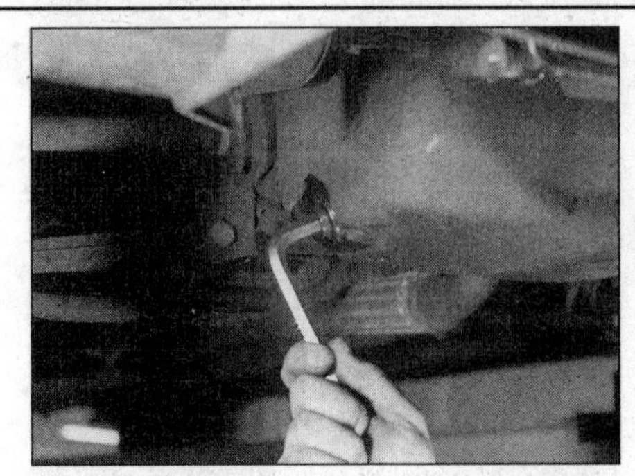

7.1a Unscrewing engine oil drain plug

7.1b Using a chain wrench to loosen oil filter

10 000 mile (15 000 km) Service

8 Idle speed check and adjustment

1 The usual type of tachometer, which works from ignition system pulses, cannot be used on diesel engines. A diagnostic socket is provided for the use of Fiat test equipment but this will not normally be available to the home mechanic. If it is not felt that adjusting the idle speed "by ear" is satisfactory. Purchase or hire an appropriate tachometer, or else leave the task to a Fiat dealer or suitably equipped specialist.

2 Before making adjustments, warm up the engine to normal operating temperature. Ensure that the accelerator cable is correctly adjusted.

3 Adjustment must be made with all electrical components (including the cooling fan) switched off. If the fan comes on during adjustment, wait until it switches off automatically before proceeding.

4 The idle adjustment screw is located on top of the fuel injection pump **(see illustration)**. To adjust idle speed, loosen the locknut and turn the screw as required then tighten the locknut.

5 On completion switch off the engine.

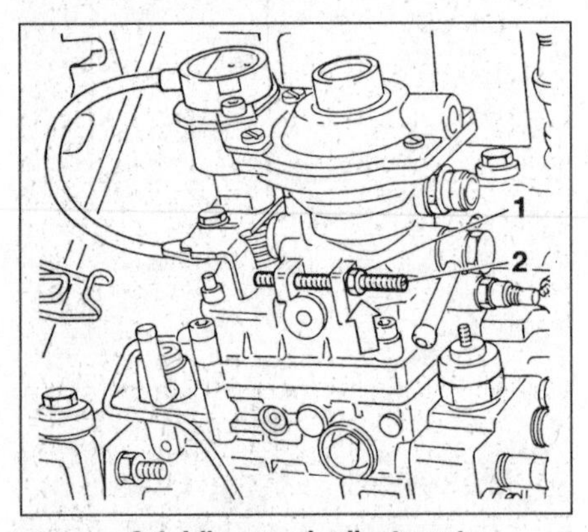

8.4 Idle speed adjustment

1 Locknut *2 Adjustment screw*

9 Fuel filter renewal

1 The fuel filter is mounted on the engine compartment bulkhead. An electrically-operated heater is located between the filter and housing.

2 Position a suitable container under the fuel filter. Loosen the bleed screw on top of the filter **(see illustration)**, then disconnect the wiring from the water sensor and loosen the water drain screw on the bottom of the filter. Allow the fuel to drain completely.

3 Tighten the drain and bleed screws, then use an oil filter strap to loosen the fuel filter **(see illustration)**.

4 Completely unscrew the filter and pour the remaining contents into the container. Ensure that the rubber sealing ring comes away with the filter and unscrew the drain screw from the bottom of the filter **(see illustration)**.

5 Wipe clean the contact surfaces then smear a little fuel on the sealing rubber of the new filter.

6 Screw the new filter fully home, using hand pressure only.

Fuel system priming and bleeding

7 Note that the injection pump is self-priming and no special procedures are necessary to prime the fuel system. However, where the system has been completely drained, it is helpful to loosen the injector union nuts while turning the engine on the starter motor in order to purge trapped air.

8 Start the engine and check for any signs of fuel leakage around the new filter.

9.2 Loosening fuel filter bleed screw

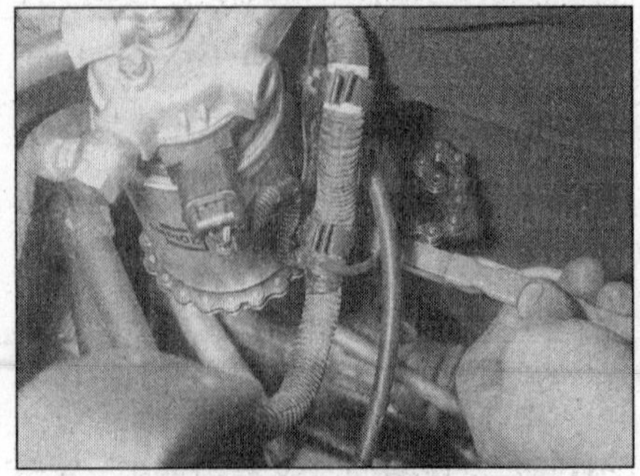

9.3 Using an oil filter strap to loosen fuel filter

9.4 Fuel filter drain screw components

20 000 mile (30 000 km) Service

10 Valve clearance check and adjustment

Valve clearance check

1 Valve clearances should be checked and adjusted with the engine cold.
2 Apply the handbrake then jack up the right-hand front of the vehicle and support it on an axle stand. Engage 4th gear. The engine can now be rotated by turning the right-hand front roadwheel.
3 Remove all four glow plugs.
4 Remove the air cleaner cover and air duct, then remove the camshaft cover.
5 Each valve clearance must be checked when the high point of the cam is pointing directly upward away from the cam follower.
6 Check the clearances in the firing order 1-3-4-2, No 1 cylinder being at the timing belt end of the engine. This will minimise the amount of crankshaft rotation required.
7 Insert the appropriate feeler blade between the heel of the cam and the cam follower shim of the first valve **(see illustration)**. If necessary, alter the thickness of the feeler blade until it is a stiff, sliding fit. Record the thickness, which will of course, represent the valve clearance for this particular valve.
8 Turn the engine, check the second valve clearance and record it.
9 Repeat the operations on all the remaining valves, recording their respective clearances.
10 Remember that the clearance for inlet and exhaust valves differs. Counting from the timing cover end of the engine, the valve sequence is:

Inlet	*2-4-5-7*
Exhaust	*1-3-6-8*

Valve clearance adjustment

11 Where clearances are incorrect, the particular shim will have to be changed. To remove the shim, turn the crankshaft until the high point of the cam is pointing directly upward. The cam follower will now have to be depressed so that the shim can be extracted. Special tools are available from your Fiat dealer to do this job, otherwise you will have to make up a forked lever to locate on the rim of the cam follower. This must allow room for the shim to be prised out by means of the cut-outs provided in the cam follower rim.

10.7 Using feeler blade to check valve clearance

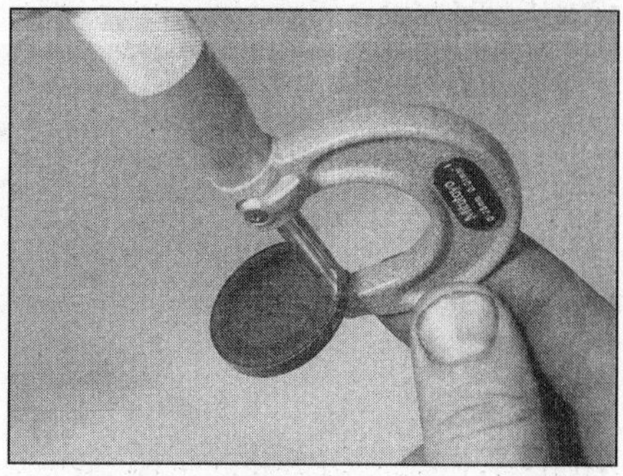
10.13 Measuring shim thickness with a micrometer

12 Once the shim is extracted, establish its thickness and change it for a thicker or thinner one to bring the previously recorded clearance within specification. For example, if the measured valve clearance was 1.27 mm too great, a shim thicker by this amount will be required. Conversely, if the clearance was 1.27 mm too small, a shim thinner by this amount will be required.
13 Shims have their thickness (in mm) engraved on them. Although the engraved side should be fitted so as not to be visible, wear still occurs and often obliterates this number. In this case, measuring their thickness with a metric micrometer is the only method to establish their thickness **(see illustration)**.
14 In practice, if several shims have to be changed, they can often be interchanged, so avoiding the necessity of having to buy more new shims than is necessary.
15 If more than two or three valve clearances are found to be incorrect, it will be more convenient to remove the camshaft for easier removal of the shims.
16 Where no clearance can be measured, even with the thinnest available shim in position, the valve will have to be removed and the end of its stem ground off squarely. This will reduce its overall length by the minimum amount to provide a clearance. This job should be entrusted to your dealer as it is important to keep the end of the valve stem square.
17 On completion, refit the camshaft cover and gasket, air cleaner and duct, and glowplugs.
18 Lower the vehicle to the ground.

11 Engine management system check

1 This check is part of the manufacturer's maintenance schedule and involves testing the engine management system using special dedicated test equipment. Such testing will allow the test equipment to read any fault codes stored in the electronic control unit memory.
2 Unless a fault is suspected, this test is not essential, although it should be noted that it is recommended by the manufacturers.
3 If access to suitable test equipment is not possible, make a thorough check of all ignition, fuel and emission control system components, hoses and wiring, for security and obvious signs of damage.

40 000 mile (60 000 km) Service

12 Timing belt check and tension

1 Refer to Section 14 for the procedure necessary to access the timing belt.
2 Turn the engine on the crankshaft pulley and inspect the full length of the timing belt for signs of oil contamination and wear of the teeth. In particular, check for cracking.
3 If in doubt as to the condition of the timing belt, then renew it immediately.
4 If the timing belt is in good condition, then refer to Section 14 and check its tension.

60 000 mile (90 000 km) Service

13 Emissions control systems check

1 A full check of the emissions control systems must be made by a Fiat dealer.

14.3 Removing upper timing cover

14.4 Removing outer cover over crankshaft pulley

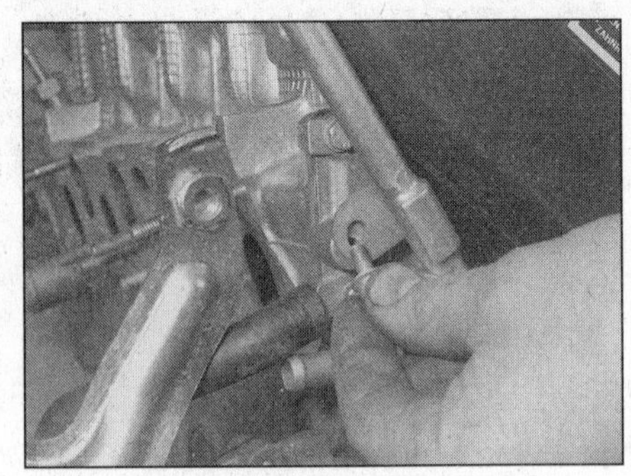
14.6a Unbolt engine oil dipstick tube . . .

70 000 mile (105 000 km) Service

14 Timing belt renewal

Caution: *Observe the direction of rotation markings on the timing belt.*

Removal

1 Jack up the front of the vehicle and support it on axle stands. Remove the right-hand front roadwheel. Disconnect the battery negative cable.

2 Unscrew the mounting bolts and move the coolant expansion tank to one side for access to the timing belt covers. Release the hose from the clips on the camshaft cover.

14.6b . . . and remove it from rubber grommet in oil pump housing

3 Release the toggle clips and remove the upper timing cover **(see illustration)**.

4 Working under the wheel arch, unbolt and remove the outer cover from over the crankshaft pulley **(see illustration)**.

5 Loosen the alternator swivel bolt and adjustment locknut, then turn the adjustment bolt to release the tension on the auxiliary drivebelt. Slip the drivebelt from the pulleys and remove it.

6 Unbolt and remove the engine oil dipstick tube, then detach it from the rubber grommet in the oil pump housing **(see illustrations)**.

7 Using a socket on the crankshaft pulley bolt, turn the engine until the TDC mark on the crankshaft pulley is aligned with the mark on the inner timing cover. Nos 1 and 4 pistons are now at TDC. If difficulty is experienced fitting a socket on the pulley centre bolt due to the pulley bolts, unscrew two diagonally opposite pulley retaining bolts then insert longer bolts by a few threads. A lever can now be used to turn the engine.

8 Check that the TDC mark on the injection pump pulley is aligned with the mark on the inner timing cover. If not, turn the crankshaft one complete turn and check again. Also check that the rear reference mark on the camshaft pulley is aligned with the hole in the top of the inner timing cover. The front reference mark on the pulley will also be aligned with the hole in the cover.

9 Unbolt and remove the lower timing cover from the cylinder block **(see illustration)**. Note that one of the bolts is located at the front of the engine.

10 Unscrew the socket-headed bolts and remove the pulley from the front of the crankshaft. Recover the spacer plate **(see illustrations)**.

11 Loosen the nut on the tensioner pulley, then turn the pulley anticlockwise to release the tension on the timing belt. Remove the belt from the camshaft, crankshaft, injection pump, idler and tensioner pulleys.

12 Examine the belt for evidence of contamination by coolant or lubricant. If this is the case, find the source of the contamination before fitting the new belt.

Refitting

13 Ensure that the crankshaft, camshaft and injection pump pulleys are still at their TDC positions.

14 Engage the new belt with the crankshaft sprocket, then locate it around the idler pulley and onto the injection pump sprocket, ensuring that it is kept tayt. Continue to locate it around the camshaft sprocket and finally around the tensioner pulley **(see illustration)**. Ensure the belt teeth seat correctly on the sprockets.

15 Tension the belt by turning the eccentrically-mounted tensioner clockwise. Two holes are provided in the side of the tensioner hub for this purpose. A pair of sturdy right-

14.9 Removing lower timing cover

14.10a Remove socket-headed bolts and spacer . . .

14.10b . . . and pull pulley from front of crankshaft

14.14 Locating timing belt around tensioner pulley

14.15a Using two bolts and a screwdriver to tension timing belt

14.15b Tightening timing belt tensioner nut

angled circlip pliers can be used to do this, or alternatively two bolts and a long screwdriver may be used. FIAT use a special tensioner tool located in the holes, which consists of a calibrated rod and weight. The weight is positioned 60 mm along the rod to provide the correct tension to the belt, then the tensioner nut is tightened. Tighten the tensioner nut to the specified torque **(see illustrations)**.

16 Turn the engine two complete turns clockwise and recheck the timing belt tension. If necessary, repeat the tensioning procedure.

17 Refit the pulley and spacer plate to the front of the crankshaft and tighten the socket-headed bolts to the specified torque.

18 Refit the lower timing belt cover and tighten the bolts.

19 Refit the engine oil dipstick and tighten the bolt.

20 Refit and tension the auxiliary drivebelt.

21 Refit the crankshaft pulley outer cover and tighten the bolts.

22 Refit the upper timing cover and secure with the toggle clips.

23 Refit the coolant expansion tank and tighten the mounting bolts. Secure the hose on the camshaft cover.

24 Refit the right-hand front roadwheel and lower the vehicle to the ground.

25 Reconnect the battery negative cable.

Chapter 4
Fiat 1698cc engine

Part B: Fuel system servicing

Contents

Specifications

Glow plugs

Type	Champion CH163

Injectors

Type	Pintle
Opening pressure:	
Bosch	150 to 158 bars
Lucas:	
New	124 to 131 bars
After running in	116 to 123 bars

Fuel injection pump

Bosch VE

Direction of rotation	Clockwise, viewed from sprocket end
Static timing:	
Engine position	No 1 piston at TDC
Pump timing measurement	0.93 ± 0.05 mm
Maximum engine speed	5200 to 5300 rpm

Lucas/CAV FT08

Direction of rotation	Clockwise, viewed from sprocket end
Static timing:	
Engine position	No 1 piston at TDC
Pump timing measurement	0° ± 1° PSM (*Value shown on pump*)
Maximum engine speed	5150 ± 50 rpm

RPM sensor

Sensor-to-flywheel ring gear teeth gap	0.25 to 1.3 mm
Winding resistance	680 ± 100 ohms

Torque wrench settings

	Nm	lbf ft
Glow plugs	15	11
Fuel injection pump	25	19
Fuel injection pump sprocket	49	36
Fuel injection pump rear bracket	29	21
Upper oil filter mounting and injection pump mounting nut	98	72
Lower oil filter mounting and injection pump mounting nut	71	52
Fuel injectors	55	41
Fuel injection pump union		
M12x1.5	32	24
M12x1.25	29	21

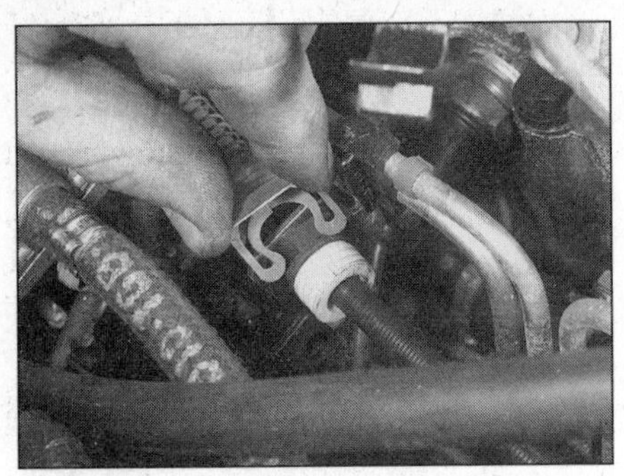

1.1 Removing accelerator cable adjustment clip

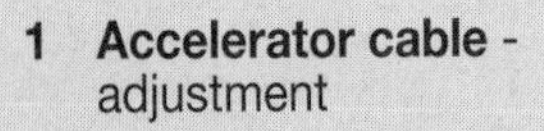

1 Accelerator cable - adjustment

1 Remove the spring clip from the accelerator cable outer **(see illustration)**. Ensuring that the control lever is against its stop, gently pull the cable out of its grommet until all free play is removed from the cable inner.

2 With the cable held in this position, refit the spring clip to the last exposed outer groove in front of the rubber grommet and washer. With the clip refitted and the cable outer released, there should be only a small amount of free play in the cable inner.

3 Have an assistant depress the accelerator pedal and check that the control lever opens fully and returns smoothly to its stop.

2 Glow plugs - removal, inspection and refitting

Caution: If the preheating system has just been energised, or if the engine has been running, the glow plugs will be very hot.

Removal

1 Disconnect the battery negative lead.

2 Remove the air inlet ducting from the front of the engine.

3 Unscrew the nut from the relevant glow plug terminal(s), and recover the washer(s). Note that the main supply cable is connected to No. 4 cylinder glow plug and an inter-

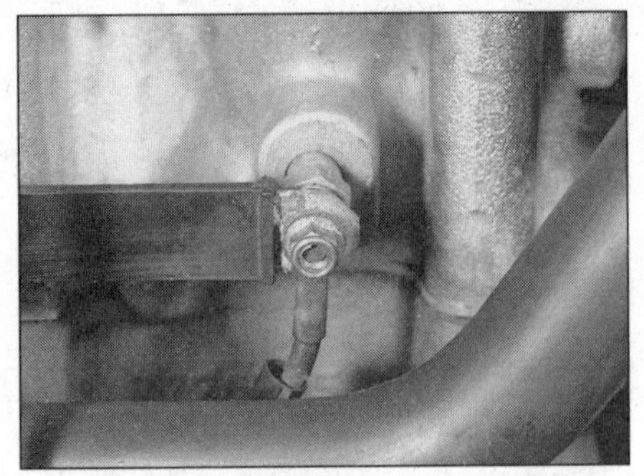

2.3 No 4 glowplug showing main supply lead and interconnecting strap

connecting strap is fitted between the four plugs **(see illustration)**.

4 Where applicable, carefully move any obstructing pipes or wires to one side to enable access to the relevant glow plug(s).

5 Unscrew the glow plug(s) and remove from the cylinder head **(see illustration)**.

Inspection

6 Inspect each glow plug for physical damage. Burnt or eroded glow plug tips can be caused by a bad injector spray pattern. Have the injectors checked if this sort of damage is found.

7 If the glow plugs are in good physical condition, check them electrically using a 12-volt test lamp or continuity tester as described in Section 6.

8 The glow plugs can be energised by applying 12 volts to them to verify that they heat up evenly and in the required time. Observe the following precautions:

a) Support the glow plug by clamping it carefully in a vice or self-locking pliers. Remember it will become red-hot.

b) Ensure that the power supply or test lead incorporates a fuse or overload trip to protect against damage from a short-circuit.

c) After testing, allow the glow plug to cool for several minutes before attempting to handle it.

9 A glow plug in good condition will start to glow red at the tip after drawing current for 5 seconds or so. Any plug which takes much longer to start glowing, or which starts glowing in the middle instead of at the tip, is defective.

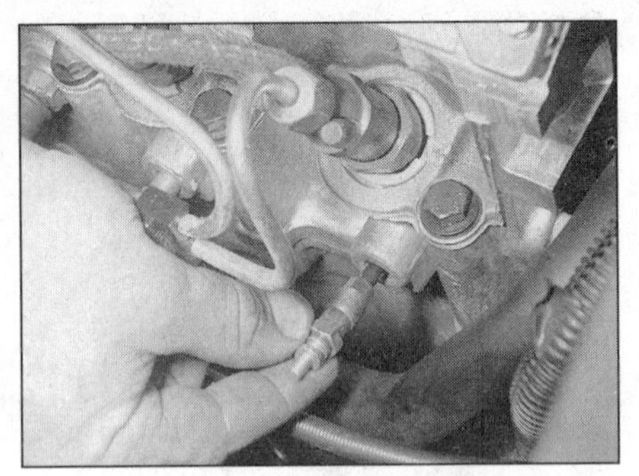

2.5 Removing a glow plug

Refitting

10 Refit by reversing the removal operations. Apply a smear of copper-based anti-seize compound to the plug threads and tighten the glow plugs to the specified torque. Do not overtighten as this can damage the glow plug element.

3 Injectors - testing, removal and refitting

Warning: Exercise extreme caution when working on the fuel injectors. Never expose the hands or any part of the body to injector spray, as the high working pressure can cause fuel to penetrate the skin, with possibly fatal results. You are strongly advised to have any work which involves testing the injectors under pressure carried out by a dealer or fuel injection specialist.

Testing

1 Injectors deteriorate with prolonged use and it is reasonable to expect them to need reconditioning or renewal after 60 000 miles (90 000 km). Accurate testing, overhaul and calibration of the injectors must be left to a specialist. A defective injector which is causing knocking or smoking can be located without dismantling as follows.

2 Run the engine at a fast idle. Slacken each injector union in turn, placing rag around the union to catch spilt fuel and being careful not to expose the skin to any spray. When the union on the defective injector is slackened, the knocking or smoking will stop.

Removal

3 Remove the air inlet ducting from the front part of the engine.

4 Carefully clean around the injectors and injector pipe union nuts.

5 Pull the leak-off pipes from the injectors **(see illustration)**.

6 Unscrew the union nuts which secure the injector pipes to the fuel injection pump. Counterhold the unions on the pump when unscrewing the nuts **(see illustration)**. Cover

3.5 Disconnecting an injector leak-off pipe

3.6 Unscrewing union nuts from injection pump

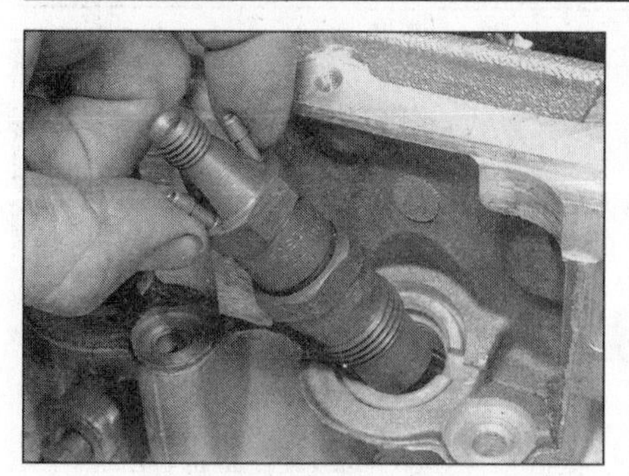
3.8 Removing an injector

3.9 Removing a fire seal washer

4.2a Remove injection pump sprocket retaining nut and washer . . .

open unions to keep dirt out by using small plastic bags or fingers cut from clean discarded rubber gloves.

7 Unscrew the union nuts and disconnect the pipes from the injectors. If necessary, the injector pipes may be completely removed. Note carefully the locations of the pipe clamps, for use when refitting. Cover the ends of the injectors to prevent dirt ingress.

8 Unscrew the injectors using a deep socket or box spanner and remove them from the cylinder head **(see illustration)**.

9 Recover the fire seal washers from the cylinder head and discard them **(see illustration)**.

Refitting

10 Obtain new fire seal washers.

11 Take care not to drop the injectors or allow the needles at their tips to become damaged. The injectors are precision-made to fine limits and must not be handled roughly. In particular, never mount them in a bench vice.

12 Commence refitting by inserting the fire seal washers (convex face uppermost).

13 Insert the injectors and tighten them to the specified torque.

14 Refit the injector pipes and tighten the union nuts. Ensure the pipe clamps are in their previously-noted positions. If the clamps are wrongly positioned or missing, problems may be experienced with pipes breaking or splitting.

15 Reconnect the leak-off pipes.

16 Refit the air ducting.

17 Start the engine. If difficulty is experienced, bleed the fuel system as described in Part A of this Chapter.

4 Fuel injection pump - removal and refitting

Removal

1 Remove the timing belt, as described in Part A of this Chapter.

2 Remove the injection pump sprocket and Woodruff key **(see illustrations)**.

3 Unscrew the bolt(s) from the injection pump rear support bracket **(see illustration)**.

4 Unscrew the pump mounting nuts/bolt, remove the special bracket, then remove the injection pump from the mounting bracket/ housing **(see illustrations)**.

4.2b . . . pull sprocket from injection pump shaft . . .

4.2c . . . followed by Woodruff key

4.3 Unscrewing pump rear support bracket bolt

4.4a Removing injection pump lower mounting bolt

4.4b Removing injection pump special mounting bracket

4.4c Removing injection pump

4.7 Tightening injection pump sprocket retaining nut

Refitting

5 Locate the injection pump in the mounting bracket, locate the special bracket and fit the nuts/bolt loosely.

6 Refit the rear support bracket and fit the bolts loosely.

7 Refit the Woodruff key and injection pump sprocket **(see illustration)**

8 Refit and tension the timing belt.

9 Finally, check and adjust the injection timing as described in Section 5. The injection pump mounting bolts are tightened at this stage.

5 Fuel injection pump - timing

Caution: Some of the injection pump settings and access plugs may be sealed by the manufacturers at the factory, using paint or locking wire and lead seals. Do not disturb the seals if the vehicle is still within the warranty period, otherwise the warranty will be invalidated. Also do not attempt the timing procedure unless accurate instrumentation is available.

Note: *To check injection pump timing, a special timing probe and mounting bracket is required. Without access to this piece of equipment, injection pump timing should be entrusted to a FIAT dealer or other suitably equipped specialist.*

1 Check the injection timing only after the injection pump has been disturbed.

2 Dynamic timing equipment does exist but it is unlikely to be available to the home mechanic. The equipment works by converting pressure pulses in an injector pipe into electrical signals. If such equipment is available, use it in accordance with the manufacturer's instructions, using the timing mark on the flywheel **(see illustration)**.

3 Static timing as described in this Section gives good results if carried out carefully. A dial test indicator will be needed, with probes and adapters appropriate to the type of injection pump. Read through the procedures before starting work to find out what is involved.

Bosch pump

4 If the injection timing is being checked with the pump in position on the engine, rather than as part of the pump fitting procedure, disconnect the battery negative lead and remove the air inlet ducting from the front of the engine.

5 Unscrew the union nuts and disconnect the injector pipes from the pump and injectors. Counterhold the unions on the pump while unscrewing the pipe-to-pump union nuts. Remove the pipes as a set. Cover open unions to keep dirt out by using small plastic bags.

6 Set the engine at TDC on No. 1 cylinder, as described in Part A of this Chapter (timing belt renewal).

7 Unscrew the access screw (situated in the centre of the four injector pipe unions) from the rear of the injection pump **(see illustration)**. As the screw is removed, position a suitable container beneath the pump to catch any escaping fuel. Mop up any spilt fuel with a clean cloth.

5.2 Remove rubber plug to reveal timing marks on flywheel and transmission casing

8 Screw the adapter into the rear of the pump and mount the dial gauge in the adapter **(see illustration)**. Position the dial gauge so that its plunger is at the mid-point of its travel and securely tighten the adapter locknut.

9 Slowly rotate the crankshaft first back then forwards whilst observing the dial gauge, to determine when the injection pump piston is at the bottom of its travel (BDC). When the piston is correctly positioned, zero the dial gauge.

10 Rotate the crankshaft slowly in the correct direction until the TDC timing marks are aligned on both the crankshaft pulley and the camshaft sprocket. The timing mark on the camshaft sprocket is viewed through the small hole in the inner timing cover.

11 The reading obtained on the dial gauge should be equal to the specified pump timing measurement. If adjustment is necessary, slacken the front and rear pump mounting nuts/bolts and slowly rotate the pump body until the point is found where the specified reading is obtained. When the pump is correctly positioned, tighten both its front and rear mounting nuts and bolts securely.

12 Rotate the crankshaft through one and three quarter rotations in the normal direction of rotation. Find the injection pump piston BDC and zero the dial gauge.

5.7 Remove access screw from rear of injection pump

5.8 Dial gauge and adapter

5.23 Removing injection pump timing inspection plug

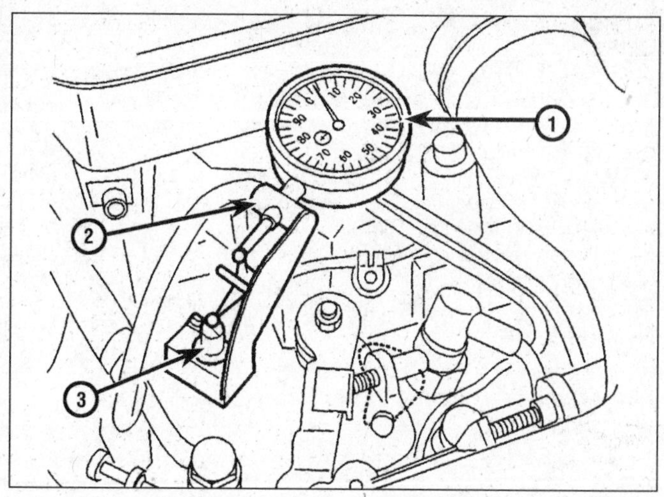

5.25 Dial gauge (1) mounting bracket (2) and setting rod (3) in position on injection pump

13 Rotate the crankshaft slowly in the correct direction of rotation until the TDC marks are aligned. Recheck the timing measurement.

14 If adjustment is necessary, slacken the pump mounting nuts and bolts and repeat the operations in paragraphs 11 to 13.

15 When the pump timing is correctly set, unscrew the adapter and remove the dial gauge.

16 Refit the screw and sealing washer to the pump and tighten it securely.

17 Refit the injector pipes, tightening their union nuts to the specified torque setting.

18 Reconnect the battery and refit the air inlet ducting.

19 Bleed the fuel system as described in Part A of this Chapter.

20 Start the engine and adjust the idle speed as described in Part A of this Chapter.

Lucas/CAV pump

21 Carry out the operations given in paragraphs 4 to 6.

22 Turn the crankshaft backwards (anti-clockwise) approximately a quarter of a turn.

23 Unscrew the access plug from the guide on the top of the pump body and recover the sealing washer **(see illustration)**.

24 Insert the special timing probe into the guide, making sure it is correctly seated against the guide sealing washer surface. Note that the timing probe must be seated against the guide sealing washer surface and not the upper lip of the guide for the measurement to be accurate.

25 Mount the bracket on the pump guide (using adapter tool) and securely mount the dial test indicator (DTI) in the bracket so that its tip is in contact with the bracket linkage **(see illustration)**. Position the dial gauge so that its plunger is at the mid-point of its travel and zero the gauge.

26 Rotate the crankshaft slowly in the correct direction of rotation (clockwise) until the crankshaft is positioned at TDC on No 1 piston.

27 With the crankshaft locked in position, read the dial gauge. The reading should correspond to the value marked on the pump (there is a tolerance of ± 0.04 mm). The timing value may be marked on a plastic disc attached to the front of the pump, or alternatively, on a tag attached to the pump control lever **(see illustrations)**.

28 If adjustment is necessary, slacken the pump front mounting nuts/bolt and the rear mounting bolt, then slowly rotate the pump body until the point is found where the specified reading is obtained on the dial gauge (access to the lower front bolt is gained through the hole in the injection pump sprocket). When the pump is correctly positioned, tighten both its front mounting nuts/bolt and the rear bolt to their specified torque settings.

29 Withdraw the timing probe slightly, so that it is positioned clear of the pump rotor dowel. Rotate the crankshaft through one and three quarter rotations in the normal direction of rotation.

30 Slide the timing probe back into position, ensuring that it is correctly seated against the guide sealing washer surface and not the upper lip, then zero the dial gauge.

5.27a Pump timing value (x) marked on plastic disc

5.27b Pump timing values marked on label (1) and tag (2)

31 Rotate the crankshaft slowly in the correct direction of rotation to the TDC position and recheck the timing measurement.
32 If adjustment is necessary, slacken the pump mounting nuts and bolt and repeat the operations in paragraphs 28 to 31.
33 When pump timing is correctly set, remove the dial gauge and mounting bracket and withdraw the timing probe.
34 Refit the screw and sealing washer to the guide and tighten it securely.
35 Carry out the operations given in paragraphs 17 to 20.

6 Preheating system - testing

1 If the preheating system malfunctions, testing is ultimately by substitution of known serviceable units but some preliminary checks may be made as follows.
2 Connect a voltmeter or 12-volt test lamp between the glow plug supply cable and earth (engine or vehicle metal). Ensure that the live connection is kept clear of the engine and bodywork.
3 Have an assistant switch on the ignition and check that voltage is applied to the glow plugs. Note the time for which the warning light is lit and the total time for which voltage is applied before the system cuts out. Switch off the ignition.
4 At an under-bonnet temperature of 20°C, typical times noted should be 5 or 6 seconds for warning light operation, followed by a further 10 seconds supply after the light goes out. Warning light time will increase with lower temperatures and decrease with higher temperatures.
5 If there is no supply at all, the relay or associated wiring is at fault.
6 To locate a defective glow plug, disconnect the main supply cable and the interconnecting strap from the top of the glow plugs. Be careful not to drop the nuts and washers.
7 Use a continuity tester or 12-volt test lamp connected to the battery positive terminal to check for continuity between each glow plug terminal and earth. The resistance of a glow plug in good condition is very low (less than 1 ohm), so if the test lamp does not light or the continuity tester shows a high resistance, the glow plug is certainly defective.
8 If an ammeter is available, the current draw of each glow plug can be checked. After an initial surge of 15 to 20 amps, each plug should draw approximately 12 amps. Any plug which draws much more or less than this is probably defective.

7 Preheating system control unit - removal and refitting

Removal

1 Disconnect the battery negative lead.
2 Unscrew the screws and remove the relay cover located at the left-hand end of the engine.
3 Disconnect the wiring then remove the control unit from the bracket.

Refitting

4 Refitting is a reversal of removal.

Chapter 5
Ford 1608cc, 1753cc and 2496cc engines
Part A: Routine maintenance and servicing

Contents

Engine application

1608cc (1.6 litre) engine	Ford Fiesta, Escort and Orion - 1984 to 1996
1753cc (1.8 litre) engine	Ford Fiesta, Escort, Orion, Sierra and Mondeo - 1984 to 1996
2496cc (2.5 litre) engine	Ford Transit - 1986 to 1995

Servicing specifications

Oil filter types

1.6 litre engine	Champion C151
1.8 litre engine	Champion C115
2.5 litre engine	Champion E103

Valve clearances (cold)

1.6 litre engine	
Inlet	0.235 to 0.365 mm
Exhaust	0.435 to 0.565 mm
1.8 litre engine	
Inlet	0.30 to 0.40 mm
Exhaust	0.45 to 0.55 mm
2.5 litre engine	
Inlet	0.20 mm
Exhaust	0.38 mm

Camshaft drivebelt tension (cold)

1.6 litre engine	
When refitting	8.5 to 10.5
Checking in service	1.0 to 8.0
1.8 litre engine	
Automatic tensioner	
2.5 litre engine	
Automatic tensioner	

Auxiliary drivebelts

Alternator

1.6 litre engine		
Type	V-belt	
Tension (using tension gauge):		
New	350 to 450 N	
Used	250 to 350 N	
1.8 litre engine - non turbocharged and Escort turbocharged		
Type	Flat "polyvee" belt	
Tension (cold belt, using tension gauge):	**New**	**Used**
Without power-assisted steering - conventional (slotted-link) belt adjustment	350 to 450 N	250 to 350 N
Without power-assisted steering rack-and-pinion belt adjustment	550 to 650N	350 to 450 N
With power-assisted steering	550 to 650N	400 to 500 N
1.8 litre engine - Mondeo turbocharged		
Type	Flat "polyvee" belt from crankshaft	
	New	**Used**
Tension (deflection at centre of belt's longest run)	1 to 2 mm	2 to 4 mm
2.5 litre engine		
Type	Flat "polyvee" belt	
Tension (deflection at centre of belt's longest run)	2.5 mm	

Power-assisted steering pump

1.8 litre engine - non turbocharged and Escort turbocharged		
See above		
1.8 litre engine - Mondeo turbocharged		
Type	Flat "polyvee" belt	
	New	**Used**
Tension (deflection at centre of belt's longest run)	1 to 2 mm	2 to 4 mm
2.5 litre engine - without air conditioning		
Type	Flat "polyvee" belt	
Tension (deflection at centre of belt's longest run)	2.0 mm	
2.5 litre engine - with air conditioning		
Type	Flat "polyvee" belt	
Tension	Automatic tensioner	

Air conditioning compressor

1.6 and 1.8 litre engines		
Type	Flat "polyvee" belt	
	New	**Used**
Tension (deflection at centre of belt's longest run)	1 to 2 mm	2 to 4 mm
2.5 litre engine		
Type	Flat "polyvee" belt	
Tension	Automatic tensioner	

Note: *A used drivebelt (V or "polyvee" type) is defined as one that has been run for at least 10 minutes.*

Note - 1.8 non turbocharged and Escort turbocharged engines: *Any tension gauge readings are nominal and are given for reference only where rack-and-pinion adjustment is found.*

Air filter types

1.6 litre engine

All models	Champion U515

1.8 litre engine

Fiesta models	Champion U557
Escort/Orion models - non turbocharged	Champion U560
Escort models - turbocharged	Champion U612
Mondeo models - turbocharged	Champion U654

2.5 litre engine

Circular air cleaner mounted on engine	Champion W184
Air cleaner mounted at side of engine	Champion U634

Fuel filter types

1.6 litre engine

Bosch:	
Early type (separate element)	N/A
Later type (spin-on cartridge)	Champion L111
CAV RotoDiesel	Champion L131 or L137

1.8 litre engine

Bosch	Champion L134
CAV RotoDiesel	Champion L131 or L137

2.5 litre engine

Type	Champion L209

Glow plug types

1.6 litre engine	Champion CH79
1.8 litre engine	Champion CH147
2.5 litre engine	N/A

Idle speed

1.6 litre engine	880 rpm
1.8 litre engine	850 rpm
2.5 litre engine:	
Non turbo	800 to 850 rpm
Turbo	800 to 900 rpm

Note: *Idle speed cannot be adjusted on turbocharged engines controlled by the Lucas EPIC engine management system, as this is a function of the system's electronic control unit.*

Torque wrench settings

	Nm	lbf ft
Camshaft drivebelt - 1.6 litre engine		
Cover bolts	8 to 11	6 to 8
Sprocket bolt	27 to 33	20 to 24
TDC setting hole plug	20 to 25	15 to 18
Tensioner pivot bolt	27 to 33	20 to 24
Camshaft drivebelt - 1.8 litre engine		
Bearing cap bolts	23	17
Cover bolts	4	3
Oil baffle nuts	20	15
Camshaft drivebelt - 2.5 litre engine		
Cover bolts	5 to 9	3.5 to 6.6
Injection pump sprocket bolts	22 to 27	16 to 20
Tensioner roller bolt	51 to 64	38 to 47
Tensioner sliding arm bolt	21 to 26	15 to 19

Lubricants, fluids and capacities

Component or system	Lubricant or fluid	Capacity
Engine - 1.6 litre	Multigrade engine oil, viscosity range SAE 10W/30 to 20W/50, to specification API SG/CD	5.0 litres - With filter
Engine - 1.8 litre non Turbo	Multigrade engine oil, viscosity range SAE 10W/30 to 20W/50, to specification API SG/CD	4.5 litres - With filter
Engine - 1.8 litre Turbo	Multigrade engine oil, to spec API SG/CD and CCMC PD2 Ford Super Motor Oil 15W/40	4.5 litres - With filter (Escort) 5.0 litres - With filter (Mondeo)
Engine - 2.5 litre	Multigrade engine oil, viscosity range SAE 5W/50 to 10W/30, to specification API SG/CD	6.15 litres - With filter (non Turbo) 6.25 litres - With filter (Turbo)
Cooling system	Ethylene glycol based antifreeze. 50% volume with water	8.5 litres (Fiesta 1.6) 9.3 litres (Fiesta 1.8, Escort, Orion, Mondeo) 11.5 litres (Transit non Turbo) 12.0 litres (Transit Turbo)
Fuel system	Commercial Diesel fuel for road vehicles (DERV)	Dependent on model type

Ford diesel engine - maintenance schedule

The maintenance schedules which follow are basically those recommended by the manufacturer. Servicing intervals are determined by mileage or time elapsed - this is because fluids and systems deteriorate with age as well as with use. Follow the time intervals if the appropriate mileage is not covered within the specified period.

Vehicles operating under adverse conditions may need more frequent maintenance. Adverse conditions include climatic extremes, full-time towing or taxi work, driving on unmade roads, and a high proportion of short journeys. The use of inferior fuel can cause early degradation of the engine oil. Consult a Ford dealer for advice on these points.

Every 250 miles (400 km), weekly or before a long journey

- ☐ Check engine oil level and top up if necessary (Section 3)
- ☐ Check coolant level and top up if necessary (Section 4)
- ☐ Check exhaust emission (Section 5)
- ☐ Check operation of glow plug warning light (Section 6)

Every 6000 miles (10 000 km) or 6 months - whichever comes first

- ☐ Renew engine oil and filter (Section 7)
- ☐ Clean engine oil filler cap - 2.5 litre engine (Section 8)
- ☐ Check auxiliary drivebelt(s) for condition and tension - 1.6 and 2.5 litre engines
- ☐ Drain water from fuel filter (Section 9)
- ☐ Check idle speed and adjust if necessary - 1.6 and 1.8 litre engines (Section 10)
- ☐ Check crankcase ventilation and engine for fluid leakage
- ☐ Check operation of brake vacuum pump - 1.6 and 1.8 litre engines (Section 11)

Every 12 000 miles (20 000 km) or 12 months

In addition to the work in the previous schedule

- ☐ Check valve clearances - 2.5 litre engine (Section 12)
- ☐ Check exhaust system security and condition
- ☐ Check auxiliary drivebelt(s) for condition and tension - 1.8 litre engine
- ☐ Check idle and anti-stall speeds and adjust if necessary - 2.5 litre engine (Section 13)

Annually, at the beginning of Winter

- ☐ Purge pre-heating flame plug fuel reservoir - 2.5 litre engine (Section 14)

Every 18 000 miles (30 000 km) or 2 years

In addition to the work in the previous schedules

- ☐ Renew fuel filter element - 1.8 litre engine (Section 15)

Every 24 000 miles (40 000 km) or 2 years

In addition to the work in the previous schedules

- ☐ Renew fuel filter element - 1.6 and 2.5 litre engines (Section 16)
- ☐ Renew air cleaner element
- ☐ Check valve clearances - 1.6 litre engine (Section 17)

Every 36 000 miles (60 000 km) or 2 years

In addition to the work in the previous schedules

- ☐ Renew engine coolant

Every 36 000 miles (60 000 km) or 3 years

In addition to the work in the previous schedules

- ☐ Renew camshaft and injection pump drivebelts - 1.8 litre engine (Section 18)
- ☐ Renew camshaft drivebelt on a precautionary basis - 1.6 litre engine (Section 19)

Every 48 000 miles (80 000 km)

In addition to the work in the previous schedules

- ☐ Check valve clearances - 1.8 litre engine (Section 20)
- ☐ Renew camshaft drivebelt - 2.5 litre engine (Section 21)

Underbonnet view of Ford Fiesta 1.6 litre Diesel engine

1 Windscreen washer reservoir
2 Camshaft drivebelt cover
3 Engine oil filler cap
4 Suspension turret
5 Coolant expansion tank
6 Cooling system bleed hose
7 Throttle cable
8 Air cleaner cover
9 Bonnet catch
10 Air intake hose
11 Crankcase ventilation hoses
12 Windscreen wiper motor
13 Brake master cylinder reservoir
14 Fuel filter head
15 Battery
16 Radiator top hose
17 Radiator fan shroud
18 Servo non-return valve
19 Cooling system bleed screw
20 Vacuum pump
21 Engine oil level dipstick
22 Thermostat housing
23 Injection pipes
24 Injection pump
25 Coolant pump connector

Underbonnet view of Ford Fiesta 1.8 litre Diesel engine

1 Coolant expansion tank
2 Suspension strut turret
3 Plastic section of inlet manifold
4 Wheel brace
5 Brake fluid reservoir
6 Camshaft cover
7 Oil filler cap
8 Air intake duct from air cleaner
9 Fuel filter
10 Brake pressure regulator
11 Air cleaner
12 Fuel injection pump
13 Radiator cooling fan
14 Top hose bleed screw
15 Vacuum pump
16 Battery
17 Washer fluid reservoir cap
18 Engine oil level dipstick

Underbonnet view of Ford Escort 1.8 litre Diesel engine

1 Engine oil level dipstick
2 Fuel injection pump
3 Coolant expansion tank
4 Engine oil filler cap
5 Suspension strut turret
6 Plastic section of inlet manifold
7 Air intake duct from air cleaner
8 Battery
9 Engine compartment relays
10 Brake fluid reservoir
11 Engine up speed control unit
12 Washer fluid reservoir cap
13 Air cleaner unit
14 Vacuum pump
15 Coolant bleed screw

Underbonnet view of Ford Escort 1.8 litre Turbo Diesel engine

1 Engine oil level dipstick
2 Fuel injection pump
3 Coolant expansion tank
4 Engine oil filler cap
5 Suspension strut turret
6 Charge air cooler
7 Turbocharger intake duct
8 Battery
9 Engine compartment relays
10 Brake fluid reservoir
11 Power steering fluid reservoir
12 Washer fluid reservoir cap
13 Air cleaner unit
14 Vacuum pump
15 Coolant bleed screw
16 Fuel pump and filter

Underbonnet view of Ford Mondeo 1.8 litre Turbo Diesel engine

1 *Engine oil level dipstick*
2 *Fuel injection pump*
3 *Coolant expansion tank*
4 *Engine oil filler cap*
5 *Suspension strut turret*
6 *Charge air cooler*
7 *Turbocharger intake duct*
8 *Battery*
9 *Engine compartment relays and fuses*
10 *Brake fluid reservoir*
11 *Power steering fluid reservoir*
12 *Washer fluid reservoir cap*
13 *Air cleaner unit*
14 *Vacuum pump*
15 *Fuel pump and filter*

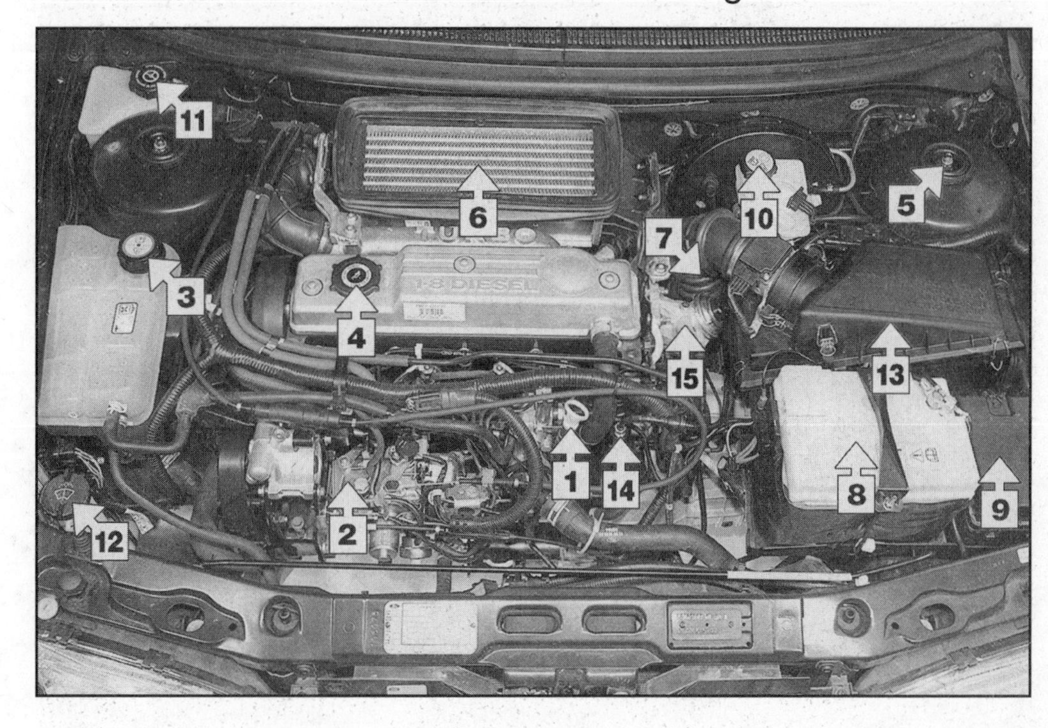

Underbonnet view of 1992 Ford Transit 2.5 litre Diesel engine

1 *Battery*
2 *Brake fluid reservoir*
3 *Coolant expansion tank*
4 *Fuel injection pump*
5 *Inlet manifold (two-piece type)*
6 *EGR valve*
7 *Oil filler cap*
8 *Air cleaner unit*
9 *Thermostat housing*
10 *Engine oil dipstick*
11 *Windscreen washer reservoir*

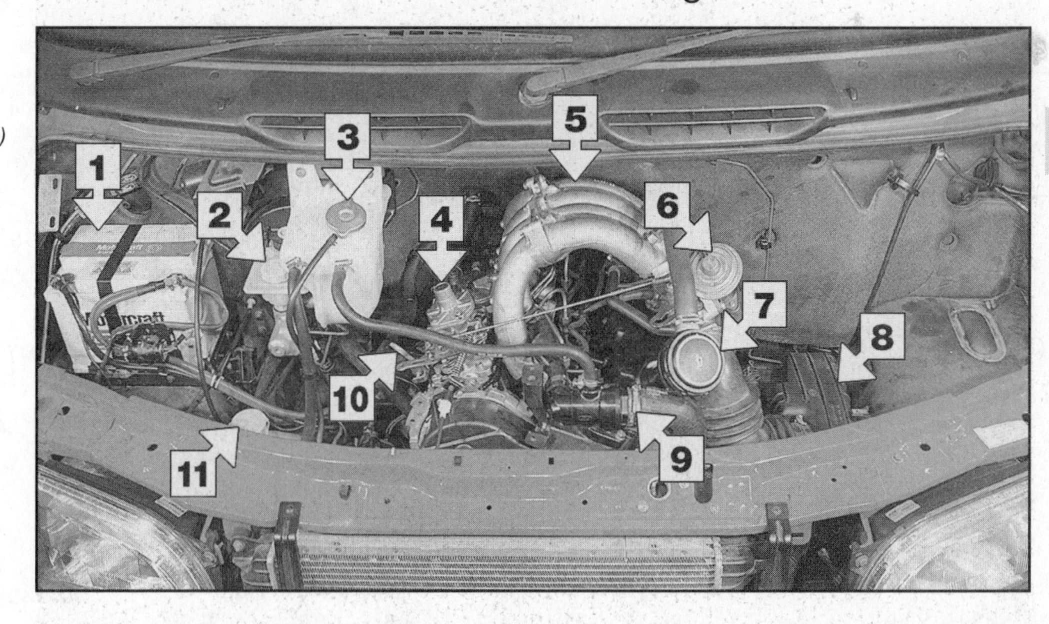

Maintenance procedures

1 Introduction

Refer to Chapter 2, Part A, Section 1.

2 Intensive maintenance

Refer to Chapter 2, Part A, Section 2.

250 mile (400 km) Service

3 Engine oil level check

1 Refer to Chapter 2, Part A, Section 3 **(see illustrations)**.

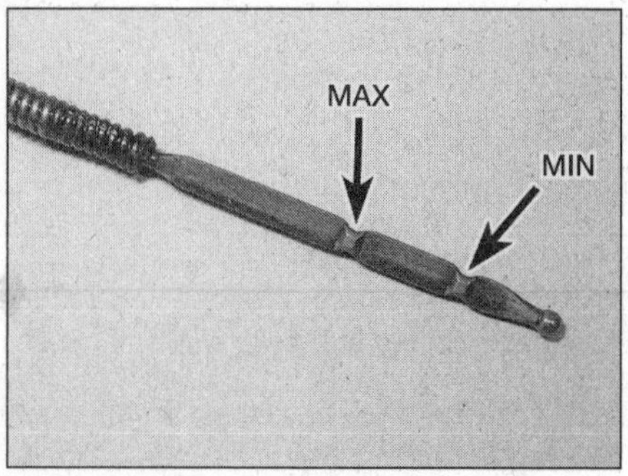

MAX
MIN

3.1a Engine oil level dipstick markings - Mondeo shown, others similar

4 Coolant level check

1 Refer to Chapter 2, Part A, Section 4. Note that the tank is translucent, so the coolant level can be verified without removing the cap. The level should be between the MAX (HOT) and MIN (COLD) marks embossed on the side of the tank. If it is below the MIN mark, remove the cap and top up with coolant to the MAX mark **(see illustration)**.

3.1b Topping-up engine oil - Mondeo shown

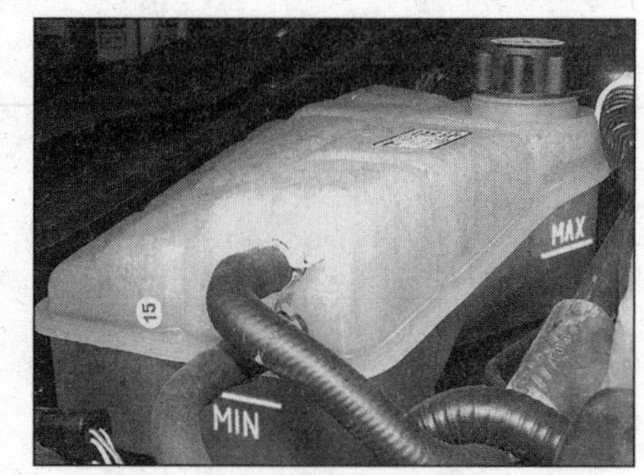

4.1 Coolant level MIN and MAX marks - Mondeo shown, others similar

5 Exhaust smoke check

1 Refer to Chapter 2, Part A, Section 5.

6 Warning light check

1 Refer to Chapter 2, Part A, Section 6.

6000 mile (10 000 km) Service

7 Engine oil and filter renewal

1 Refer to Chapter 2, Part A, Section 7 **(see illustrations)**.

8 Engine oil filler cap check - 2.5 litre engine

1 Remove and inspect the oil filler cap to ensure that it is in good condition and not blocked with sludge.

2 Disconnect the hoses at the cap and, if necessary, clean it by brushing the inner mesh filter with solvent and blowing through with light pressure from an air line. Renew the cap if badly congested.

9 Fuel filter water drainage

1.6 litre engine

Early type Bosch filter (separate element)

1 Disconnect the battery earth lead.

2 Attach a tube to the drain spigot on the base of the fuel filter. Place the other end of the tube in a clean jar or can.

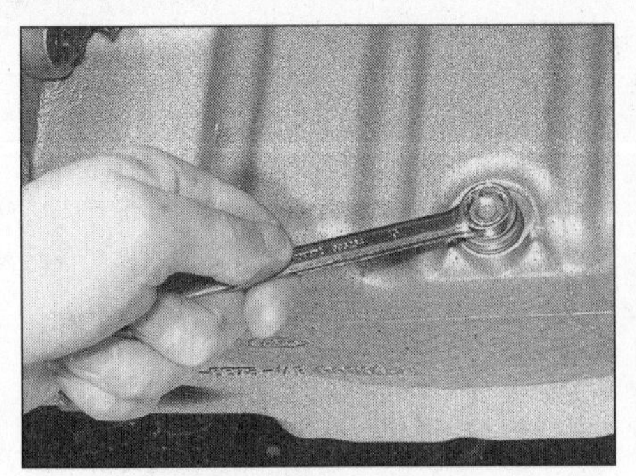

7.1a Removing engine oil drain plug - Mondeo shown

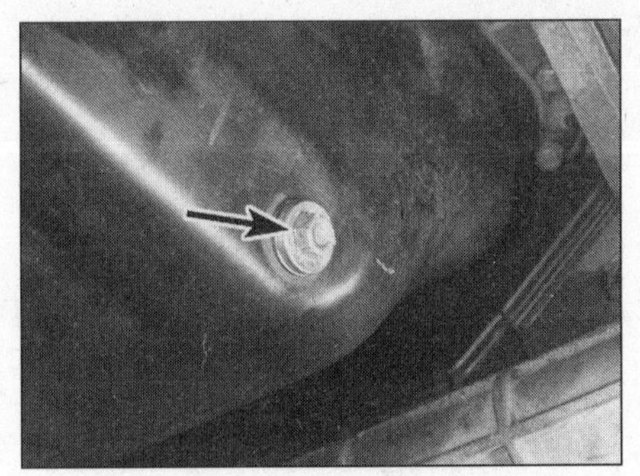

7.1b Engine oil drain plug (arrowed) - Transit shown

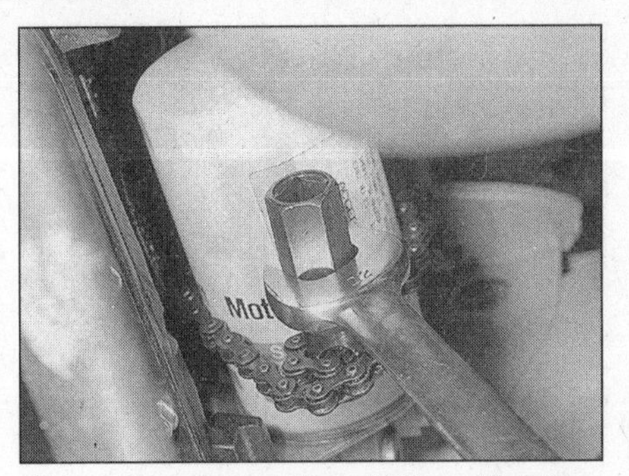

7.1c Removing engine oil filter - Mondeo shown, others similar

3 Open the drain cock by unscrewing the knurled wheel.

4 Allow the filter to drain until clean fuel, free of dirt or water, emerges from the tube. If no fuel emerges, use the procedure given below for the later type of filter. Close the drain cock and remove the tube.

5 Dispose of the contaminated fuel safely.

6 Reconnect the battery earth lead.

Later type Bosch filter (spin-on cartridge)

7 Disconnect the battery earth lead.

8 In addition to taking the precautions noted above to catch any fuel spillages, connect a tube to the drain spigot on the base of the fuel filter. Place the other end of the tube in a clean jar or can.

9 Open the drain cock by unscrewing the knurled wheel.

10 Allow the filter to drain until clean fuel, free of dirt or water, emerges from the tube (approximately 100 cc is usually sufficient). Close the drain cock and remove the tube, containers and rag, mopping up any spilt fuel.

11 If, as often happens, no fuel emerges on opening the drain cock, slacken the vent screw on the filter head to allow sufficient air into the filter for fuel to flow. If this does not work, remove the filter cartridge and check it carefully until the reason for the lack of flow can be identified and is cured. It is unwise simply to probe the drain cock with a piece of wire in an attempt to clear the obstruction; the small seals in the drain cock may be damaged or dislodged. Note that the system may require bleeding if the vent screw is disturbed or the filter unscrewed.

12 On completion, dispose safely of the drained fuel and reconnect the battery earth lead. Check carefully all disturbed components to ensure that there are no leaks (of air or fuel) when the engine is restarted.

CAV RotoDiesel filter

13 Disconnect the battery earth lead.

14 Connect a tube to the drain spigot (where fitted) on the base of the fuel filter. Place the other end of the tube in a clean jar or can.

15 Open the drain cock either by unscrewing the knurled wheel/thumbscrew or by using a spanner, as appropriate **(see illustration)**.

16 Allow the filter to drain until clean fuel, free of dirt or water, emerges from the tube (approximately 100 cc is usually sufficient). Close the drain cock and remove the tube, containers and rag, mopping up any split fuel.

17 If, as often happens, no fuel emerges on opening the drain cock, either operate the hand-priming pump to get fuel flowing or slacken the bleed nipple on the filter outlet union to allow sufficient air into the filter for fuel to flow. If this does not work, remove the filter element and check the element and bowl carefully until the reason for the lack of flow can be identified and is cured. In some cases, it would appear that the drain cock passage in the bowl was never made on manufacture. In such cases, either the filter element must be removed at each draining interval so that any water or foreign matter can be tipped out of the filter bowl, or the necessary replacement parts must be obtained so that the drain cock can be used as described above. It is unwise simply to probe the drain cock with a piece of wire in an attempt to clear the obstruction as the small seals in the drain cock may be damaged or dislodged. Note that the system may require bleeding if the bleed nipple is disturbed or the filter dismantled.

18 On completion, refit the air cleaner duct (if removed), dispose safely of the drained fuel and reconnect the battery earth lead. Check carefully all disturbed components to ensure that there are no leaks (of air or fuel) when the engine is restarted.

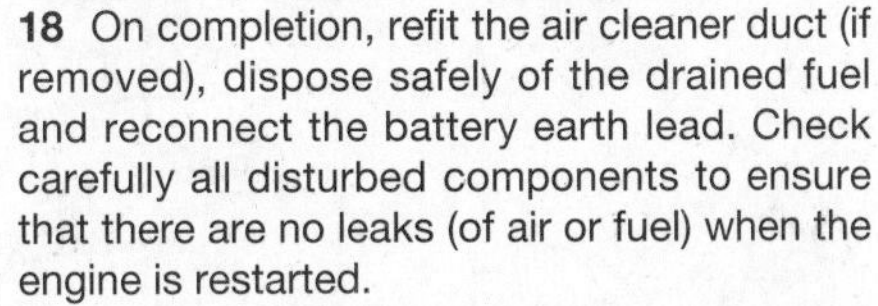

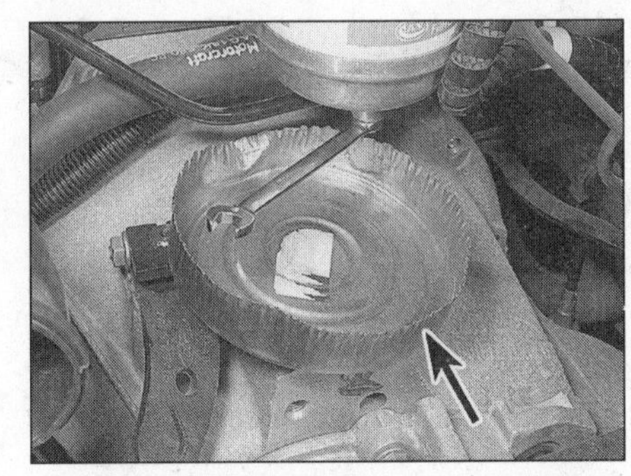

9.15 Draining water from CAV fuel filter using container (arrowed) to prevent spillage

1.8 litre engine

Bosch clamp-fixing cartridge filter

19 Proceed as described for the later type Bosch spin-on cartridge filter fitted to the 1.6 litre engine, noting that on this filter the vent screw is the single (slotted, hexagon-headed) screw on the top of the filter itself. Access to the fuel filter assembly may be much improved on Escort/Orion models if the duct from the air cleaner to the inlet manifold is first removed.

CAV RotoDiesel filter

20 This process is as described for the same filter type fitted to the 1.6 litre engine but note that on Escort/Orion models with 1.8 litre engines, access to the fuel filter assembly may be much improved if the duct from the air cleaner to the inlet manifold is first removed.

2.5 litre engine

21 Disconnect the battery negative lead.

22 Prevent damage to the starter motor from escaping fuel by covering it with a plastic bag. Also place a container beneath the filter to collect any escaping fuel.

23 Slacken the drain screw at the bottom of the filter. If fuel does not flow out, also slacken the bleed screw or the fuel inlet connection on the filter head.

24 When fuel which is free from water flows out of the drain screw, tighten the screw and, if slackened, the bleed screw or inlet connection.

25 If a hand-priming pump is fitted to the filter head, operate it until resistance is felt. If a hand-priming pump is not fitted, the fuel system will self-bleed while the engine is being started.

26 Remove any bags or containers and reconnect the battery.

27 Dispose of the drained fuel/water safely.

10 Idle speed check and adjustment - 1.6 and 1.8 litre engines

All engines

1 The usual type of tachometer (rev counter), which works from ignition system pulses, cannot be used on diesel engines. If it is not

10.4 Adjusting idle speed screw and locknut

felt that adjusting the idle speed by ear is satisfactory, one of the following alternatives must be used:

a) *Purchase or hire of an appropriate tachometer*
b) *Delegation of the job to a Ford dealer or other specialist*
c) *Timing light (strobe) operated by a petrol engine running at the desired speed. If the timing light is pointed at a chalk mark on the diesel engine crankshaft pulley, the mark will appear stationary when the two engines are running at the same speed (or multiples of that speed)*
d) *Calculating the mph/rpm relationship for a particular gear and running the engine, in that gear, with the front wheels free. The speedometer accuracy may not be adequate, especially at low speeds. Stringent safety precautions must be observed*

1.6 litre engine

Bosch injection pump

2 Warm up the engine until it is at normal operating temperature.

3 Connect the tachometer, if used, or make the necessary alternative arrangements. Start the engine and allow it to idle. Compare the idle speed with that specified.

4 If adjustment is necessary, slacken the idle speed screw locknut on the fuel injection pump **(see illustration)**. Turn the idle speed screw clockwise to increase the speed, anti-clockwise to decrease it. When the speed is correct, tighten the locknut without disturbing the position or the screw.

5 Disconnect the tachometer or other instruments, as appropriate.

CAV RotoDiesel injection pump

Note: *A special (spacer) service tool (23-016) will be required for this operation. If not available, this can be replaced by the (careful) use of spacers.*

6 Run the engine to normal operating temperature and check the idle speed.

7 If the idle speed exceeds 910 rpm, slacken the idle speed screw locknut (C) **(see illustration)** and adjust the idle speed screw until the engine idles at 880 ± 30 rpm. Tighten the locknut.

8 Insert a 2.0 mm thick spacer between the adjusting screw and the idle stop lever as shown **(see illustration)**. The idle speed should fall by approximately 100 rpm. No change in speed indicates the need for anti-stall adjustment.

9 If the engine idle speed when originally checked was less than 850 rpm, insert a 2.0 mm thick spacer between the adjusting screw and the idle stop lever. If the engine speed does not alter, carry out the anti-stall adjustment. If the speed alters when the spacer is inserted, then the idle speed should be set to specification.

1.8 litre engine - non turbocharged

Bosch injection pump

10 Refer first to paragraphs 1 to 3 of this Section. The pump adjustments should only be disturbed if the idle speed is unreliable, or significantly above or below the specified range.

11 If the idle speed recorded was incorrect, reset to 850 rpm using the idle speed adjusting screw (B) **(see illustration)**. Once the idle speed is correct, insert a spacer 0.5 mm thick between the throttle lever and the residual capacity adjusting screw (A). The idle speed should not alter. If the speed does alter, carry out the basic idle setting procedure described below. If the speed does not alter remove the spacer and replace it with one 1.0 mm thick, whereupon the speed should increase very slightly, by about 10 or 20 rpm. If the speed does increase, check the fast idle speed as described below. If it does not increase, carry out the basic idle setting procedure.

Basic idle setting procedure

12 Using the idle speed adjusting screw (B), set the idle speed to 850 rpm, release the fast idle waxstat device cable end stop and reposition it at the end of the cable so that it can have no effect. Insert a spacer 0.5 mm thick between the throttle lever and the residual capacity adjusting screw (A), then slacken its locknut and turn the screw anti-clockwise (away from the throttle lever) one full turn. Readjust the idle speed to 850 rpm using the idle speed adjusting screw. Repeat the procedure until turning the residual capacity adjusting screw has no effect on the idle speed (to ensure that the engine is not idling on the residual capacity adjusting screw).

13 Remove the 0.5 mm spacer and replace it with one 1.0 mm thick, then adjust the

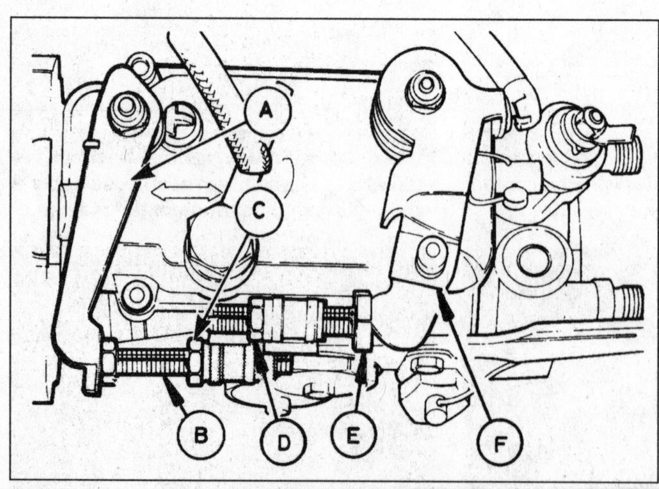

10.7 Idle speed and anti-stall adjustment - CAV fuel injection pump

A Idle speed/stop lever
B Idle speed adjusting screw
C Locknut
D Locknut
E Anti-stall adjustment screw
F Throttle lever

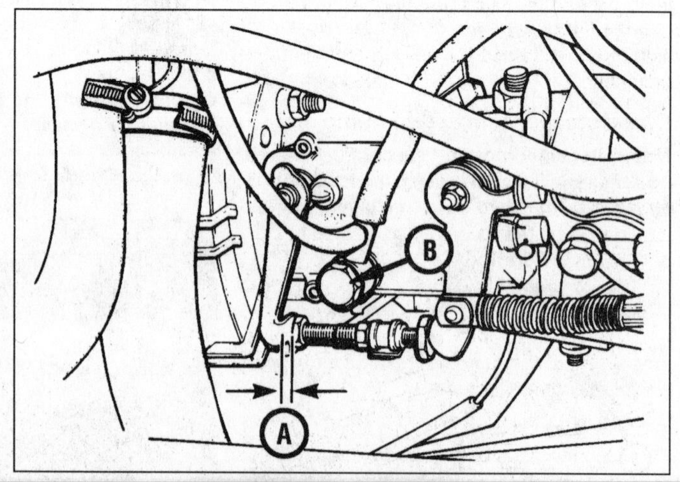

10.8 Idle speed adjustment - CAV fuel injection pump

A Insert spacer between idle speed/stop lever and idle speed adjusting screw at point indicated
B Fuel return banjo union

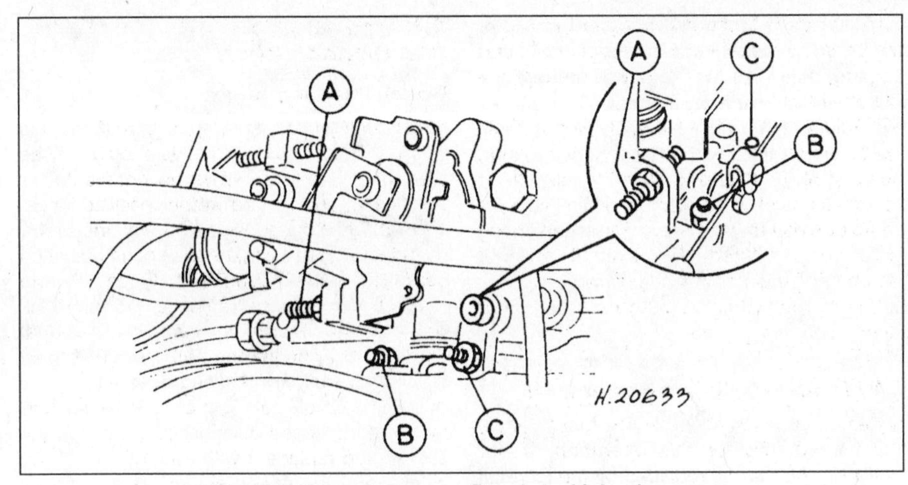

10.11 Adjustment screws - Bosch fuel injection pump

A Residual capacity (anti-stall) adjusting screw
B Idle speed adjusting screw
C Fast idle adjuster screw

residual capacity adjusting screw to give an engine speed of 860 to 870 rpm and tighten the screw's locknut. Remove the 1.0 mm spacer and note the idle speed, then replace the spacer with the 0.5 mm thick one. The idle speed should not change. If the idle speed does change, repeat the full procedure. When the basic idle setting is correct, reset the fast idle waxstat device cable and stop to give a 1.0 mm gap between the idle lever and the fast idle adjuster screw (C) when the engine is hot (waxstat in hot mode), then proceed to check the fast idle speed.

Fast idle speed check

14 To check the fast idle, ensure that the engine is thoroughly hot, then ensure that there is a gap of 1.0 mm between the idle lever and the fast idle adjuster screw (C). Adjust if necessary by repositioning the stop on the end of the fast idle waxstat device cable. With the engine idling, move the idle lever against the fast idle adjuster screw and check that speed rises to 1180 to 1200 rpm. Adjust if necessary by turning the fast idle adjuster screw.

CAV RotoDiesel injection pump

Note: *A special tool, the spacer 23-076, will be required. If not available, the tool can be replaced by the (careful) use of spacer(s).*

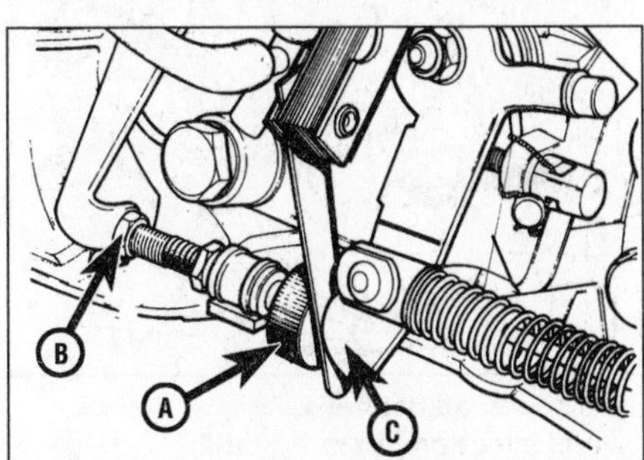

10.15 Fit spacer (A) and 1.0 mm thick feeler blade between anti-stall screw (B) and throttle lever (C)

15 Fit the special tool or alternative and a 1.0 mm thick feeler blade (to a total thickness of 4.0 mm) between the anti-stall screw and the throttle lever, as shown **(see illustration)**.

16 Using a 20.0 mm thick spacer, hold the idle speed lever (A) away from the adjusting screw, as shown in illustrations 10.7, 10.8 and 10.15.

17 Slacken the locknut (D) and turn the anti-stall adjustment screw (E) to give an engine idle speed of 900 ± 100 rpm.

18 Remove the 20.0 mm thick spacer. The idle speed stop lever must return and contact the adjuster screw (B).

10.22a Check for play in waxstat cable at pump end . . .

10.24 Insert 4.0 mm gauge between residual fuel screw and throttle lever

19 Remove the special tool and the feeler blade. Slacken the idle speed adjuster screw locknut and turn the screw to obtain an idle speed of between 840 and 870 rpm.

20 Should any problems of slow deceleration or stalling be evident, recheck the preceding adjustment. If the faults persist, then stalling may be corrected by turning the throttle lever anti-stall screw (by a maximum of a quarter of a turn) clockwise. To eliminate slow deceleration, turn the throttle lever anti-stall screw (again, by no more than a quarter turn) anti-clockwise.

1.8 litre engine - turbocharged

Note: *Pump adjustments should only be disturbed if the idle speed is unreliable, or much above or below the specified range.*

Stage 1 - Idle and residual fuel setting checks

21 Run the engine until it reaches normal operating temperature, that is until the cooling fan cuts in.

22 Check that there is 2.0 mm of play on the waxstat cable at the pump end. If necessary, use the cable adjuster to alter the amount of play **(see illustrations)**.

23 Take a note of the idle speed.

24 Insert a 4.0 mm feeler blade between the residual fuel screw and throttle lever **(see illustration)**.

25 Rotate the stop lever in a clockwise direction and insert a 3.0 mm diameter pin through the idle lever **(see illustration)**.

26 Take a note of the residual idle speed.

27 If the idle and residual speeds are correct, then check that the engine deceleration time

10.22b . . . and, if necessary, use cable adjuster to alter amount of play

10.25 Rotate stop lever in clockwise direction and insert 3.0 mm diameter pin through idle lever

from maximum no load speed to idle is no more than 5 seconds without stalling or undershoot. If an adjustment is required, proceed as follows:

Stage 2 - Idle resetting procedure

28 Insert a 4.0 mm feeler blade between the residual fuel screw and throttle lever.

29 Rotate the stop lever in a clockwise direction and insert a 3.0 mm diameter pin through the idle lever.

30 Adjust the residual fuel screw to give an engine speed of 900 ± 100 rpm.

31 Remove the feeler blade and pin.

32 Turning the idle speed adjuster screw (illustration 10.25), set the idle speed to 850 ± 50 rpm.

33 Now check that the engine deceleration time from maximum no load speed to idle is no more than 5 seconds without stalling or undershoot.

34 If the engine stalls, turn the residual fuel screw anti-clockwise (viewed from the rear of the pump) one quarter turn.

35 Recheck all operations from paragraph 28.

36 If the deceleration time exceeds 5 seconds, turn the residual fuel screw clockwise (viewed from the rear of the pump) one quarter turn.

37 Recheck all operations from paragraph 28.

11 Vacuum pump check - 1.6 and 1.8 litre engines

1 Inspect the vacuum pump for oil leaks, the security and condition of hoses and security of mountings **(see illustration)**.

11.1 Inspect vacuum pump hoses for leakage and security

2 Check the operation of the pump as follows.

3 With the engine stopped, operate the footbrake several times to destroy any residual vacuum in the servo. Keep the brake pedal depressed and start the engine. The pedal should be felt to move downwards as the vacuum pump operates on the servo. If not, there is a fault in the pump, the servo or their connecting pipe (not forgetting the non-return valve).

4 A defective vacuum pump must be renewed - no spares are available.

12 000 mile (20 000 km) Service

12 Valve clearance check - 2.5 litre engine

1 Remove the cylinder head rocker cover.

2 Remove the rubber bung from the front of the crankshaft pulley. Turn the crankshaft clockwise by using a spanner on the crankshaft pulley bolt, until the first two valves listed in the table below are fully open. In this position, check the clearance of the first two valves specified below:

Valves fully open	Valves to adjust
1 and 6	4 (In) and 7 (Ex)
2 and 3	5 (Ex) and 8 (In)
4 and 7	1 (Ex) and 6 (In)
5 and 8	2(In) and 3 (Ex)

3 Clearances for the inlet and exhaust valves differ. Use a feeler blade of the appropriate thickness to check each clearance between the end of the valve stem and the rocker arm **(see illustration)**. The blade should be a firm sliding fit. Where adjustment is necessary, turn the adjuster bolt as required with a ring spanner to set the clearance to that specified. The adjuster bolts are of stiff-thread type and require no locking nut.

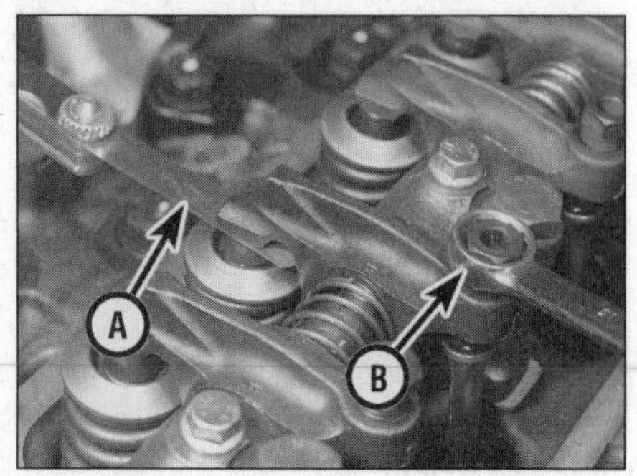

12.3 Checking/adjusting valve clearances using feeler blade (A) and ring spanner (B)

4 When the clearance is correct for the first pair of valves, rotate the crankshaft clockwise again until the next pair of valves listed are fully open. Check/adjust the second pair of valves listed, then repeat the procedure until all are done.

5 On completion, refit the rubber bung to the crankshaft pulley then refit the rocker cover.

13 Idle and anti-stall speed check and adjustment - 2.5 litre engine

Note: *On turbocharged engines with the Lucas EPIC engine management system, all injection pump parameters are controlled by the system electronic control unit and adjustments are not possible. The following adjustments are applicable to normally-aspirated engines and earlier turbocharged engines without engine management systems. Note also that in general, this is not a routine service operation and should only require attention at this service interval if the settings are believed to be incorrect.*

1 The usual type of tachometer (rev counter) which works from ignition system pulses cannot be used on Diesel engines. If it is not felt that adjusting the idle speed by ear is satisfactory, one of the following alternatives may be used:

a) *Purchase or hire an appropriate tachometer.*
b) *Delegate the job to a Ford dealer or other specialist.*
c) *Timing light (strobe) operated by a petrol engine running at the desired speed. If the timing light is pointed at a mark on the crankshaft pulley, the mark will appear stationary when the two engines are running at the same speed.*

2 Before making adjustments, warm-up the engine to its normal operating temperature. Ensure that the accelerator cable is correctly adjusted.

Idle speed

3 Ensure that, with the accelerator pedal released, the accelerator lever on the fuel injection pump is resting against its stop.

4 On engines with a fast idle thermostatic sensor, ensure that the sensor cable is correctly adjusted.

5 Allow the engine to idle and check its speed. If adjustment is necessary, turn the idle speed adjustment screw until the idle speed is correct **(see illustrations)**.

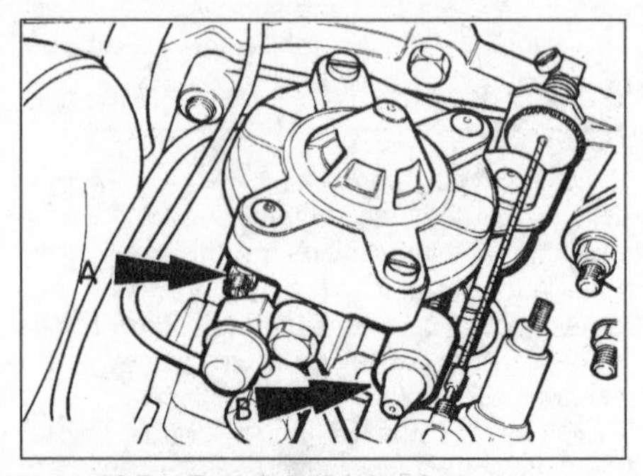

13.5a Bosch fuel injection pump adjustment points

A Idle speed adjustment screw
B Maximum speed adjustment screw (under cap)

Anti-stall speed

6 On models with a Lucas/CAV fuel injection pump, accelerate the engine and allow it to return to idle. If it shows a tendency to stall or is slow to decelerate, adjust the anti-stall setting as follows.

7 Remove the tamperproof cap or seal from the anti-stall screw. Slacken the screw locknut, give the screw a quarter-turn clockwise, then repeat the deceleration check and observe the effect.

8 Continue to adjust the anti-stall screw until deceleration and idling are satisfactory, then tighten the locknut and fit a new tamperproof seal. Note that if engine speed rises when the anti-stall screw is turned, this suggests a fault in the pump. Consult a Lucas/CAV agent or other specialist.

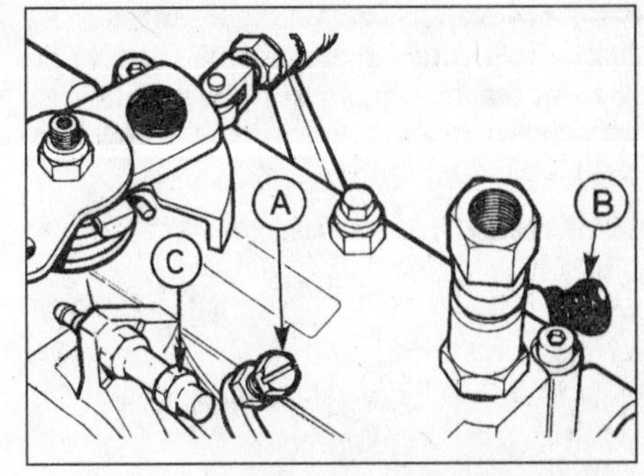

13.5b Lucas/CAV fuel injection pump adjustment points

A Idle speed adjustment screw
B Anti-stall adjustment screw (under cap)
C Maximum speed adjustment screw (under cap)

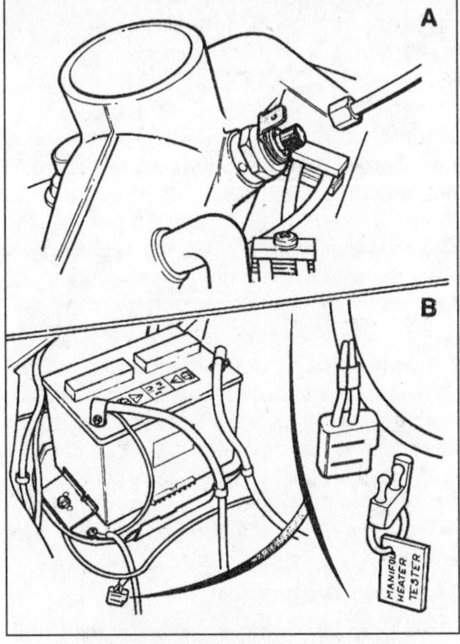

14.2 Purging preheating system flame plug fuel reservoir

A Disconnect fuel supply pipe
B Bridge test connector terminals

Annually, at the beginning of Winter

14 Pre-heating flame plug fuel reservoir purging - 2.5 litre engine

1 On engines equipped with the optional preheating system, the fuel reservoir should be purged of summer-grade fuel at the beginning of Winter. If this is not done, the fuel in the reservoir may suffer from waxing when cold weather begins.

2 Disconnect the fuel supply pipe from the flame plug and place the end of the pipe in a suitable container **(see illustration)**.

3 Locate the preheating system test connector below the battery tray. Bridge the connector terminals using an insulated wire link with two male connectors.

4 Switch the ignition on for 25 seconds. The preheating warning light will come on for 5 seconds then go out. Switch off the ignition momentarily, then switch on again for a further 25 seconds. Switch off again.

5 Dispose of the fuel which has flowed into the container. Reconnect the fuel supply pipe and remove the test connector bridging wire.

18 000 mile (30 000 km) Service

15 Fuel filter element renewal - 1.8 litre engine

Bosch clamp-fixing cartridge filter

1 Drain the filter completely.

2 Note carefully the orientation of the fuel inlet and outlet hoses and the filter vent screw **(see illustration)**. Clean them thoroughly and obtain new hose clamps and/or flexible hoses if the condition of those fitted is in any way suspect.

3 Releasing the clamps with pliers, disconnect the fuel inlet and outlet hoses from the filter stubs. Plug or cap hoses and unions to keep fuel in and dirt out.

4 Slacken the clamp screw and withdraw the filter from its bracket, taking care to spill as little as possible of any remaining fuel.

5 Fit the new filter to the clamp, aligning its stubs with the hoses as noted on removal and observing any directional markings on the filter. Fit the new flexible hoses and/or clamps (if required), then connect the hoses to the filter and fasten them securely with the clamps.

6 Tighten the filter mounting clamp screw, but be careful not to overtighten it (nominal torque wrench setting of 1.5 to 2.5 Nm/ 1 to 2 lbf ft only), or the filter may be crushed. Check that the drain cock is closed.

7 Reconnect the battery earth lead and restart the engine. Considerable cranking may be required to bleed the air from the system. To spare the battery, this time may be reduced by filling the filter with clean fuel via its vent screw opening but it is essential that no dirt is introduced into the system and that no diesel fuel is poured over vulnerable components when doing this.

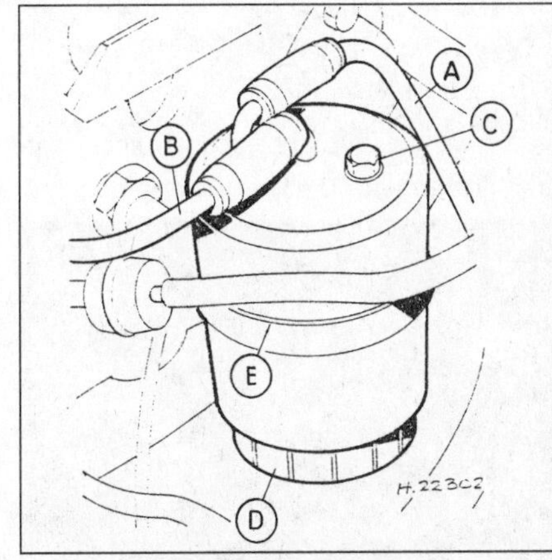

15.2 Bosch clamp-fixing cartridge filter

A Fuel inlet hose
B Fuel outlet hose
C Vent screw
D Drain cock
E Clamp

8 On completion, dispose safely of the old filter and the drained fuel. Check carefully all disturbed components to ensure that there are no leaks (or air or fuel) when the engine is restarted.

CAV RotoDiesel filter

9 Drain the filter completely.

10 Support the filter bowl and unscrew the through-bolt from the filter head **(see illustration)**. Withdraw the filter bowl and the element, taking care to spill as little as possible of any remaining fuel.

11 Using a small mirror and a torch if necessary, check that all seals are removed from above and below the filter element, from the through-bolt and from (the underside of) the filter head. Precise details of seal type and location will vary according to engine and model, as well as depending on the make of filter element used, but all these seals must be renewed as a matter of course before the filter is reassembled; usually they will be supplied with the new element.

15.10 CAV filter through-bolt (arrowed)

12 Wipe clean the filter head and bowl. Check that the drain cock in the filter bowl is clean, that its seals are in good condition and correctly located, then tighten it securely closed.

13 Ensuring that all seals are renewed, fitted as noted on removal and are correctly located, refit the element to the filter head, followed by the filter bowl, then ensure that the seals above and below the element are not distorted or dislodged as the through-bolt is refitted and tightened securely.

14 Reconnect the battery earth lead, bleed the system, then restart the engine.

15 On completion, dispose safely of the old filter and the drained fuel. Check carefully all disturbed components to ensure that there are no leaks (of air or fuel) when the engine is restarted.

24 000 mile (40 000 km) Service

16 Fuel filter element renewal - 1.6 and 2.5 litre engines

1.6 litre engine

Early type Bosch filter (separate element)

1 Drain the filter completely. Clean around the sealing area between the filter head and body.

2 Unscrew and remove the filter body. Use a chain or strap wrench if it is tight **(see illustration)**. Remove and discard the element and seal **(see illustration)**.

3 Using a clean, non-fluffy rag, wipe clean the filter head and body. Fit the new element into the filter body and apply clean fuel to the new sealing ring. Screw the filter body into position, tightening it by hand only. Make sure that the drain cock is closed.

4 Reconnect the battery and start the engine. Considerable cranking may be necessary to purge the air from the system. The filter can be filled with clean fuel via the vent plug on its head if wished, but it is extremely important that no dirt be introduced.

16.2a Using chain wrench to unscrew Bosch fuel filter element

5 Check for leaks from the filter seal, tightening further if necessary. Stop the engine and remove the clutch housing protection material.

Later type Bosch filter (spin-on cartridge)

6 Drain the filter completely. Using a chain or strap wrench, unscrew the filter cartridge from the filter head and remove it, taking care to spill as little as possible of any remaining fuel.

7 Check that both seals on the top of the new filter cartridge are correctly located in the groove and retainer provided (as applicable) and ensure that its drain cock is closed. Smear the seals with clean fuel and screw on the new cartridge, tightening it by hand only, or as directed by the manufacturer.

8 Reconnect the battery earth lead and restart the engine. Considerable cranking may be required to bleed the air from the system. To spare the battery, this time may be reduced by filling the filter with clean fuel via the vent screw opening on the filter head but it is essential that no dirt is introduced into the system and that no diesel fuel is poured over vulnerable components when doing this.

9 On completion, dispose safely of the old filter and the drained fuel. Check carefully all disturbed components to ensure that there are no leaks (of air or fuel) when the engine is restarted.

CAV RotoDiesel filter

10 Refer to the procedure given for the same type of filter fitted to the 1.8 litre engine.

2.5 litre engine

11 Drain the fuel filter.

12 Slacken the wing nut on the filter securing clamp as far as possible, then remove the old filter **(see illustrations)**. Make sure that the old seal comes away with the filter.

13 If the original filter contains a water-in-fuel sensor, this should be transferred to the new filter prior to fitting **(see illustration)**.

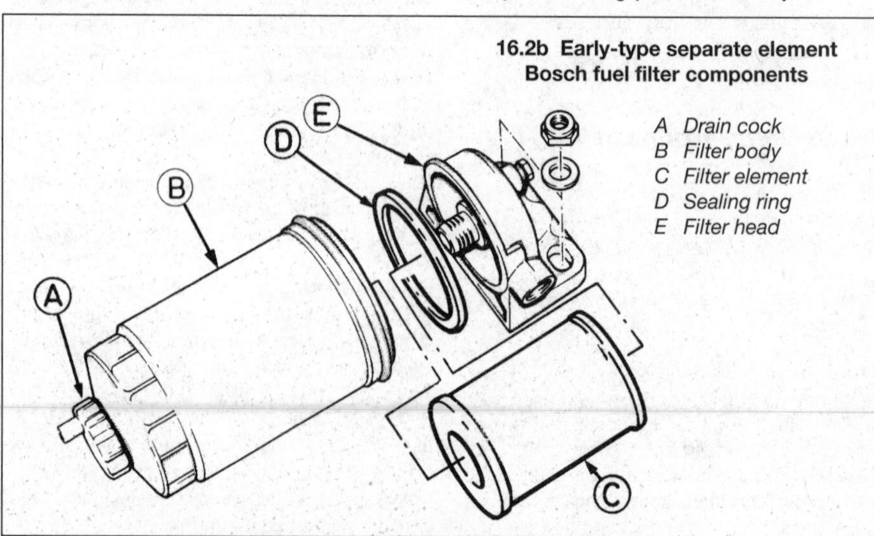

16.2b Early-type separate element Bosch fuel filter components

16.12a Slacken wing nut on fuel filter securing clamp (arrowed) . . .

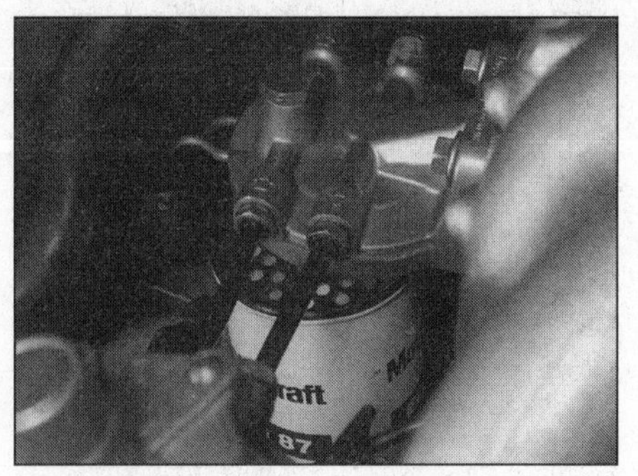
16.12b . . . then remove fuel filter

16.13 Fuel filter water-in-fuel sensor components

14 Smear a little clean fuel onto the sealing ring of the new filter. Insert the filter into the filter head, using a pushing and twisting action to seat it.

15 Tighten the securing clamp wing nut, holding the filter in place until it is gripped. Do not overtighten the wing nut, or the filter may be distorted and will leak.

16 If a hand-priming pump is fitted to the filter head, operate it until resistance is felt. When no priming pump is fitted, prime the system by cranking the engine in ten-second bursts until it starts.

17 Run the engine and check that there are no leaks around the filter.

17 Valve clearance check - 1.6 litre engine

1 Release the breather hoses and remove the camshaft cover. It is secured by 10 bolts. Recover the washers and the reinforcing strips, noting their locations. Remove the gasket, sealing strip and plug. Obtain new ones for reassembly if necessary.

2 Turn the engine in the normal direction of rotation until two cam lobes for any one cylinder are pointing upwards (relative to the engine) at the same angle. It is permissible to "bounce" the engine round on the starter motor for this procedure, but disconnect the fuel shut-off solenoid first.

3 Measure the clearance between the bases of the two cam lobes and the underlying shims using feeler blades **(see illustration)**. Record the thickness of blade(s) required to give a firm sliding fit. The desired clearances are given in Specifications. Note that the clearances for inlet and exhaust valves are different. From the pulley end of the engine, the valve sequence is:

I-E-I-E-I-E-I-E

4 If adjustment is required, proceed as follows:

5 Turn the engine in the normal direction of rotation through approximately 90°, to bring the pistons to mid-stroke. If this is not done, the pistons at TDC will prevent the tappets being depressed and damage may result. Depress the tappets and then either shim can be withdrawn, providing that the peak of the cam does not prevent access. The Ford tools for this operation are Nos 21-106 and 21-107, but with care and patience, we found that a C-spanner or screwdriver can be used to depress the tappet and the shim can be flicked out with a small screwdriver **(see illustration)**.

6 If the valve clearance was too small, a thinner shim must be fitted. If the clearance was too large, a thicker shim must be fitted. The thickness of the shim (in mm) is engraved on the side facing away from the camshaft **(see illustration)**. If the marking is missing or illegible, a micrometer will be needed to establish shim thickness.

7 When the shim thickness and the valve clearance are known, the required thickness of the new shim can be calculated as follows:

Sample calculation - clearance too small
Desired clearance (A) = 0.50 mm
Measured clearance (B) = 0.35 mm
Shim thickness found (C) = 3.95 mm
Shim thickness req'd (D) = C + B - A = 3.80 mm

Sample calculation - clearance too large
Desired clearance (A) = 0.30 mm
Measured clearance (B) = 0.40 mm
Shim thickness found (C) = 4.05 mm
Shim thickness req'd (D) = C + B - A = 4.15 mm

8 With the correct shim fitted, release the tappet depressing tool. Turn the engine back so that the cam lobes are again pointing upwards and check that the clearance is now correct.

9 Repeat the process for the remaining valves, turning the engine each time to bring a pair of cam lobes upwards.

10 It will be helpful for future adjustment if a record is kept of the thickness of shim fitted at each position. The shims required can be purchased in advance once the clearances and the existing shim thicknesses are known.

11 It is permissible to interchange shims between tappets to achieve the correct clearances but it is not advisable to turn the camshaft with any shims removed, since there is a risk that the cam lobe will jam in the empty tappet.

12 When all the clearances are correct, refit the camshaft cover, using a new gasket etc. if necessary. Fit the bolts with washers and reinforcing strips. Tighten the bolts progressively to the specified torque.

13 Secure the breather hoses.

14 If it was disconnected, reconnect the fuel shut-off solenoid.

17.3 Measuring a valve clearance

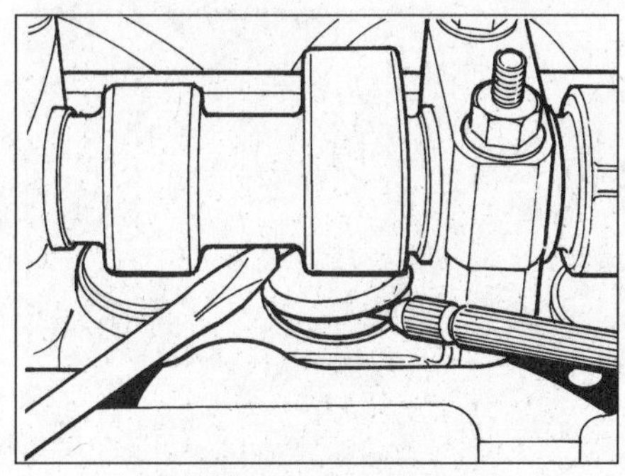
17.5 Depressing a tappet and removing a shim

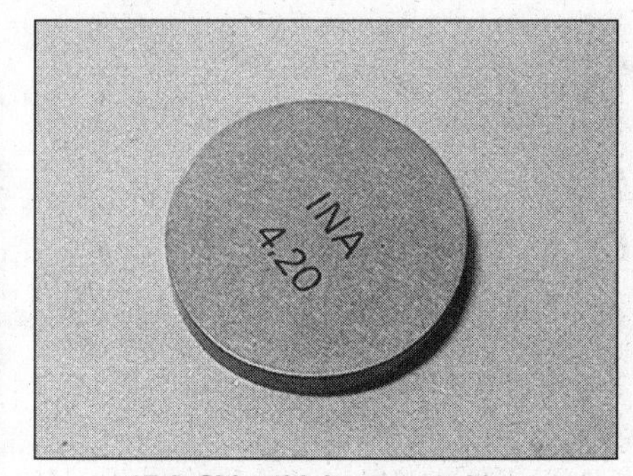

17.6 Shim thickness marking

36 000 mile (60 000 km) Service

18 Camshaft and injection pump drivebelt renewal - 1.8 litre engine

Removal

1 Begin by carrying out the following preliminary dismantling procedures:

a) *Jack up the front right-hand side of the vehicle and support it on axle stands.*
b) *Disconnect the battery earth (negative) lead.*
c) *Detaching the shield(s) and/or cover(s) as necessary **(see illustration)**, remove the alternator/coolant pump drivebelt.*
d) *On Fiesta models (Escort/Orion as well depending on the task to be carried out and the tools available) the front right-hand roadwheel and the wheel arch liner should also be removed.*
e) *With the engine still in the vehicle, it will probably be necessary to remove the alternator and, if fitted, the power-assisted steering pump to reach the TDC pin hole plug and to insert a timing pin.*
f) *Improved access may be gained by unbolting the coolant expansion tank and, if fitted, the power-assisted steering fluid reservoir on Escort/Orion models so that these can be moved aside (without disconnecting them) as required. On Fiesta models the air cleaner assembly must be removed.*
g) *Where applicable, slacken the engine lifting eye retaining nut(s) or bolt(s) and swing it clear of the drivebelt cover. Where a throttle damper is fitted which will prevent the removal of the cover, this must first be removed.*

2 Working under the vehicle, first unscrew the front (vertical) retaining bolt and the rear (horizontal) pivot bolt, then carefully withdraw the drivebelt lower cover from the crankshaft pulley/vibration damper **(see illustrations)**.

3 If not already removed, detach the plastic fuel deflector from the alternator mounting bracket **(see illustration)**.

4 Returning to the engine compartment, release the three camshaft drivebelt cover retaining clips and unscrew the single (central) 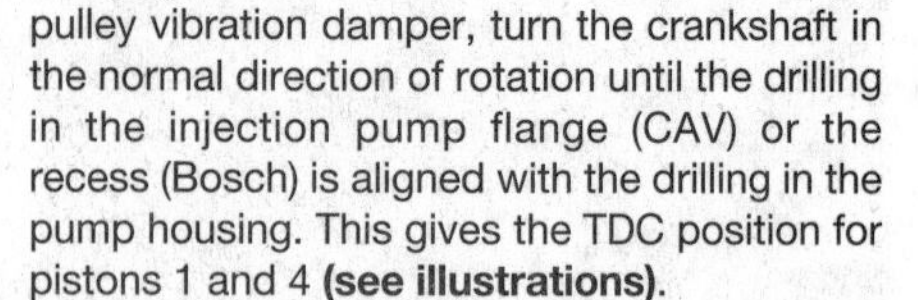retaining bolt, then manoeuvre the cover upwards and withdraw it **(see illustrations)**.

5 Using the bolt in the centre of the crankshaft pulley vibration damper, turn the crankshaft in the normal direction of rotation until the drilling in the injection pump flange (CAV) or the recess (Bosch) is aligned with the drilling in the pump housing. This gives the TDC position for pistons 1 and 4 **(see illustrations)**.

6 Release the belt tensioner and then remove the camshaft drivebelt. If the injection pump drivebelt is to be renewed, then its tensioner should be removed and the belt withdrawn.

7 Align the camshaft sprocket and the injection pump sprocket, so that the drillings and the recess in the sprockets are aligned with the drillings in the cylinder head and the pump housing.

18.1 Detaching alternator/coolant pump drivebelt cover

18.2a Remove drivebelt lower cover retaining screw . . .

18.2b . . . and swivel cover downwards

18.3 Detach plastic fuel deflector from alternator mounting bracket

18.4a Release three camshaft drivebelt cover retaining clips . . .

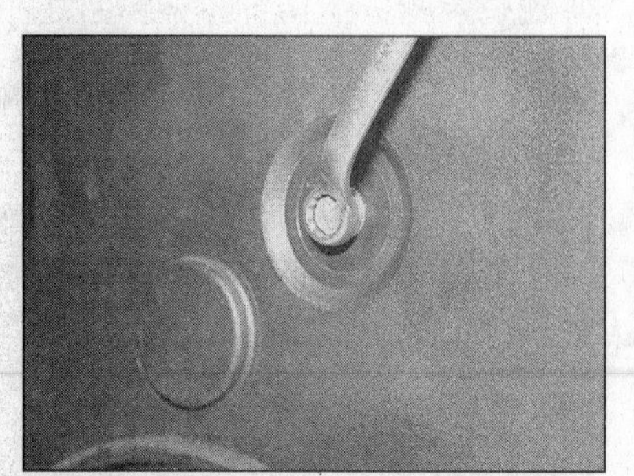

18.4b . . . and unscrew single (central) cover retaining bolt

18.4c Manoeuvre cover upwards and withdraw it . . .

18.4d . . . to provide access to drivebelt

18.5a Toothed belt and sprocket identification

1 *Camshaft sprocket*
2 *Idler sprocket*
3 *Fuel pump sprocket*
4 *Fuel pump belt tensioner*
5 *Crankshaft pulley vibration damper*
6 *Auxiliary shaft sprocket*
7 *Coolant pump sprocket*
8 *Camshaft belt tensioner*

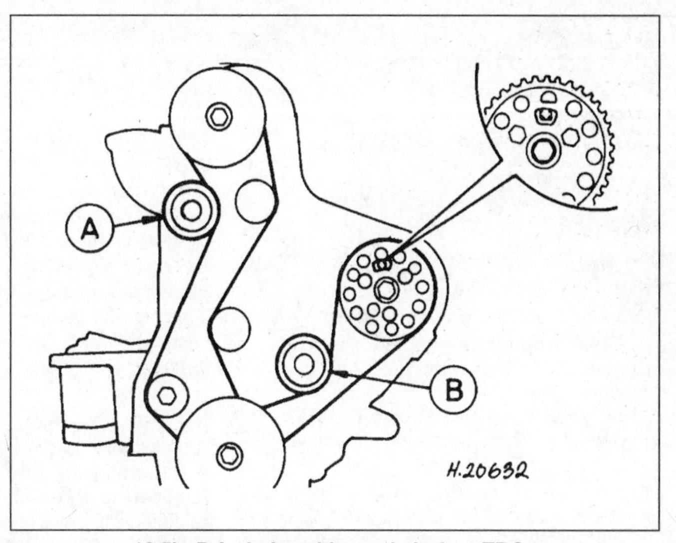

18.5b Drivebelts with crankshaft at TDC - Nos 1 and 4 pistons

A *Camshaft drivebelt tensioner*
B *Fuel injection pump drivebelt tensioner*

8 A special pin will now be required to time the camshaft sprocket and the injection pump sprocket. If a CAV pump is fitted, then pins number 23-019 will time both sprockets, but if a Bosch pump is fitted, pin number 23-029 will be required for the pump sprocket, and one pin 23-019 for the camshaft sprocket.

9 Twist drills will serve as substitute pins, but they must be in unworn condition and be long enough to enter the holes in the pump or cylinder head. A drill of 9.5 mm diameter will be required for the Bosch type pump, plus one of 6.0 mm diameter for the camshaft sprocket.

10 Two drills of 6.0 mm diameter will be required for the CAV type pump (one for the camshaft sprocket and one for the pump).

11 Insert the appropriate timing pins **(see illustrations)**.

12 Remove the plug and screw in the TDC setting pin. Make sure that the crankshaft is in contact with the timing pin **(see illustrations)**.

18.11a Fuel pump sprocket timing pin

18.11b Camshaft sprocket timing pin

18.12a TDC pin hole plug

18.12b Screwing in TDC setting pin

Fitting and tensioning

13 Fit the new injection pump drivebelt so that it is taut between the crankshaft and pump sprockets. Ensure the directional arrows are pointing the correct way.

14 Slacken the injection pump sprocket bolts half a turn. Also slacken the belt tensioner bolts half a turn. Allow the belt tensioner to snap against the belt. Retighten all the slackened bolts but make sure that the bolts are not at the ends of their slots, otherwise any further adjustment would be impossible.

15 Fit the new camshaft drivebelt with the directional arrows correct for normal crankshaft rotational directional. The belt should be slack on the tensioner side and taut between sprockets.

16 Slacken the camshaft sprocket bolts and the tensioner bolts half a turn. Allow the tensioner to snap against the belt.

17 Retighten all slackened bolts. Remove all the timing pins and turn the crankshaft through two revolutions in the normal direction of rotation until the slot in the injection pump sprocket is at the highest point (12 o'clock).

18 Now turn the crankshaft anti-clockwise until the slot in the injection pump sprocket is at the 11 o'clock position.

19 Screw in the TDC setting pin.

20 Slowly turn the crankshaft clockwise until the crankshaft contacts the timing pin.

21 Insert the timing pins in the camshaft and the injection pump sprockets.

22 Slacken the bolts (through half a turn) that secure the camshaft and injection pump sprockets and the belt tensioners.

23 Depress both drivebelts on the taut side opposite to the tensioners and then release them.

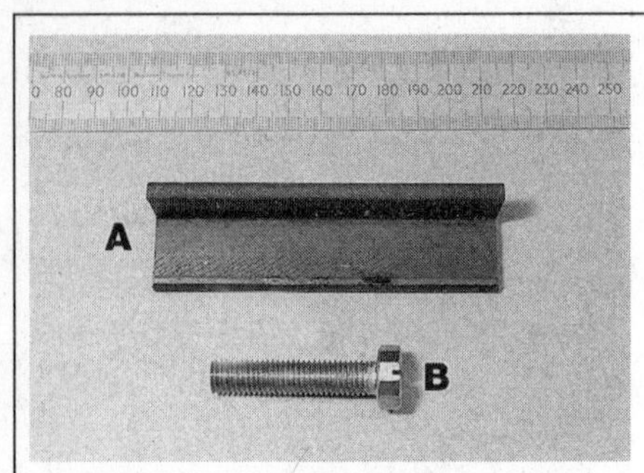

19.0 Home-made tools for setting valve timing

A Camshaft setting tool - Fabricated from angle iron - Dimensions 25 x 25 x 100 mm approx. and 5.0 mm thick.
B TDC setting pin - Fabricated from M10 bolt, ground to 47.5 mm length from underside of bolt head to tip.

Note that an ordinary bolt cannot be inserted without first removing alternator bracket, as there is insufficient clearance for bolt head. Therefore bolt head must be ground down and a screw slot cut in it. If difficulty is experienced in using bolt, it is necessary to grind down first 36 mm of threaded end of bolt to 6.0 mm diameter.

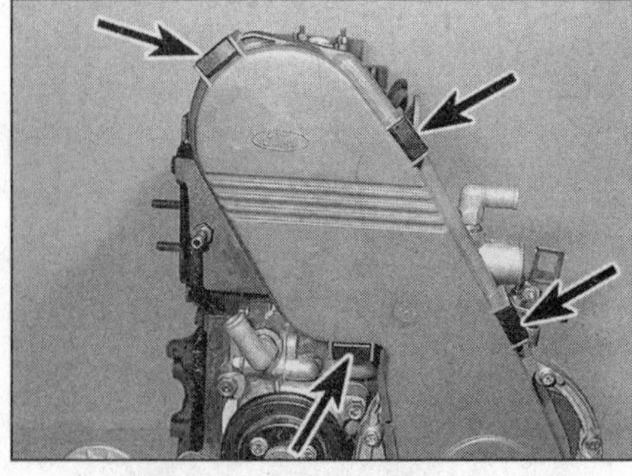

19.3 Unclip camshaft drivebelt cover (clips arrowed)

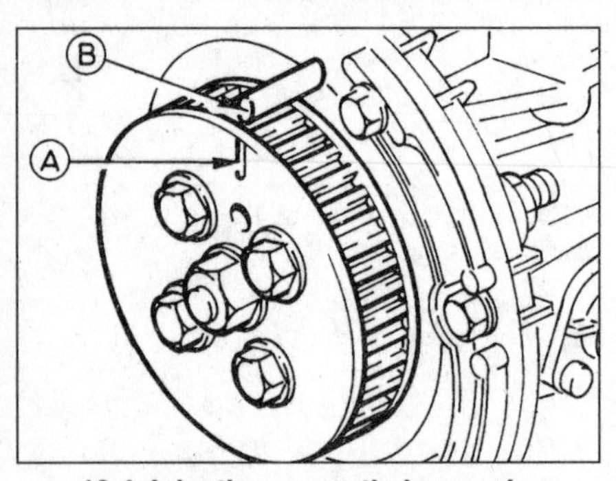

19.4 Injection pump timing marks
A Sprocket mark B Timing cover mark

19.5a Remove plug from crankcase . . .

19.5b . . . and insert TDC setting pin (arrowed)

24 Retighten all slackened bolts.
25 Remove all timing pins and screw in the TDC pin hole plug.
26 Refit the belt covers.
27 Refit and tension the alternator drivebelt, then refit all components removed for better access.
28 Reconnect the battery.

19 Camshaft drivebelt renewal - 1.6 litre engine

Note: *Two special tools will have to be bought or made for this operation. They are needed to position the crankshaft and camshaft accurately at TDC, No. 1 cylinder firing* ***(see illustration)****.*

Removal

1 Disconnect the battery earth (negative) lead.
2 Release the breather hoses and remove the camshaft cover. It is secured by ten bolts. Recover the washers and reinforcing strips, noting their location. Remove the gasket, sealing strip and plug, obtaining new ones for reassembly if necessary.
3 Unclip and remove the camshaft drivebelt cover **(see illustration)**.
4 Turn the engine in the normal direction of rotation until the timing mark on the injection pump sprocket is aligned with the mark on the timing cover **(see illustration)**.
5 Remove the plug from the crankcase and insert the TDC setting pin **(see illustrations)**. Carefully turn the engine further until the crankshaft web contacts the pin.
6 Insert the camshaft setting tool so that it is a snug fit in the camshaft tail **(see illustration)**.
7 Counterhold the camshaft sprocket and slacken its bolt.
8 Slacken the drivebelt tensioner pivot bolt. This bolt is of the Torx type, so the appropriate key will be needed to deal with it. Access is restricted with the engine installed; the key must be of the angled type.
9 Mark the running direction of the drivebelt if it is to be re-used. Slip the belt off the sprockets and remove it.
10 Do not rotate the camshaft or crankshaft with the belt removed. Piston/valve contact may occur.
11 Ensure that the camshaft sprocket is free to turn. Break the taper if necessary by tapping the sprocket with a wooden or plastic mallet.

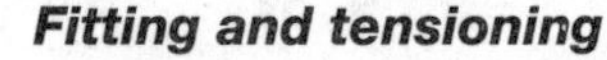

Fitting and tensioning

12 Place the new belt over the sprockets, observing its running direction **(see illustration)**. Tension the belt initially by levering the tensioner anti-clockwise and

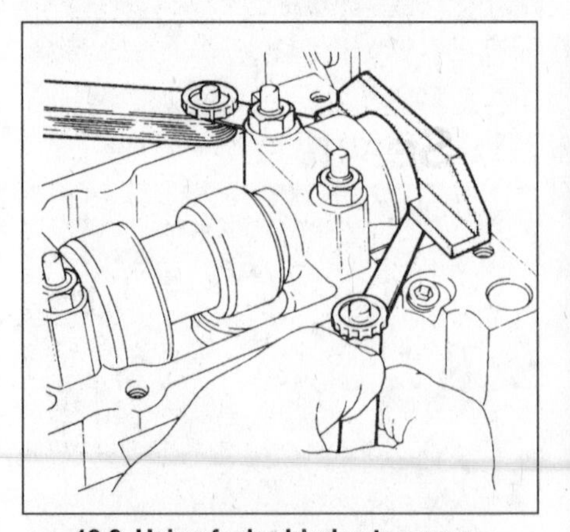

19.6 Using feeler blades to ensure camshaft setting tool is snug fit in camshaft

19.12a Commence drivebelt fitting by placing belt over sprockets

19.12b Tension belt initially by levering tensioner anti-clockwise and nipping up pivot bolt

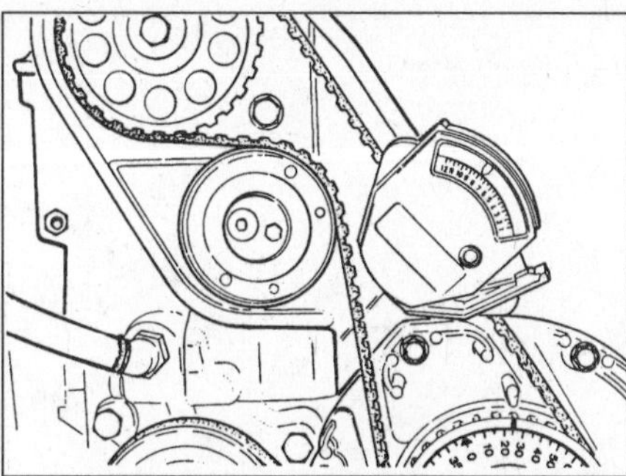

19.13 Fit belt tension gauge to longest run of drivebelt

nipping up the pivot bolt **(see illustration)**. An Allen key will be required to lever the tensioner.

13 Fit the belt tension gauge (tool No. 21 - 113) to the longest run of the belt **(see illustration)** following the instructions supplied with the gauge. Read the belt tension and compare it with the specified value. Adjust if necessary by slackening the tensioner pivot bolt, moving the tensioner and retightening the bolt. Note that the camshaft sprocket must be free on its taper during tensioner movement.

14 In the absence of the proper belt tension gauge, correct tension can be estimated by attempting to twist the belt, with finger and thumb, in the middle of its longest run. A correctly tensioned belt should not be capable of being twisted more than 90° by anyone of average strength. A belt which is too tight will hum or honk in use and a slack belt may wear rapidly or even jump sprocket

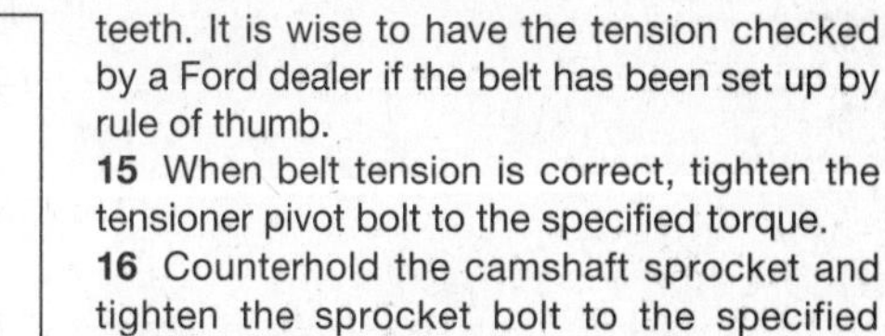

teeth. It is wise to have the tension checked by a Ford dealer if the belt has been set up by rule of thumb.

15 When belt tension is correct, tighten the tensioner pivot bolt to the specified torque.

16 Counterhold the camshaft sprocket and tighten the sprocket bolt to the specified torque.

17 Remove the camshaft setting tool and the TDC setting pin. Refit the setting hole plug and tighten it to the specified torque. Refit the camshaft drivebelt cover.

18 Refit the camshaft cover, if necessary using a new gasket, sealing strip and plug **(see illustrations)**. Secure with the bolts, washers and reinforcing strips **(see illustrations)**. Tighten the bolts to the specified torque.

19 Refit the breather hoses.

20 Reconnect the battery earth lead.

19.18a Camshaft cover sealing strip (arrowed)

19.18b Camshaft cover sealing plug

19.18c Reinforcing strip (arrowed) - pulley end, rear side

19.18d Reinforcing strip (arrowed) - pulley end, front side

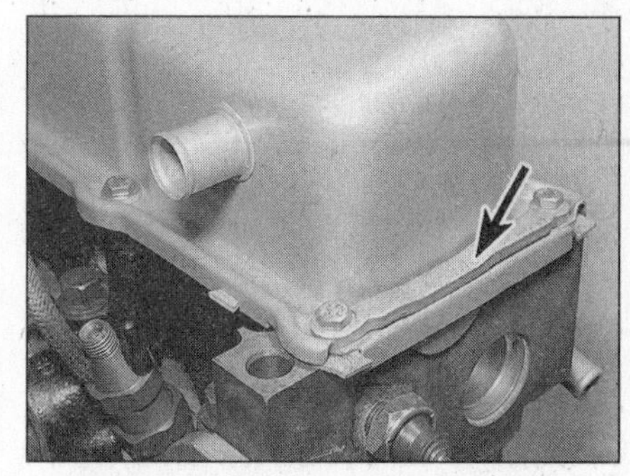

19.18e Reinforcing strip (arrowed) - flywheel end. This one is marked TOP

48 000 mile (80 000 km) Service

20 Valve clearance check - 1.8 litre engine

1 Refer to Section 17 (valve clearance check for the 1.6 litre engine) whilst noting the following points:

a) The camshaft cover is secured by three bolts on all engines.

b) When the camshaft cover is removed to reveal an oil baffle (later non turbo and turbocharged engines) ***(see illustration)****, unscrew the retaining nuts and withdraw the baffle, then refit the nuts (which also secure the camshaft bearing caps), tightening them to the specified torque.*

c) Check the valve clearances, noting the clearances specified.

d) Unscrew the retaining nuts, refit the baffle, then tighten all ten camshaft bearing cap nuts to the specified torque wrench setting and refit the camshaft cover.

2 If adjustment is required, refer to Section 17 whilst keeping in mind the aforementioned points.

20.1 Camshaft oil baffle (arrowed) fitted to later engines

21 Camshaft drivebelt renewal - 2.5 litre engine

Note: *It is a wise precaution to check the coolant pump for signs of leakage when renewing the camshaft drivebelt. This may avoid the need to remove the belt again at a later stage should the pump fail.*

Removal

1 Disconnect the battery negative lead.

2 Remove the radiator and the viscous cooling fan clutch.

3 Remove the alternator/coolant pump drivebelt.

4 Undo the four bolts each and remove the coolant pump pulley and fan pulley.

5 Undo the seven Torx bolts securing the timing belt cover to the engine **(see illustration)**. To facilitate removal of the cover over the crankshaft pulley, slacken the two small bolts just above the crankshaft pulley and push the splash guard upwards to the extent of the elongated bolt slots **(see illustration)**.

6 Pivot the lower portion of the timing belt cover downwards, then manipulate the cover around the crankshaft pulley and off the engine **(see illustrations)**.

7 Set No 1 piston to TDC then lock the crankshaft, camshaft and injection pump sprockets in position. To carry out this procedure, two drill bits, dowel rods or proprietary timing pins of appropriate diameters will be needed. Locking pins are available as Ford special tools or as complete kits from Diesel injection equipment specialists. The pin tool numbers and their diameters are as follows:

Crankshaft - *Ford tool No. 23-020 - 13.0 mm*
Camshaft - *Ford tool No. 21-123 - 8.0 mm*
Injection pump:
Lucas/CAV and early Bosch -
Ford tool No. 23-019 - 6.0 mm
Bosch with Stanadyne injectors (1989 model year on) -
Ford tool No. 23-029 - 9.0 mm

8 Remove the large rubber bung from the front of the crankshaft pulley.

9 Remove the plastic plug from the

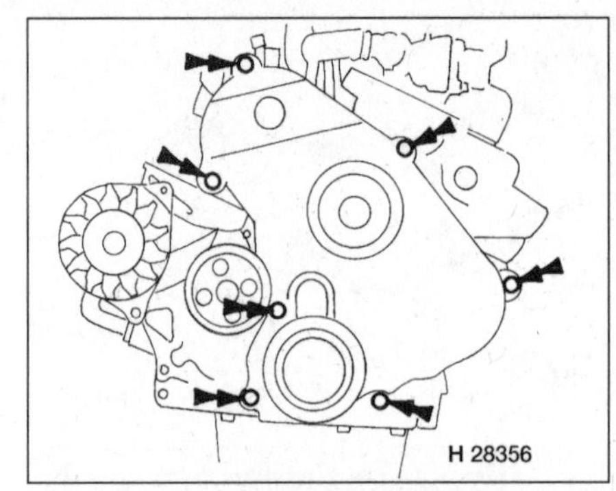

21.5a Undo timing belt cover securing bolts (arrowed) . . .

21.5b . . . slacken two small bolts just above crankshaft pulley (arrowed) and push splash guard upwards

21.6a Pivot lower portion of timing belt cover downwards . . .

21.6b . . . and manipulate cover around crankshaft pulley

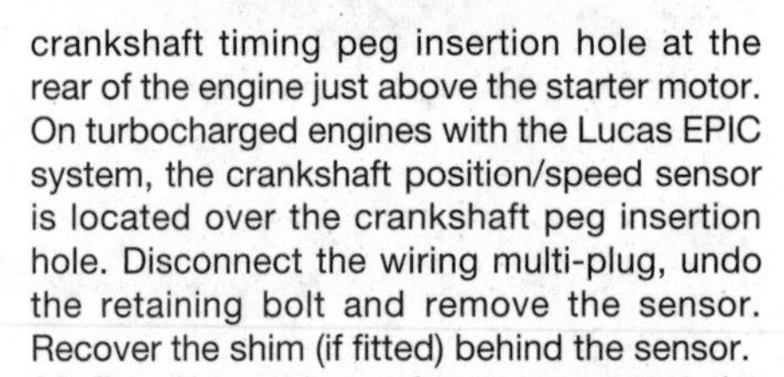

crankshaft timing peg insertion hole at the rear of the engine just above the starter motor. On turbocharged engines with the Lucas EPIC system, the crankshaft position/speed sensor is located over the crankshaft peg insertion hole. Disconnect the wiring multi-plug, undo the retaining bolt and remove the sensor. Recover the shim (if fitted) behind the sensor.

10 Turn the engine, using a spanner on the crankshaft pulley bolt, until the U-shaped cut-out in the injection pump sprocket is located just before the 12 o'clock position.

11 Insert the crankshaft timing peg into its hole, apply gentle pressure to the peg and slowly turn the engine back and forth slightly until the peg engages with the hole in the flywheel **(see illustration)**.

12 Fit the injection pump timing peg through the U-shaped cut-out and into the drilling behind it **(see illustration)**.

13 Using the camshaft timing peg, lock the camshaft sprocket by inserting the peg through the hole in the sprocket and into the drilling behind it

14 The crankshaft, camshaft and injection pump are now locked in position, with No 1 piston at TDC.

15 If the engine is to be left in this state for a long period of time, it is a good idea to place suitable warning notices inside the vehicle and engine compartment. This will reduce the possibility of the engine being accidentally cranked on the starter motor, which is likely to cause damage with the locking tools in place.

16 Slacken the belt tensioner roller and sliding arm retaining bolts, then push the tensioner back (using a lever if necessary) to release the tension on the belt **(see illustration)**. Hold the tensioner in this position and retighten the retaining bolts.

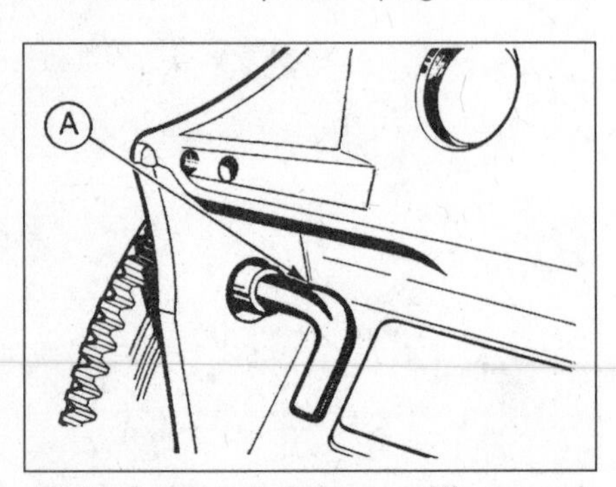

21.11 Crankshaft timing peg (A) engaged with hole in cylinder block and flywheel

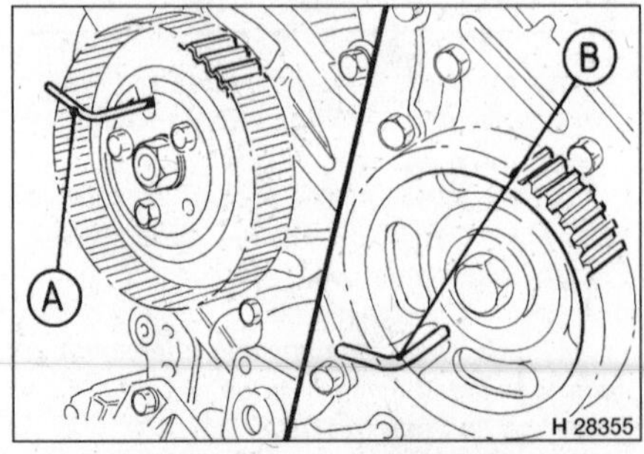

21.12 Injection pump sprocket timing peg (A) and camshaft sprocket timing peg (B) engaged with respective locating holes

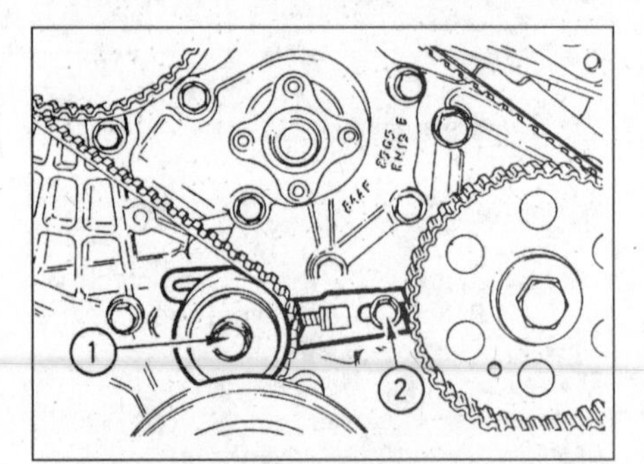

21.16 Timing belt tensioner roller retaining bolt (1) and sliding arm retaining bolt (2)

21.17 Removing timing belt from sprockets

17 Remove the belt from the sprockets **(see illustration)**.

18 If the belt is contaminated with oil, fuel or coolant, rectify the cause of the leak.

19 Ensure that the correct type of new belt is obtained, according to vehicle model year. Pre 1992 model year vehicles use a belt with a 2.5 mm tooth depth. From 1992 on, the tooth depth was increased to 3.5 mm **(see illustration)**.

Fitting and tensioning

20 Ensure that No 1 piston is still at TDC and the timing pegs still inserted.

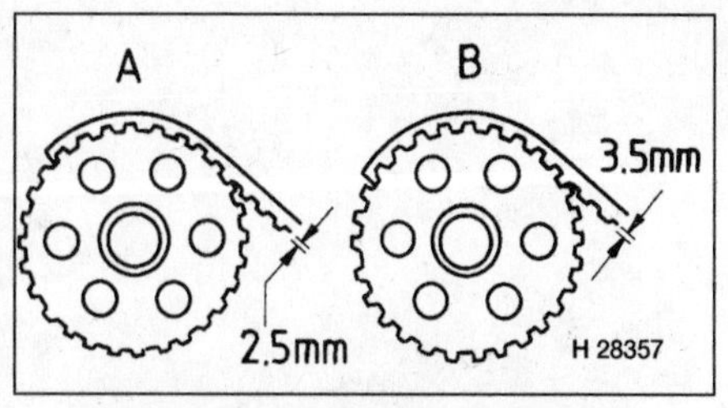

21.19 Timing belt tooth details
A Pre 1992 engines B Post 1992 engines

21 Slacken the four injection pump sprocket retaining bolts and turn the sprocket so that the bolts are in the centre of their elongated slots.

22 Locate the new belt over the crankshaft sprocket, making sure that the direction-of-rotation arrow is facing the correct way.

23 Hold the belt in place on the crankshaft sprocket, then feed it over the camshaft sprocket and injection pump sprocket, keeping it taut. If necessary, turn the injection pump sprocket, within the limits of the bolt holes, to aid fitting.

24 Pull the belt down and around the tensioner, then slacken the tensioner retaining bolts and allow the tensioner to spring back. Tighten the bolts again securely.

25 Tighten the injection pump sprocket retaining bolts to the specified torque.

26 Remove all timing pegs and rotate the crankshaft by 1-and-7/8 turns in a clockwise direction.

27 Slacken the two timing belt tensioner retaining bolts once more, then press down firmly on the timing belt in the centre of its longest run to actuate the tensioner. Retighten the tensioner bolts to the specified torque.

28 Turn the crankshaft 1/8 of a turn clockwise until the crankshaft timing peg can again be inserted.

29 Check that the injection pump timing peg can be inserted. If not, slacken the injection pump sprocket retaining bolts and tap the bolts one way or the other slightly until the timing peg goes in. Now tighten the bolts to the specified torque.

30 Remove all timing pegs and refit the plastic plug in the crankshaft peg hole. On engines with a crankshaft position sensor, refit the sensor and spacing shim, if fitted.

31 Locate the timing belt cover in position and refit the seven retaining bolts, tightened to the specified torque.

32 Slide the splash guard down to its original position and tighten the two small bolts.

33 Refit the coolant pump and fan pulleys, then tighten the bolts to the specified torque.

34 Refit the alternator/coolant pump drivebelt and the fan clutch and radiator.

35 Reconnect the battery.

Chapter 5
Ford 1608cc, 1753cc and 2496cc engines

Part B: Fuel system servicing

Contents

Specifications

Glow plugs

1.6 litre engine	Champion CH79
1.8 litre engine	Champion CH147
2.5 litre engine	Not applicable

Injectors

1.6 litre engine

Bosch:	
Type	Pintle
Opening pressure	143 ± 7 bar (2074 ± 102 lbf/in²)
Back leakage time (from 125 to 100 bar/1813 to 1450 lbf/in²)	More than 5 seconds
Needle seat leakage	No visible droplets after 10 seconds at 10 bar (145 lbf/in²) below opening pressure
CAV:	
Type	Pintle
Opening pressure	120 ± 6 bar (1740 ± 87 lbf/in²)
Back leakage time (from 100 to 70 bar/1450 to 1015 lbf/in²)	More than 5 seconds
Needle seat leakage	Holds 100 bar (1450 lbf/in² for 10 seconds)

1.8 litre engine

Type	Bosch
Needle seat leakage	Holds 125 bar (1813 lbf/in²) for 10 seconds

2.5 litre engine

Type:	
Pre-1989	Bosch or Lucas/CAV, 4-hole
1989 on	Bosch or Lucas/CAV, 5-hole Stanadyne type
Opening pressure:	
Pre-1989:	
Bosch	250 bars
Lucas/CAV	260 bars
1989-on:	
New	275 bars
Used	241 bars

5B

Fuel injection pump

1.6 litre engine

Type	Bosch VE or CAV RotoDiesel
Timing:	
Bosch	0.92 ± 0.01 mm at TDC
CAV RotoDiesel	1.40 ± 0.07 mm at TDC
Rotation (viewed from crankshaft pulley end)	Clockwise
Drive	By gear from crankshaft

1.8 litre engine

Type	Bosch VE or CAV RotoDiesel
Timing	By timing pegs, at TDC
Rotation (viewed from crankshaft pulley end)	Clockwise
Drive	By toothed belt from crankshaft

2.5 litre engine

Type	Bosch or Lucas/CAV
Static timing	11° BTDC, using timing pegs
Rotation (viewed from sprocket end)	Clockwise

Idle speed

1.6 litre engine	880 ± 50 rpm
1.8 litre engine	850 ± 50 rpm
2.5 litre engine:	
Non turbo	800 to 850 rpm
Turbo	800 to 900 rpm

Maximum speed

1.6 litre engine

No load	5350 ± 50 rpm

1.8 litre engine

Continuous	4800 rpm
Intermittent:	
Non-turbo	5350 ± 50 rpm
Turbo	5200 ± 50 rpm

2.5 litre engine

No load:	
Bosch injection pump	4320 to 4560 rpm
Lucas/CAV injection pump	4280 to 4480 rpm
Full load	4000 rpm

Deceleration time

1.6 litre engine	5 seconds maximum (no load at idle)

Torque wrench settings

1.6 litre engine

Fuel injection pump	Nm	lbf ft
Drivebelt sprocket to pump gear	18 to 22	13 to 16
Injection pipe unions	15 to 25	11 to 18
Pump bracket to block	18 to 22	13 to 16
Pump shaft nut	40 to 50	30 to 37
Pump to timing case	18 to 22	13 to 16

1.8 litre engine

Fuel injection pump	Nm	lbf ft
Pump belt tensioner to cylinder block	45	33
Pump pulley bolts	20 to 25	15 to 18
Pump pulley to flange	23	17
Pump support bracket-to-cylinder block	18 to 27	13 to 20
Pump-to-engine front plate	18 to 28	13 to 21
Pump-to-rear support bracket	18 to 22	13 to 16
Fuel regulating thermostat		
Thermostat to thermostat housing	23	17

Torque wrench settings (continued)	Nm	lbf ft
1.8 litre engine (continued)		
EGR system		
EGR vacuum regulator valve-to-pump bolts	2 to 3	1 to 2
EGR valve exhaust supply pipe bolts	20 to 25	15 to 18
EGR valve-to-inlet manifold Allen bolts	17 to 22	12 to 16
1.6 & 1.8 litre engines		
Fuel pipe banjo union bolts	16 to 20	12 to 15
Fuel shut-off solenoid - CAV RotoDiesel pump	16 to 20	12 to 15
Glow plugs	28	21
Injectors:		
Injectors to head	60 to 80	44 to 59
Feed pipe unions	15 to 25	11 to 18
2.5 litre engine		
Fuel injection pump		
Pump front mounting nuts and bolts	21 to 26	15 to 19
Pump rear support bracket	21 to 26	15 to 19
Pump sprocket bolts	22 to 27	16 to 20
Fuel injectors		
Injector clamp bolts (Stanadyne injectors)	37 to 42	27 to 31
Injector clamp nuts (pre-1989 model year)	12 to 15	9 to 11
Injector delivery pipe unions	18 to 20	13 to 14
Fast idle thermostatic sensor		
Sensor to thermostat housing	15 to 20	11 to 14
EGR system		
EGR connecting hose to valve and manifold	20 to 25	14 to 18
EGR valve to throttle housing:		
Normally-aspirated engines	20 to 25	14 to 18
Turbocharged engines	15 to 20	11 to 14

1 Accelerator cable - adjustment

1.6 and 1.8 litre engines

1 Adjust the accelerator cable so that with the pedal released, there is a small amount of slack in the cable inner.

2 Have an assistant operate the pedal and check that the throttle lever on the injection pump moves through its full range of travel (as limited by the idle and maximum speed adjusting screws).

3 If necessary, readjust the cable.

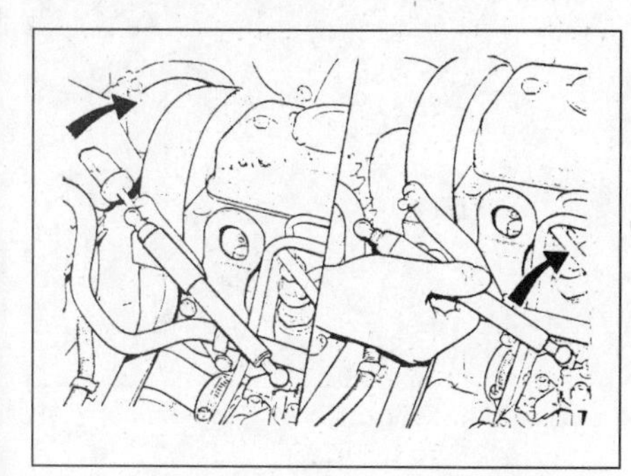

2.2 Throttle damper removal

2.5 litre engine

4 Have an assistant fully depress the accelerator pedal, then check that the injection pump control lever is in the full-throttle position. If not, turn the adjuster on the cable outer as necessary.

5 Release the accelerator pedal and check that the injection pump control lever returns to the idle position.

2 Throttle damper (1.8 litre engine) - removal and refitting

1 A revised throttle damper unit can be fitted to Escort, Orion and Mondeo models equipped with the Bosch fuel injection system, where the vehicle is regularly used under low speed and light throttle application, to help prevent vehicle shake and power "on/off" effect at low engine speeds.

2 The throttle damper is detached by prising free the top balljoint and moving the damper up so that the lower joint disconnects from the throttle end **(see illustration)**.

3 When refitting the damper, press it into position on the top and bottom end joints. Ensure that the large diameter end joint is fitted at the top.

3 Anti-stall speed (1.6 litre engine) - checking and adjustment

Note: *A service tool (23-016) will be required for this operation. If not available, this can be replaced by the (careful) use of spacers.*

1 The following operation applies to the CAV RotoDiesel fuel injection pump.

2 Ensure that the engine is at normal operating temperature. Fit the service tool (23-016) or suitable alternatives, plus a 1.0 mm thick feeler blade (to a total thickness of 4.0 mm) between the anti-stall screw and throttle lever **(see illustration)**.

3 Insert a 3.0 mm thick spacer between the head of the idle speed screw and idle stop lever **(see illustration)**.

4 Release the locknut on the anti-stall adjustment screw, start the engine and turn the anti-stall adjustment screw until the engine is idling at between 900 ± 100 rpm.

5 Remove the 3.0 mm spacer and check that the idle stop lever returns to make contact with the head of the idle speed adjuster screw.

6 Remove the service tool or alternative.

7 Release the locknut on the idle speed adjusting screw and turn the screw until the engine idles at 880 ± 30 rpm.

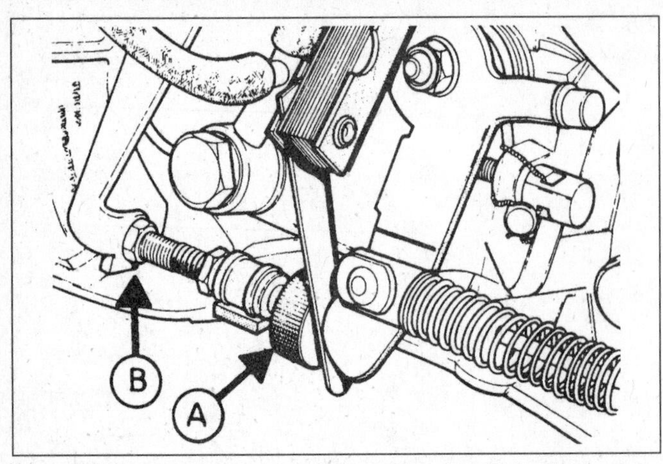

3.2 Anti-stall adjustment - CAV RotoDiesel fuel injection pump

A Service tool 23-016 and 1.0 mm feeler blade (total thickness 4.0 mm) inserted between throttle lever and anti-stall adjustment screw
B Insert spacer (thickness according to engine - refer to text) between idle speed/stop lever and idle speed adjusting screw

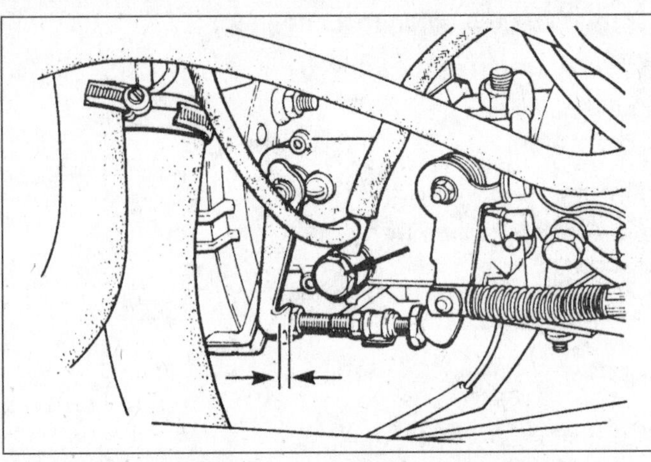

3.3 Idle speed adjustment - CAV RotoDiesel fuel injection pump. Insert spacer between idle speed/stop lever and idle speed adjusting screw at point indicated

***Note:** Fuel return pipe union arrowed*

8 Stalling and slow engine deceleration should not occur if the idle and anti-stall adjustments have been correctly carried out. However, if stalling continues, turn the anti-stall adjusting screw by no more than one quarter of a turn clockwise. If slow deceleration is a problem, turn the anti-stall adjusting screw (again, by not more than) one quarter of a turn (maximum) anti-clockwise.

4 Idle up speed control system (1.8 litre engine) - checking, adjustment and renewal

Checking

1 An idle up speed device may be fitted to Escort, Orion and Mondeo models to automatically raise the engine speed and prevent stalling when reverse gear is selected. The unit is attached to a bracket on the left-hand inner wing panel in the engine compartment. The glow plug relay has been moved from its original position and is now secured to the up speed unit bracket **(see illustrations)**.

2 The control unit operates in conjunction with the reversing light circuit and the brake vacuum system. It differs according to the fuel injection type (CAV RotoDiesel or Bosch).

3 To check the idle up speed system for satisfactory operation, first check that the system wiring and vacuum hoses are in good condition and securely connected.

Adjustment

4 Check that the operating cable adjustment is as follows according to system type:

5 On the CAV RotoDiesel system, ensure that the idle operating cable is fully released and there is no vacuum in the servo, then check that there is a clearance of 0.5 to 1.0 mm between the idle up speed operating cable clamp and the idle lever **(see illustration)**. If necessary, loosen off the adjuster clamp screw and move the clamp to set the clearance, then retighten the screw.

6 On the Bosch system, fully extend the waxstat operating cable by switching on the ignition and leaving it in position "II" for a period of three minutes, then check that the clearance between the cable clamp and the idle lever is 0.5 mm **(see illustration)**.

7 If adjustment is required on either system, loosen off the cable clamp screw and set the clamp as required.

8 Start the engine and allow it to idle for a period of 5 minutes, then engage reverse gear. The idle speed should rise and then level off within three seconds of reverse gear being

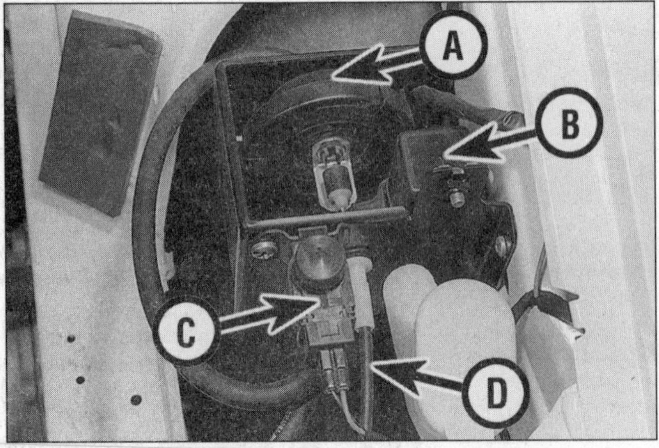

4.1a Idle up speed control system components - Escort with CAV fuel injection system

A Vacuum diaphragm
B Glow plug relay
C Reverse light switch circuit connector
D Up speed operating cable

4.1b Idle up speed device (viewed from beneath vehicle) - Mondeo

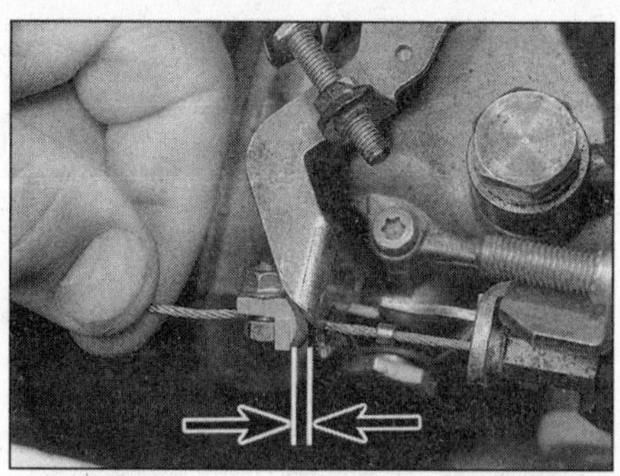

4.5 Adjust up speed operating cable to allow required clearance between clamp and lever

engaged. Now disengage reverse gear and check that the idle speed drops and levels off within three seconds of disengagement.

Renewal

9 To remove the idle up speed device, first disconnect the battery earth lead.
10 Unplug the electrical connector from the device.
11 Pull the lower vacuum pipe off the device.
12 Disconnect the cable from the fuel injection pump.
13 Remove the retaining bolts and withdraw the idle up speed device from the vehicle.
14 Refitting is the reverse of the removal procedure. Adjust the operating cable as described above.

5 Maximum speed - checking and adjustment

Caution: The maximum speed adjustment screw is fitted only to certain versions of fuel injection pump and is sealed by the manufacturers with paint or locking wire and a lead seal. Do not disturb the adjustment screw if the vehicle is still within the warranty period, otherwise the warranty will be invalidated.
1 The usual type of tachometer (rev counter), which works from ignition system pulses, cannot be used on diesel engines. If it is not

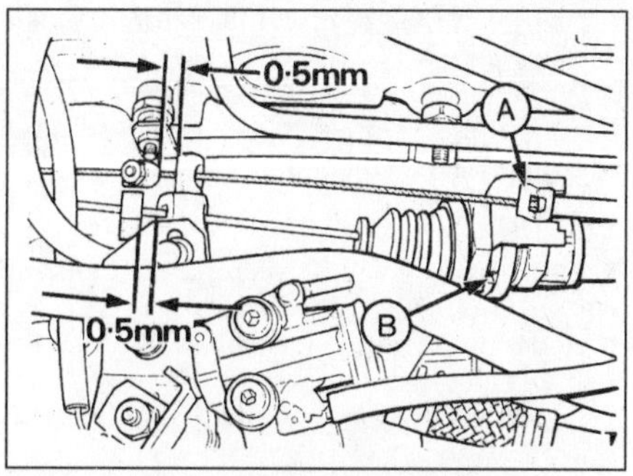

4.6 Idle up speed control system cable adjustment - Bosch injection system shown

A Up speed cable clip - on fast idle waxstat device cable bracket
B Slot in bracket for cable removal and refitting

felt that adjusting the maximum no load speed "by ear" is satisfactory, one of the following alternatives may be used:

a) Purchase or hire of an appropriate tachometer
b) Delegation of the job to a Ford dealer or other specialist
c) Timing light (strobe) operated by a petrol engine running at the desired speed. If the timing light is pointed at a chalk mark on the diesel engine crankshaft pulley, the mark will appear stationary when the two engines are running at the same speed (or multiples of that speed)
d) Calculating the mph/rpm relationship for a particular gear and running the engine, in that gear, with the front wheels free. The speedometer accuracy may not be adequate, especially at low speeds. Stringent safety precautions must be observed because of the risk of damage or injury if anything goes wrong

2 Run the engine to normal operating temperature.
3 When checking maximum speed, do not hold the engine at this speed for more than 3 seconds. Keep well clear of the coolant pump/alternator drivebelt and pulleys.
4 If adjustment is necessary, stop the engine, loosen the adjustment screw locknut and turn

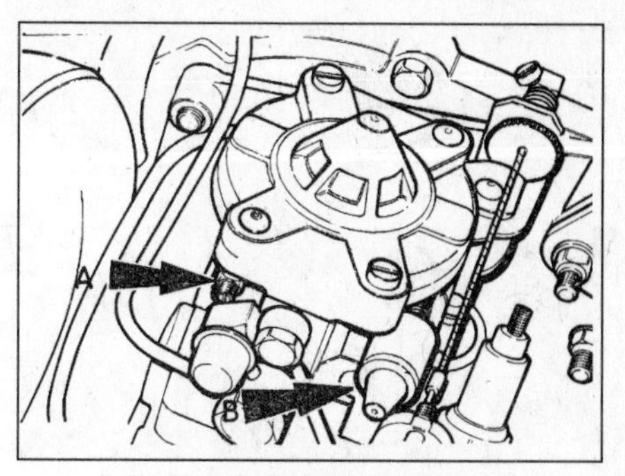

5.4a Bosch fuel injection pump adjustment points

A Idle speed adjustment screw
B Maximum speed adjustment screw (under cap)

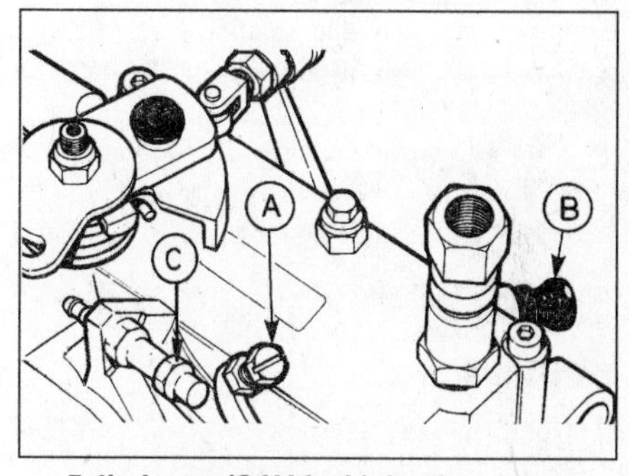

5.4b Lucas/CAV fuel injection pump adjustment points

A Idle speed adjustment screw
B Anti-stall adjustment screw (under cap)
C Maximum speed adjustment screw (under cap)

the screw as necessary. Retighten the locknut on completion **(see illustrations)**.
5 The engine speed should drop from maximum to idle within the specified time when the throttle is released. If not, check that the throttle linkage is not binding or obstructed. If this is in order, seek specialist advice.

6 Fuel shut-off solenoid - removal and refitting

Caution: Take care not to allow dirt into the fuel injection pump during this procedure.

Removal

1 Disconnect the battery earth lead.
2 Check that the ignition key is removed from the ignition switch.
3 Withdraw the rubber boot (where applicable), then disconnect the electrical lead from the solenoid **(see illustration)**.
4 Wipe clean around the solenoid, then unscrew it from the fuel injection pump using a deep socket or box spanner. If the solenoid has recently been energised, it may be hot.
5 Recover the spring and plunger **(see illustration)**. Discard the solenoid O-ring.

6.3 Side view of Bosch fuel injection pump

A Cold start element
B Fuel shut-off solenoid

6.5 Solenoid, spring and plunger (O-ring arrowed)

8.2 Location of fuel heater multiplug (arrowed)

Refitting

6 Refitting is a reversal of removal. Use a new O-ring and tighten the solenoid to the specified torque wrench setting.

7 On completion, run the engine to check for correct operation.

7 Cold start element (1.6 and 1.8 litre engine) - renewal

Removal

1 The electrically-operated cold start element is screwed into the advance device - see illustration 6.3. No test data are available. If the element is suspect, it can be renewed as follows.

2 Disconnect the battery earth lead.

3 Disconnect the electrical lead from the cold start element.

4 Wipe clean around the element, then unscrew and remove it. If it has just been energised, the element may be hot.

Fitting

5 Fit the new element, using a new sealing washer. Tighten it moderately.

6 Reconnect the electrical lead and the battery earth lead.

7 Run the engine to check for correct operation.

8 Fuel heater (1.8 litre engine) - removal and refitting

Removal

1 Obtain a container in which to catch any fuel spillage.

2 Disconnect the battery negative (earth) lead and then the multi-plug from the base of the fuel heater **(see illustration)**.

3 Separate the quick release connectors of the fuel inlet and outlet lines to the heater, catching any fuel spillage.

4 Remove the two retaining screws and detach the heater from the engine.

Refitting

5 Refitting is the reverse of the removal procedure. On completion, prime the fuel system and carry out leak checks directly after the engine is started.

9 Glow plugs and relay (1.6 litre engine) - removal and refitting

Note: *As from October 1986, a modified controller relay has been fitted to increase glow duration at cold starting. Earlier models may be fitted with the later type relay if cold starting is a problem, this assumes that injection pump timing and all other factors (starter motor, fuel supply, etc.) are in order.*

Glow plugs

1 Disconnect the battery earth lead and glow plug relay.

2 Disconnect the feed wire from the bus bar **(see illustration)**.

3 Unscrew the terminal nut from each plug to be removed **(see illustration)**. Remove the nuts, washers and bus bar.

4 Clean around the glow plug seats then unscrew and remove them **(see illustration)**.

5 When refitting, apply a little anti-seize compound to the glow plug threads. Screw the glow plugs into place and tighten them to the specified torque.

6 Refit the bus bar and washers and secure with the nuts. Make sure that the clamping areas are clean.

7 Reconnect the feed wire and the battery earth lead.

Relay

8 The relay is located on the left-hand side of the engine bay. It is secured by a single screw **(see illustration)**.

9 Disconnect the battery earth lead, then remove the relay securing screw.

10 Peel back the rubber boot and unplug the electrical connector from the relay **(see illustration)**.

11 Refit in the reverse order to removal.

10 Glow plugs, relay and fuse (1.8 litre engine) - removal and refitting

1 Refer to Section 9 but note that the glow plug relay on later models is located under the jack stowage position.

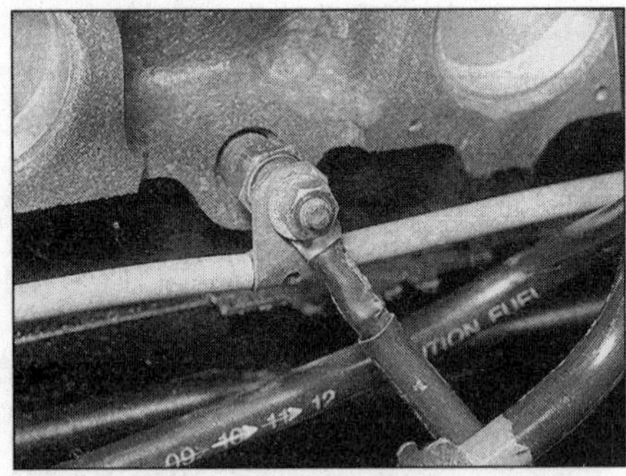

9.2 Glow plug feed wire connection

9.3 Unscrewing a glow plug terminal nut

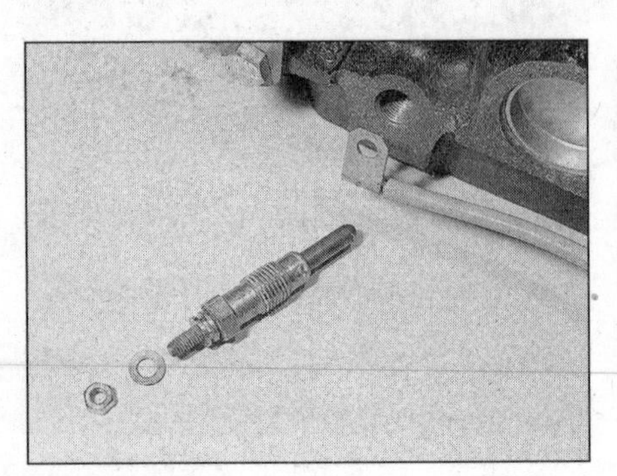

9.4 Glow plug removed from cylinder head

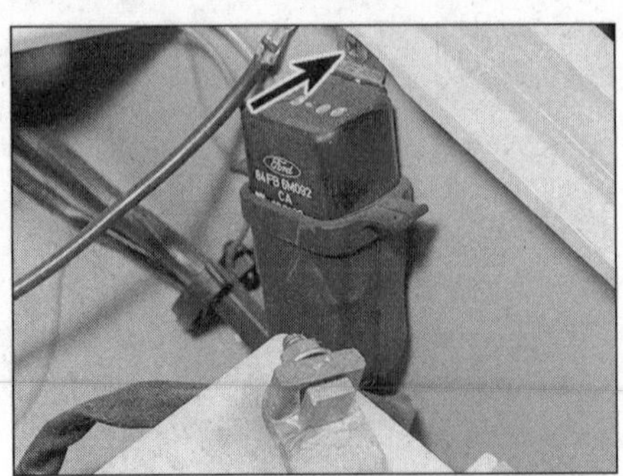

9.8 Glow plug relay - securing screw arrowed

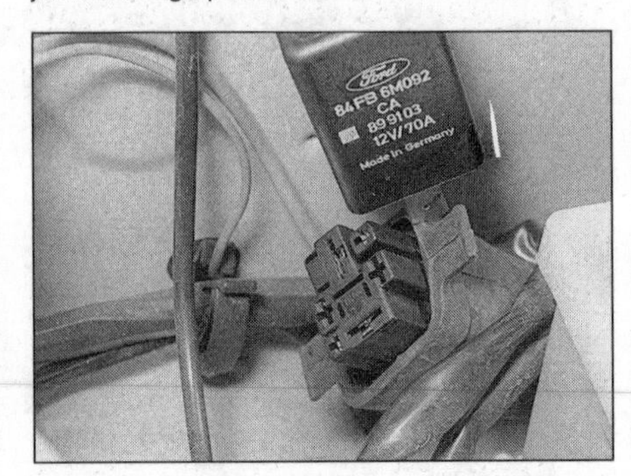

9.10 Electrical connector unplugged from glow plug relay

10.2a Fuel system glow plug relay location (arrowed) - later Fiesta

10.2b Fuel system glow plug relay location (arrowed) - later Escort fitted with engine up speed system

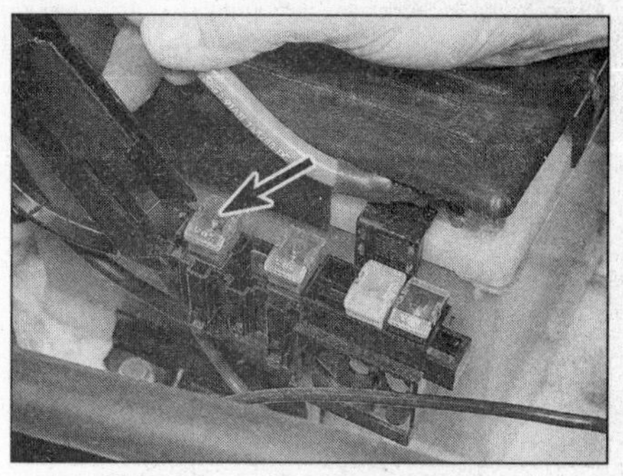

10.3 Glow plug fuse location - later models

2 On models fitted with an engine up speed system, the relay is attached to a bracket on the left-hand inner wing panel in the engine compartment **(see illustrations)**.

3 The glow plug circuit fuse is in the additional fuse block located in front of the battery **(see illustration)**.

11 Injectors - testing, removal and refitting

Warning: Exercise extreme caution when working on fuel injectors. Never expose the hands or any part of the body to injector spray, as the high working pressure can cause fuel to penetrate the skin, with possibly fatal results. You are strongly advised to have any work which involves testing the injectors under pressure carried out by a dealer or fuel injection specialist.

11.6 Disconnecting fuel return hose from an injector

Testing

Fitted

1 Injectors deteriorate with prolonged use and it is reasonable to expect them to need reconditioning or renewal after 60 000 miles (90 000 km). Accurate testing, overhaul and calibration of the injectors must be left to a specialist. A defective injector which is causing knocking or smoking can be located without removal as follows.

2 Run the engine at a fast idle. Slacken each injector union in turn, placing rag around the union to catch spilt fuel and being careful not to expose the skin to any fuel spray. When the union on the defective injector is slackened, the knocking or smoking will stop.

Removed

3 Testing of removed injectors is quite simple but requires a special high pressure pump and gauge. Should such equipment be available, use it in accordance with the manufacturer's instructions, referring to Specifications for the desired values.

4 Defective injectors should be renewed or professionally repaired. DIY repair is not a practical proposition.

Removal

1.6 and 1.8 litre engines

5 Disconnect the battery earth lead. Clean around the injectors and the pipe unions.

6 Remove the fuel return hoses from the injectors **(see illustration)**.

7 Remove the injection pipes.

8 Unscrew and remove the injectors. A 27mm box spanner or deep socket will be required **(see illustration)**.

9 Retrieve the heat protection washers from the injector bores **(see illustration)**. Obtain new washers for reassembly.

10 Take care not to drop the injectors, nor allow the needles at their tips to become damaged.

2.5 litre engine - Bosch or Lucas/CAV injectors

11 Fuel injectors of either Bosch or Lucas/CAV type are fitted to all engines manufactured before 1989.

12 Disconnect the battery negative lead.

13 Remove the air cleaner assembly.

14 Carefully clean around the injectors and injector pipe union nuts.

15 Undo the fuel supply union nuts and the leak-off pipe banjo bolts. Withdraw the pipes from the injectors and plug or cap the open unions. Recover the two copper washers from each banjo bolt union **(see illustration)**.

16 Unscrew the injector clamp nuts and remove the clamp from each injector.

5B

11.8 Withdrawing an injector . . .

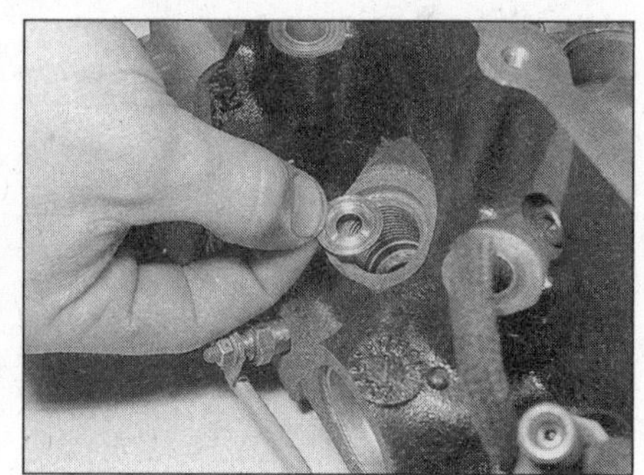

11.9 . . . followed by heat protection washer

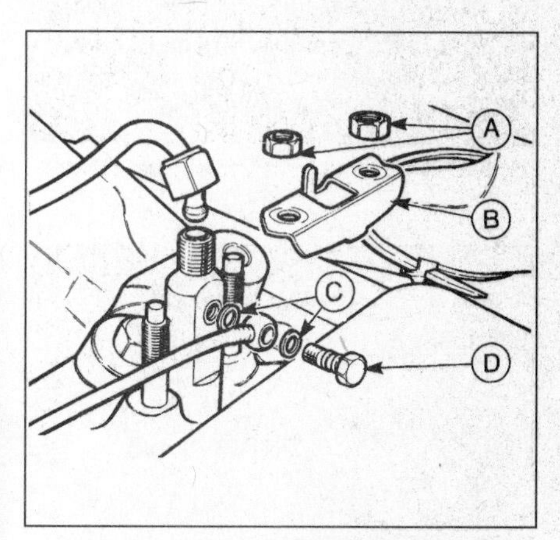

11.15 Fuel injector fittings on pre-1989 model year vehicles

A Clamp nuts
B Clamp
C Banjo union washers
D Banjo bolt

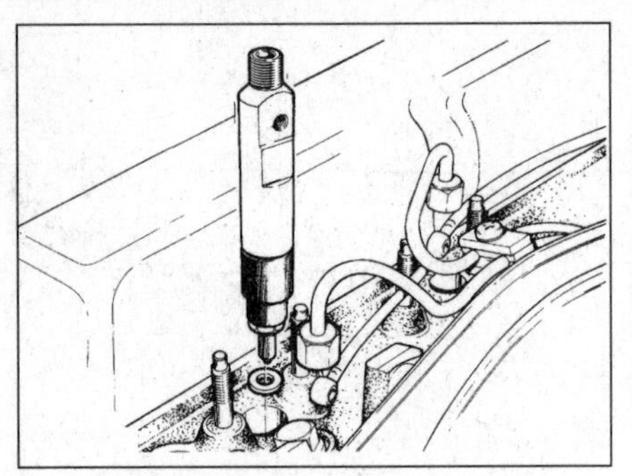

11.17 Pull each injector out of the cylinder head

11.22 Unscrew fuel supply pipe unions from injectors

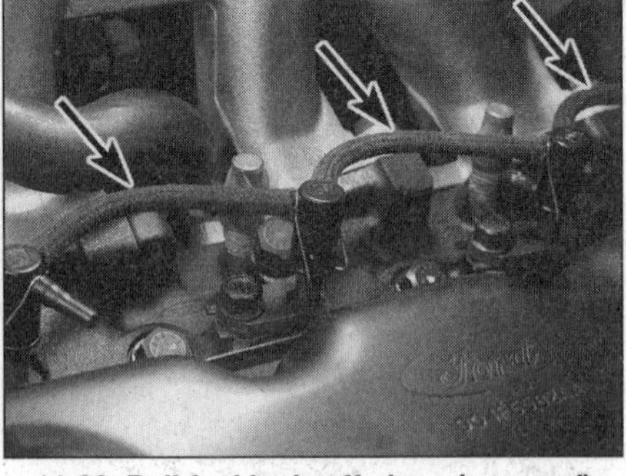

11.23 Pull fuel leak-off pipes (arrowed) from injectors

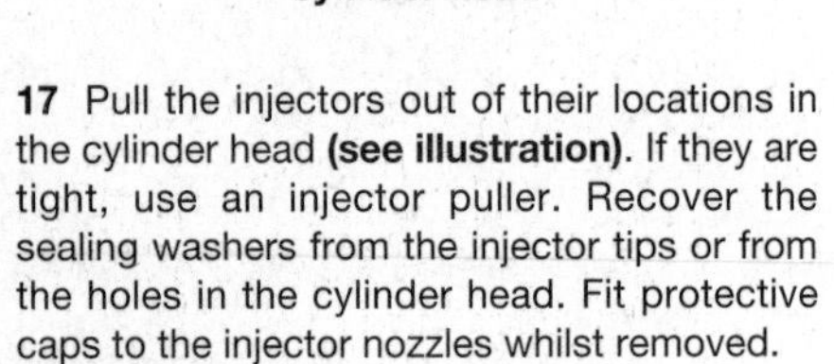

17 Pull the injectors out of their locations in the cylinder head **(see illustration)**. If they are tight, use an injector puller. Recover the sealing washers from the injector tips or from the holes in the cylinder head. Fit protective caps to the injector nozzles whilst removed.

2.5 litre engine - Stanadyne "slim-tip" injectors

18 Stanadyne "slim-tip" fuel injectors are fitted to all engines manufactured after 1989.
19 Disconnect the battery negative lead.
20 Remove the air cleaner assembly.
21 Carefully clean around the injectors and injector pipe union nuts.
22 Unscrew the fuel supply pipe unions from the injectors **(see illustration)**. If necessary, use a second spanner to counterhold the injector as the pipe union is undone. Plug or cap the open unions.
23 Carefully pull the fuel leak-off pipes from the injectors **(see illustration)**.
24 Undo the injector clamp bolts and remove the clamp plate assemblies.
25 Pull the injectors out of their locations in the cylinder head. If they are stuck, use Ford removal tool 23-030 or a proprietary injector puller. Do not try to lever the injectors free **(see illustration)**.
26 Remove the dust-seal washers from the injector bodies **(see illustration)**. Remove the PTFE sealing washers from the injector tips by carefully cutting them with a knife, then ease them off using pliers. Obtain new dust-seal and sealing washers for refitting. Fit protective caps to the injector nozzles while they are removed.

Refitting

1.6 and 1.8 litre engines

27 Commence refitting by inserting new heat protection washers (domed faces downwards) to the injector bores.
28 Insert the injectors and screw them in by hand, then tighten them to the specified torque. No outer sealing washer is used and the injectors are a taper fit in the head.
29 Reconnect the fuel return hoses. Ensure that a blanking cap is fitted to the unused connector on No 4 injector.
30 Refit the injection pipes.
31 Reconnect the battery and run the engine for a minute or two. Check for leaks around the disturbed components.

2.5 litre engine

32 On all injector types, refitting is a reversal of removal, noting the following points:

a) *Use new injector sealing washers, PTFE washers and banjo union copper washers, as applicable.*
b) *If working on the Bosch or Lucas/CAV injectors, note that the injector leak-off pipe connections face towards the rocker cover and the pointed ends of the injector clamps face the front of the engine.*
c) *If working on the Stanadyne injectors, fit the new PTFE sealing washers with their recesses facing upwards. Fit the washers by placing them in the handle of tool 23-030, or in a suitably-sized socket or shouldered tube clamped in a vice. Push the injector tip through the washer **(see illustration)**.*
d) *Tighten all fastenings and unions to the specified torque. Make sure that the injector pipes are not under strain.*
e) *Prime the fuel system, then start the engine and check for fuel leaks.*

12 Fuel injection pipes - removal and refitting

1.6 and 1.8 litre engines

Removal

1 The injection pipes should be removed as a set. Individual pipes may then be renewed if necessary after slackening the anti-rattle clips.
2 Disconnect the battery earth lead. Clean around the pipe unions at the injectors and at the pump.
3 Protect the alternator against fuel spillage. Counterhold the pump adapters and unscrew the pipe union nuts **(see illustration)**.
4 Similarly, unscrew the injector union nuts, counterholding the injector bodies as the nuts are slackened **(see illustration)**.

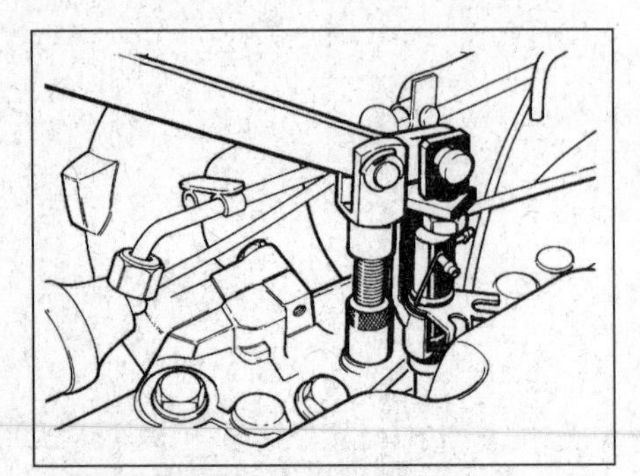

11.25 Pulling injector out of cylinder head with Ford tool 23-030

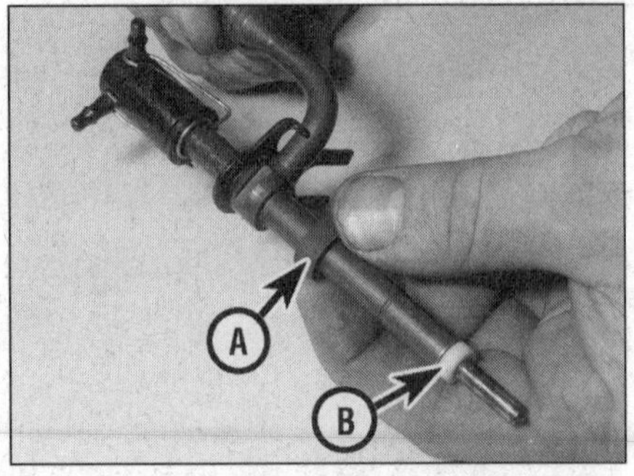

11.26 Removing seals from injector body

A Dust seal *B PTFE seal*

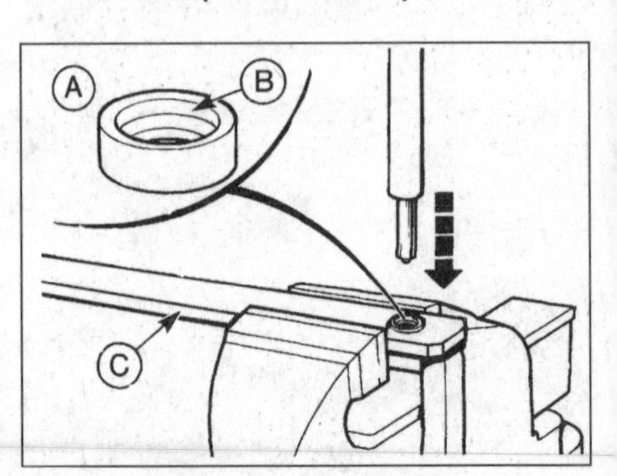

11.32 Correct fitting of Stanadyne injector PTFE sealing washer (A)

B Recess *C Fitting tool*

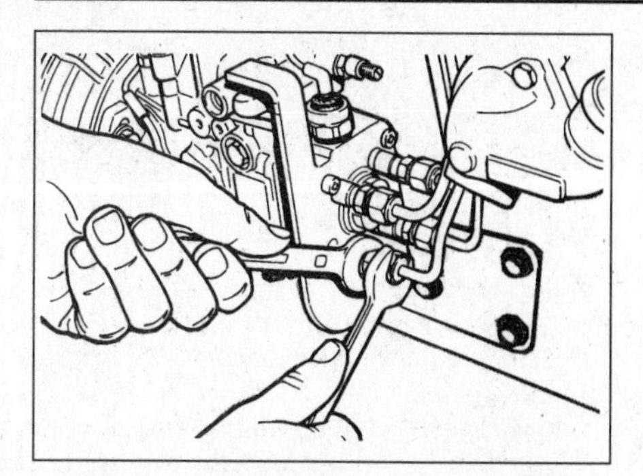
12.3 Counterhold pump adapter when slackening or tightening a pipe union nut

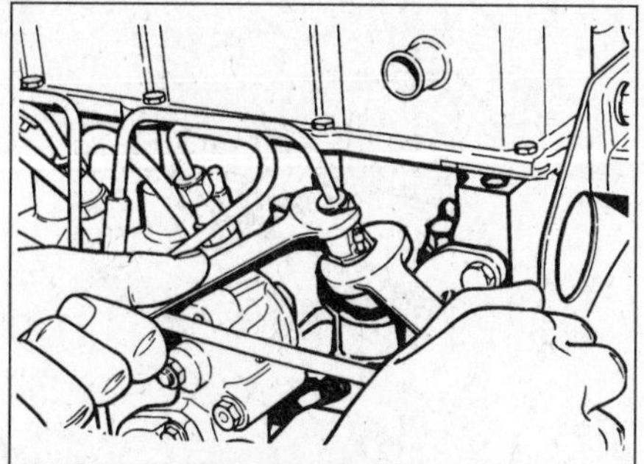
12.4 Counterhold injector body when slackening a pipe union nut

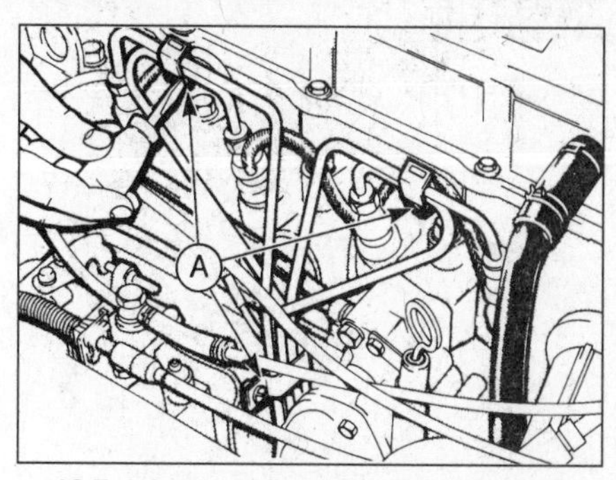

12.7 Injection pipe anti-rattle clips (A)

5 Remove the pipe assembly. Plug or cap open unions to keep fuel in and dirt out.
6 The pipes of the Bosch and CAV systems look similar but they have different bore sizes. To identify a pipe, insert a new twist drill of specified diameter into the pipe bore. The bore sizes are as follows:

Bosch pipe internal diameter - 2.0 mm
CAV RotoDiesel pipe internal diameter - 2.5 mm

Refitting

7 When refitting, ensure that all the anti-rattle clips are in place **(see illustration)**. Do not bend or strain the pipes. Blow through the pipes with compressed air (from an air line or a foot pump) to expel any debris.
8 Counterhold the pump adapters and tighten the pump union nuts.
9 Reconnect the battery earth lead.
10 With the injector union nuts finger-tight, have an assistant crank the engine on the starter in short bursts until fuel emerges from the unions. Tighten the injector unions. There is no need to counterhold the injectors.
11 Run the engine for a minute or two to purge any remaining air from the system. Check the disturbed unions for leaks.

2.5 litre engine

Removal

12 Disconnect the battery negative lead.
13 For improved access to the injection pump, remove the air cleaner assembly if necessary.
14 Cover the starter motor with a plastic bag, as a precaution against spillage of fuel.
15 Remove the clamps from the injector pipes, then unscrew the pipe unions at the injectors and fuel injection pump. Use a second spanner to counterhold the injector if necessary as the pipe union is undone. Plug or cap the open unions.
16 Carefully remove the injector pipes from the engine, taking care not to bend or distort them as they are removed.

Refitting

17 Refitting is a reversal of removal, noting the following points:

a) *Tighten all the pipe unions finger-tight initially, then tighten them fully once they all are connected.*
b) *Tighten all unions to the specified torque. Ensure that the injector pipes are not under strain.*
c) *Prime the fuel system, then start the engine and check for fuel leaks.*

13 Fuel injection pump (1.6 litre engine) - removal and refitting

Bosch

Removal

1 Disconnect the battery earth lead.
2 Depressurise the cooling system by removing the expansion tank filler cap, taking precautions against scalding if the system is hot.
3 Disconnect the coolant vent hose from the thermostat housing and cylinder head. Be prepared for some coolant spillage. Move the vent hose out of the way.
4 It is not essential, but access will be greatly improved if the radiator and cooling fan are removed.
5 Remove the camshaft drivebelt cover.
6 Disconnect the throttle cable from the pump.
7 Clean around the unions, then disconnect the fuel supply and return hoses from the pump **(see illustrations)**. Be prepared for fuel spillage. Protect the alternator against the entry of fuel. Plug or cap hoses and unions to keep fuel in and dirt out.
8 Disconnect the electrical leads from the fuel shut-off solenoid and the cold start device
9 Remove the injection pipes and plug or cap open unions.
10 Release the nut which secures the pump driveshaft to its gear. Unscrew it as far as the end of the shaft.
11 Turn the engine until the timing marks on the pump sprocket and the timing cover are aligned.
12 Obtain or make a TDC setting pin - see Section 19 in Part A of this Chapter. Remove the screw plug and insert the pin, then turn the engine clockwise until the crankshaft web contacts the pin.
13 Make alignment marks between the pump flange and the timing case, then remove the three nuts and washers which secure the pump to the timing case. Slacken, but do not remove, the pump bracket nut and bolt **(see illustration)**.

13.7a Fuel supply pipe union (arrowed) at pump

13.7b Either remove return pipe banjo union or disconnect hoses (arrowed) from it

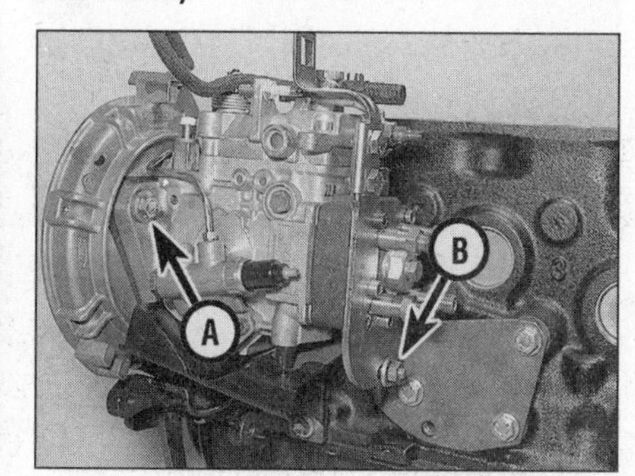

13.13 One of three flange nuts (A) and bracket nut and bolt (B)

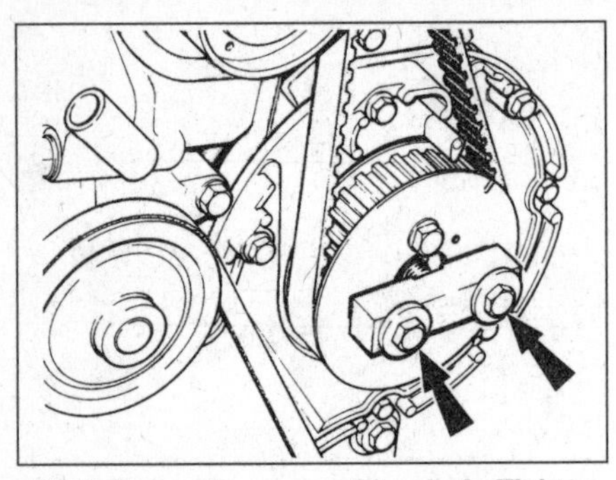

13.14 **Releasing pump driveshaft. Tighten bolts (arrowed) to break taper . . .**

14 Remove two opposite bolts from the pump sprocket. Use two longer M8 bolts (not the sprocket bolts), a suitably drilled bar and some washers or spacers to release the pump shaft from its taper fit in the gear **(see illustration)**. The correct length of bolt will depend on the thickness of the bar. If too long or too short, damage to the gear or timing case may result. Tighten the bolts evenly to break the taper.

15 Remove the bolts, bar, etc. and transfer them to a position suitable for restraining the pump sprocket from moving **(see illustration)**. When the pump is removed, the sprocket and gear will not be positively located. If the gear comes out of mesh with the idler, it will be necessary to remove the timing cover to re-engage it.

16 Remove the pump driveshaft nut and the bracket nut and bolt. Withdraw the pump and bracket, being careful not to lose the Woodruff key. Recover the gasket.

Refitting

17 Commence refitting by placing a new gasket on the timing case. Offer the pump to the case, with the Woodruff key positioned to enter the keyway in the gear. Take care not to push the gear out of mesh. Fit the securing nuts and washers but only tighten them finger tight at this stage. Loosely fit the bracket nut and bolt.

18 Apply sealant to the screw thread on the pump shaft. Fit the shaft nut and carefully tighten it to draw the shaft taper into the gear. When satisfied that the shaft has entered the gear without jamming, tighten the nut to the specified torque.

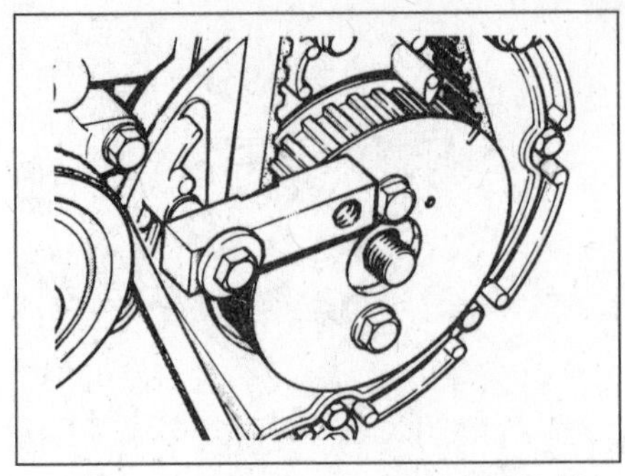

13.15 **. . . and using same tool to hold sprocket in position**

19 Remove the gear puller/restrainer components. Refit and tighten the pump sprocket bolts.

20 Adjust the pump timing. The alignment marks made during removal will provide a starting point if the original pump is being refitted.

21 Refit the injection pipes.

22 Reconnect the fuel shut-off solenoid, the cold start device and the throttle cable.

23 Refit the camshaft drivebelt cover.

24 Refit the radiator and fan, if removed.

25 Reconnect the coolant vent hose. Refill or top-up the cooling system as necessary.

26 Prime the pump by pouring or injecting clean fuel into the fuel inlet and outlet orifices. Take great care not to introduce dirt or foreign matter into the pump.

27 Reconnect the fuel supply and return hoses.

28 Reconnect the battery earth lead.

29 Start the engine. A good deal of cranking may be necessary and the self-bleeding process can be speeded up by slackening each injector pipe union in turn whilst an assistant cranks the engine on the starter motor. Tighten the unions when fuel emerges.

30 Run the engine for a minute or two to purge any remaining air from the injection system. Check the disturbed components for leaks of fuel, oil or coolant.

CAV RotoDiesel

31 The procedures are basically as described for the Bosch pump, whilst noting the following:

a) According to the manufacturers, there is no need to drain the cooling system or move the coolant vent hose
b) There is no separate electrical feed to a cold start device
c) It is necessary to remove the alternator shield when fitted
d) It will be necessary to remove the pump rear support bracket completely
e) Before refitting, drain the fuel from the pump (if applicable) by removing the lower of the two plugs in the side of the pump.
f) Before refitting the rear support bracket, set the pump timing.
g) Prime a new pump with clean fuel via the fuel return banjo connection.
h) Before attempting to start the engine, prime the system then bleed any trapped air out when the engine is restarted.

14 Fuel injection pump (1.8 litre engine) - removal and refitting

Non turbocharged engine - Bosch pump

Removal

1 Open the bonnet and disconnect the battery.

2 Slowly release the coolant expansion tank cap and then disconnect the air bleed tube from the tank.

3 Release the fixing clips and bolt from the timing belt upper cover.

4 Raise the front of the vehicle and remove the under-wing splash shield from the right-hand side.

5 Unscrew the lower timing belt cover fixing bolt, release the cover pivot bolt and allow the cover to swing downwards **(see illustrations)**.

6 Lower the vehicle, and remove the belt upper cover.

7 Disconnect the fuel feed and return hoses from the injection pump. Banjo type unions are used. Plug or cap the openings to prevent the entry of dirt. Disconnect the injector high pressure pipes **(see illustration)**.

14.5a **Remove lower belt cover retaining screw . . .**

14.5b **. . . and swivel cover downwards**

14.7 **Fuel return union at pump**

14.11 Fuel injection pump rear bracket

14.22a Fitting fuel injection pump

14.22b Tightening fuel injection pump fixing screws

8 Disconnect the electrical connections from the fuel shut-off solenoid device and (where fitted) the up speed control system cables waxstat fast idle and the cold start device.
9 Carefully identify the two vacuum hoses and disconnect them from the vacuum regulator valve (EGR system only).
10 Disconnect the throttle cable from the operating arm on the injection pump, then remove the cable bracket.
11 Remove the bolts from the injection pump rear support bracket and slacken the bolts which hold the bracket to the cylinder block **(see illustration)**.
12 Engage 4th gear, raise the right-hand front roadwheel and turn it, while at the same time observing the injection pump timing pin slot. When the slot is at the 11 o'clock position, stop turning the roadwheel.
13 Remove the alternator protective cover.
14 Remove the crankshaft TDC gauge pin plug from the cylinder block and screw in the pin (refer to Part A of this Chapter).
15 Using the roadwheel, slowly turn the crankshaft in its normal direction of rotation, until the crankshaft web contacts the TDC pin.
16 Insert the camshaft timing peg.
17 Slacken the injection pump timing belt tensioner and secure the tensioner away from the belt.
18 Unscrew and remove the injection pump belt sprocket bolts, then slide off the sprocket and belt.
19 Support the weight of the pump, remove the fixing screws and remove it from the engine.

Refitting

20 Before fitting a new pump, remove the blanking plugs and prime it with clean fuel, poured in through the return port.
21 Align the peg cut-outs of the pump body and drive flange.
22 Bolt the pump into position, making sure that the mounting surfaces are clean **(see illustrations)**.
23 Bolt the pump rear support bracket into position.
24 Locate the belt sprocket on the pump flange but leave the fixing bolts slack **(see illustration)**.
25 Insert the timing peg so that is passes through the sprocket, flange and pump body.
26 Centralise the sprocket bolts in the centres of their elongated slots by rotating the sprocket. Nip up the bolts.
27 Slide the toothed belt onto the pump sprocket, making sure that the slack side of the belt is on the tensioner side.
28 Slacken the pump sprocket bolts.
29 Release the tensioner and allow it to snap against the belt to take up the slack.
30 Tighten the tensioner bolt but check that they are not at the ends of their slots. If they are, adjust the belt tension to correct the situation.
31 Tighten the sprocket bolts to the specified torque, then remove the timing peg.
32 Remove the TDC pin from the crankcase.
33 Turn the crankshaft through two complete revolutions until the injection pump sprocket peg slot is at the 11 o'clock position.
34 Refit the TDC pin and then continue turning the crankshaft slowly until the crankshaft web contacts the TDC pin.
35 Now check that the timing peg will enter the pump sprocket and pass into the pump body. If the cut-outs are not in alignment, slacken the sprocket bolts and turn the pump flange until they are.
36 Tighten the sprocket bolts and remove the peg.
37 Remake the electrical and hose connections and connect the fast idle and up speed cables.
38 Reconnect the injector high-pressure pipes but do not fully tighten the connections at the injectors yet. Prime the system as far as is possible.
39 Remove the TDC pin and fit the plug to the crankcase.
40 Fit the alternator cover.
41 Reconnect the throttle cable, making sure that the idle and full-throttle positions can be obtained.
42 Refit the belt covers and the splash shield.
43 Reconnect the expansion tank hose and top-up the coolant.
44 Reconnect the battery and disengage 4th gear.
45 Operate the starter until fuel is seen to be ejected from the untightened injector pipes then tighten the pipes.
46 Start the engine and bring it to operating temperature. Check and adjust the idle speed then (where appropriate) check the adjustment of the EGR system vacuum regulator valve.

Non-turbocharged engine - CAV RotoDiesel pump

Removal

47 Carry out the operations described in paragraphs 1 to 8, 10 and 13 for the Bosch type pump, but note that only the electrical wiring for the fuel shut-off solenoid need be disconnected.
48 Remove the bolts from the injection pump rear support bracket and then slacken the bolts which hold the bracket to the cylinder block.
49 Engage 4th gear, raise the right-hand front roadwheel and turn it, while at the same time observing the injection pump sprocket timing pin slot. Stop turning when it is at 12 o'clock. The camshaft sprocket timing pin slot will be at 8 o'clock.
50 Now turn the crankshaft anti-clockwise until the pump timing slot is at the 11 o'clock position.
51 Remove the plug and screw in the crankcase TDC pin. Rotate the crankshaft slowly until the crankshaft web contacts the TDC pin.
52 Insert the timing pegs into the camshaft and the injection pump sprockets.
53 Slacken the pump drivebelt tensioner bolt, relieve the tension on the belt and lock the tensioner away from the belt.
54 Unscrew and remove the bolts from the injection pump belt sprocket. Withdraw the sprocket and belt from the pump.
55 Unscrew the T40 Torx bolts, and remove the fuel injection pump.

14.24 Fitting fuel injection pump sprocket bolts

14.84 Fuel injection pump connections
A Throttle cable end fitting
B Idle up speed cable end clamp
C Waxstat cable grommet
D Throttle cable bracket screw
E Fuel supply connection

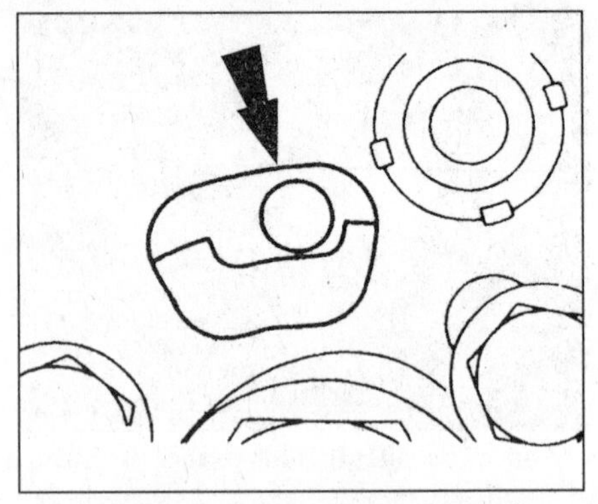

14.100 Ensure that cut out of injection pump flange aligns with slot in sprocket (arrowed)

Refitting

56 Before fitting a new pump, remove the blanking plugs and prime it by pouring in clean fuel.
57 Align the timing peg holes in the pump body and the drive flange.
58 Insert a timing peg through the flange hole into the body hole. If it is tight, it is permissible to use a 5.5 mm drill bit.
59 Fit the pump and tighten the Torx bolts to the specified torque.
60 Locate the pump sprocket and screw in the fixing bolts finger-tight. Ensure that the timing peg passes through all three holes (sprocket, flange and pump body).
61 Centralise the sprocket bolts in the middle of their elongated slots.
62 Engage the drivebelt with the pump sprocket, so that the slack side is towards the tensioner.
63 Release the tensioner so that it snaps against the belt and takes up any slackness.
64 Tighten the tensioner bolt.
65 Tighten the pump sprocket bolts to the specified torque.
66 Remove both timing pegs and the TDC pin.
67 Using the roadwheel, turn the crankshaft through two complete revolutions until the injection pump sprocket timing peg hole is at 12 o'clock and the one in the camshaft sprocket is at 8 o'clock.
68 Now turn the crankshaft anti-clockwise until the pump timing hole is at the 11 o'clock position.
69 Refit the crankcase TDC pin and then turn the crankshaft slowly, until the crankshaft web contacts the pin.
70 Refit the pump and camshaft sprocket pegs. If necessary, slacken the pump sprocket bolts and adjust the mounting flange to enable the peg to be inserted fully into the pump body. Should this adjustment of the flange position have to be carried out, then repeat the operations described in paragraphs 65 to 70.
71 Remove the timing pegs and TDC pin. Screw in the crankcase plug.
72 Refit the injection pump bracket.
73 Reconnect the injector high-pressure pipes (do not tighten yet) and the fuel hoses, using new copper sealing washers.
74 Reconnect the throttle cable and (if fitted) the up speed cable and the fuel shut-off solenoid wiring.
75 Refit the timing belt covers and splash shield.
76 Reconnect the battery. Disengage 4th gear.
77 Using the hand primer on the fuel filter, prime the system.
78 Reconnect the expansion tank hose and top-up the coolant.
79 Crank the engine by operating the starter motor until fuel is seen to be ejected from the untightened injector pipes, then tighten the pipes.
80 Start the engine and bring it to operating temperature. Check and adjust the idle speed as described earlier.

Turbocharged engine

Removal

81 Disconnect the battery earth lead.
82 Remove the alternator and the air conditioning compressor (where fitted) drivebelts.
83 Disconnect the fuel pipes from the pump and the injectors. Blank off all open connections to prevent the ingress of dirt and moisture.
84 Detach the throttle cable from the pump **(see illustration)**.
85 Disconnect the waxstat and idle up speed cables from the pump.
86 Undo the throttle cable bracket retaining screw and detach the bracket from the pump.
87 Disconnect the pump electrical connections by separating the multi-plugs.
88 Disconnect the fuel supply line and the remaining pipes from the pump.
89 Disconnect the hose and rigid pipe from the power steering pump, remove the pump drivebelt cover and loosen the locking bolt to slacken the drivebelt. Remove the drivebelt and the drive pulley.
90 Slowly release the coolant expansion tank cap and then drain the cooling system.
91 Support the engine and remove the right-hand engine mounting.
92 Detach the coolant hose to facilitate removal of the timing belt covers.
93 With the timing belt covers removed, remove the blanking plug and insert the TDC pin into the cylinder block - see Part A of this Chapter.
94 Engage 4th gear, raise the right-hand front roadwheel and carefully turn it to rotate the engine clockwise until it is stopped by the pin.
95 Insert a 6.0 mm diameter pin into the pump timing slots.
96 Insert the camshaft timing pin.
97 Release the camshaft and fuel pump drivebelt tensioners and remove both belts.
98 Remove the pump sprocket retaining bolts, remove the timing pin, followed by the sprocket and belt.
99 Support the weight of the pump, remove the three retaining bolts and remove the pump from the engine.

Refitting

100 Refitting the pump is a reversal of the removal procedure, noting the following:
a) Before fitting a new pump, remove the blanking plugs and prime it with clean fuel, poured in through the return port
b) Align the peg cut-outs of the pump body and drive flange before fitting
c) Ensure that the mounting surfaces are clean before bolting the pump into position
*d) Ensure that the cut out of the pump flange aligns with the sprocket slot when fitting the sprocket **(see illustration)***
e) Tighten the sprocket retaining bolts finger-tight only, until the drivebelt is tensioned
f) With the pin reinserted through the sprocket and the belt refitted, tension the belt, see Part A of this Chapter
g) Refer to Part A of this Chapter and fit and tension the camshaft drivebelt
h) With all the pins removed, rotate the engine two full turns clockwise. Reinsert the pins to confirm the timing. If the pins cannot be inserted, then repeat the timing procedure
i) Tighten all fasteners to the specified torque loading figures

15.4a Undo fuel injection pump sprocket bolts . . .

15.4b . . . then withdraw plate . . .

15.4c . . . and sprocket

j) Clean all electrical connectors before reconnection

k) On completion, check for correct throttle cable operation and signs of fuel leakage

15 Fuel injection pump (2.5 litre engine) - removal and refitting

Removal

1 Disconnect the battery negative lead.

2 On vehicles manufactured after 1995, release the heater element from the cooling system expansion tank, then undo the two retaining bolts and move the tank to one side.

3 Refer to Part A of this Chapter and remove the timing belt.

4 Undo the fuel injection pump sprocket bolts, then withdraw the plate and sprocket **(see illustrations)**.

5 If necessary, remove the air cleaner assembly for improved access to the injection pump.

6 Cover the starter motor with a plastic bag, as a precaution against spillage of fuel.

7 Disconnect the fuel supply pipe from the injection pump. Recover the sealing washers from the banjo union, where applicable. Cover the open end of the pipe and refit and cover the banjo bolt to keep dirt out.

8 Disconnect the main fuel return pipe and where fitted, the injector leak-off return pipe banjo union **(see illustration)**. Recover the sealing washers from the banjo union. Again, cover the open end of the hose and the banjo bolt, to keep dirt out.

9 Disconnect all relevant wiring from the pump. Note that on certain Bosch pumps, this can be achieved by simply disconnecting the wiring connectors at the brackets on the pump. On some pumps, it will be necessary to disconnect the wiring from the individual components (some connections may be protected by rubber covers). On turbocharged models with Lucas EPIC engine management, disconnect the large wiring multi-plug from the socket at the rear of the pump. Cover the opening in the pump after disconnection.

10 Unscrew the union nuts securing the injector pipes to the fuel injection pump and injectors. Counterhold the unions on the pump, while unscrewing the pipe-to-pump union nuts. Remove the pipes as a set. Cover open unions to keep dirt out **(see illustration)**.

11 Disconnect the accelerator cable from the injection pump **(see illustrations)**. Where fitted, disconnect the EGR throttle valve control rod **(see illustration)**.

15.8 Disconnect injector leak-off return pipe banjo union (arrowed) from fuel injection pump

15.10 Cover open fuel unions using small plastic bags, or fingers cut from rubber gloves

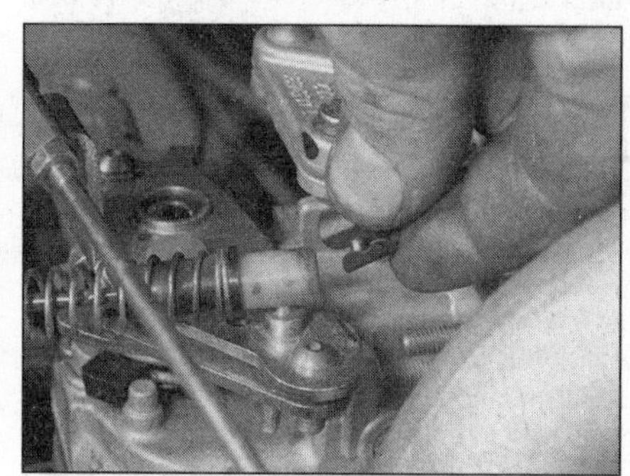

15.11a Extract accelerator cable retaining clip . . .

15.11b . . . and disconnect cable inner from injection pump control lever

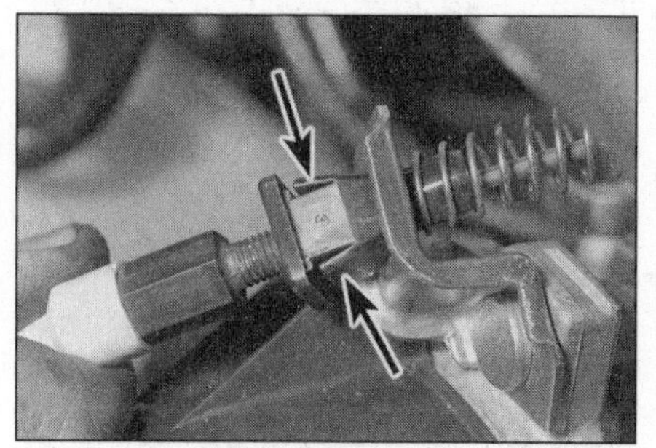

15.11c Depress plastic legs (arrowed) and withdraw accelerator cable from support bracket

15.11d Disconnect EGR throttle valve control rod

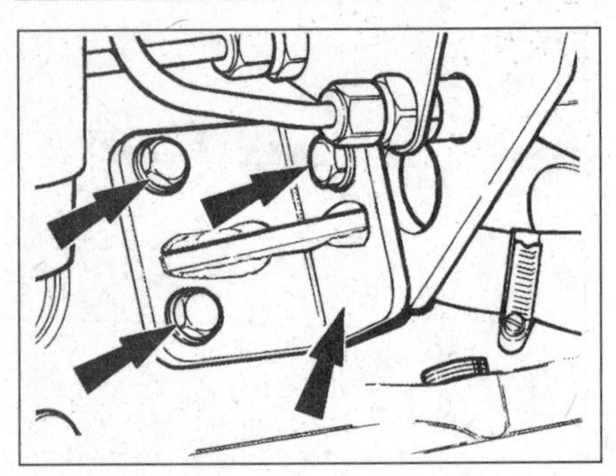
15.13 Undo injection pump rear support bracket bolts (arrowed)

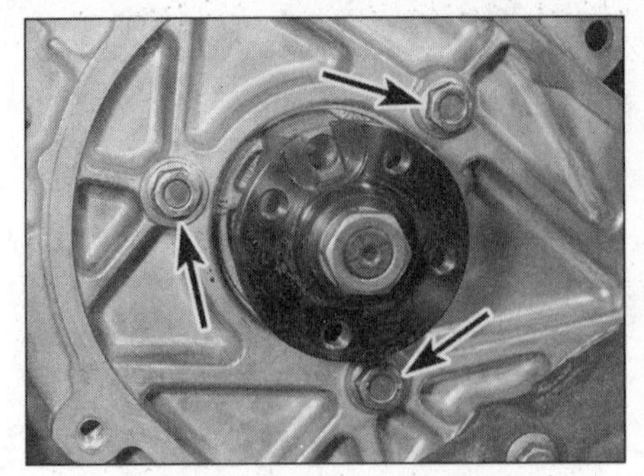
15.14a Undo front mounting bolts . . .

15.14b . . . and lift pump up and off engine

12 Where applicable, disconnect the fast idle cable from the injection pump.
13 Undo the bolts and remove the injection pump rear support bracket **(see illustration)**.
14 Support the injection pump and undo the front mounting nuts or bolts. Lift the pump up and off the engine **(see illustrations)**.

Refitting

15 Commence refitting the injection pump by fitting the rear support bracket to the pump.
16 Locate the pump on the engine and refit the front mounting nuts and bolts, tightening to the specified torque. Ensure that the rear support bracket does not prevent the pump from seating squarely on the engine front mounting flange.
17 Reconnect the fuel supply and return hoses, and tighten the unions, as applicable. Use new sealing washers on the banjo unions.
18 Refit and reconnect the injector fuel pipes.
19 Secure the injection pump rear support bracket to the cylinder block, then tighten the bolts to the specified torque.
20 Reconnect all relevant wiring to the pump.
21 Refit the fuel injection pump sprocket and plate assembly. Ensure that the retaining bolts are in the mid position of the pulley slots.
22 Refit and adjust the timing belt as described in Part A of this Chapter.
23 Where applicable, reconnect the fast idle cable to the fuel injection pump.
24 Reconnect the accelerator cable to the fuel injection pump.
25 Refit the air cleaner, if removed.
26 Reconnect the battery negative lead.
27 Remove the protective plastic bag from the starter motor.
28 Bleed the fuel system.
29 Start the engine and check the fuel injection pump adjustment.

16 Fuel injection pump (1.6 and 1.8 litre engines) - timing

Bosch

1 This operation should only be necessary if the pump has been disturbed, after fitting a new pump, or if the crankshaft pulley bolt has been disturbed. Whenever the crankshaft pulley bolt is slackened, it is possible for the drive gear to move very slightly in relation to the crankshaft, hence the need to check the injection pump timing.
2 Two special tools will be needed, a TDC setting pin and a dial test indicator with a suitable mounting or stand.
3 Slacken the pump mountings so that it is just free to be twisted back and forth within the limits of its slotted fixing holes.
4 Remove the camshaft drivebelt cover. Turn the engine until the pump sprocket timing mark is aligned with the pointer on the timing cover **(see illustration)**.
5 Remove the screw plug and insert the TDC setting pin. Carefully turn the engine in the normal direction of rotation until the crankshaft web contacts the setting pin, showing that No. 1 piston is at TDC.
6 Protect the alternator against fuel spillage, then unscrew and remove the central plug from the rear of the pump **(see illustration)**.
7 Mount the dial test indicator (DTI) so that its probe enters the plug hole and bears on the plunger inside. It is preferable, though not essential, that the indicator be mounted on the pump rather than on the block. Depending on the length of the indicator probe, it may be necessary to remove the injection pipes.
8 Turn the engine slowly anti-clockwise, observing the DTI. The reading will decrease and then become steady. Stop turning when the reading is steady and zero the indicator **(see illustration)**.
9 Turn the engine clockwise again until the setting pin is contacted. Read the DTI. The value shown should correspond to that specified for pump timing. If not, turn the pump one way or the other until it does.
10 Tighten the pump mountings. If the DTI is mounted on the block, tightening the mountings may cause the reading to change. This does not matter provided that the indicator is reset to its new zero.
11 Repeat the operations from paragraph 8 onwards, until the correct result is obtained with the pump mountings tightened.
12 Remove the DTI and the TDC setting pin.
13 Refit the disturbed components, not forgetting the screw plug for the TDC pin hole.
14 Run the engine for a minute or two to bleed any air from the fuel

CAV RotoDiesel

15 For these operations, a dial gauge, a TDC gauge pin and a dial gauge holding fixture will be required. The dial gauge fixture (Ford tool No 21-100) can probably be dispensed with if the radiator and cooling fan are removed to improve access.

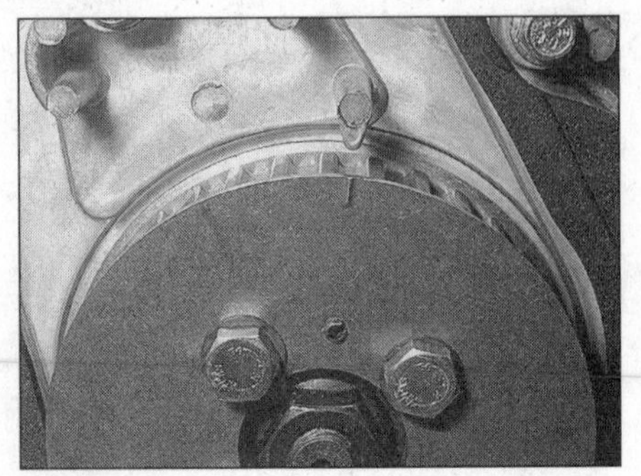
16.4 Pump sprocket mark aligned with pointer on timing cover

16.6 Removing central plug (arrowed) from rear of pump

16.8 Dial test indicator with probe in plug hole

16.20 Checking CAV RotoDiesel fuel injection pump (static) timing

16 Injection pump timing will only be required if the pump has been removed and refitted, or the crankshaft pulley vibration damper bolt has been disturbed. Whenever the sprocket bolt is slackened, it is possible for the sprocket to move very slightly in relation to the crankshaft, hence the need to check the injection pump timing.

17 If timing is being carried out for a reason other than pump removal or refitting, take off the camshaft drivebelt cover and alternator shield and remove the TDC gauge pin hole blanking plug, see Part A of this Chapter.

18 Turn the crankshaft in a clockwise direction until the injection pump sprocket and front cover timing marks are in alignment.

19 Remove the lower plug from the side of the pump body. Be prepared to catch any released fuel and prevent it from entering the alternator.

20 Fit the TDC gauge pin into its hole, then fit the dial gauge and its holding fixture to the fuel injection pump **(see illustration)**.

21 Turn the crankshaft clockwise until the dial gauge stops moving and then zero the gauge.

22 Continue turning the crankshaft until the crankshaft locks against the TDC pin. The dial gauge should register 1.40 ± 0.07 mm.

23 If the gauge reading is outside the specified range, release the pump mounting nuts and bolts and rotate the pump until the correct reading is indicated on the gauge.

17.7 Insert crankshaft timing peg (arrowed) into hole at rear of engine

17.4a Remove blanking plug (arrowed) from timing belt cover . . .

24 Now turn the crankshaft anti-clockwise until the pump sprocket and front cover marks are in alignment. Tighten the pump nuts and bolts.

25 Repeat the operations described in paragraphs 21 and 22 to check the setting.

26 Remove the dial gauge, holding fixture and TDC pin. Refit the plug.

27 Fit the alternator plastic fuel deflector and camshaft drivebelt cover where applicable.

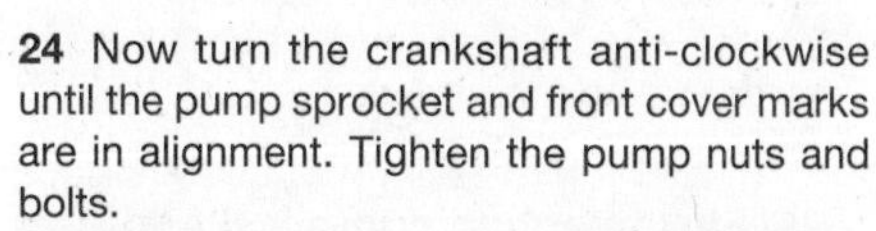

17 Fuel injection pump (2.5 litre engine) - timing

Note: *Timing pegs will be necessary for the following checks and adjustment. Do not attempt to rotate the engine with any of these pegs in position, and do not use the pegs as a method of preventing engine rotation when slackening or tightening retaining nuts or bolts.*

1 Checking the injection timing is only necessary after the injection pump or timing belt has been disturbed. Checking and adjustment is carried out by using pegs to lock the crankshaft, camshaft sprocket and injection pump sprocket. For checking, only the crankshaft and injection pump sprocket pegs are needed.

2 Locking pegs are available as Ford special tools or as complete kits from Diesel injection equipment specialists. Alternatively, rods or drill bits of the correct sizes will suffice. The peg tool numbers and their diameters are as follows:

Crankshaft (Ford tool No. 23-020) - 13.0 mm
Camshaft (Ford tool No. 21-123) - 8.0 mm
Injection pump:
Lucas/CAV and early Bosch (Ford tool No. 23-019) - 6.0 mm
Bosch with Stanadyne injectors - 1989 on (Ford tool No. 23-029) - 9.0 mm

3 Start by disconnecting the battery negative lead.

4 Remove the blanking plug from the timing belt cover and the rubber bung from the front of the crankshaft pulley **(see illustrations)**.

5 Remove the plastic plug from the crankshaft peg insertion hole at the rear of the engine, just above the starter motor. On turbocharged engines with the Lucas EPIC system, the crankshaft position/speed sensor is located over the crankshaft peg insertion hole. Disconnect the wiring multi-plug, undo the retaining bolt and remove the sensor. Recover the shim (if fitted) behind the sensor.

17.4b . . . and rubber bung from front of crankshaft pulley

6 Turn the engine by using a spanner on the crankshaft pulley bolt, until the U-shaped cut-out in the injection pump sprocket becomes visible through the hole in the timing belt cover. It may be necessary to use a mirror to accurately observe the sprocket through the timing belt cover hole.

7 Insert the crankshaft timing peg into its hole, apply gentle pressure to the peg and slowly turn the engine back and forth slightly until the peg engages with the hole in the flywheel **(see illustration)**.

8 With the crankshaft peg inserted, try to fit the injection pump timing peg through the U-shaped cut-out and into the drilling behind it **(see illustration)**. If the peg enters easily, the injection pump timing is correct. Remove the timing pegs, refit the plugs and bungs and reconnect the battery. On engines with a crankshaft position sensor, refit the sensor and spacing shim, if fitted.

9 If the timing peg will not go in, the injection pump timing must be adjusted as follows.

10 Remove the timing belt cover.

11 If not already in place, insert the crankshaft timing peg into its hole.

12 Using the camshaft timing peg, lock the camshaft sprocket by inserting the peg

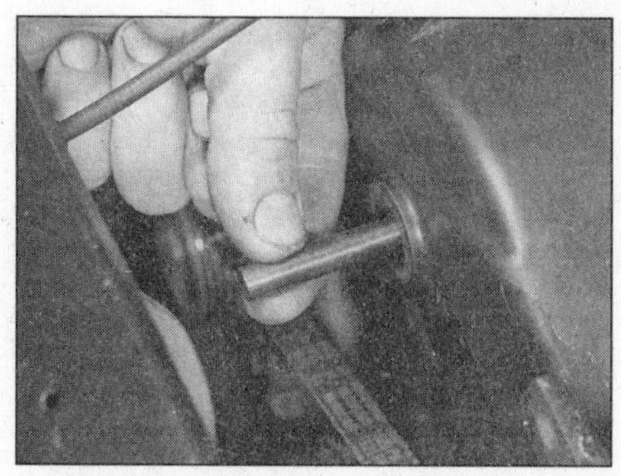

17.8 Fit injection pump timing peg through U-shaped cut-out and into drilling behind it

17.12 Lock camshaft sprocket by inserting peg through hole in sprocket and into drilling behind it

through the hole in the sprocket and into the drilling behind it **(see illustration)**.

13 Slacken the injection pump sprocket retaining bolts and carefully tap one of the slackened bolts with a soft-faced mallet, in one direction or the other, until the timing peg can be fully inserted. Once the peg is in place, tighten the pump sprocket retaining bolts.

14 If there is insufficient movement allowed by the slots of the pump sprocket to enable the timing peg to be fitted, then it will be necessary to remove the timing belt and reposition it on the sprockets.

15 On completion, remove the timing pegs and refit all disturbed components.

18 Fuel system - bleeding

Note: *When working on the 1.8 litre engine, note that the valve fitted between the filter and the fuel injection pump on later engines is used at the factory only to fill and bleed the system on production. Check regularly that it is tightly closed.*

Bosch system

1 As this system is intended to be self-bleeding, no hand-priming pump or separate bleed screws/nipples are fitted.

2 When any part of the system has been disturbed, air must be purged from the system by cranking the engine on the starter motor until it starts. When it has started, keep the engine running for approximately 5 minutes to ensure that all air has been removed from the system. To minimise the strain on the battery and starter motor when trying to start the engine, crank it in 10-second bursts, pausing for 30 seconds each time until the engine starts.

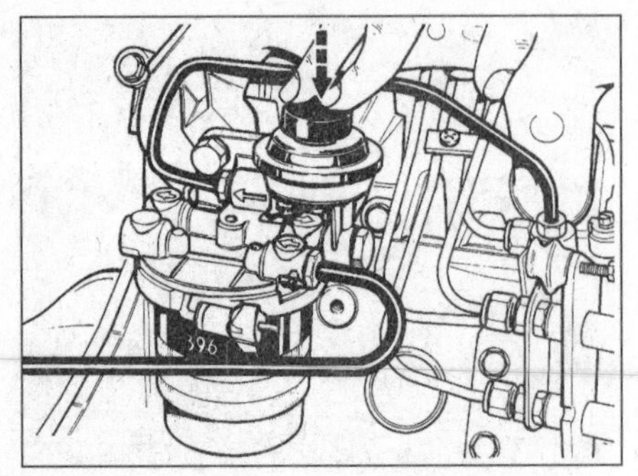

18.5 Hand-operated priming pump on Lucas/CAV injection system

3 Depending on the work carried out, it may be possible to partially prime the system so as to spare the battery by reducing as much as possible the amount of cranking time required to start the engine. To spare the battery, fill the filter with clean fuel via its vent screw opening. It is essential that no dirt is introduced into the system and that no fuel is poured over vulnerable components when doing this.

4 If a hand-operated vacuum pump is available, this can be connected to the pump's fuel return union and used to suck fuel through the supply lines and filter. This will obviously save the battery a good deal of work. If a long length of clear plastic tubing is used to connect the vacuum pump to the injection pump union, it will be easier to see when fuel emerges free from air bubbles. Do not forget to energise the fuel shut-off solenoid by switching on the ignition, to position "II" so that fuel can pass through the pump.

CAV RotoDiesel system

5 This system is fitted with a hand-priming pump which is operated by depressing repeatedly the black button on the top of the filter assembly **(see illustration)**. If air has entered the system, always purge it from the filter bleed nipple first, then (if required) from the pump union and the injector pipes. Ensure that rags are placed underneath the bleeding point to catch the spilt fuel. Diesel fuel must not be allowed to contaminate vulnerable components, especially the clutch, alternator and starter motor.

6 To bleed air from the system as far as the fuel filter, slacken the bleed nipple on the filter outlet union and operate the hand-priming pump until fuel emerges free from air bubbles. Tighten securely the bleed nipple, mop up any spilt fuel and operate the hand-priming pump until increased resistance is felt.

7 If air has reached the fuel injection pump, energise the fuel shut-off solenoid by switching on the ignition to position "II", slacken the pump's fuel return union and operate the hand-priming pump until fuel emerges free from air bubbles. Tighten securely the union banjo bolt, mop up any spilt fuel and operate the hand-priming pump until increased resistance is felt. Switch off the ignition.

8 Finally, start the engine and keep it running for approximately 5 minutes to ensure that all air is removed from the system.

Both systems

9 If air has entered the injector pipes, slacken each union at the injectors and crank the engine until fuel emerges, then tighten securely all unions and mop up the spilt fuel. Start the engine and keep it running for a few minutes to ensure that all air has been expelled.

19 Preheater system (1.6 and 1.8 litre engines) - testing

Note: *The whole preheater system is protected by a fusible link which will melt in the event of a short-circuit.*

1 If the preheater system malfunctions, testing is ultimately by substitution of known good units but some preliminary checks may be made as follows.

2 Connect a voltmeter (0 to 20 volt) or 12 volt test lamp between any glow plug terminal and earth. Have an assistant switch on the ignition. The test lamp or voltmeter should give a positive indication for several seconds, corresponding to the preheating period, then give a zero reading or go out. If not, the relay (or associated wiring) is at fault. Switch off the ignition.

3 If an ammeter of suitable range (0 to 50 amp approx) is available, connect it between the glow plug feed wire and the bus bar. During the preheating period, the ammeter should show a current draw of approximately 8 amps per working plug, ie. 32 amps if all four plugs are working.

4 If one or more plugs appear not to be drawing current, remove the bus bar and check each plug separately with a continuity tester or self-powered test lamp. Before condemning a plug, ensure that the problem is not simply a loose or dirty connection.

20 Fast idle thermostatic sensor (2.5 litre engine) - removal, refitting and adjustment

1 On pre-1992 engines, a thermostatic sensor in the cooling system operates a fast idle lever on the injection pump to increase the idle speed when the engine is cold. The thermostatic sensor is located in the side of the thermostat housing.

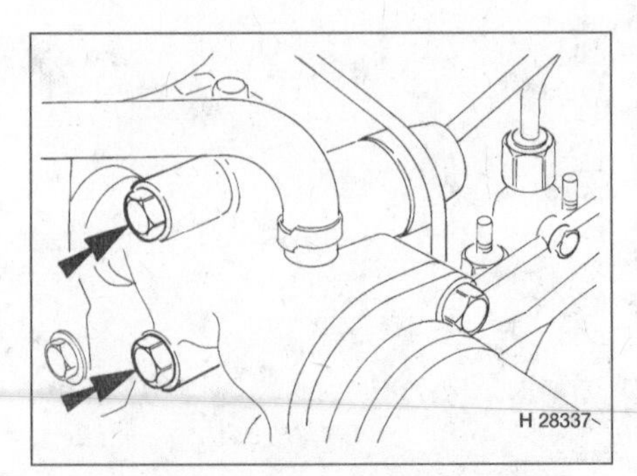

20.5 Thermostatic sensor to thermostat housing retaining bolts (arrowed)

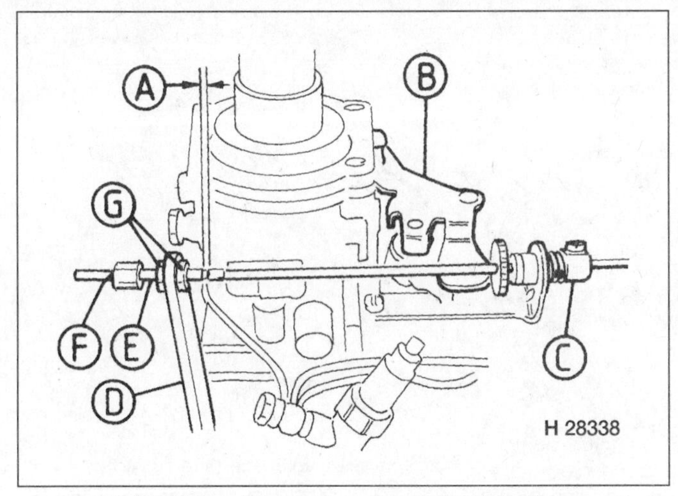

20.13a Fast idle adjustment on Bosch fuel injection pump

A 2 to 3 mm gap
B Fast idle control lever
C Spring-loaded end fitting
D Support bracket
E Adjustment thread
F Outer cable
G Locknuts

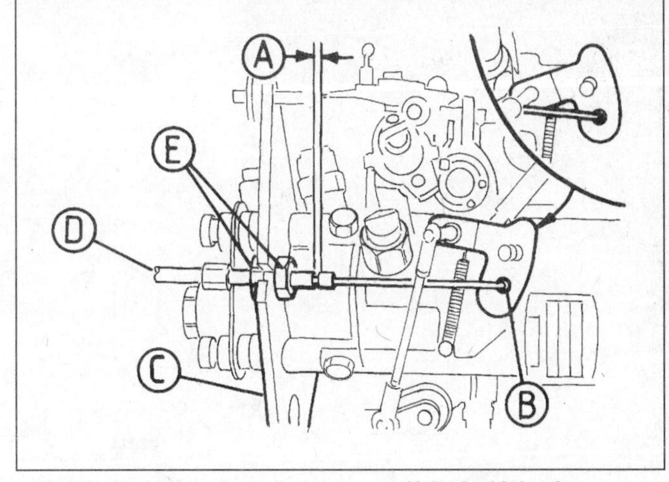

20.13b Fast idle adjustment on Lucas/CAV fuel injection pump

A 2 to 3 mm gap
B Fast idle control lever
C Support bracket
D Outer cable
E Locknuts
(Inset shows fast idle control lever in normal idle position)

2 On later engines, the thermostatic sensor forms part of the injection pump assembly and is non-serviceable.

Removal

3 Disconnect the battery negative lead.
4 Drain the cooling system.
5 Undo the two bolts securing the thermostatic sensor assembly to the thermostat housing **(see illustration)**. Withdraw the sensor assembly and gasket from its location in the housing. Note that a new gasket will be required when refitting.
6 Release the cable outer locknuts from the support bracket on the injection pump.
7 Release the cable inner end fitting from the injection pump fast idle lever. On the Bosch injection pump, the cable inner is released by slackening the screw securing the cable to the spring-loaded end fitting.
8 Remove the thermostatic sensor and cable assembly from the engine.

Refitting

9 Thoroughly clean all traces of old gasket from the thermostat housing and sensor mating faces, then place a new gasket in position.
10 Fit the sensor assembly and secure with the retaining bolts.
11 Refit the cable using the reverse of the removal procedure but leave the cable outer locknuts (and securing screw of the spring-loaded end fitting on Bosch pumps) slack ready for adjustment.
12 Adjust the cable as follows, then refill the cooling system and reconnect the battery.

Adjustment

13 Move the fast idle control lever on the injection pump to the fast idle position and temporarily secure it in this position **(see illustrations)**.
14 On the Bosch injection pump, push the spring-loaded cable end fitting hard against the fast idle stop bracket and tighten the screw to secure the inner cable to the end fitting.
15 Adjust the position of the locknuts so that a 2 to 3 mm gap exists between the end of the cable outer and the ferrule on the cable inner. Tighten the locknuts.
16 Check that, with the cable outer pulled towards the rear of the engine to tension the cable, the spring-loaded end fitting is against its stop (Bosch injection pump), or the fast idle control lever should be hard against the cold operation stop (Lucas/CAV injection pump). The 2 to 3 mm gap should still exist between the cable outer and the ferrule on the cable inner.
17 Release the fast idle control lever.

21 Exhaust Gas Recirculation system (1.8 litre engine) - testing, removal and refitting

1 An Exhaust Gas Recirculation (EGR) system is fitted to some 1.8 litre models to ensure that the vehicle complies with the appropriate emission control legislation. Only vehicles with the Bosch fuel injection system are so equipped. The system comprises the following components:

a) The Thermal-Operated Vacuum Switch - fitted to the thermostat housing. This is closed until the coolant temperature reaches 60°C, thus preventing the system from operating while the engine is warming up
b) The Vacuum Regulator Valve - mounted on the top of the fuel injection pump. This regulates according to throttle opening the amount of vacuum applied to the EGR valve
c) The Vacuum Delay Valve - fitted in the vacuum line to control the rate at which vacuum is applied to the EGR valve
d) The Exhaust Gas Recirculation (EGR) Valve - bolted to the inlet manifold and connected by a supply pipe to the exhaust manifold. This opens under the control of the vacuum switch, regulator and delay valves, using the depression created by the vacuum pump which allows a proportion of the exhaust gases to flow up into the inlet manifold and into the combustion chamber

System testing

2 Whenever the fuel injection pump is removed, the vacuum regulator valve setting must be checked and, if necessary, adjusted.
3 To check system operation, warm the engine up to normal operating temperature and allow it to idle. Disconnect and reconnect several times the vacuum pipe from the top of the EGR valve **(see illustration)**. The valve should be heard to operate each time.
4 If the EGR valve does not operate and vacuum can be felt at the pipe end, first check the setting of the vacuum regulator valve.

21.3 EGR valve vacuum pipe (arrowed)

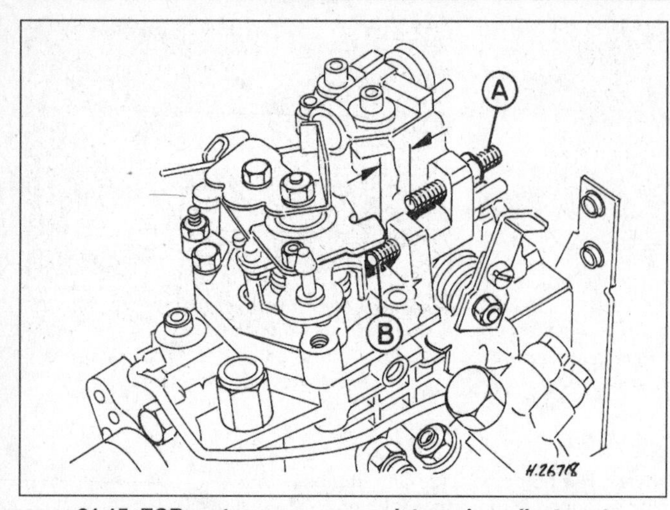

21.15 EGR system vacuum regulator valve adjustment

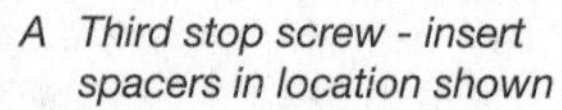
A Third stop screw - insert spacers in location shown
B Maximum speed adjusting screw

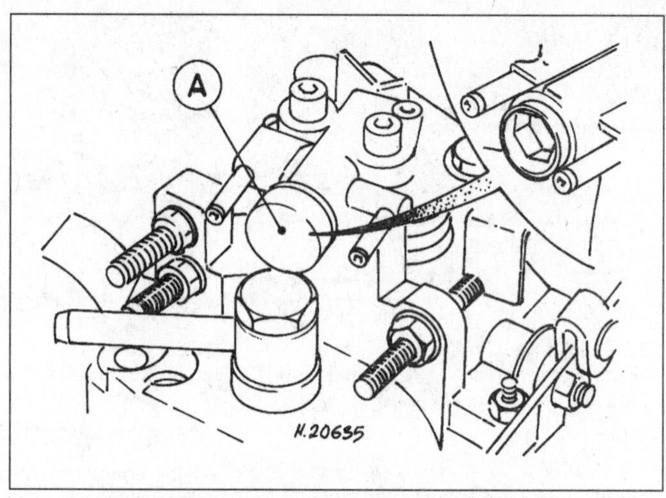

21.18 EGR system vacuum regulator valve adjustment screw under tamperproof cap (A)

5 If the vacuum regulator valve is functioning correctly, the fault must be in the EGR valve, which must then be renewed. If the valve is to be renewed, it is always worth first trying the effect of cleaning any carbon build-up from its passages to check whether this is the reason for the failure. If the valve diaphragm has failed, there is no alternative to the renewal of the complete valve unit.

6 If no vacuum can be felt, check back through the system until the leak or blockage is found and rectified.

Thermal-operated vacuum switch - removal and refitting

7 This unit is screwed into the vacuum pump side of the thermostat housing and can be identified by the two vacuum pipes connected to it.

8 Drain the cooling system, either completely or down as far as the thermostat.

9 Disconnect the vacuum pipes and unscrew the switch.

10 On fitting the new switch, either ensure that a new sealing washer is used or apply a smear of suitable sealant to its threads, as applicable. Tighten the switch securely.

11 Refill the cooling system.

Vacuum regulator valve - adjustment

12 Checking and adjustment of the vacuum regulator valve is only possible if a hand-operated vacuum pump/gauge is available.

13 Connect the pump/gauge to the inlet port (the one nearest the engine) of the regulator valve.

14 Hold the throttle in the fully open position and operate the hand pump continuously. Note the vacuum reading on the gauge, which should be around 0.6 bar (8.7 lbf/in^2).

15 Fit an 11.8 mm thick spacer between the throttle lever and third stop screw (A) **(see illustration)**.

16 Push the throttle lever against the spacer and then operate the vacuum pump. The recorded vacuum pressure should be as previously noted.

17 Change the spacer for one 12.1 mm thick. This spacer should hold the regulator valve open, so that no vacuum reading can be obtained when the vacuum pump is operated.

18 If the regulator valve does not behave as indicated, remove the tamperproof cover (A) **(see illustration)**.

19 Hold the throttle lever hard against the maximum speed adjusting screw (B).

20 Using the vacuum pump, the vacuum pressure should be between 0.6 and 0.7 bar.

21 Fit a 12.0 mm thick spacer between the throttle lever and the third stop screw. Retain the throttle in this position, and operate the vacuum pump.

22 Turn the regulator adjuster screw to set the vacuum pressure to 0.35 bar.

23 Now recheck the vacuum readings using the 11.8 mm and 12.1 mm spacers as previously described.

24 Fit a new tamperproof cap, remove the pump and refit the original hose connections.

Vacuum regulator valve - removal and refitting

25 Note that the valve's inlet pipe (from the vacuum pump) is connected to the union nearest the engine. The valve's outlet union (to the EGR valve) is the union nearest the radiator. On later models this pipe will be marked with a yellow tracer.

26 If no identifying mark can be found, use paint to make your own before disconnecting either pipe.

27 Unbolt and remove the regulator valve.

28 Refitting is a reversal of removal but if a new valve is being fitted, it must be adjusted as described above.

Vacuum delay valve - removal and refitting

29 At the time of writing, no information was available concerning the precise location of this unit, or whether it is available separately from the vacuum pipes. See your local Ford dealer for details.

30 Note that valves of this type are usually clearly marked to show which way round they are to be fitted. Note any such markings or other identifying details of this unit before disturbing it. Ensure that the valve is fitted the correct way round, as noted on removal, and that the vacuum pipes are securely fastened to each end.

EGR valve - removal and refitting

31 Disconnect the battery earth (negative) terminal.

32 Disconnect the vacuum pipe from the top of the valve.

33 Unscrew the two bolts securing the supply pipe to the valve's underside. Withdraw and discard the gasket.

34 Unbolt the EGR valve from the inlet manifold and withdraw it. Withdraw and discard the gasket.

35 If the supply pipe is ever disturbed, always renew the gaskets at its upper and lower ends. Tighten the bolts to the torque wrench setting specified and ensure that the securing clamps are securely fastened on reassembly.

36 On refitting, always renew the gaskets and tighten the bolts to their specified torque wrench settings. Connect the vacuum pipe to the valve, start the engine and check that the system is operating correctly, as described above.

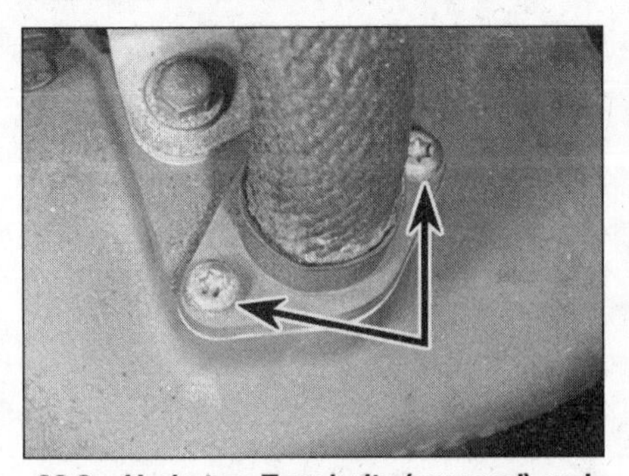

22.8a Undo two Torx bolts (arrowed) and detach EGR connecting hose at exhaust manifold

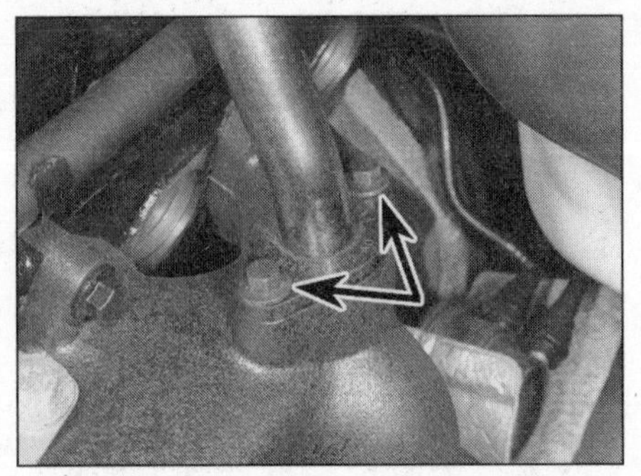

22.8b Alternative EGR connecting pipe-to-manifold connection on later models . . .

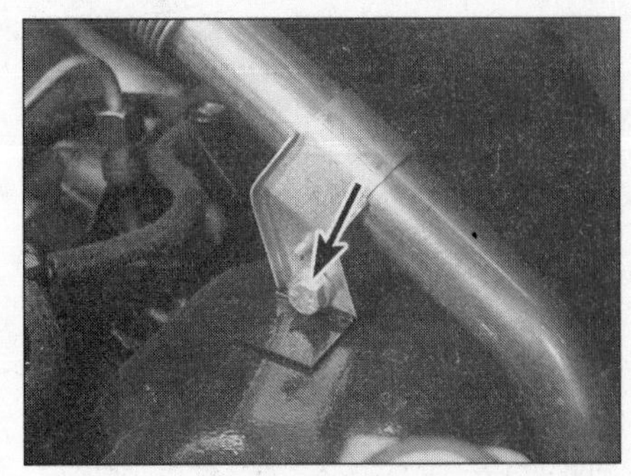

22.8c . . . and connecting pipe support bracket bolt (arrowed)

22 Exhaust Gas Recirculation system (2.5 litre engine) - testing, removal and refitting

1 The Exhaust Gas Recirculation (EGR) system fitted to 2.5 litre engines is designed to recirculate small quantities of exhaust gas into the inlet tract and therefore into the combustion process. This reduces the level of oxides of nitrogen present in the final exhaust gas which is released into the atmosphere.

2 The volume of exhaust gas recirculated is controlled by vacuum (supplied from the inlet manifold downstream of the throttle valve) via an EGR valve mounted on the inlet manifold or turbocharger. Before reaching the EGR valve, the vacuum from the manifold passes to a vacuum valve. The purpose of this is to modify the vacuum supplied to the EGR valve according to engine operating conditions.

3 The throttle valve mounted on the inlet manifold allows the ratio of air-to-recirculated exhaust gas to be controlled. The throttle valve also enables the exhaust gases to be drawn into the inlet manifold at idle or under light load. Without the throttle valve, the inlet manifold would be effectively at atmospheric pressure and the vacuum created by the opening of the engine inlet valves would not be sufficient to cause the exhaust gas to circulate.

4 On turbocharged engines manufactured after 1992, the EGR system operates in conjunction with the Lucas Electronic Programmed Injection Control (EPIC) engine management system. The EGR system is controlled by the EPIC electronic control unit, which receives information on engine operating parameters from an accelerator pedal position sensor, a manifold absolute pressure sensor, a crankshaft position/speed sensor, an engine coolant temperature sensor and an inlet air temperature sensor.

5 The operating principles of the EGR system fitted to turbocharged engines are essentially the same as on normally-aspirated versions but before reaching the EGR valve, the vacuum from the manifold passes to a vacuum flow controller mounted on the engine compartment bulkhead. The purpose of the vacuum flow controller is to modify the vacuum supplied to the EGR valve according to information supplied by the electronic control unit.

6 From 1995, certain turbocharged models are fitted with an EGR charge cooler incorporated in the engine coolant circuit.

System testing

7 Any testing and adjustment of the system should be entrusted to a Ford dealer.

EGR valve (non turbo engines) - removal and refitting

8 Undo the two Torx bolts or clamp ring and detach the EGR connecting hose/pipe at the EGR valve and exhaust manifold. Recover the metal gasket. Where applicable, undo the connecting hose/pipe support bracket bolt **(see illustrations)**.

9 Slacken the hose clip and detach the air inlet hose from the throttle housing **(see illustration)**.

10 Disconnect the throttle actuating lever from the throttle valve linkage.

11 On engines with a one-piece inlet manifold, disconnect the EGR valve vacuum hose, undo the two throttle housing retaining bolts and remove the throttle housing, complete with EGR valve, from the inlet manifold **(see illustration)**. Undo the four Torx bolts and separate the EGR valve and connecting hose from the throttle housing.

12 On engines with a two-piece inlet manifold, undo the bolt securing the manifold to the support bracket. Undo the nuts and bolts, and separate the manifold upper section from the lower section. Recover the gasket between the two halves. Disconnect the EGR valve vacuum hose, then undo the four Torx bolts and separate the EGR valve and connecting hose from the throttle housing.

13 Refitting is a reversal of removal. Use new gaskets at the manifold and EGR valve joints (as applicable) and tighten all nuts and bolts to the specified torque.

EGR valve (turbocharged engines) - removal and refitting

14 Slacken the hose clips and disconnect the air inlet pipe at the hose connection on the inlet manifold.

15 Undo the bolts, detach the air inlet pipe connection at the turbocharger end and recover the gasket. Release the pipe from the support bracket and remove it from the engine. Close off the turbocharger inlet using a suitable cap or clean rag.

16 Disconnect the EGR valve wiring multi-plug and vacuum hose.

17 Undo the two Torx bolts and remove the throttle housing complete with EGR valve. Undo the remaining two Torx bolts and separate the valve from the housing.

18 Refitting is a reversal of removal. Use new gaskets as applicable and tighten all nuts and bolts to the specified torque.

22.9 Slacken hose clip and detach air inlet hose from throttle housing

22.11 Disconnect EGR valve vacuum hose (arrowed)

EGR charge cooler (turbocharged engines, 1995 on) - removal and refitting

19 Disconnect the battery negative lead.
20 Drain the cooling system.
21 Undo the two bolts, disconnect the EGR connecting pipe at the exhaust manifold and recover the metal gasket.
22 Undo the clamp bolt and slip off the clamp securing the other end of the EGR connecting pipe to the charge cooler. Remove the pipe.
23 Disconnect the EGR valve wiring multi-plug and vacuum hose.
24 Undo the two Torx bolts, remove the EGR valve and recover the metal gasket.
25 Release the clips and disconnect the coolant hoses from the charge cooler **(see illustration)**.
26 Undo the retaining bracket bolts and the flange bolts, then remove the charge cooler.
27 Refitting is a reversal of removal, using new gaskets as applicable.

23 Lucas EPIC system (2.5 litre engines) - component testing, removal and refitting

Note: *Before disconnecting any system component, always disconnect the battery negative lead.*

1 From 1992, fuel and emissions control systems on turbocharged engines are controlled by the Lucas Electronic Programmed Injection Control (EPIC) engine management system **(see illustration - on opposite page)**.
2 This system provides programmed electronic control of the fuel injection pump and electronic control of the exhaust gas recirculation system via the EPIC electronic control module (ECU).
3 For the ECU to assess fuel system requirements under all operating conditions, sensors are provided to monitor accelerator pedal position, manifold absolute pressure, crankshaft speed/position, engine coolant temperature and inlet air temperature. Operation of the EGR valve is also controlled by the ECU, in conjunction with a vacuum flow controller.
4 A unique feature of this system is the "drive-by-wire" throttle control. Instead of the accelerator cable being connected to the fuel injection pump, as it is in the normal mechanical system, the cable is connected to a pedal position sensor. This sensor sends pedal position signals to the ECU, which in turn controls the fuel injection pump electronically.
5 When working on the system, observe the following precautions:

a) Disconnect the battery negative lead before removing any of the system's electrical connectors.
b) When installing a battery, be particularly careful to avoid reversing the positive and negative battery leads.

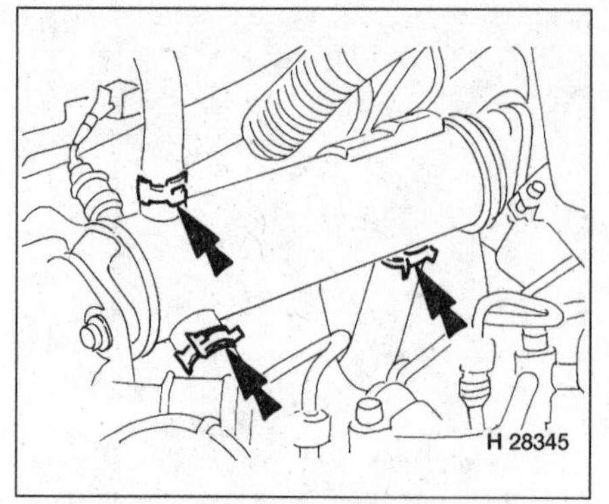

22.25 Release clips (arrowed) and disconnect coolant hoses from EGR charge cooler

c) Do not subject any system components to severe impact during removal or installation.
d) Never attempt to work on the ECU, to test it, or to open its cover.
e) Ensure that water does not enter any component. When washing the engine compartment, do not spray components or their electrical connectors.

System testing

6 The various components of the fuel and emissions control systems are so closely interlinked that diagnosis of a fault in any one component is virtually impossible using traditional methods.
7 So that faults can be quickly and accurately traced and rectified, the ECU is provided with a built-in self-diagnosis facility which detects malfunctions in the system's components. When a fault occurs, the ECU identifies the fault, stores a corresponding code in its memory, and (in most cases) runs the system using back-up values pre-programmed into its memory. Some form of driveability is thus maintained, to enable the vehicle to be driven to a garage for attention.
8 Accurate testing of the system requires the use of Ford test equipment and a methodical test procedure. Therefore, testing should be entrusted to a suitably-equipped Ford garage.

ECU (Electronic Control Unit) - removal and refitting

Pre 1995 models

9 Turn the two retaining catches inside the glove compartment anti-clockwise, push the ECU holding tray slightly forwards and lower the tray with the ECU **(see illustration)**.
10 Push the ECU retaining bracket inwards to release it from the slot in the tray and lift the unit upwards off the tray.
11 Pull the wiring multi-plug locking clip outwards to release it, then unhook the other end and disconnect the plug. Remove the ECU.
12 Refitting is a reversal of removal.

Post 1995 models

13 Undo the two multi-plug rubber boot retaining nuts on the engine compartment bulkhead, pull back the boot and disconnect the multi-plug.
14 Using a screwdriver and protective pad, prise out the stowage tray from the top of the facia on the passenger's side.
15 Working through the stowage tray aperture, undo the mounting bracket bolt and remove the ECU.
16 Refitting is a reversal of removal.

Crankshaft position/speed sensor - removal and refitting

17 The crankshaft position/speed sensor is located at the rear of the engine, just above the starter motor.
18 Disconnect the wiring multi-plug, then undo the retaining bolt and remove the sensor. Recover the shim, if fitted, behind the sensor.
19 Refitting is a reversal of removal, ensuring that the shim (if fitted) is positioned behind the sensor.

Coolant temperature sensor - removal and refitting

20 Drain the cooling system.
21 Unplug the electrical connector from the sensor, located on the thermostat housing.
22 Unscrew the sensor and withdraw it.
23 Refitting is a reversal of removal. Apply a light coat of sealant to the sensor's threads prior to installation and top-up the cooling system on completion.

Inlet air temperature sensor - removal and refitting

24 If necessary, remove the air cleaner assembly or air inlet ducting as necessary, to gain access to the sensor.
25 Disconnect the wiring multi-plug, then unscrew the sensor from the air cleaner casing.
26 Refitting is a reversal of removal.

Accelerator pedal position sensor - removal and refitting

Pre 1995 models

27 Undo the two retaining nuts and withdraw the pedal position sensor mounting bracket assembly from its location in the engine compartment **(see illustration)**.

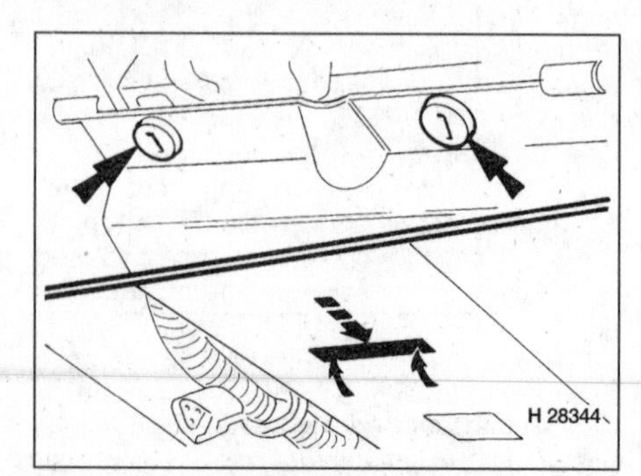

23.9 ECU tray retaining catches (arrowed) and retaining bracket slot

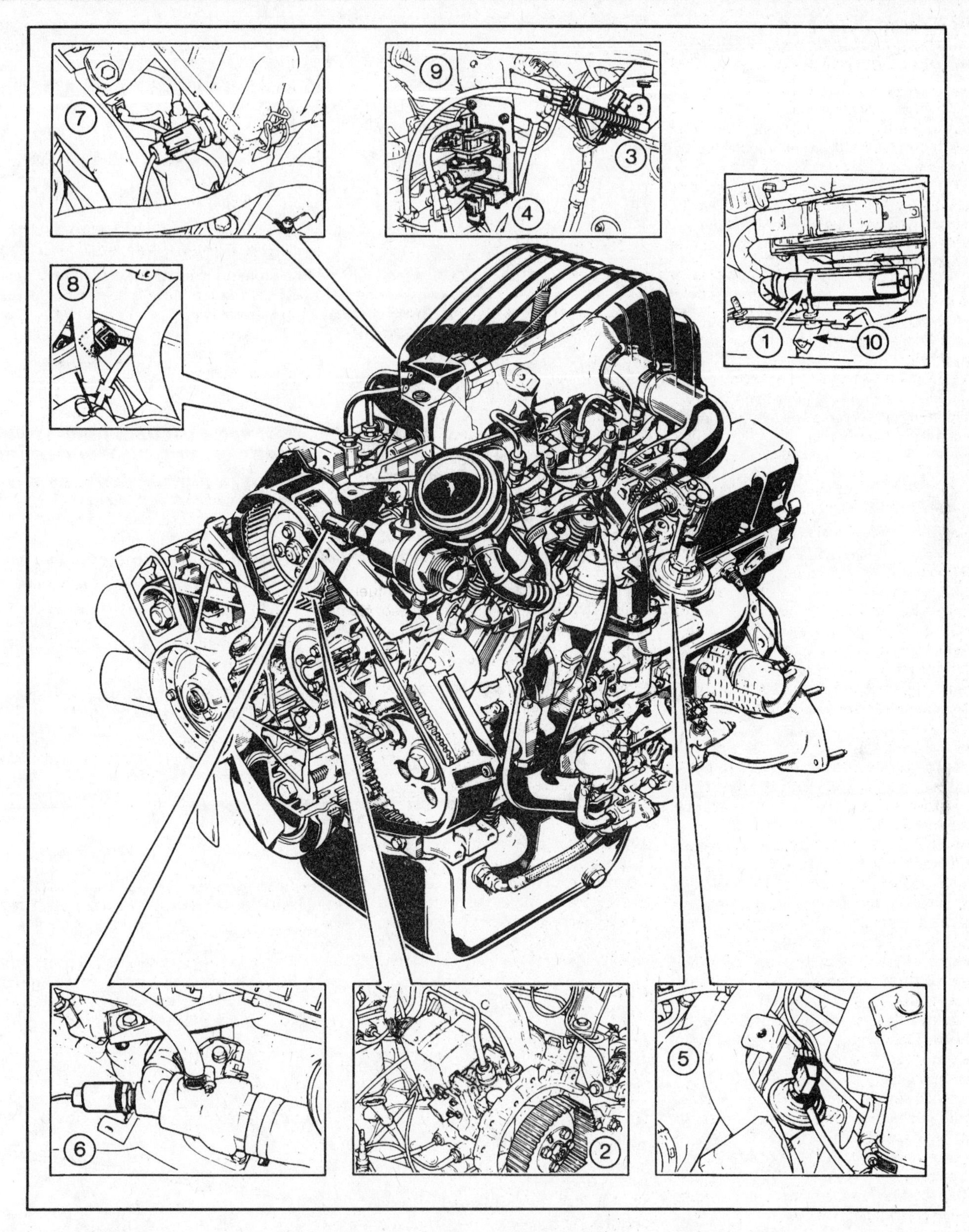

23.1 Lucas EPIC engine management system component location

1 Electronic control unit
2 Fuel injection pump
3 Accelerator pedal position sensor
4 Manifold absolute pressure sensor
5 Exhaust gas recirculation valve
6 Engine coolant temperature sensor
7 Inlet air temperature sensor
8 Crankshaft position/speed sensor
9 EGR vacuum flow controller
10 Self test connector

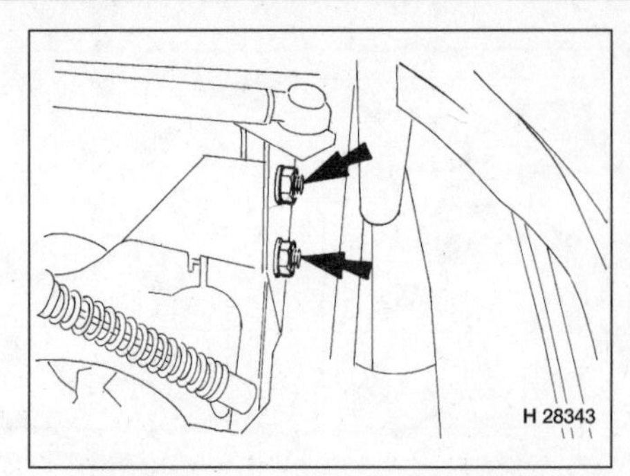

23.27 Undo retaining nuts (arrowed) and withdraw accelerator pedal position sensor mounting bracket assembly

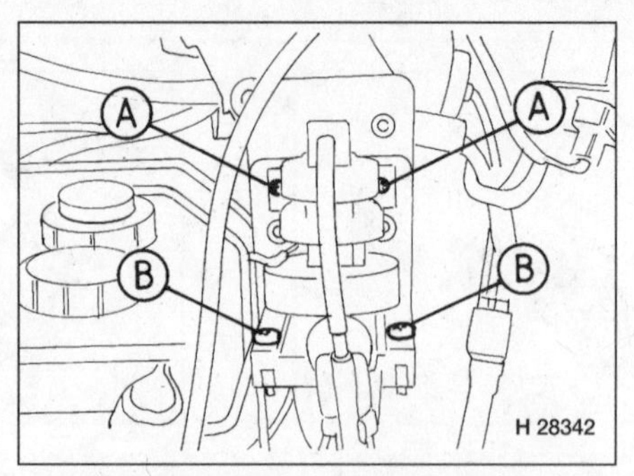

23.32 Manifold absolute pressure sensor retaining screws (B) and EGR vacuum flow controller retaining screws (A)

28 Disconnect the accelerator cable from the sensor link stud.

29 Disconnect the wiring multi-plug, then undo the two retaining nuts and withdraw the sensor from the mounting bracket.

30 Refitting is a reversal of removal.

Post 1995 models

31 On these models, the sensor is an integral part of the accelerator pedal assembly and is removed with it.

Manifold absolute pressure (MAP) sensor - removal and refitting

32 The sensor is located on a bracket attached to the bulkhead at the rear of the engine compartment **(see illustration)**.

33 Undo the mounting bracket bolts and lower the bracket.

34 Disconnect the wiring multi-plug and detach the vacuum hose from the base of the sensor.

35 Undo the two retaining screws and withdraw the sensor from its bracket.

36 Refitting is a reversal of removal.

EGR valve vacuum flow controller - removal and refitting

37 The vacuum flow controller is mounted, together with the manifold absolute pressure sensor, on a bracket attached to the bulkhead at the rear of the engine compartment. Removal and refitting procedures are the same as for the MAP sensor.

Chapter 6
Land Rover 2286cc & 2495cc engines

Part A: Routine maintenance and servicing

Contents

Engine application

2286cc engine . . . . . Land Rover Series IIA & III, 90, 110 and Defender - 1958 to 1995
2495cc engine . . . . . Land Rover Discovery, 90, 110 and Defender - 1983 to 1995

Manufacturer's engine codes

Discovery

2495cc - 200 TDi engine 12L00001
2495cc - 300 TDi engine:
- Manual gearbox and EDC (Electronic Diesel Control) 17L00001
- Manual gearbox and DETOX system (not UK) 18L00001
- Automatic transmission and EDC (Electronic Diesel Control) 19L00001
- Automatic transmission and DETOX system (not UK) 20L00001
- Manual gearbox and EGR (Exhaust Gas Recirculation) 21L00001
- Automatic transmission and EGR (Exhaust Gas Recirculation) 22L00001

90, 110 and Defender

2286 cc - Normally-aspirated (1983 to 1984) 10J
2495 cc - Normally-aspirated (1984 to 1986) 12J
2495 cc - Turbocharged (1986 to September 1990) 19J
2495 cc - Turbocharged and intercooled:
- September 1990 to 1994 . . . . . 200 TDi
- 1994 on . . . . . 300 TDi

Servicing specifications

Oil filter

Discovery	Champion C105
Defender:	
10J engine	Champion X117
All except 10J engine	Champion C105
Series IIA & III	Champion X117

Valve clearances (cold)

Discovery (inlet and exhaust)	0.20 mm
Defender (inlet and exhaust):	
10J, 12J and 19J engines	0.25 mm
200 TDi and 300 TDi engines	0.20 mm
Series IIA & III (inlet and exhaust)	0.25 mm

Timing belt

Type	Toothed belt

Discovery

Tension (using gauge-type torque wrench):	
200 TDi engine	18 to 20 Nm
300 TDi engine:	
New belt	14 to 16 Nm
Used belt	11 to 13 Nm

Defender

Tension (using gauge-type torque wrench):	**New belt**	**Used belt**
12J and 19J engines	24 to 29 Nm	19 to 24 Nm
200 TDi engine	19 Nm	17 Nm
300 TDi engine	14 to 16 Nm	11 to 13 Nm

Auxiliary drivebelts tension

Discovery:	
200 TDi engine	0.5 mm deflection for every 25.0 mm of belt run. Measured midway between pulleys
300 TDi engine	Automatic
Defender - 10J, 12J and 19J engines:	
Alternator/coolant pump	9.0 mm deflection, midway between pulleys on longest run
Power steering pump	12.0 mm deflection, midway between pulleys on longest run
Air conditioning compressor	12.0 mm deflection, midway between pulleys on longest run
Defender:	
200 TDi engine:	
Alternator/coolant pump/power steering pump	0.5 mm deflection for every 25.0 mm of belt run. Measured midway between pulleys
Air conditioning compressor	12.0 mm deflection, midway between pulleys on longest run
300 TDi engine:	
Alternator/coolant pump/power steering pump	Automatic
Air conditioning compressor	35 Nm (using gauge-type torque wrench)
Series IIA & III	13.0 mm deflection, midway between pulleys on longest run

Air filter

Discovery	Champion W709
Defender:	
19J engine	Champion W709
200 TDi engine	Champion W710
All other engines	No recommendation at time of writing
Series IIA & III:	
Type	AC centrifugal oil bath
Oil capacity	0.85 litre

Fuel filter

Discovery	Champion L111
Defender:	
10J and 12J engines	Champion L131 or L137
19J and 200 TDi engines	Champion L111
300 TDi engine	No recommendation at time of writing
Series IIA & III	Champion L131 or L137

Glow plugs

Discovery	Champion CH70
Defender:	
Non-turbocharged engines	Champion CH63
Turbocharged engines	Champion CH70
Series IIA & III	Champion CH63

Idle speed

Discovery	720 ± 20 rpm
Defender:	
10J and 12J engines	650 ± 20 rpm
19J engine	670 ± 20 rpm
200 TDi engine	780 to 800 rpm
300 TDi engine	720 ± 20 rpm
Series IIA & III	590 ± 20 rpm

Fast idle speed

Discovery	Determined by idle speed - no adjustment possible

Turbocharger maximum boost pressure

Discovery	0.8 to 1.0 bar
Defender:	
19J engine	0.64 bar
200 TDi engine	0.78 bar
300 TDi engine	0.83 to 1.04 bar

Torque wrench settings

	Nm	lbf ft
Discovery		
Camshaft sprocket bolt - 200 TDi engine	45	33
Camshaft sprocket hub-to-camshaft bolt - 300 TDi engine	80	59
Camshaft sprocket-to-camshaft hub bolts - 300 TDi engine	25	18
Coolant pump securing bolts - 200 TDi engine	26	19
Crankshaft pulley bolt - 300 TDi engine:		
Stage 1	80	59
Stage 2	Angle-tighten through a further 90°	
Engine sump drain plug:		
200 TDi engine	45	33
300 TDi engine	35	26
Fuel injection pump sprocket-to-hub bolts	25	18
Glow plugs	23	17
Tappet adjuster nut:		
200 TDi engine	25	18
300 TDi engine	16	12
Timing belt cover bolts	25	18
Timing belt idler pulley nut	45	33
Timing belt tensioner bolt	45	33
Defender		
200 TDi and 300 TDi engines	As for Discovery	
Engine sump drain plug:		
10J, 12J and 19J engines	35	26
Series IIA & III		
Fuel injector securing nuts	6 to 8	0.8 to 1.1

Lubricants, fluids and capacities

Component or system	Lubricant or fluid	Capacity
Discovery		
Engine	Multigrade engine oil, viscosity range SAE 5W/30 to 25W/50, to specification RES.22.OL.PD-2 or CCMC PD-2	6.0 litres - 200 TDi without filter 5.8 litres - 300 TDi without filter
Cooling system	Ethylene glycol based antifreeze. 50% volume with water	11.5 litres
Fuel system	Commercial Diesel fuel for road vehicles (DERV)	81.8 litres - Pre March 1993 89.0 litres - Post April 1993
Defender		
Engine	Multigrade engine oil, viscosity range SAE 5W/30 to 25W/50, to specification RES.22.OL.PD-2 or CCMC PD-2	6.0 litres - All except 300TDi without filter 5.8 litres - 300 TDi without filter
Cooling system	Ethylene glycol based antifreeze. 50% volume with water	10.8 litres - 10J and 12J engines 11.1 litres - 19J, 200 TDi and 300 TDi
Fuel system	Commercial Diesel fuel for road vehicles (DERV)	79.5 litres - Rear-mounted tank 45.5 litres - Side-mounted tank on Station Wagon 68.2 litres - Side-mounted tank on all other models
Series IIA & III		
Engine	Multigrade engine oil, viscosity range SAE 10W/40 to 20W/50, to specification API SE or SF	6.0 litres - without filter
Cooling system	Ethylene glycol based antifreeze. 50% volume with water	10.0 litres - Series IIA 7.8 litres - Series III
Fuel system	Commercial Diesel fuel for road vehicles (DERV)	45.0 litres - 88 models 68.0 litres - 109 models

Land Rover diesel engine - maintenance schedule

The maintenance schedules which follow are basically those recommended by the manufacturer. Servicing intervals are determined by mileage or time elapsed - this is because fluids and systems deteriorate with age as well as with use. Follow the time intervals if the appropriate mileage is not covered within the specified period.

Vehicles operating under adverse conditions may need more frequent maintenance. Adverse conditions include climatic extremes, full-time towing or taxi work, driving on unmade roads, and a high proportion of short journeys. The use of inferior fuel can cause early degradation of the engine oil. Consult a Land Rover dealer for advice on these points.

Every 250 miles (400 km), weekly, or before a long journey - All models

- ☐ Check engine oil level and top up if necessary (Section 3)
- ☐ Check coolant level and top up if necessary (Section 4)
- ☐ Check exhaust smoke (Section 5)
- ☐ Check operation of glow plug warning light (Section 6)

Every 4000 miles (6000 km) - Series IIA & III

- ☐ Renew engine oil and filter (Section 7)
- ☐ Renew oil in oil bath type air cleaner
- ☐ Drain water from fuel filter and sedimenter (Section 8)
- ☐ Check condition and tension of auxiliary drivebelt
- ☐ Drain flywheel housing (Section 9)

Every 6000 miles (10 000 km) - Discovery

- ☐ Renew engine oil and filter (Section 10)
- ☐ Check valve clearances* (Section 15)
- ☐ Check engine idle speed* (Section 16)

**Check at first 6000 miles (10 000 km), then at 12 000 miles (20 000 km) intervals*

Every 6000 miles (10 000 km) - Defender

- ☐ Renew engine oil and filter (Section 10)
- ☐ Check valve clearances* (Section 22)
- ☐ Check engine idle speed (Section 11)
- ☐ Check engine compartment hoses for security and leaks
- ☐ Check condition and tension of auxiliary drivebelts
- ☐ Clean fuel sedimenter - 1995 models on (Section 12)

**Check at first 6000 miles (10 000 km), then at 12 000 miles (20 000 km), and every 12 000 miles (20 000 km) thereafter*

Every 8000 miles (12 000 km) - Series IIA & III

- ☐ Clean engine breather filters (Section 13)
- ☐ Check valve clearances (Section 14)

Every 12 000 miles (20 000 km) - Discovery

- ☐ Check valve clearances (Section 15)
- ☐ Check engine idle speed (Section 16)
- ☐ Renew fuel filter element (Section 17)
- ☐ Renew air cleaner element
- ☐ Clean engine breather filter (Section 18)
- ☐ Check engine compartment hoses for security and leaks
- ☐ Check condition and security of glow plug wiring
- ☐ Check condition of air cleaner dump valve - 200 TDi engine (Section 19)
- ☐ Check condition and tension of auxiliary drivebelts
- ☐ Check security and condition of exhaust system
- ☐ Clean fuel sedimenter (Section 20)
- ☐ Drain flywheel and timing belt housings (Section 21)

Every 12 000 miles (20 000 km) - Defender

- ☐ Check valve clearances (Section 22)
- ☐ Renew fuel filter element (Section 23)
- ☐ Renew air cleaner element
- ☐ Clean engine breather filter (Section 24)
- ☐ Check condition and security of glow plug wiring
- ☐ Check condition of air cleaner dump valve - 200 TDi engine (Section 25)
- ☐ Check security and condition of exhaust system
- ☐ Clean fuel sedimenter - Pre 1995 models (Section 26)
- ☐ Drain flywheel and timing belt housings (Section 27)

Every 12 000 miles (20 000 km) - Series IIA & III

- ☐ Check fuel injectors (Section 28)
- ☐ Renew fuel filter element (Section 29)
- ☐ Clean fuel sedimenter (Section 30)
- ☐ Clean fuel sediment bowl (Section 31)

Every 20 000 miles (30 000 km) - Series IIA & III

- ☐ Clean emission control flame-trap

Every 24 000 miles (40 000 km) - Discovery

- ☐ Check turbocharger boost pressure (Section 32)

Every 24 000 miles (40 000 km) - Defender

- ☐ Check turbocharger boost pressure (Section 33)
- ☐ Check fuel injectors for leaks (Section 34)
- ☐ Check fuel injector spray pattern - 10J, 12J and 19J engines (Section 35)

Every 2 years - Discovery & Defender

- ☐ Renew engine coolant

Every 48 000 miles (80 000 km) - Discovery and Defender

- ☐ Clean intercooler element (Section 36)

Every 60 000 miles (100 000 km) or 5 years - Discovery

- ☐ Renew timing belt (Section 37)

Every 60 000 miles (100 000 km) or 5 years - Defender (12J & 19J engines)

- ☐ Renew timing belt (Section 38)

Every 72 000 miles (120 000 km) or 6 years - Defender (200 TDi & 300 TDi engines)

- ☐ Renew timing belt (Section 39)

Every 96 000 miles (154 000 km) - Discovery & Defender

- ☐ Renew catalytic converter

Underbonnet view of 300 TDi Diesel engine in Land Rover Discovery

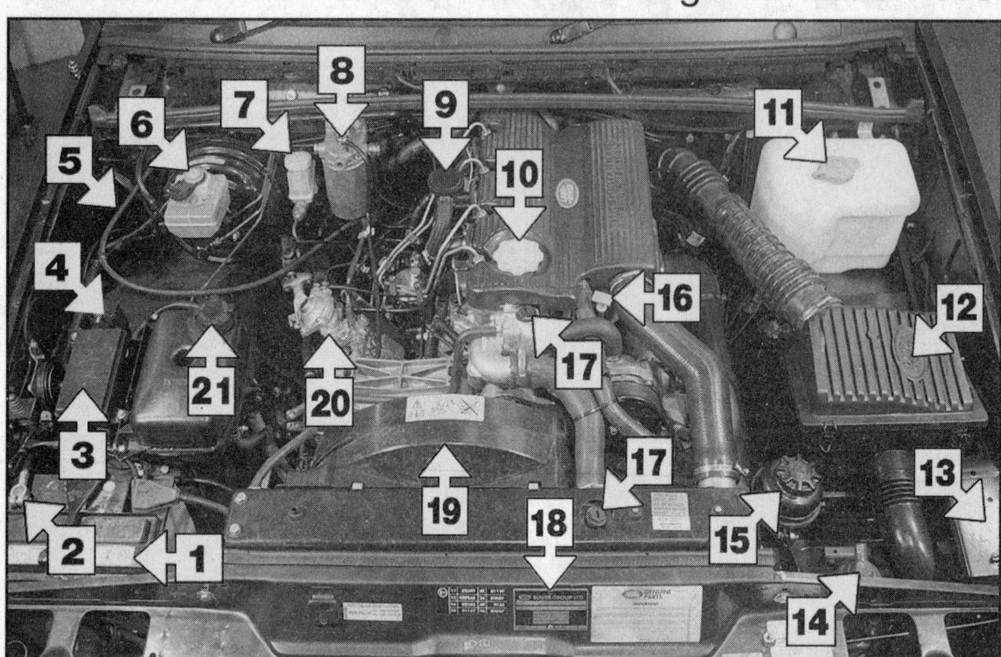

1 Battery
2 Battery negative lead
3 Fusebox
4 Preheating system relay/timer unit
5 Accelerator cable
6 Brake fluid reservoir
7 Clutch fluid reservoir
8 Fuel filter assembly
9 Engine breather filter
10 Engine oil filler cap
11 Washer fluid reservoir
12 Air cleaner casing
13 Wheel chock
14 Jack
15 Power steering fluid reservoir
16 Engine oil level dipstick
17 Cooling system bleed screw
18 VIN plate
19 Cooling fan cowl
20 Fuel injection pump
21 Coolant expansion tank cap

Underbonnet view of 19J Diesel engine in Land Rover Defender

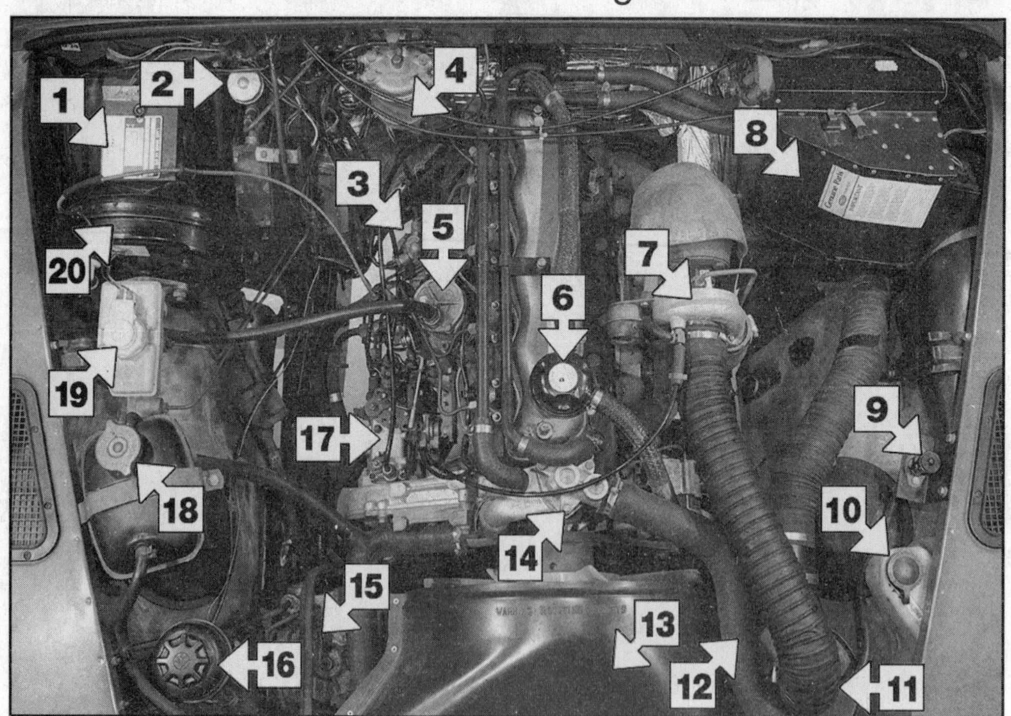

1 VIN plate
2 Clutch fluid reservoir
3 Fuel lift pump
4 Fuel filter
5 Brake vacuum pump
6 Engine oil filler cap
7 Turbocharger
8 Heater
9 Air filter element condition indicator
10 Washer fluid reservoir
11 Air cleaner
12 Radiator top hose
13 Cooling fan cowl
14 Thermostat housing
15 Steering box
16 Power steering fluid reservoir
17 Fuel injection pump
18 Coolant expansion tank
19 Brake fluid reservoir
20 Brake vacuum servo

Maintenance procedures

1 Introduction

Refer to Chapter 2, Part A, Section 1.

2 Intensive maintenance

Refer to Chapter 2, Part A, Section 2.

250 mile (400 km) Service - all models

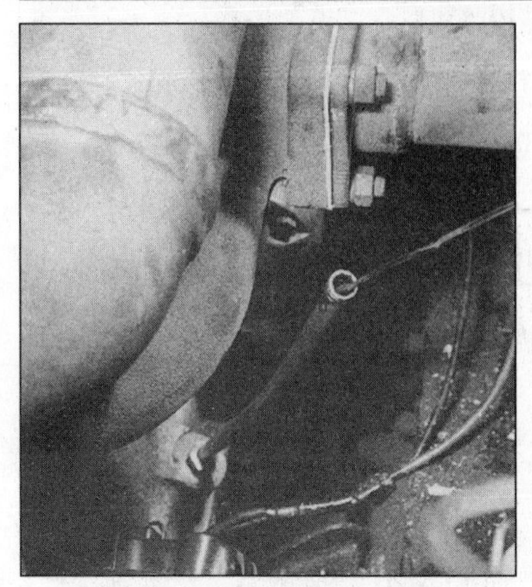
3.1a Engine oil dipstick location - Series IIA and III

3 Engine oil level check

1 Refer to Chapter 2, Part A, Section 3 **(see illustrations)**.

4 Coolant level check

Series IIA & III

1 Refer to Chapter 2, Part A, Section 4, whilst noting the following.

2 On early models not fitted with a cooling system expansion tank, the coolant level should be no higher than within 13.0 mm of the radiator filler cap orifice.

3 On later models fitted with an expansion tank, fill the tank with sufficient coolant to cover the end of the overflow pipe from the radiator **(see illustration)**.

Discovery and Defender

4 Refer to Chapter 2, Part A, Section 4 **(see illustration)**.

5 Exhaust smoke check

1 Refer to Chapter 2, Part A, Section 5.

6 Warning light check

1 Refer to Chapter 2, Part A, Section 6.

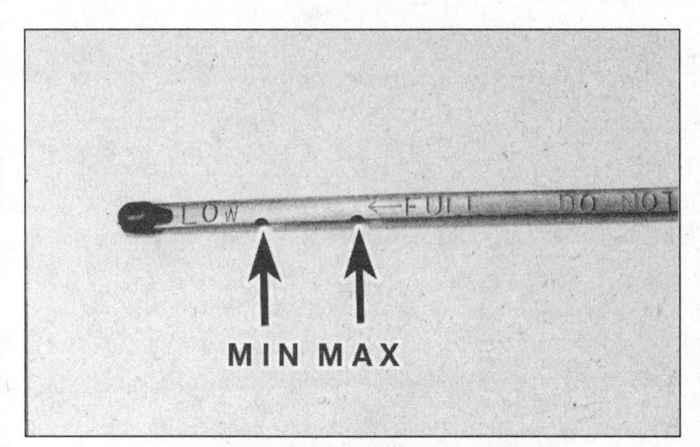

3.1b Engine oil level dipstick markings - Discovery shown, others similar

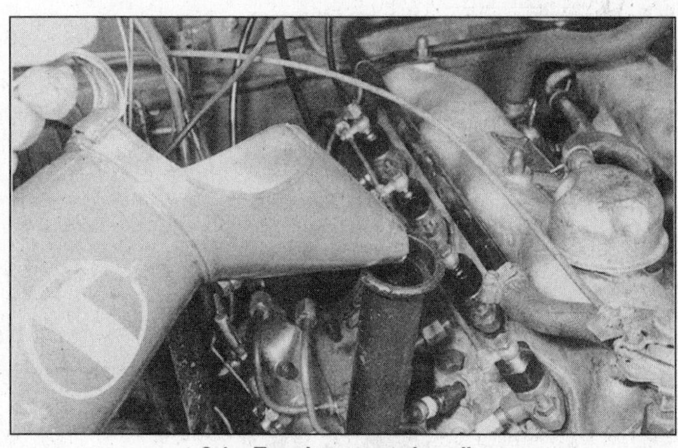
3.1c Topping-up engine oil - Series IIA and III

6A

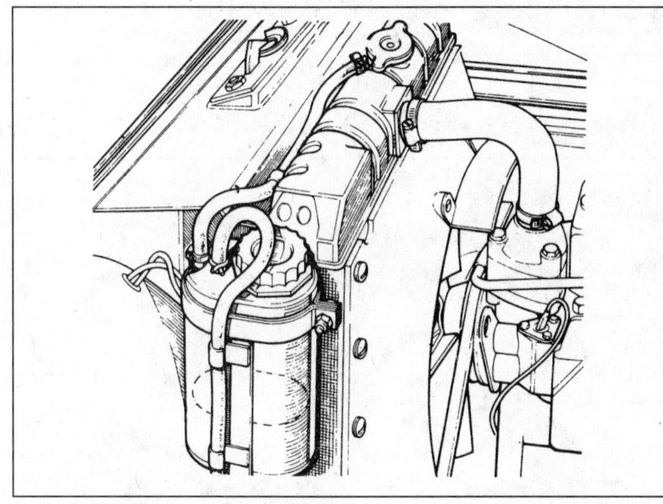
4.3 Expansion tank location - later Series IIA and III

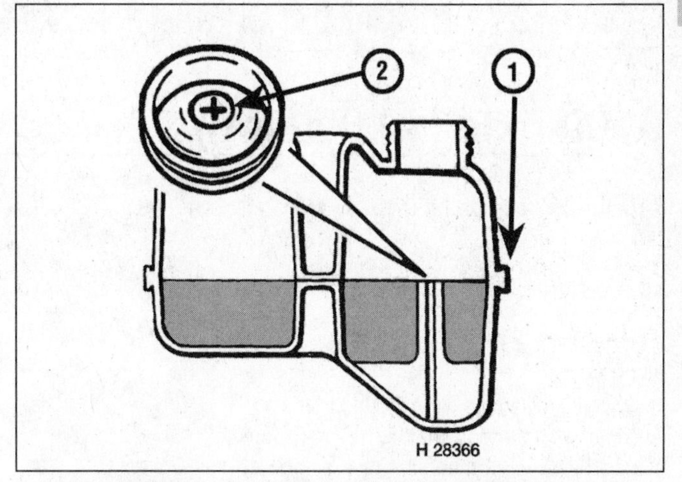

4.4 Coolant level must be up to ridge (1) on front of expansion tank. On later models, a level indicator (2) may also be visible through tank neck - Discovery and Defender

7.1 Engine oil drain plug location - Series IIA and III

7.4a Position new oil filter sealing ring . . .

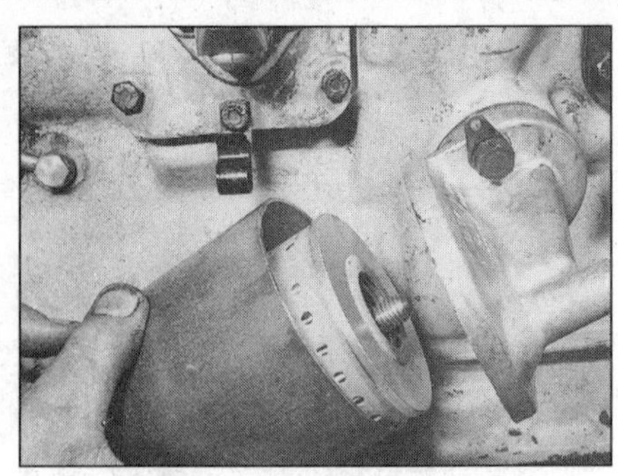
7.4b . . . and refit oil filter

4000 mile (6000 km) Service - Series IIA & III

7 Engine oil and filter renewal

Oil renewal

1 The procedure for renewing engine oil is similar to that given in Chapter 2, Part A, Section 7 **(see illustration)**.

Filter renewal

2 Remove the oil filter element casing by unscrewing its central retaining bolt. As the casing is withdrawn, oil trapped within it will be spilt, so have a suitable container at the ready to catch the oil.

3 Discard the filter element and sealing rings. The new element will be supplied complete with new sealing rings.

4 Refitting is a reversal of removal. Wipe all new seals with clean engine oil before fitting and do not overtighten the central retaining bolt **(see illustrations)**.

8 Fuel filter and sedimenter draining

Fuel filter

1 The main fuel filter is mounted on the engine (early models) or on the engine compartment bulkhead (later models).

2 Drain any water from the filter by slackening the plug on the bottom of the filter body **(see illustration)**.

3 Drain off water and sediment into a suitable container until clean fuel flows from the filter.

4 Immediately close the drain plug when fuel flows from it. Failure to do so may result in the fuel system requiring bleeding.

Sedimenter

5 To drain the sedimenter of water, follow a procedure similar to that given for the main fuel filter.

9 Flywheel housing draining

1 A plug can be fitted to the oil drain hole in the flywheel housing, to seal the housing if the vehicle is likely to be used off-road in very muddy conditions or under severe wading conditions. A suitable plug can be obtained from a Land Rover dealer **(see illustration)**.

2 If the plug is permanently fitted, it should be removed to allow any accumulated oil to drain from the flywheel housing.

3 Clean the plug before refitting.

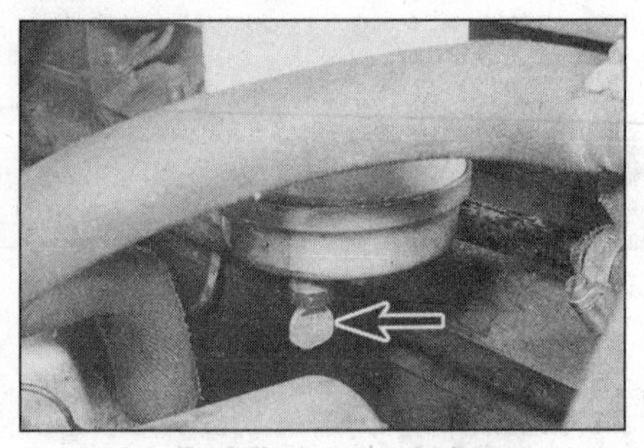
8.2 Fuel filter water drain tap

9.1 Flywheel housing drain hole and plug

6000 mile (10 000 km) Service - Discovery & Defender

10 Engine oil and filter renewal

1 Refer to Chapter 2, Part A, Section 7 **(see illustrations)**.

2 When changing the oil filter fitted to the 10J - engined Defender model, refer to the procedure given for the Series IIA & III models in Section 7 of this Chapter.

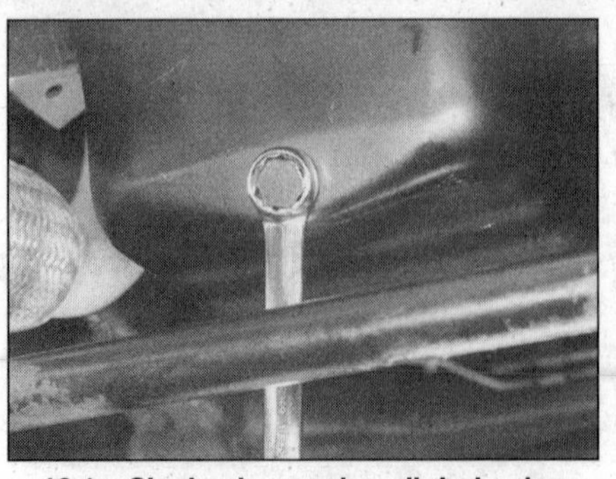
10.1a Slackening engine oil drain plug

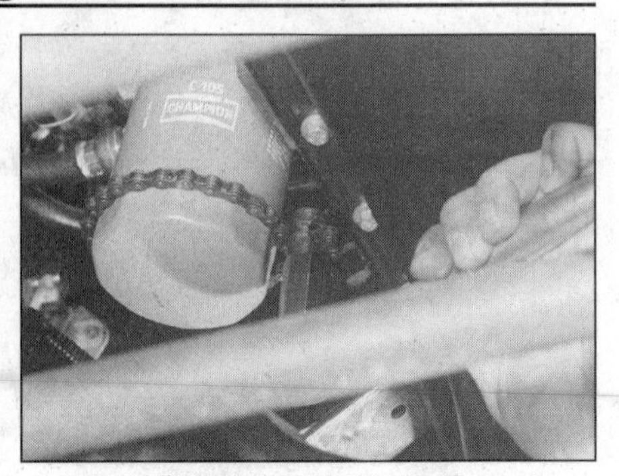

10.1b Slackening oil filter with chain wrench

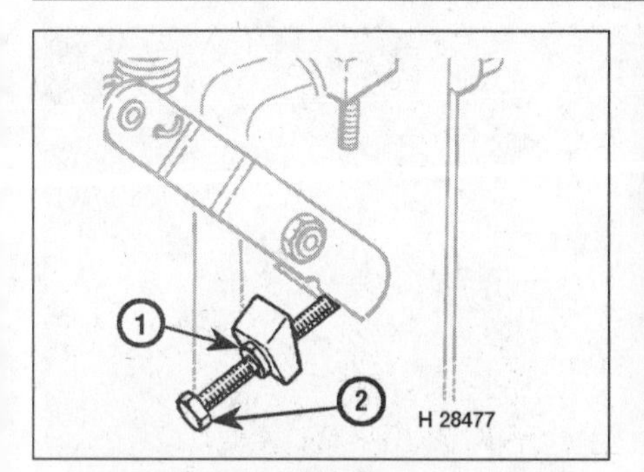

11.4a Idle speed adjustment screw (1) and locknut (2) - 10J engine

11.4b Idle speed adjustment screw (1) and locknut (2) - 19J engine

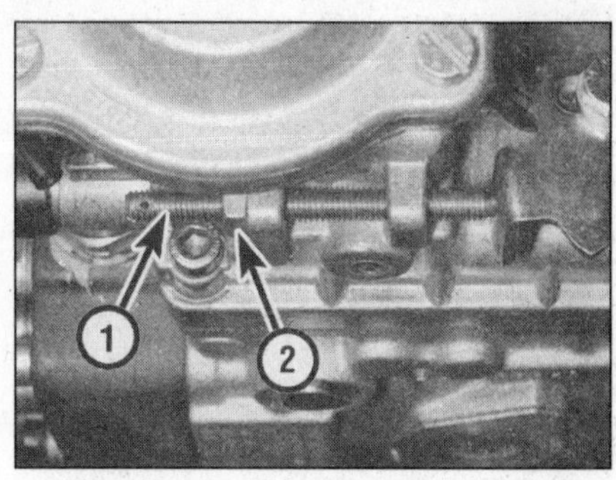

11.4c Idle speed adjustment screw (1) and locknut (2) - 300 TDi engine

6000 mile (10 000 km) Service - Defender

11 Idle speed check

Note: *Fast idle speed is automatically set by setting the idle speed and cannot be adjusted independently. Adjustment of the idle speed is permitted in service but the manufacturers recommend that any other fuel injection pump adjustments are entrusted to authorised Bosch agents.*

1 The usual type of tachometer (rev counter) which works from ignition system pulses, cannot be used on Diesel engines. If it is not felt that adjusting the idle speed by ear is satisfactory, one of the following alternatives may be used:

a) *Purchase or hire of an appropriate tachometer.*

b) *Delegation of the job to a Land Rover dealer or other specialist.*

c) *Timing light (strobe) operated by a petrol engine running at the desired speed. If the timing light is pointed at a mark on the camshaft or injection pump sprocket, the mark will appear stationary when the two engines are running at the same speed (or multiples of that speed). The sprocket will be rotating at half the crankshaft speed but this will not affect the adjustment. In practice, it was found impossible to use this method on the crankshaft pulley, due to the acute viewing angle.*

2 Before making adjustments, warm-up the engine to normal operating temperature. Ensure that the accelerator cable is correctly adjusted.

3 With the accelerator lever resting against the idle stop, check that the engine idles at the specified speed.

4 If adjustment is necessary, loosen the idle speed adjustment screw locknut and turn the screw as necessary to give the desired engine speed **(see illustrations)**. Turn the screw clockwise to increase engine speed, or anti-clockwise to decrease engine speed.

5 Operate the accelerator lever to increase engine speed for a few seconds, then re-check the idle speed.

6 When adjustment is correct, hold the adjustment screw steady as the locknut is tightened.

7 On completion, stop the engine and, where applicable, disconnect the tachometer.

12 Fuel sedimenter cleaning - 1995 models on

1 The fuel sedimenter is designed to increase the life of the fuel filter by removing the larger droplets of water and dirt from the fuel before it reaches the filter.

2 Unit location varies according to model. It is usually mounted under the vehicle on a bracket attached to the chassis, near the fuel tank.

3 Before cleaning the sedimenter element, drain off any water as follows. Remove the drain plug at the bottom of the sedimenter body and allow the water to run out **(see illustration)**. When clean, uncontaminated fuel runs from the drain hole, refit and tighten the drain plug.

4 Disconnect the fuel inlet pipe from the sedimenter and lift the pipe above the level of the fuel tank. Alternatively, plug the end of the pipe to prevent fuel draining from the tank.

5 Support the sedimenter bowl, then unscrew the bolt at the top of the sedimenter head until the bowl can be removed.

6 Remove the sedimenter sleeve from the bowl and recover the plastic collar, then clean the components in clean paraffin.

7 Fit new seals to the sedimenter head and fit a new seal to the top of the bowl, then fit the sleeve to the bowl **(see illustration)**.

8 Fit the plastic collar to the sedimenter head, then fit the bowl/sleeve assembly **(see illustration)**.

9 Tighten the bolt to secure the bowl.

10 Reconnect the fuel pipe and tighten the union.

11 Slacken the drain plug at the bottom of the sedimenter body and tighten the plug when clean, uncontaminated fuel runs from the drain hole.

12 Refer to Part B of this Chapter and prime the fuel system.

13 With the engine running, check for fuel leaks around the sedimenter.

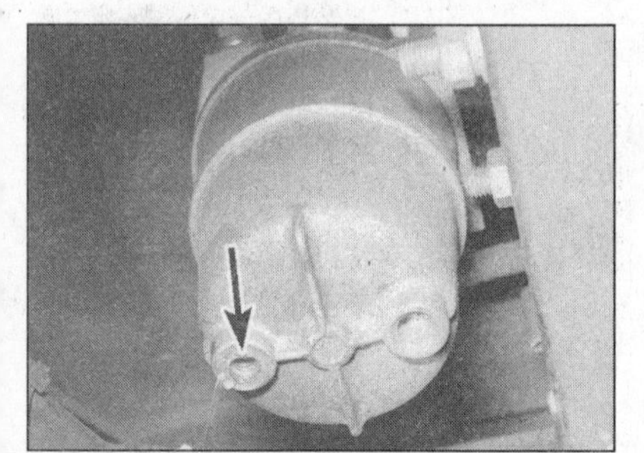
12.3 Allow water to drain from fuel sedimenter drain hole (arrowed)

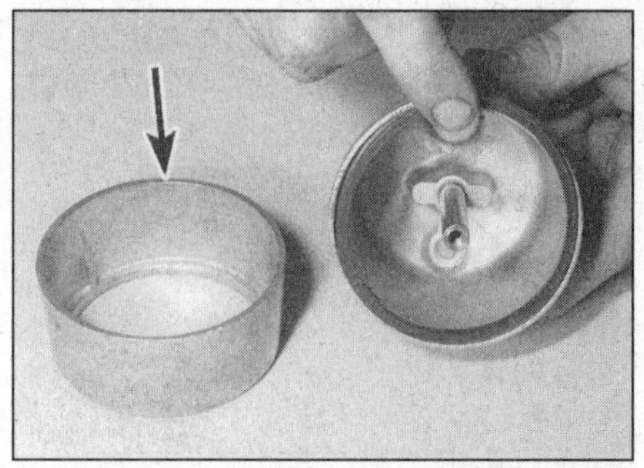
12.7 Fit new seal to top of sedimenter bowl - sleeve arrowed

12.8 Fitting plastic collar to sedimenter head - seals arrowed

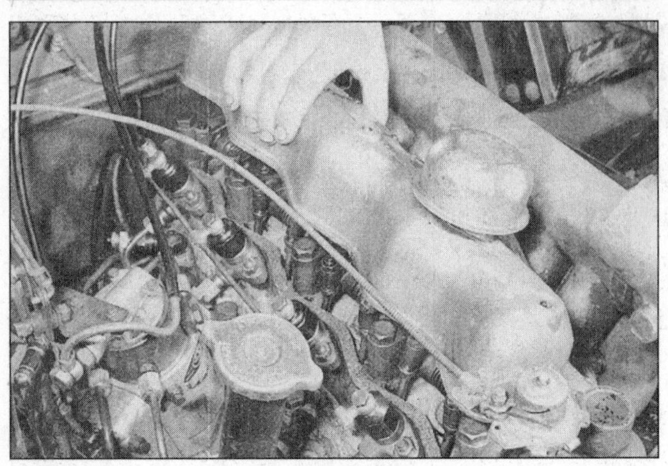
14.1 Removing valve cover

14.4 Adjusting a valve clearance

8000 mile (12 000 km) Service - Series IIA & III

13 Engine breather filter cleaning

1 Remove all breather filters from the engine and immerse them in clean paraffin to dissolve any oily deposits which may have formed on them.

2 When each filter is clean, remove it from the paraffin and dry it thoroughly. All filters must be absolutely dry before refitting.

14 Valve clearance check

Warning: If the crankshaft is rotated with excessive valve clearances, it is possible for the pushrods to become dislodged and fracture the tappet slides. To prevent the possibility of damage, turn the adjusters to eliminate all clearance from any loose rocker arms before turning the crankshaft to check the valve clearances.

1 Remove the valve cover and gasket **(see illustration)**.

2 Using a spanner or socket on the crankshaft pulley bolt, turn the crankshaft until No 8 valve is fully open (valve spring fully compressed). The valves are numbered from the front of the engine. Turning the engine will be much easier if the glow plugs are first removed.

3 Using a feeler blade of the specified thickness, check the clearance between the top of No 1 valve stem and the valve stem contact face of the rocker arm.

4 If the clearance is not as specified, slacken the adjuster locknut and turn the tappet adjuster screw as required to give the correct clearance. Turn the adjuster screw clockwise to reduce the clearance and anti-clockwise to increase the clearance **(see illustration)**.

5 When the clearance is correct, tighten the adjuster locknut. Hold the adjuster screw stationary as the locknut is tightened.

6 With the locknut tightened, re-check the clearance and re-adjust if necessary.

7 Turn the crankshaft and continue to check the remaining valve clearances in the following sequence:

Valve fully open	Valve clearance to be checked
No 6	No 3
No 4	No 5
No 7	No 2
No 1	No 8
No 3	No 6
No 5	No 4
No 2	No 7

8 When all valve clearances have been checked, refit the valve cover.

12 000 mile (20 000 km) Service - Discovery

15 Valve clearance check

Refer to Section 14.

16 Idle speed check

Refer to Section 11.

17.2a Loosen bleed screw . . .

17.2b . . . and unscrew drain tap (arrowed)

17 Fuel filter element renewal

1 The fuel filter assembly is located on the engine compartment bulkhead, to the right-hand side of the engine.

2 Before the filter is renewed, any water should be drained from the filter bowl as follows:

*a) Loosen the bleed screw on the top of the filter head **(see illustration)**.*

*b) Hold a small container beneath the drain tap at the bottom of the filter, then unscrew the tap by half a turn **(see illustration)**.*

c) Drain off water and sediment until clean fuel flows from the tap.

d) Immediately close the tap when fuel flows from it. Failure to do so may result in the fuel system requiring bleeding.

3 Clean the area around the filter head and place a container beneath the filter.
4 Unscrew the filter element and catch the fuel which is released **(see illustration)**. A strap wrench can be used to grip the base of the filter element if necessary.
5 Lubricate the seals of the new filter with a little fuel.
6 Screw the new filter into position and tighten the filter firmly by hand only.
7 Ensure that the drain tap at the base of the filter is closed.
8 Prime the fuel system by operating the priming lever on the fuel lift pump until fuel which is free from air bubbles emerges from the bleed screw on the filter head, then tighten the bleed screw.
9 Start the engine and check for leaks around the filter.

18 Engine breather filter cleaning

Note: *A new gasket will be required when refitting this filter.*
1 The engine breather filter is located at the rear right-hand corner of the valve cover **(see illustration)**.
2 Loosen the clips securing the hoses to the top and bottom of the filter, noting their locations to ensure correct refitting.
3 Unscrew the two bolts securing the filter to the valve cover, then carefully pull the filter away from the valve cover and recover the gasket.
4 Fill a suitable container with clean paraffin, then immerse the filter in the paraffin to dissolve any oily deposits which may have formed inside.
5 When the filter is clean, remove it from the paraffin and dry it thoroughly. The filter must be absolutely dry before it is refitted to the engine.

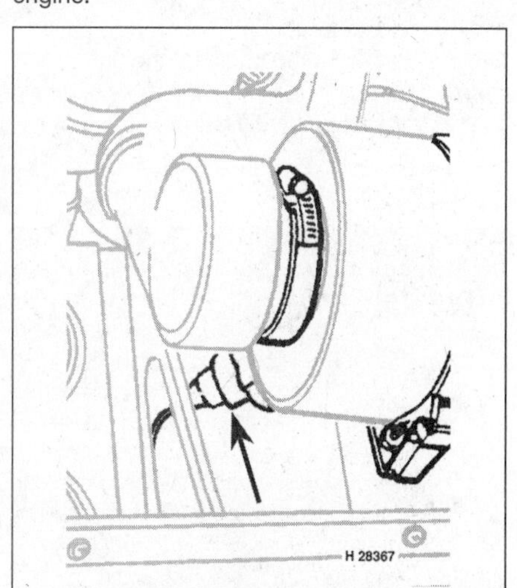

19.3 Dump valve connection (arrowed) - 200 TDi engine

17.4 Removing fuel filter element

6 Refit the filter to the valve cover using a new gasket and tighten the securing bolts.
7 Reconnect the two hoses to the filter, ensuring that the clips are securely tightened to produce a gas-tight seal.

19 Air cleaner dump valve check - 200 TDi engine

1 Remove the air cleaner element from its casing.
2 Thoroughly clean the inside of the casing and lid.
3 Squeeze open the air cleaner dump valve, which is located at the bottom of the casing **(see illustration)**. Check that the valve is flexible and in good condition.
4 If it needs cleaning, pull the dump valve from the air cleaner casing. Fit a new valve if necessary.
5 Fit a new air cleaner element, ensuring that its sealing rubber is towards the air cleaner outlet.

20 Fuel sedimenter cleaning

1 Refer to the procedure given in Section 12 whilst noting the following:
a) The sedimenter is located under the vehicle, on the inboard right-hand side of the chassis, forward of the rear axle.

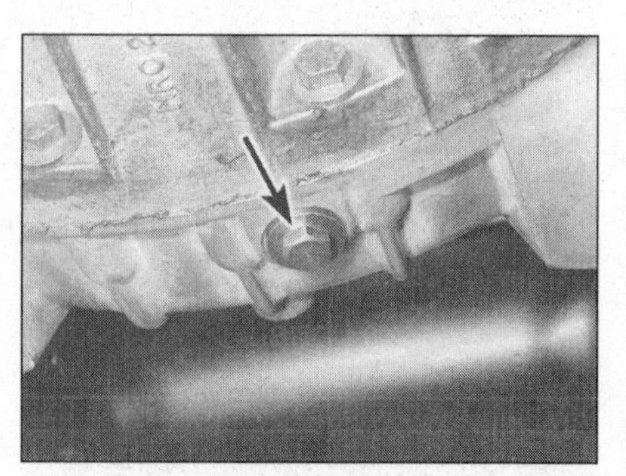

21.1 Flywheel housing drain plug location (arrowed)

18.1 Engine breather filter (arrowed) - 300 TDi engine

b) Refer to the instructions given for 200 TDi and 300 TDi engines when priming the fuel system

21 Flywheel housing and timing belt housing draining

Flywheel housing

1 In production, a flywheel housing plug is not normally fitted. A plug can be fitted to the oil drain hole in the housing, to seal the housing if the vehicle is likely to be used off-road in very muddy conditions or under severe wading conditions. A suitable plug can be obtained from a Land Rover dealer **(see illustration)**.
2 If the vehicle is regularly used in adverse conditions, then the plug should be fitted permanently but if the vehicle is normally used on the road, the plug should be removed.
3 If the plug is permanently fitted, it should be removed to allow any accumulated oil to drain from the housing.
4 Clean the plug before refitting.

Timing belt housing

5 Refer to paragraphs 1 to 4, but note that the plug should be treated as an inspection plug. There should be no oil in the timing belt housing **(see illustration)**.
6 If oil is present, investigate the cause immediately as the timing belt will deteriorate if contaminated with oil.

21.5 Timing belt housing inspection hole (arrowed)

23.2 Secure filter bowl with through-bolt - 19J engine

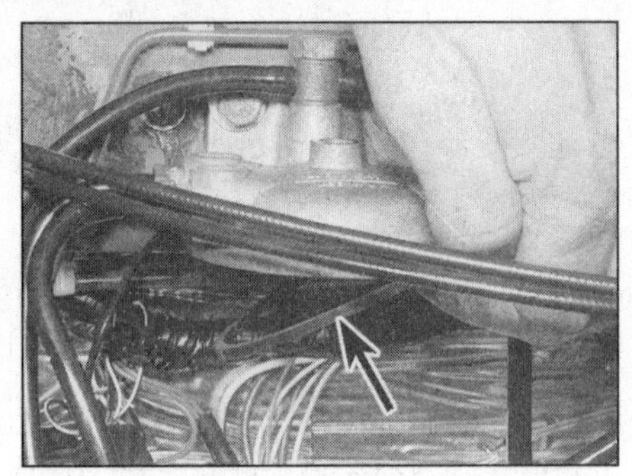
23.5a Fit new large . . .

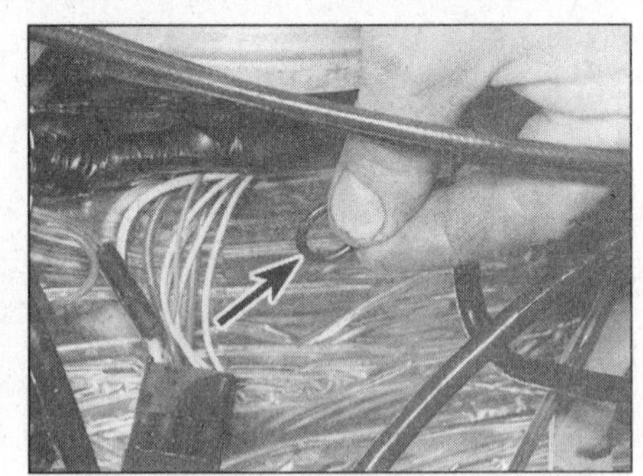
23.5b . . . and small sealing rings to filter head - 19J engine

12 000 mile (20 000 km) Service - Defender

22 Valve clearance check

Refer to Section 14.

23 Fuel filter element renewal

All engines

1 Refer to paragraphs 1 to 3 inclusive in Section 17.

10J, 12J and 19J engines

2 Unscrew the through-bolt from the top of the filter head and withdraw the filter bowl and element **(see illustration)**.
3 Discard the old element and rubber seals. New seals should be supplied with the new element.
4 Thoroughly clean the inside of the filter head and bowl.
5 Fit new large and small sealing rings to the filter head, then push the new filter element into position in the head with the holes in the element uppermost **(see illustrations)**.
6 Fit a new seal to the filter bowl, then refit the bowl and secure with the through-bolt **(see illustration)**.

200 TDi and 300 TDi engines

7 Refer to paragraphs 4 to 6 inclusive in Section 17.

All engines

8 Refer to paragraphs 7 to 9 inclusive in Section 17.

24 Engine breather filter cleaning

10J, 12J and 19J engines

1 The engine breather filter is incorporated in the engine oil filler cap.
2 Disconnect the breather hose(s) and remove the filler cap.
3 Fill a suitable container with clean paraffin, then immerse the cap in the paraffin to dissolve any oily deposits which have formed inside the gauze filter.
4 When the filter is clean, remove it from the paraffin and dry it thoroughly. The filter must be absolutely dry before it is refitted to the engine.
5 Refit the oil filler cap and reconnect the breather hose(s).

200 TDi and 300 TDi engines

6 Refer to Section 18.

25 Air cleaner dump valve check - 200 TDi engine

Refer to Section 19.

26 Fuel sedimenter cleaning - Pre 1995 models

Refer to Section 12.

27 Flywheel housing and timing belt housing draining

1 Refer to Section 21.
2 Note that on some engines, the timing belt housing plug can be screwed into a plate next to the drain hole **(see illustrations)**.

23.6 Fitting new seal to filter bowl

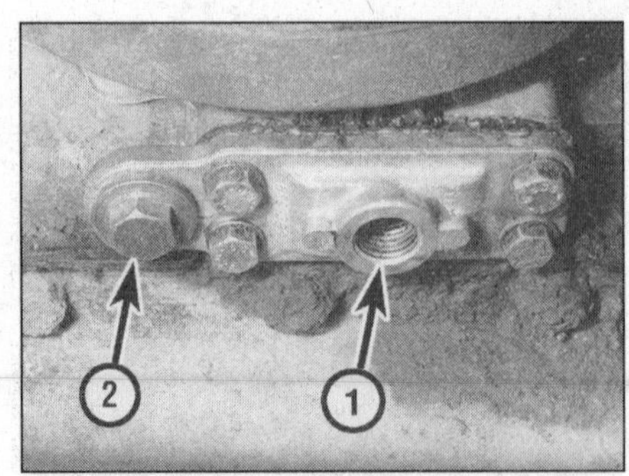

27.2a Timing belt housing inspection hole (1) and plug storage location (2) - 19J engine

27.2b Timing belt housing inspection hole (arrowed) - 300 TDi engine

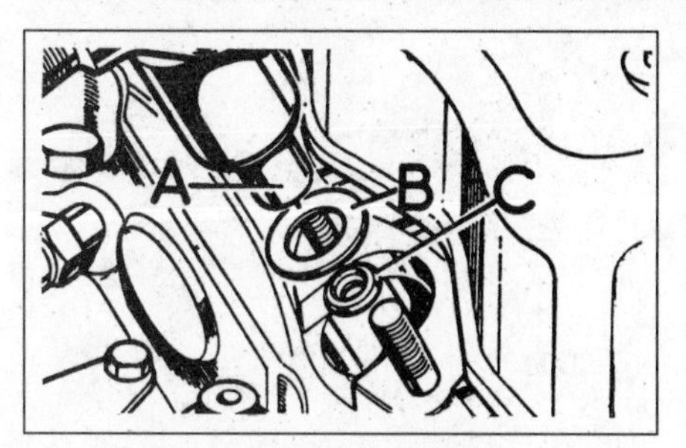

28.6 Injector sealing washer location

A Injector
B Copper sealing washer
C Corrugated sealing washer

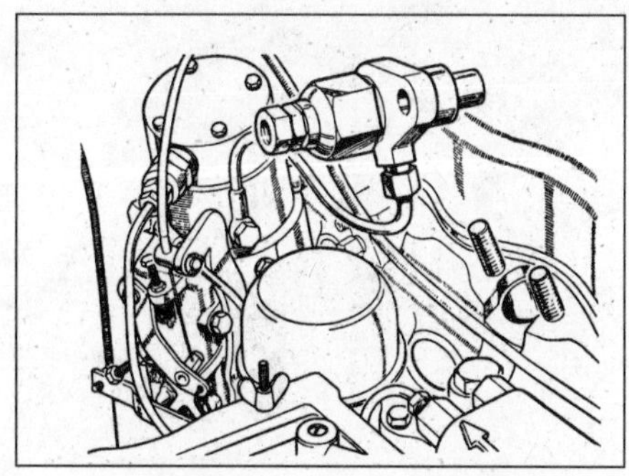

28.9 Testing injector on engine

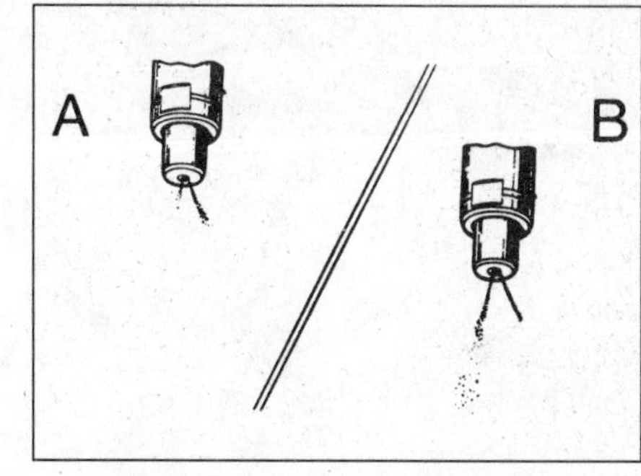

28.12 Fuel injection spray form

A Correct *B Incorrect*

12 000 mile (20 000 km) Service - Series IIA & III

28 Fuel injector check

Warning: Exercise extreme caution when working on fuel injectors. Never expose any part of the body to injector spray, as working pressure can cause the fuel to penetrate the skin with possibly fatal results. You are strongly advised to have any work which involves testing the injectors under pressure carried out by a dealer or fuel injection specialist

1 Remove and test each fuel injector in turn as follows:

Removal

2 Remove the air cleaner.

3 Slacken the fuel pipe union at the injection pump and remove the pipe completely from the injector.

4 Unscrew and remove the union securing the spill pipe to the injector and detach the pipe. Take care not to lose the copper washers under the union and spill pipe fixings.

5 Undo and remove the nuts (and bracket on early engines) securing the injector to the cylinder head.

6 Carefully lift out the injector from its location in the cylinder head and recover the two washers **(see illustration)**. Ensure that none of the washers are left behind in the injector housing. Handle the injector with care as there is a small needle valve protruding from its end which is easily damaged.

Testing

7 Test each injector as follows:

8 With the injector removed, slacken the fuel inlet unions on the remaining injectors.

9 Reconnect the fuel inlet pipe to the removed injector and position it in such a way that the fuel emission may be observed **(see illustration)**.

10 Place rags over the engine compartment to protect it from fuel spray.

11 Have an assistant operate the starter switch and with the engine cranking, observe the spray form emitting from the end of the injector.

12 Compare the observed spray form with the correct form shown **(see illustration)**.

13 With the engine turning over at starter speed, there should be a fine spray ejected from the auxiliary hole with very little fuel emitted from the main spray hole.

14 If the ejected fuel is more in the form of a liquid rather than a spray or if excessive fuel is emitted from the main spray hole, this indicates that the injector is in need of renewal or overhaul.

15 It is not recommended that any attempt be made to dismantle or repair a fuel injector as this requires specialist knowledge and equipment outside the scope of the average DIY mechanic. The best policy is to renew a faulty injector or have it reconditioned by your Land Rover dealer or diesel injection specialists.

16 On completion of testing, refit each injector as follows:

Refitting

17 Refitting is the reverse procedure to removal, bearing in mind the following points:

a) Always use new copper and steel sealing washers and fit the steel washers with the raised corrugation uppermost.
b) Tighten the retaining bolts to the specified torque figure.
c) Prime the fuel system as follows.

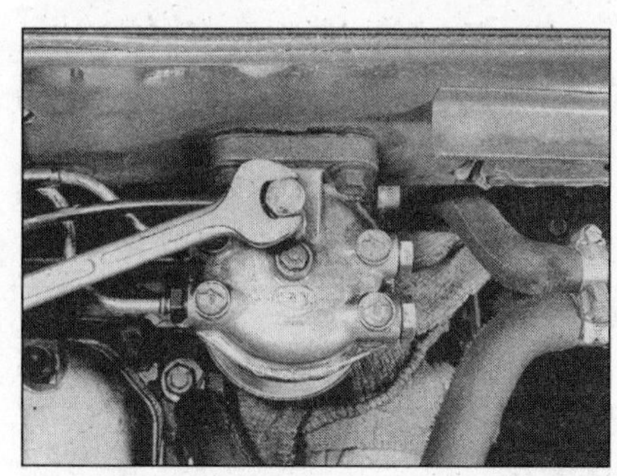

28.18 Loosening fuel filter bleed union

Priming

18 Prime each fuel filter as follows:

*a) Slacken the filter air vent or bleed pipe union **(see illustration)**.*
b) Operate the fuel pump hand priming lever until fuel which is free from air bubbles emerges from the air vent or bleed pipe.
c) Tighten the air vent or bleed pipe union whilst still pumping.
d) Operate the hand priming lever twice more to clear any remaining air bubbles into the bleed pipe.
e) Start the engine in the normal way and carefully check for any fuel leaks.

19 Now prime the fuel injection/distributor pump as follows:

*a) Slacken the air vent screw on the side of the pump **(see illustration)**.*
b) Operate the fuel pump hand priming lever until fuel which is free from air bubbles emerges from the air vent.
c) Tighten the air vent screw whilst pumping.
d) Slacken the air vent screw on the pump control cover and repeat b) and c).
e) Start the engine in the normal way and carefully check for any fuel leaks.

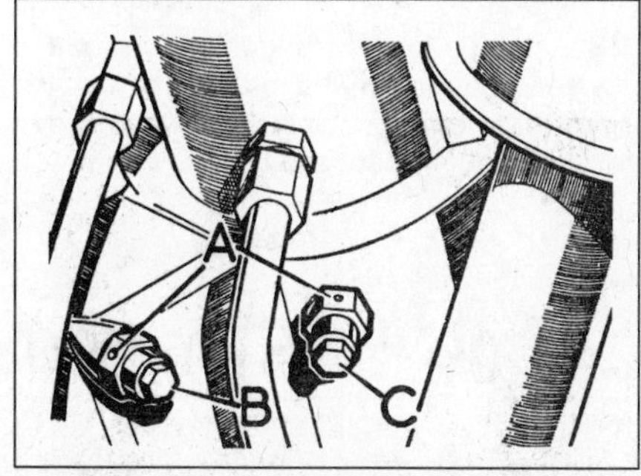

28.19 Fuel injection pump air vent screw location

A Fuel orifice
B Air vent screw on pump body
C Air vent screw on control cover

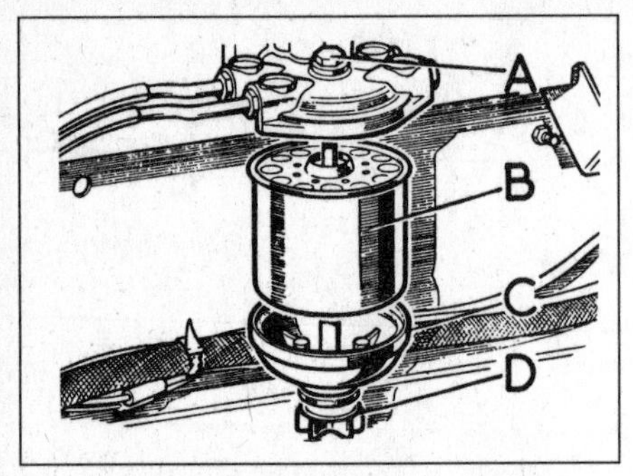

29.9 Latest type of main fuel filter assembly

A Retaining bolt
B Filter element
C Filter element holder
D Water drain plug

29 Fuel filter element renewal

Early type - engine mounted

1 Slacken the plug on the bottom of the main fuel filter body and drain the fuel into a suitable container.
2 Unscrew and remove the bleed back pipe from the top of the filter unit.
3 Support the filter body and unscrew and remove the centre cap securing nut on top of the filter.
4 Withdraw the filter body, complete with the small sealing ring on the top of the element. Recover the large sealing ring from the underside of the filter cover.
5 Discard the filter element and wash the container and all components thoroughly in clean diesel fuel.
6 Inspect the sealing rings. If worn or damaged, they must be renewed.
7 Place a new element in position in the container and refit using the reverse procedure to removal.
8 Prime the fuel system as described in Section 28.

Later type - bulkhead mounted

9 Support the element holder from below and unscrew and remove the retaining bolt on the top of the main filter body **(see illustration)**. Withdraw the element and holder.

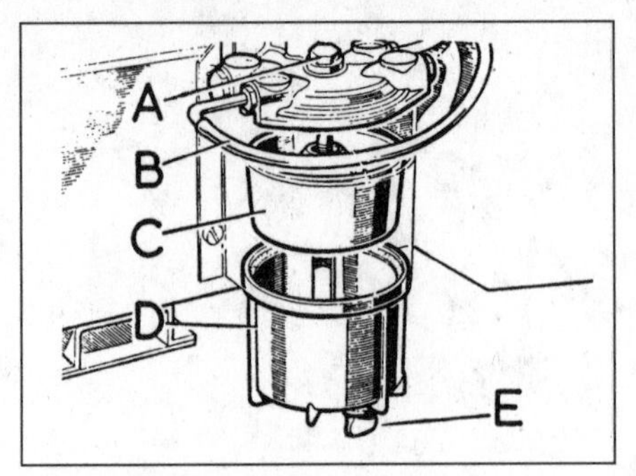

30.1 Fuel sedimenter assembly

A Retaining bolt
B Inlet pipe
C Element
D Bowl
E Water drain plug

10 Discard the element and thoroughly wash the element holder in clean diesel fuel.
11 Inspect the sealing rings. If worn or damaged, they must be renewed.
12 Place a new element in position on the filter body with the perforated holes uppermost. Refit the element holder and secure the assembly with the retaining bolt.
13 Prime the fuel system as described in Section 28.
14 If an additional filter of the same type is fitted alongside the main filter, then it may be removed and serviced in the same manner. If the additional filter is of the sedimenter type, refer to Section 30 for servicing procedures.

30 Fuel sedimenter cleaning

1 Unscrew and remove the fuel inlet pipe union and position the pipe above fuel tank level to prevent syphoning **(see illustration)**.
2 Support the sediment bowl and unscrew and remove the securing bolt on the top of the main body. Lift off the sediment bowl and element.
3 Thoroughly clean all components in clean diesel fuel.
4 Inspect the seals and renew if worn or damaged.
5 Refitting is the reversal of the removal procedure.
6 Prime the fuel system as described in Section 28.

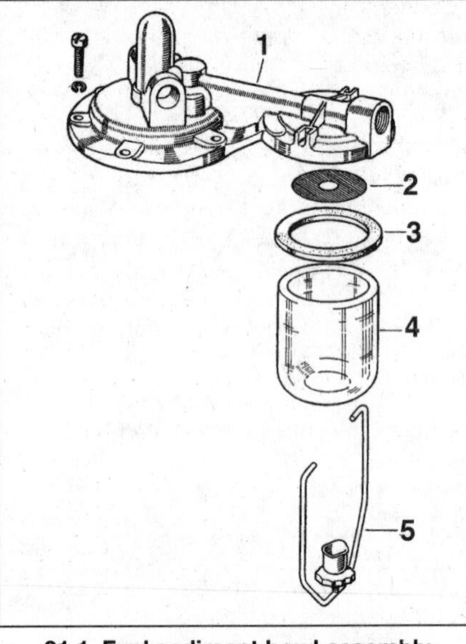

31.1 Fuel sediment bowl assembly

1 Pump top cover
2 Gauze filter disc
3 Lock sealing gasket
4 Sediment bowl
5 Bowl retainer

31 Fuel sediment bowl cleaning

1 The following procedure is for earlier fuel pumps, which incorporate a glass filter bowl **(see illustration)**.
2 Clean the outside of the pump and wipe dry using a dry non-fluffy rag.
3 Unscrew the filter bowl stirrup retaining screw and swing the stirrup clear of the bowl whilst holding the bowl in position. Lift away the bowl, followed by the cork seal and gauze filter.
4 Inspect the cork seal for signs of damage or flattening and, if necessary, obtain a new one.
5 Thoroughly clean the bowl in clean diesel fuel and inspect it for cracks.
6 Clean and inspect the gauze filter for damage or blockage, renewing it if necessary.
7 Refitting the bowl is the reversal of the removal procedure Tighten the stirrup retaining screw lightly, just enough to ensure a fuel tight joint, as overtightening will crack the bowl.

24 000 mile (40 000 km) Service - Discovery

32 Turbocharger boost pressure check

Note: *A pressure gauge capable of registering 1.0 bar will be required for this check.*

1 Disconnect the hose connecting the waste-gate actuator to the turbocharger, at the turbocharger.
2 Connect the hose to a T-piece, then use a short length of hose to connect the T-piece to the turbocharger **(see illustration)**.
3 Obtain a length of hose long enough to run from the T-piece to the passenger compartment, to enable a pressure gauge to be read by the driver or passenger whilst the vehicle is being driven. Note that the hose must be long enough to be routed so that it is not trapped when the bonnet is closed.

4 Connect the hose to the T-piece and pressure gauge. Carefully lower the bonnet, taking care not to trap the hose. Do not fully close the bonnet (as this will trap the hose) but ensure that the safety catch is engaged so that there is no risk of the bonnet opening when the vehicle is driven. As a safety precaution, it is advisable to secure the bonnet by using a length of string or a cable-tie around the lock and striker.
5 Start the engine and drive the vehicle normally until the engine reaches normal operating temperature.
6 When the engine is warm, drive the vehicle normally up a suitable shallow hill, in such a manner that full throttle can be maintained with the engine speed held steady between 2500 and 3000 rpm.
7 Under these conditions, the maximum boost pressure should be as specified.
8 If the reading is not as specified, it is likely that there is a fault with the turbocharger wastegate. In this case, have the problem investigated by a Land Rover dealer.

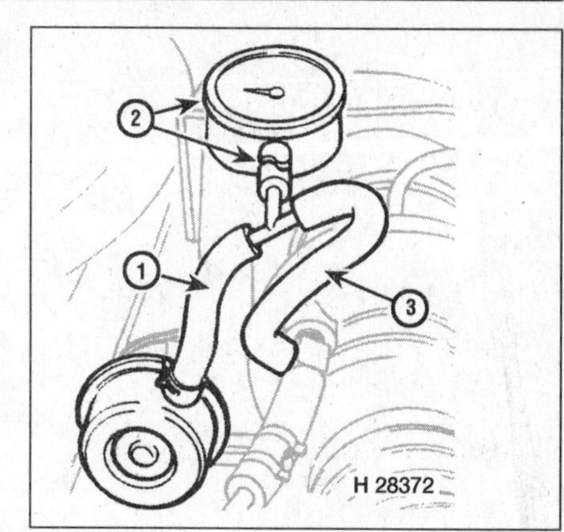

32.2 Turbocharger boost pressure check
1 Wastegate actuator hose
2 T-piece and vacuum gauge
3 Hose to turbocharger

24 000 mile (40 000 km) Service - Defender

33 Turbocharger boost pressure check

Refer to Section 32.

34 Fuel injector leak check

1 Check the fuel injector seating areas in the cylinder head for any signs of fuel leakage.
2 Similarly, check the fuel supply pipe unions and the fuel leak-off pipe unions.
3 Rectify any leaks without delay. Do not over-tighten the unions in an attempt to cure leaks.

35 Fuel injector spray pattern check - 10J, 12J and 19J engines

1 This check requires the use of specialist equipment and must be entrusted to a Land Rover dealer of a Diesel fuel injection specialist.

48 000 mile (80 000 km) Service - Discovery & Defender

36 Intercooler element cleaning

1 To expose the intercooler element, remove the intercooler as follows:

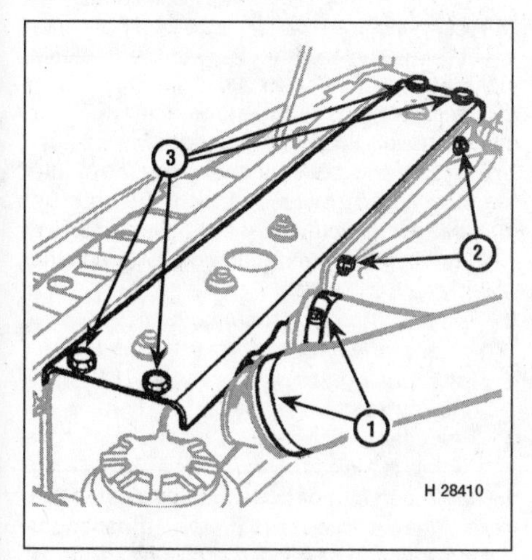

36.3 Intercooler mounting details
1 Intercooler hose clips
2 Cooling fan cowl-to-radiator nuts
3 Radiator top cover bolts

200 TDi engine

Discovery

2 Disconnect the battery negative lead.
3 Loosen the clips securing the two hoses to the intercooler and carefully pull the hoses from the intercooler stubs **(see illustration)**.
4 Unscrew the two nuts and washers securing the upper cooling fan cowl to the radiator.
5 Ease the fan cowl upwards to disengage the lower section from the securing clips, then move the cowl towards the rear of the vehicle over the fan blades.
6 Remove the four bolts (two at each side) securing the radiator top cover, then withdraw the cover.
7 Lift the intercooler upwards from the support frame.

Defender

8 Disconnect the battery negative lead.
9 Remove the viscous cooling fan and coupling, then the fan cowl.
10 Loosen the clips securing the two hoses to the intercooler, then carefully pull the hoses from the intercooler stubs **(see illustration)**.
11 Remove the four bolts (two at each side) securing the two radiator mounting brackets to the front body panel. Withdraw the brackets.
12 Remove the four bolts (two at each side) securing the radiator top cover and withdraw the cover.

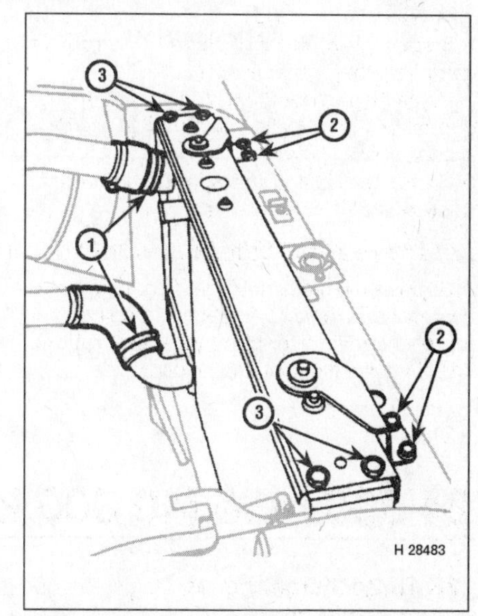

36.10 Intercooler fixings - 200 TDi engine
1 Hose clips
2 Radiator mounting bracket bolts
3 Radiator top cover bolts

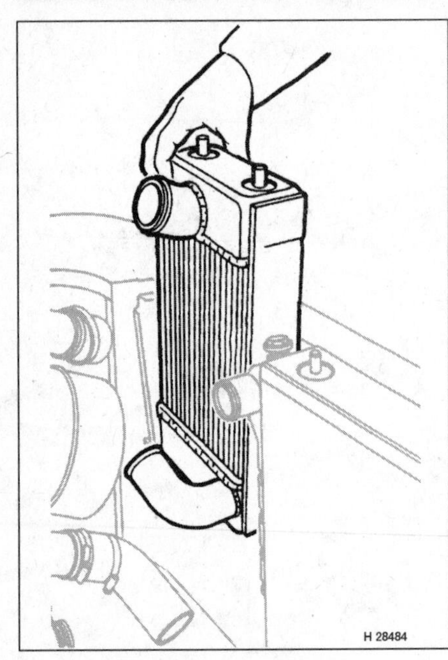

36.13 Lifting out intercooler - 200 TDi engine

13 Lift the intercooler upwards from the support frame **(see illustration)**.

300 TDi engine

Discovery

14 Disconnect the battery negative lead.

15 Release the two clips securing the cooling fan cowl to the radiator top cover.

16 Remove the four bolts (two at each side) securing the radiator top cover, then withdraw the cover **(see illustration)**.

17 Unscrew the nut and bolt securing the power steering pump bracket to the body front panel **(see illustration)**. Recover the washer.

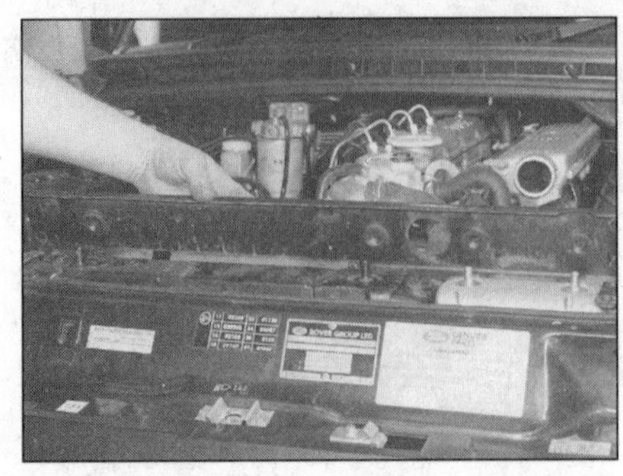

36.16 Withdrawing radiator top cover

18 Release the power steering pump bracket from the locating lug, then position the bracket and power steering fluid reservoir assembly to one side.

19 Pull the side bracket away from the intercooler.

20 Loosen the two securing clips and disconnect the sleeve connecting the top hose to the intercooler.

21 Similarly, disconnect the sleeve connecting the bottom hose to the intercooler.

22 Lift the intercooler upwards clear of the cooling fan shroud **(see illustration)**.

Defender

23 This procedure is as described for the 200 TDi engine but instead of removing the viscous cooling fan and coupling and the fan shroud, simply remove the two nuts securing the top of the cooling fan cowl to the radiator top cover.

Both engines

24 Check the element for damage and deterioration. Renew it if necessary.

25 If the original element is to be refitted, flush the element with ICI "Genklene" or a suitable alternative, following the instructions supplied with the cleaner.

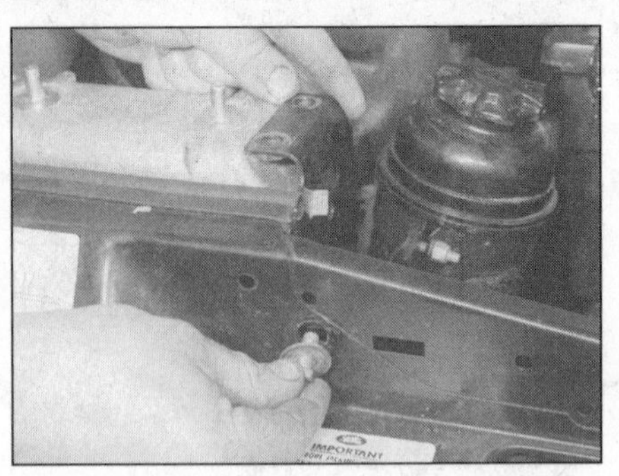

36.17 Remove nut and bolt securing power steering pump bracket

36.22 Lift intercooler upwards and remove from the vehicle

26 Dry the element thoroughly.

27 Before refitting, check the condition of the intercooler locating lug grommets in the lower body panel and the radiator top cover, and renew if necessary. Also check the condition of the foam insulating pad and ensure that it is securely attached to the intercooler.

28 Refitting is a reversal of removal, ensuring that the hose sleeves are securely reconnected.

60 000 mile (100 000 km) Service - Discovery

37 Timing belt renewal

Note: *Timing belts must be stored on edge on a clean surface. Do not bend a belt through acute angles (radius less than 50 mm) as damage and premature failure may result. A gauge-type torque wrench will be required to tension the belt during fitting. A break-type torque wrench is not suitable. New gaskets must be used on refitting and it is advisable to fit a new crankshaft dust seal to the cover.*

Removal

1 To expose the timing belt, remove its cover as follows:

200 TDi engine

2 Remove the crankshaft pulley and damper. Note that the damper securing bolt is tightened to a very high torque and both the damper and bolt are coated with thread-locking compound. Suitable thread-locking compound will be required to coat the threads of the bolt and damper on refitting. Proceed as follows:

a) Disconnect the battery negative lead.

b) On models with air conditioning, remove the compressor drivebelt and disconnect the wiring from the temperature sensor located in the thermostat housing. Remove the four bolts securing the compressor to the engine and move the compressor to one side. Take care not to strain the refrigerant hoses and do not under any circumstances disconnect the hoses.

c) Drain the cooling system.

d) Remove the viscous cooling fan and coupling.

e) Disconnect the intercooler-to-inlet manifold air trunking at the manifold.

f) Remove the radiator top hose.

g) Unscrew the two nuts securing the cooling fan cowl to the top of the radiator and withdraw the cowl.

h) Remove the alternator and power steering pump drivebelts.

i) Unscrew the four securing bolts, and remove the crankshaft pulley from the crankshaft damper.

j) A suitable tool will now be required to hold the damper stationary as the damper bolt is loosened. This is most easily achieved by bolting a suitable metal bar to the damper, using bolts screwed into at least two of the pulley bolt holes.

k) Remove the damper bolt and recover the washer.

l) Withdraw the damper from the crankshaft, using a suitable puller if necessary.

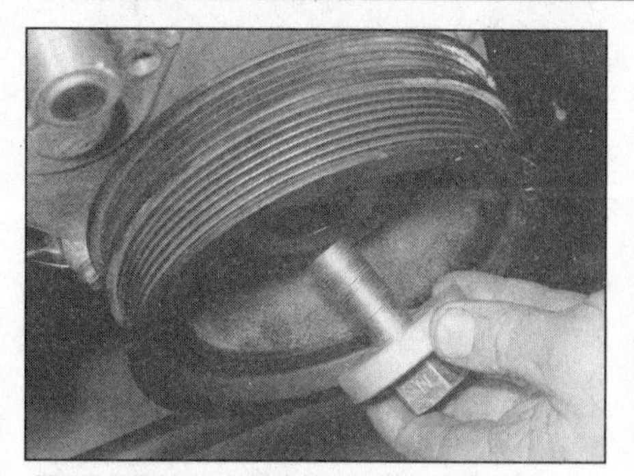
37.11a Remove pulley bolt and washer . . .

37.11b . . . and withdraw pulley

37.17a Camshaft sprocket timing mark aligned with web on timing belt housing

3 Disconnect the hoses from the coolant pump.

4 If necessary, hold the coolant pump pulley stationary by wrapping the drivebelt tightly round the pulley, then unscrew the three securing bolts and withdraw the pulley.

5 Unscrew the securing bolts and withdraw the coolant pump. Recover the gasket.

6 Loosen the hose clips and withdraw the air trunking connecting the air cleaner to the turbocharger. Where applicable, disconnect the breather hose from the air trunking.

7 Disconnect the wiring from the alternator. Unscrew the through-bolt and nut and remove the alternator from its mounting bracket.

8 Unscrew the through-bolt and nut, then remove the power steering pump from the mounting bracket. There is no need to disconnect the fluid hoses. Move the pump to one side clear of the working area, taking care not to strain the hoses.

9 Unscrew the securing bolts and remove the alternator/power steering pump mounting bracket.

10 Unscrew the nine securing bolts and remove the timing belt cover. Note the location of each bolt, as they are of different lengths. Recover the gasket.

300 TDi engine

11 Remove the crankshaft pulley. Note that the pulley securing bolt is coated with thread-locking compound. Suitable thread-locking compound will be required to coat the threads of the bolt refitting. Proceed as follows:

a) Disconnect the battery negative lead.
b) Drain the cooling system.
c) Disconnect the radiator top hose.
d) Remove the air trunking connecting the intercooler to the inlet manifold.
e) Remove the viscous fan unit and cowl.
f) Remove the auxiliary drivebelt.
g) Hold the pulley stationary by applying the handbrake, engaging differential lock and engaging the LOW range in the transfer gearbox. On manual gearbox models, engage first gear in the main gearbox. On automatic transmission models, move the selector lever to position P. Remove the ignition key.
h) Loosen the pulley bolt, using a suitable socket and extension bar.
*i) Remove the pulley bolt and washer **(see illustration)**.*
*j) Withdraw the pulley from the crankshaft, using a suitable puller if necessary **(see illustration)**.*

12 Unscrew and withdraw the fourteen bolts securing the timing belt cover to the housing. Note the location of each bolt, as they are of different lengths. Note also that the top two bolts secure the thermostat coolant hose clips.

13 Unbolt the viscous fan pulley if desired.

14 Withdraw the timing belt cover and recover its gasket. Where applicable, also recover the small gasket located around the cover centre securing bolt boss.

Both engines

15 If the camshaft sprocket (sprocket hub on 300 TDi engines) is to be removed for any reason, the sprocket/hub securing bolt should be loosened at this stage, before the timing belt is removed.

16 Temporarily refit the crankshaft damper/pulley bolt to the end of the crankshaft, then turn the crankshaft (using a suitable spanner or socket on the damper/pulley bolt) to bring No 1 piston to TDC.

17 Check that the timing marks are aligned as follows:

*a) The timing mark on the camshaft sprocket should be aligned with the web on the timing belt housing **(see illustration)**.*
*b) The Woodruff key in the end of the crankshaft should be aligned with the arrow on the timing belt housing **(see illustration)**.*

18 Slacken the belt tensioner pulley bolt.

19 Slide the timing belt from the sprockets **(see illustration)**. Do not turn the camshaft once the timing belt had been removed.

20 If the belt cannot easily be slid from the sprockets, unscrew the securing nut and remove the belt idler pulley.

Fitting and tensioning

Note: *During fitting, the timing belt tensioning procedure is effectively carried out twice. This double-tensioning procedure must be carried out as described, to avoid the possibility of belt failure and resultant engine damage.*

21 Slacken the three bolts securing the injection pump sprocket to the pump hub **(see illustration)**.

22 Carefully fit the belt over the sprockets, ensuring that its direction of rotation marks are correctly orientated. Take care not to move the sprockets and ensure that the timing marks are still aligned.

37.17b Crankshaft Woodruff key aligned with arrow on timing belt housing

37.19 Slacken belt tensioner pulley bolt (arrowed) and slide off timing belt

37.21 Unscrew three bolts (arrowed) securing injection pump sprocket to hub

37.27 Tensioning timing belt

23 Where applicable, refit the idler pulley and tighten the securing nut.

24 If necessary, adjust the position of the belt so that it sits correctly on the sprockets with the timing marks still aligned.

25 Tighten the belt tensioner pulley bolt finger-tight.

26 Engage a 13.0 mm square-drive extension bar with the hole in the tensioner pulley mounting plate.

27 Using a gauge-type torque wrench held vertically, turn the extension bar to tension the belt to the specified torque. Tighten the tensioner pulley bolt, taking care to maintain the correct torque **(see illustration)**.

28 Tighten the injection pump sprocket-to-hub securing bolts to the specified torque.

29 Remove the pump timing pin from the injection pump sprocket and withdraw the flywheel locking tool centre pin from the slot in the flywheel.

30 Turn the crankshaft clockwise through two complete turns until the timing marks are aligned again.

31 Slacken the tensioner pulley bolt and repeat the tensioning procedure.

32 Turn the crankshaft clockwise again until the timing marks are aligned, then fit the pump timing pin through the pump hub into the pump body and engage the flywheel locking tool with the slot in the flywheel. If the flywheel locking tool centre pin cannot be engaged easily with the timing slot in the flywheel, proceed as follows.

33 Withdraw the flywheel locking tool centre pin from the slot in the flywheel, then turn the crankshaft as necessary until the timing pin can be inserted easily into the injection pump.

34 Loosen the pump locking screw and remove the keeper plate (located at the front of the pump, behind the timing belt housing). Tighten the locking screw to lock the pump spindle in position.

35 Loosen the three pump sprocket-to-hub bolts.

36 Turn the crankshaft the small amount to TDC and engage the flywheel locking tool centre pin with the timing slot in the flywheel.

37 Re-check to ensure that the pump timing pin is an easy sliding fit in the pump.

38 Tighten the pump sprocket-to-hub bolts to the specified torque.

39 Loosen the pump locking screw then refit the keeper plate and tighten the locking screw.

40 Remove the timing pin from the pump and withdraw the flywheel locking tool centre pin from the slot in the flywheel.

41 Refit the timing belt cover as follows:

200 TDi engine

42 Clean all traces of old gasket from the mating faces of the timing belt cover and housing.

43 It is advisable to fit a new crankshaft dust seal to the cover, as follows:

a) Prise the old seal from the aperture in the cover using a suitable screwdriver.

b) Clean the seal seat in the cover.

c) Press a new seal into position using a suitable socket or tube. Take care not to damage the seal lips.

44 Refit the cover to the housing, using a new gasket, then refit the securing bolts in their correct locations, as noted before removal **(see illustration)**. Tighten the bolts to the specified torque.

45 Refit the alternator/power steering pump mounting bracket and tighten the securing bolts.

46 Refit the power steering pump and alternator to the bracket and reconnect the alternator wiring.

47 Refit the air trunking and tighten the securing clips.

48 Clean all traces of old gasket from the mating faces of the coolant pump and housing, then refit the coolant pump using a new gasket. Tighten the securing bolts to the specified torque.

49 Refit the coolant pump pulley and tighten the securing bolts. Hold the pulley using the drivebelt, as during removal.

50 Reconnect the hoses to the coolant pump.

51 Refit the crankshaft damper and pulley as follows:

a) Clean all traces of thread-locking compound from the damper and bolt.

b) Smear the crankshaft contact surfaces of the damper spigot with thread-locking compound.

c) Fit the damper to the crankshaft, then fit the washer and bolt.

d) Hold the damper stationary, as during removal and tighten the bolt to pull the damper into position on the nose of the crankshaft.

e) Unscrew the bolt, then apply thread-locking compound to the bolt threads.

f) Refit the bolt and tighten to the specified torque.

g) Further refitting is a reversal of removal. Tighten the crankshaft pulley bolts securely and on completion, refill the cooling system.

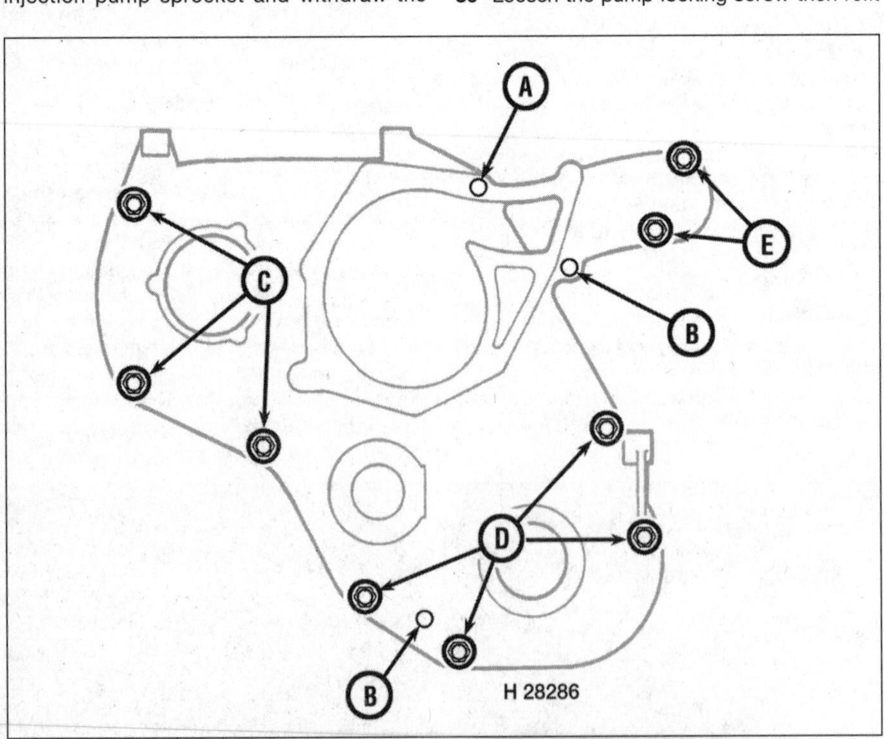

37.44 Timing belt cover securing bolt locations - 200 TDi engine

A Stud hole
B Dowel hole
C 25 mm long bolt
D 80 mm long bolt
E 90 mm long bolt

300 TDi engine

52 Clean all traces of old gasket from the mating faces of the timing belt cover and housing.

53 It is advisable to fit a new crankshaft dust seal to the cover, as follows:

a) Prise the old seal from the aperture in the cover using a suitable screwdriver.
b) Clean the seal seat in the cover.
c) Press a new seal into position using a suitable socket or tube. Take care not to damage the seal lips. Note that the seal fits with the lips facing towards the outside of the timing belt cover.

54 Refit the cover to the housing, using new gaskets, then refit the securing bolts in their correct locations, as noted before removal **(see illustration)**. Tighten the bolts to the specified torque.

55 Refitting the crankshaft pulley is a reversal of removal, bearing in mind the following:

a) Lightly grease the pulley spigot before fitting.
b) Apply suitable thread-locking compound to the bolt threads and tighten the bolt to the specified torque, holding the pulley stationary as during removal.
c) On completion, refill the cooling system.

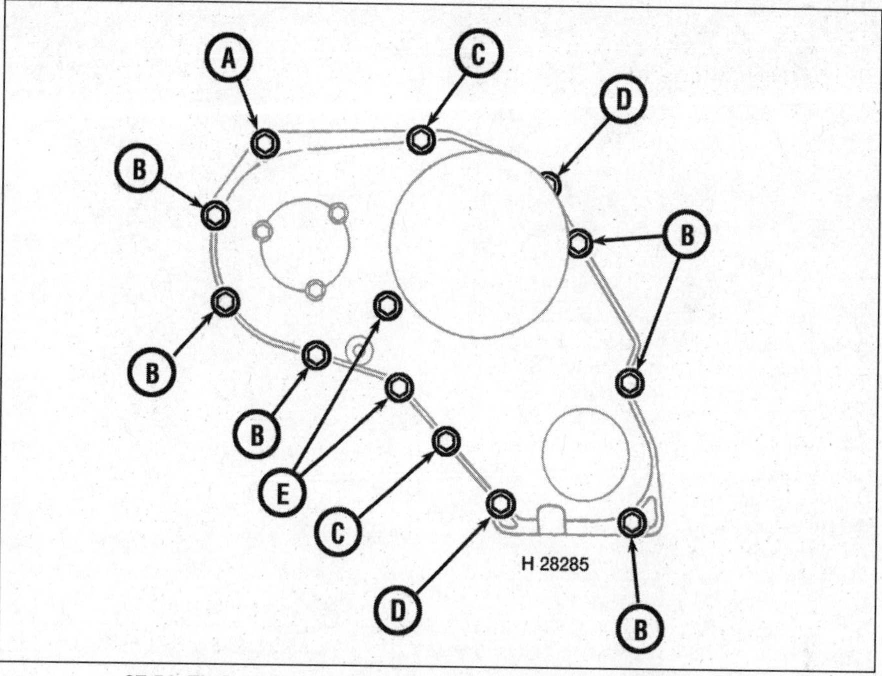

37.54 Timing belt cover securing bolt locations - 300 TDi engine

A 25 mm long bolt
B 35 mm long bolt
C 50 mm long bolt
D 100 mm long bolt
E 110 mm long bolt

60 000 mile (100 000 km) Service - Defender

38 Timing belt renewal - 12J and 19J engines

Note: *Timing belts must be stored on edge on a clean surface. Do not bend a belt through acute angles (radius less than 50 mm) as damage and premature failure may result. A gauge-type torque wrench will be required to tension the belt during fitting. A break-type torque wrench is not suitable. New gaskets must be used on refitting and it is advisable to fit a new crankshaft dust seal to the cover.*

Removal

1 Remove the timing belt cover as follows.

2 Remove the crankshaft pulley, using the following procedure:

a) Disconnect the battery negative lead.
b) On models with air conditioning, remove the compressor drivebelt and disconnect the wiring from the temperature sensor. Remove the bolts securing the compressor to the engine and move the compressor to one side. Do not strain the refrigerant hoses and do not under any circumstances disconnect the hoses.
c) Remove the cooling fan cowl and the fan.
d) Remove the auxiliary drivebelt(s).
e) Hold the crankshaft stationary by removing the starter motor and jamming the starter ring gear with a large screwdriver. Unscrew the crankshaft pulley nut or bolt/starter dog (as applicable). Note that the nut/bolt is very tight!
f) Remove the pulley nut/bolt and recover the washer, where applicable.
g) Withdraw the pulley from the crankshaft, using a suitable puller to free it if necessary ***(see illustration)****.*

3 Remove the coolant pump.

4 Where applicable, unclip the coolant hose from the bracket on the cover.

5 Working at the bottom of the cover, unscrew the four securing bolts and withdraw the breather cover plate and gauze filter **(see illustration)**. Recover the gasket.

6 Unscrew the cover securing bolts whilst noting each bolt location, as several different lengths of bolt are used. Recover the washers, then withdraw the cover **(see illustration)**. The cover locates on dowels in the timing belt housing. If necessary, lever between the cover

38.2 Removing crankshaft pulley - 19J engine

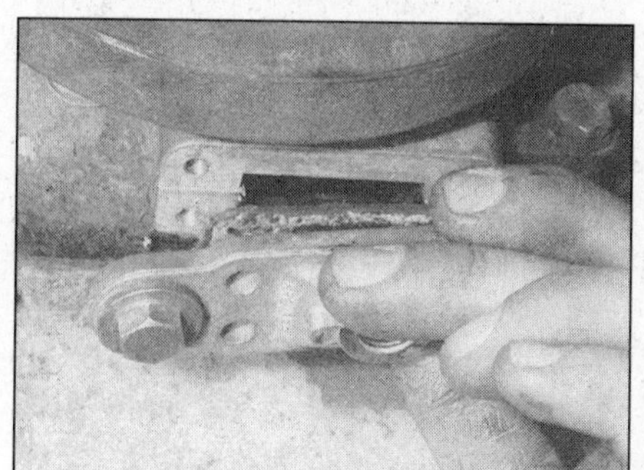

38.5 Withdrawing breather cover plate and gauze

38.6 Withdrawing timing belt cover

38.11 Slacken belt tensioner pulley bolt (arrowed) and slide off timing belt - 300 TDi engine shown

and housing mating faces to free the cover but take care not to damage the mating faces. Note the location of any brackets secured by the bolts.

7 Recover the gasket. Where applicable, also recover the smaller circular gasket from the centre cover securing bolt lug.

8 If the camshaft sprocket is to be removed for any reason, then its securing bolt should now be loosened. Similarly, if the fuel injection pump sprocket is to be removed, its securing nut should be loosened.

9 Temporarily refit the crankshaft damper/pulley bolt to the end of the crankshaft, then turn the crankshaft (using a suitable spanner or socket on the damper/pulley bolt) to bring No 1 piston to TDC, with the timing marks aligned.

10 Slacken the belt tensioner pulley bolt, or the two nuts, as applicable.

11 Slide the timing belt from the sprockets **(see illustration)**. Do not turn the camshaft or crankshaft once the timing belt had been removed.

Fitting and tensioning

Note: *During fitting, the timing belt tensioning procedure is effectively carried out twice. This double-tensioning procedure must be carried out as described, to avoid the possibility of belt failure and resultant engine damage.*

12 Carefully fit the belt over the sprockets. Start with the crankshaft sprocket, followed by the camshaft and fuel injection pump sprockets, then the tensioner. Ensure that the belt direction of rotation marks are correctly orientated. Take care not to move the sprockets and ensure that the timing marks are still aligned. If necessary, adjust the position of the belt so that it sits correctly on the sprockets with the timing marks still aligned. If the belt teeth do not quite mate with the sprocket grooves, move the camshaft sprocket (and if necessary, the fuel injection pump sprocket) slightly clockwise until the teeth engage with the sprocket grooves.

13 Tighten the belt tensioner pulley bolt or nuts (as applicable) finger-tight.

14 Engage a suitable square-drive extension with the hole in the tensioner pulley mounting plate.

15 Using a gauge-type torque wrench held vertically, turn the extension to tension the belt to the specified torque. Tighten the tensioner pulley bolt/nuts, taking care to maintain the correct torque.

16 If the camshaft or fuel injection pump sprockets have been removed, then tighten each securing bolt (or nut) to the specified torque.

17 Turn the crankshaft clockwise through two complete turns, until the timing marks are aligned again with No 1 piston at TDC.

18 Slacken the tensioner pulley bolt/nuts and repeat the tensioning procedure.

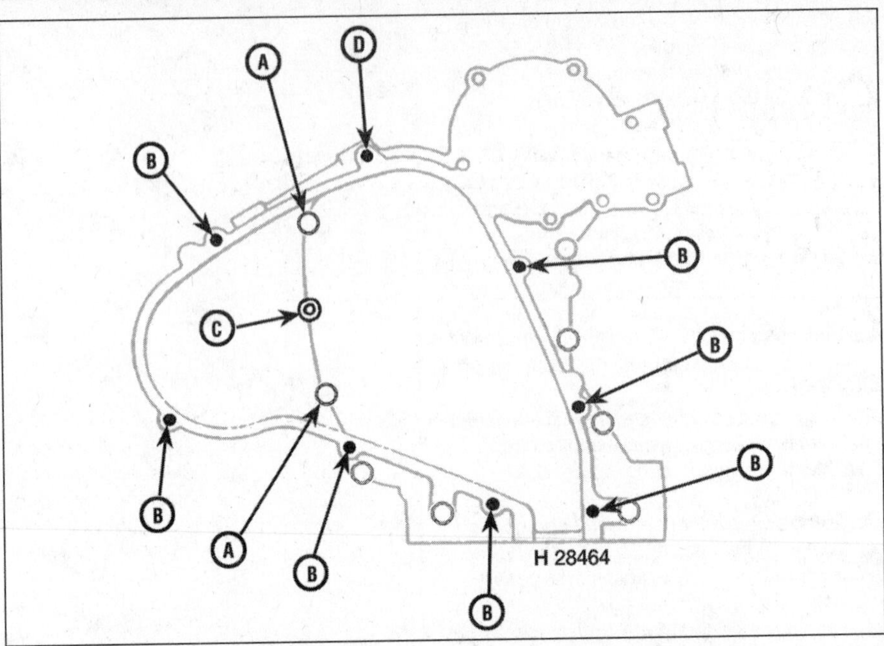

38.22 Timing belt cover securing bolt locations - 12J and 19J engines

A 20 mm long bolt B 25 mm long bolt C 65 mm long bolt D 95 mm long bolt

19 Check the fuel injection pump timing.

20 Clean all traces of old gasket from the mating faces of the timing belt cover and housing.

21 It is advisable to fit a new crankshaft dust seal to the cover, as follows:

a) Prise the old seal from the aperture in the cover using a suitable screwdriver.
b) Clean the seal seat in the cover.
c) Press a new seal into position using a suitable socket or tube. Take care not to damage the seal lips.

22 Refit the cover to the housing, using a new gasket (and a new centre lug gasket, where applicable), then refit the securing bolts in their correct locations, as noted during removal **(see illustration)**. Tighten the bolts to the specified torque.

23 Refit the coolant pump.

24 Refitting the crankshaft pulley is a reversal of removal, bearing in mind the following:

a) Lightly grease the pulley spigot before fitting.
b) Tighten the pulley nut or bolt/starter dog to the specified torque.
c) On completion, refill the cooling system.

72 000 mile (120 000 km) Service - Defender

39 Timing belt renewal -
200 TDi and 300 TDi engines

Refer to Section 37.

Chapter 6
Land Rover 2286cc and 2495cc engines

Part B: Fuel system servicing

Contents

Specifications

Glow plugs

Discovery	Champion CH70
Defender:	
Non turbo	Champion CH63
Turbo	Champion CH70
Series IIA & III	Champion CH63

Injectors

Discovery

Type	Pintle
Opening pressure:	
Initial	200 bars
Secondary:	
200 TDi engine	280 bars
300 TDi engine	300 bars

Defender

Type	Pintle
Opening pressure:	
10J and 12J engines	135 bars
19J engine	135 to 140 bars
200 TDi engine:	
Initial	200 bars
Secondary	280 bars
300 TDi engine:	
Initial	200 bars
Secondary	300 bars

Series IIA & III

Type	CAV Pintaux

Injection pump

Discovery

Pump rotation	Clockwise (viewed from timing belt end)
Timing:	
200 TDi engine	1.54 mm lift at TDC
300 TDi engine:	
Without Electronic Diesel Control or Exhaust Gas Recirculation	1.54 mm lift at TDC
With EDC	0.45 mm lift at TDC
With EGR	1.40 mm lift at TDC

Defender

Pump rotation:	
10J engine	Anti-clockwise (viewed from above)
All except 10J engine	Clockwise (viewed from timing belt end)
Timing:	
10J engine	Set using special tool RO605863 - see text
12J and 19J engines	Set using special tool 18G1458 or DTI and probe - see text
200 TDi and 300 TDi engines	Set using flywheel and pump locking tools - see text

Series IIA & III

Timing:	
Early models	16° BTDC
Later models:	
Pre 1973	15° BTDC
Post 1973	13°BTDC

Accelerator cable

Discovery and Defender

Freeplay (maximum)	1.57 mm

Idle speed - see Part A specifications

Fast idle speed - see Part A specifications

Maximum speed

Discovery

No-load	4600 (+ 40 / - 120) rpm
Full load (cut-off begins)	4000 rpm

Defender

No-load:	
10J engine	4200 rpm
12J and 19J engines	4400 ± 80 rpm
200 TDi engine	4180 ± 80 rpm
300 TDi engine	4600 (+ 40 / -120) rpm

Series IIA & III

All engines	4200 ± 20 rpm

EGR throttle position sensor

Discovery and Defender

Resistance across terminals 1 and 3	1000 to 1050 ohms
Resistance across terminals 1 and 2	850 to 900 ohms

Torque wrench settings

	Nm	lbf ft
Discovery		
Fuel hose-to-fuel lift pump unions:		
200 TDi engine	12	9
300 TDi engine	33	24
Fuel injection pump sprocket-to-hub bolts	25	18
Fuel injector clamp plate nuts	25	18
Fuel injector pipe unions	25	18
Fuel supply hose-to-fuel injection pump union:		
200 TDi engine	12	9
300 TDi engine	25	18
200 TDi engine	2	1
300 TDi engine	10	7

Torque wrench settings (continued)

	Nm	lbf ft
Defender		
Fuel hose-to-fuel filter unions:		
200 TDi engine	15	11
300 TDi engine	33	24
Fuel hose-to-fuel lift pump unions	20	15
Fuel leak-off pipe-to-injector unions	10	7
Fuel injection pump sprocket nut - 12J and 19J engines	45	33
Fuel injection pump sprocket-to-hub bolts - 200 TDi & 300 TDi engines	25	18
Fuel injector clamp plate nuts - 200 and 300 TDi engines	25	18
Fuel injector securing nuts - 10J, 12J and 19J engines	7	5
Fuel injector pipe unions:		
10J, 12J and 19J engines	17	12
200 TDi and 300 TDi engines	25	18
Fuel supply hose-to-fuel injection pump union:		
200 TDi engine	12	9
300 TDi engine	25	18
Discovery and Defender		
Boost pressure pipe-to-fuel injection pump union	10	7
EGR delivery pipe bolts	25	18
EGR valve securing bolts	25	18
Fuel injection pump front securing nuts	25	18
Fuel injection pump hub cover plate screws	25	18
Fuel injection pump rear bracket fixings	25	18
Fuel leak-off pipe-to-fuel injection pump union	25	18
Fuel lift pump securing bolts	25	18
Glow plug wiring nuts	2	1
Glow plugs	23	17
Series IIA & III		
Fuel injector securing nuts	6 to 8	0.8 to 1.1

1 Accelerator cable (Discovery and Defender) - adjustment

Discovery

1 Hold the pump accelerator lever in the fully-closed position.

2 Adjust the cable by turning the knurled adjustment wheel to give the specified freeplay in the cable inner.

3 Check that the accelerator lever moves to the full-throttle position when the accelerator pedal is fully depressed.

Defender

4 Hold the injection pump accelerator lever, or the throttle linkage bellcrank, as applicable, in the fully closed position.

5 Turn the knurled adjuster wheel at the bracket on the fuel injection pump, to eliminate all freeplay from the cable inner **(see illustration)**.

6 Working in the driver's footwell, remove the trim panel for access to the pedals.

7 Slacken the locknut on the pedal stop screw.

8 Fully depress the accelerator pedal by hand until the accelerator lever, or the throttle linkage bellcrank (as applicable) is in the full-throttle position. Hold the pedal in this position, ensuring that the cable is not under strain.

9 Turn the pedal stop screw until it just touches the bulkhead panel **(see illustration)**.

1.5 Throttle cable adjuster wheel (arrowed) - 19J engine

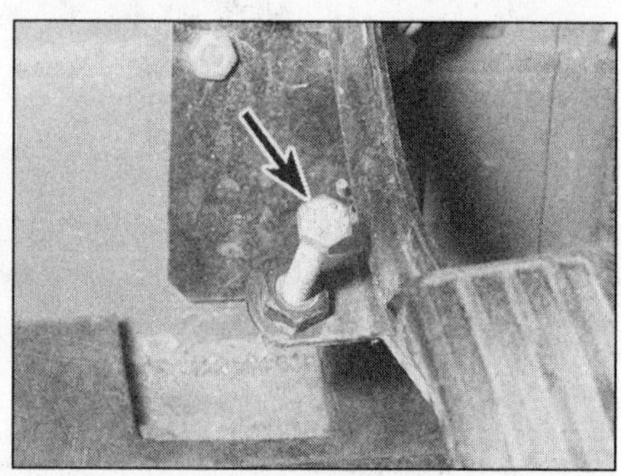

1.9 Throttle pedal stop screw (arrowed)

10 Again, check that the throttle cable is not under strain then, where applicable, tighten the locknut on the pedal stop screw.

11 Refit the footwell trim panel.

2 Accelerator linkage (Series IIA & III) - adjustment

1 Before adjusting the accelerator linkage, ensure that there is no free play in the control rod ends.

2 Check that the control arm on the fuel injection pump opens fully with the accelerator pedal pressed down onto its stop and closes fully when the pedal is released.

3 Adjust the linkage as necessary by unscrewing the adjuster locknut and turning the control rod. Retighten each locknut on completion.

3 Inlet manifold butterfly valve (Series IIA & III) - adjustment

1 Correct adjustment of the inlet manifold butterfly valve is important for two reasons. Firstly, if the butterfly valve does not open slightly in advance of the accelerator linkage, then instances of excessive black smoke from the exhaust can occur. Secondly, if the butterfly valve does not close slightly in advance of the

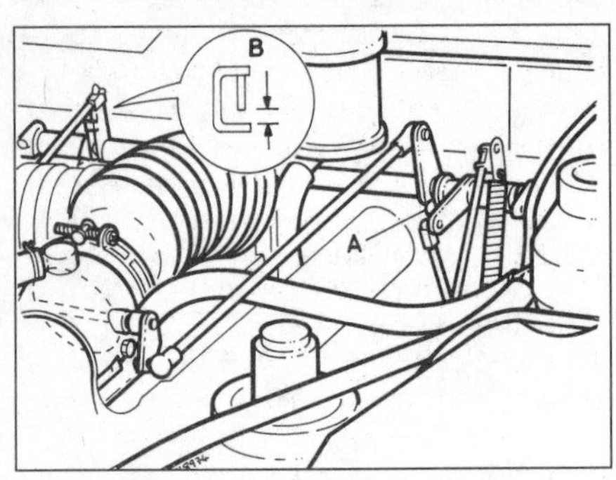

3.2 Inlet manifold butterfly valve adjustment

A Pinch bolt
B Forked shaft lost-motion gap

accelerator linkage, then ineffective brake servo action can result. The correct procedure for butterfly valve adjustment is as follows.

2 Remove the air inlet hose from the inlet manifold and check the butterfly valve is fully closed when the accelerator linkage is in the idle position. If it is not, adjustment is made at the pinch-bolt which secures the butterfly valve linkage to the accelerator cross-shaft **(see illustration).**

3 Where adjustment is required on earlier rod-operated pump linkage, ensure that the gap between the front and rear arms of the forked shaft, which actuates the injection pump linkage, provides a "lost motion" period when the accelerator cross-shaft rotates but the pump linkage does not.

4 This "lost motion" period on vehicles with the later cable-operated pump linkage is obtained by adjusting the cable lever to allow a small amount of movement in the accelerator cross-shaft before the cable begins to operate the injection pump.

4 Stop cable (Series IIA & III) - adjustment

Vehicles without steering lock

1 Ensure that the fuel injection pump cut-off lever moves through its complete range.

2 Adjust by releasing the cable end fixing. Tighten the cable fixing on completion.

Vehicles with steering lock

3 Loosen the cable inner fixing on the cut-off lever.

4 Pull the control knob fully out and position the cable in the "engine stop" position.

5 Move the cut-off lever on the fuel injection/distributor pump to the stop position and tighten the cable fixing.

6 Check that the cable moves into the start position when the key is turned to its "II" position and that with the key removed, the cable remains engaged in the stop position when pulled out.

5 Maximum speed (Discovery and Defender) - checking and adjustment

Caution: The maximum speed screw is sealed by the manufacturers at the factory, using paint or locking wire and a lead seal. Do not disturb the screw if the vehicle is still within the warranty period, otherwise the warranty will be invalidated. This adjustment requires the use of a tachometer.

5.3 Maximum speed adjustment screw (1) and locknut cover (2) - viewed from rear of pump

Discovery

Conventional fuel injection system

1 Run the engine to operating temperature.

2 Have an assistant fully depress the accelerator pedal and check that the maximum engine speed is as specified. Do not keep the engine at maximum speed for more than two or three seconds.

3 If adjustment is necessary, stop the engine then loosen the locknut, turn the maximum speed adjustment screw as necessary, then retighten the locknut. Note that the locknut may be sealed using a plastic cover **(see illustration).**

4 Repeat the procedure in paragraph 2 to check adjustment.

5 Stop the engine and disconnect the tachometer.

Electronic Diesel Control (EDC) system

6 The maximum speed is controlled by the EDC system and no adjustment is possible.

Defender

7 Follow the procedure given in paragraphs 1 to 5 inclusive **(see illustrations).**

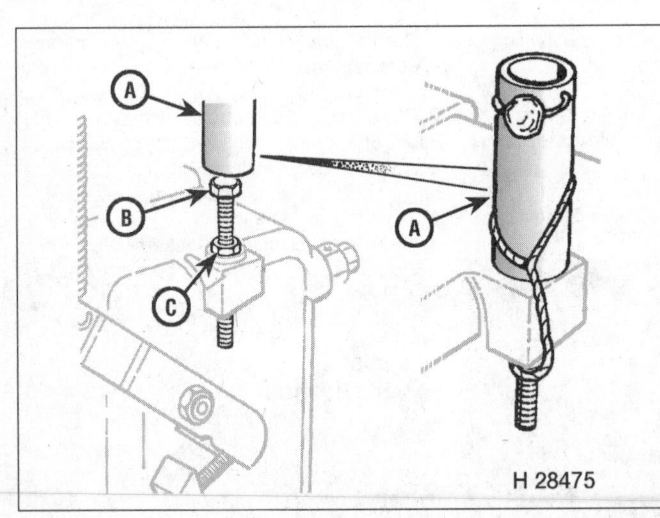

5.7a Maximum speed adjustment screw details - 10J engine

A Screw cover
B Maximum speed adjustment screw
C Locknut

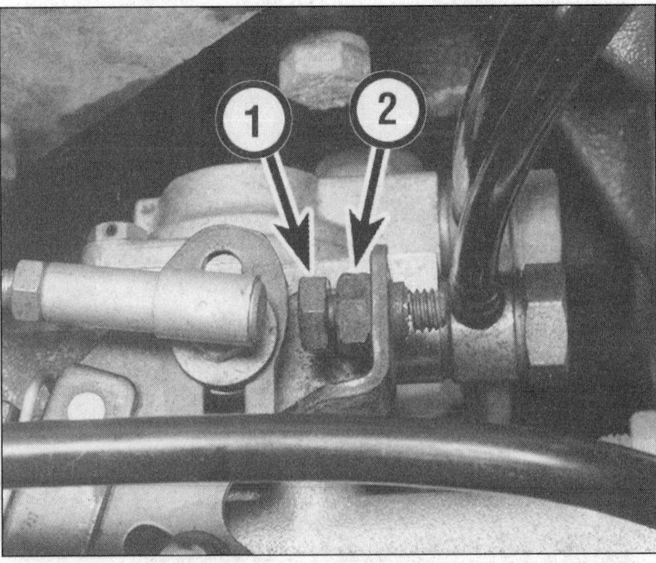

5.7b Maximum speed adjustment screw (1) and locknut (2) - 19J engine

6.2a Disconnecting wiring from stop solenoid - 19J engine

6.2b Stop solenoid location (arrowed) in rear of injection pump - 300 TDi engine

6 Stop solenoid (Discovery and Defender) - removal and refitting

Caution : Be careful not to allow dirt into the injection pump. A new sealing washer or O-ring must be used on refitting.

Removal

1 Disconnect the battery negative lead.

2 Withdraw the rubber boot (where applicable), then unscrew the terminal nut and disconnect the wire from the top of the solenoid **(see illustrations)**.

3 Carefully clean around the solenoid, then unscrew and withdraw the solenoid and recover the sealing washer or O-ring (as applicable).

4 Recover the solenoid plunger and spring if they remain in the pump. Operate the hand-priming lever on the fuel lift pump as the solenoid is removed, to flush away any dirt.

Refitting

5 Refitting is a reversal of removal. Use a new sealing washer or O-ring.

7 Glow plugs (Discovery and Defender) - removal, inspection and refitting

Note: *Where applicable, a new crankcase ventilation valve O-ring will be required on refitting.*

Caution: If the preheating system has just been energised, or if the engine has been running, the glow plugs will be very hot.

Removal

1 Disconnect the battery negative lead.

2 If No 1 cylinder (timing belt end) glow plug is to be removed on 300 TDi engine models with air conditioning, remove the air conditioning compressor drivebelt. To provide access to the glow plug, remove the four securing bolts and move the air conditioning compressor to one side. Do not disconnect the refrigerant lines from the compressor.

3 If No 3 cylinder glow plug is to be removed on 300 TDi engine models, remove the securing bolt and withdraw the crankcase ventilation system valve from the valve cover. Move the valve to one side for access to the glow plug.

4 Unscrew the nut from the relevant glow plug terminal and recover the washer **(see illustration)**.

5 Disconnect the wiring, noting the routing if all the glow plugs are to be removed.

6 Unscrew each glow plug and remove it from the cylinder head **(see illustrations)**.

Inspection

7 Inspect the glow plugs for physical damage. Burnt or eroded glow plug tips can be caused by a bad injector spray pattern. Have the injectors checked if this sort of damage is found.

8 If the glow plugs are in good physical condition, then they can be energised by applying 12 volts to them to verify that they heat up evenly and in the required time. Observe the following precautions:

a) Support the glow plug by clamping it carefully in a vice or self-locking pliers. Remember, it will become red-hot.

b) Ensure that the power supply or test lead incorporates a fuse or overload trip, to protect against damage from a short-circuit.

c) After testing, allow the glow plug to cool for several minutes before attempting to handle it.

9 A glow plug in good condition will start to glow red at the tip after drawing current for 5 seconds or so. Any plug which takes much longer to start glowing, or which starts glowing in the middle instead of at the tip, is defective.

Refitting

10 Refitting is a reversal of removal, bearing in mind the following points:

a) Apply a smear of copper-based anti-seize compound to the plug threads and tighten the glow plugs to the specified torque. Do not overtighten, as this can damage the glow plug element.

b) Ensure that the glow plug wiring is routed as noted before removal.

c) Where applicable, use a new O-ring lubricated with clean engine oil when refitting the crankcase ventilation valve.

d) Where applicable, refit and tension the air conditioning compressor drivebelt.

8 Glow plugs (Series IIA & III) - removal, inspection and refitting

Caution: If the preheating system has just been energised, or if the engine has been running, the glow plugs will be very hot.

Removal

1 Disconnect the electrical lead from each plug, taking care to avoid distortion of the central rod. On early engines, use two spanners at each terminal to prevent the insulating rod or central tube twisting.

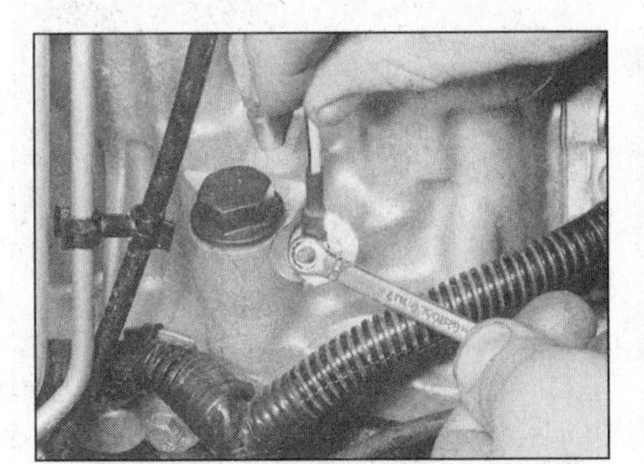

7.4 Unscrewing glow plug wiring nut

7.6a Removing a glow plug - 19J engine

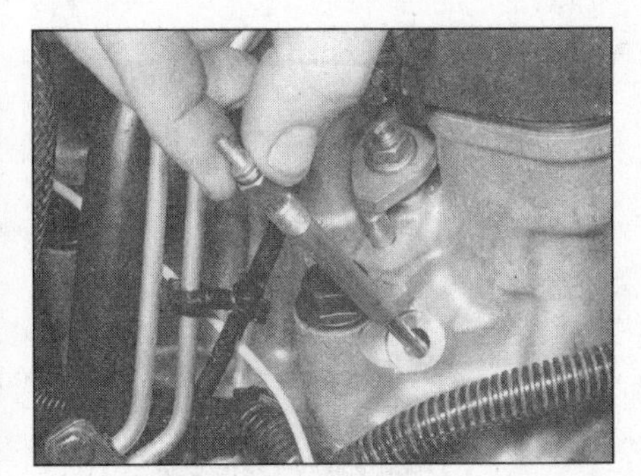

7.6b Removing a glow plug - 300 TDi engine

8.2 Removing glow plug from cylinder head

2 Unscrew and remove each glow plug from the cylinder head **(see illustration)**.
3 Scrape off any carbon from the base of the plug and element. Do not use ordinary spark plug sandblasting equipment.

Inspection

4 Refer to Section 7, paragraphs 7 to 9 inclusive.

Refitting

5 Refitting the glow plugs is the reverse sequence to removal. Do not overtighten the plugs as this can damage their elements.

9 Injectors (Discovery and Defender) - testing, removal and refitting

Warning: Exercise extreme caution when working on fuel injectors. Never expose the hands or any part of the body to injector spray, as the high working pressure can cause fuel to penetrate the skin, with possibly fatal results. You are strongly advised to have any work which involves testing the injectors under pressure carried out by a Land Rover dealer or fuel injection specialist.

Note: *Take care not to allow dirt into the injectors or fuel pipes during removal and refitting. New sealing washers must be used when refitting the injectors.*

Discovery

Testing

1 Injectors do deteriorate with prolonged use and it is reasonable to expect them to need reconditioning or renewal after 60 000 miles (90 000 km) or so. Accurate testing, overhaul and calibration of the injectors must be left to a specialist.
2 A defective injector which is causing knocking or smoking can be located without dismantling. Run the engine at a fast idle. Slacken each injector union in turn, placing rag around the union to catch spilt fuel and being careful not to expose the skin to any spray. When the union on the defective injector is slackened, the knocking or smoking will stop.

Removal

3 Where applicable, remove the engine oil filler cap and unclip the plastic cover from the top of the valve cover.
4 Carefully clean around the relevant injector and injector pipe union nuts.
5 Unscrew the banjo bolt and disconnect the leak-off pipe(s) from the injector **(see illustration)**.
6 Unscrew the union nut securing the injector pipe to the fuel injector **(see illustration)**. Cover the open ends of the injector and the pipe.
7 Counterhold the union on the pump and slacken the union nut securing the relevant injector pipe to the injection pump. There should be no need to disconnect the pipe from the pump.
8 If working on No 4 fuel injector on engines fitted with EDC, separate the two halves of the fuel injector wiring connector (the injector incorporates the EDC injection timing sensor).
9 Unscrew the nut securing the injector clamp plate to the cylinder head **(see illustration)**.
10 Withdraw the clamp plate and the injector from the cylinder head **(see illustrations)**.
11 Recover the copper washer from the cylinder head.
12 Take care not to drop the injectors, nor allow the needles at their tips to become damaged. The injectors are precision-made to fine limits and must not be handled roughly. In particular, do not mount them in a bench vice.

Refitting

13 Fit a new copper washer to the cylinder head, with the concave side towards the injector. The washer can be guided into position by sliding it down the shaft of a screwdriver positioned over the injector hole in the cylinder head.
14 Place the injector in position, with the hole for the leak-off pipe union facing away from the cylinder head, then refit the clamp plate, locating it over the cylinder head stud.
15 Refit the clamp nut and tighten to the specified torque.
16 Reconnect the injector pipe to the fuel injector and tighten the union.
17 Tighten the injector pipe union at the injection pump.
18 Reconnect the leak-off pipe to the injector and tighten the banjo bolt.
19 Where applicable, reconnect the two halves of the fuel injector wiring connector.
20 Start the engine. If difficulty is experienced, bleed the fuel system.
21 Where applicable, refit the plastic cover and the oil filler cap to the valve cover.

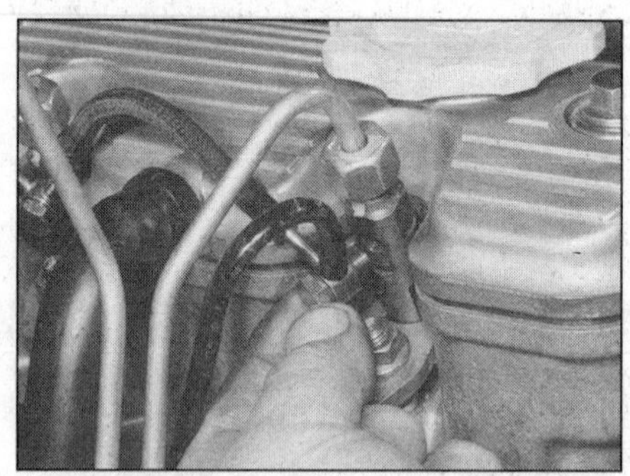
9.5 Disconnecting leak-off pipes . . .

9.6 . . . and injector pipe from fuel injector

9.9 Unscrew securing nut . . .

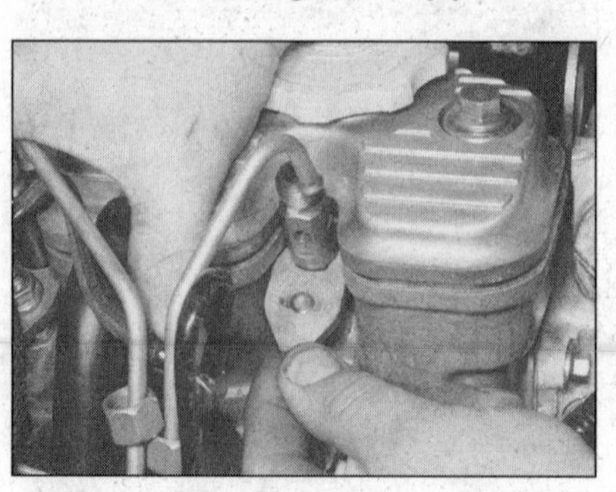
9.10a . . . then withdraw clamp plate . . .

9.10b . . . and injector

9.22a Unscrew securing nuts . . .

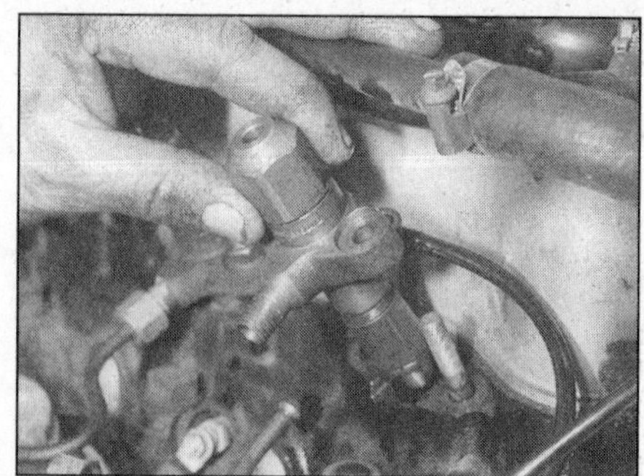

9.22b . . . and withdraw fuel injector - 19J engine

Defender

22 Carry out those procedures given in paragraphs 1 to 21 inclusive, whilst noting the following:

a) On models with a rigid leak-off pipe connected to all injectors, disconnect the pipe from all injectors and remove it. Recover the sealing washers and plug the openings in the injectors, to keep dirt out.

b) On some models, it may be necessary to completely remove the injector to injection pump pipes.

c) On 10J, 12J, and 19J engines, unscrew the two nuts (recovering the washers) securing the injector to the studs on the cylinder head. Carefully lift the injector from the cylinder head and recover the two washers from the base of the injector, or from the recesses in the cylinder head, as applicable **(see illustrations)**.

d) On 10J, 12J and 19J engines, fit a new steel sealing washer to the cylinder head, with the raised corrugation uppermost. Lightly grease a new copper washer and fit it to the injector.

e) On 10J, 12J and 19J engines, the hole for the injector pipe union should face away from the cylinder head.

f) On 200 TDi engines, the hole for the leak-off pipe union should face towards the rear of the engine.

g) On 300 TDi engines, the hole for the leak-off pipe union should face away from the cylinder head.

10 Injectors (Series IIA & III) - testing, removal and refitting

1 Refer to Part A, Section 28.

11 Fuel injection pump (Discovery) - removal and refitting

Note: *To remove the fuel injection pump without disturbing the timing belt, Land Rover special tool LRT-12-045 will be required to retain the pump sprocket in position. If a suitable tool is not available, the timing belt must be removed. Tools will be required to lock the flywheel and the fuel injection pump spindle in position. The Land Rover special tool available to lock the flywheel is LRT-12-044 for models with a conventional fuel injection system, or LRT-12-085 for models with EDC. Special flywheel locking tool LRT-12-044 can be improvised by obtaining a spare flywheel housing blanking plug and accurately drilling a hole though its centre to accept a 3/16 in twist drill. To lock the fuel injection pump sprocket, special tool LRT-12-045 will be required, however, this tool can be improvised using a short length (approx. 50.0 mm) of 9.5 mm diameter round bar. A new pump front gasket and a new pump hub cover plate gasket must be used on refitting.*

Conventional fuel injection system - using special tool LRT-12-045

Removal

1 Disconnect the battery negative lead.

2 Turn the crankshaft to bring No 1 piston to TDC on the compression stroke and fit the tools to lock the crankshaft and injection pump spindle in position, as follows.

3 On models with a manual gearbox, unscrew the blanking plug from the timing hole in the base of the flywheel housing.

4 On models with automatic transmission, unscrew the larger bolt from the cover plate located on the engine backplate, to the rear of the sump. Pivot the cover plate away from the bolt hole.

5 Screw the appropriate flywheel locking tool into the timing hole on models with a manual gearbox, or into the larger cover plate bolt hole on models with automatic transmission. Do not engage the locking tool centre pin at this stage **(see illustrations)**.

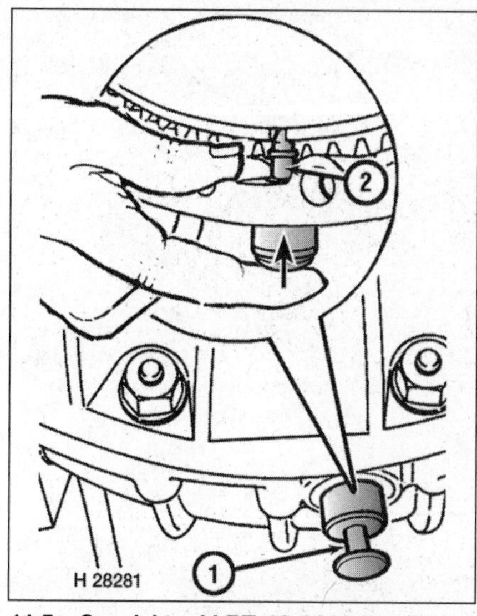

11.5a Special tool LRT-12-044 in position - manual gearbox

1 Special tool LRT-12-044
2 Tool centre pin

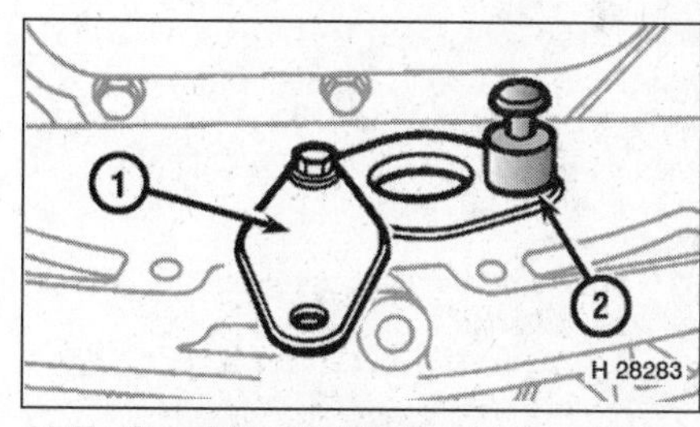

11.5b Special tool LRT-12-044 in position - automatic transmission

1 Cover plate
2 Special tool LRT-12-044

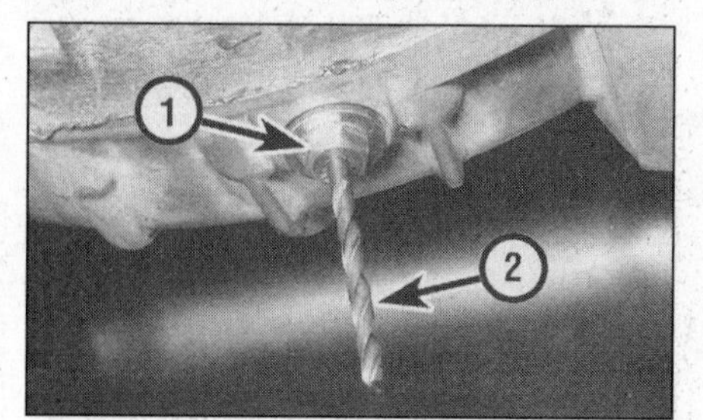

11.5c Improvised flywheel locking tool in position - manual gearbox
1 Blanking plug 2 3/16 in twist drill

6 On models with air conditioning, remove the air conditioning compressor drivebelt. If desired, unscrew the securing bolts and move the compressor to one side, clear of the working area. Do not disconnect the refrigerant lines.

7 Remove the three screws and withdraw the injection pump hub cover plate from the timing belt cover **(see illustration)**. Note that on

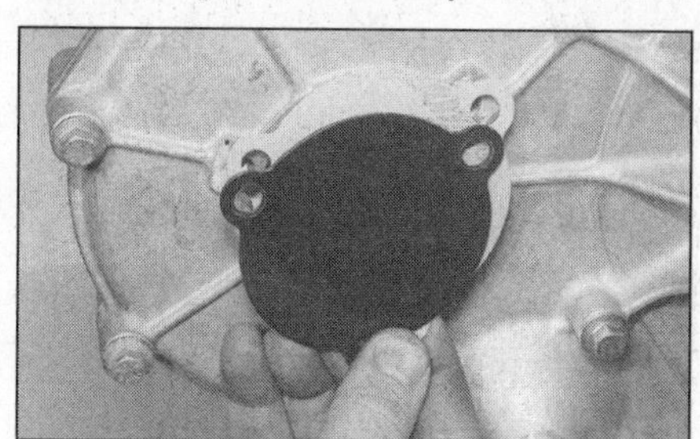

11.7 Remove injection pump hub cover plate and gasket - viewed with engine removed

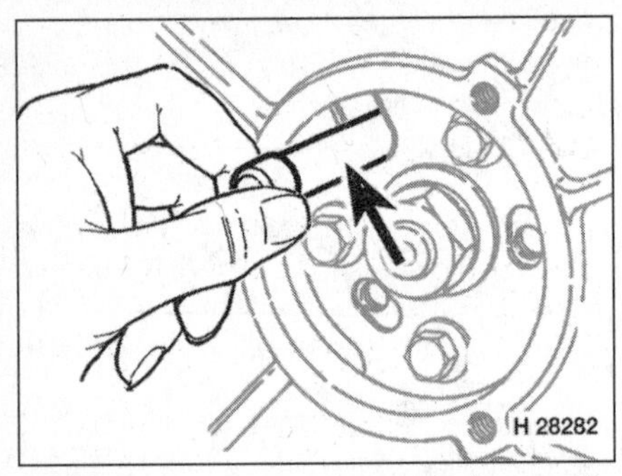

11.8 Injection pump timing pin (arrowed) in position

11.9 Improvised flywheel locking tool centre pin engaged with flywheel - gearbox removed

11.11a Unclip wiring harness (arrowed) from pump bracket . . .

models with air conditioning, the air conditioning drivebelt tensioner pulley is secured to the cover plate. Recover the gasket.
8 Insert the pump timing pin (Tool No LRT-12-045) or an improvised equivalent, through the U-shaped slot in the pump hub then, using a suitable tool on the crankshaft pulley/damper bolt, turn the crankshaft until the timing pin can be slid through the pump hub into the pump body **(see illustration)**. The tool should slide easily into position.
9 The flywheel locking tool centre pin should now slide easily into engagement with the timing slot in the flywheel. If the tool does not slide easily into position, this indicates that the injection pump timing is incorrect **(see illustration)**.
10 The engine is now locked with No 1 piston at top dead centre, proceed as follows.

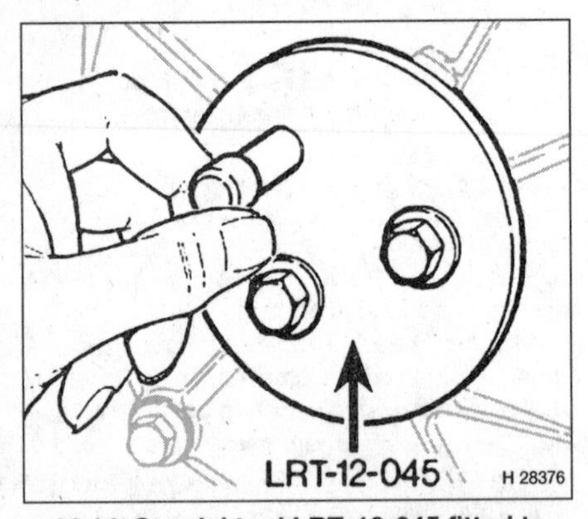

11.14 Special tool LRT-12-045 fitted to retain fuel injection pump sprocket

11 Loosen the pump locking screw and remove the keeper plate (located at the front of the pump, behind the timing belt housing). Tighten the locking screw to lock the pump in position **(see illustrations)**.
12 Remove the three pump sprocket-to-hub bolts and withdraw the sprocket retaining plate. If necessary, counterhold the injection pump hub using a socket on the hub nut. Do not rely on the pump spindle locking screw to hold the sprocket in position whilst loosening the pump sprocket-to-hub bolts.
13 Withdraw the pump timing pin.
14 Fit the sprocket retaining tool (LRT-12-045), with a 1.5 to 2.0 mm thick, 8.0 mm washer under each bolt head, in addition to the washers supplied with the tool. Tighten the two retaining tool bolts, then re-insert the timing pin through the hole provided in the retaining tool plate **(see illustration)**.
15 Disconnect the wiring from the stop solenoid.
16 Disconnect the accelerator cable from the pump. On models with automatic transmission, also disconnect the kickdown cable from the pump.
17 Unscrew the banjo bolt and the union nut, then disconnect the fuel supply and return pipes from the pump **(see illustrations)**. Be prepared for fuel spillage. Recover the sealing washers from the banjo union. Cover the open ends of the pipes and plug the openings in the injection pump to keep dirt out (the banjo bolt can be refitted to the pump and covered).
18 Similarly, disconnect the boost pressure pipe from the pump.

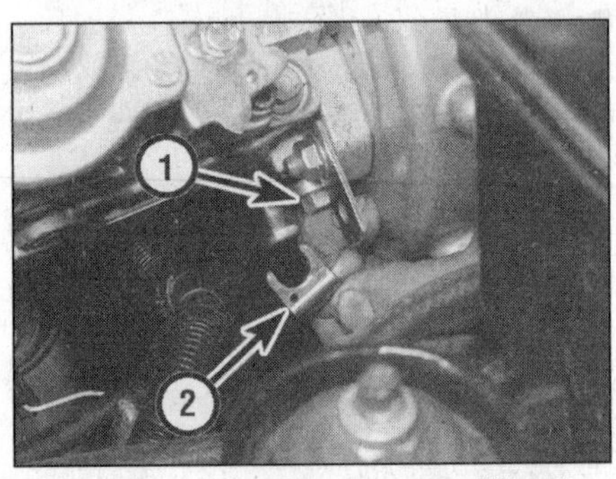

11.11b . . . then loosen screw (1) and remove keeper plate (2) - 300 TDi engine

19 Unscrew the union nuts and disconnect the injector pipes from the rear of the pump and from the injectors. Remove the pipes. Plug or cover the open ends of the pump, pipes and injectors, to prevent dirt ingress.
20 Working at the rear of the pump, counterhold the bolts and unscrew the two nuts securing the pump to the rear support bracket **(see illustration)**.
21 Unscrew the three nuts securing the pump to the studs at the rear of the timing belt housing, then withdraw the pump and recover the gasket. Where applicable, note the location of any brackets on the studs **(see illustrations)**.

Refitting

22 Thoroughly clean the mating faces of the pump flange and the timing belt housing.
23 Place the new gasket in position over the pump mounting studs.

11.17a Disconnecting fuel supply pipe from pump

11.17b Counterhold union on pump when unscrewing fuel return pipe union nut

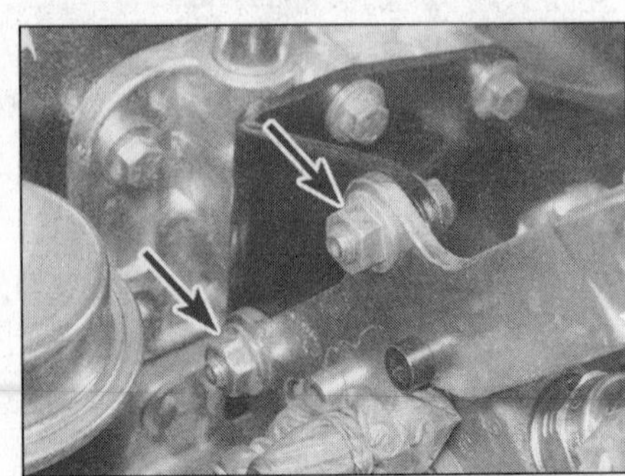
11.20 Unscrew two nuts and bolts (arrowed) securing pump to rear support bracket

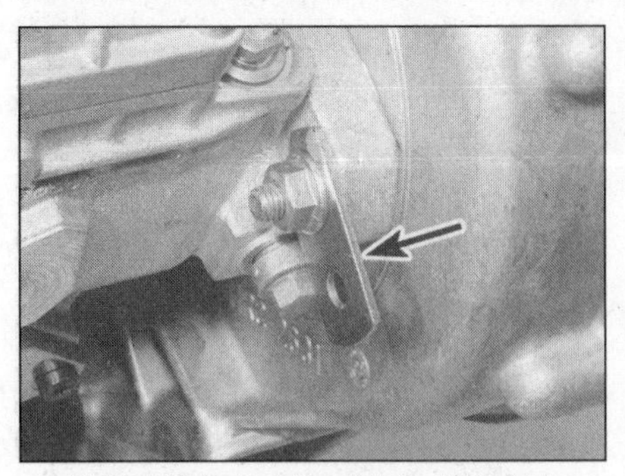

11.21a Note location of any brackets (arrowed) on timing belt housing studs

11.21b Withdrawing fuel injection pump

24 If a new pump is being fitted, proceed as follows:

a) *Fit the timing pin to the pump. If necessary, rotate the pump spindle to allow the pin to locate fully.*
b) *Slacken the pump locking screw, remove the keeper plate, then tighten the screw to lock the pump.*
c) *Remove the timing pin from the pump.*

25 Place the pump in position on the mounting studs, ensuring that the gasket is correctly located. Tighten the mounting nuts to the specified torque.

26 Refit the pump rear mounting bracket to the cylinder block but do not fully tighten the bolts at this stage.

27 Refit the nuts and bolts securing the pump to the rear mounting bracket but again, do not fully tighten at this stage.

28 Tighten the rear mounting bracket-to-cylinder block bolts, followed by the pump-to-mounting bracket bolts.

29 Refit and reconnect the injector pipes and tighten the union nuts.

30 Reconnect the boost pressure pipe to the pump.

31 Reconnect the fuel supply and return pipes to the pump.

32 Reconnect the accelerator cable to the pump and adjust the cable as described in Section 1. On models with automatic transmission, also reconnect and adjust the kickdown cable, as follows:

a) *From beneath the vehicle, loosen the kickdown cable outer locknut at the cable mounting bracket on the transmission.*
b) *Ensure that the throttle linkage on the injection pump is fully closed.*
c) *Working at the transmission bracket, adjust the cable outer by turning the adjuster nut as required, so as to achieve the desired gap between the end of the cable outer and the crimped collar on the cable inner **(see illustration).***
d) *When the gap is correct, tighten the locknut.*
e) *Recheck that the throttle linkage is fully closed, then recheck the gap and re-adjust if necessary.*

33 Reconnect the stop solenoid wiring.

34 Unscrew the securing bolts and remove the injection pump sprocket retaining tool.

35 Refit the sprocket retaining plate, then refit the pump timing pin through the pump hub into the pump body.

36 Refit and tighten the pump sprocket-to-hub bolts.

37 Loosen the pump locking screw, then refit the keeper plate and tighten the locking screw.

38 Remove the timing pin from the pump and withdraw the flywheel locking tool centre pin from the slot in the flywheel.

39 Turn the crankshaft through two complete revolutions, then re-engage the flywheel locking tool centre pin with the slot in the flywheel and check that the pump timing pin can still be inserted easily.

40 If the timing tool cannot be easily inserted into position, proceed as follows.

41 Withdraw the flywheel locking tool centre pin from the slot in the flywheel, then turn the crankshaft as necessary until the timing pin can be inserted easily into the injection pump.

42 Loosen the pump locking screw and remove the keeper plate, then tighten the locking screw to lock the pump in position.

43 Loosen the three pump sprocket-to-hub bolts.

44 Turn the crankshaft back to TDC and engage the flywheel locking tool centre pin with the timing slot in the flywheel.

45 Re-check to ensure that the pump timing pin is an easy sliding fit in the pump.

46 Tighten the pump sprocket-to-hub bolts to the specified torque.

47 Loosen the pump locking screw, then refit the keeper plate and tighten the locking screw.

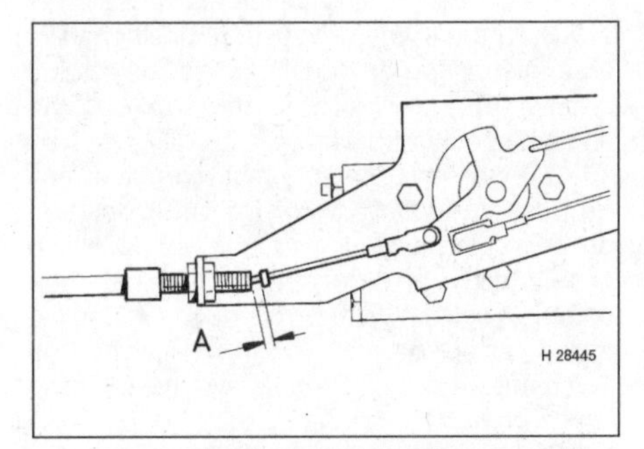

11.32 Kickdown cable adjustment

A = 0.25 to 1.25 mm

48 Remove the timing pin from the pump and withdraw the flywheel locking tool centre pin from the slot in the flywheel.

49 Refit the blanking plug or cover plate bolt, as applicable, to the flywheel locking tool aperture. On models with a blanking plug, coat the threads of the plug with thread-locking compound before refitting.

50 Refit the injection pump hub cover plate, using a new gasket.

51 Where applicable, refit the air conditioning compressor and drivebelt.

52 Reconnect the battery negative lead.

Conventional fuel injection system - without special tool LRT-12-045

Removal

53 Remove the timing belt, as described in Part A of this Chapter.

54 Loosen the pump locking screw and remove the keeper plate (located at the front of the pump, behind the timing belt housing). Tighten the locking screw to lock the pump spindle in position.

55 Withdraw the pump timing pin from the pump sprocket.

56 Remove the pump sprocket-to-hub securing bolts, then withdraw the sprocket retaining plate and the sprocket.

57 Proceed as described in paragraphs 15 to 21 inclusive.

Refitting

58 Proceed as described in paragraphs 22 to 33 inclusive.

59 Refit the pump sprocket and retaining plate (noting that the U-shaped slot in the retaining plate should align with the slot in the pump hub), then refit the sprocket-to-hub bolts. Do not fully tighten the bolts at this stage.

60 Refit the pump timing pin through the sprocket into the pump body.

61 Loosen the pump locking screw, then refit the keeper plate and tighten the locking screw.

62 Refit the timing belt as described in Part A of this Chapter.

Electronic Diesel Control (EDC) system

63 The removal and refitting procedure is as described previously for models with a conventional fuel injection system, bearing in mind the following points:

a) *Ignore all references to the accelerator cable.*
b) *Disconnect all relevant wiring from the pump, noting the routing of the harnesses.*

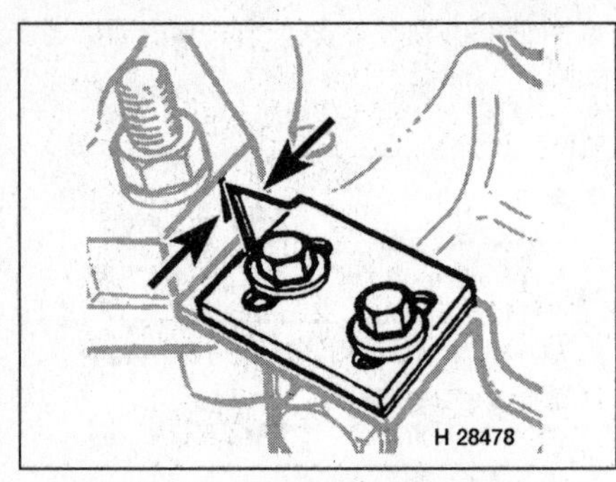

12.7 Mark on pump flange aligned with pump timing pointer (arrowed) - 10J engine

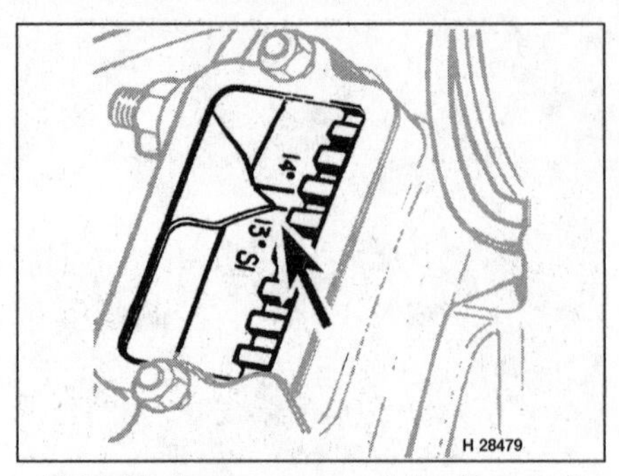

12.12 Timing aperture pointer (arrowed) aligned with 13° mark on flywheel - 10J engine

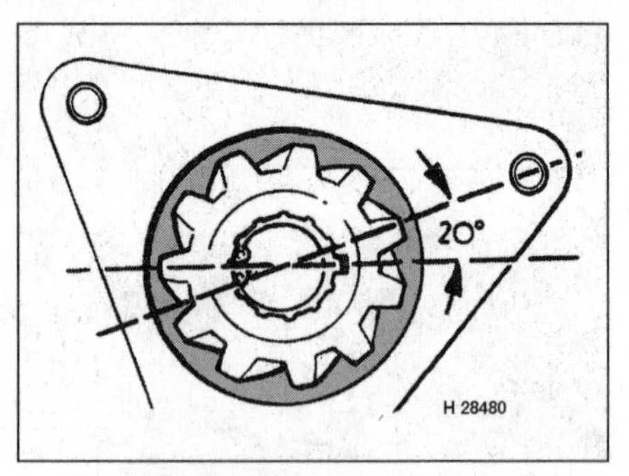

12.14 Fuel injection pump drivegear master spline (arrowed) positioned at 20° to crankshaft axis - 10J engine

12 Fuel injection pump (Defender) - removal and refitting

10J engines

Note: *A new pump gasket and a new timing aperture cover plate gasket will be required on refitting.*

Removal

1 Disconnect the battery negative lead.

2 To improve access, remove the bonnet.

3 Disconnect the wiring from the stop solenoid.

4 Disconnect the accelerator cable from the injection pump.

5 Unscrew the unions and disconnect the fuel supply and return pipes from the pump. Be prepared for fuel spillage. Where applicable, recover the sealing washers from the banjo union. Cover the open ends of the pipes and plug the openings in the injection pump to keep dirt out.

6 Unscrew the union nuts and disconnect the injector pipes from the pump and from the injectors. Remove the pipes, noting their locations to aid refitting. Plug or cover the open ends of the pump, pipes and injectors, to prevent dirt ingress.

7 Check that there is a clear alignment mark on the pump flange, in line with the pump timing pointer, which is mounted on the cylinder block side cover plate in front of the pump **(see illustration)**. Make an appropriate mark if necessary.

12.18 Special gauge RO605863 in position in injection pump drivegear aperture - 10J engine

1 *Special gauge RO605863*
2 *Timing mark on gauge flange*
3 *Timing pointer securing bolts*

8 Unscrew the three securing nuts, recover the washers and withdraw the pump. Recover the gasket.

9 Withdraw the pump driveshaft from the drivegear.

Refitting

10 Unscrew the two securing nuts and recover the washers securing the timing aperture cover plate to the flywheel housing on the right-hand side of the engine. Lift off the cover plate and recover the gasket.

11 Look to see if a timing pointer is visible in the aperture. If no pointer is visible, a suitable pointer can be obtained under Land Rover part No ERC 2250. Where applicable, fit the timing pointer and secure with the two nuts. Note that the pointer arrow should be positioned on the gearbox side of the timing aperture.

12 Using a socket or spanner on the crankshaft pulley bolt, turn the crankshaft until the 13° mark on the flywheel is aligned with the pointer in the timing aperture **(see illustration)**.

13 If the crankshaft is inadvertently turned beyond the 13° mark, do not turn the crankshaft back but continue to turn in a clockwise direction until the mark is precisely aligned with the pointer.

14 Look through the injection pump drivegear aperture and check that the master spline on the pump drivegear is positioned at an angle of approximately 20° to the engine crankshaft axis, towards the front of the engine **(see illustration)**.

15 It is possible that the master spline may be positioned 180° away from the position described in the previous paragraph, in which case, turn the crankshaft through one complete revolution to bring the master spline to the correct position. Again, check that the 13° mark on the flywheel is aligned with the timing pointer.

16 Insert special gauge tool RO605863 through the drivegear aperture into the drivegear.

17 Turn the gauge handle firmly clockwise to take up backlash in the timing gears, then hold the gauge in this position.

18 Check that the mark on the edge of the gauge is aligned with the pump timing pointer on the engine. If not, slacken the two bolts securing the pointer, reposition the pointer to align with the gauge mark, then tighten the bolts **(see illustration)**.

19 Remove the gauge then refit the pump driveshaft, engaging the master spline with the master spline on the drivegear. Note that the longer-splined end of the driveshaft engages with the drivegear.

20 Locate a new pump gasket on the drive-gear housing.

21 Turn the injection pump spindle to align the master spline on the spindle with the master spline on the driveshaft, then lower the pump into position. Turn the pump as necessary to align the timing mark on the pump flange with the pump timing pointer on the engine.

22 Refit the washers and the pump securing nuts, then tighten the nuts. Check that the timing mark on the pump flange is still aligned with the pointer on the engine.

23 Refit the injector pipes to their original locations and tighten the union nuts.

24 Reconnect the fuel supply and return pipes to the pump and tighten the unions.

25 Reconnect the wiring to the stop solenoid.

26 Reconnect the accelerator cable and check cable adjustment.

27 Refit the timing aperture cover plate to the flywheel housing, using a new gasket, then tighten the securing nuts.

28 Reconnect the battery negative lead.

29 Bleed the fuel system, then check the idle speed and maximum speed.

30 On completion, refit the bonnet.

12J and 19J engines

Note: *If Land Rover special tool 18G 1457 is available, the pump can be removed without disturbing the timing belt, working through the access hole in the timing belt cover. At the time of writing, no information was available regarding the use of this special tool. The following procedure assumes that the special tool is not available, in which case the timing belt must be removed. A new pump front mounting gasket will be required on refitting.*

12.34 Levering accelerator linkage rod from fuel injection pump lever - 19J engine

12.36 Disconnecting fuel injector pipe from fuel injection pump - 19J engine

12.38 Disconnect fuel leak-off pipe (1) and boost pressure pipe (2) from injection pump - 19J engine

Removal

31 To improve access, remove the bonnet.

32 Remove the timing belt and the fuel injection pump sprocket.

33 Disconnect the wiring from the stop solenoid.

34 Using a small screwdriver, carefully lever the accelerator linkage rod from the lever on the injection pump **(see illustration)**.

35 Unscrew the unions and disconnect the fuel supply and return pipes from the pump. Be prepared for fuel spillage. Where applicable, recover the sealing washers from the banjo union. Cover the open ends of the pipes and plug the openings in the injection pump, to keep dirt out.

36 Unscrew the union nuts and disconnect the injector pipes from the pump and from the injectors **(see illustration)**. Remove the pipes, noting their locations to aid refitting. Plug or cover the open ends of the pump, pipes and injectors, to prevent dirt ingress.

37 Similarly, disconnect the fuel leak-off pipe from the pump.

38 On 19J engines, unscrew the union bolt and disconnect the boost pressure pipe from the pump **(see illustration)**.

39 Unbolt the oil filter adapter assembly from the cylinder block, to allow sufficient clearance to withdraw the pump. Be prepared for oil spillage and recover the gasket.

40 Ensure that there is an alignment mark on the pump flange, in line with the pump timing pointer (bolted to the rear of the timing belt housing). Make a suitable mark if necessary. If no timing pointer is fitted, simply make alignment marks between the pump flange and the timing belt housing.

41 Unscrew the nut and bolt securing the pump to the rear support bracket.

42 Unscrew the three nuts (recovering the washers) securing the pump to the studs at the rear of the timing belt housing, then withdraw the pump and recover the gasket.

Refitting

43 Commence refitting by thoroughly cleaning the mating faces of the pump flange and the timing belt housing.

44 Place the new gasket in position over the pump mounting studs.

45 Place the pump in position on the mounting studs, ensuring that the gasket is correctly located, then refit the washers and securing nuts. Do not fully tighten the nuts at this stage. Position the pump so that the mark on the pump flange is aligned with the timing pointer or the mark (as applicable) on the timing belt housing.

46 Refit the nut and bolt securing the pump to the rear mounting bracket. Again, do not fully tighten at this stage.

47 Thoroughly clean the mating faces of the oil filter adapter assembly and cylinder block, then refit the assembly, using a new gasket. Tighten the securing bolts.

48 Refit the fuel injection pump sprocket and the timing belt.

49 Set up the injection pump timing.

50 With all pump mountings tightened, refit the injector pipes and tighten the unions.

51 Reconnect the fuel supply and return pipes.

52 Reconnect the fuel leak-off pipe and where applicable, the boost pressure pipe.

53 Reconnect the accelerator linkage rod to the lever on the pump, then check the accelerator cable adjustment.

54 Reconnect the wiring to the stop solenoid.

55 On completion, start the engine and check the idle speed and maximum engine speed. Refit the bonnet.

200 TDi and 300 TDi engines

56 Refer to Section 11 and follow the procedure given for 200 TDi and 300 TDi engines fitted with a conventional fuel injection system.

13 Fuel injection pump (Series IIA & III) - removal, refitting and timing

Early and later (pre 1973) pumps

1 Early pumps have internal timing marks, viewed through an inspection window. Later pumps, fitted before 1973, are identified by DPA No. 3248760 stamped on the manufacturer's label and have an external timing mark on the lower flange, which is used in conjunction with a pointer on the engine.

2 For efficient running of the engine, accurate fuel injection/distributor pump timing is essential. Providing the following procedures are strictly followed, no problems should be encountered. However, if a new or reconditioned injection pump is to be fitted, Land Rover special tool No. 605863 will be required to accurately set the injection timing. This tool is only necessary on later type injection pumps with external timing marks.

Removal

3 Disconnect the battery earth terminal.

4 Remove the air cleaner.

5 Disconnect the engine stop cable from the injection pump and remove the stop spring.

6 Prise off the retaining clip and lift off the accelerator linkage rod from the bellcrank lever on the injection pump upper body.

7 Slacken the fuel inlet pipe unions at the injectors and remove all the fuel pipes from the injection pump. If necessary, mark their positions to aid reassembly **(see illustration)**.

8 Accurately mark the pump mounting flange in relation to the cylinder block, using a scribe or a centre punch. This is most important as the injection pump must be refitted in exactly the same position, otherwise the injection timing will be incorrect.

9 Undo and remove the three nuts and washers securing the pump to the engine and lift off the pump.

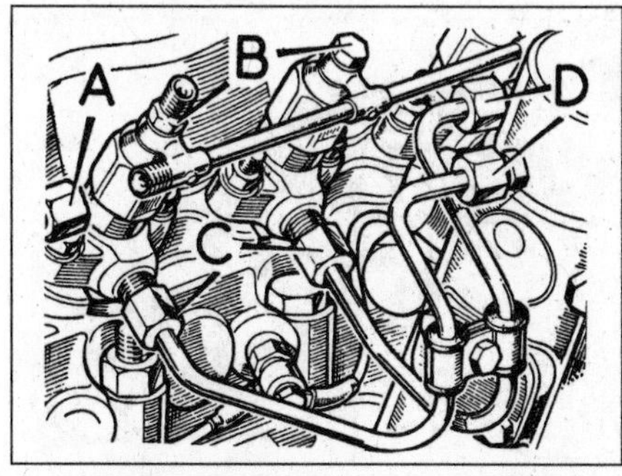

13.7 Fuel injection pump and fuel lines

A Spill pipe union
B Injector spill pipe fixings
C Fuel lines to injectors
D Fuel lines to fuel injection distributor pump

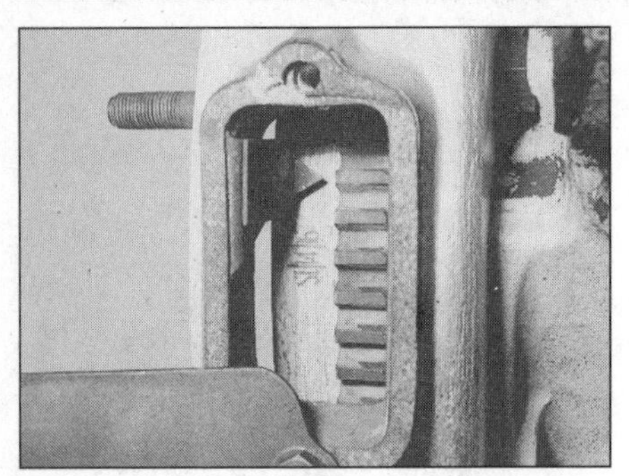

13.12 Aligning timing marks on flywheel with pointer

Refitting and timing

10 To refit the pump, remove the valve rocker cover and the inspection cover for the timing pointer on the flywheel housing.

11 Turn the engine in the normal direction of rotation until both valves on No 1 cylinder are closed and there is a clearance between the valve stems and rockers.

12 Continue turning slowly in the normal direction of rotation until the applicable timing mark is in line with the timing pointer on the flywheel housing **(see illustration)**.

13 On early injection pumps, set the pointer adjacent to the 16° mark on the flywheel.

14 On later injection pumps fitted to engines having a 14° and 16° mark stamped on the flywheel, set the timing at 15°, that is midway between the two marks. If the flywheel is stamped with 13° and 14° marks set the timing at 13°. Ensure that the marks approach the pointer In the normal direction of rotation. If the pointer is passed, start again.

15 Using a protractor, scribe a line at 20° to the horizontal on the fuel injection/distributor pump mating face of the cylinder block **(see illustration)**.

16 Observe the injection pump vertical drive gear master spline and ensure that it is in line with the scribed mark **(see illustration)**.

17 If the original pump is being used, it may now be refitted using the reverse sequence to removal. Ensure that the previously made marks on the pump flange and cylinder block are in line before tightening the securing nuts. With the pump in position and all the fittings reconnected, refer to paragraphs 27 to 30 inclusive.

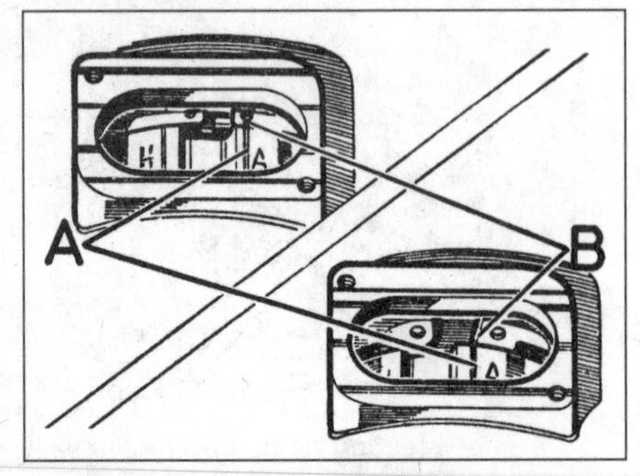

13.18 Early-type fuel injection pump timing markings

A *Timing mark on pump rotor*
B *Scribed mark on straight edge as applicable*

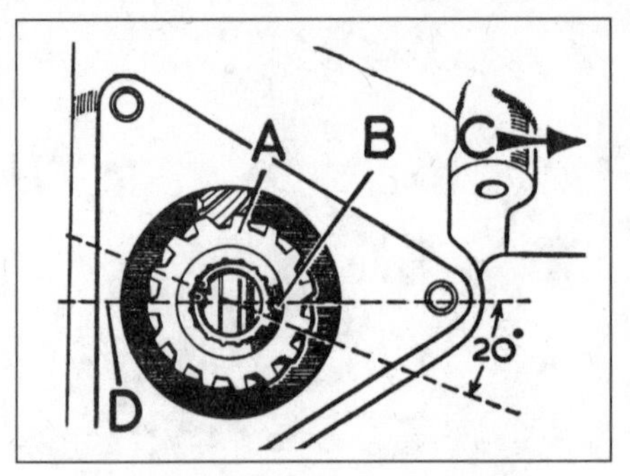

13.15 Vertical drive gear positioning

A *Vertical drive gear*
B *Master spline at 20° to engine centre line*
C *Front of engine*
D *Line parallel with engine centre line*

18 If a new or reconditioned pump of the early type is being fitted, remove the inspection cover from the side of the pump and observe the driving plate through the viewing window. Rotate the spindle until the line marked A on the driving plate is in line with the mark on the circlip **(see illustration)**.

19 Place the pump in position on the engine and engage the drive. Refit the securing nuts and washers but do not fully tighten at this stage.

20 Observe the timing marks through the viewing window and make any final corrections necessary to bring them in line, by turning the pump body. When turning the pump in the normal direction of rotation, hold the driving plate against the direction of rotation to take up any backlash in the gears. Now fully tighten the securing nuts.

21 Reconnect all pipes and fittings using the reverse sequence to removal, then refer to paragraphs 27 to 30 inclusive.

22 If a new or reconditioned pump of the later type is being fitted, remove the short drive shaft from the vertical drive gear and place the timing gauge (Land Rover tool No. 605863) in position - see illustration 12.18.

23 Turn the gauge clockwise to take up any backlash in the gears and hold it in this position. The arrow on the timing pointer should now be in line with the mark on the timing gauge. If necessary slacken the bolts and reposition the pointer.

13.25 Fuel injection pump timing mark in line with pointer

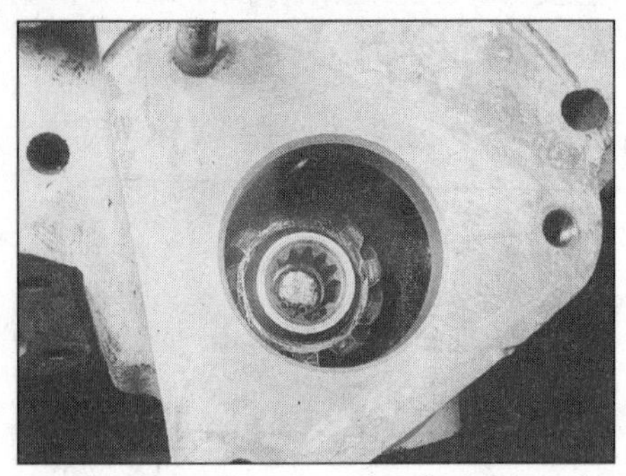

13.16 Vertical drive gear master spline set at 20° to horizontal

24 Remove the timing gauge and refit the drive gear, narrow portion first.

25 Position the master spline on the pump spindle to line up with the master spline on the drive gear and place the pump in position on the engine. Align the mark on the pump flange with the pointer and refit and fully tighten the securing nuts and washers **(see illustration)**.

26 Reconnect all pipes and fittings using the reverse sequence to removal.

27 With all components reconnected, undo the two air vent screws on the side of the pump body and operate the hand priming lever on the fuel pump until fuel emerges with no trace of air bubbles, then tighten the air vent screws.

28 With an assistant operating the starter switch and the engine turning on the starter motor, slacken the fuel feed pipe to one of the injectors. When fuel free from air bubbles emerges, tighten the feed pipe.

29 Start the engine and check for any fuel leaks.

30 If a new or reconditioned pump has been fitted, set the engine slow running control screw on the pump to give the slowest possible tickover consistent with even

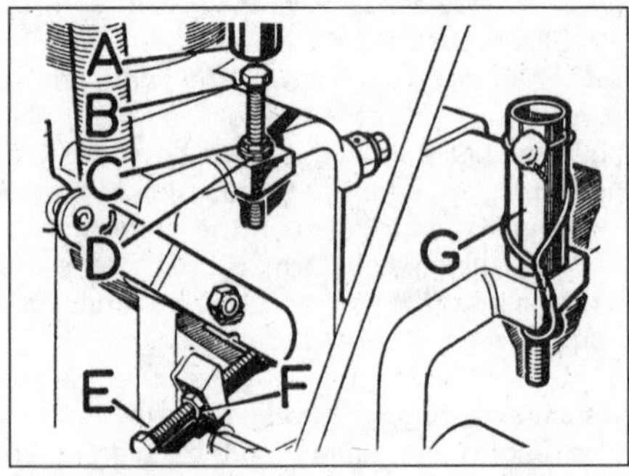

13.30 Fuel injection pump control screws

A *Collar*
B *Maximum output control screw*
C *Locknut*
D *Screw retainer*
E *Slow running screw*
F *Locknut*
G *Screw collar lockwired after setting*

running. The pump maximum output control screw should be set to give a maximum engine speed of 4200 rpm. This can be set by a road test, 4200 rpm being equal to 48 mph (77 kph) in third gear **(see illustration)**.

Post 1973 pumps

Note: *The following procedure for resetting the timing pointer requires the use of special tool No MS 67 B which probably will not be available to the home mechanic. Therefore, do not disturb the timing pointer.*

Removal

31 Remove the injection pump, as described in paragraphs 3 to 9 inclusive.

Refitting and timing

32 Remove the engine rocker cover.

33 Gain access to the pointer and timing marks on the engine flywheel.

34 Turn the engine in its normal direction of rotation until both valves on No 1 cylinder are closed and the piston is ascending on its compression stroke.

35 Keep turning the engine until the 13° mark on the flywheel lines up exactly with the pointer when viewed from directly above. If the engine is turned too far, then the operation must be repeated as it is important this position is reached with the engine turning in its normal direction of rotation.

36 The master spline on the drivegear should now be facing 20° away from the centre line of the engine, viewed from the front. If the special timing gauge is not available, continue from paragraph 42.

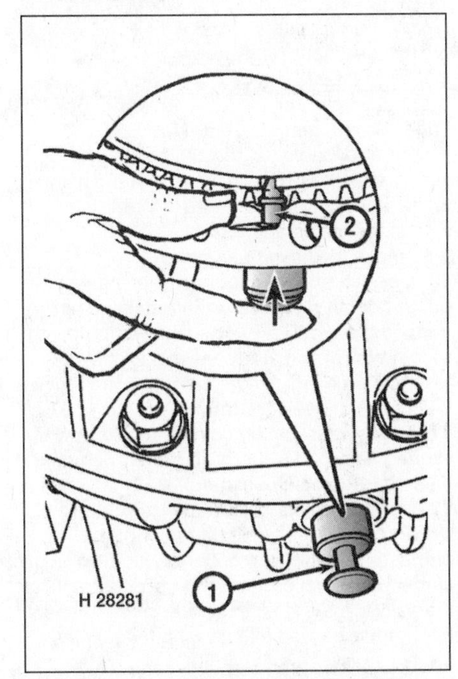

14.3a Special tool LRT-12-044 in position - 300 TDi engine

1 *Special tool LRT-12-044*
2 *Tool centre pin*

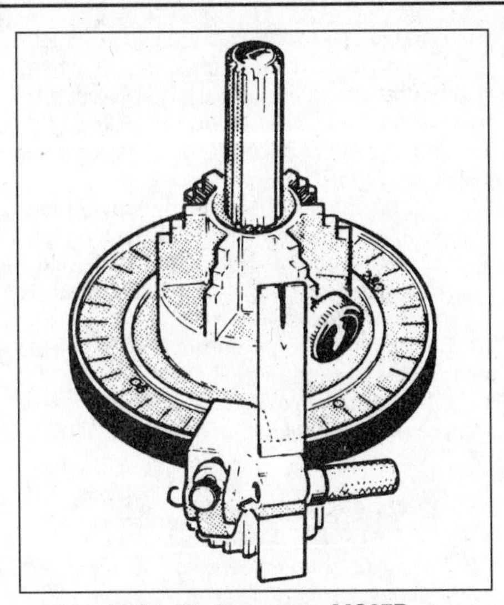

13.37 Timing gauge MS67B

37 Set the timing gauge (tool No MS 67 B) to 22° and lock it in this position **(see illustration)**.

38 Now invert the timing gauge and insert it into the pump housing on the engine, ensuring it engages with the injection pump drive splines.

39 Slide the body of the tool down the centre shaft, engaging it in the injection pump drivegear hub. Tighten the knurled retaining screw.

40 Turn the tool gently in a clockwise direction to take up any backlash or wear in gears. Hold it in this position.

41 Slacken the retaining bolts and adjust the timing pointer to align with the pointer on the timing gauge. Tighten the bolts in this position, then remove the timing gauge.

42 Rotate the driving gear on the pump to line up the master spline with that on the engine drive spline and offer up the pump to the engine, checking that the timing mark on the pump body lines up with the timing pointer.

43 Tighten the sump retaining nuts.

44 Referring to the procedure given for pre 1973 pumps, complete refitting of the pump and prime the fuel system.

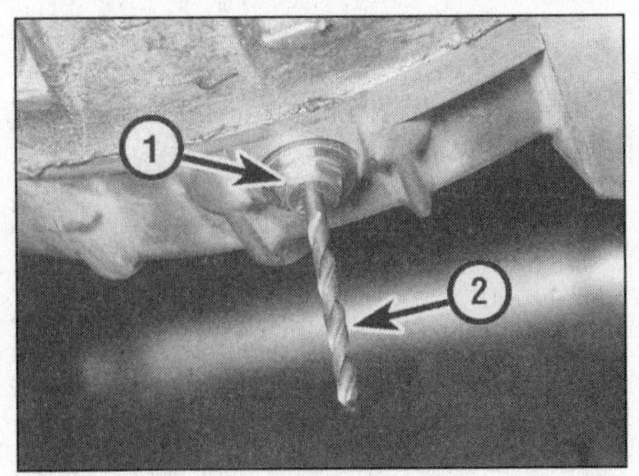

14.3b Improvised flywheel locking tool in position - manual gearbox

1 *Blanking plug*
2 *3/16 in twist drill*

14 Fuel injection pump (Discovery) - timing

Caution: The maximum engine speed and transfer pressure settings, together with timing access plugs, are sealed by the manufacturers with locking wire and lead seals. Do not disturb the wire if the vehicle is still within the warranty period, otherwise the warranty will be invalidated. Also, do not attempt the timing procedure unless accurate locking tools are available. A new injection pump hub cover plate gasket must be used on refitting.

1 It is only necessary to check the injection timing after the injection pump has been disturbed.

2 Dynamic timing equipment does exist but it is unlikely to be available to the home mechanic. The equipment works by converting pressure pulses in an injector pipe into electrical signals. If such equipment is available, use it in accordance with the manufacturer's instructions.

3 Static timing can be carried out very accurately, provided that the appropriate flywheel and injection pump spindle locking tools are available. The Land Rover tool required to lock the flywheel is LRT-12-044 **(see illustration)** for models with a conventional fuel injection system, or LRT-12-085 for models with EDC. Special flywheel locking tool LRT-12-044 can be improvised by obtaining a spare flywheel housing blanking plug and accurately drilling a hole though its centre to accept a 3/16 in drill. To lock the fuel injection pump sprocket, special tool LRT-12-045 will be required. This tool can be improvised using a short length (approx 50.0 mm) of 9.5 mm diameter round bar **(see illustrations)**. Proceed as follows.

4 Disconnect the battery negative lead.

5 Turn the crankshaft to bring No 1 piston to TDC on the compression stroke and fit the tools to lock the flywheel and the injection pump sprocket in position, as described in Section 11. If the flywheel and injection pump

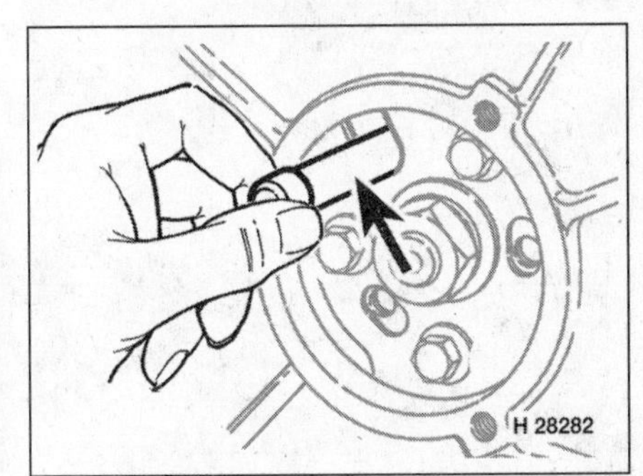

14.3c Injection pump timing pin (arrowed) can be improvised using length of 9.5 mm diameter bar

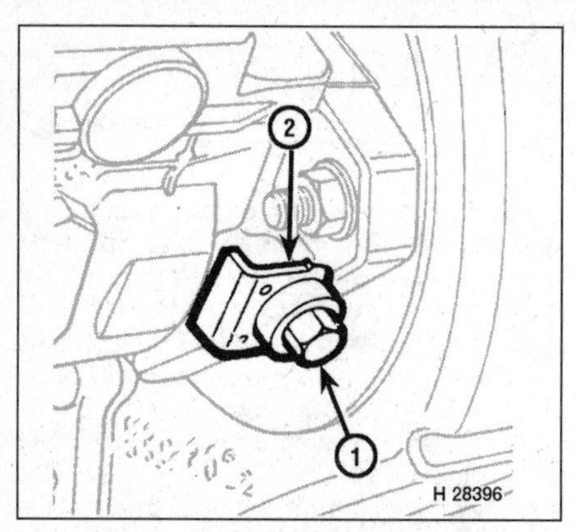

14.8 Pump locking screw (1) and keeper plate (2)

sprocket can be locked using the tools as described, the injection pump timing is correct.

6 If the flywheel locking tool centre pin cannot be engaged easily with the timing slot in the flywheel, proceed as follows.

7 Withdraw the flywheel locking tool centre pin from the slot in the flywheel, then turn the crankshaft as necessary, until the timing pin can be inserted easily into the injection pump.

8 Loosen the pump locking screw and remove the keeper plate (located at the front of the pump, behind the timing belt housing). Tighten the locking screw to lock the pump in position **(see illustration)**.

9 Loosen the three pump sprocket-to-hub bolts.

10 Turn the crankshaft back the small amount to TDC, then engage the flywheel locking tool centre pin with the timing slot in the flywheel.

11 Re-check to ensure that the pump timing pin is an easy sliding fit in the pump.

12 Tighten the pump sprocket-to-hub bolts to the specified torque.

13 Loosen the pump locking screw, then refit the keeper plate and tighten the locking screw.

14 Remove the timing pin from the pump and withdraw the flywheel locking tool centre pin from the slot in the flywheel.

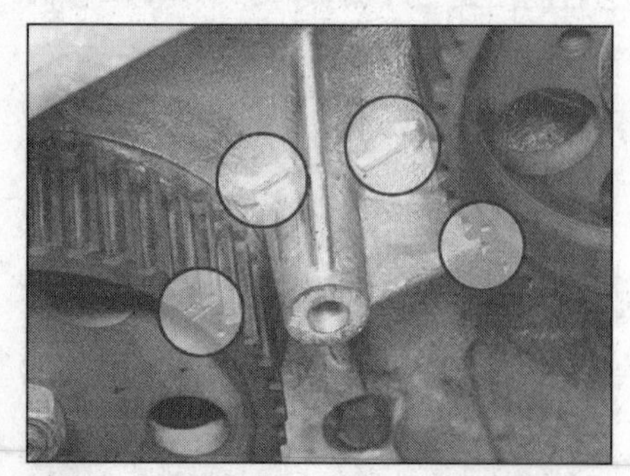

15.10 Fuel injection pump and camshaft sprocket timing marks aligned with arrows on timing belt housing. Note marks do not appear to align due to viewing angle - 19J engine

15 Turn the crankshaft through two complete revolutions and check that the flywheel locking tool and the pump timing pin can still be inserted easily, both at the same time.

16 Withdraw the timing pin and the flywheel locking tool.

17 Refit the blanking plug (or the cover plate bolt, as applicable) to the flywheel locking tool aperture. On models with a blanking plug, coat the threads of the plug with thread-locking compound before refitting.

18 Refit the injection pump hub cover plate, using a new gasket.

19 Where applicable, refit the air conditioning compressor and refit the drivebelt.

15 Fuel injection pump (Defender) - timing

Caution: The maximum engine speed and transfer pressure settings, together with timing access plugs, are sealed by the manufacturers with locking wire and lead seals. Do not disturb the wire if the vehicle is still within the warranty period, otherwise the warranty will be invalidated. Also, do not attempt the timing procedure unless suitable tools are available.

1 Checking the injection timing is only necessary after the injection pump has been disturbed.

2 Dynamic timing equipment does exist but it is unlikely to be available to the home mechanic. If such equipment is available, use it in accordance with the manufacturer's instructions. There should be no need to carry out dynamic timing on the engines fitted to the Defender.

3 Static timing can be carried out very accurately, provided that the appropriate tools are available.

10J engines

4 The injection pump must be removed to check its timing. The timing procedure is included as part of the pump removal and refitting procedure in Section 12. Note that Land Rover special tool RO605863 will be required.

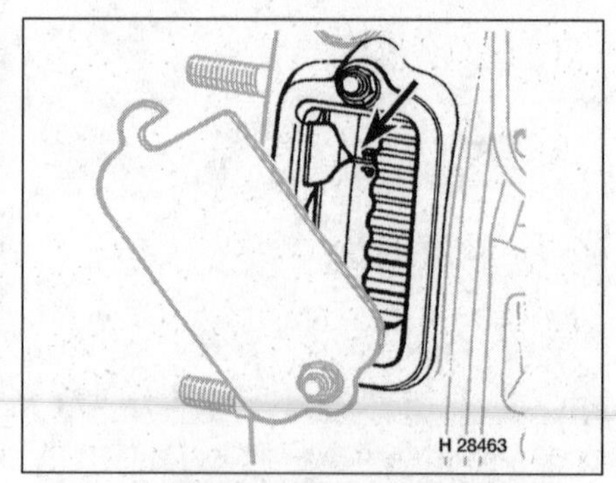

15.11 Flywheel E.P. mark (arrowed) aligned with timing pointer - 10J and early 12J engines

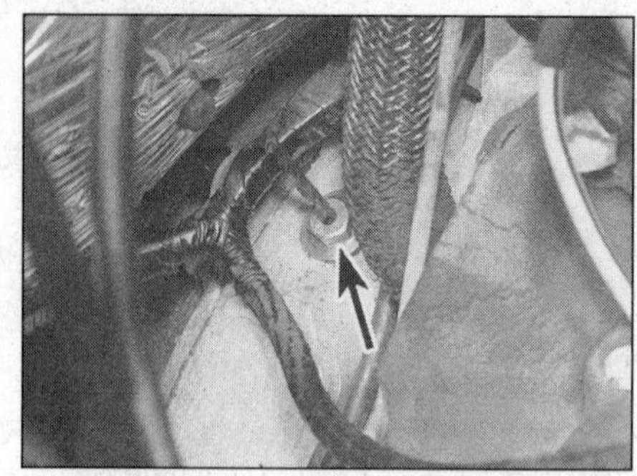

15.5 Improvised flywheel locking tool (arrowed) in position - 19J engine

12J and 19J engines

5 Timing can be carried out very accurately, providing that the appropriate injection pump spindle locking tool (and where applicable, flywheel locking tool) is available **(see illustration)**. The Land Rover tool needed to lock the injection pump is 18G 1458. This tool can be improvised by obtaining a spare injection pump timing aperture blanking plug and accurately drilling a hole through its centre to accept a 5/32 in twist drill. Proceed as follows:

6 Turn the crankshaft to bring No 1 piston to TDC as follows.

Early 12J engine with timing marks on flywheel

Note: *A timing pointer may be required for this operation and a new timing aperture cover gasket should be used on refitting.*

7 Unscrew the two securing nuts and washers and remove the cover from the timing aperture in the upper right-hand side of the flywheel housing. Recover the gasket.

8 If no pointer is visible in the timing aperture, a suitable pointer can be obtained from a Land Rover dealer (Part No. ERC 2250). Where applicable, fit the timing pointer and secure with the two nuts. Note that the pointer arrow should be positioned on the gearbox side of the timing aperture.

9 Remove the timing belt cover.

10 Using a suitable tool on the crankshaft pulley bolt, turn the crankshaft until the timing dots on the camshaft and fuel injection pump sprockets are exactly aligned with their respective timing arrows cast into the timing belt housing **(see illustration)**.

11 The flywheel timing pointer should now be aligned with a line on the flywheel periphery marked E.P **(see illustration)**.

12 If the crankshaft is inadvertently turned beyond the TDC position, do not turn the crankshaft back but continue to turn in a clockwise direction until the sprocket timing marks are again in alignment and the flywheel E.P mark is aligned exactly with the pointer.

13 No 1 piston is now at TDC.

Later 12J and 19J engines with timing slot in flywheel

Note: *A suitable tool will be required to lock the flywheel in position during this operation.*

The Land Rover tool for this purpose is LRT-12-044. This tool can be improvised by obtaining a spare flywheel housing blanking plug and accurately drilling a hole though its centre to accept a 3/16 in twist drill.

14 Unscrew the blanking plug from the timing hole in the upper right-hand side of the flywheel housing.

15 Screw the flywheel locking tool into the timing hole. Do not engage the locking tool centre pin at this stage.

16 Remove the timing belt cover.

17 Using a suitable tool on the crankshaft pulley bolt, turn the crankshaft until the timing dots on the camshaft and fuel injection pump sprockets are exactly aligned with their respective timing arrows cast into the timing belt housing - see illustration 15.10.

18 The flywheel locking tool centre pin should now slide easily into engagement with the timing slot in the flywheel - see illustration 15.5.

19 If the crankshaft is inadvertently turned beyond the TDC position, do not turn the crankshaft back but continue to turn in a clockwise direction until the sprocket timing marks are again in alignment and the locking tool centre pin can be fully engaged with the flywheel slot.

20 The engine is now locked with No 1 piston at top dead centre.

Both engines

21 Unscrew the timing aperture blanking plug from the side of the injection pump **(see illustration)**.

22 Insert the timing tool 18G 1458 (or improvised tool) into the timing aperture and attempt to screw the tool fully into the pump so that the centre pin engages with the pump spindle (or insert the twist drill into the hole in the pump spindle), locking the spindle in position. Do not force the tool. To ensure that the tool centre pin has engaged with the pump spindle, remove the flywheel locking tool (where applicable), then attempt to turn the crankshaft slightly. Do not force the crankshaft. It will be obvious when the timing tool centre pin engages with the hole in the pump spindle **(see illustration)**.

23 If it is possible to engage the timing tool centre pin with the pump spindle with the crankshaft at TDC, the pump timing is correct, and no adjustment is required.

24 If it is necessary to turn the crankshaft away from the TDC position in order to engage the timing tool centre pin with the pump spindle, withdraw the tool from the pump spindle, then turn the crankshaft in the normal direction of rotation (clockwise) back to TDC. Where applicable, engage the flywheel locking tool with the slot in the flywheel. Proceed as follows.

a) Unscrew the union nuts securing the injector pipes to the rear of the pump. Counterhold the unions on the pump when unscrewing the nuts. Cover the open unions to keep dirt out.

15.21 Removing timing aperture blanking plug from injection pump - 19J engine

b) Slacken the rear pump mounting nut and bolt and the three front pump mounting nuts.

c) Rotate the pump body slightly, until the timing tool centre pin can be engaged with the hole in the pump spindle.

d) Check that the engine timing marks are still aligned. The flywheel timing mark/slot and camshaft and fuel injection pump sprocket marks should be in alignment with No 1 piston at TDC.

e) Tighten the pump mounting nuts and bolt.

25 Check to see if a pump timing pointer is fitted to the rear of the timing belt housing, this pointer was deleted on later models. The pointer is secured by two bolts and serves as a reference to help preserve the pump timing when removing and refitting the pump.

26 If a pointer is fitted, check to see if there is a corresponding alignment mark on the pump flange.

27 If a mark is present but it is not aligned with the pointer, loosen the two pointer securing screws and move the pointer until it aligns with the mark. Tighten the pointer securing screws.

28 If no mark is present on the pump flange, make a suitable mark in the centre of the machined area on the flange. Loosen the two pointer securing screws, align the timing pointer with the mark and tighten the screws.

29 Withdraw the timing tool from the aperture in the pump, then refit the blanking plug.

30 On engines with timing marks on the flywheel, where applicable remove the timing pointer, then refit the timing aperture cover using a new gasket and tighten the securing nuts.

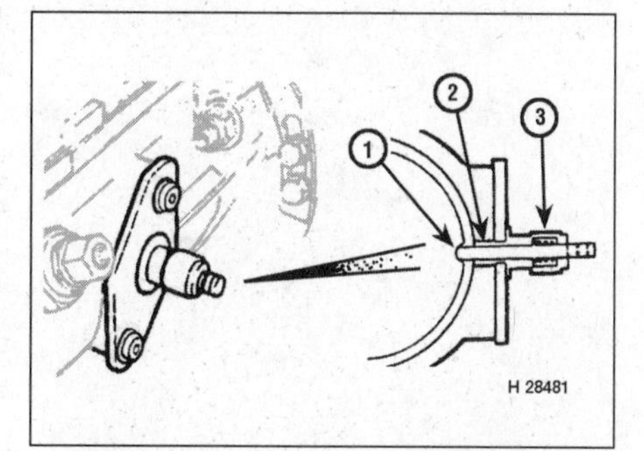

15.22 Timing tool screwed into timing aperture in injection pump - 19J engine

1 Hole in pump spindle
2 Tool centre pin
3 Tool body

31 On engines with a timing slot in the flywheel, remove the timing pin from the flywheel housing and refit the blanking plug.

32 Refit the timing belt cover.

200 TDi and 300 TDi engines

33 Follow the procedure given in Section 14.

16 Fuel injection pump filter (Series IIA & III) - removal, cleaning and refitting

1 Unscrew and remove the inlet pipe union from the fuel filter **(see illustration)**.

2 Unscrew and remove the large pipe connection from the fuel injection pump head and withdraw the gauze filter.

3 Wash the filter in clean diesel fuel and if possible, blow through with an air line.

4 Refit the filter in the pump head, followed by the pipe connection and inlet pipe union. Before tightening the inlet pipe, operate the hand priming lever on the fuel pump until all the air is removed and clean diesel fuel emerges from the union. Fully tighten the union while operating the priming lever.

17 Fuel lift pump (Discovery and Defender) - removal and refitting

Note: *New gasket(s) must be used when refitting the fuel lift pump.*

Removal

1 Disconnect the battery negative lead.

2 Where applicable, to improve access, remove the air cleaner assembly.

3 Similarly, where necessary to improve access, unscrew the union nuts and disconnect the upper two fuel pipes connecting the fuel injectors to the fuel injection pump, from the fuel injectors. Be prepared for fuel spillage and plug the open

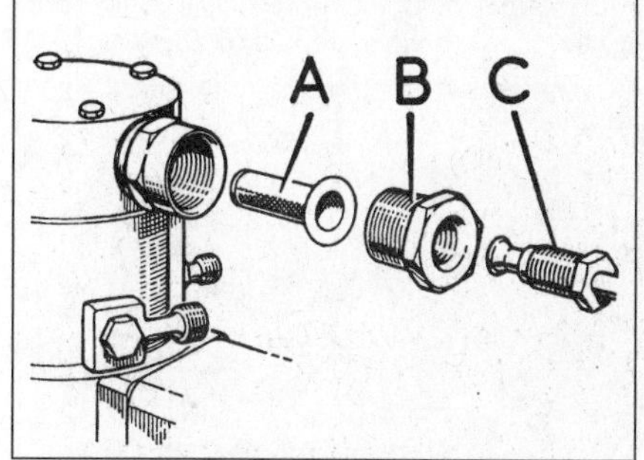

16.1 Fuel injection pump filter components

A Filter
B Union nut
C Inlet pipe

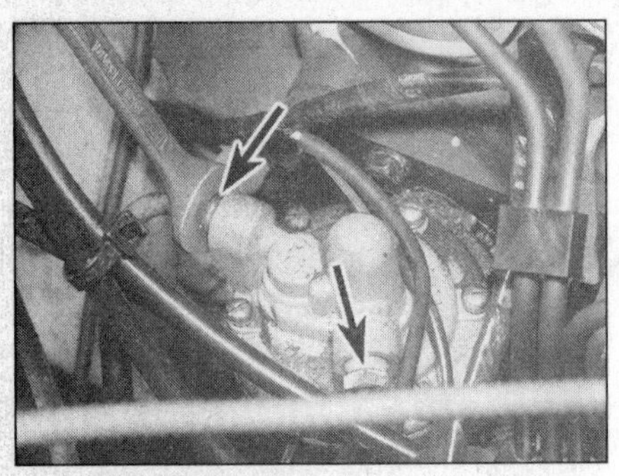
17.4a Disconnecting pipe unions (arrowed) from fuel lift pump - 19J engine

17.4b Disconnecting hose from fuel lift pump - 300 TDi engine

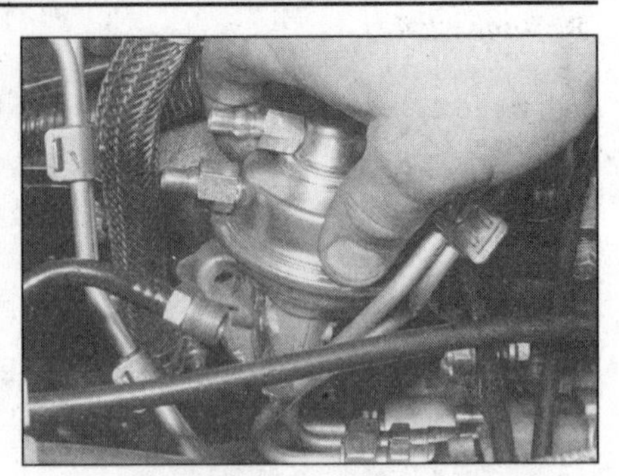
17.5a Remove fuel lift pump . . .

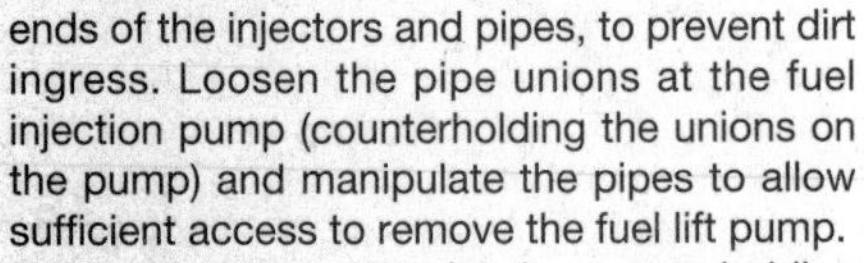
ends of the injectors and pipes, to prevent dirt ingress. Loosen the pipe unions at the fuel injection pump (counterholding the unions on the pump) and manipulate the pipes to allow sufficient access to remove the fuel lift pump.

4 Unscrew the unions (again, counterholding the unions on the pump) and disconnect the fuel supply and feed hoses from the fuel lift pump **(see illustrations)**. Again, plug or cover the open ends of the hoses and pump.

5 Unscrew the two securing nuts or bolts (as applicable), then withdraw the pump and the gasket(s) **(see illustrations)**. Discard the gasket(s), noting that some models may be fitted with a plastic insulating block sandwiched between two gaskets.

6 On all except 300 TDi engines, if desired, the fuel lift pump housing can be unbolted from the cylinder block. Note the location of any brackets secured by the bolts. Recover the gasket.

Refitting

7 Commence refitting by cleaning all traces of old gasket from the mating faces of the pump and housing (and the insulating block, where applicable).

8 Similarly, where applicable, clean the mating faces of the fuel pump housing and refit the housing using a new gasket.

9 Refit the pump, and the insulating block where applicable, using new gasket(s). Ensure that the pump operating lever engages correctly with the camshaft as the pump is refitted.

10 Refit the pump securing bolts or nuts and tighten them to the specified torque.

11 Reconnect the fuel hoses to the lift pump and where applicable, reconnect the injector pipes to the injectors. Ensure that all unions are securely tightened. Where applicable, refit the air cleaner assembly.

12 Reconnect the battery negative lead, and start the engine. If difficulty is experienced, bleed the fuel system.

18 Fuel pump (Series IIA & III) - removal, servicing and refitting

Removal

1 Remove the air cleaner.

2 Undo and remove the inlet and outlet fuel pipe unions from the pump body **(see illustration)**.

3 Remove the two securing nuts and withdraw the pump and gasket **(see illustration)**. If difficulty is experienced in removing the two nuts, undo the four bolts and remove the pump complete with side cover plate and gasket.

Dismantling

4 The following procedure is for pumps incorporating a glass filter bowl. Later pumps are identical with the exception of the filter bowl which is omitted **(see illustration)**.

5 Clean the outside of the pump and wipe dry using a dry non-fluffy rag.

6 Using a file, mark the flanges of the upper and lower pump bodies to ensure that they are correctly reassembled.

18.2 Fuel pump and pipe fittings

18.3 Removing fuel pump

17.5b . . . and recover gasket - 300 TDi engine

7 Unscrew the stirrup thumb screw and swing the stirrup out of the way. Hold the glass bowl to ensure that it does not drop. Lift away the sediment bowl followed by the cork seal and gauze filter. Inspect the cork gasket for signs of damage or flattening and obtain a new one ready for reassembling.

8 Undo and remove the six body securing screws and spring washers and separate the two halves.

9 Invert the upper body and undo the two valve retaining plate screws and lift away the screws, retaining plate, the two valve assemblies and the valve gasket from the upper body.

10 Note the position of the lip on the diaphragm relative to the lower body, to ensure correct reassembly, then remove the diaphragm by rotating through 90° in an anti-clockwise direction and lifting it away from the lower body and the link.

11 It is recommended that the lower body parts are not dismantled unless either the seal, hand priming lever on the link assembly require attention.

Examination

12 Check the condition of the cork sediment bowl sealing washer, if hardened or broken then it must be renewed. The diaphragm should also be checked and renewed if faulty. Clean the pump thoroughly and agitate the valves in paraffin or petrol to clean them out. This will also improve the contact between the valve seat and the valve. Check the pump body for fractures.

Reassembly

13 If the lower body has been dismantled, refit the rocker arm assembly comprising the operating link, rocker arm, anti-rattle spring and washers in their relative positions in the lower body. Align the holes in the body and insert the pivot pin.

14 Refit the circlips to the grooves in each end of the pivot pin. On later models, the pivot pin is held in place by two retainers. After refitting the pivot pin, tap the retainers into their grooves and secure them in place by lightly peening over the ends of the grooves with a small chisel.

15 Invert the upper body and fit the gasket, valves, valve retaining plate and tighten the two plate retaining screws. The two valves are interchangeable so care must be taken to ensure they are fitted the correct way round. The inlet valve should be fitted into the offset and shallower part with its spring facing the diaphragm, whilst the outlet valve is fitted to the centre part with its spring facing away from the diaphragm.

16 Place the seal and retainer in the lower body and place the diaphragm spring over them.

17 Refit the diaphragm and pullrod assembly with the pullrod downwards and ensure the small tab on the diaphragm lines up to the previously noted position, which should have been adjacent to the centre of the flange and rocker arm.

18 With the body of the pump held so that the rocker arm is facing away, press down the diaphragm, turning it a quarter of a turn to the left at the same time. This engages the slot on the pullrod with the operating lever. The small tab on the diaphragm should now be at an angle of 90° to the rocker arm and the diaphragm should be firmly located.

19 Move the rocker arm until the diaphragm is level with the body flanges and hold the arm in this position. Reassemble the two halves of the pump, ensuring that the previously made marks on the flanges are adjacent to each other.

20 Insert the six screws and lockwashers and tighten them down finger-tight.

21 Move the rocker arm up and down several times to centralise the diaphragm, then with the arm held down, tighten the screws securely in a diagonal sequence.

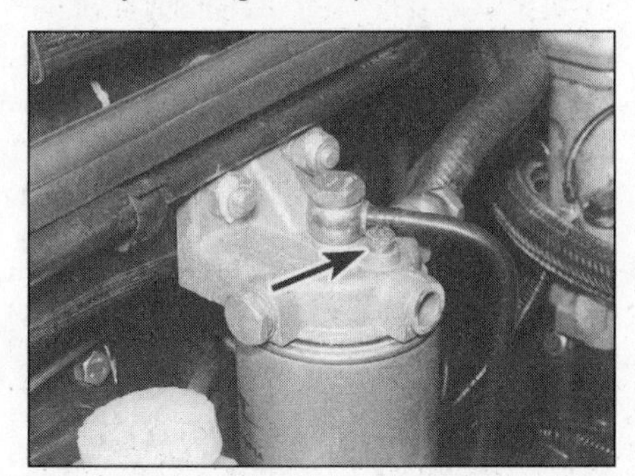

19.3 Fuel filter head bleed screw (arrowed) - 300 TDi engine

18.4 Fuel pump components

1 Top cover
2 Securing screws
3 Spring washer
4 Valve gasket
5 Valves
6 Retainer for valves
7 Screw for retainer
8 Gauze filter disc
9 Lock sealing gasket
10 Sediment bowl
11 Bowl retainer
12 Diaphragm assembly
13 Diaphragm spring
14 Oil seal retainer
15 Sealing washers
16 Pump body
17 Hand priming lever
18 Return spring for hand lever
19 Hand rocker
20 Cork washers
21 Rocker arm pivot pin, early type
22 Operating link
23 Plain washers
24 Rocker arm
25 Return spring
26 Joint washer
27 Oil seal retainer
28 Oil seal
29 Pump body
30 Rocker arm pivot pin type
31 Retainer for pivot pin

22 Fit the gauze filter, cork washer and sediment bowl and refit the stirrup thumbscrew to the base of the sediment bowl. Tighten lightly only to ensure a fuel tight joint, as overtightening will crack the bowl.

Refitting

23 Refitting the pump is a reversal of removal. Ensure that a new gasket is fitted and prime the fuel system on completion.

19 Fuel system - priming and bleeding

Discovery

1 After disconnecting part of the fuel supply system or after running out of fuel, it is necessary to prime the system and bleed off any air which may have entered system components.

2 All models are fitted with a hand-operated priming lever on the fuel lift pump. Note that if the engine has stopped with the lift pump lever fully raised on its cam, it will not be possible to operate the hand priming lever. In this case, turn the engine (using a suitable spanner or socket on the crankshaft pulley bolt if necessary), until the lever can be operated.

3 To prime the system, loosen the bleed screw, located on the fuel filter head **(see illustration)**.

4 Operate the priming lever until fuel free from air bubbles emerges from the bleed screw, then retighten the screw. To operate the lever, push the lever down to release it from the catch, then pump the lever up and down.

5 Switch on the ignition to activate the stop solenoid and continue operating the priming lever until firm resistance is felt, then pump a few more times.

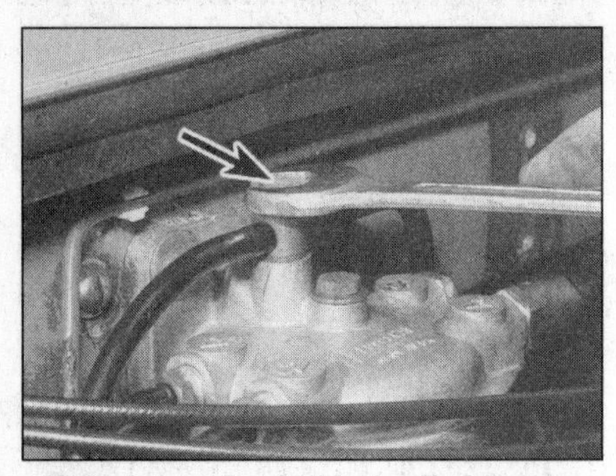
19.9a Loosening fuel leak-off pipe union on filter head - 19J engine

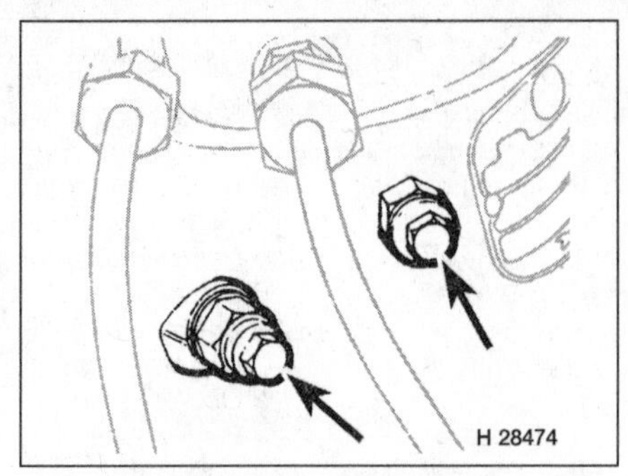

19.9b Fuel injection pump bleed screws (arrowed) - 10J engine

19.9c Fuel injection pump bleed screw (arrowed) - 19J engine

6 If a large amount of air has entered the fuel injection pump, place a wad of rag around the fuel return union on the fuel injection pump to absorb spilt fuel, then slacken the union. Operate the priming lever with the ignition switched on to activate the stop solenoid, or crank the engine on the starter motor in 10-second bursts, until fuel free from air bubbles emerges from the fuel union. Tighten the union and mop up any split fuel. Be prepared to stop the engine if it should fire, to avoid excessive fuel spray and spillage.

7 If air has entered the injector pipes, place wads of rag around the injector pipe unions at the injectors to absorb spilt fuel, then slacken the unions. Crank the engine on the starter motor until fuel emerges from the unions, then stop cranking the engine and retighten the unions. Mop up any spilt fuel.

8 Start the engine with the accelerator pedal fully depressed. Additional cranking may be necessary to finally bleed the system before the engine starts.

Defender

9 Carry out those procedures given in paragraphs 1 to 8 inclusive for the 200 TDi and 300 TDi engines, whilst noting the following:

a) *To prime the fuel system on 10J, 12J and 19J engines, loosen the fuel leak-off pipe union bolt on the top of the fuel filter head* ***(see illustration)****.*

b) *To bleed the fuel system on 10J engines, slacken the two bleed screws on the side of the pump body* ***(see illustration)****.*

c) *To bleed the fuel system on 12J and 19J engines, slacken the bleed screw on the top of the pump* ***(see illustration)****.*

Series IIA & III

10 Refer to Section 28 in Part A of this Chapter.

20 Preheating system (Discovery and Defender) - component testing, removal and refitting

Discovery

System testing

1 If the preheating system malfunctions, testing is ultimately by substitution of known good units but some preliminary checks may be made as follows.

2 Connect a voltmeter or 12-volt test light between the glow plug supply cable and earth (engine or vehicle metal). Ensure that the live connection is kept clear of the engine and bodywork.

3 Have an assistant switch on the ignition and check that voltage is applied to the glow plugs. Note the time for which the warning light is lit and the total time for which voltage is applied before the system cuts out. Switch off the ignition.

4 At an underbonnet temperature of 20°C, typical times noted should be 5 or 6 seconds for warning light operation, followed by a further 4 to 5 seconds supply after the light goes out (provided that the starter motor is not operated). Warning light time will increase with lower temperatures and decrease with higher temperatures.

5 If there is no supply at all, the relay or associated wiring is at fault.

6 To locate a defective glow plug, disconnect the main supply cable and the interconnecting wire or strap from the top of the glow plugs. Be careful not to drop the nuts and washers.

7 Use a continuity tester or a 12-volt test light connected to the battery positive terminal to check for continuity between each glow plug terminal and earth. The resistance of a glow plug in good condition is very low (less than 1 ohm) so if the test light does not light, or the continuity tester shows a high resistance, the glow plug is certainly defective.

8 If an ammeter is available, the current draw of each glow plug can be checked. After an initial surge of around 15 to 20 amps, each plug should draw around 10 amps. Any plug which draws much more or less than this is probably defective.

9 As a final check, the glow plugs can be removed and inspected.

Relay/timer unit - removal and refitting

10 On 200 TDi engine models, the relay/timer unit is located on the right-hand side of the engine compartment bulkhead. On 300 TDi engine models, the unit is located on the right-hand side of the engine compartment, on a bracket attached to the rear of the fusebox.

11 Disconnect the battery negative lead.

12 Disconnect the wiring plug from the relay/timer unit **(see illustration)**.

20.12 Disconnecting wiring plug from preheating system relay/timer unit - 300 TDi engine

13 Unscrew the bolt or the nut and bolt, as applicable, and withdraw the unit.

14 Refitting is a reversal of removal.

Defender

System testing - 10J, 12J and 19J engines

15 Early models are fitted with glow plugs which are wired to the supply cable in series. Later models have the plugs wired in parallel. If any one plug fails on an engine with series-wired plugs, the supply to all plugs will be interrupted. Testing of series-wired plugs must not be done by applying 12 volts to them directly, or they will burn out.

16 To test the supply to the plugs, connect a 12-volt test light (approximately 5 watts) between the glow plug supply cable and earth (engine or vehicle metal). Ensure that the live connection is kept well clear of the engine and bodywork.

17 Have an assistant switch on the ignition (position II) and check that voltage is applied to the glow plugs.

18 If there is no supply, the wiring or associated fuse is at fault.

19 To locate a defective glow plug, disconnect the wiring from the plugs and test each plug individually by connecting a 12-volt battery to the plug in series with a 12-volt (approximately 5 watt) test bulb. If the light comes on, the plug is working.

System testing - 200 TDi and 300 TDi engines

20 Carry out those procedures given in paragraphs 1 to 9 inclusive

Relay/timer unit - 200 TDi and 300 TDi engines

21 Carry out those procedures given in paragraphs 10 to 14 inclusive

21 Electronic Diesel Control system (Discovery) - component removal and refitting

1 The Electronic Diesel Control (EDC) system replaces certain mechanical systems used to control a conventional Diesel fuel injection system with electronic controls **(see illustration)**.

2 The most notable feature of the EDC system is that a "drive-by-wire" accelerator control system is used, with no mechanical link (accelerator cable) between the accelerator pedal and the fuel injection pump.

3 The EDC system supplies the exact amount of fuel required by the engine, according to prevailing engine operating conditions. The engine is fitted with various sensors which monitor the engine operating conditions and transmit data to the EDC electronic control unit. The control unit processes the data from the various sensors and determines the optimum amount of fuel required and the injection timing for the prevailing running conditions. Additionally, the control unit activates the fuel injection pump stop solenoid and on models fitted with EGR, the electronic control unit also determines the degree of exhaust gas recirculation.

4 The system incorporates the following sensors:

a) *Injection timing sensor - an inductive sensor incorporated in No 4 fuel injector.*
b) *Airflow sensor - positioned in the air inlet trunking between the air cleaner and the turbocharger.*
c) *Engine speed sensor - an inductive sensor mounted on the flywheel housing, activated by slots in the flywheel.*
d) *Vehicle speed sensor - located in the transfer gearbox and also acts as a speedometer sender unit.*
e) *Brake and clutch switches - located in the pedal box.*
f) *Throttle position sensor - located in the pedal box.*
g) *Turbocharger boost pressure sensor - located on the engine compartment bulkhead.*
h) *Coolant temperature sensor - located in the cylinder head.*
i) *Air temperature sensor.*
j) *Fuel temperature sensor - located in the fuel injection pump.*

5 To control fuelling of the engine, the system uses the following actuators:

a) *Fuel delivery actuator - incorporated in the fuel injection pump.*
b) *Injection timing solenoid - incorporated in the fuel injection pump.*
c) *EGR control solenoid - mounted at the front left-hand corner of the engine compartment.*
d) *Engine stop solenoid - located in the fuel injection pump.*

6 Safety features are built into the system to protect the engine against overspeed and overheating damage. If a component in the system fails, the electronic control unit activates a "limp-home" mode, where a default value is substituted for the failed component. This will allow the engine to start and run but a noticeable loss in engine performance may occur.

7 Electronic control units are very sensitive components and certain precautions must be taken, to avoid damage to the EDC control unit when working on the vehicle. These are as follows:

a) *When carrying out welding operations on the vehicle, disconnect the battery and alternator.*
b) *Underbonnet-mounted modules can be adversely affected by excess heat or*

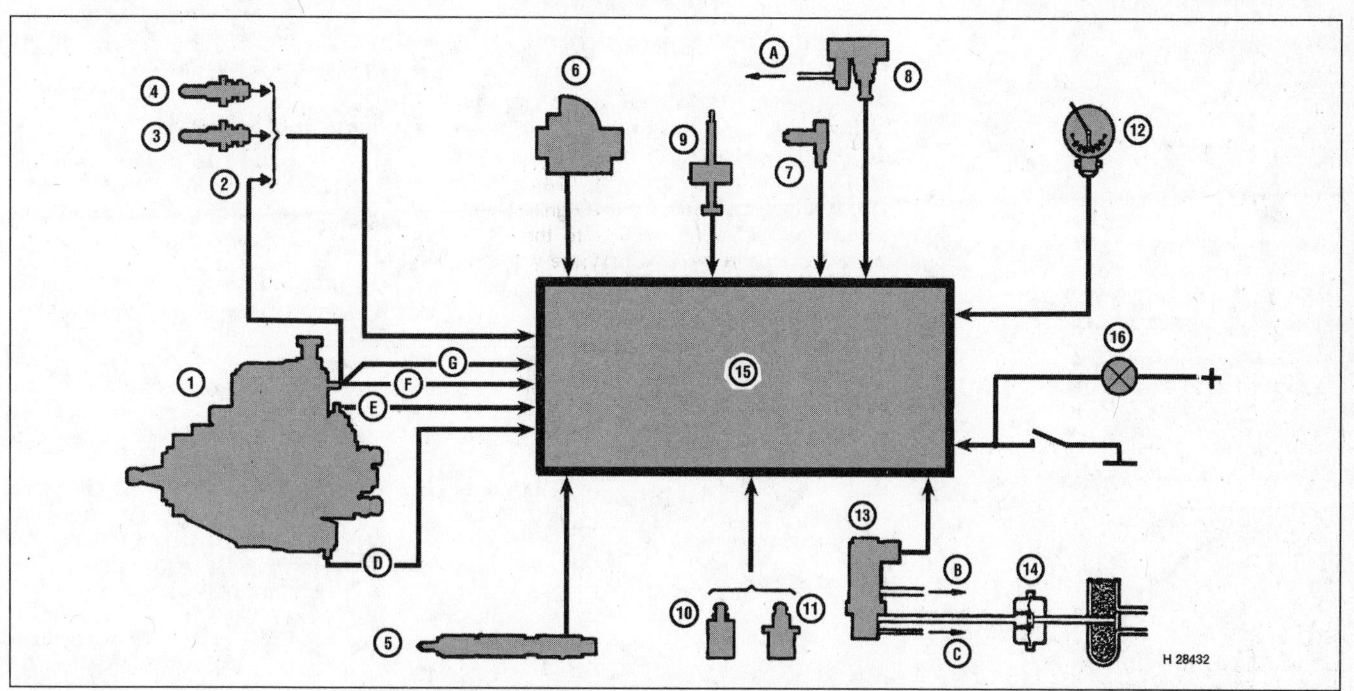

21.1 Electronic Diesel Control system layout

1 *Fuel injection pump*
2 *Fuel temperature sensor*
3 *Air temperature sensor*
4 *Coolant temperature sensor*
5 *Injection timing sensor (No 4 injector)*
6 *Airflow sensor*
7 *Engine speed sensor*
8 *Turbocharger boost pressure sensor*
9 *Vehicle speed sensor*
10 *Clutch switch*
11 *Brake switch*
12 *Throttle position sensor*
13 *EGR control solenoid*
14 *EGR valve*
15 *Electronic control unit*
16 *Diagnostic indicator*
A *To turbocharger*
B *To air cleaner*
C *To brake servo vacuum hose T-piece*
D *Injection timing solenoid*
E *Engine stop solenoid*
F *Actuator current*
G *Fuel delivery actuator*

moisture. If using welding equipment or pressure-washing equipment in the vicinity of a module, take care not to direct heat or jets of water or steam at the module. If this cannot be avoided, remove the module from the vehicle and protect its wiring plug with a plastic bag.

c) Before disconnecting any wiring or removing components, always ensure that the ignition is switched off.

d) Do not attempt to improvise fault diagnosis procedures using a test light or multi-meter, as irreparable damage could be caused to a module.

e) After working on any of the EDC system components, ensure that all wiring is correctly reconnected before reconnecting the battery or operating the ignition switch.

Injection timing sensor - removal and refitting

8 The sensor is incorporated in No 4 fuel injector.

9 The removal and refitting procedure for the fuel injectors is given in Section 9.

Airflow sensor - removal and refitting

10 The sensor is located in the air trunking between the air cleaner and the turbocharger **(see illustration)**.

11 Disconnect the battery negative lead.

12 Where applicable, disconnect the vacuum pipe from the EGR valve.

13 Disconnect the airflow sensor wiring plug.

14 Loosen the securing clips and disconnect the air trunking from the airflow sensor.

15 Unscrew the three bolts securing the airflow sensor to the mounting bracket and withdraw the airflow sensor.

16 Refitting is a reversal of removal. Ensure that the wiring plug is securely reconnected and that the air trunking clips are securely tightened, to prevent air leaks.

Engine speed sensor - removal and refitting

17 The sensor is located in the gearbox bellhousing and access is obtained from under the vehicle **(see illustration)**.

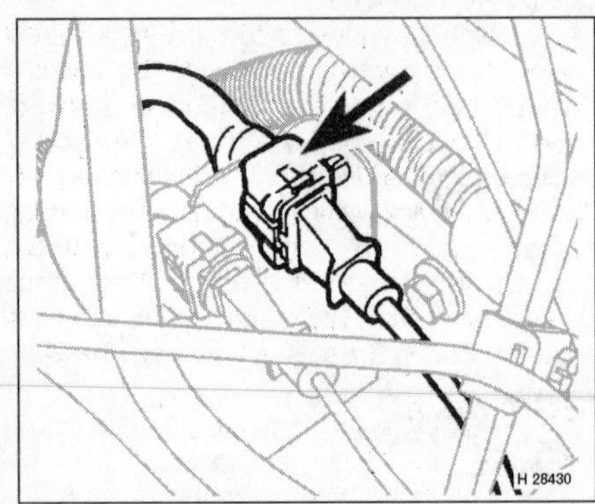

21.20 Engine speed sensor wiring connector location (arrowed)

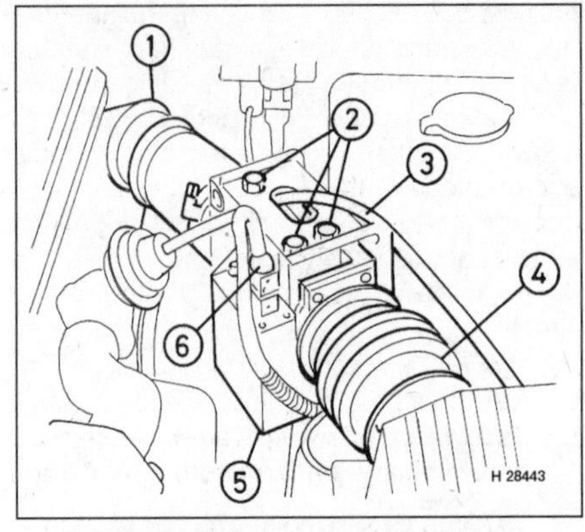

21.10 Airflow sensor location

1 Air outlet hose
2 Airflow sensor mounting bolts
3 EGR valve vacuum pipe
4 Air inlet hose
5 Airflow sensor
6 Wiring plug

18 Disconnect the battery negative lead.

19 Jack up the front of vehicle and support securely on axle stands.

20 Unclip the sensor wiring connector from the top of the transfer gearbox, then separate the two halves of the connector **(see illustration)**.

21 Unscrew the securing bolt and withdraw the sensor from the bellhousing.

22 Refitting is a reversal of removal.

Vehicle speed sensor - removal and refitting

23 The sensor is located in the transfer gearbox casing **(see illustration)**.

24 Disconnect the battery negative lead.

25 Disconnect the sensor wiring plug.

26 Unscrew the sensor securing bolt and recover the washer.

27 Withdraw the sensor from the transfer gearbox.

28 Refitting is a reversal of removal.

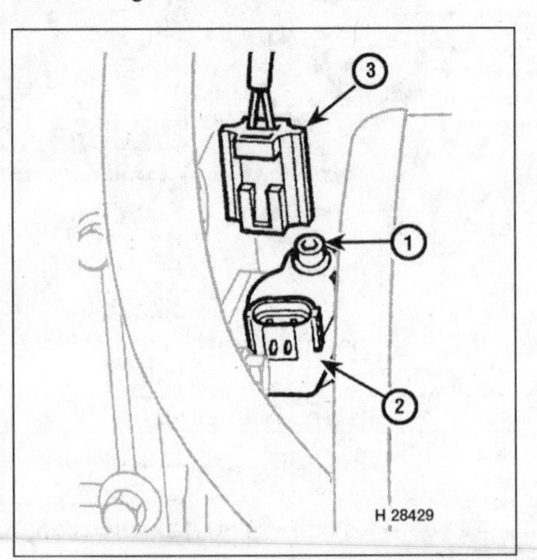

21.23 Vehicle speed sensor location

1 Securing bolt
2 Sensor
3 Wiring plug

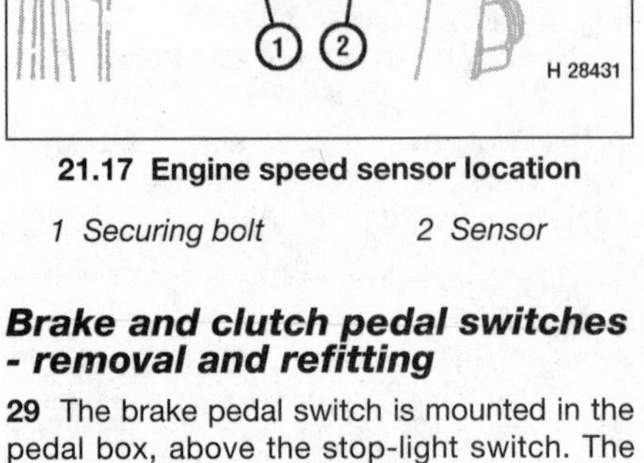

21.17 Engine speed sensor location

1 Securing bolt
2 Sensor

Brake and clutch pedal switches - removal and refitting

29 The brake pedal switch is mounted in the pedal box, above the stop-light switch. The clutch pedal switch is mounted at the top of the clutch pedal.

30 Disconnect the battery negative lead.

31 Release the securing clips and withdraw the driver's side lower facia panel for access to the pedals.

32 Disconnect the wiring from the switch.

33 Loosen the locknut at the rear of the switch, then unscrew the front securing nut and withdraw the switch from the bracket.

34 Refitting is a reversal of removal.

Throttle position sensor - removal and refitting

Warning: Do not operate the accelerator pedal if the sensor is loosely fitted, as damage to the sensor may result.

35 The sensor is located in the pedal box **(see illustration)**.

36 Disconnect the battery negative lead.

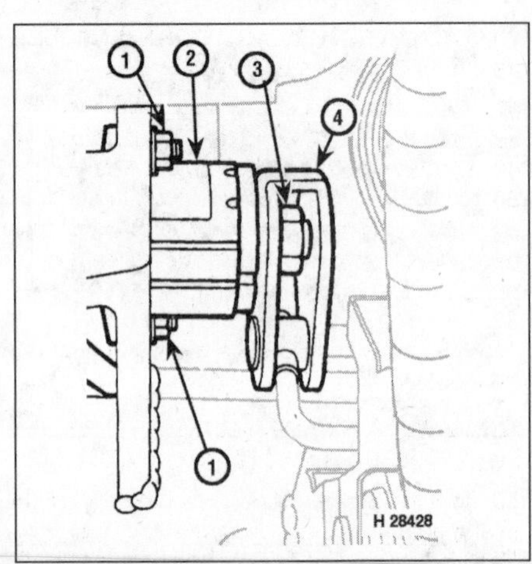

21.35 Throttle position sensor location

1 Sensor securing nuts
2 Sensor
3 Pedal quadrant-to-sensor nut
4 Pedal quadrant

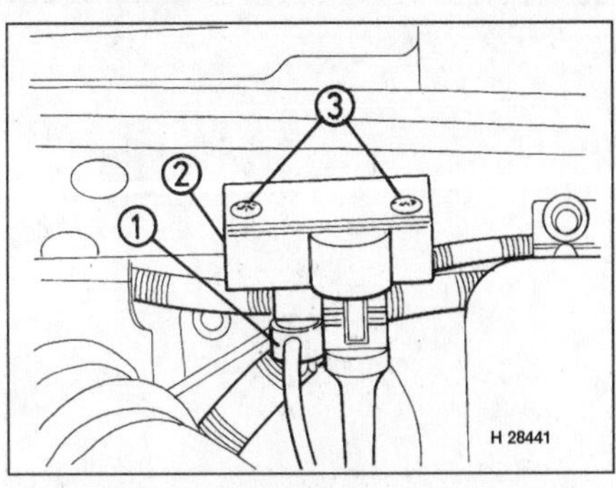

21.42 Turbocharger boost pressure sensor

1 Banjo union
2 Sensor
3 Sensor securing screws

37 Release the securing clips and withdraw the driver's side lower facia panel for access to the pedals.
38 Working in the driver's footwell, disconnect the wiring plug from the sensor.
39 Unscrew the nut securing the accelerator pedal quadrant to the sensor and disconnect the quadrant.
40 Unscrew the two nuts securing the sensor to the pedal box and withdraw the sensor.
41 Refitting is a reversal of removal.

Turbocharger boost pressure sensor - removal and refitting

42 The sensor is located on a bracket attached to the engine compartment bulkhead **(see illustration)**.
43 Disconnect the battery negative lead.
44 Disconnect the sensor wiring plug.
45 Unscrew the banjo bolt and disconnect the pressure pipe from the sensor. Recover the copper washers.
46 Remove the two screws securing the sensor to the mounting bracket and withdraw the sensor.
47 Refitting is a reversal of removal. Use new copper washers when reconnecting the pressure pipe.

Coolant temperature sensor - removal and refitting

48 The sensor is located in the top left-hand side of the cylinder head **(see illustration)**.
49 Disconnect the battery negative lead.
50 Disconnect the sensor wiring plug.
51 Unscrew the sensor from the cylinder head and recover the copper washer. Be prepared for coolant spillage.
52 Refitting is a reversal of removal. Use a new copper washer and on completion, check the coolant level.

Air temperature sensor - removal and refitting

53 The sensor is located in the rear of the inlet manifold.
54 Disconnect the battery negative lead, then disconnect the wiring plug from the sensor.
55 Unscrew the sensor from the manifold and where applicable, recover the sealing ring.

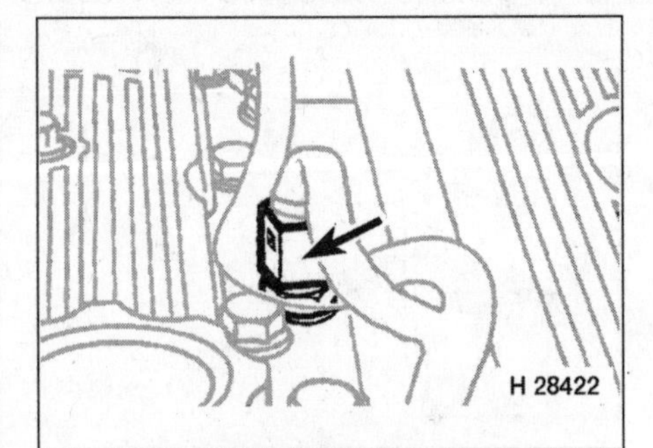

21.48 Coolant temperature sensor location (arrowed)

56 Refitting is a reversal of removal. Where applicable, use a new sealing ring.

Fuel temperature sensor - removal and refitting

57 The fuel temperature sensor is integral with the fuel injection pump.

EGR control solenoid - removal and refitting

58 The solenoid is located at the front left-hand corner of the engine compartment **(see illustration)**.
59 Disconnect the battery negative lead.
60 Disconnect the wiring plug from the solenoid.
61 Disconnect the three vacuum hoses from the modulator, noting their locations to ensure correct refitting.
62 Unscrew the securing nut and withdraw the solenoid from the body panel.
63 Refitting is a reversal of removal.

Electronic control unit - removal and refitting

64 The unit is located behind the right-hand A-pillar trim panel **(see illustration)**.
65 Remove the A-pillar trim panel.
66 Disconnect the battery negative lead.

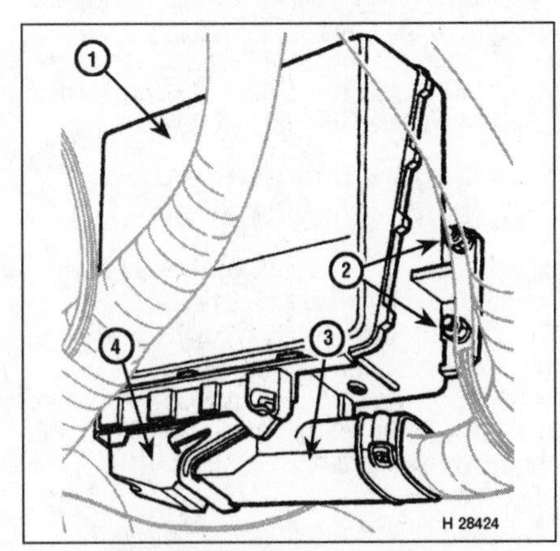

21.64 Electronic control unit location

1 Electronic control module
2 Securing nuts
3 Wiring plug
4 Wiring plug securing screw

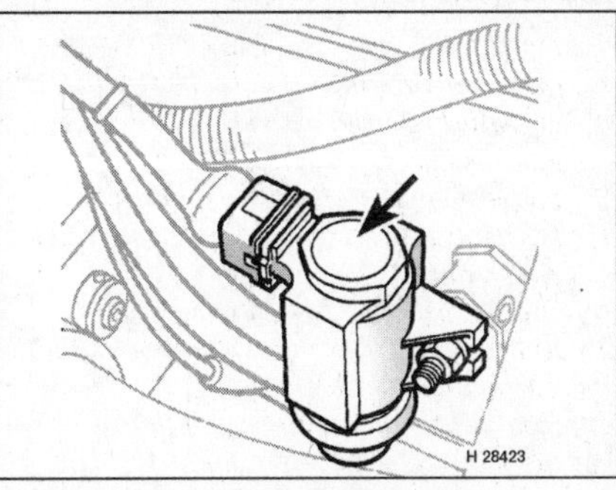

21.58 EGR control solenoid location (arrowed)

67 Loosen the control unit wiring plug securing screw and disconnect the wiring plug. Move the wiring plug and the harness to one side.
68 Unscrew the securing nuts and withdraw the control unit.
69 Refitting is a reversal of removal.

22 EGR system (Discovery and Defender) - component testing, removal and refitting

1 The Exhaust gas recirculation (EGR) system is fitted to certain models with a conventional fuel injection system and all models with Electronic Diesel Control (EDC). The system is designed to recirculate small quantities of exhaust gas into the inlet tract and therefore into the combustion process. This process reduces the level of oxides of nitrogen present in the final exhaust gas which is released into the atmosphere, and also lowers the combustion temperature.
2 The volume of exhaust gas recirculated is controlled by vacuum, via a solenoid valve. The solenoid valve is controlled by a fuel injection pump-mounted sensor on models with a conventional fuel injection system, or by the EDC electronic control unit on models with EDC.
3 A vacuum-operated recirculation valve is fitted to the exhaust manifold, to regulate the quantity of exhaust gas recirculated. The valve is operated by the vacuum supplied via the solenoid valve.
4 Between idle speed and a pre-determined engine load, power is supplied to the solenoid valve, which allows the recirculation valve to open. Under full-load conditions, the exhaust gas recirculation is cut off. Additional control is provided by the engine temperature sensor, which cuts off the vacuum supply until the coolant temperature reaches 40°C, thus preventing the recirculation valve from opening during the engine warm-up phase.

EGR valve

Testing

5 Testing of the EGR valve should be entrusted to a Land Rover dealer.

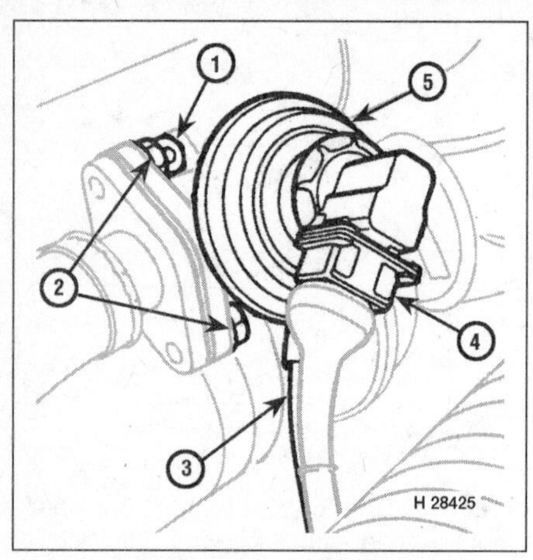

22.7 EGR valve location

1 Valve securing bolts
2 EGR delivery pipe securing bolts
3 Vacuum hose
4 Wiring plug
5 Valve

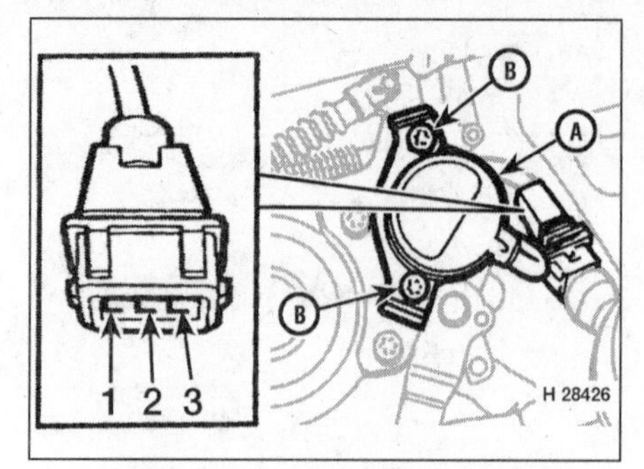

22.24 EGR throttle position sensor location - plug terminal numbers inset

A Sensor
B Securing screws

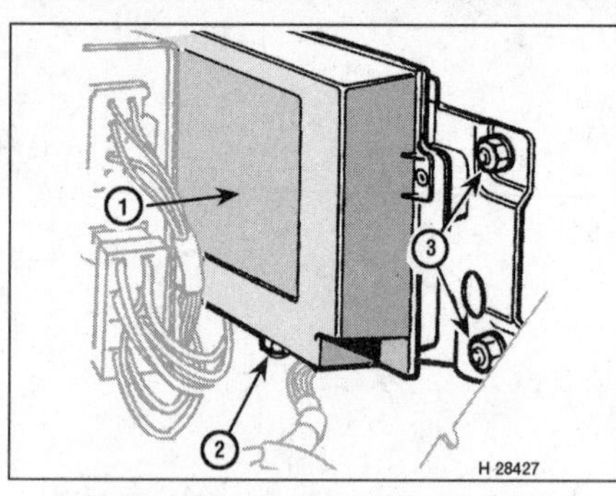

22.34 EGR electronic control unit

1 Control unit
2 Securing nuts
3 Wiring plug

Removal

6 Disconnect the battery negative lead, then where applicable, disconnect the wiring plug from the valve.

7 Disconnect the vacuum hose from the valve **(see illustration)**.

8 Unscrew the two bolts securing the valve to the exhaust manifold.

9 Remove the two securing bolts and disconnect the EGR delivery pipe from the valve.

10 Withdraw the valve and recover the gaskets.

Refitting

11 Refitting is a reversal of removal. Use new gaskets when refitting the valve and reconnecting the delivery pipe.

Coolant temperature sensor

Testing

12 The system uses the coolant temperature gauge sender unit. This sender unit is screwed into the thermostat housing.

13 If the temperature gauge needle remains at the cold end of the scale with the engine running, then stop the engine and disconnect the sender wire and earth it to the cylinder head. If the needle then deflects when the ignition is switched on, the sender unit is proved faulty and should be renewed. If the needle still does not move, remove the instrument panel and check the continuity of the wiring between the sender unit and the gauge, and the feed to the gauge unit. If continuity is shown and the fault still exists, then the gauge is faulty and should be renewed.

14 If the gauge needle remains at the hot end of the scale, disconnect the sender wire. If the needle then returns to the cold end of the scale when the ignition is switched on, the sender unit is proved faulty and should be renewed.

Removal

15 Either partially drain the cooling system to just below the level of the sender or have ready a suitable plug which can be used to plug the sender aperture whilst it is removed. If a plug is used, take care not to damage the sender unit threads and do not use anything which will allow foreign matter to enter the cooling system.

16 Disconnect the battery negative lead.

17 Disconnect the wiring from the sender, then unscrew the unit from the thermostat housing and recover the sealing washer (where fitted).

Refitting

18 If the sender unit was fitted with a sealing washer, fit a new washer. Where no washer was fitted, ensure that the sender threads are clean and apply a smear of suitable sealant to them.

19 Refit the sender, tightening it securely. Reconnect the wiring.

20 Top-up the cooling system.

21 On completion, start the engine and check the operation of the temperature gauge. Also check for coolant leaks.

Throttle position sensor

Testing

22 Start the engine and run it until normal operating temperature is reached.

23 Stop the engine and disconnect the throttle position sensor wiring plug.

24 Connect an ohmmeter across pins 1 and 3 of the wiring plug. The reading on the ohmmeter should be as specified **(see illustration)**.

25 Connect the ohmmeter between pins 1 and 2 of the wiring plug. Again, the reading should be as specified.

26 If the readings are not as specified, loosen the two sensor retaining screws and rotate the sensor to achieve the correct readings. Tighten the retaining screws when the readings are correct.

27 If the correct readings cannot be obtained by rotating the sensor, then it is faulty and should be renewed.

28 Reconnect the wiring plug on completion.

Removal

29 This sensor is only used on models with a conventional fuel injection system and is located on the fuel injection pump.

30 Disconnect the battery negative lead, then disconnect the wiring plug from the sensor.

31 Unscrew the two securing screws and withdraw the sensor.

Refitting

32 Refitting is a reversal of removal. Before tightening the securing screws, adjust the position of the sensor as described previously during testing.

Electronic control unit

Testing

33 Testing of the control unit is only possible using specialist test equipment. Do not attempt to test the unit using a test meter or a test light, as irreparable damage could be caused. Any suspected faults should be referred to a Land Rover dealer.

Removal

34 The unit is located in the passenger compartment, behind the right-hand side of the facia **(see illustration)**.

35 Release the two glovebox stays from the facia and pivot the glovebox fully downwards.

36 Unscrew the control unit plastic securing nuts and release the unit from its mountings.

37 Disconnect the wiring plug and withdraw the unit.

Refitting

38 Refitting is a reversal of removal.

Chapter 7
Mercedes-Benz 1988cc, 1997cc, 2399cc, 2404cc, 2497cc, 2996cc & 2998cc engines

Part A: Routine maintenance and servicing

Contents

Engine application

1988cc engine	Mercedes-Benz 200D 123 Series - 1976 to 1985
1997cc engine	Mercedes-Benz 200 124 Series - 1985 to 1993
2399cc engine	Mercedes-Benz 240D & TD 123 Series - 1976 to 1985
2404cc engine	Mercedes-Benz 240D 123 Series - 1976 to 1985
2497cc engine	Mercedes-Benz 250 124 Series - 1985 to 1993
2996cc engine	Mercedes-Benz 300 124 Series - 1985 to 1993
2998cc engine	Mercedes-Benz 300D & TD 123 Series - 1976 to 1985

Manufacturer's engine codes

123 Series	
1988 cc engine	615.940
2399 cc engine	616.916
2404 cc engine	616.912146.7
2998 cc engine	617.912
124 Series	
1997cc (2.0 litre, 4-cylinder) engine	601.912
2497cc (2.5 litre, 5-cylinder) engine:	
Non Turbo	602.912
Turbo	602.962
2996cc (3.0 litre, 6-cylinder) engine:	
Non Turbo	603.912
Turbo	603.960, 603.962, or 603.963

7A

Servicing specifications

Oil filter

123 Series	Champion X104
124 Series	Champion X103

Valve clearances

123 Series

Cold:	
Intake	0.10 mm*
Exhaust:	
Turbo	0.30 mm
Non-turbo	0.35 mm
Warm:	
Intake	0.15 mm*
Exhaust:	
Turbo	0.35 mm
Non-turbo	0.40 mm

**At ambient temperatures below -20°C, add 0.05 mm*

124 Series

Maximum clearance between cam lobe and valve lifter	0.40 mm

Timing chain

Type	Duplex
Tension	Automatic hydraulic tensioner

Auxiliary drivebelt

123 Series

Type	V-belt	
Tension - Gates gauge:	**New belt**	**Used belt**
616, 617.91 engine	50	45 to 50
Tension - Borroughs gauge:		
V-belt measuring 9.5 mm (green zone)	10 to 10.5	9 to 10
V-belt measuring 12.5 mm (red zone)	11 to 12	10.5 to 11

124 Series

Type	Multi-ribbed
Tension	Automatic sprung tensioner

Air filter

123 Series	Champion W149
124 Series:	
2.0 litre	Champion U516
2.5 litre non Turbo	Champion U563
2.5 litre Turbo	Champion U563
3.0 litre non Turbo	Champion U517
3.0 litre Turbo	Champion W196

Fuel filter

123 Series	Champion L105 or L133
124 Series	Champion L105 or L116

Glow plugs

123 Series

1988 cc engine:	
Pre July 1980	Champion CH61
Post Aug 1980	Champion CH68
2399 cc engine:	
Feb 1976 to Mar 1979	Champion CH61
2404 cc engine:	
Pre July 1980	Champion CH61
Post Aug 1980	Champion CH68
2998 cc engine:	
Aug 1980 to Nov 1985	Champion CH68

124 Series

2.0 litre:	
Pre Jan 1989	Champion CH68
Post Feb 1989	Champion CH156
2.5 litre non Turbo:	
Pre Jan 1989	Champion CH68
Post Feb 1989	Champion CH156
2.5 litre Turbo:	
Post May 1988	Champion CH156
3.0 litre non Turbo:	
Pre Jan 1989	Champion CH68
Post Feb 1989	Champion CH156
3.0 litre Turbo:	
Pre Jan 1989	Champion CH68
Post Feb 1989	Champion CH156

Idle speed

123 Series

1975 model year	700 to 800 rpm
1976 model year:	
2399 cc & 2404 cc engines	700 to 780 rpm
2998 cc engine	680 to 760 rpm
1978 model year on	750 rpm

124 Series

4-cylinder engines with pneumatic idle speed increase	750 ± 50 rpm
4-cylinder engines with electronic idle speed control (ELR)	720 ± 20 rpm
5-cylinder engines with pneumatic idle speed increase	700 ± 50 rpm
5-cylinder engines with electronic idle speed control (ELR)	680 ± 20 rpm
6-cylinder engines	630 ± 20

Fuel injection start of delivery

123 Series:	
Turbocharged	23 to 25° BTDC
Non turbocharged:	
1988 cc	26° BTDC
2399 cc & 2404 cc	24° BTDC

Torque wrench settings

	Nm	lbf ft
123 Series		
Camshaft cover bolts	10	14
Engine oil drain plug	26 to 33	35 to 45
Engine oil filter cover bolts	15 to 18	20 to 25
Glow plugs	50	37
124 Series		
Auxiliary drivebelt tensioner lever bolt	10	7
Engine oil drain plug:		
M12 plug	30	22
M14 plug	25	18
Engine oil filter housing cover nuts	25	18
Engine oil filter return pipe	25	18
Glow plugs	20	15

Lubricants, fluids and capacities

Component or system	Lubricant or fluid	Capacity
123 Series		
Engine	Multigrade engine oil, viscosity range SAE 10W/40 to 15W/50, to specification API SG/CD	6.5 litres - Non Turbo with filter 7.5 litres - Turbo with filter
Cooling system	Ethylene glycol based antifreeze. 50% volume with water	11.0 litres
Fuel system	Commercial Diesel fuel for road vehicles (DERV)	70 litres (approximate)
124 Series		
Engine	Multigrade engine oil, viscosity range SAE 10W/40 to 15W/50, to specification API SG/CD	6.5 litres - 2.0 litre with filter 8.0 litres - 2.5 litre Turbo with filter 7.0 litres - 2.5 litre non Turbo with filter 8.0 litres - 3.0 litre Turbo with filter 7.5 litres - 3.0 litre non Turbo with filter
Cooling system	Ethylene glycol based antifreeze. 50% volume with water	8.5 litres - 2.0 litre models 10.0 litres - 2.5 & 3.0 litre Turbo 9.0 litres - 2.5 & 3.0 litre non Turbo
Fuel system	Commercial Diesel fuel for road vehicles (DERV)	72 litres (approximate)

Mercedes-Benz diesel engine - maintenance schedule

The maintenance schedules which follow are basically those recommended by the manufacturer. Servicing intervals are determined by mileage or time elapsed - this is because fluids and systems deteriorate with age as well as with use. Follow the time intervals if the appropriate mileage is not covered within the specified period.

Vehicles operating under adverse conditions may need more frequent maintenance. Adverse conditions include climatic extremes, full-time towing or taxi work, driving on unmade roads, and a high proportion of short journeys. The use of inferior fuel can cause early degradation of the engine oil. Consult a Mercedes-Benz dealer for advice on these points.

Every 250 miles (400 km), weekly, or before a long journey - all models

- ☐ Check engine oil level and top up if necessary (Section 3)
- ☐ Check coolant level and top up if necessary (Section 4)
- ☐ Check exhaust emission (Section 5)
- ☐ Check operation of glow plug warning light (Section 6)

Every 5000 miles (7500 km) - 123 Series

- ☐ Renew engine oil and filter (Section 7)
- ☐ Check exhaust system for security and damage

Change to 6000 mile (10 000 km) service interval on models manufactured after August 1982
Under severe operating conditions, renew engine oil and filter every 2500 miles (3750 km)

Every 6000 miles (10 000 km) - 124 Series

- ☐ Renew engine oil and filter (Section 8)

Every 10 000 miles (15 000 km) - 123 Series

- ☐ Check engine compartment hoses for security and leaks
- ☐ Check valve clearances (Section 9)
- ☐ Check condition and tension of auxiliary drivebelts
- ☐ Check engine idle speed - pre-1979 models (Section 10)
- ☐ Clean air filter element
- ☐ Check idle speed adjusting knob - non-Turbo models (Section 11)

Change to 12 000 mile (20 000 km) service interval on models manufactured after August 1982

Every 12 000 miles (20 000 km) - 124 Series

- ☐ Check engine compartment hoses for security and leaks
- ☐ Check condition and tension of auxiliary drivebelt(s)
- ☐ Check engine idle speed (Section 12)
- ☐ Check exhaust system for security and damage

Every 28 000 miles (45 000 km) or 30 months - 123 Series

- ☐ Renew engine coolant
- ☐ Renew fuel filter and prefilter (Section 13)
- ☐ Check engine idle speed - 1980-on models (Section 14)
- ☐ Check fuel injection start of delivery (Section 15)
- ☐ Renew air filter element

Change to 36 000 mile (60 000 km) service interval on models manufactured after August 1982
Under severe operating conditions, renew air filter element every 15 000 miles (22 500 km)

Every 36 000 miles (60 000 km) - 124 Series

- ☐ Renew air filter element
- ☐ Renew fuel filter and pre-filter (Section 16)

Every 3 years, regardless of mileage - 124 Series

- ☐ Renew engine coolant

Typical underbonnet view of Diesel engine in Mercedes 123 Series

1 Battery
2 Air filter housing
3 Ventilation hose
4 Camshaft cover
5 Throttle linkage
6 Oil filter
7 Windscreen wiper
8 Brake master cylinder
9 Fuse box
10 Fuel filter housing
11 Washer fluid reservoir
12 Headlight
13 Oil cooler
14 Power steering pump
15 Radiator hose
16 Radiator
17 Oil filler cap
18 Bonnet latch
19 EGR valve
20 Level control system dipstick
21 Coolant expansion tank
22 Coolant filler cap

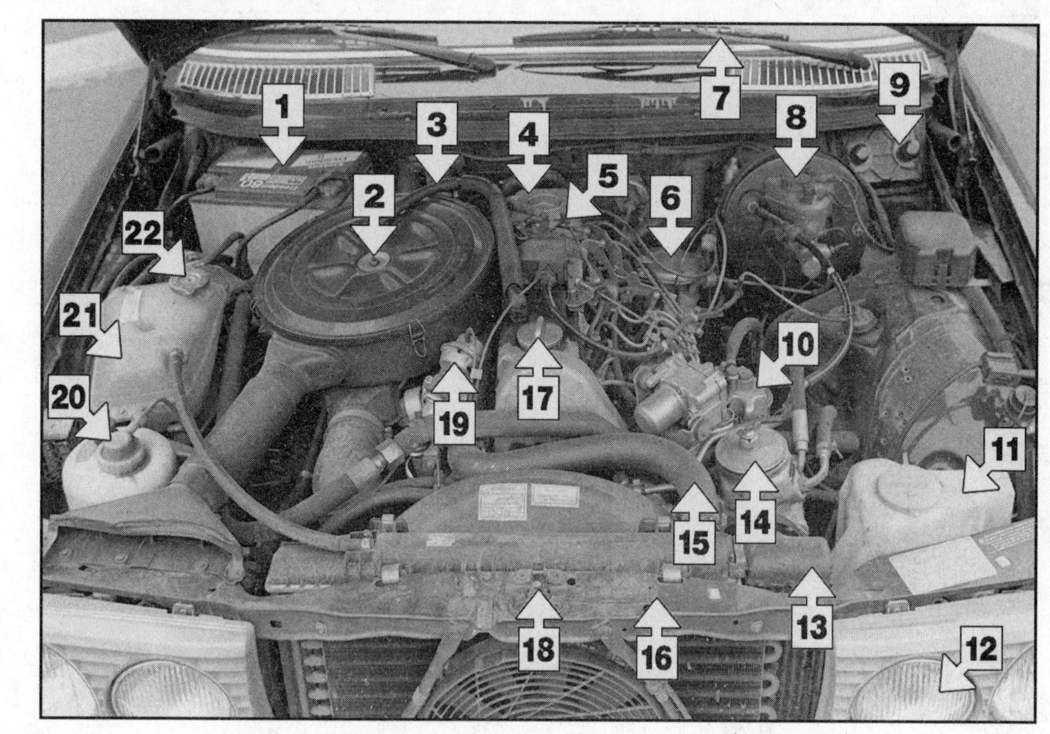

Underbonnet view of 2.5 litre Diesel engine in Mercedes 124 Series

1 *Engine oil filler cap*
2 *Engine oil level dipstick*
3 *Battery*
4 *Brake and clutch fluid reservoir*
5 *Fuse/relay box*
6 *Coolant expansion tank*
7 *Suspension strut upper mounting*
8 *Air filter housing*
9 *Fuel filter*
10 *Power steering pump*
11 *Glow plug control unit*
12 *Oil filter*
13 *Washer fluid reservoir*
14 *Anti-lock braking system (ABS) hydraulic unit*
15 *Steering box*

Maintenance procedures

1 Introduction

Refer to Chapter 2, Part A, Section 1.

2 Intensive maintenance

Refer to Chapter 2, Part A, Section 2.

250 mile (400 km) Service - all models

3 Engine oil level check

1 Refer to Chapter 2, Part A, Section 3 **(see illustrations)**.

4 Coolant level check

1 Refer to Chapter 2, Part A, Section 4. Note that early 123 Series models may not have an expansion tank, in which case the coolant level should be checked by removing the radiator cap and checking that the coolant is just covering the tab in the radiator neck **(see illustration)**.

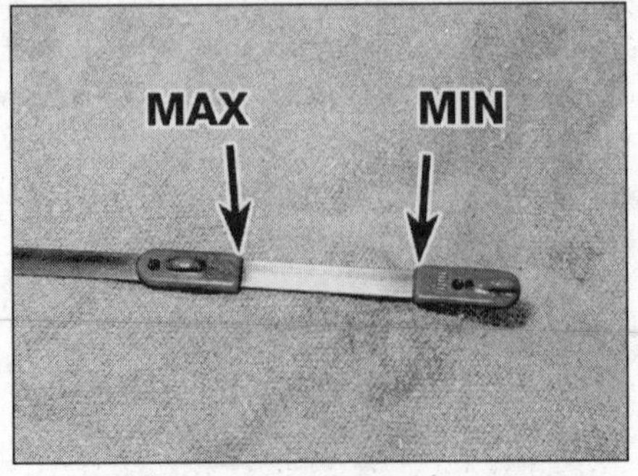

3.1a Engine oil level dipstick markings

3.1b Topping-up engine oil

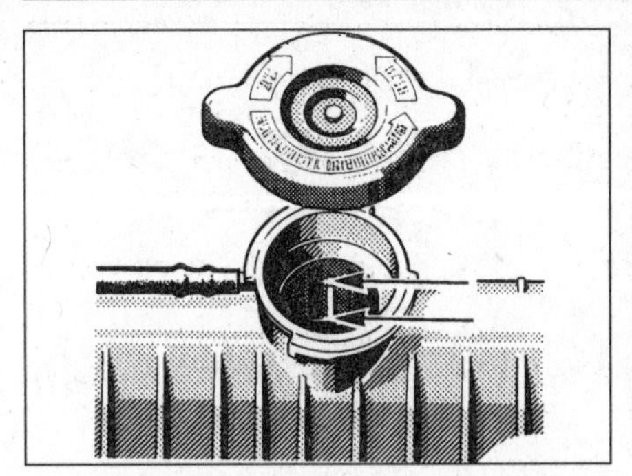

4.1 On models without expansion tank, coolant level should be at tab in radiator filler neck (arrowed)

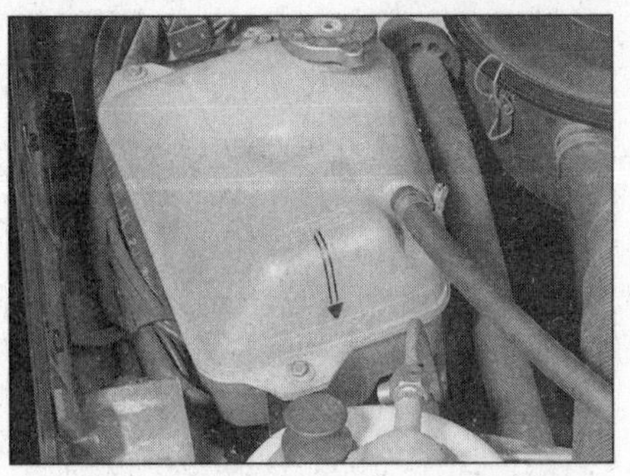

4.2 Coolant level must be kept at line marked by arrow

2 All other models have a translucent expansion tank, so that the coolant level can be verified without removing the tank cap. The level should always be kept at the line marked by the arrow embossed on the side of the tank. If the coolant level is below this line, remove the cap and top up with coolant **(see illustration)**.

5 Exhaust smoke check

1 Refer to Chapter 2, Part A, Section 5.

6 Warning light check

1 Refer to Chapter 2, Part A, Section 6.

5000 mile (7500 km) Service - 123 Series

7 Engine oil and filter renewal

Oil draining

1 Refer to Chapter 2, Part A, Section 7 **(see illustrations)**.

Filter renewal

2 Place a wad of rag around the bottom of the oil filter housing to absorb any spilt oil.
3 Remove the retaining nuts and lift off the filter housing cover **(see illustration)**.
4 Lift the old filter element out of the housing **(see illustration)**.
5 Compare the old filter element with the new one to make sure they are of the same type.
6 Lower the new filter into the housing, ensuring it seats securely.
7 Refit the filter housing cover, making sure the gasket seats securely. Fit and tighten its retaining nuts.
8 Remove all tools and rag from the engine compartment.

Oil refilling and engine checks

9 Refer to Chapter 2, Part A, Section 7.

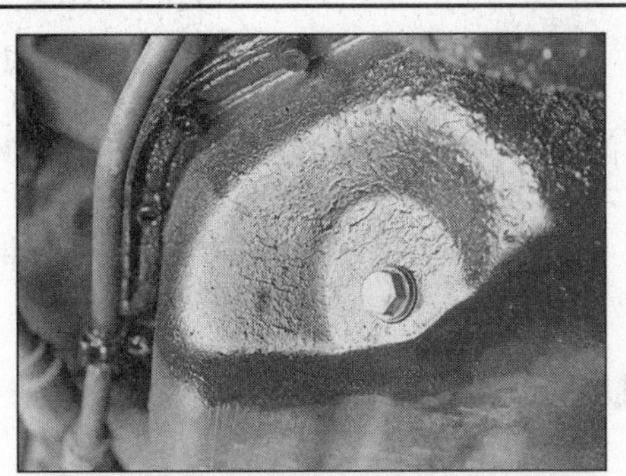

7.1a Engine oil drain plug - 123 Series

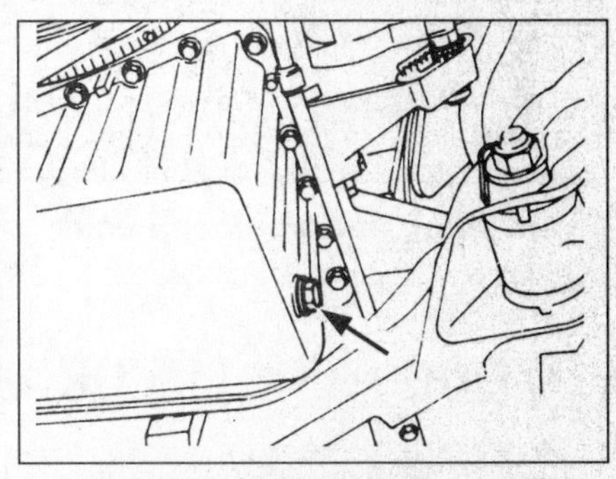

7.1b Engine oil drain plug (arrowed) - 124 Series

7.3 Engine oil filter cover nuts (arrowed)

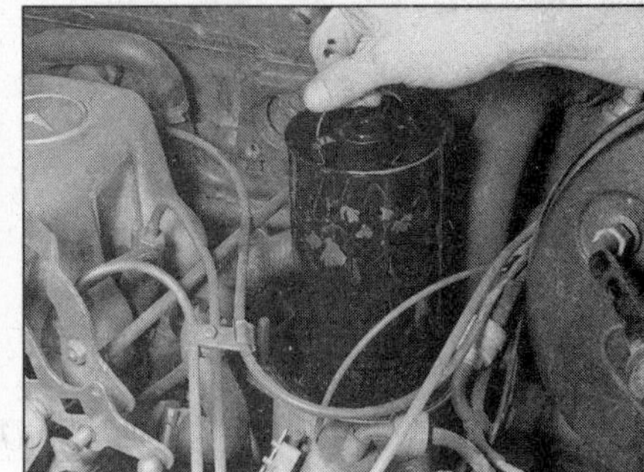

7.4 Lifting oil filter from housing

6000 mile (10 000 km) Service - 124 Series

8 Engine oil and filter renewal

Oil draining

1 Refer to Chapter 2, Part A, Section 7.

Filter renewal

Note: *A new oil filter housing cover O-ring and, where applicable, a new oil return pipe O-ring will be required on refitting.*

2 Locate the oil filter housing at the left-hand rear corner of the engine, behind the inlet manifold.
3 Place a wad of rag around the bottom of the housing to absorb any spilt oil.
4 Pull off the retaining clip, or remove the screw (as applicable), and pull the rubber weatherstrip from the bulkhead at the rear of the engine compartment, in order to improve access to the oil filter housing **(see illustration)**.

5 On models with an oil return pipe protruding from the centre of the oil filter housing cover, unscrew the pipe and withdraw it from the housing/cover assembly **(see illustration)**. Where applicable, recover the O-ring from the top of the pipe and discard it. A new O-ring must be used on refitting.
6 Unscrew the two securing nuts, then lift off the filter housing cover - see illustration 7.3. Recover the O-ring from the cover and discard it. A new O-ring must be used on refitting.
7 Lift the oil filter element from the housing, using the handle provided - see illustration 7.4.
8 Wipe out the oil filter housing and cover, using a clean rag.
9 Check the oil return pipe (either separate, or part of the cover) for blockage. It should be possible to blow through the small hole in the top of the pipe and feel air escaping from the bottom of the pipe **(see illustration)**. Clean the pipe and blow through with compressed air if necessary.
10 Fit a new O-ring to the oil filter housing cover **(see illustration)**.
11 Fit a new oil filter element to the housing (handle at the top), then refit the cover and tighten the nuts to the specified torque.
12 Where applicable, fit a new O-ring to the top of the oil return pipe, then refit the return pipe and tighten to the specified torque.

Oil refilling and engine checks

13 Refer to Chapter 2, Part A, Section 7.

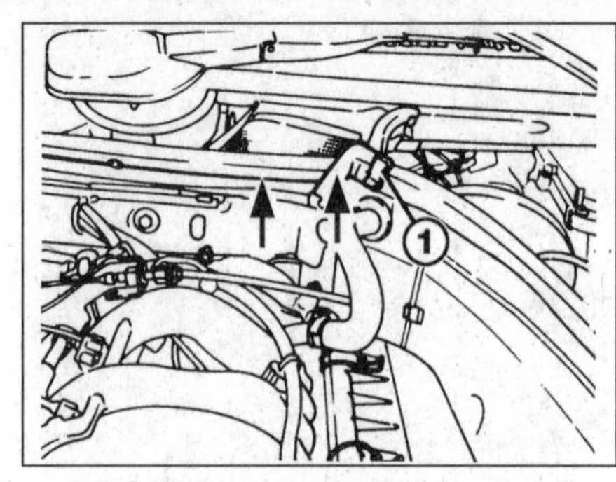

8.4 Pull off retaining clip (1) and pull weatherstrip from bulkhead

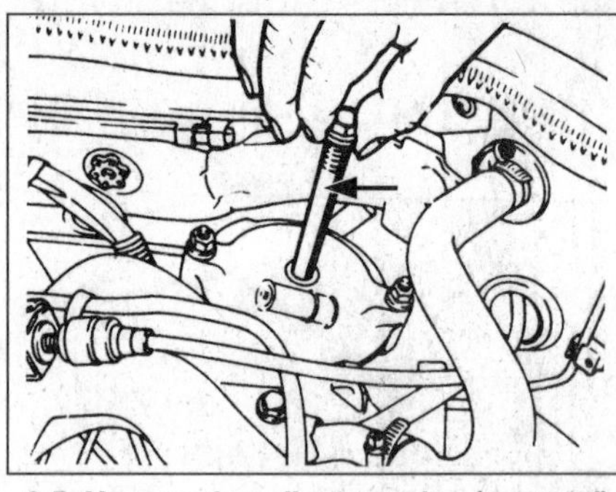

8.5 Unscrewing oil return pipe (arrowed)

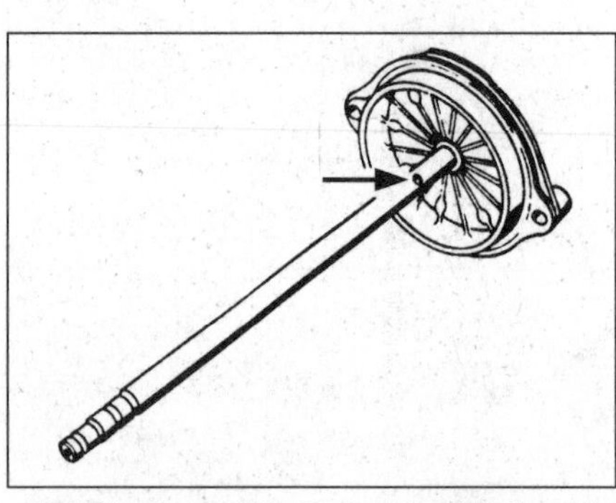

8.9 Check small hole (arrowed) in top of oil return pipe for blockage

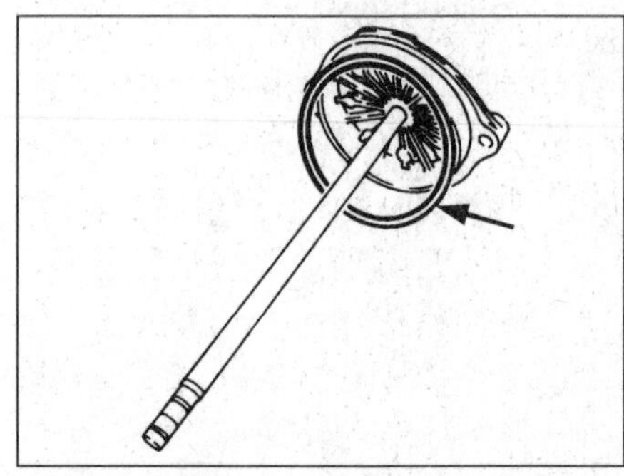

8.10 Fit new O-ring (arrowed) to oil filter housing cover

10 000 mile (15 000 km) Service - 123 Series

9 Valve clearance check

1 Remove the ventilation hose and vacuum connectors (if equipped) from the camshaft cover **(see illustration)**.
2 Disconnect the throttle linkage **(see illustrations)**.
3 Unbolt the throttle linkage from the camshaft cover and move it to one side **(see illustration)**.
4 Remove the retaining bolts and lift the camshaft cover with gasket from the engine.
5 Each valve clearance is measured between the rocker arm and camshaft base circle, with the lobe positioned opposite the arm as shown **(see illustration)**. Depending on engine type, follow the sequence shown **(see illustrations)**.
6 Slowly turn the engine over in a clockwise direction by slipping a socket over the large bolt at the front of the crankshaft, until the first rocker arm and camshaft lobe (this will be the exhaust valve) are correctly positioned so the clearance can be checked. Repeat this procedure on each valve in turn, working from the front of the engine to the rear. Take care to differentiate between the intake and

9.1 Unplug hose and connectors from camshaft cover

9.2a Using screwdriver to disconnect throttle linkage

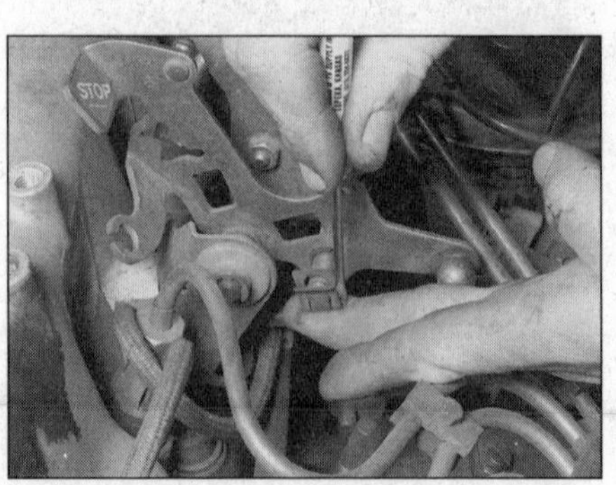

9.2b Using small screwdriver to remove throttle linkage clip on camshaft cover

9.2c Using needle-nose pliers to remove throttle rod pin

9.3 Throttle linkage assembly-to-camshaft cover bolts (arrowed)

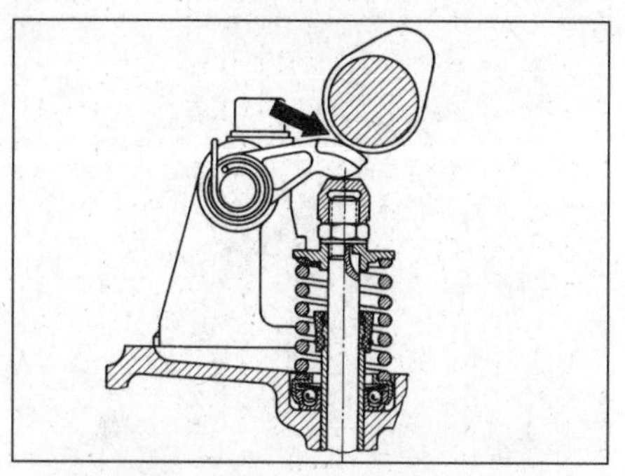
9.5a Measure valve clearance between rocker arm and camshaft base circle (arrowed)

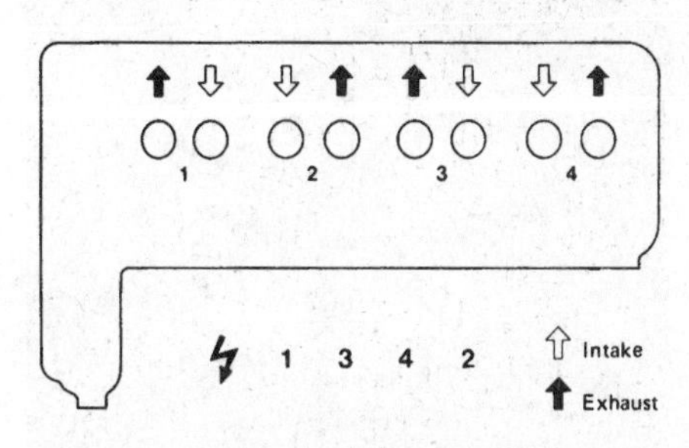

9.5b Valve adjustment sequence - 4 cylinder engine

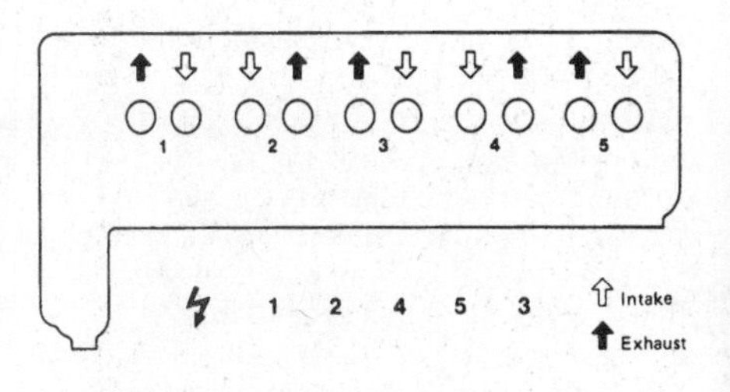

9.5c Valve adjustment sequence - 5 cylinder engine

9.7 Using feeler gauge to measure valve clearance

9.8 Valve adjusting nut (A) locknut (B) and valve spring collar (C)

exhaust valves, as the clearance between the two differ.

7 Insert the specified size of feeler gauge between the rocker arm and camshaft **(see illustration)**. If the gauge fits with some slight drag, then the clearance is correct and no adjustment is required.

8 If the feeler gauge does not fit, or if it is loose, use two spanners to loosen the adjusting nut locknut. It may also be necessary to hold the valve spring collar in position **(see illustration)**.

9 Carefully tighten or loosen the adjusting nut until you can feel a slight drag on the feeler gauge as it is withdrawn.

10 Hold the adjusting nut with one spanner to keep it from turning, then tighten the locknut securely **(see illustration)**. Recheck the clearance.

11 After checking (and adjusting, if necessary) all the valve clearances, refit the camshaft cover. Use a new cover gasket if the old one is dried out or brittle, and tighten the retaining bolts in a diagonal sequence to the specified torque.

12 Refit the throttle linkage and vacuum line connector.

13 Start the engine and check for oil leakage around the camshaft cover.

10 Idle speed check and adjustment - pre-1979 models

1 Run the engine until it reaches normal operating temperature.

2 Turn the idle speed adjusting knob fully to the right.

3 On models equipped with a fuel injection pump with a pneumatic governor, disconnect the regulating rod and adjust idle speed on the throttle unit **(see illustration)**.

4 On mechanical governor equipped fuel injection pumps, disconnect the regulating rod and adjust idle by turning the screw after loosening the locknut **(see illustration)**.

9.10 Using two spanners to tighten locknut

10.3 On pneumatic governor equipped fuel injection pumps, disconnect regulating rod (3) and adjust idle speed screw (4)

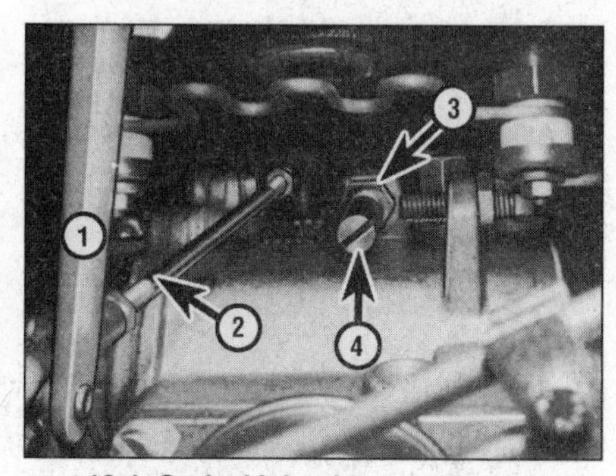

10.4 On fuel injection pumps with mechanical governors, disconnect regulating rod (2) from lever (1) loosen locknut (3) and adjust idle speed screw (4)

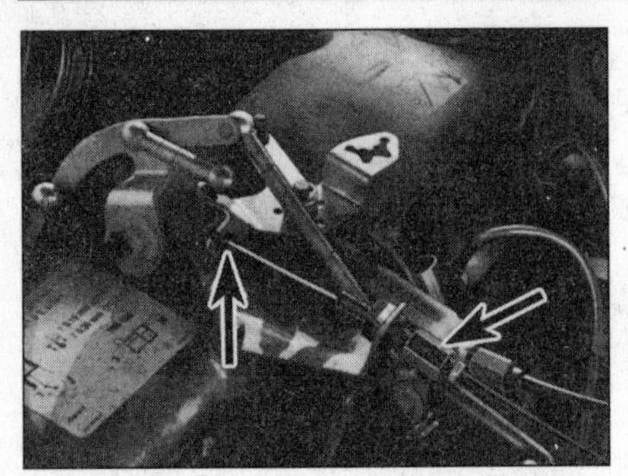

10.5 Adjust cruise control Bowden wire tension after loosening adjusting locknut (arrowed)

11.3 Adjust the engine idle speed knob on mechanical governor equipped fuel injection pumps by measuring the clearance between adjusting ring or nipple and spring (arrowed) - pre-1979 models

11.4 Idle speed knob cable locking grommet (arrowed) adjusting nut (2) and throttle rod (4) - post-1980 models

5 After adjustment of the idle speed, check the cruise control (if equipped) Bowden wire adjustment as follows:

a) *Push the stop lever against the regulating lever.*

b) *The wire should now be free of tension and rest against the regulating lever.*

c) *If necessary, adjust the wire by means of the adjusting nut **(see illustration)**.*

11 Idle speed adjusting knob check - non Turbo models

1 Some non Turbo models are equipped with an idle speed adjuster knob which is sited on the instrument panel. This allows engine idle speed to be adjusted manually, for ease of starting and driveability. Check the idle speed adjuster clearance as follows:

2 On models with pneumatic governor equipped fuel injection pumps, turn the preglow starter switch fully clockwise, then turn it anti-clockwise. Make sure there is a half turn of travel until the idle speed increases. Adjust the locknut on the cable at the bracket as necessary.

3 On injection pumps with mechanical governors, turn the idle speed adjusting knob fully to the right and check that the clearance between the adjusting nipple or ring and spring is 1.0 mm **(see illustration)**.

4 With the engine off, depress the accelerator pedal while turning the knob fully clockwise. Start the engine and check that it runs at no more than 1000 rpm, as otherwise the engine speed can climb to full throttle. Adjust by turning the adjusting screw on the end of the cable wire (early models) or the adjusting nut on the cable and bracket **(see illustration)**.

12 000 mile (20 000 km) Service - 124 Series

12 Idle speed check and adjustment

Checking

1 Check that adjustment of the accelerator cable is correct.

2 Start the engine and run it at a fast idle until it reaches its normal operating temperature, or else take the vehicle on a short journey. With the parking brake applied and the transmission in neutral, allow the engine to idle. Check that all electrical consumers are switched off (including air conditioning, where applicable).

3 Using a Diesel engine tachometer, check that the engine idle speed is as specified. If adjustment is necessary, proceed as follows.

Adjustment

Engines with pneumatic idle speed increase

4 Loosen the locknut on top of the idle speed vacuum unit, which is fitted to the rear of the injection pump.

5 Using an open-ended spanner, gradually turn the vacuum unit until the idle speed is as specified. On completion, tighten the locknut.

Engines with ELR idle speed control

6 Unplug the electrical wiring from the electromagnetic actuator, which is fitted to the rear of the injection pump.

7 Locate the idle speed adjustment screw, which is directly above the electromagnetic actuator body. Loosen the locknut and turn the adjustment screw until the engine idle speed is as specified. Turning the screw to the left raises the idle speed, turning it to the right lowers the idle speed.

8 On completion, tighten the locknut and reconnect the actuator wiring.

Engines with EDS electronic engine control

9 Proceed as described in paragraphs 6 to 8 inclusive, but note that the basic idle speed setting can also be altered electronically by means of a trimming socket.

10 The socket is mounted in the accessories compartment, at the rear right hand side of the engine bay, behind the false bulkhead panel.

11 The position of the resistive plug can be altered by pulling it from the trimming socket, rotating it and refitting it. The positions are indicated by numbers, ranging from 1 to 7, marked on the rear of the resistive plug.

12 Position No 1 equates to roughly 600 rpm and position No 7 equates roughly to 700 rpm.

28 000 mile (45 000 km) Service - 123 Series

13 Fuel filter and pre-filter renewal

1 Two filters are fitted, a main spin-on type mounted on a housing adjacent to the front of the cylinder head and a pre-filter in the fuel line, which is located on the left-hand side of the engine compartment. Both are of the disposable type.
2 To minimise fuel spillage, position a small container beneath each filter and pad the surrounding area with absorbent rags.
3 Disconnect the battery negative cable and position it well away from the terminal.

Main filter

4 Loosen the large bolt on top of the filter housing **(see illustration)**.
5 Unscrew the filter while holding the bolt **(see illustration)**.
6 Install the new filter and tighten the bolt.

Pre-filter

7 Loosen each filter hose retaining clamp, sliding it clear of the filter **(see illustration)**.
8 Note the direction in which the prefilter is installed and remove each hose.
9 Fit each hose to the new prefilter and secure it with its clamp.

Fuel system bleeding

10 After replacing either filter, all air must be bled from the system.
11 Loosen the large bolt at the top of the filter housing and bleed the fuel system as follows until no air bubbles can be seen escaping.
12 Ensure the fuel tank is full and unscrew the primer pump handle by rotating it in an anti-clockwise direction **(see illustration)**.
13 Operate the pump until air can be heard (a hissing noise) at the bypass valve located in the fuel filter housing.
14 After bleeding, tighten the pump handle.
15 Tighten the filter housing bolt.

14 Idle speed check and adjustment - 1980-on models

1 Idle speed adjustment on vehicles manufactured after 1980 requires the use of special tools and techniques. The job should therefore be left to a Mercedes dealer.

15 Fuel injection start of delivery check

Note: *This procedure determines the start of fuel delivery of the fuel injection pump number one element when the number one piston is at the start of the compression stroke. Before beginning this procedure, obtain a start of delivery overflow pipe spout, tool no. 636 589 02 23 00 from your dealer.*
1 Remove the fuel injection pump-to-injector pipe assembly.
2 Disconnect the vacuum hose from the fuel pump vacuum control unit.
3 Disconnect the throttle linkage from the pump and use a piece of wire to fasten the control lever in the full load position **(see illustration)**.
4 Remove the No 1 pump element from the pump and then remove the delivery valve and spring from the element **(see illustrations)**.
5 Reinstall the element, minus the delivery valve and spring.

13.4 Loosening fuel filter centre bolt

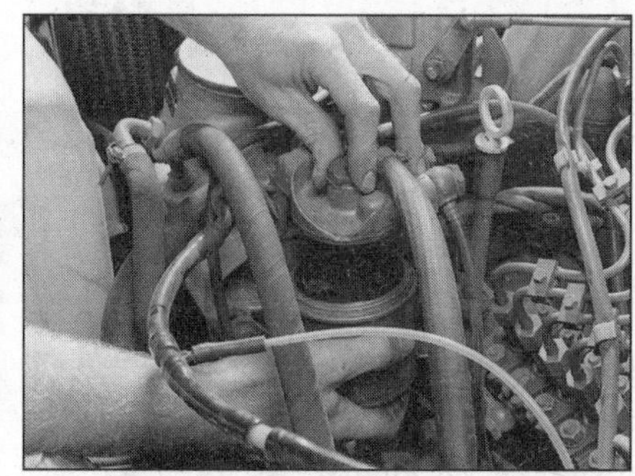
13.5 Holding centre bolt while unscrewing fuel filter

13.7 Loosening fuel prefilter clamp screws

13.12 Unlocking primer pump handle

15.3 Wiring pump lever (arrowed) in full load position

15.4a Unscrew No 1 fuel element from the pump . . .

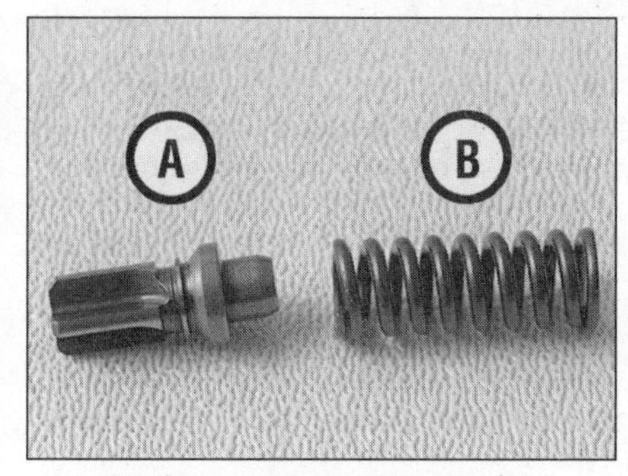

15.4b . . . and remove valve (A) and spring (B)

15.6 **Fuel injection start of delivery tool must be installed with spout facing engine (arrowed)**

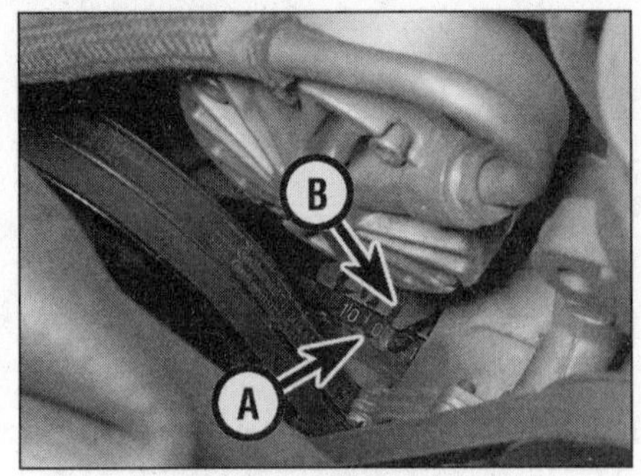

15.7 Engine timing marks (A) and pointer (B) with engine at TDC

15.8a Loosening fuel filter union bolt (arrowed)

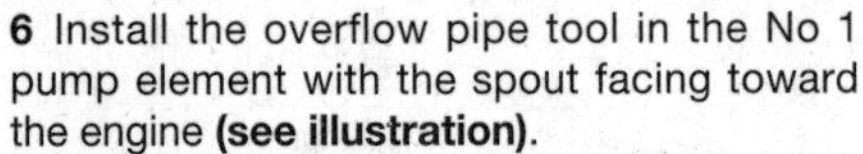

6 Install the overflow pipe tool in the No 1 pump element with the spout facing toward the engine **(see illustration)**.

7 Turn the engine over by hand in the normal direction of rotation (clockwise when facing the front of the vehicle) until the beginning of compression pressure can be felt. Rotate the engine until the timing pointer on the front of the engine is aligned with the specified start of delivery degrees on the balancer **(see illustration)**. Remove the oil filler cap. Check to see that both camshaft lobes for the front (No 1) cylinder are facing upwards. With this done, the No 1 piston is at the start of its compression stroke.

8 Loosen the fuel union bolt at the top of the fuel filter and bleed any air from the system by pumping the hand pump until fuel with no air bubbles issues from the top of the filter and the overflow tool spout **(see illustrations)**.

9 Stop pumping the hand pump and the flow from the spout of the overflow tool should slow until a rate of one droplet per second is reached.

15.8b Air-free fuel escaping from start of delivery spout (arrowed)

15.10 Rotate fuel injection pump to achieve proper start of delivery

10 If the flow is not correct, loosen the injection pump mounting bolts, repeat the procedure and rotate the pump until one droplet per second is achieved **(see illustration)**.

11 Once the proper start of delivery is obtained, tighten the pump mounting bolts, remove the spout tool and reinstall the delivery valve and spring in the element. Install the fuel pipe assembly and connect the throttle linkage and vacuum hose.

36 000 mile (60 000 km) Service - 124 Series

16 Fuel filter and pre-filter renewal

1 Disconnect the battery negative cable and position it away from the terminal.

2 To minimise fuel spillage, position a small container underneath the filter canister and pad the surrounding area with absorbent rags.

3 Support the fuel filter with one hand, then slacken and remove the banjo bolt at from the top of the fuel filter housing. Recover both O-ring seals and discard them. New seals must be used on refitting **(see illustration)**.

4 Remove the filter canister from the engine bay, keeping the mating face upwards to minimise fuel spillage.

5 With the filter removed, check that the restriction orifice in the fuel return line on the mating surface of the filter housing is clean and free from blockage.

6 Take the new filter canister and moisten the rubber seal with a little clean fuel.

7 Offer the filter up to the housing, then insert the banjo bolt (using new O-rings) and tighten it securely.

8 The pre-filter is positioned to the left hand side of the fuel injection pump. Clamp off the fuel supply hose from the fuel tank downstream of the pre-filter, then slacken the clips and detach the fuel hoses from either side of the pre-filter. Fit the new unit in its place and tighten the hose clips securely.

9 Reconnect the battery, then start and run the engine at idle and check the filter for leaks. The pump is self priming but may take a few seconds of cranking before the engine starts.

10 Raise engine speed to about 2000 rpm several times, then allow the engine to idle again. This should bleed air bubbles from the filter canister. If engine idle is at all rough or hesitant, repeat the action until the fuel system clears itself.

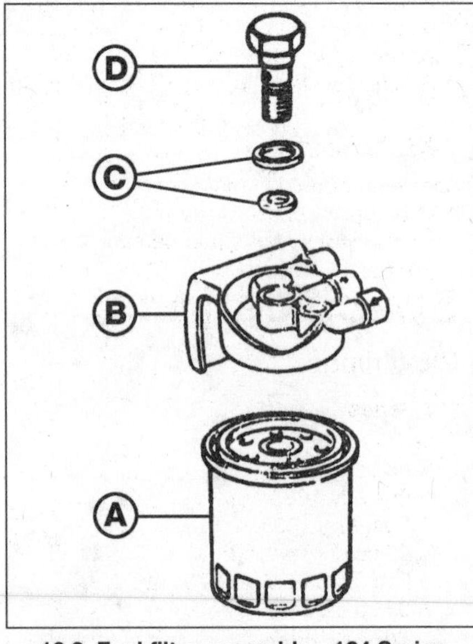

16.3 Fuel filter assembly - 124 Series

A Fuel filter canister
B Filter housing
C Sealing washers
D Banjo bolt

Chapter 7
Mercedes-Benz 1988cc, 1997cc, 2399cc, 2404cc, 2497cc, 2996cc & 2998cc engines

Part B: Fuel system servicing

Contents

Specifications

Glow plugs

123 Series

Type:	
1988 cc engine:	
Pre July 1980	Champion CH61
Post Aug 1980	Champion CH68
2399 cc engine:	
Feb 1976 to Mar 1979	Champion CH61
2404 cc engine:	
Pre July 1980	Champion CH61
Post Aug 1980	Champion CH68
2998 cc engine:	
Aug 1980 to Nov 1985	Champion CH68

Glow plugs (continued)

124 Series

Nominal operating voltage	11.5 V
Electrical resistance	0.75 to 1.5 ohms (approx - at operating temperature)
Current consumption	8 - 15A (per glow plug, after approx. 8 secs of operation)
Type:	
2.0 litre:	
Pre Jan 1989	Champion CH68
Post Feb 1989	Champion CH156
2.5 litre non Turbo:	
Pre Jan 1989	Champion CH68
Post Feb 1989	Champion CH156
2.5 litre Turbo:	
Post May 1988	Champion CH156
3.0 litre non Turbo:	
Pre Jan 1989	Champion CH68
Post Feb 1989	Champion CH156
3.0 litre Turbo:	
Pre Jan 1989	Champion CH68
Post Feb 1989	Champion CH156

Fuel injection pump

123 Series

Start of delivery:	
Turbocharged	23 to 25° BTDC
Non-turbocharged:	
1988 cc	26° BTDC
2399 cc & 2404 cc	24° BTDC

124 Series

Start of delivery	15° ATDC on No 1 cylinder

Idle speed

123 Series

1975 model year	700 to 800 rpm
1976 model year:	
2399 cc & 2404 cc engines	700 to 780 rpm
2998 cc engine	680 to 760 rpm
1978 model year on	750 rpm

124 Series

4-cylinder engines with pneumatic idle speed increase	750 ± 50 rpm
4-cylinder engines with electronic idle speed control (ELR)	720 ± 20 rpm
5-cylinder engines with pneumatic idle speed increase	700 ± 50 rpm
5-cylinder engines with electronic idle speed control (ELR)	680 ± 20 rpm
6-cylinder engines	630 ± 20

Maximum no-load speed

124 Series	5150 ± 50 rpm

Torque wrench settings

	Nm	lbf ft
123 Series		
Glow plugs	50	37
Fuel injection lines	18	25
Injectors	52 to 59	70 to 80
124 Series		
Glow plugs	20	15
Glow plug electrical terminals	4	3
Injection pump to rear mounting bracket	25	18
Injection pump to front mounting bolts	25	18
Injection pump sprocket bolt	45	33
Injection pump inspection hole plug	35	26
Injector fuel pipe unions	15	11
Injectors	75	55

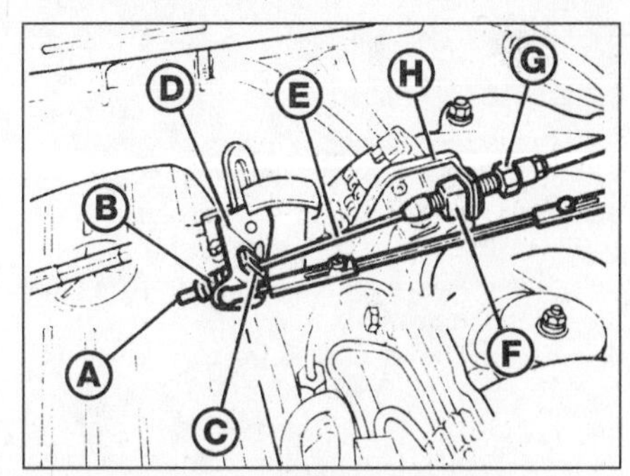

1.2a Accelerator cable linkage - 4 and 5-cylinder engines

A Accelerator cable end
B Compression spring
C Retaining block
D Guide lever
E Accelerator cable inner
F Plastic retainer
G Adjustment nut
H Guide bracket

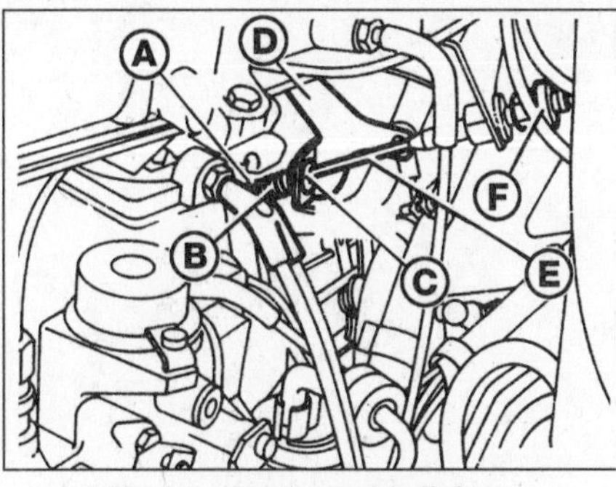

1.2b Accelerator cable linkage - 6-cylinder engines

A Accelerator cable end
B Compression spring
C Retaining block
D Guide lever
E Accelerator cable inner
F Adjustment nut

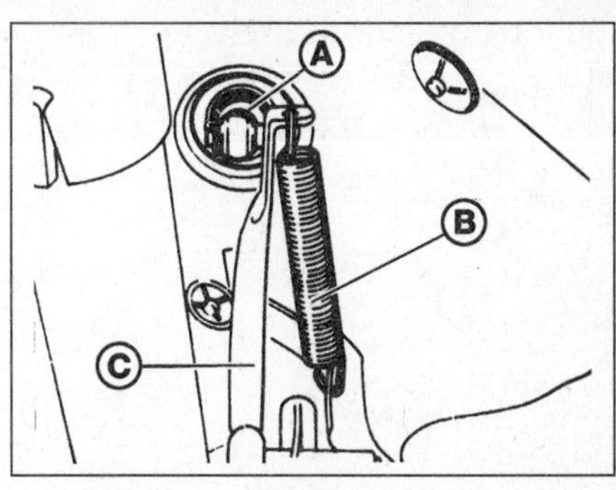

1.3 Cable adjustment knob at accelerator pedal

A Adjustment knob
B Return spring
C Accelerator pedal

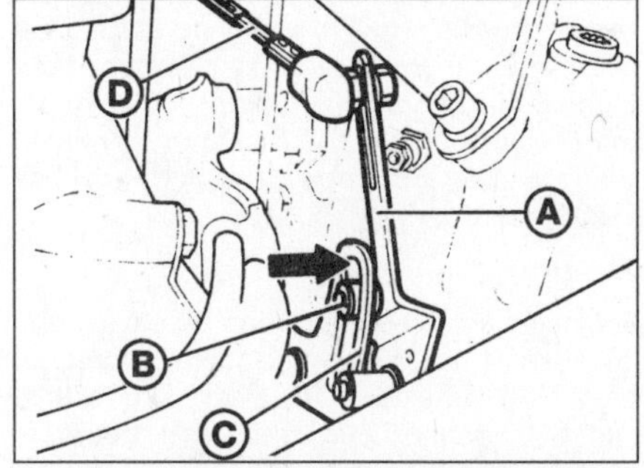

1.4a At idle, roller pivot should be resting against end (arrowed) of slot in fulcrum lever - 4 and 5-cylinder engines shown

A Relay lever
B Roller pivot
C Fulcrum lever
D Connecting rod

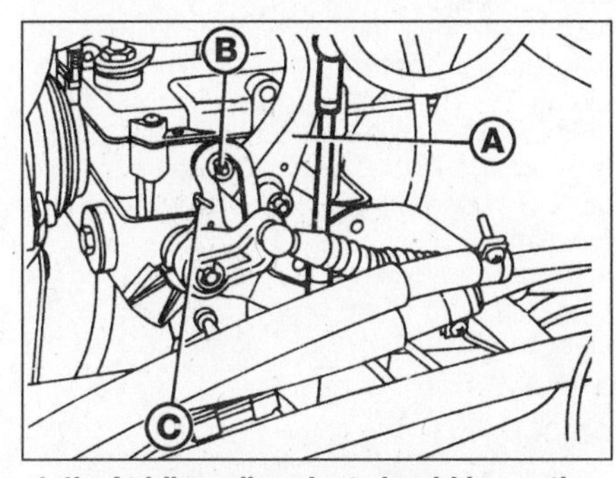

1.4b At idle, roller pivot should be resting against end (arrowed) of slot in fulcrum lever - 6-cylinder engine shown

A Relay lever B Roller pivot C Fulcrum lever

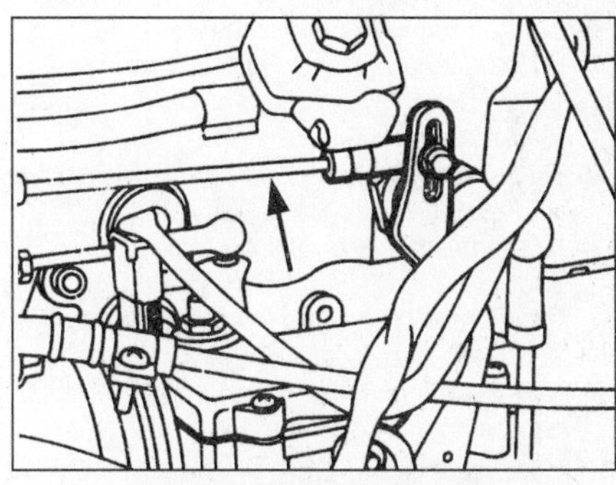

1.4c Adjust length of connecting rod (arrowed)

1 Accelerator cable (124 Series) - adjustment

1 Before attempting adjustment of the accelerator cable, check that the route taken by the cable avoids kinking, crushing or exceptionally tight bends. Operate the accelerator pedal through its full stroke and check that no resistance can be felt.

2 With the accelerator linkage in the idle position, check that the spring plate at the end of the accelerator cable is resting lightly against compression spring, without tension **(see illustrations).**

3 If this is not the case, remove the trim panel above the relevant footwell to expose the grommeted hole in the bulkhead, where the accelerator cable passes from the footwell into the engine bay **(see illustration)**. Turn the adjustment knob at the bulkhead until the conditions in paragraph 2 are met.

4 With the relay lever in the idle position, the roller pivot should be resting against the end of the slotted section of the fulcrum lever. Adjust the length of the connecting rod if required **(see illustrations)**.

5 Pull the accelerator control lever through its full travel. Check that the fuel injection pump control lever rests against the full load stop. In this position, also check that the relay lever pivot stops approximately 1mm short of the end of the slotted section of the fulcrum lever **(see illustration)**.

6 If this not the case, slacken the locknut at the ball socket on the end of the connecting rod and reposition the socket within the relay lever slotted section to achieve the correct travel **(see illustrations)**. On completion, tighten the locknut.

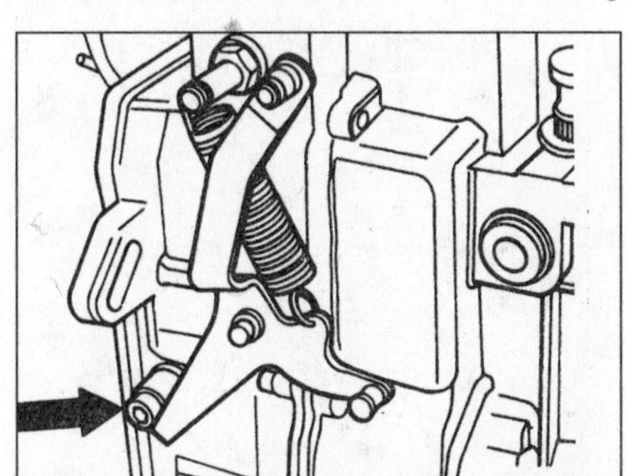

1.5 Check that fuel injection pump control lever rests against full load stop (arrowed)

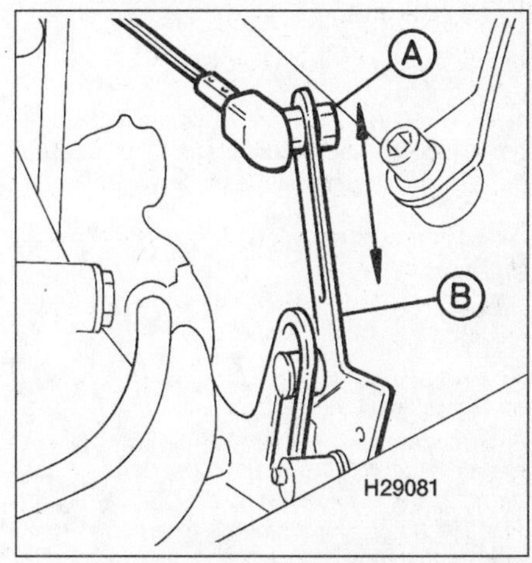

1.6a Slacken locknut at ball socket on end of connecting rod - 4 and 5-cylinder engines shown

A Locknut B Relay lever

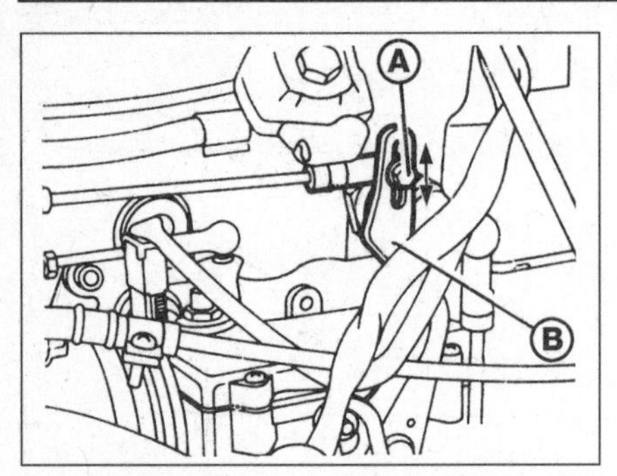

1.6b Slacken the locknut at the ball socket on the end of the connecting rod - 6-cylinder engine shown

A Locknut B Relay lever

7 On automatic transmission models, adjust the control pressure cable as follows:

a) Disconnect the control pressure cable from the balljoint on the throttle linkage.

*b) Loosen the clamping screw(s) on the throttle lever connecting plate, then pull the two sections of the plate apart as far as the stop **(see illustration)**.*

c) Pull the control pressure cable forwards until slight resistance is felt.

d) At the point where resistance is just felt, it should be possible to fit the cable end back onto the throttle linkage balljoint. If necessary, adjust the length of the connecting plate until the cable end can be easily refitted to the balljoint.

8 Have an assistant press the accelerator pedal to the end of its travel, then check that the fuel injection pump control lever rests against the full load stop. If required, turn the adjustment nut at the accelerator guide bracket to achieve the correct travel - see illustrations 1.2a and 1.2b.

9 On completion, repeat the operations described in paragraphs 2 and 3.

2 Glow plugs (123 Series) - testing, removal and refitting

1 Pre-1980 123 Series models use a filament-type glow plug whilst later models are equipped with pencil-type glow plugs.

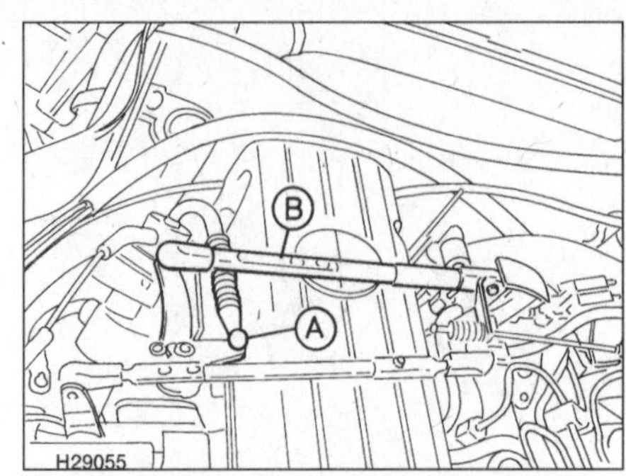

1.7 Control pressure cable adjustment - except 6-cylinder Turbo Diesel

A Control pressure cable end fitting
B Throttle lever connecting plate

2 The filament-type glow plugs are wired in series to maintain the proper resistance throughout the preheating system. The current flows from No 4 cylinder (No 5 on five-cylinder engines) through to No 1 cylinder and then to earth. Consequently a failure or short circuit in one plug will cause problems in those wired in series after it.

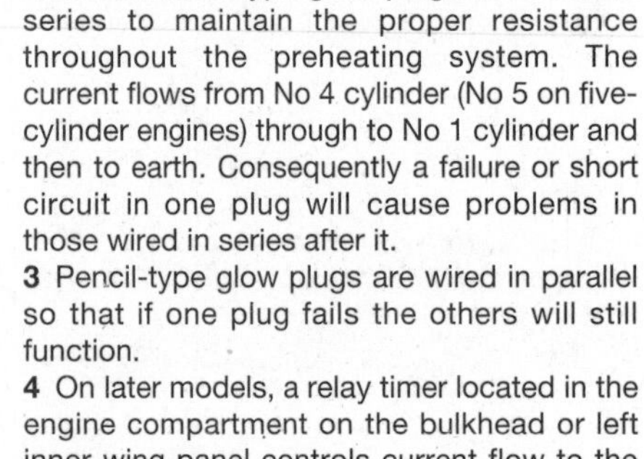

3 Pencil-type glow plugs are wired in parallel so that if one plug fails the others will still function.

4 On later models, a relay timer located in the engine compartment on the bulkhead or left inner wing panel controls current flow to the glow plugs.

Testing

Filament-type plugs

5 With the preheating system on, connect the negative probe of a voltmeter (set at the 0 to 30 volt range) to a good earth point and the positive probe to first the input and then the output of the No 4 (or No 5, if applicable) glow plug **(see illustration)**.

6 If voltage is measured at the glow plug input and 0 volts at the output, then the glow plug is faulty and must be replaced with a new one. If voltage passes through the plug, repeat the check on the remaining plugs, in order. Do not short out the glow plugs to earth, such as would happen if a screwdriver were placed between them and the engine block. This could seriously damage the timer relay.

Pencil-type plugs

7 Unplug the glow plug connector at the relay **(see illustration)**.

8 With the ignition off, connect an ohmmeter (set on the 200 scale) to earth and each of the numbered glow plug terminals in turn **(see illustration)**. An infinity reading on any plug terminal indicates that the plug or its related wiring is faulty and a new glow plug should be installed or the wiring repaired.

Removal

9 Disconnect the battery negative cable.

10 Remove the nut and disconnect the glow plug wire. Unscrew the glow plug with a suitable spanner and remove it from the cylinder head **(see illustrations)**.

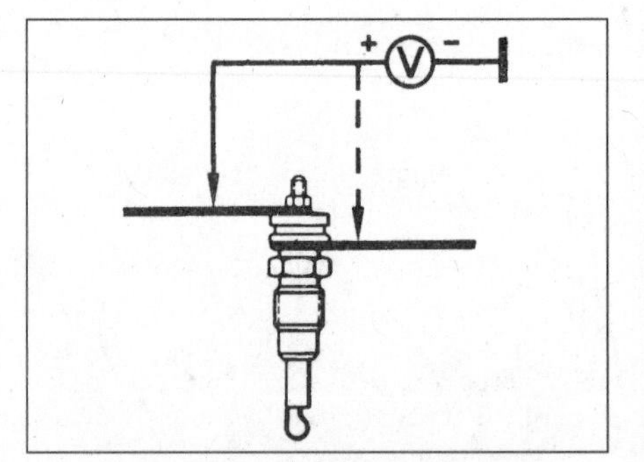

2.5 Filament-type glow plug check

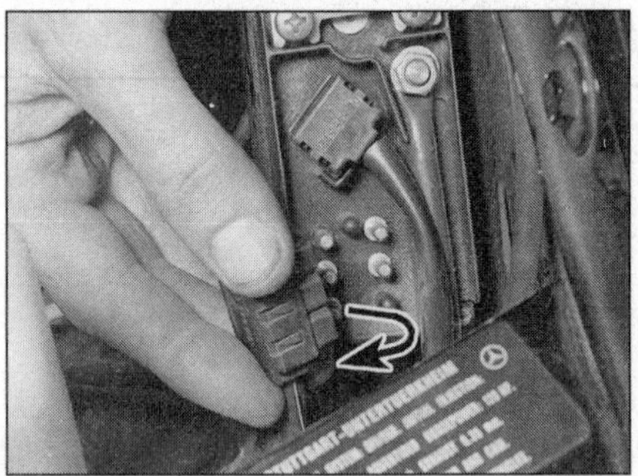

2.7 Pull glow plug connector off timer relay in direction arrowed

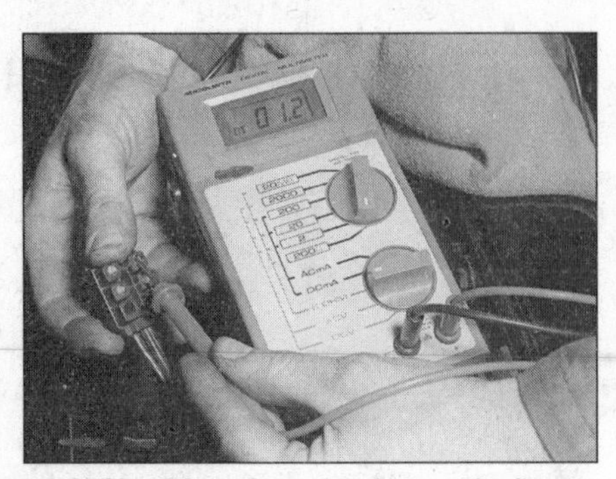

2.8 Checking glow plug for continuity at timer relay connector

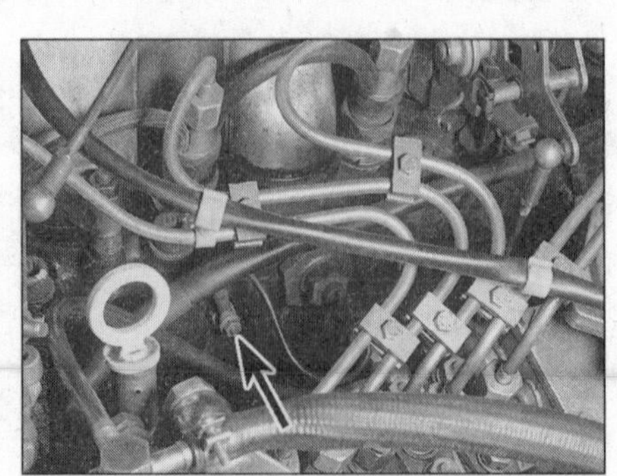

2.10a Glow plug electrical connector is retained by nut (arrowed)

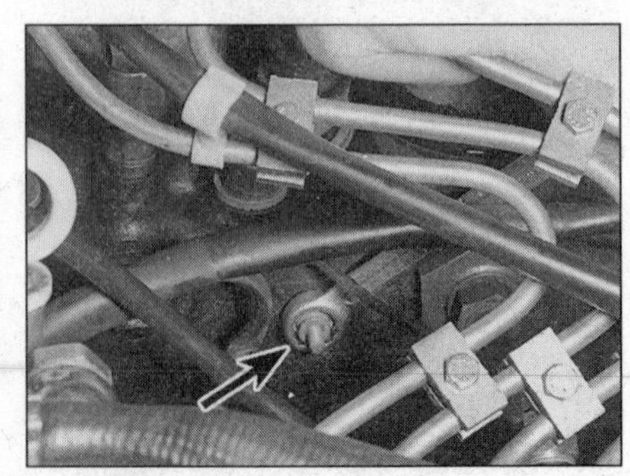

2.10b Unscrewing glow plug from cylinder head

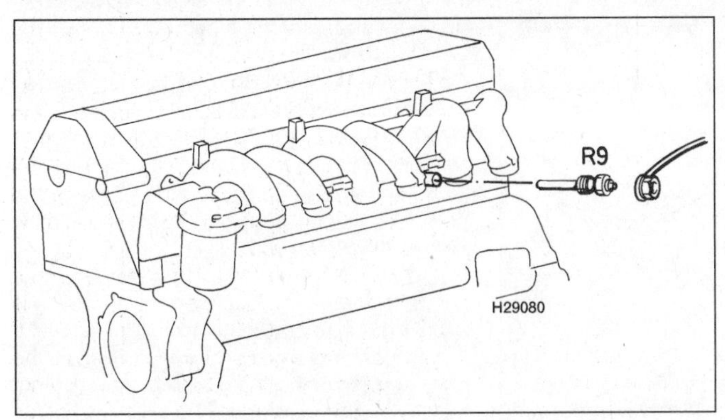

3.10a Glow plug location - non turbo 124 Series engines

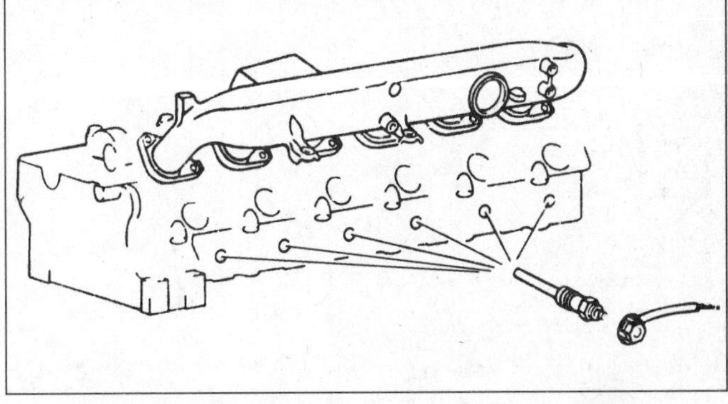
3.10b Glow plug location - turbo 124 Series engines

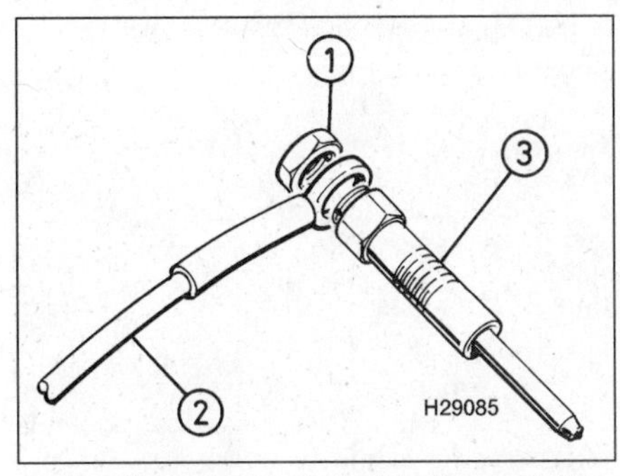

3.10c Glow plug and electrical connection

1 Terminal nut *3 Glow plug*
2 Supply cable

Refitting

11 Refitting each glow plug is a reversal of removal. Tighten each one securely into the cylinder head and reconnect the wire.

3 Glow plugs (124 Series) - testing, removal and refitting

Testing

1 If the system malfunctions, testing is ultimately by substitution of known good units but some preliminary checks may be made as follows.

2 Connect a voltmeter or 12 Volt test lamp between the glow plug supply cable and a good earth point on the engine. Ensure that the live connection is kept well clear of the engine and bodywork.

3 Have an assistant activate the pre-heating system by turning the ignition key to the second position and check that battery voltage is applied to the glow plug electrical connection. The supply voltage will be less than battery voltage initially but will rise and settle as the glow plug heats up. It will then drop to zero when the pre-heating period ends and the safety cut-out operates.

4 If no supply voltage can be detected at the glow plug, then either the plug relay (where applicable) or the supply cabling must be faulty.

5 To locate a faulty glow plug, first operate the pre-heating system to get the glow plugs up to working temperature, then disconnect the battery negative cable and position it away from the terminal.

6 Remove the supply cabling from the glow plug terminal. Measure the electrical resistance between the glow plug terminal and the engine earth. A reading of anything more than a few Ohms indicates that the plug is defective.

7 If a suitable heavy duty ammeter is available, connect it between the glow plug and its supply cable and measure the steady state current consumption (ignore the initial current surge which will be about 50% higher). Compare the result with that specified. High current consumption (or no current draw at all) indicates a faulty glow plug.

8 As a final check, remove the glow plugs and inspect them visually.

Removal

9 Disconnect the battery negative cable and position it away from the terminal.

10 Slacken the nuts at the glow plug terminal. Lift off the cable connector **(see illustration)**. Note that the nuts are captive in the cable connector.

11 Slacken and withdraw the glow plug **(see illustrations)**.

12 Inspect the glow plug probe for signs of damage. A badly burned or charred probe is usually an indication of a faulty fuel injector.

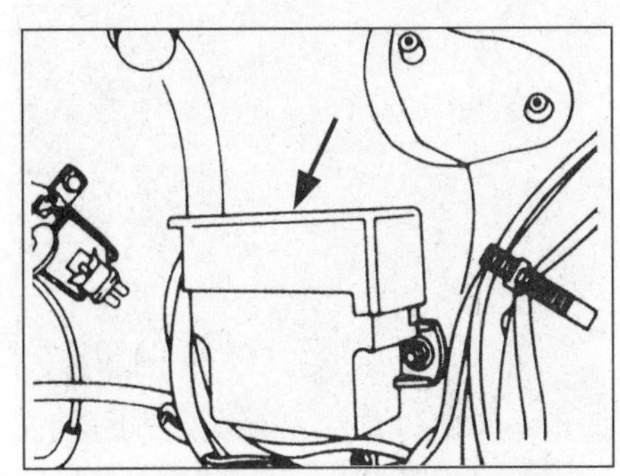
4.1 Glow plug control unit (arrowed)

Refitting

13 Refitting is a reversal of removal. Tighten each glow plug to the specified torque.

4 Glow plug control unit (124 Series) - removal and refitting

Removal

1 The glow plug control unit is located in the engine bay, on the left hand inner wing **(see illustration)**.

2 Disconnect the battery negative cable and position it away from the terminal.

3 Prise the protective cap from the top of the control unit, to expose the fuse and electrical connections.

4 Disconnect the wiring harness from the control unit at the connectors.

5 Remove the retaining nuts lift the control unit away from the wing.

Refitting

6 Refitting is a reversal of removal.

5 Injectors - testing, removal and refitting

Warning: Exercise extreme caution when working on fuel injectors. Never expose the hands or any part of the body to injector spray, as the high working pressure can cause fuel to penetrate the skin, with possibly fatal results. You are strongly advised to have any work which involves testing injectors under pressure carried out by a dealer or fuel injection specialist.

Note: *Take great care not to allow dirt into the injectors or fuel pipes. Do not drop the injectors or allow the needles at their tips to become damaged. Injectors are precision-made to fine limits and must not be handled roughly.*

Testing

1 Injectors deteriorate with prolonged use and it is reasonable to expect them to need

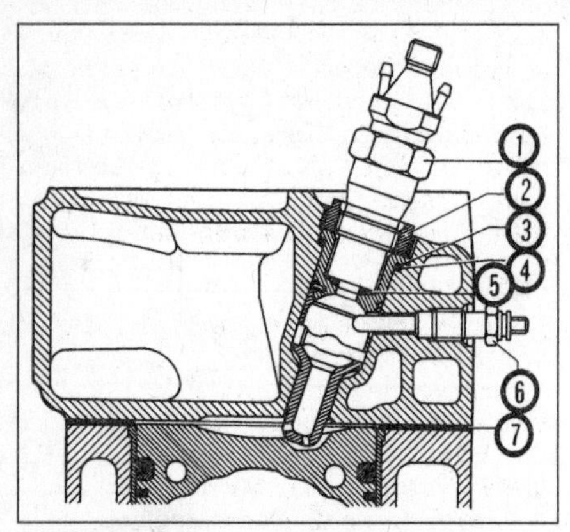

5.6 Fuel injection nozzle - 123 Series

1 Injection nozzle
2 Collar
3 Precombustion chamber
4 Sealing ring
5 Nozzle plate
6 Glow plug
7 Cylinder head gasket

reconditioning or renewal after 60 000 miles (90 000 km) or so. Accurate testing, overhaul and calibration of the injectors must be left to a specialist. A defective injector which is causing knocking or smoking can be located without dismantling as follows.

2 Run the engine at a fast idle. Slacken each injector union in turn, placing rag around the union to catch spilt fuel and being careful not to expose the skin to any spray. When the union on the defective injector is slackened, the knocking or smoking will stop.

Removal

123 Series

3 Remove the cable from the negative battery terminal.

4 Due to the rigid nature of the injection pipes, it is best to unscrew all the pipes from the injectors, even if only one injector is being serviced.

5 Pull the overflow tube from each injector.

6 Unscrew each injector from the cylinder head with a socket wrench, such as Mercedes tool no. 000 589 68 03 00. If such a tool is not available, remove the camshaft cover to provide the proper clearance and remove the nozzle with a suitable size spanner **(see illustration)**.

124 Series

7 Disconnect the battery negative cable and position it away from the terminal.

8 To improve access, remove the inlet manifold.

9 Carefully clean around the injectors and pipe union nuts **(see illustration)**. Slacken the clips (where applicable) and pull the bleed hose(s) from the injector.

10 Pad the area around the injector union with absorbent rags. Wipe clean the pipe unions then slacken the union nut securing the relevant high pressure pipe to the top of the injector.

11 Slacken the relevant union nut securing

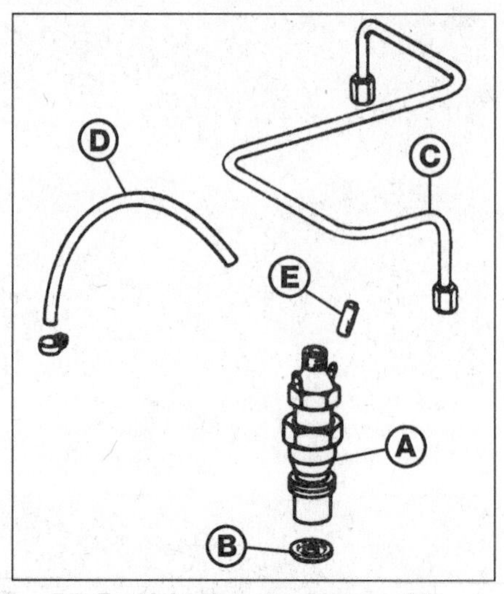

5.9 Fuel injection nozzle assembly - 124 Series

A Injector body
B Washer
C High pressure pipe
D Bleed hose
E End cap

the high pressure pipe to the top of the injection pump. As each pump union nut is slackened, retain the adapter with a suitable open-ended spanner to prevent it being unscrewed from the pump. With the union nuts undone, remove the injector pipes from the engine. Cover the injector and pipe unions to prevent the entry of dirt into the system.

12 Unscrew the injector, using a deep socket or box spanner, and remove it from the cylinder head. Unscrew the injector by the hexagonal section closest to the cylinder head. Do not unscrew it by the upper hexagonal section or the injector will fall apart.

13 Recover the washer, noting which way up it is fitted.

Refitting

123 Series

14 Refitting is the reverse of removal. Tighten each injector to the specified torque.

124 Series

15 Fit a new washer to the cylinder head, then screw the injector into position and tighten it to the specified torque.

16 Refit the injector pipes and tighten the union nuts to the specified torque setting. Position any clips attached to the pipes as noted before removal.

17 Reconnect the bleed pipe(s) securely to the injector and tighten the hose clips (where applicable).

18 Restore the battery connection and check the running of the engine.

6 Fuel injection pump (123 Series) - removal and refitting

Removal

1 Disconnect the cable from the battery negative terminal.

2 On some models it will be necessary to remove the oil filter housing assembly. Drain the engine oil then disconnect the oil cooler line and oil pressure gauge connection. Hold the cooler line nut fitting on the housing with a thin backup spanner while unscrewing the fitting to avoid twisting the line **(see illustration)**.

3 If equipped, remove the turbocharger cooler line from under the filter housing **(see illustration)**. Remove the bolts using a suitable Allen key and lift the filter housing from the engine. It may be necessary to cut off a short piece of Allen key with a hacksaw and hold it with locking pliers to remove the bolts on some models because of the restricted working area around the oil filter housing.

4 Disconnect the throttle linkage at the fuel injection pump.

5 Mark the injection pump vacuum hoses for ease of fitting and disconnect them.

6 Remove the fuel injection pump-to-injector pipe assembly. Be sure to hold the fittings in the injection pump with a back-up spanner to prevent them from turning.

7 From under the engine, disconnect the throttle return spring and remove the lower pump retaining bolts **(see illustration)**.

8 Remove the fuel union bolts and disconnect the lines from the injection pump **(see illustration)**.

9 Remove the remaining pump retaining

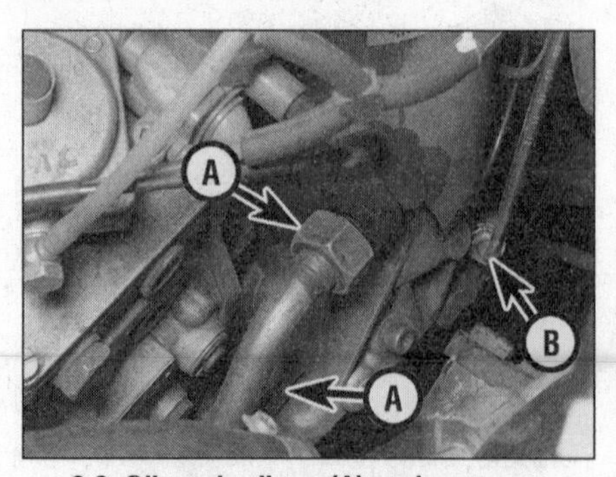

6.2 Oil cooler lines (A) and pressure gauge line (B) connections

6.3 Turbocharger oil line located at bottom of oil filter housing

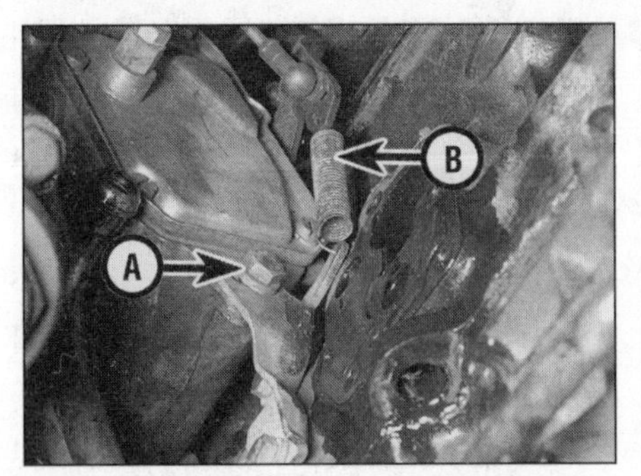

6.7 Fuel injection pump lower bolt (A) and throttle return spring (B)

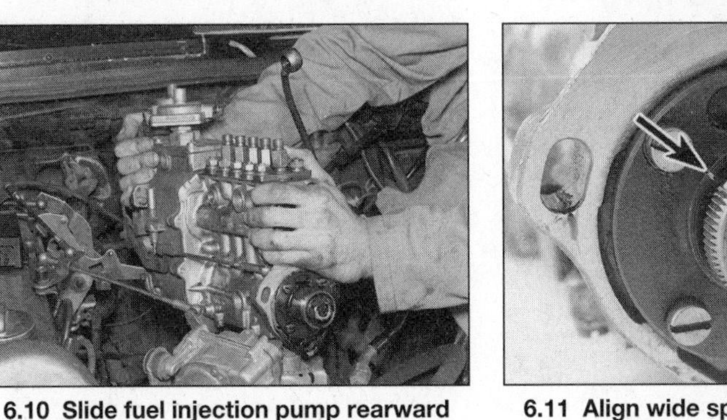

6.10 Slide fuel injection pump rearward and lift from engine

6.11 Align wide spline and mark on fuel injection pump (arrowed)

bolts. Use a curved spanner to loosen the bottom one.

10 Grasp the pump securely as it is heavy, slide it rearward and then lift it from the engine compartment **(see illustration)**.

Refitting

11 Prior to refitting the injection pump, remove the front collar and align the mark on the splines with the mark on the housing **(see illustration)**.

12 Install the collar on the pump. The engine must be at the specified start of delivery point.

13 Fit the pump into the engine as near as possible to it's original angle. A good way to check this is to place the fuel injection pipe assembly temporarily in place to make sure the connections line up.

6.8 Prior to injection pump removal, disconnect two fuel lines (A) and oil feed line (B)

14 Fit the retaining bolts (finger-tight) and then the fuel lines.

15 Bleed the air from the fuel system.

16 Check and adjust the fuel start of delivery, see Part A of this Chapter. Fully tighten the pump mounting bolts.

17 The remainder of refitting is the reverse of removal. Loosen the clamps between the fuel injection pipes to ease installation and prevent cross threading.

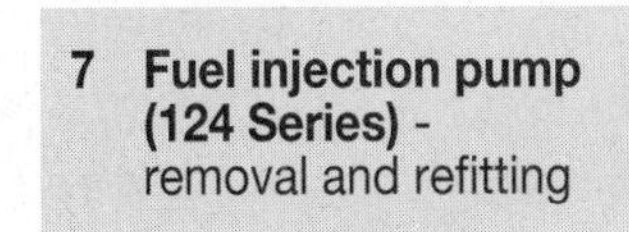

7 Fuel injection pump (124 Series) - removal and refitting

Note: *Following removal, the injection pump shaft must be locked in position using a specially shaped locking tool. Fabrication of an accurate substitute would be very difficult and its use could risk internal damage to the injection pump. For these reasons, it is recommend that a locking tool is borrowed from a Mercedes-Benz dealer or a Bosch diesel fuel injection system specialist.*

Removal

1 Disconnect the battery negative cable and position it away from the terminal.

2 Remove the fixings and lower the sound insulating panel away from the underside of the engine bay.

3 Remove the auxiliary belt tensioner.

4 Remove the cooling fan and shroud.

5 Remove the vacuum pump from the timing cover. Note that the gasket must be renewed on refitting.

6 Access can be improved, if desired, by removing the inlet manifold.

7 On 6-cylinder engines with cruise control, unbolt the cruise control actuator and position it to one side.

8 Counterhold the crankshaft, then slacken and remove the injection pump timing sprocket centre bolt **(see illustration)**. Note that this bolt has a left-hand thread. Recover the washer.

9 Using a socket and wrench on the crankshaft pulley centre bolt, turn the crankshaft in its normal direction of rotation until the engine is set to 15° after top dead centre (ATDC) on No 1 cylinder. Use the pointer on the timing cover and the graduated markings on the vibration damper to achieve the correct alignment **(see illustration)**.

10 Remove the timing chain tensioner **(see illustration)**.

11 Using a suitable open ended spanner, or a wrench and crow's foot adapter, slacken the unions and detach the high pressure injector fuel lines from the injection pump. Be prepared for an amount of fuel loss and pad the surrounding area with absorbent rags **(see illustration)**.

12 Similarly, slacken and withdraw the banjo bolts, then disconnect the fuel supply, delivery and return hoses from the injection pump. Recover the seals and discard them.

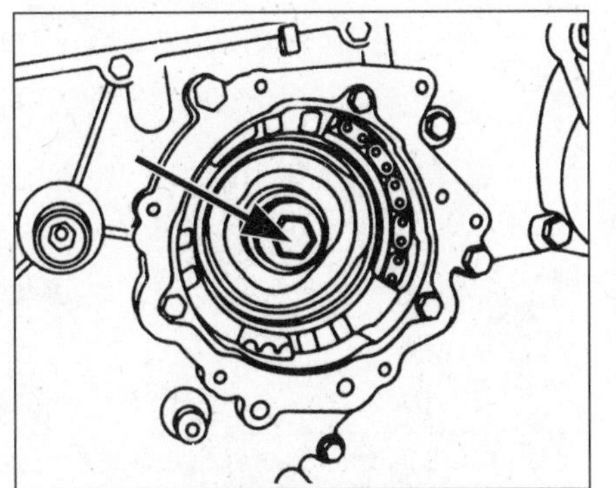

7.8 Remove injection pump timing sprocket centre bolt (arrowed)
Note bolt has LEFT-HAND THREAD

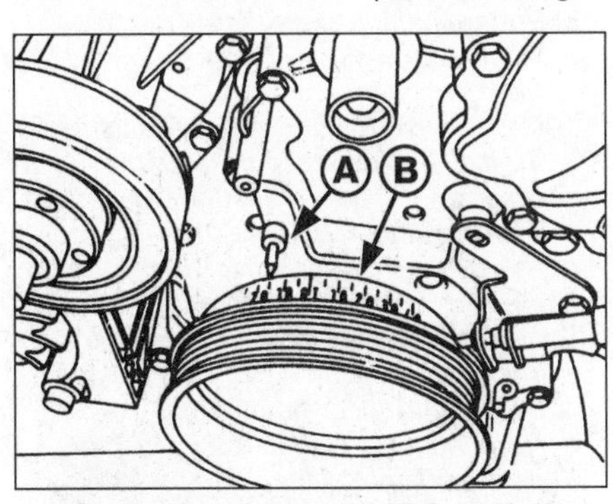

7.9 Set engine to 15° ATDC on No 1 cylinder, using pointer on timing cover and graduated markings on vibration damper
A Pointer B Graduated markings

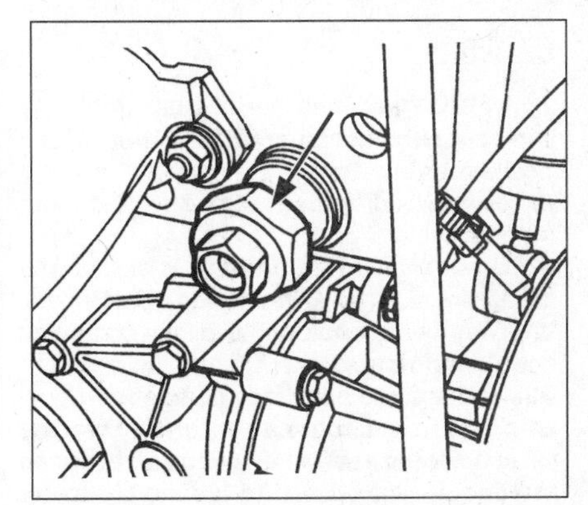

7.10 Remove timing chain tensioner (arrowed)

New seals must be used on refitting. Clamp off the flexible section of the hoses to prevent further fuel loss.

13 Unplug all vacuum hoses from the actuators on the top and rear of the injection pump, noting their fitted positions to aid refitting later.

14 Similarly, unplug all electrical wiring from the actuators and sensors on the top and rear of the injection pump at the connectors, noting the fitted position of each to aid refitting.

15 Detach the accelerator linkage from the injection pump control lever.

16 Mark the body of the injection pump in relation to the rear surface of its mounting flange, to allow approximate alignment during refitting.

17 When the injection pump is removed, it will be necessary to hold the sprocket (and timing device) in place in the timing chain casing, so that it cannot disengage from the timing chain, but in a manner which still allows it to rotate, if the engine is turned over by hand. On later models, a special retaining cage is fitted for this purpose. Owners who have earlier models, not fitted with this special device, should proceed from paragraph 18 onwards.

18 On earlier models, not fitted with a sprocket retaining cage, have ready a length of metal tubing, of roughly the same outside diameter as the threaded section of the injection pump sprocket centre bolt.

19 Unscrew and withdraw the mounting bolts that secure the front of the injection pump to its mounting flange **(see illustration)**. Remove the bolt that secures the rear of the injection pump to the support bracket, then lift the injection pump away from its mountings. At the same time, support the pump sprocket (and timing device) to keep it in place. Be prepared for an amount of engine oil loss as the injection pump is removed from its mounting flange and do not allow the sprocket to disengage from the timing chain.

20 Where applicable on earlier models not fitted with a sprocket retaining cage, slide the metal tubing through the sprocket centre hole. Pass a length of sturdy wire or a large nylon cable-tie through the tubing, then secure it and the sprocket over the top of the timing chain casing.

21 Unbolt the fuel thermostat from the injection pump body and position it to one side **(see illustration)**. It should not be necessary to disconnect the fuel lines from the thermostat.

22 Cover all exposed fuel unions to minimise fuel loss and prevent the ingress of dirt.

23 With the injection pump on a workbench, unbolt and remove the timing plug from the side of the pump body **(see illustration)**.

24 Using a suitable pair of grips, turn the injection pump shaft in its normal direction of rotation, whilst observing the movement of the governor body through the timing plug hole. Continue turning the shaft until the lug

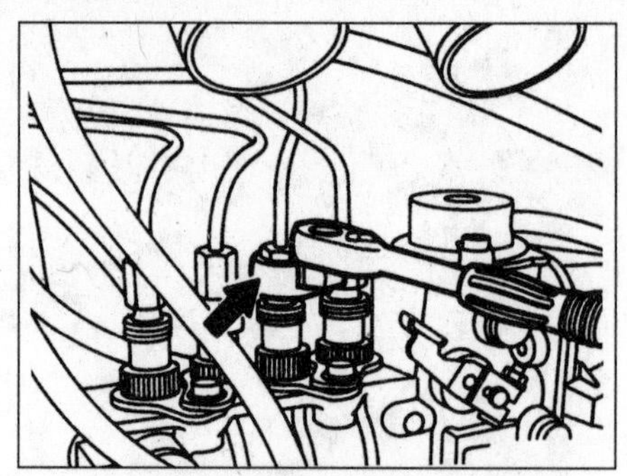

7.11 Slacken unions and detach high pressure injector fuel lines from the injection pump

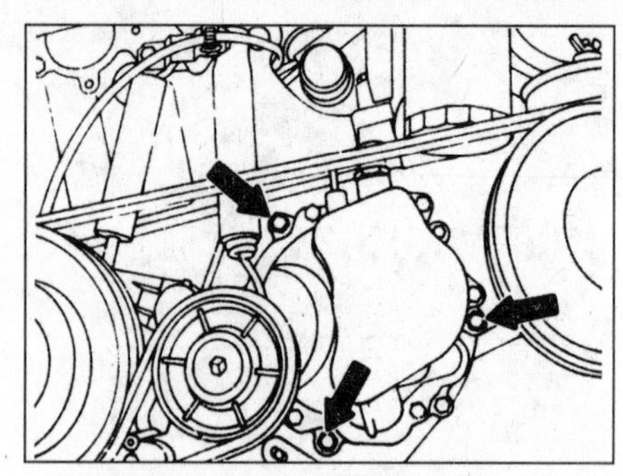

7.19 Unscrew and withdraw mounting bolts (arrowed) securing front of injection pump to mounting flange

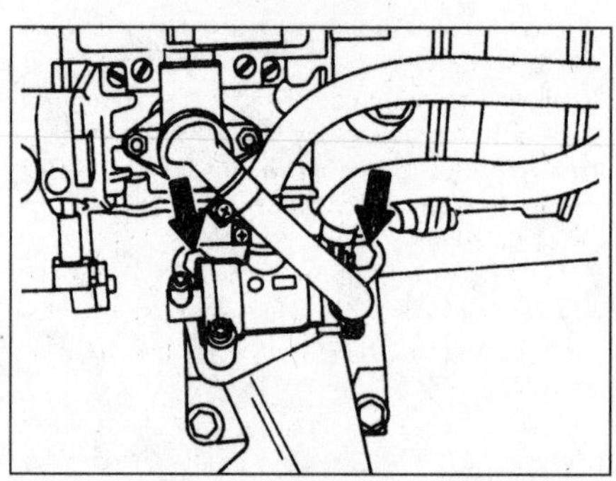

7.21 Undo bolts (arrowed) and remove fuel thermostat from injection pump body

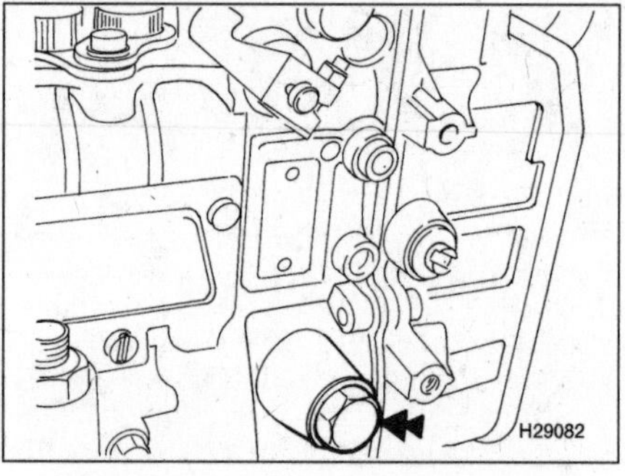

7.23 Unbolt and remove timing plug (arrowed) from side of pump body

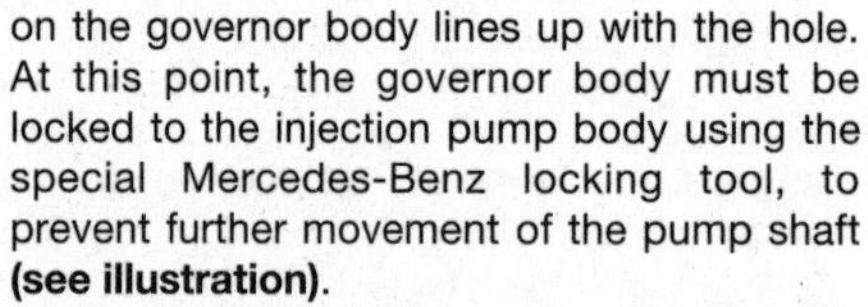

on the governor body lines up with the hole. At this point, the governor body must be locked to the injection pump body using the special Mercedes-Benz locking tool, to prevent further movement of the pump shaft **(see illustration)**.

25 Recover the O-ring from the front of the injection pump and discard it. A new O-ring must be used on refitting.

Refitting

26 Refit the pump by following the removal procedure in reverse, noting these points:

a) Fit a new O-ring to the injection pump mating face and lubricate it lightly with clean engine oil.

b) Ensure that the engine is still set to 15° ATDC on No 1 cylinder before refitting the injection pump.

c) Counterhold the crankshaft and tighten the injection pump sprocket to the specified torque, noting that the bolt has a left-hand thread..

d) Remove the locking tool from the injection pump timing hole (and refit the plug) before turning over the engine.

e) Tighten the injection pump mounting bolts to the specified torque.

f) Reconnect the high pressure injector pipes and tighten the union to the specified torque.

g) New sealing washers must be fitted to the fuel supply, delivery and return banjo bolt unions at the injection pump.

h) A new seal must be used when the vacuum pump is refitted.

i) On completion, check and if necessary adjust the injection pump start of delivery.

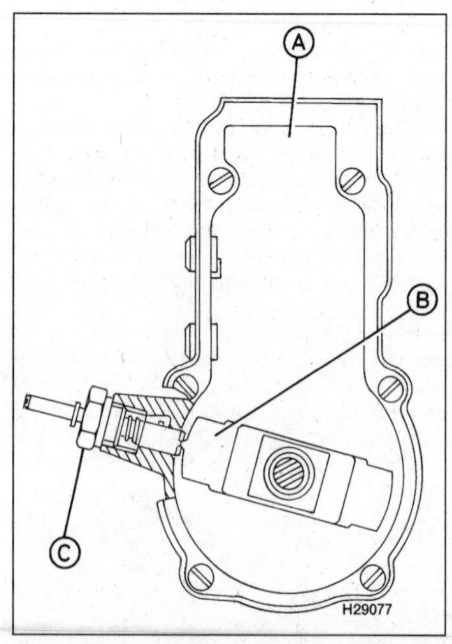

7.24 Turn injection pump shaft until lug on governor body lines up with inspection hole

A Injection pump - viewed from rear
B Governor body C Locking tool

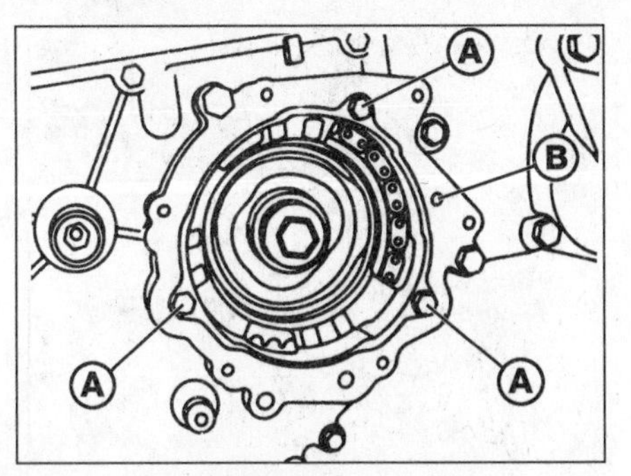

8.7 Sprocket retaining cage
A Mounting bolts B Locking pin

8 Fuel injection pump timing device and sprocket (124 Series) - removal and refitting

Note: *Following removal of the timing device and sprocket, the injection pump shaft must be locked in position using a specially shaped locking tool. Fabrication of an accurate substitute would be very difficult and its use could risk internal damage to the injection pump. For these reasons, it is recommend that a locking tool is borrowed from a Mercedes-Benz dealer or a Bosch diesel fuel injection system specialist.*

Removal

1 Disconnect the battery negative cable and position it away from the terminal.
2 Remove the fixings and lower the sound insulating panel away from the underside of the engine bay.
3 Remove the auxiliary belt tensioner.
4 Remove the cooling fan and shroud.
5 Remove the vacuum pump from the timing cover. Note that the gasket must be renewed on refitting.
6 Using a socket and wrench on the crankshaft pulley centre bolt, turn the crankshaft in its normal direction of rotation until the engine is set to 15° after top dead centre (ATDC) on No 1 cylinder. Use the pointer on the timing cover and the graduated markings on the vibration damper to achieve the correct alignment - see illustration 7.9.
7 Where applicable, unbolt the retaining cage from the front of the injection pump sprocket **(see illustration)**. On later models, the cage is secured with a locking pin. Remove the pin by threading an M6 bolt into the end of it, then attaching a slide hammer or impact puller to the bolt head and gradually drawing the pin out.
8 Remove the cylinder head cover and timing chain tensioner. Slacken and withdraw the securing bolt and washer for the camshaft timing chain sprocket.
9 Preserve the relationship between the camshaft sprocket and the timing chain by passing one or more nylon cable straps (or similar) through both and securing them tightly.

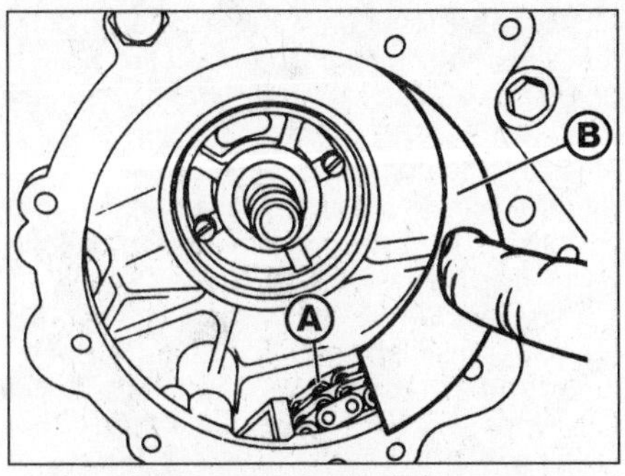

8.14 Expand home-made tool to push timing chain off sprocket teeth
A Timing chain B Home made tool

10 Slide the camshaft sprocket off the end of the camshaft, with the chain still strapped to it and allow it to rest in the timing chain housing.
11 Unbolt the assembly cage from the front of the injection pump sprocket. Slacken and remove the injection pump sprocket centre bolt, noting that it has a left-hand thread.
12 At this point, mark the relationship between the injection pump sprocket and the timing chain by using a small dab of paint. This will aid alignment during refitting.
13 The timing chain must now be pushed off the injection pump sprocket teeth, to allow the sprocket and timing device to be withdrawn. Fabricate a tool from a sheet of thin scrap metal for this purpose by cutting out a rectangle measuring 140mm by 70 mm (approx) and bending it into a partial circle, so that it is about the same shape as the injection pump sprocket.
14 Press this tool against the front of the injection pump sprocket, then expand it so that it pushes the timing chain off the sprocket teeth and retains it in that position **(see illustration)**.
15 With the chain now clear of the sprocket teeth, withdraw the timing device, together with the sprocket from the timing chain housing using a large pair of pliers or grips.
16 Remove the timing plug from the side of pump body.
17 Using a suitable pair of grips, turn the injection pump shaft in its normal direction of rotation, whilst observing the movement of the governor body through the timing plug hole. Continue turning the shaft until the lug on the governor body lines up with the hole. At this point, the governor body must be locked to the injection pump body using the special Mercedes-Benz locking tool, to prevent further movement of the pump shaft - see illustration 7.24. This step must not be omitted, as it is the only means of ensuring correct injection pump timing during reassembly.

Refitting

18 Refitting is a reversal of removal, noting the following **(see illustration)**:

a) *Ensure that the engine is still set to 15° ATDC on No 1 cylinder before refitting the sprocket and timing device to the injection pump shaft.*
b) *Use the paint marks made during removal to align the injection pump sprocket with the timing chain.*
c) *Counterhold the crankshaft and tighten the injection pump sprocket to the*

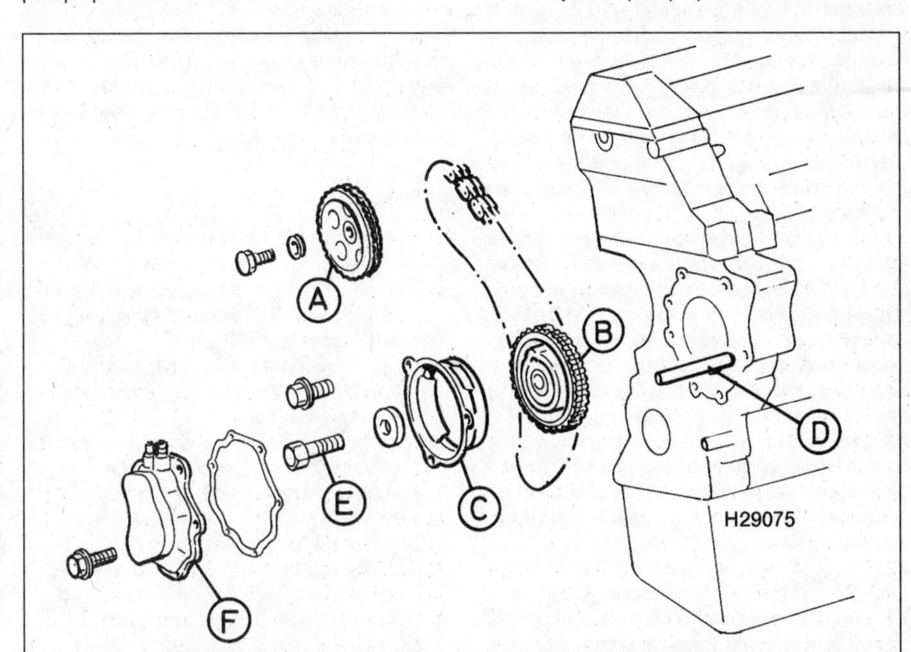

8.18 Injection pump sprocket and timing device assembly

A Camshaft sprocket
B Injection pump sprocket and timing device
C Retaining cage
D Locking pin
E Injection pump sprocket bolt
F Vacuum pump

specified torque, noting that the bolt has a left-hand thread.

d) Remove the locking tool from the injection pump timing hole and refit the plug before turning over the engine.

e) Refit the timing sprocket to the camshaft. To verify camshaft timing, rotate the engine through one complete crankshaft revolution and check that the camshaft and crankshaft TDC markings line up correctly.

f) A new seal must be used when the vacuum pump is refitted.

g) On completion, check and if necessary adjust, the injection pump start of delivery

9 Fuel injection pump start of delivery (124 Series) - checking and adjustment

1 To ensure that the fuel injection pump delivers fuel to each cylinder at the correct time during the engine cycle, the start of delivery must be checked and if necessary adjusted if the injection pump, or any of its associated components, have been disturbed.

2 The injection pump has a timing inspection hole bored into its body. During normal operation this hole is closed off with a threaded metal plug. Start of delivery to cylinder No 1 is indicated when an alignment lug, mounted on the governor body inside the injection pump, passes directly behind the inspection hole.

3 When the lug is aligned exactly with the centre of the inspection hole, the position of the crankshaft can then be read off by using the pointer on the timing chain cover and the graduated markings on the crankshaft vibration damper. The relationship between the angle of the crankshaft and the injection pump at this point, provides an indirect start of delivery measurement.

4 Ideally, the measurement should be carried out electronically by using a sensor that screws into the injection pump inspection hole. However, as this equipment is only available to Mercedes-Benz dealers and Bosch diesel fuel injection specialists, an alternative method is described here. It should be noted that this method provides an approximate reading only, to allow the engine to be started. The vehicle must be taken to a dealer or Bosch injection specialist at the earliest opportunity to have the reading accurately checked.

Checking

5 Disconnect the battery negative cable and position it away from the terminal.

6 Remove the cooling fan and shroud, to improve access to crankshaft pulley and vibration damper.

7 Unscrew the inspection hole plug from the side of the injection pump body. Be prepared for an amount of fuel loss.

8 With a small mirror, observe the edge of the governor body through the inspection hole.

9 Using a socket and wrench on the crankshaft pulley centre bolt, turn over the engine in its normal direction of rotation until the alignment lug on the edge of the governor body is aligned exactly with the centre of the inspection hole - see illustration 7.24.

10 Prevent further engine rotation, then read off the crankshaft angle by using the pointer on the timing chain cover and the graduated markings on the vibration damper - see illustration 7.9.

11 Compare the reading with that specified and adjust if required. Refit the inspection hole plug, observing the correct torque.

Adjustment

12 With reference to the previous sub-section, turn the crankshaft by hand until the engine is set to its nominal start of delivery test value. Refer to Specifications for the exact figure.

13 Slacken the three mounting bolts that secure the front of the injection pump to its mounting flange. Similarly, slacken the bolt that secures the rear of the injection pump to the support bracket.

14 Unscrew the inspection hole plug from the side of the injection pump body. Be prepared for an amount of fuel loss.

15 With a small mirror, observe the edge of the governor body through the inspection hole. Turn the delivery adjusting screw at the side of the injection pump until the alignment lug on the edge of the governor body is exactly aligned with the centre of the inspection hole **(see illustration)**. Turning this screw to the right retards the start of delivery, turning it to the left advances the start of delivery.

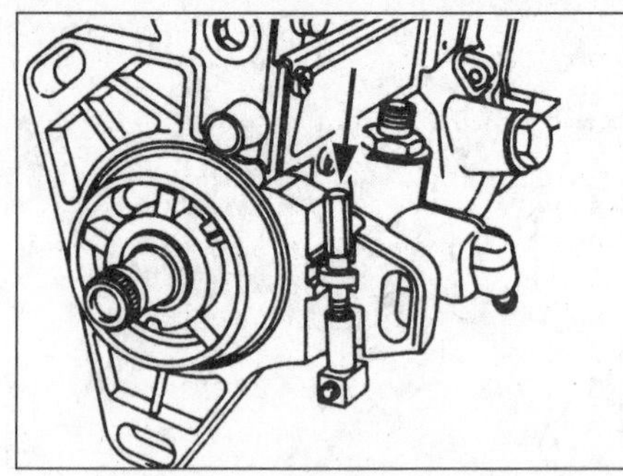

9.15 Injection pump start of delivery adjustment screw (arrowed)

16 When alignment is correct, tighten the front and rear injection pump mounting bolts, observing the correct torque settings.

17 Refit the inspection hole plug and tighten it to the correct torque.

18 The method described here provides an approximate setting only, to allow the engine to be started. The vehicle must now be taken to a Mercedes-Benz dealer or Bosch diesel injection specialist at the earliest opportunity to have the reading accurately verified.

10 Fuel lift pump (124 Series) - removal and refitting

Removal

1 Disconnect the battery negative cable and position it away from the terminal.

2 On non turbo engines, remove the air cleaner cover.

3 Clamp off the fuel supply line using a proprietary hose clamp **(see illustration)**. Slacken the clip and detach the fuel line from

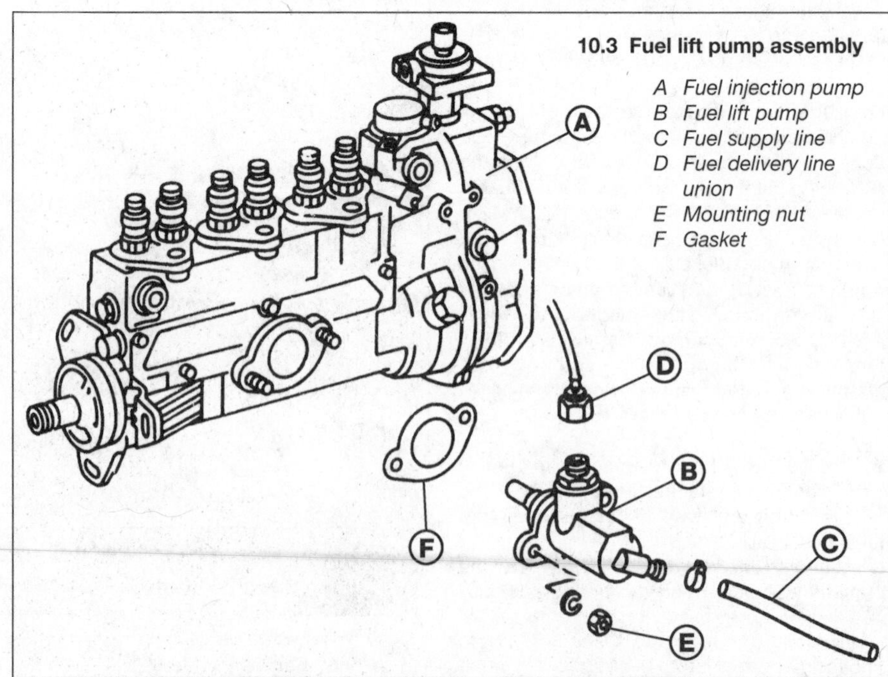

10.3 Fuel lift pump assembly

A Fuel injection pump
B Fuel lift pump
C Fuel supply line
D Fuel delivery line union
E Mounting nut
F Gasket

the port at the rear of the lift pump. Be prepared for an amount of fuel loss. Position a container underneath the pump and pad the surrounding area with absorbent rags.
4 Slacken the union at the top of the lift pump and detach the delivery line to the fuel filter. Again be prepared for an amount of fuel loss.
5 When the lift pump is removed, there will be a small amount of engine oil loss. Position a container underneath the pump for this.
6 Slacken and withdraw the retaining nuts then pull the lift pump away from the injection pump body. Recover the washers and the pump gasket.

Refitting

7 Refitting is a reversal of removal, noting the following:

a) If the pump is to be renewed, unscrew the lower half of the fuel filter delivery union from the top of the pump and transfer it to the new unit.
b) Use a new gasket when refitting the lift pump to the injection pump.
c) On completion, tighten the lift pump retaining nuts securely.

11 Fuel thermostat (124 Series) - removal and refitting

Removal

1 The fuel thermostat is bolted to a bracket, adjacent to the fuel injection pump, upstream of the fuel pre-filter.
2 Disconnect the battery negative cable and position it away from the terminal.
3 Clamp off the fuel hoses using proprietary hose clamps. Slacken the hose clips and detach the hoses from the ports on the thermostat. Be prepared for an amount of fuel spillage. Pad the surrounding area with absorbent rags.
4 Slacken and withdraw the bolts and remove the thermostat from its mounting bracket.

Refitting

5 Refitting is a reversal of removal.

12 Fuel filter assembly (123 Series) - removal and refitting

Note: *If only the fuel filter cartridge is being replaced, refer to Part A of this Chapter.*

Removal

1 Disconnect the battery negative cable.
2 Place rags under the filter to catch any spilt fuel.
3 Remove the four fuel union screws and disconnect the fuel lines from the filter housing.
4 Remove the retaining bolts and lift the housing assembly from the engine.

14.3 Glow plug timer relay (arrowed) - located on inner wing on later models

Refitting

5 Refitting is the reverse of removal, taking care to tighten the union screws securely. In order to prevent leaks, use new sealing rings.

13 Fuel system - bleeding

123 Series

1 Refer to Part A, Section 13 of this Chapter.

124 Series

2 The fuel injection pump is self priming but it may take a few seconds of cranking before the engine starts.
3 Once started, raise engine speed to about 2000 rpm several times then allow the engine to idle. This should bleed air bubbles from the filter canister. If engine idle is at all rough or hesitant, repeat the action until the fuel system clears itself of air.

14 Preheating system (123 Series) - testing, component removal and refitting

System testing

1 Due to the variety of preheating systems used and the special equipment and techniques required, testing of the preheating system by the home mechanic is confined to checking for loose or damaged connections and checking of the glow plugs.

15.3 When vacuum is applied, EGR shaft should move through slot (arrowed)

Timer relay

Removal

2 Disconnect the battery negative cable.
3 Remove the cover from the top of the relay. Disconnect the electrical power lead retaining bolt and unplug the connectors from the relay **(see illustration)**.
4 Remove the retaining bolts and lift the relay from the engine compartment.

Refitting

5 Refitting is the reverse of removal.

15 Exhaust Gas Recirculation system (123 Series) - testing, removal and refitting

1 Common engine problems associated with the Exhaust Gas Recirculation (EGR) system are poor engine performance, black or blue smoke, poor starting and combustion knocking under partial load. Usually, when a problem develops in the system, it is due to a stuck or corroded EGR valve.

EGR valve - testing

2 The EGR valve is located on the intake manifold, adjacent to the air cleaner.
3 With the engine cold, connect a vacuum pump to the EGR valve and apply vacuum while watching the diaphragm rod through the slot in the valve **(see illustration)**.
4 If the diaphragm does not move, replace the EGR valve with a new one. If in doubt about its condition, compare the free movement of your EGR valve with a new valve.
5 If the EGR valve appears to be in proper operating condition, carefully check all hoses connected to the valve for breaks, leaks or kinks. Replace or repair the valve/hoses as necessary. Further checking should be left to your dealer or a diesel specialist because of the special tools and techniques required.

EGR valve - renewal

6 The EGR valve can be renewed by disconnecting the vacuum hose and valve-to-exhaust manifold crossover pipe and then removing the retaining bolts **(see illustration)**.

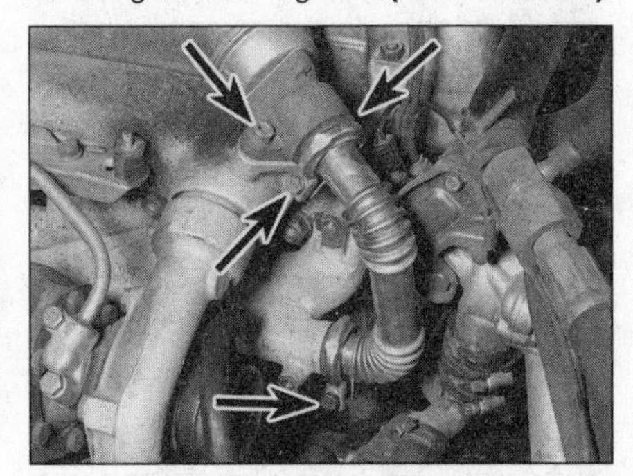

15.6 Remove bolts (arrowed) and separate flexible pipe to remove EGR valve

16 Exhaust Gas Recirculation system (124 Series) - component renewal

1 Several different versions of this system have been fitted to the 124 Series. The type of system fitted and its mode of operation will depend on the age of vehicle, engine type and the market for which the vehicle is specified.

2 In-depth coverage of each system type is beyond the scope of this manual, therefore the procedures described in this Section are limited to the renewal of the major components that are common to each system.

Vacuum solenoid valve

Removal

3 The solenoid valve is located on the right hand side of the engine bay.

4 Ensure that the ignition is switched off, then unplug the wiring from the solenoid valve at the connector.

5 Make a careful note of their order of connection, then pull the vacuum hoses from the ports on the solenoid valve.

6 Undo the screws and remove the valve from the engine bay.

Refitting

7 Refitting is a reversal of removal, but ensure that the vacuum hoses are reconnected to the correct ports on the solenoid valve.

EGR valve

Removal

8 Ensure that the engine has cooled completely before starting work.

9 Unplug the vacuum hose from the port on the top of the EGR valve.

10 Where applicable, undo the nuts and separate the recirculation pipe from the EGR valve flange. Recover the gasket.

11 Slacken and remove the nuts and lift the EGR valve from the exhaust manifold.

Refitting

12 Refitting is a reversal of removal. Ensure that the securing nuts are tightened to the correct torque.

17 ELR idle speed control system (124 Series) - component removal and refitting

Crankshaft speed sensor

Removal

1 Disconnect the battery negative cable and position it away from the terminal.

2 Unplug the crank sensor wiring from the harness at the connector, located in the engine bay, behind the battery.

3 The sensor is located at the mating surface between the cylinder block and transmission bellhousing, above the starter motor aperture. Unscrew the retaining bolt and withdraw the sensor from the bellhousing. Recover the spacer, where fitted.

Refitting

4 Refit the crank sensor by following the removal procedure in reverse. Where applicable, ensure that the spacer is fitted to the sensor probe before inserting it into the bellhousing.

Coolant temperature sensor

Removal

5 Partially drain the cooling system. Ensure that the ignition is switched off.

6 The coolant sensor is threaded into the upper surface of the cylinder head on the left hand side of the engine. Do not confuse it with the temperature gauge sender unit.

7 Unplug the wiring from the sensor at the connector.

8 Unscrew the sensor from the housing and recover the O-ring.

Refitting

9 Refitting is a reversal of removal. On completion, top-up the cooling system.

Electronic control unit

Removal

10 The ELR electronic control unit is located at the rear of the engine bay, behind the false bulkhead panel.

11 Disconnect the battery negative cable and position it away from the terminal.

12 Unplug the wiring from the control unit at the multi-plug connector.

13 Remove the securing screws and lift the unit away from the bulkhead.

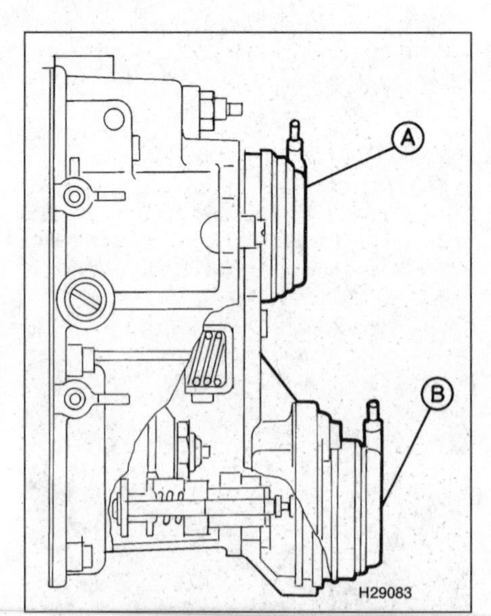

17.15 Actuator location on rear of injection pump

A ELR electromagnetic actuator
B ARA electromagnetic actuator

Refitting

14 Refitting is a reversal of removal.

Electromagnetic actuator

Removal

15 The ELR electromagnetic actuator is bolted to the rear of the injection pump body. On vehicles equipped with ELR electronic idle speed control and ARA anti-jerk control, the ELR electromagnetic actuator is the upper of the two **(see illustration)**.

16 Disconnect the battery negative cable and position it away from the terminal.

17 On non turbo engines, remove the complete air cleaner assembly.

18 Unplug the wiring from the actuator at the connector.

19 Slacken and withdraw the two securing screws at the rear of the actuator. Lift off the associated brackets.

20 Remove the actuator body, recovering the O-ring, shim(s) (where applicable), and intermediate plate (where applicable).

Refitting

21 Refitting is a reversal of removal, noting the following:

a) Transfer the shims to the new actuator, if the existing unit is to be renewed.
b) Renew the O-ring.
c) Ensure the electrical connector is facing upwards when the actuator is refitted.

18 ARA anti-jerk control system (124 Series) - component removal and refitting

Electronic control unit

Removal

1 On models with ELR electronic idle speed control, the ARA function is managed by the ELR electronic control unit.

2 On models with a pneumatic idle speed control system, the ARA electronic control unit is located at the rear of the engine bay, behind the false bulkhead panel.

3 Disconnect the battery negative cable and position it away from the terminal.

4 Unplug the wiring from the control unit at the multi-plug connector.

5 Remove the securing screws and lift the unit away from the bulkhead.

Refitting

6 Refitting is a reversal of removal.

Crankshaft speed sensor

7 Refer to the information given in Section 17.

Coolant temperature sensor

8 Refer to the information given in Section 17.

Electromagnetic actuator

Removal

9 The ARA electromagnetic actuator is bolted to the rear of the injection pump body. On vehicles equipped with ELR electronic idle speed control and ARA anti-jerk control, the ARA electromagnetic actuator is the lower of the two - see illustration 17.15.

10 Disconnect the battery negative cable and position it away from the terminal.

11 On non turbo engines, remove the complete air cleaner assembly.

12 Unplug the wiring from the actuator at the connector.

13 Slacken and withdraw the two securing screws at the rear of the actuator. Lift off the associated brackets.

14 Remove the actuator body, recovering the O-ring and pushrod.

Refitting

15 Refitting is a reversal of removal. Transfer the push rod to the new actuator, if the existing unit is to be renewed. Renew the O-ring.

19 Diesel engine control system (124 Series) - component removal and refitting

Electronic control unit

Removal

1 The electronic diesel engine control system (EDS) control unit is located at the rear of the engine bay, behind the false bulkhead panel.

2 Disconnect the battery negative cable and position it away from the terminal.

3 Unplug the wiring from the control unit at the multi-plug connector.

4 Remove the securing screws and lift the unit away from the bulkhead.

Refitting

5 Refitting is a reversal of removal.

Over-voltage protection relay

Removal

6 This relay is mounted on a base unit, adjacent to the EDS ECU. It contains fuses and diodes which protect the EDS system from current overload and high supply voltage peaks.

7 Disconnect the battery negative cable and position it away from the terminal.

8 Carefully pull the relay from its base.

Refitting

9 Refitting is a reversal of removal.

Crankshaft speed sensor

10 Refer to the information in Section 17.

Coolant temperature sensor

11 Refer to the information in Section 17.

ELR electromagnetic actuator

12 Refer to the information in Section 17.

EGR vacuum solenoid valve

13 Refer to the information in Section 16.

Air flow meter

Removal

14 Disconnect the battery negative cable and position it away from the terminal. Remove the air cleaner assembly.

15 Unbolt the air cleaner support bracket from the air flow meter body.

16 Slacken the hose clips and detach the inlet elbow and ducting from either side of the air flow meter. Recover the sealing rings.

17 Unplug the wiring from the air flow meter at the connector.

18 Remove the securing nuts and bolts, then lift the air flow meter away from its mounting bracket. Handle the air flow meter carefully as it is a delicate component.

Refitting

19 Refitting is a reversal of removal.

Inlet air temperature sensor

20 The inlet air temperature sensor is integral with the air flow meter.

20 Engine overload protection system (124 Series) - component removal and refitting

Note: *This system is only fitted to turbo-diesel engines.*

Pressure switch

Removal

1 The switch is mounted on the side of the inlet manifold plenum chamber, adjacent to the washer fluid container .

2 Unplug the wiring from the switch at the connector.

3 Unscrew the switch from the manifold and recover the sealing ring.

Refitting

4 Refitting is a reversal of removal.

Vacuum solenoid valve

Removal

5 The vacuum solenoid valve is mounted at the rear of the engine bay, on the front left hand side of the false bulkhead panel.

6 Unplug the wiring from the switch at the connector.

7 Disconnect the vacuum hoses from the ports on the solenoid valve. Make a careful note of the hose positions to aid refitting later.

8 Undo the securing screw and lift off the solenoid valve.

Refitting

9 Refitting is a reversal of removal. Take great care to ensure that the vacuum hoses are refitted correctly, or engine performance could be seriously affected.

Notes

Chapter 8
Peugeot 1360cc, 1527cc, 1769cc and 1905cc engines

Part A: Routine maintenance and servicing

Contents

Engine application

1360cc and 1527cc engines	Peugeot 106 - 1991 to 1996
1769cc engine	Peugeot 205, 305, 306, 309, 405 - 1982 to 1996
1905cc engine	Peugeot 305, 306, 309, 405 - 1982 to 1996

Manufacturer's engine codes

Peugeot 106	
1360cc non turbo	K9A (TUD3L1)
1527cc non turbo	VJY or VJZ (TUD5)
Peugeot 205	
1769cc non turbo	161A (XUD7) or A9A (XUD7L)
1769cc turbo	A8A/B (XUD7T/E)
Peugeot 305	
1769cc non turbo	161A (XUD7) or A9A (XUD7L)
1905cc non turbo	162 (XUD9) or D9A (XUD9A and XUD9L)
Peugeot 306	
1769cc non turbo	A9A (XUD7L)
1905cc non turbo	D9B (XUD9A/L) or DJZ (XUD9Y)
1905cc turbo	D8A (XUD9TE/L) or DHY (XUD9TE/Y)
Peugeot 309	
1769cc turbo	A8A/B (XUD7T/E)
1905cc non turbo	162 (XUD9) or D9A (XUD9A and XUD9L)
Peugeot 405	
1769cc turbo	A8A (XUD7TE/L)
1905cc non turbo, non catalyst/EGR	D9B (XUD9A/L)
1905cc non turbo with catalyst/EGR	DJZ (XUD9Y)
1905cc turbo, non-catalyst/EGR	D8A (XUD9TE/L)
1905cc turbo with catalyst/EGR	DHY (XUD9TE/Y)

8A

Servicing specifications

Oil filter

Type	Champion F104

Valve clearances (cold)

Inlet	0.15 ± 0.05 mm
Exhaust	0.30 ± 0.05 mm

Timing belt

Peugeot 106

Type	Toothed belt
Tension:*	
1360cc:	
Stage 1	50 units
Stage 2	39 units
Final stage	51 ± 3 units
1527cc:	
New belt:	
Stage 1	98 units
Stage 2	54 units
Final stage	54 ± 3 units
Used belt:	
Stage 1	75 units
Stage 2	44 units
Final stage	44 ± 3 units

**Using Peugeot electronic measuring equipment*

All other models

Type	Toothed belt
Tension	Automatic sprung tensioner

Auxiliary drivebelt tension

Peugeot 106	5.0 mm deflection, midway between pulleys on longest run
Other models:	
Later models with power steering and air conditioning	By automatic tensioner
All other models*	60 SEEM units or 5.0 mm deflection, midway between pulleys on longest run
Vacuum pump (early models)	3.0 mm deflection, midway between pulleys on longest run

**On engines where the auxiliary drivebelt tension is manually set, Peugeot specify the use of a special electronic tool (SEEM C.TRONIC type 105 belt tensioning measuring tool) to correctly set belt tension. If access to this equipment cannot be obtained, the approximate setting of 5.0 mm deflection stated above can be used but the tension must be rechecked with the special tool at the earliest opportunity.*

Air filter

106:	
1360cc	Champion U543
1527cc	Champion V414
205:	
Non turbo	Champion W117
Turbo	Champion W233
305	Champion W117
306:	
Turbo	Champion V433
Non turbo	Champion W233
309	Champion W117
405	Champion U543

Fuel filter

106:	
1360cc	Champion L120
1527cc	Champion L113
205 and 309:	
Pre April 1992:	
Lucas/CAV pump	Champion L132
Bosch pump	Champion L135
May 1992 on	Champion L141
305:	
Lucas/CAV pump	Champion L131 or L137
Bosch pump	Champion L136

Fuel filter (continued)

306	Champion L141
405:	
Early models - fuel filter mounted on battery tray:	
Lucas CAV/Roto-diesel filter	Champion L132
Bosch filter	Champion L135
Later models - integral fuel filter/thermostat housing	Champion L141

Glow plugs

106:	
1360cc	Champion CH147
1527cc	Champion listing not available at time of writing
205	Champion CH68
305	Champion CH68
306:	
XUD9TE engine	Champion CH163
Other engines	Champion CH68
309	Champion CH68
405:	
XUD9TE engine	Champion CH163
Other engines	Champion CH68

Idle speed

Without air conditioning	750 to 800 rpm
With air conditioning	800 to 850 rpm

Fast idle speed

Peugeot 106 - 1527cc engine	900 to 1100 rpm
All other engines	900 to 1000 rpm

Anti-stall speed

Peugeot 106

1360cc (1.0 mm shim)	1600 rpm
1527cc (1.5 mm shim)	1500 to 1700 rpm

Peugeot 205, 305 and 309

Lucas CAV/Roto-diesel injection pump (3.0 mm shim)	850 to 950 rpm
Bosch injection pump - 1984 on (1.0 mm shim)	50 rpm above idle speed

Peugeot 306

Lucas injection pump (4.0 mm shim)	1500 rpm
Bosch injection pump:	
1769cc (1.0 mm shim)	770 to 820 rpm
1905cc non turbo, DJZ (1.0 mm shim)	795 to 845 rpm
1905cc non turbo, D9B (3.0 mm shim)	1200 to 1300 rpm
1905cc turbo (3.0 mm shim)	1200 to 1300 rpm

Peugeot 405

Lucas CAV/Roto-diesel injection pump (3.0 mm shim)	850 to 950 rpm
Bosch injection pump (1.0 mm shim)	20 to 50 rpm above idle speed

Torque wrench settings

	Nm	lbf ft
Peugeot 106		
Camshaft sprocket hub bolts (1527cc)	25	18
Camshaft sprocket retaining bolt	80	59
Crankshaft pulley bolts	16	12
Injection pump sprocket hub bolts (1527cc)	25	18
Injection pump sprocket nut (1360cc)	50	37
Sump drain plug	30	22
Timing belt cover bolts:		
1360cc:		
Upper cover	5	5
Centre and lower covers	8	6
1527cc:		
All covers	10	7
Timing belt tensioner pulley nut:		
1360cc	15	11
1527cc	20	15

Torque wrench settings	Nm	lbf ft
All other models		
Crankshaft pulley bolt:		
Stage 1	40	30
Stage 2	Tighten through a further 60°	
Engine right-hand mounting:		
Engine (tensioner assembly) bracket bolts	18	13
Mounting bracket retaining nuts	45	33
Curved retaining plate bolts	20	15
Timing belt cover bolts	8	6
Timing belt tensioner:		
Adjustment bolt	18	13
Pivot nut	18	13

Lubricants, fluids and capacities

Component or system	Lubricant or fluid	Capacity
Peugeot 106		
Engine	Multigrade engine oil, viscosity range SAE 10W/40 to 15W/50, to specification API SG/CD	3.2 litres - without filter
Cooling system	Ethylene glycol based antifreeze. 50% volume with water	6.0 litres
Fuel system	Commercial Diesel fuel for road vehicles (DERV)	45.0 litres
Peugeot 205		
Engine	Multigrade engine oil, viscosity range SAE 15W/40 to specification API SG/CD	4.5 litres - Non turbo without filter 4.8 litres - Turbo without filter
Cooling system	Ethylene glycol based antifreeze. 50% volume with water	8.3 litres
Fuel system	Commercial Diesel fuel for road vehicles (DERV)	50.0 litres
Peugeot 305		
Engine	Multigrade engine oil, viscosity range SAE 15W/40 to specification API SG/CD	4.5 litres - without filter
Cooling system	Ethylene glycol based antifreeze. 50% volume with water	9.5 litres
Fuel system	Commercial Diesel fuel for road vehicles (DERV)	43.0 litres
Peugeot 306		
Engine	Multigrade engine oil, viscosity range SAE 10W/40 to 15W/50, to specification API SG/CD	4.5 litres - Non turbo without filter 4.8 litres - Turbo without filter
Cooling system	Ethylene glycol based antifreeze. 50% volume with water	9.0 litres
Fuel system	Commercial Diesel fuel for road vehicles (DERV)	60.0 litres
Peugeot 309		
Engine	Multigrade engine oil, viscosity range SAE 15W/40 to specification API SG/CD	4.5 litres - Non turbo without filter 4.8 litres - Turbo without filter
Cooling system	Ethylene glycol based antifreeze. 50% volume with water	7.8 litres - GRD turbo 8.5 litres - All other models
Fuel system	Commercial Diesel fuel for road vehicles (DERV)	55.0 litres
Peugeot 405		
Engine	Multigrade engine oil, viscosity range SAE 10W/40 to 20W/50, to specification API SG/CD	4.5 litres - Non turbo without filter 4.8 litres - Turbo without filter
Cooling system	Ethylene glycol based antifreeze. 50% volume with water	7.0 litres - 1905cc turbo 7.8 litres - All other engines
Fuel system	Commercial Diesel fuel for road vehicles (DERV)	70.0 litres

Peugeot diesel engine - maintenance schedule

The maintenance schedules which follow are basically those recommended by the manufacturer. Servicing intervals are determined by mileage or time elapsed - this is because fluids and systems deteriorate with age as well as with use. Follow the time intervals if the appropriate mileage is not covered within the specified period.

Vehicles operating under adverse conditions may need more frequent maintenance. Adverse conditions include climatic extremes, full-time towing or taxi work, driving on unmade roads, and a high proportion of short journeys. The use of inferior fuel can cause early degradation of the engine oil. Consult a Peugeot dealer for advice on these points.

Every 250 miles (400 km), weekly, or before a long journey - all models

- ☐ Check engine oil level and top up if necessary (Section 3)
- ☐ Check coolant level and top up if necessary (Section 4)
- ☐ Check exhaust emission (Section 5)
- ☐ Check operation of glow plug warning light (Section 6)

Every 6000 miles (10 000 km) or 12 months - all models

- ☐ Renew engine oil and filter (Section 7)
- ☐ Drain water from fuel filter (Section 8)
- ☐ Check engine compartment hoses for security and leaks

On 205, 305 and 309 models manufactured before 1989, this maintenance interval should be at 5 000 miles (7500 km), the time interval remaining the same.

Every 12 000 miles (20 000 km) - Peugeot 106

- ☐ Check engine idle speed and anti-stall speed (Section 9)
- ☐ Check emission control system (Section 10)
- ☐ Check condition and tension of auxiliary drivebelt(s)
- ☐ Renew fuel filter (Section 11)
- ☐ Clean fuel pick-up filter (at fuel tank)

Every 12 000 miles (20 000 km) - Peugeot 205, 305 and 309

- ☐ Check engine idle speed and anti-stall speed (Section 12)
- ☐ Check emission control system (Section 13)
- ☐ Renew fuel filter (Section 14)
- ☐ Clean oil filler cap (Section 15)

On models manufactured before 1989, this maintenance interval should be at 10 000 miles (15 000 km)

Every 12 000 miles (20 000 km) - Peugeot 306 and 405

- ☐ Check engine idle speed and anti-stall speed (Section 16)
- ☐ Check emission control system (Section 17)
- ☐ Check condition and tension of auxiliary drivebelt(s)

Every 18 000 miles (30 000 km) - Peugeot 205, 305 and 309

- ☐ Renew air filter element
- ☐ Check condition and tension of auxiliary drivebelt(s)
- ☐ Check vacuum pump (Section 18)

On models manufactured before 1989, this maintenance interval should be at 15 000 miles (22 500 km)

Every 18 000 miles (30 000 km) - Peugeot 306 and 405

- ☐ Renew air filter element
- ☐ Renew fuel filter (Section 19)

Every 24 000 miles (40 000 km) - Peugeot 106

- ☐ Renew air filter element

On models manufactured after 1994, this maintenance interval changes to 36 000 miles (60 000 km)

Every 30 000 miles (45 000 km) - Peugeot 205, 305 and 309

- ☐ Renew engine coolant

Every 36 000 miles (60 000 km) - all models

- ☐ Renew timing belt (Sections 20, 21 and 22)

Peugeot recommend renewal of the timing belt at 72 000 mile (120 000 km) intervals. It is strongly recommended that this interval is halved on vehicles which are subjected to intensive use, ie. mainly short journeys or a lot of stop-start driving. The actual belt renewal interval is therefore very much up to the individual owner but bear in mind that severe engine damage will result if the belt breaks.

Every 2 years (regardless of mileage) - Peugeot 106, 306 and 405

- ☐ Renew engine coolant

Underbonnet view of 1360 cc Diesel engine in Peugeot 106

1 Engine oil filler cap
2 Engine oil dipstick
3 Battery earth (negative) terminal
4 Master cylinder/brake fluid reservoir
5 Auxiliary fusebox
6 Fuel injection pump
7 Expansion tank filler cap
8 Braking system vacuum pump
9 Washer fluid reservoir filler cap
10 Braking system vacuum servo unit
11 Preheating control unit
12 Relay box
13 Suspension strut upper mounting
14 Air cleaner housing
15 Fuel system priming bulb

Underbonnet view of 1769 cc Diesel engine in Peugeot 205 GRD -

Air cleaner removed for clarity

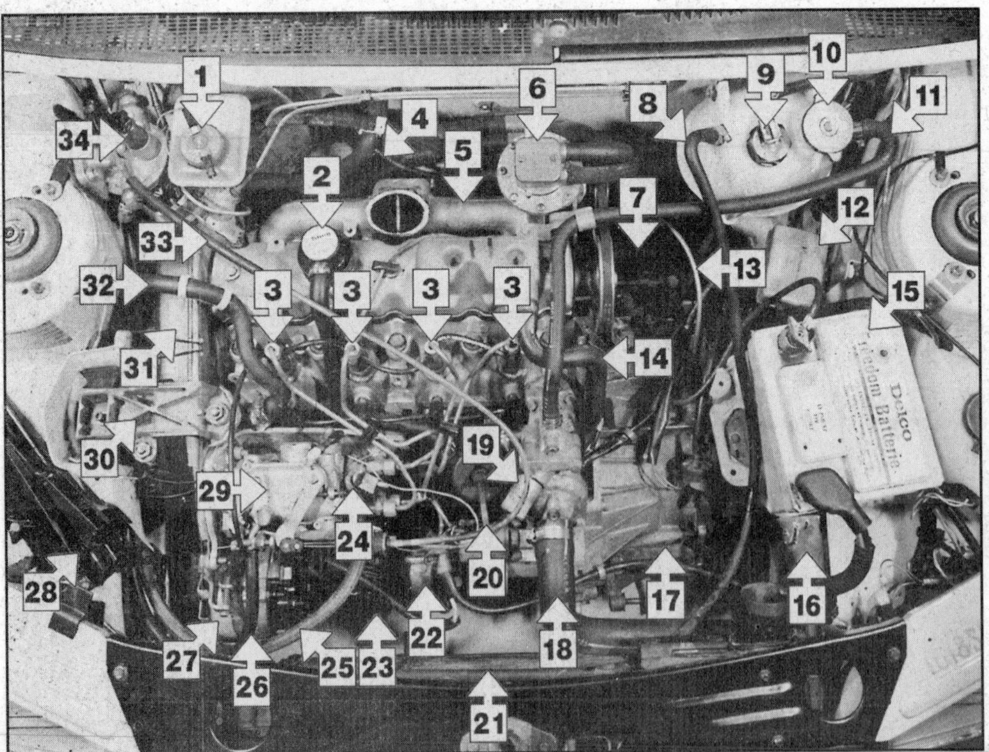

1 Brake fluid reservoir and filler cap
2 Engine oil filler cap
3 Injectors
4 Speedometer cable
5 Inlet manifold
6 Brake vacuum pump (exhauster)
7 Steering gear
8 Expansion tank vent hose
9 Coolant low level warning switch
10 Coolant filler/pressure cap
11 Expansion tank supply hose
12 Preheater plug relay
13 Reverse gear stop cable
14 Crankcase ventilation hose
15 Battery
16 Electric cooling fan relay
17 Clutch relay lever
18 Top hose
19 Fast idle thermostatic unit
20 Engine oil dipstick
21 Radiator
22 Starter motor
23 Oil filter
24 Stop solenoid
25 Fuel supply hose
26 Fuel return hose
27 Alternator
28 Vehicle lifting jack
29 Injection pump
30 Right hand engine mounting bracket
31 Timing cover
32 Coolant bypass hose
33 Accelerator cable
34 Fuel filter

Underbonnet view of 1905 cc non Turbo Diesel engine in Peugeot 306

1 *Engine oil filler cap/dipstick*
2 *Engine oil filter and oil cooler*
3 *Battery*
4 *Master cylinder brake fluid reservoir*
5 *Relay box*
6 *Alternator*
7 *Radiator filler cap*
8 *Windscreen/tailgate washer fluid reservoir filler cap*
9 *Power steering fluid reservoir filler cap*
10 *Suspension strut upper mounting*
11 *Injection pump*
12 *Fuel system priming pump*
13 *Air cleaner housing*
14 *Fuel filter*

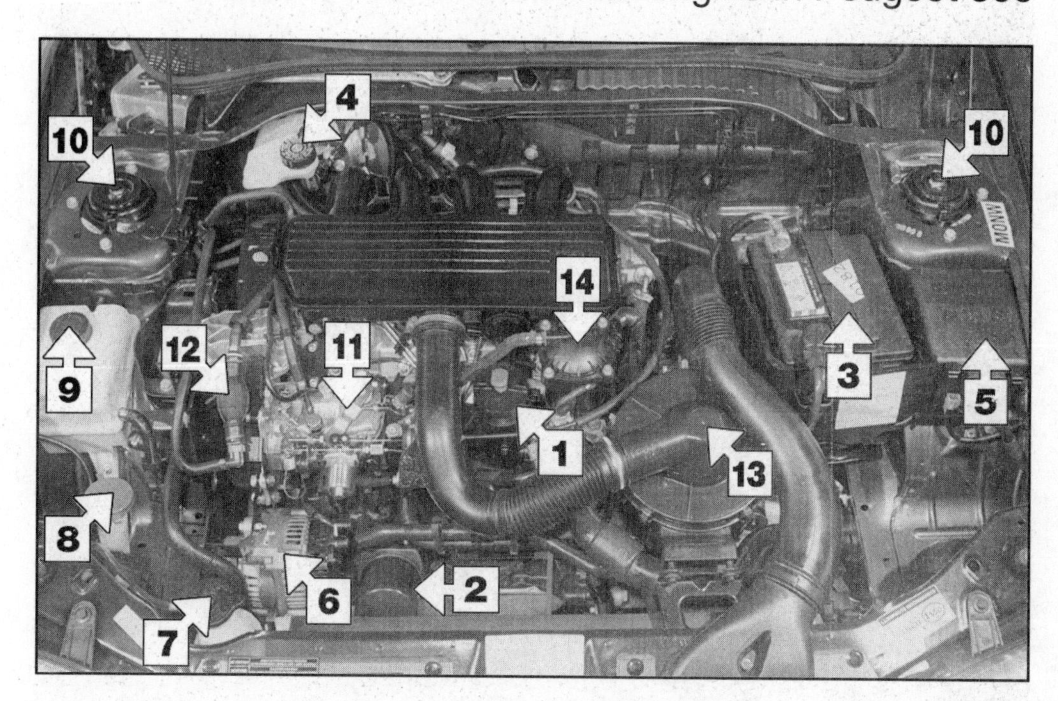

Underbonnet view of 1905 cc Turbo Diesel engine in Peugeot 306

1 *Engine oil filler cap/dipstick*
2 *Intercooler*
3 *Battery*
4 *Master cylinder brake fluid reservoir*
5 *Relay box*
6 *Alternator*
7 *Radiator filler cap*
8 *Windscreen/tailgate washer fluid reservoir filler cap*
9 *Power steering fluid reservoir filler cap*
10 *Suspension strut upper mounting*
11 *Injection pump*
12 *Fuel system priming pump*
13 *Air cleaner housing*
14 *Fuel filter*

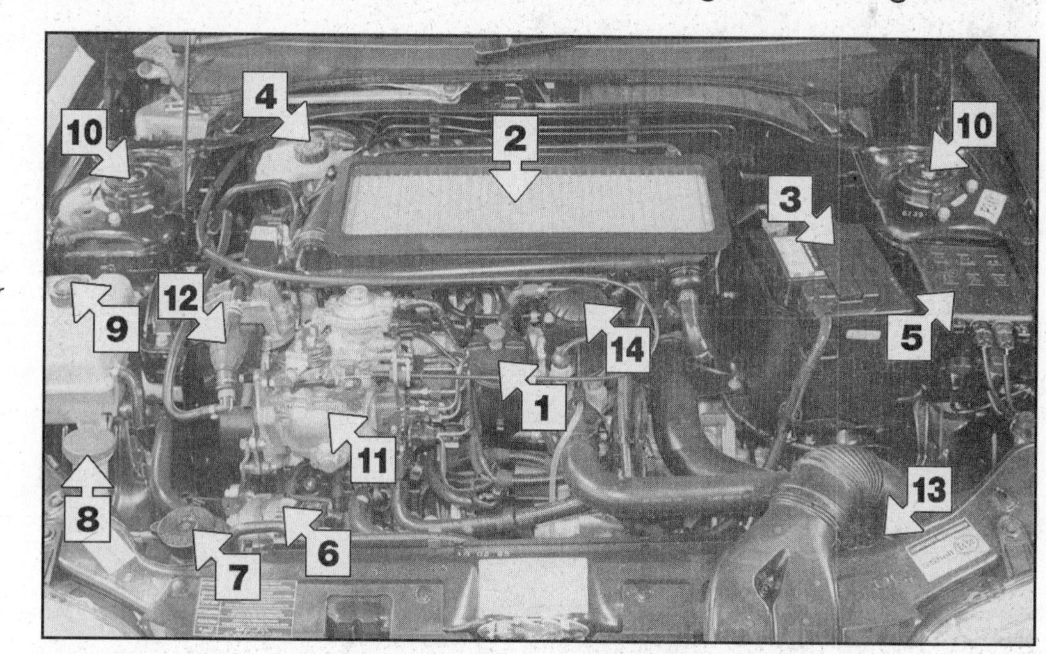

Underbonnet view of 1769 cc Turbo Diesel engine in Peugeot 309 GRD

1 Brake fluid reservoir
2 Boost pressure hose
3 Air intake trunking
4 Crankcase ventilation oil trap
5 Vacuum pump
6 Fuel filter
7 Expansion tank filler cap
8 Heater plug relay
9 Battery
10 Air cleaner inlet hose
11 Power steering fluid reservoir
12 Radiator cap
13 Air cleaner
14 Thermostat housing
15 Engine oil dipstick/oil filler cap
16 Oil filter
17 Fuel injection pump
18 Fuel injectors
19 Throttle cable
20 Headlight beam adjusters

Underbonnet view of 1905 cc non Turbo Diesel engine in Peugeot 405

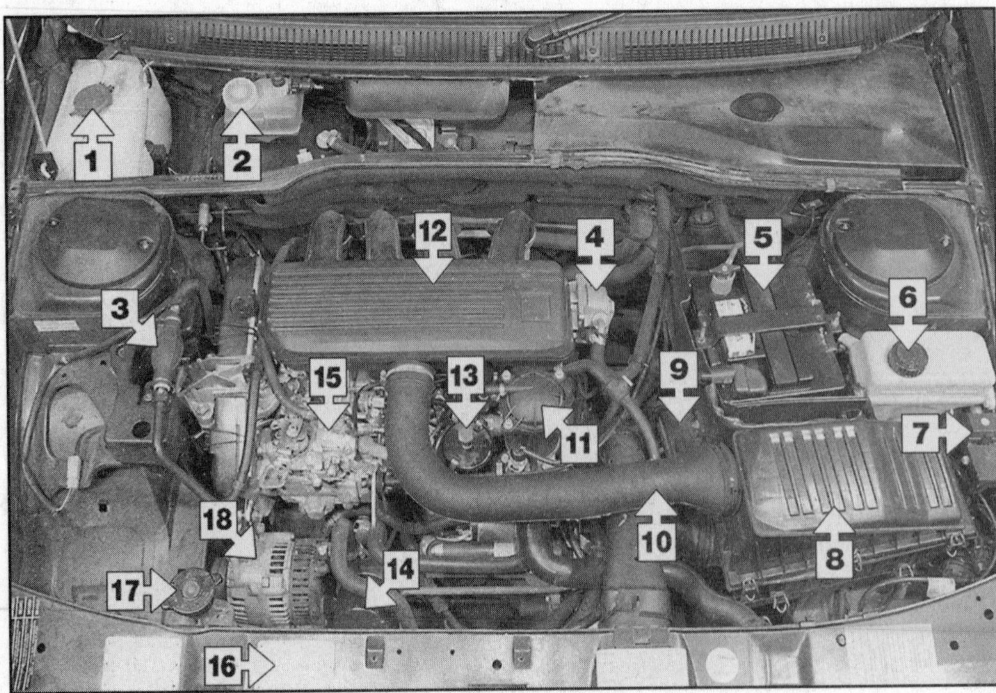

1 Washer fluid reservoir
2 Brake fluid reservoir
3 Fuel system priming bulb
4 Brake vacuum pump
5 Battery
6 Power steering fluid reservoir
7 Fusebox
8 Air cleaner housing
9 Preheating system control unit
10 Air ducting
11 Fuel filter housing
12 Air distribution housing
13 Engine oil level dipstick and oil filler cap
14 Oil filter
15 Fuel injection pump
16 Vehicle Identification Number (VIN) plate
17 Coolant expansion tank
18 Alternator

Underbonnet view of 1905 cc Turbo Diesel engine in Peugeot 405

1 Washer fluid reservoir
2 Brake fluid reservoir
3 Fuel system priming bulb
4 Intercooler
5 Battery
6 Power steering fluid reservoir
7 Fusebox
8 Air cleaner housing
9 Preheating system control unit
10 Air intake hose
11 Fuel filter housing
12 Engine oil level dipstick and oil filler cap
13 Fuel injection pump
14 Coolant expansion tank
15 Power steering pump
16 Air cleaner-to-intercooler tubing
17 Fuse/relay/junction box

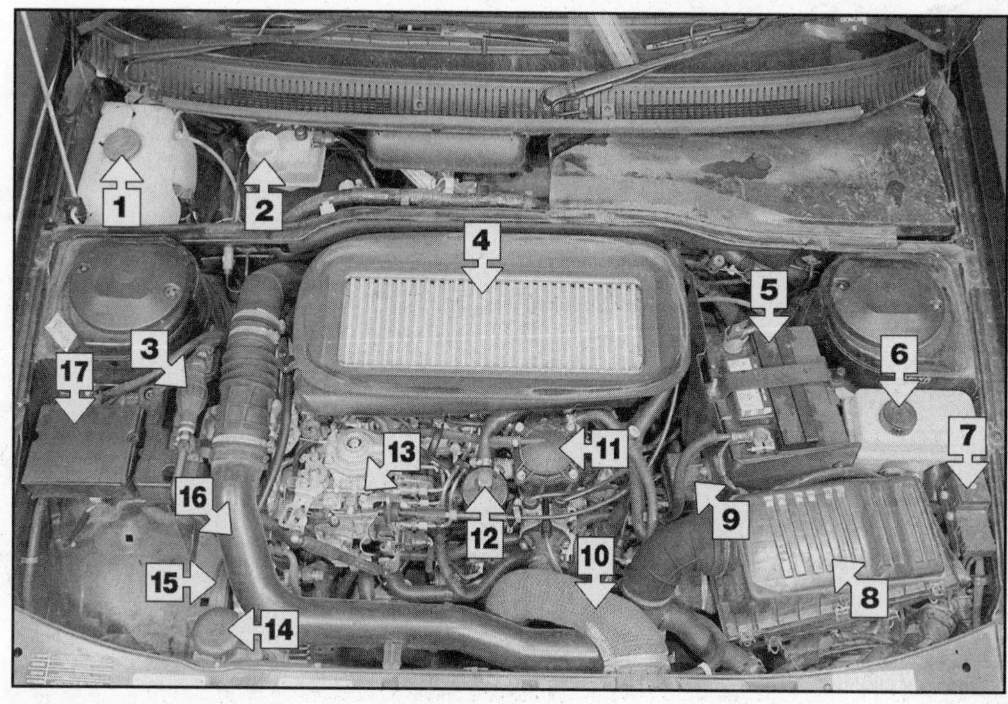

Maintenance procedures

1 Introduction

Refer to Chapter 2, Part A, Section 1.

2 Intensive maintenance

Refer to Chapter 2, Part A, Section 2.

250 mile (400 km) Service - all models

3 Engine oil level check

1 Refer to Chapter 2, Part A, Section 3 **(see illustrations)**.

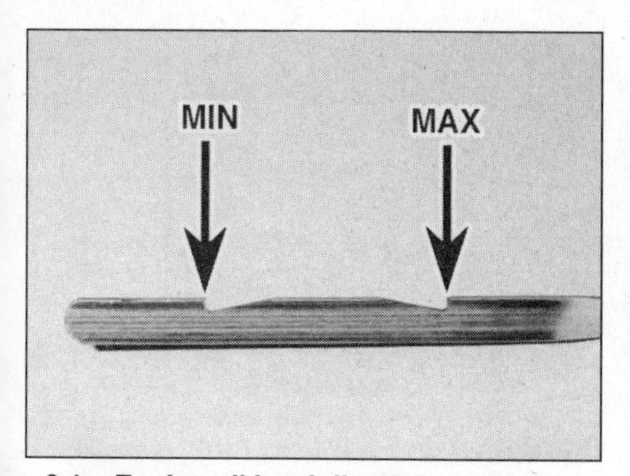

3.1a Engine oil level dipstick markings - Peugeot 106 shown, others similar

4 Coolant level check

1 Refer to Chapter 2, Part A, Section 4, whilst noting the following.

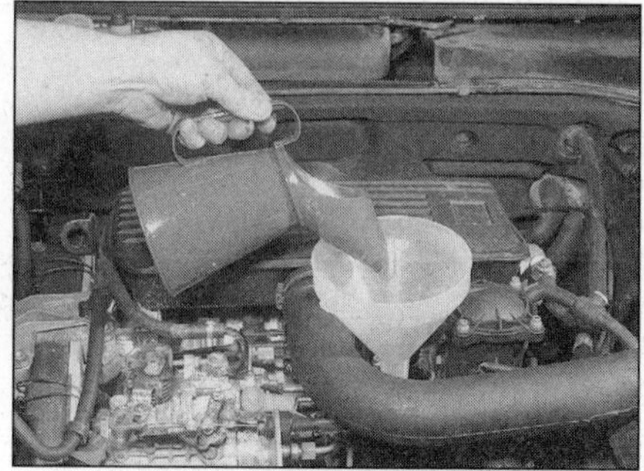

3.1b Topping-up engine oil - Peugeot 405 shown

Peugeot 106

2 The cooling system expansion tank is located on the right-hand side of the engine compartment. With the engine cold, the coolant level should be between the MIN and MAX marks on the side of the tank. With the engine hot, the level may rise slightly above the MAX mark. The maximum coolant level is indicated by a red marker visible inside the expansion tank when the pressure cap has been removed.

Peugeot 205, 305 and 309

3 On early models the cooling system expansion tank incorporates a level plate or tube, similar to that described in Section 4 in Part 1 of this Chapter.

4 On later models, the cooling system expansion tank is translucent, so the coolant level can be verified without removing the filler cap. The coolant level should be between the MAX (HOT) and MIN (COLD) marks embossed

4.5 Coolant level MAX mark - Peugeot 405

on the side of the tank. If it is below the MIN mark, remove the cap and top up with coolant to the MAX mark.

Peugeot 306 and 405

5 The cooling system expansion tank is incorporated into the right-hand side of the radiator. The coolant level should be between the MAX (HOT) and MIN (COLD) marks embossed on the side of the tank. If it is below the MIN mark, remove the cap and top up with coolant to the MAX mark **(see illustration)**.

5 Exhaust smoke check

1 Refer to Chapter 2, Part A, Section 5.

6 Warning light check

1 Refer to Chapter 2, Part A, Section 6.

6000 mile (10 000 km) Service - all models

7 Engine oil and filter renewal

1 Refer to Chapter 2, Part A, Section 7 **(see illustrations)**.

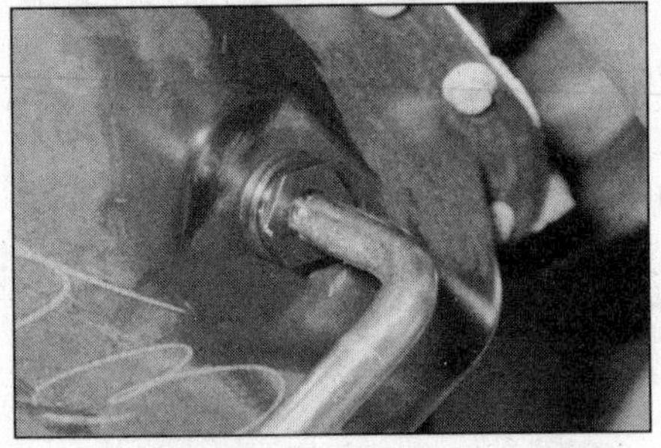
7.1a Removing engine oil drain plug

7.1b Removing engine oil filter

8 Fuel filter water draining

1 A water drain screw is provided at the base of the fuel filter housing. On 106, 306, and late 205, 305, 309 and 405 models, which are equipped with an integral thermostat/fuel filter housing, a plastic tube is attached to the drain screw to aid the draining procedure **(see illustrations)**.

8.1a Fuel filter drain screw (arrowed) - Peugeot 106

8.1b Opening fuel filter drain screw - Peugeot 306

2 Place a suitable container beneath the drain screw/tube. Where necessary, cover the clutch bellhousing to prevent water entering the housing.

3 Open the drain screw by turning it anti-clockwise. Allow fuel and water to drain, until fuel which is free from water emerges from the end of the screw/tube. Close the drain screw, tightening it securely.

4 Dispose of the drained fuel safely.

5 Start the engine. If difficulty is experienced, bleed the fuel system as follows:

Fuel system priming and bleeding

6 All models are fitted with a hand-operated priming pump. On early models, the priming pump consists of a push-button mounted on

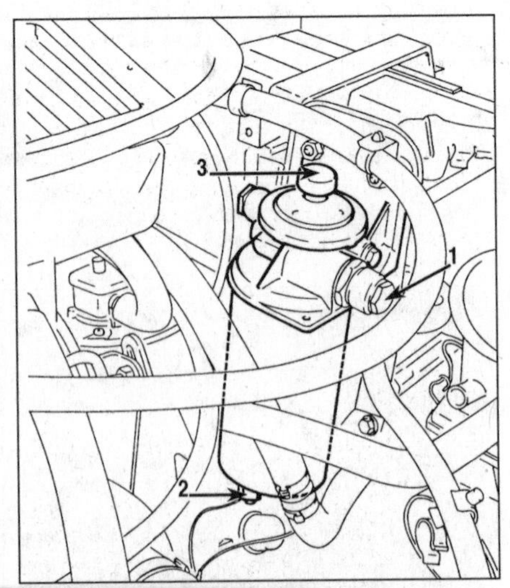

8.6a Fuel system priming pump on early models - Bosch filter assembly

1 Air bleed screw
2 Water drain screw
3 Priming push-button

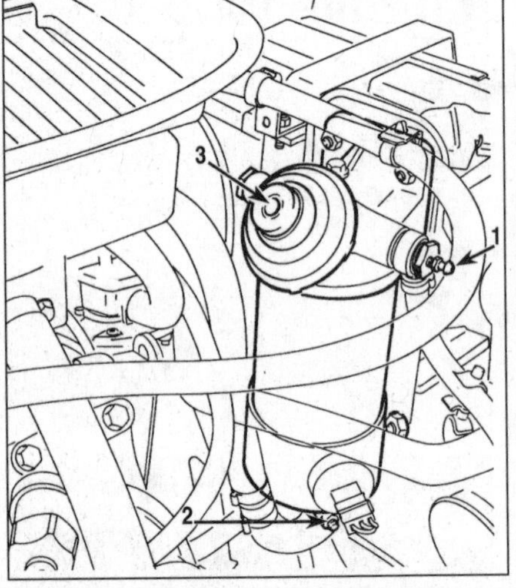

8.6b Fuel system priming pump on early models - Lucas CAV/Roto-diesel filter assembly

1 Air bleed screw
2 Water drain screw
3 Priming push-button

top of the fuel filter head. On models equipped with an integral thermostat/fuel filter housing, the priming pump consists of a rubber bulb **(see illustrations)**.

7 To prime the system, loosen the bleed screw located on the fuel filter head or in the injection pump inlet pipe union bolt, depending on model **(see illustration)**.

8 Pump the priming pump until fuel which is free from air bubbles emerges from the bleed screw. Retighten the bleed screw.

9 Switch on the ignition (to activate the stop solenoid) and continue pumping the priming plunger until firm resistance is felt, then pump a few more times.

10 If a large amount of air has entered the fuel injection pump, place a wad of rag around the fuel return union on the pump (to absorb spilt fuel), then slacken the union. Operate the priming plunger (with the ignition switched on to activate the stop solenoid), or crank the engine on the starter motor in 10 second bursts, until fuel which is free from air bubbles emerges from the fuel union. Tighten the union and mop up split fuel.

8.6c Fuel system priming pump - Later models

8.7 Fuel system bleed screw (arrowed) located on top of fuel filter housing

11 If air has entered the injector pipes, place wads of rag around the injector pipe unions at the injectors (to absorb spilt fuel), then slacken the unions. Crank the engine on the starter motor until fuel emerges from the unions, then stop cranking the engine and retighten the unions. Mop up spilt fuel

12 Start the engine with the accelerator pedal fully depressed. Additional cranking may be necessary to finally bleed the system before the engine starts.

12 000 mile (20 000 km) Service - Peugeot 106

9 Idle speed and anti-stall speed check

1 The usual type of tachometer (rev counter) which works from ignition system pulses, cannot be used on diesel engines. A diagnostic socket is provided for the use of Peugeot test equipment but this will not normally be available to the home mechanic. If it is not felt that adjusting the idle speed by ear is satisfactory, it will be necessary to purchase or hire an appropriate tachometer, or else leave the task to a Peugeot dealer or other suitably equipped specialist.

9.4a Slacken locknut (arrowed) . . .

2 Before making adjustments, warm up the engine to normal operating temperature and ensure that the accelerator cable is correctly adjusted.

Idle speed

3 Check that the engine idles at the specified speed. If necessary, adjustments can be made using the idle speed adjustment screw on the top of the fuel injection pump.

4 Loosen the locknut, then adjust the screw (as necessary) until a position is found where the engine is idling at the specified speed **(see illustrations)**. Once the screw is correctly positioned, securely tighten the locknut.

5 Check the anti-stall speed.

Anti-stall speed

6 Adjust the idle speed then switch off the engine.

7 Insert a shim or feeler blade of the specified thickness between the fuel injection pump accelerator lever and the anti-stall adjustment screw **(see illustration)**.

8 Start the engine and allow it to idle. The engine should now run at the specified anti-stall speed.

9 If adjustment is necessary, loosen the locknut and turn the anti-stall adjustment screw as required, until the anti-stall speed is correct **(see illustration)**. Hold the screw in this position, and securely tighten the locknut.

10 Remove the shim or feeler blade, then recheck the idle speed.

11 Move the accelerator lever to increase the engine speed to approximately 3000 rpm, then quickly release the lever. The deceleration period should be between 2.5 and 3.5 seconds, and the engine speed should drop to approximately 50 rpm below idle.

9.4b . . . then turn idle speed screw as necessary

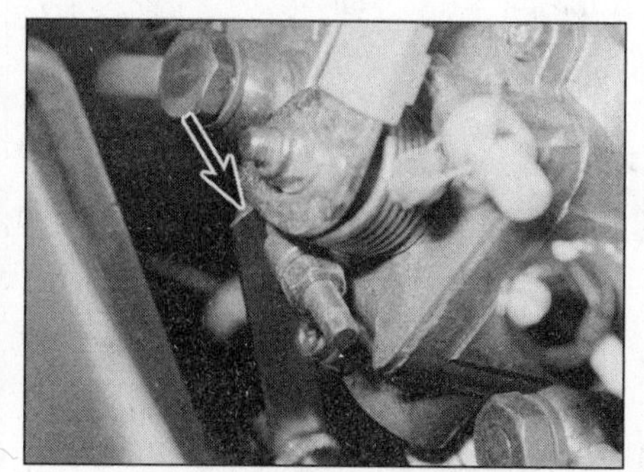

9.7 Insert feeler blade (arrowed) between anti-stall adjustment screw and accelerator lever . . .

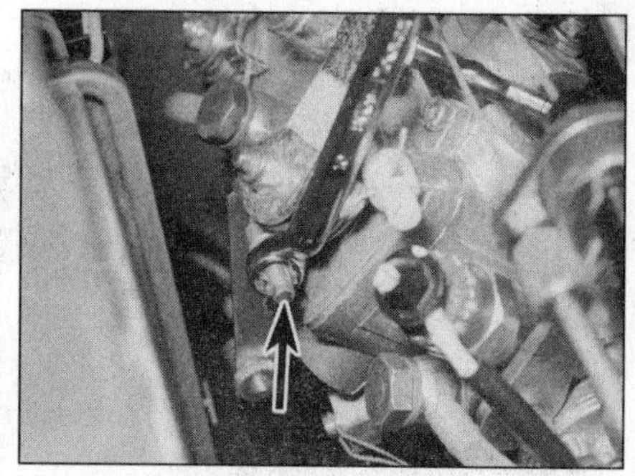

9.9 . . . then slacken locknut and turn screw (arrowed) to set anti-stall speed

12 If deceleration is too fast and the engine stalls, screw the anti-stall adjustment screw in a quarter of a turn towards the accelerator lever. If deceleration is too slow, resulting in poor engine braking, unscrew it a quarter of a turn away from the lever. Adjust as necessary, then securely retighten the locknut.
13 Recheck the idle speed and readjust if necessary.
14 With the engine idling, check the operation of the manual stop control by turning the stop lever anti-clockwise. The engine must stop instantly.
15 Where applicable, disconnect the tachometer on completion.

10 Emission control system check

1 Detailed checking and testing of the evaporative and/or exhaust emission systems (as applicable) should be entrusted to a Peugeot dealer.

11 Fuel filter renewal

1 The fuel filter is screwed onto the underside of the filter/thermostat housing on the left-hand end of the cylinder head. To improve access to the filter, remove the battery.
2 Cover the clutch bellhousing with a piece of plastic sheeting, to protect the clutch from fuel spillage.
3 Position a suitable container under the end of the fuel filter drain hose. Open the drain screw on the base of the filter and allow the fuel to drain completely.
4 When the filter has drained, close the bleed screw and unscrew the filter. In the absence of the special fuel filter socket (Purflux no. F76, a shaped socket that fits the base of the filter), the filter can be unscrewed using a suitable strap or chain wrench **(see illustration)**.
5 Remove the filter and dispose of it safely. Ensure that the sealing ring comes away with the filter and does not stick to the filter/thermostat housing mating surface.
6 Apply a smear of clean diesel to the filter sealing ring, and wipe clean the housing mating surface. Screw the filter on until its sealing ring lightly contacts the housing mating surface, then tighten it through a further three-quarters of a turn.

11.4 Using chain wrench to unscrew fuel filter

7 Prime the fuel system as described in Section 8.
8 Open the drain screw until clean fuel flows from the hose, then close the drain screw and withdraw the container from under the hose.
9 Refit the battery and start the engine. If difficulty is encountered, bleed the fuel system as described in Section 8.

12 000 mile (20 000 km) Service - Peugeot 205, 305 and 309

12 Idle speed and anti-stall speed check

Refer to Section 16.

13 Emission control system check

1 Detailed checking and testing of the evaporative and/or exhaust emission systems (as applicable) should be entrusted to a Peugeot dealer.

14 Fuel filter renewal

Pre-1993 models

1 Refer to the instructions given for early 405 models in Section 19, whilst noting the following
2 The filter is located on the right-hand side of the engine compartment, except for 305 models, where it will be found on the left.
3 Where applicable, disconnect the water detector wiring from the end cap or chamber before unscrewing the through-bolt.

Post 1993 models (except 205 and 309 turbo)

4 Refer to the instructions given for 306 and later 405 models in Section 19.

15 Engine oil filler cap cleaning

Note: *This procedure is only applicable to models with the cap fitted to the valve cover.*
1 Pull the oil filler cap from the top of the valve cover then loosen the clip and disconnect the crankcase ventilation hose.
2 Clean the wire mesh filter in paraffin and allow it to dry.
3 If the cap is blocked with sludge then it must be renewed.
4 Refit the hose to the filler cap and fit the cap to the valve cover.

12 000 mile (20 000 km) Service - Peugeot 306 and 405

16 Idle speed and anti-stall speed check

1 The usual type of tachometer (rev counter), which works from ignition system pulses, cannot be used on diesel engines. A diagnostic socket is provided for the use of Peugeot test equipment but this will not normally be available to the home mechanic. If it is not felt that adjusting the idle speed by ear is satisfactory, it will be necessary to purchase or hire an appropriate tachometer, or else leave the task to a Peugeot dealer or other suitably equipped specialist.
2 Before making adjustments, warm up the engine to normal operating temperature. Ensure that the accelerator and fast idle cables are correctly adjusted.

Lucas CAV/Roto-diesel fuel injection pump

3 Place a shim of the specified thickness between the pump control lever and the anti-stall adjustment screw **(see illustration)**.

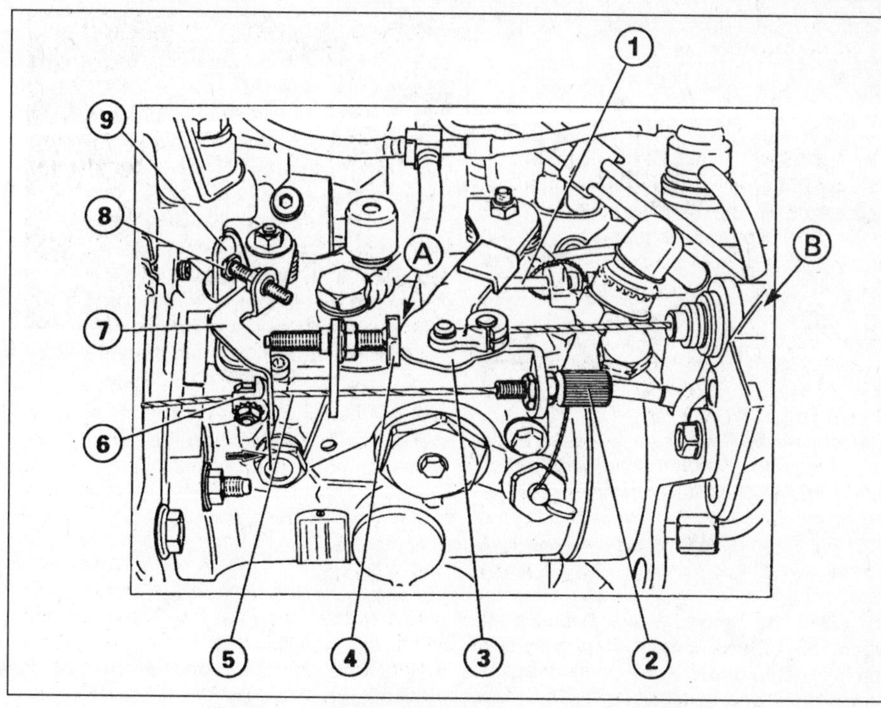

16.3 Lucas fuel injection pump adjustment points

1 Maximum speed screw
2 Fast idle cable screw
3 Pump control lever
4 Anti-stall screw
5 Fast idle cable
6 Fast idle cable end fitting
7 Fast idle lever
8 Idle speed screw
9 Manual stop lever
A Anti-stall shim location
B Accelerator cable clip

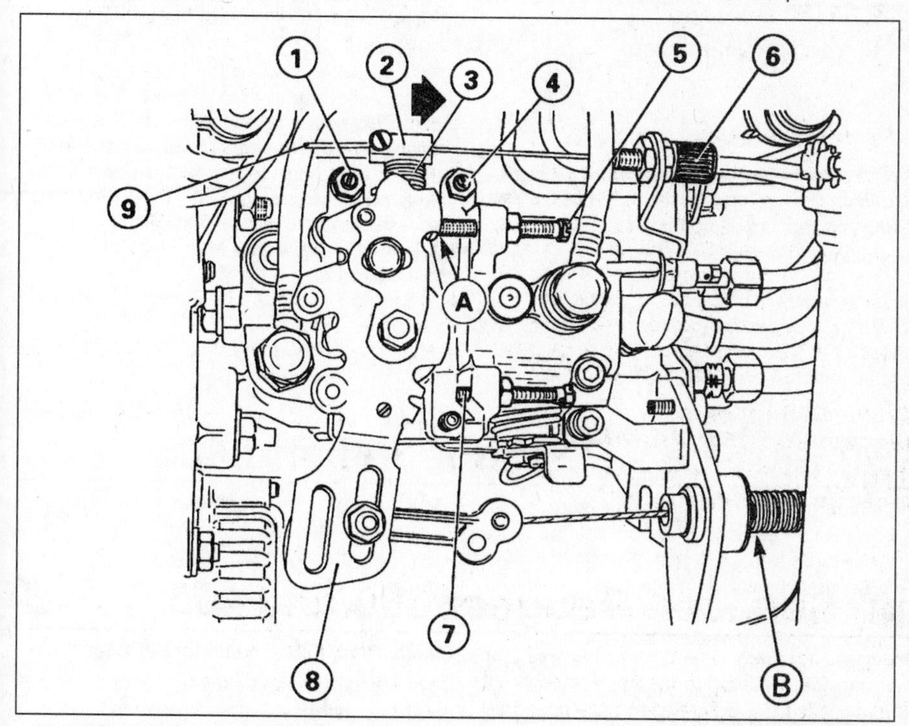

16.14 Bosch fuel injection pump adjustment points - non Turbo engine (Turbo similar)

1 Fast idle lever stop screw
2 Fast idle cable end fitting
3 Fast idle lever
4 Idle speed screw
5 Anti-stall speed screw
6 Fast idle cable screw
7 Maximum speed screw
8 Pump control lever
9 Fast idle cable
A Anti-stall adjustment shim location
B Accelerator cable clip

16.12 Hand-operated stop lever (arrowed) - Lucas pump

4 Push the manual stop lever back against its stop and hold it in position by inserting a 3 mm diameter rod/drill through the hole in the fast idle lever.

5 The engine speed should be as specified for the anti-stall speed.

6 If adjustment is necessary, loosen the locknut, turn the anti-stall adjustment screw as required, then tighten the locknut.

7 Remove the rod/drill and the shim, then check that the engine is idling at the specified speed.

8 If adjustment is necessary, loosen the locknut on the idle speed adjustment screw. Turn the screw as required and retighten the locknut.

9 Move the pump control lever to increase the engine speed to approximately 3000 rpm, then quickly release the lever. The deceleration period should be between 2.5 and 3.5 seconds and the engine speed should drop to approximately 50 rpm below idle.

10 If deceleration is too fast and the engine stalls, unscrew the anti-stall adjustment screw a quarter-turn towards the control lever. If deceleration is too slow, resulting in poor engine braking, turn the screw a quarter-turn away from the lever.

11 Retighten the locknut after making an adjustment. Recheck the idle speed and adjust if necessary as described previously.

12 With the engine idling, check the operation of the manual stop control by turning the stop lever clockwise **(see illustration)**. The engine must stop instantly.

13 Where applicable, disconnect the tachometer on completion.

Bosch fuel injection pump

Non turbo

14 Loosen the locknut and unscrew the anti-stall adjustment screw until it is clear of the pump control lever **(see illustration)**.

15 Check the idle speed with the figure specified. If adjustment is required, loosen the locknut and turn the idle speed adjustment screw as necessary, then retighten the locknut.

16 Insert a shim or feeler blade of the specified thickness between the pump control lever and the anti-stall adjustment screw.

16.21 Hand-operated stop lever (arrowed) - Bosch pump

17 Start the engine and allow it to idle. The engine speed should be as specified for the anti-stall speed.
18 If adjustment is necessary, loosen the locknut and turn the anti-stall adjustment screw as required. Retighten the locknut.
19 Remove the shim or feeler blade and allow the engine to idle.
20 Move the fast idle lever fully towards the flywheel end of the engine and check that the engine speed increases to the specified fast idle speed. If necessary, loosen the locknut and turn the fast idle adjusting screw as required, then retighten the locknut.

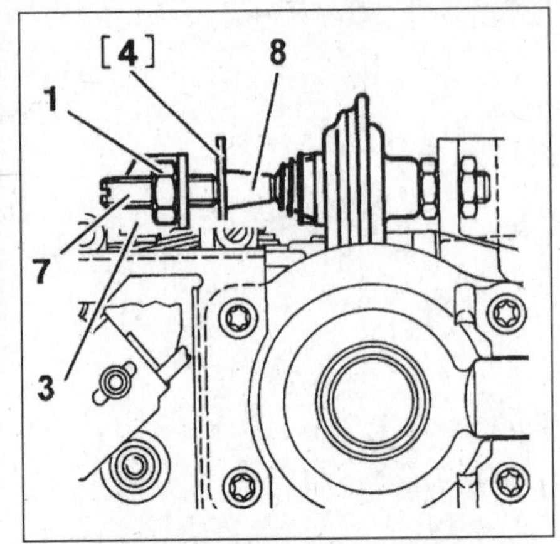

16.24 Fuel injection pump damper adjustment details - Turbo engine

1 Locknut
3 Pump control lever
4 Shim
7 Adjustment screw
8 Damper rod

21 With the engine idling, check the operation of the manual stop control by turning the stop lever **(see illustration)**. The engine must stop instantly.
22 Where applicable, disconnect the tachometer on completion.

Turbo

23 Carry out the operations described in paragraphs 14 to 19.
24 Slacken the locknut and unscrew the control lever damper adjustment screw, located on the rear of the lever. Insert the shim or feeler blade between the damper rod and adjustment screw **(see illustration)**.
25 Ensure the pump control lever is in the idle position then position the adjustment screw so that the feeler blade/shim is a light, sliding fit between the screw and damper rod. Hold the screw in this position and securely tighten its locknut.
26 Carry out the operations described in paragraphs 19 to 22.

17 Emission control system check

1 Detailed checking and testing of the evaporative and/or exhaust emission systems (as applicable) should be entrusted to a Peugeot dealer.

18 000 mile (30 000 km) Service - Peugeot 205, 305 and 309

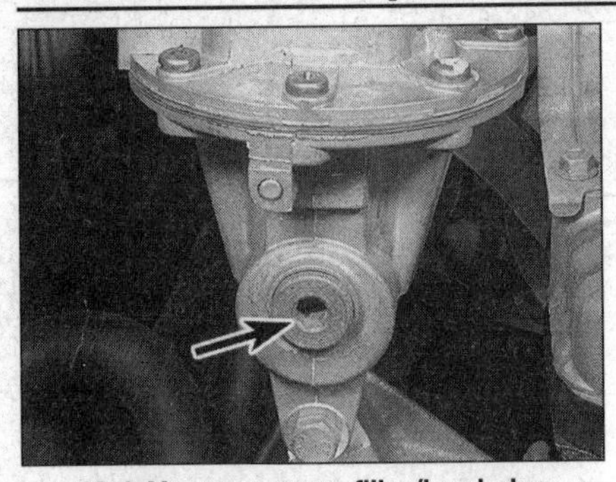

18.4 Vacuum pump filler/level plug (arrowed)

18 Vacuum pump check

1 Examine the hose between the brake servo unit and vacuum pump for cracks, deterioration or damage. Renew if necessary.
2 Check the vacuum pump body for signs of oil leakage.
3 Turn the engine so that the mark on the pump pulley shoulder is in line with the mark on the pump (i.e. uppermost).
4 Unscrew the filler/level plug and check that the oil level is up to the bottom of the plug hole **(see illustration)**. If not, top-up with 15W/40 viscosity oil.
5 Refit and tighten the plug.

18 000 mile (30 000 km) Service - Peugeot 306 and 405

19 Fuel filter renewal

Early 405 models

1 On these models, the fuel filter is mounted on a bracket bolted to the battery tray on the left-hand side of the engine compartment **(see illustrations)**.
2 Place a suitable container beneath the filter.
3 Loosen the water drain screw on the bottom of the filter and slacken the air bleed screw. Allow the fuel to drain completely.
4 Securely tighten the drain screw, then unscrew the through-bolt from the top (Lucas CAV/Roto-diesel) or bottom (Bosch) of the filter.
5 On the Lucas CAV/Roto-diesel assembly, this will release the end cap and enable the filter cartage and seals to be removed.
6 On the Bosch assembly, remove the chamber, followed by the filter element and seals.
7 Clean the filter head and the end cap or chamber, as applicable.
8 Ensure that the old seals are removed, then locate the new seals in position and fit the new cartridge or element using a reversal of the removal procedure.
9 Prime the fuel system as described in Section 8.
10 Open the drain screw until clean fuel flows from the hose, then close the drain screw and withdraw the container from under the hose.

306 and later 405 models

11 On these models, the fuel filter is integral with the thermostat housing and is located in a plastic housing at the front of the engine.
12 Where applicable, cover the clutch bellhousing with a piece of plastic sheeting, to protect the clutch from fuel spillage.
13 Position a suitable container under the end of the fuel filter drain hose. Open the drain

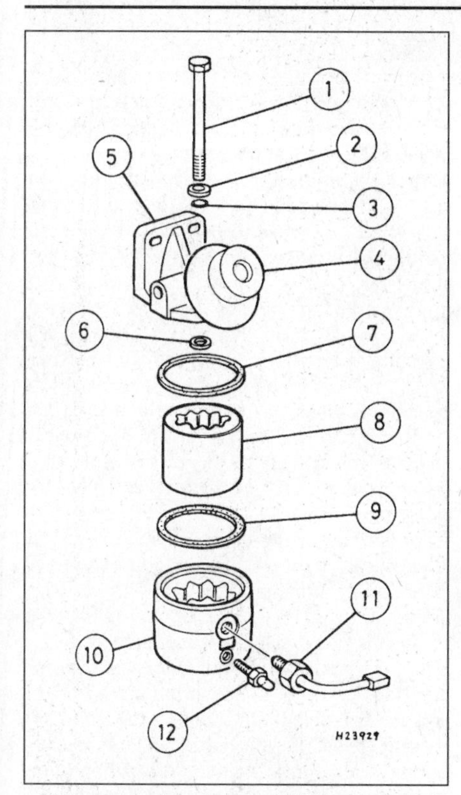

19.1a Early-type Lucas CAV/Roto-diesel fuel filter components

1 *Through-bolt*
2 *Washer*
3 *Seal*
4 *Priming pump*
5 *Filter head*
6 *Seal*
7 *Seal*
8 *Filter cartridge*
9 *Seal*
10 *End cap*
11 *Water sensor (not fitted to all models)*
12 *Water drain screw*

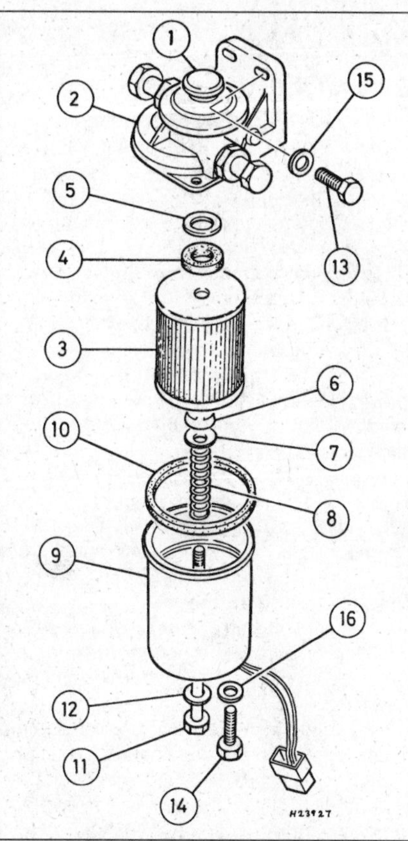

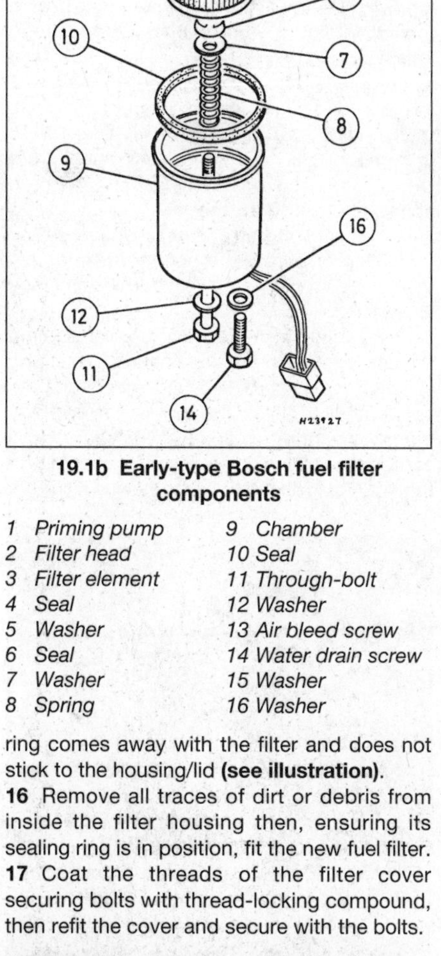

19.1b Early-type Bosch fuel filter components

1 *Priming pump*
2 *Filter head*
3 *Filter element*
4 *Seal*
5 *Washer*
6 *Seal*
7 *Washer*
8 *Spring*
9 *Chamber*
10 *Seal*
11 *Through-bolt*
12 *Washer*
13 *Air bleed screw*
14 *Water drain screw*
15 *Washer*
16 *Washer*

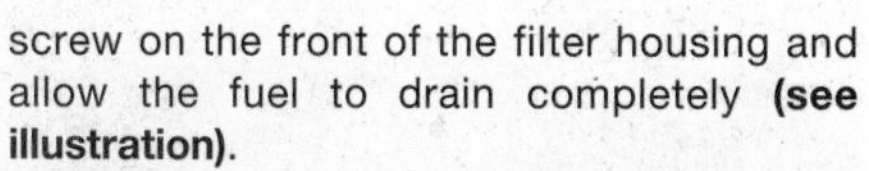

screw on the front of the filter housing and allow the fuel to drain completely **(see illustration)**.

14 Securely tighten the drain screw, then undo the four retaining screws and lift off the filter housing cover **(see illustration)**.

15 Lift the filter from the housing **(see illustration)**. Ensure that the rubber sealing ring comes away with the filter and does not stick to the housing/lid **(see illustration)**.

16 Remove all traces of dirt or debris from inside the filter housing then, ensuring its sealing ring is in position, fit the new fuel filter.

17 Coat the threads of the filter cover securing bolts with thread-locking compound, then refit the cover and secure with the bolts.

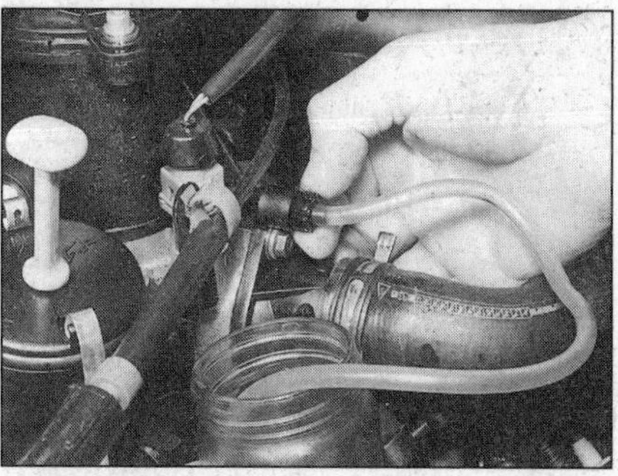

19.13 Draining fuel from filter housing

19.14 Lift off fuel filter cover . . .

19.15a . . . then lift filter from housing - later models

18 Removal of the water detector is straightforward **(see illustrations)**.

19 Prime the fuel system as described in Section 8.

20 Open the drain screw until clean fuel flows from the hose, then close the drain screw and withdraw the container from under the hose.

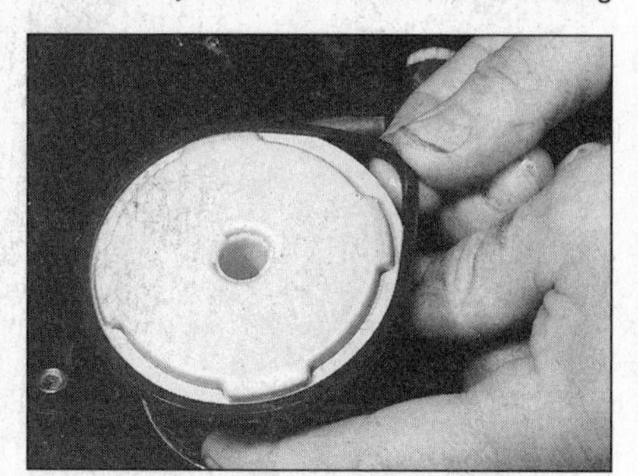

19.15b Checking sealing rubber

19.18a Disconnecting wiring plug . . .

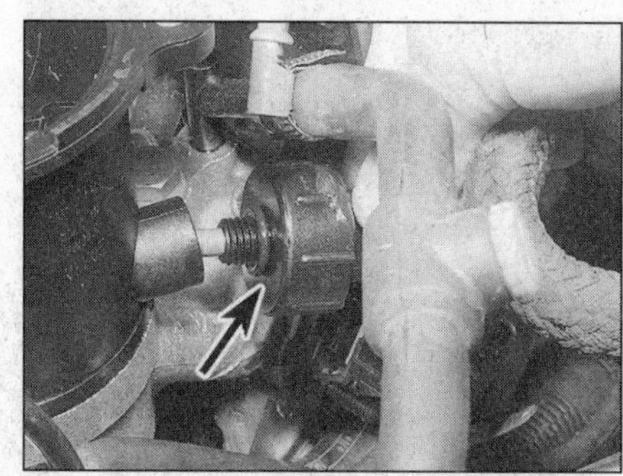

19.18b . . . and removing water detector (arrowed)

36 000 mile (60 000 km) Service - all models

20 Timing belt renewal - Peugeot 106

Note: *Whenever renewing the timing belt, it is a wise precaution to check the coolant pump for signs of coolant leakage at the same time. This may avoid the need to remove the timing belt again at a later stage, should the coolant pump fail.*

Warning: Do not attempt to rotate the engine whilst the crankshaft/camshaft/ injection pump are locked in position.

20.3 Removing timing belt upper cover

Removal

1 Disconnect the battery negative terminal.

2 Timing holes are drilled in the camshaft sprocket, injection pump sprocket and flywheel. These holes are used to align the crankshaft, camshaft and injection pump, and to prevent the possibility of the valves contacting the pistons when fitting a timing belt. With the timing holes aligned, No 4 cylinder (at timing belt end of engine) is at TDC on its compression stroke.

3 Remove the timing belt upper cover by removing its three retaining screws and lifting the cover from the cylinder head **(see illustration)**.

4 To remove the timing belt centre cover, first turn the roadwheels onto full right-hand lock, then prise out the rubber plug from underneath the right-hand front wheel arch. Unscrew the cover retaining bolt, which is accessible through the hole in the wing valance **(see illustrations)**. Unscrew the remaining bolt from the centre of the cover, then manoeuvre the cover out of position **(see illustration)**.

5 The crankshaft must now be turned until the timing holes in the camshaft sprocket and injection pump sprocket are aligned with the corresponding holes in the cylinder head and pump mounting bracket. The holes are aligned when the camshaft sprocket hole is in the 4 o'clock position, when viewed from the right-hand end of the engine. The crankshaft can be turned by using a spanner on the crankshaft sprocket bolt, noting that it should always be rotated in a clockwise direction (viewed from the right-hand end of the engine). If necessary, firmly apply the handbrake then jack up the front of the car, support it on axle stands and remove the right-hand roadwheel to improve access to the crankshaft pulley. Turning the engine will be much easier if the glow plugs are removed.

6 With the camshaft sprocket hole correctly positioned, insert a 6 mm diameter bolt or drill bit through the hole in the front left-hand flange of the cylinder block and locate it in the timing hole in the flywheel **(see illustration)**. Note that it may be necessary to rotate the crankshaft slightly to get the holes to align.

7 With the flywheel correctly positioned, insert an 8 mm diameter bolt through the timing hole in the camshaft sprocket and screw it into the cylinder head. Also insert an 8 mm diameter bolt through each of the two timing holes on the injection pump sprocket and screw them into the holes in the mounting bracket **(see illustrations)**.

8 The crankshaft, camshaft and injection pump are now locked in position.

9 With the auxiliary drivebelt removed, undo the crankshaft pulley retaining bolts and remove the pulley, noting which way round it is fitted **(see illustrations)**.

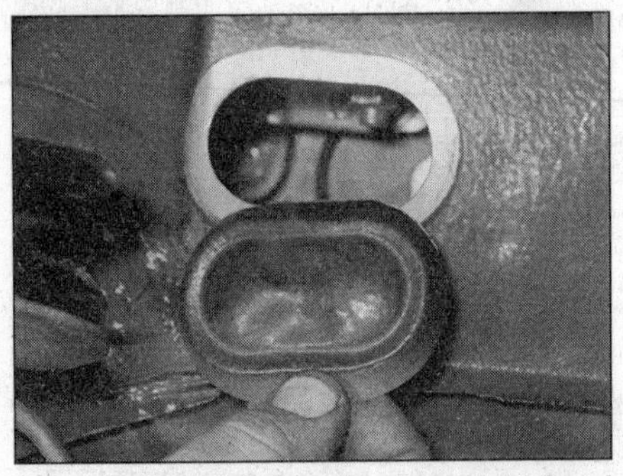

20.4a Remove rubber plug from right-hand wing valance . . .

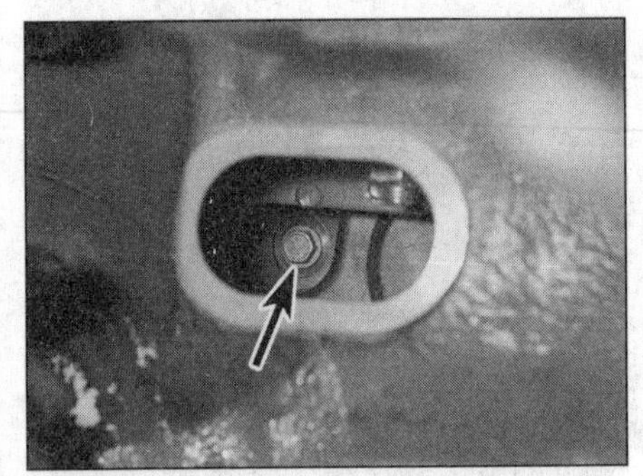

20.4b . . . to gain access to timing belt centre cover bolt (arrowed)

20.4c Unscrew remaining bolt (arrowed) and remove centre cover

20.6 Insert 6 mm bolt (arrowed) through hole in cylinder block flange and into timing hole in flywheel

20.7a Insert 8 mm bolt (arrowed) through camshaft sprocket timing hole and screw into cylinder head . . .

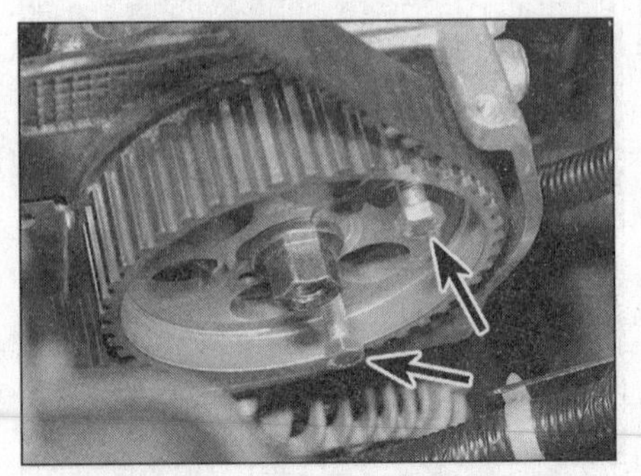

20.7b . . . then insert two 8 mm bolts (arrowed) into injection pump sprocket holes and screw into mounting bracket

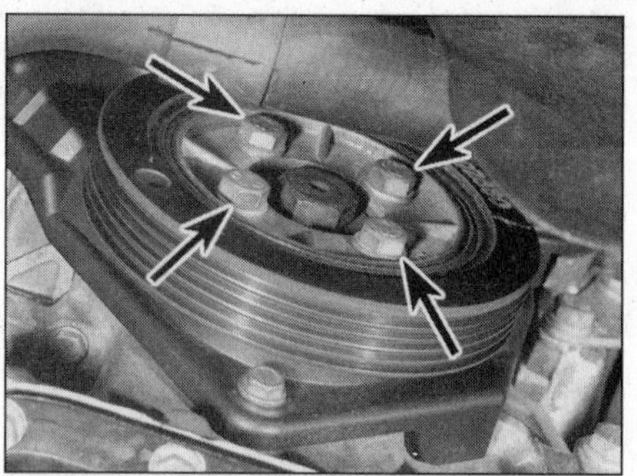
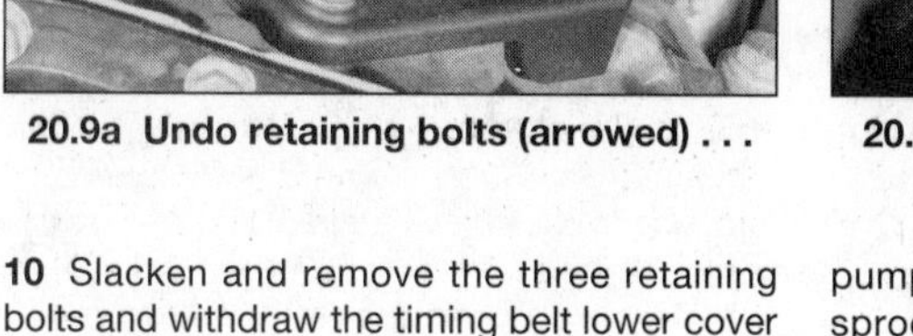

20.9a Undo retaining bolts (arrowed) . . .

20.9b . . . and remove crankshaft pulley from engine

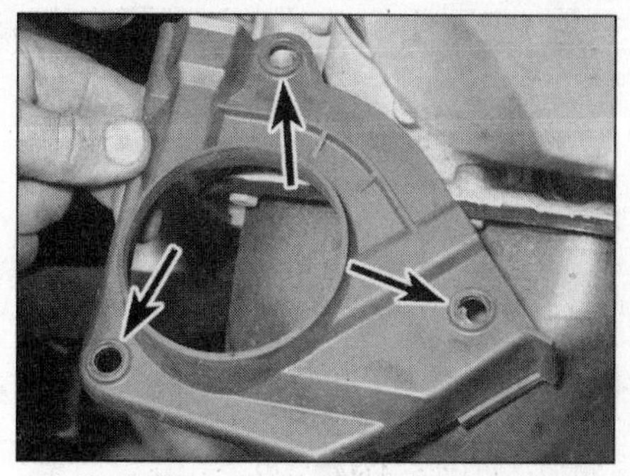

20.10 Undo retaining bolts (arrowed) and remove lower cover

10 Slacken and remove the three retaining bolts and withdraw the timing belt lower cover over the crankshaft sprocket outer flange **(see illustration)**.

11 Remove the right-hand headlight unit.

12 Loosen the timing belt tensioner pulley retaining nut. Pivot the pulley in a clockwise direction, using a square-section key fitted to the hole in the pulley hub, then retighten the retaining nut.

13 Slip the timing belt off the sprockets, idler and tensioner, then remove it from the engine.

Refitting and tensioning

14 Prior to refitting, thoroughly clean the timing belt sprockets. If signs of oil contamination are found, trace the source of the oil leak and rectify it. Wash down the engine timing belt area and all related components, to remove all traces of oil.

15 Check that both the tensioner and idler pulleys rotate freely, without any sign of roughness. Renew any damaged pulley. Ensure that all locking tools are still in position.

1360cc engines

16 Manoeuvre the new timing belt into position, ensuring that the arrows on the belt are pointing in the direction of rotation (clockwise when viewed from the right-hand end of the engine). Do not twist the belt sharply while refitting it.

17 First locate the belt over the crankshaft sprocket then, keeping the belt taut, feed it over the idler pulley, around the injection pump sprocket and over the camshaft sprocket **(see illustration)**. Locate the belt over the tensioner pulley, then finally over the coolant pump sprocket. Ensure that the belt teeth are seated centrally in the sprockets and that any slack is in the section of the belt between the camshaft and coolant pump sprockets.

18 Loosen the tensioner pulley retaining nut. Pivot the pulley anti-clockwise to remove all free play from the timing belt, then retighten the nut **(see illustration)**. Tension the timing belt as described under the relevant sub-heading.

1527cc engines

19 Slacken the six (three on each) camshaft and injection pump hub bolts **(see illustration)**. Ensure that the sprockets move freely on their hubs. Finger-tighten the six sprocket hub bolts, then slacken them all by just under a quarter of a turn.

20 Move the camshaft and injection pump sprockets to the bottom of their slot by turning them in the direction of engine rotation (clockwise).

21 Locate the timing belt, fully taut, firstly on the crankshaft sprocket then on the tension roller nearest to the injection pump. Wrap the belt around the injection pump sprocket, ensuring that the belt does not "jump" on the crankshaft sprocket. If necessary, move the injection pump sprocket anti-clockwise by no more than one tooth to enable the belt to seat properly.

22 Fit the belt on the camshaft sprocket in the same way. Feed the belt around the remaining tension roller and on around the coolant pump sprocket. Continue on to paragraph 32.

Tensioning - without electronic measuring tool

Note: *If this method is used, ensure that the belt tension is checked by a Peugeot dealer at the earliest possible opportunity.*

23 Peugeot dealers use a special tool to tension the timing belt **(see illustration)**. A similar tool may be fabricated using a suitable square-section bar attached to an arm made from a metal strip. A hole should be drilled in the strip at a distance of 80 mm from the centre of the square-section bar. Fit the tool to the hole in the tensioner pulley, keeping the tool arm as close to the horizontal as possible, and hang a 2.0 kg weight from the hole in the tool. In the absence of an object of the specified weight, a spring balance can be used to exert the required force. Ensure that

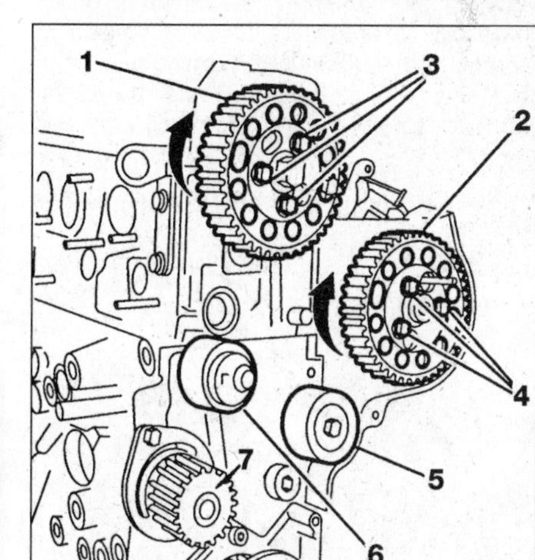

20.19 Camshaft and injection pump sprocket hub bolts - 1527 cc engine

1 *Camshaft sprocket*
2 *Injection pump sprocket*
3 *Camshaft sprocket hub bolts*
4 *Injection pump sprocket hub bolts*
5 & 6 *Tension rollers*
7 *Coolant pump sprocket*

20.17 Engage timing belt with sprockets

20.18 Remove all freeplay from belt, then securely tighten tensioner pulley retaining nut

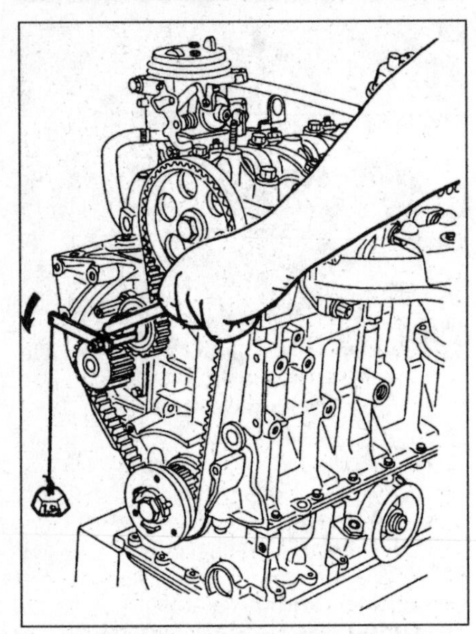

20.23a Using Peugeot special tool to tension timing belt

the spring balance is held at 90° to the tool arm **(see illustration)**. Slacken the pulley retaining nut, allowing the weight or force exerted (as applicable) to push the tensioner pulley against the belt. Now push down on the tool to exert some additional force and retighten the pulley nut. This effectively over-tensions the belt, to allow it to settle in before the final tensioning.

24 If this special tool is not available, an approximate setting may be achieved by pivoting the tensioner pulley anti-clockwise until it is just possible to turn the timing belt through 45° by finger and thumb, midway between the camshaft and injection pump sprockets. Once the belt has been tensioned, securely tighten the pulley retaining nut.

25 Remove the locking tools from the camshaft sprocket, injection pump sprocket and flywheel.

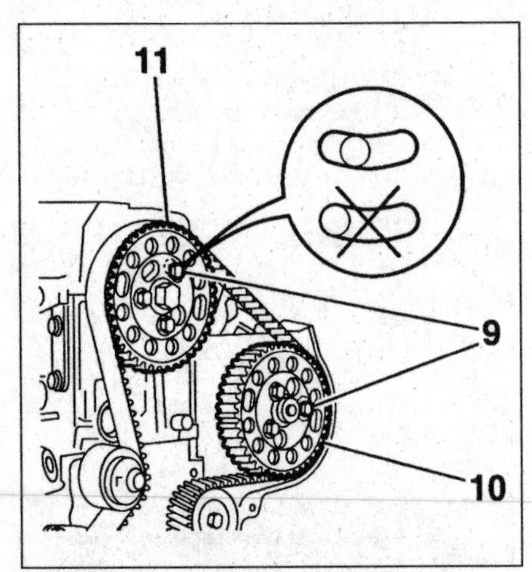

20.33 Correct location of camshaft and injection pump sprocket hub bolts - 1527 cc engine

20.23b Using home-made tool and spring balance to tension timing belt

26 Using a suitable socket and extension bar on the crankshaft sprocket bolt, rotate the crankshaft through four complete rotations in a clockwise direction (viewed from the right-hand end of the engine). Do not at any time rotate the crankshaft anti-clockwise.

27 Allow the belt to stand for approximately one minute, then slacken the tensioner pulley nut.

28 Where the special tool is being used, allow the weight of the tool to tension the belt then tighten the pulley retaining nut to the specified torque. Do not exert any extra force on the tool this time.

29 Where tensioning is being carried out without the special tool, re-tension the belt as described in paragraph 24, then tighten the tensioner pulley nut to the specified torque. Note that this method is only an initial setting. Do not drive the vehicle over large distances, or use high engine speeds, until the belt tension is known to be correct.

30 Rotate the crankshaft through a further two turns clockwise, then check that the camshaft sprocket, injection pump and flywheel timing holes are still correctly aligned.

31 If all is well, refit the timing belt covers then the headlight.

Tensioning - with electronic measuring tool

32 Fit the special belt tensioning measuring equipment to the front run of the timing belt, midway between the camshaft and injection pump sprockets. Position the tensioner pulley so that the belt is tensioned to Stage 1 of the specified setting, then retighten its retaining nut without moving the tensioner.

33 On 1527cc engines, ensure that the camshaft and injection sprocket hub bolts are located in the centre of the slot **(see illustration)**. If they are at either end, refit the timing belt. Fully tighten all six bolts to their correct torque.

34 Remove the locking tools from the camshaft sprocket, injection pump sprocket and flywheel, then remove the measuring tool from the belt.

35 Using a socket and extension bar on the crankshaft sprocket bolt, rotate the crankshaft through four (two on 1527cc engines) complete rotations in a clockwise direction (viewed from the right-hand end of the engine). Do not at any time rotate the crankshaft anti-clockwise.

36 Refit the locking tools and allow the belt to stand for approximately one minute, then slacken the tensioner pulley retaining nut (and six sprocket hub bolts) and refit the measuring tool to the belt. Position the tensioner pulley so that the belt is tensioned to the Stage 2 setting, then tighten the pulley retaining nut to the specified torque setting. On 1527cc engines, tighten the six camshaft and injection pump hub sprocket bolts.

37 Remove the measuring tool from the belt. Then on 1360cc engines, rotate the crankshaft through another two complete rotations in a clockwise direction, so that the camshaft and injection pump sprocket and flywheel timing holes are realigned. Do not at any time rotate the crankshaft anti-clockwise. Refit the measuring tool to the belt and check that the belt tension is as specified at the Final Stage.

38 If the belt tension is incorrect, repeat the procedures in paragraphs 36 and 37.

39 With the belt tension correctly set, remove all locking tools, refit the timing belt covers and refit the headlight.

21 Timing belt renewal - Peugeot 205, 305 and 309

1 Refer to Section 22. As part of preparation for belt removal, note the following:

a) *On all models, remove the engine splash guard from under the right-hand front wheel arch.*

b) *On all models, for extra working space, drain the cooling system and disconnect the bottom hose from the coolant pump inlet.*

c) *On 205 and 309 models only, also remove the intermediate metal coolant tube after removing the cross head screws.*

22 Timing belt renewal - Peugeot 306 and 405

Note: *Whenever renewing the timing belt, it is a wise precaution to check the coolant pump for signs of coolant leakage at the same time. This may avoid the need to remove the timing belt again at a later stage, should the coolant pump fail.*

Note: *Do not attempt to rotate the engine whilst the crankshaft/camshaft/injection pump are locked in position. Three 8.0 mm diameter bolts and one 8.0 mm diameter rod or drill will be required for this operation.*

Note: *It is advisable to use a new crankshaft pulley retaining bolt on refitting.*

Removal

1 Timing holes are drilled in the camshaft sprocket, injection pump sprocket and flywheel.

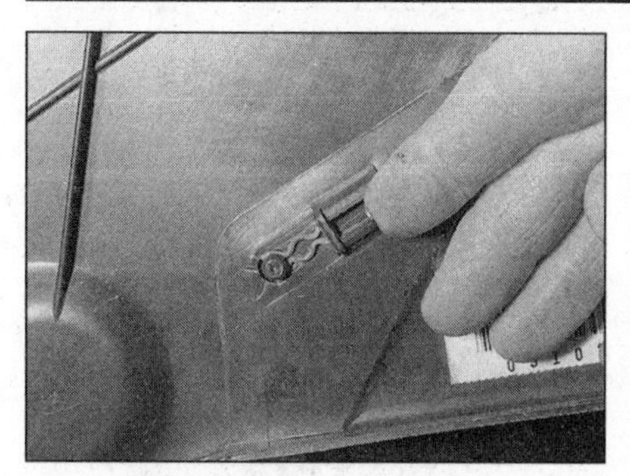

22.3a Timing cover front clip (early engines) . . .

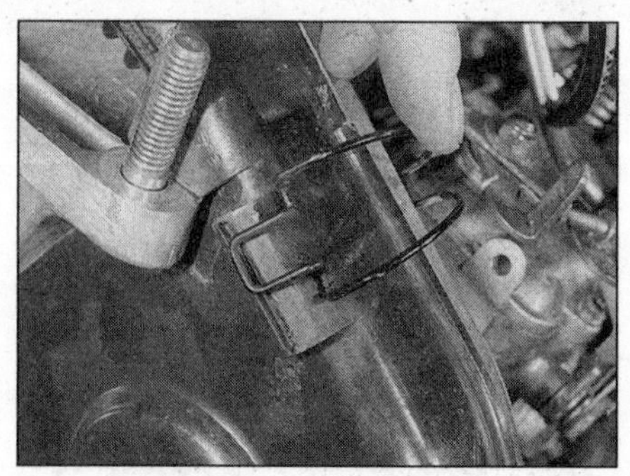

22.3b . . . and spring clips

22.3c Removing upper rear timing belt cover - early engines

These holes are used to align the crankshaft, camshaft and injection pump, and to prevent the possibility of the valves contacting the pistons when fitting a timing belt.

2 With the timing holes aligned with their corresponding holes in the cylinder head and cylinder block (as appropriate), suitable diameter bolts/pins can be inserted to lock the camshaft, injection pump and crankshaft in position, preventing them from rotating unnecessarily. With the timing holes aligned, No 4 cylinder (at timing belt end of engine) will be at TDC on its compression stroke.

3 Remove the timing belt upper covers. On early models, this will necessitate removal of the right-hand engine mounting-to-body bracket and, where applicable, the air trunking from the top of the cover. On later models, removal of the air trunking from the top of the cover is necessary **(see illustrations)**.

4 Turn the crankshaft in a clockwise direction (viewed from the right-hand side of the vehicle) to align the timing holes. The crankshaft can be turned by using a socket and extension bar on the pulley bolt. To gain access to the pulley bolt from underneath the front of the car, prise out the retaining clips and remove the screws (as applicable), then withdraw the plastic cover from the wing valance. Access is easier with the car jacked up, supported on axle stands and with the roadwheel removed. Where necessary, unclip the coolant hoses from the bracket to improve access further.

5 Insert an 8 mm diameter rod or drill through the hole in the left-hand flange of the cylinder block by the starter motor. If necessary, carefully turn the crankshaft either way until the rod enters the timing hole in the flywheel **(see illustrations)**.

6 Insert three 8 mm bolts through the holes in the camshaft and fuel injection pump sprockets, screwing them into the engine, finger-tight **(see illustrations)**.

7 The crankshaft, camshaft and injection pump are now locked in position.

8 Remove the crankshaft pulley by first detaching the auxiliary drivebelt.

9 To prevent the crankshaft turning whilst the pulley retaining bolt is being slackened, select top gear and have an assistant apply the brakes firmly. If it proves impossible to hold on the brakes, remove the starter motor and use the locking tool shown to retain the flywheel **(see illustration)**. If the engine has been removed from the vehicle, lock the flywheel ring gear. Do not attempt to lock the pulley by inserting a bolt/drill through the timing hole. If the locking pin is in position, temporarily remove it prior to slackening the pulley bolt, then refit it once the bolt has been slackened.

22.3d Lower timing belt cover securing bolts (arrowed)

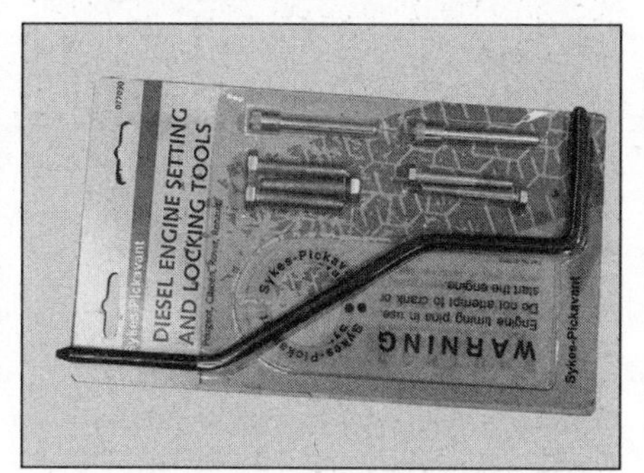

22.5a Suitable tools available for locking engine in position

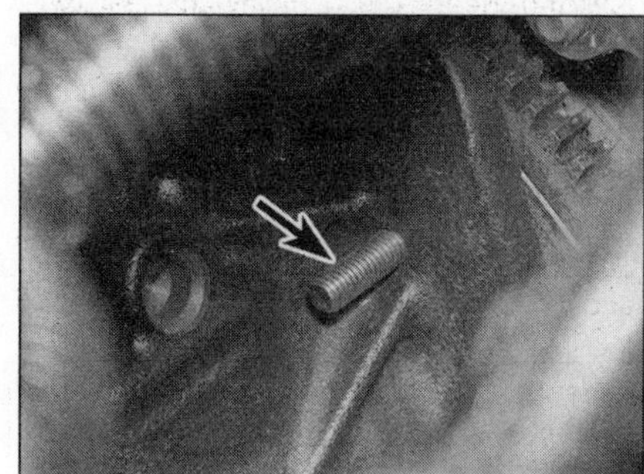

22.5b Rod (arrowed) inserted through cylinder block into timing hole in flywheel

22.6a Bolt (arrowed) inserted through timing hole in camshaft sprocket

22.6b Bolts (arrowed) inserted through timing holes in fuel injection pump sprocket

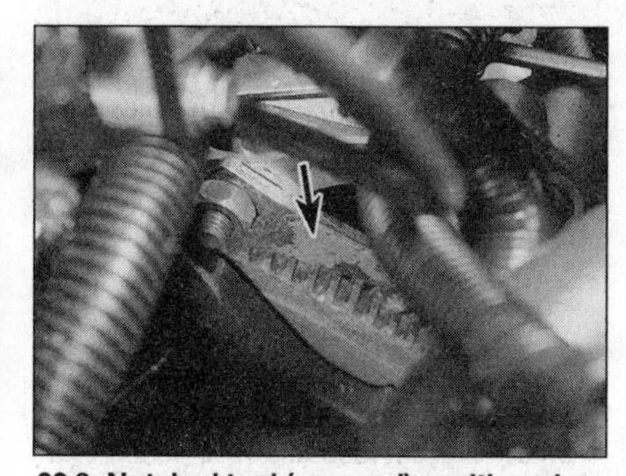

22.9 Notched tool (arrowed) positioned on ring gear teeth to lock flywheel

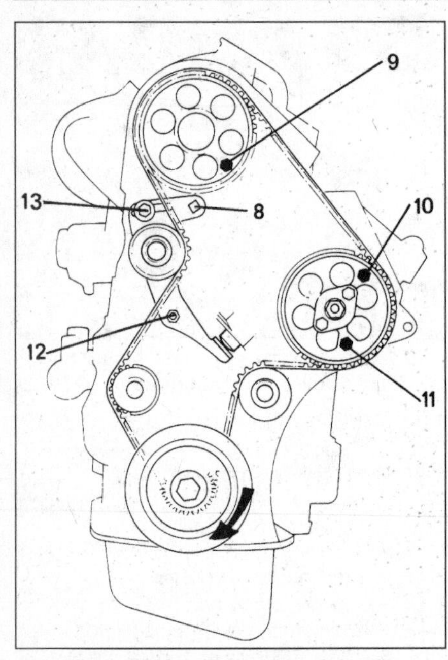

22.12 Timing belt removal details

8 Square hole
9 to 11 Bolts
12 Tensioner pivot nut
13 Adjustment bolt

10 Unscrew the retaining bolt and washer, then slide the pulley off the end of the crankshaft. If the pulley locating roll pin or Woodruff key (as applicable) is a loose fit, remove it and store it with the pulley for safe-keeping. If the pulley is a tight fit, it can be drawn off the crankshaft using a suitable puller.

11 If not already done, remove the right-hand engine mounting-to-body bracket.

12 Loosen the timing belt tensioner pivot nut and adjustment bolt, then turn the tensioner bracket anti-clockwise to release the tension. Retighten the adjustment bolt to hold the tensioner in the released position. If available, use a 10 mm square drive extension in the hole provided to turn the tensioner bracket against the spring tension **(see illustration)**.

13 Remove the belt from its sprockets **(see illustration)**.

22.13 Removing timing belt

Refitting and tensioning

14 Commence fitting of the new belt by ensuring that the 8 mm bolts are still fitted to the camshaft and fuel injection pump sprockets, and that the rod/drill is positioned in the timing hole in the flywheel.

15 Locate the timing belt on the crankshaft sprocket, ensuring that where applicable, the direction of rotation arrow is facing the correct way.

16 Engage the timing belt with the crankshaft sprocket, hold it in position, then feed the belt over the remaining sprockets in the following order **(see illustrations)**:

a) Idler roller.
b) Fuel injection pump.
c) Camshaft.
d) Tensioner roller.
e) Coolant pump.

17 Be careful not to kink or twist the belt. To ensure correct engagement, locate only a half-width on the injection pump sprocket before feeding the belt onto the camshaft sprocket, keeping the belt taut and fully engaged with the crankshaft sprocket. Locate the belt fully onto the sprockets.

18 Unscrew and remove the bolts from the camshaft and fuel injection pump sprockets, and remove the rod/drill from the timing hole in the flywheel.

19 With the pivot nut loose, slacken the tensioner adjustment bolt while holding the bracket against the spring tension. Slowly release the bracket until the roller presses against the timing belt. Retighten the adjustment bolt and the pivot nut.

20 Rotate the crankshaft through two complete turns in the normal running direction (clockwise). Do not rotate the crankshaft backwards, as the timing belt must be kept tight between the crankshaft, fuel injection pump and camshaft sprockets.

21 Loosen the tensioner adjustment bolt and the pivot nut to allow the tensioner spring to push the roller against the timing belt, then tighten both the adjustment bolt and pivot nut to the specified torque.

22 Check that the timing holes are all correctly positioned by reinserting the sprocket locking bolts and the rod/drill in the flywheel timing hole. If the timing holes are not correctly positioned, the timing belt has been incorrectly fitted (possibly one tooth out on one of the sprockets). In this case, repeat the fitting procedure from the beginning.

23 Refit the timing belt covers by using a reversal of the removal procedure. Ensure that each cover section is correctly located and that its retaining nuts and/or bolts are tightened to the specified torque. Do not lower the vehicle to the ground until the engine mounting-to-body bracket has been refitted.

24 Ensure that the crankshaft pulley Woodruff key is correctly located in the crankshaft groove, or that the roll pin is in position (as applicable). Refit the pulley to the end of the crankshaft, aligning its locating groove or hole with the Woodruff key or pin.

25 It is recommended that the crankshaft pulley retaining bolt is renewed whenever disturbed. Thoroughly clean the threads of the bolt, then apply a coat of locking compound. Peugeot recommend the use of Loctite but in the absence of this, any good-quality locking compound may be used.

26 Refit the crankshaft pulley retaining bolt and washer. Tighten the bolt to the specified torque, preventing the crankshaft from turning by using the method employed on removal.

27 Refit and tension the auxiliary drivebelt.

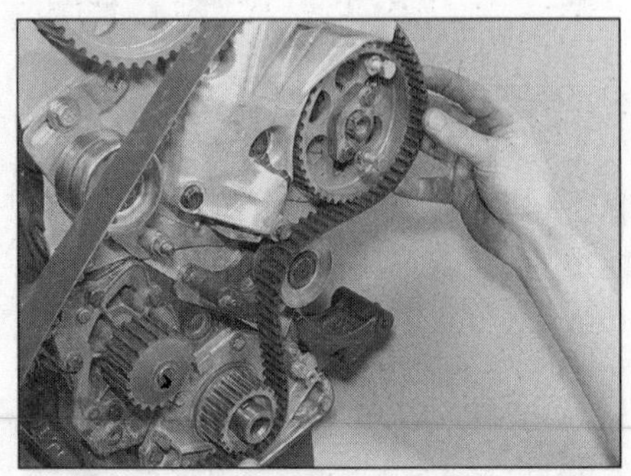

22.16a Fitting timing belt over injection pump sprocket . . .

22.16b . . . camshaft sprocket . . .

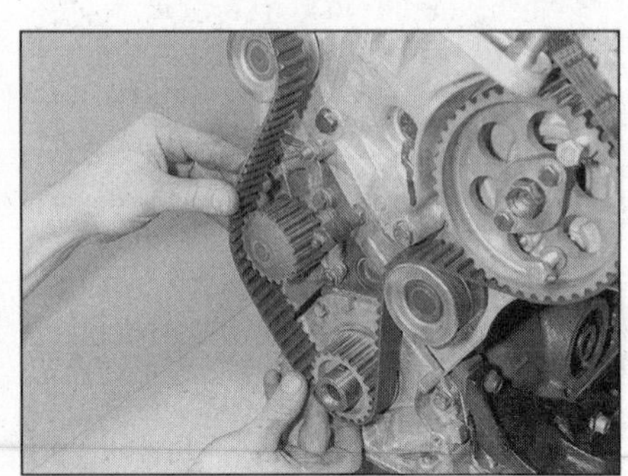

22.16c . . . and coolant pump sprocket

Chapter 8
Peugeot 1360cc, 1527cc, 1769cc and 1905cc engines

Part B: Fuel system servicing

Contents

Specifications

Glow plugs

Peugeot 106:	
1360cc	Champion CH147
1527cc	Champion listing not available at time of writing
Peugeot 205, 305 and 309	Champion CH68
Peugeot 306 and 405:	
XUD9TE engine	Champion CH163
Other engines	Champion CH68

Injectors

Type (all models)	Pintle
Opening pressure:	
Peugeot 106:	
1360 cc	125 to 130 bar
1527 cc	130 to 135 bar
Peugeot 205, 305 and 309:	
Lucas/Roto-Diesel:	
205 and 309 Turbo	130 ± 5 bar
All other models	115 ± 5 bar
Bosch	130 ± 5 bar
Peugeot 306:	
Lucas CAV/Roto-Diesel injection pump	125 to 135 bar
Bosch injection pump:	
Non turbo engines	130 to 135 bar
Turbo engines	175 to 180 bar
Peugeot 405:	
1769 cc Turbo engines	130 bar
1905 cc non Turbo engines:	
Bosch injection pump	130 bar
Lucas CAV/Roto-diesel injection pump	125 bar
1905 cc turbo engines	175 bar

Fuel injection pump

Direction of rotation (all models) .... Clockwise, viewed from timing belt end

Peugeot 106

Static timing:
- Engine position .... No 4 piston at TDC
- Pump position .... Value shown on pump

Dynamic timing at idle:
- 1360 cc non turbo .... 12° BTDC
- 1527 cc non turbo .... Not available

Peugeot 205, 305 and 309 - Lucas type

Static advance:
- 205 and 309 turbo .... Value shown on pump
- All other models .... 2.26 ± 0.05 mm BTDC (equivalent to 16° BTDC)

Dynamic advance:
- 205 and 309 turbo .... 12° BTDC at 775 rpm
- XUD 9 pumps with suffix 160A .... 13.5° BTDC at 800 rpm
- All other models .... 14° BTDC at 800 rpm

Peugeot 205, 305 and 309 - Bosch type

Static advance:
- 1769 cc models .... 0.80 ± 0.03 mm BTDC
- 1905 cc models .... 0.50 ± 0.03 mm BTDC

Dynamic advance:
- 1769 cc models .... 14° BTDC at 800 rpm
- 1905 cc models .... 13.5° BTDC at 800 rpm

Peugeot 306 - Lucas type

Static timing:
- Engine position .... No 4 piston at TDC
- Pump position .... Value shown on pump

Dynamic timing at idle .... 12° ± 1°

Peugeot 306 - Bosch type

Static timing:
- Engine position .... No 4 piston at TDC
- Pump timing measurement:
  - 1769cc engine .... 0.90 ± 0.02 mm
  - 1905cc non turbo:
    - D9B code .... 1.07 ± 0.02 mm
    - DJZ code .... 0.77 ± 0.02 mm
  - 1905cc turbo:
    - D8A code .... 0.66 ± 0.02 mm
    - DHZ code .... 0.63 ± 0.02 mm

Dynamic timing at idle:
- 1769cc engine .... 15° ± 1°
- 1905cc non turbo:
  - D9B code .... 18° ± 1°
  - DJZ code .... 12° ± 1°
- 1905cc turbo:
  - D8A code .... 11° ± 1°
  - DHZ code .... 10.5° ± 1°

Peugeot 405 - Lucas type

Static timing:
- Engine position .... No 4 piston at TDC
- Pump position .... Value shown on pump

Dynamic timing at idle:
- A8A engine .... 9°
- D8A engine .... 11° ± 1°
- D9B engine .... 15° ± 1°
- DHY engine .... 11° ± 1°
- DJZ engine:
  - Pre 1992 .... 13.5° ± 1°
  - Post 1993 .... 12° ± 1°

Peugeot 405 - Bosch type

Static timing:
- Engine position .... No 4 piston at TDC

Peugeot 405 - Bosch type (continued)

Pump timing measurement:	
1769 cc (A8A) turbo	0.80 ± 0.02 mm
1905 cc non turbo:	
D9B code	0.90 ± 0.02 mm
DJZ code	0.77 ± 0.02 mm
1905 cc turbo:	
D8A code	0.66 ± 0.02 mm
DHY code	0.66 ± 0.02 mm
Dynamic timing at idle:	
1769 cc (A8A) turbo	14° ± 1°
1905 cc non turbo:	
D9B code	15° ± 1°
DJZ code	13.5° ± 1°
1905 cc turbo:	
D8A code	11° ± 1°
DHY code	11° ± 1°

Fast idle speed

Peugeot 106 - 1527cc engine	900 to 1100 rpm
All other engines	900 to 1000 rpm

Maximum speed

Peugeot 106

1360 cc non turbo	5500 rpm
1527 cc non turbo	5450 ± 100 rpm

Peugeot 205, 305 and 309

No load	5100 ± 100 rpm

Peugeot 306

Non turbo	5150 ± 125 rpm
Turbo	5100 ± 80 rpm

Peugeot 405

1769 cc turbo	4800 rpm
1905 cc:	
Non turbo	5150 ± 125 rpm
Turbo	5100 ± 80 rpm

Torque wrench settings

	Nm	lbf ft
Peugeot 106		
Injectors:		
1360 cc non turbo	70	52
1527 cc non turbo	55	40
Injector pipe:		
Union nuts:		
1360 cc non turbo	20	15
1527 cc non turbo	25	18
Union bolts	25	18
Injection pump:		
Mounting nuts/bolts:		
1360 cc non turbo:		
Front	18	12
Rear	23	17
1527 cc non turbo	20	15
Glow plugs	22	16
Peugeot 205, 305 and 309		
Injectors:		
Bosch	90	66
Roto-Diesel	130	96
Injector pipe union nuts	20	15
Injection pump:		
Mounting nuts/bolts	18	13
Blanking plug (Bosch)	20	15
Sprocket nut	50	37
Glow plugs	22	16

Torque wrench settings (continued)

	Nm	lbf ft
Peugeot 306 and 405		
Injectors	90	66
Fuel pipe union nuts	20	15
Injection pump:		
Mounting nuts/bolts	20	15
Sprocket nut	50	37
Sprocket puller bolts	10	7
Timing hole blanking plug:		
Lucas	6	4
Bosch	15	11
No 4 cylinder TDC blanking plug	30	22
Stop solenoid:		
Lucas pump	15	11
Bosch pump	20	15
Glow plugs	22	16

1.1 Removing spring clip from accelerator cable groove

1 Accelerator cable - adjustment

1 Remove the spring clip from the accelerator cable outer **(see illustration)**.

2 Ensuring that the control lever is against its stop, gently pull the cable out of its grommet until all free play is removed from the cable inner.

3 With the cable held in this position, ensure that the flat washer is pressed securely against the grommet.

4 Refit the spring clip to the last exposed cable outer groove, in front of the grommet and washer.

5 With the clip refitted and the cable outer released, there should be only a small amount of free play in the cable inner.

6 Have an assistant depress the accelerator pedal and check that the control lever opens fully and returns smoothly to its stop.

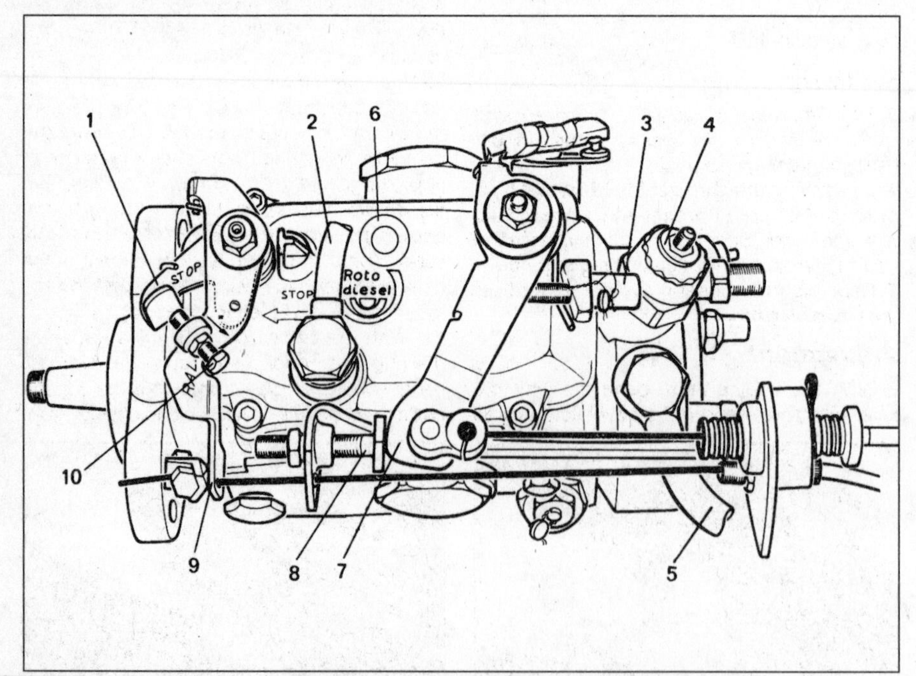

2.4a Lucas fuel injection pump adjustment points

1 Manual stop lever
2 Fuel return pipe
3 Maximum speed adjustment screw
4 Stop solenoid
5 Fuel inlet
6 Timing access plug
7 Control (accelerator) lever
8 Anti-stall adjustment screw
9 Fast idle lever
10 Idle speed adjustment screw

2 Maximum speed - checking and adjustment

Caution: The maximum speed adjustment screw is sealed by the manufacturers, with paint or locking wire and a lead seal. Do not disturb the screw if the vehicle is still within the warranty period, otherwise the warranty will be invalidated. Maximum speed adjustment requires the use of a tachometer.

1 Run the engine to normal operating temperature.

2 If the vehicle does not have a tachometer (rev counter), connect a suitable instrument in accordance with its manufacturer's instructions.

3 Have an assistant fully depress the accelerator pedal and check that the maximum engine speed is as specified. Do not keep the engine at maximum speed for more than two or three seconds.

4 If adjustment is necessary, stop the engine, then loosen the locknut, turn the maximum speed adjustment screw as necessary and retighten the locknut **(see illustrations)**.

5 Repeat the procedure in paragraph 3 to check adjustment.

6 Stop the engine and disconnect the tachometer.

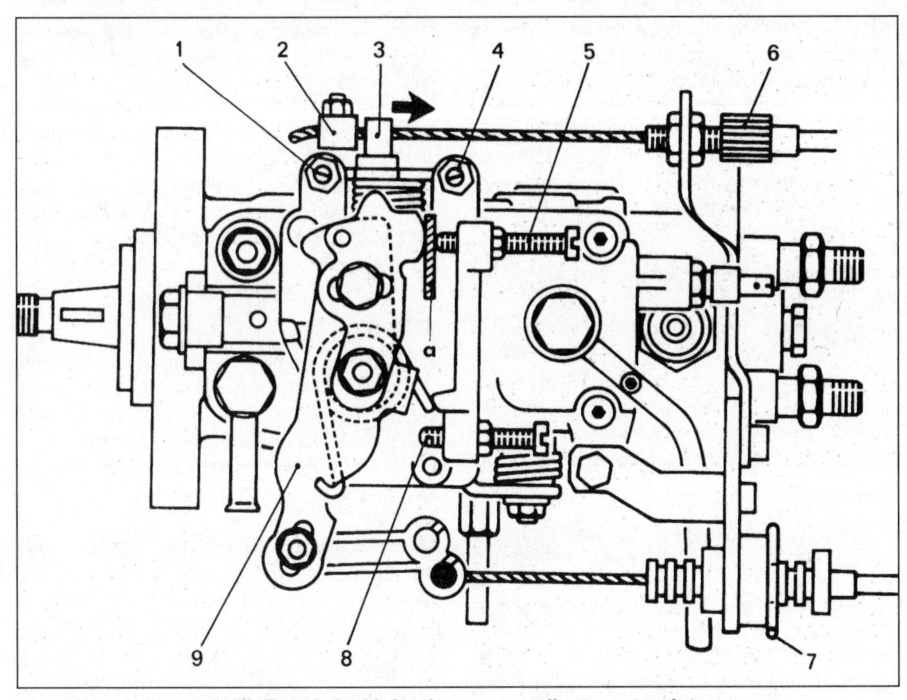

2.4b Bosch fuel injection pump adjustment points

1 *Fast idle adjustment screw*
2 *Cable end fitting*
3 *Fast idle lever*
4 *Idle speed adjustment screw*
5 *Anti-stall adjustment screw*
6 *Fast idle cable adjustment screw*
7 *Accelerator cable adjustment clip*
8 *Maximum speed adjustment screw*
9 *Control (accelerator) lever*
a *Shim for anti-stall adjustment*

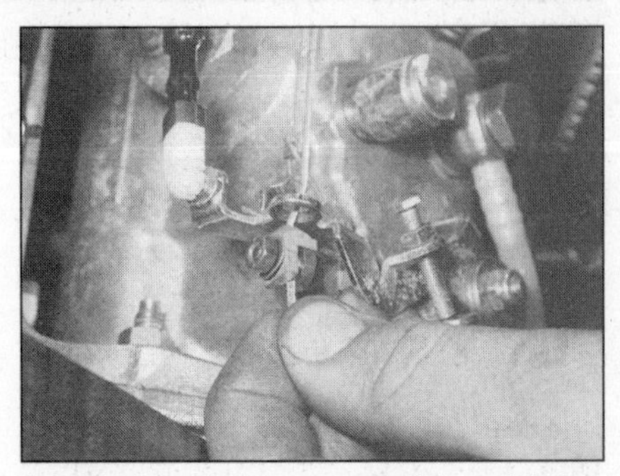

3.2 Slacken clamp nut and slide end fitting off fast idle cable

3.3 Slide fast idle cable from adjustment screw

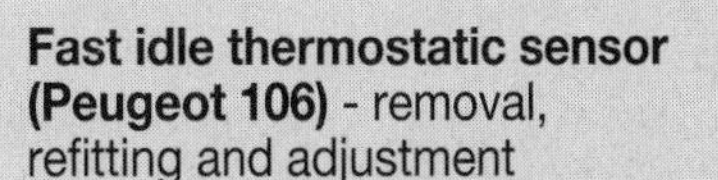

3 Fast idle thermostatic sensor (Peugeot 106) - removal, refitting and adjustment

Note: *A new sealing washer must be used when refitting the thermostatic sensor.*

Removal

1 Disconnect the battery negative terminal and partially drain the cooling system.

2 Loosen the clamp nut and slide the fast idle cable end fitting off the fuel injection pump end of the cable inner **(see illustration)**.

3 Free the fast idle cable from the bracket on the injection pump **(see illustration)**.

4 Unscrew the thermostatic sensor from the cylinder head and remove the sensor and cable assembly. Recover the sealing washer **(see illustrations)**.

Refitting

5 Fit a new sealing washer to the sensor and screw the sensor into position in the cylinder head, tightening it securely.

6 Insert the cable through the injection pump bracket, then pass the cable inner through the fast idle lever. Slide the end fitting onto the cable inner and lightly tighten its clamp nut.

7 Replenish the cooling system and adjust the cable as follows.

Adjustment

8 With the engine cold, push the fast idle lever fully to the end of its travel (ie. towards the rear of the injection pump). Hold it in position and slide the cable end fitting along the cable until its abuts the fast idle lever. Securely tighten the clamp nut.

9 Start the engine. As the engine warms up, the fast idle cable should extend so that the fast idle lever returns to is stop.

10 Wait until the cooling fan has cut in and cut out, then switch off the engine. Measure the clearance between the fast idle lever and the cable end fitting. There should be a gap of approximately 0.5 to 1.0 mm. If not, slacken the clamp nut, move the end fitting to the correct position, then securely retighten the screw or nut. Note that fine adjustment of the cable can be made using the adjuster on the mounting bracket **(see illustration)**.

11 With the cable correctly adjusted, allow the engine to cool. As it cools, the fast idle cable should be drawn back into the sensor, pulling the fast idle lever back against its stop.

3.4a Unscrew fast idle valve (arrowed) from cylinder head . . .

3.4b . . . and remove valve with sealing washer (arrowed)

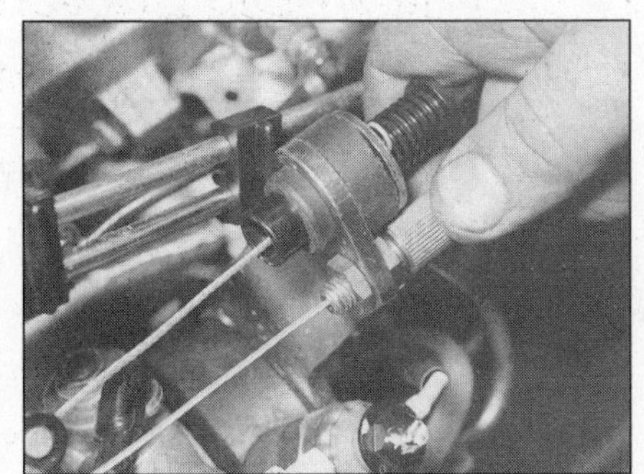

3.10 Fine adjustment of fast idle cable is made using adjuster on mounting bracket

4 Fast idle thermostatic sensor (Peugeot 205, 305 and 309) - removal, refitting and adjustment

Note: *Refer to the illustrations in Section 3 before carrying out the following procedure.*
Note: *A new sealing washer must be used when refitting the thermostatic sensor.*

Removal

1 Remove the air cleaner and ducting, as necessary.
2 Drain the cooling system.
3 Loosen the clamp screw or nut and remove the end fitting from the cable inner.
4 Unscrew the locknut and remove the adjustment ferrule and cable outer from the bracket on the fuel injection pump.
5 Unscrew the thermostatic sensor from the thermostat housing cover and recover the sealing washer.

Refitting

6 Fit the thermostatic sensor and new washer, then tighten it.
7 Insert the cable and ferrule in the bracket and screw on the locknut finger-tight.
8 Insert the cable end through the lever and fit the end fitting loosely.

Adjustment

9 With the engine cold, push the fast idle lever or the knurled adjuster (pre January 1984 Bosch injection pumps) fully towards the flywheel end of the engine. Then tighten the clamp screw or nut with the end fitting touching the lever or adjuster.
10 Adjust the ferrule to ensure that the fast idle lever is touching its stop, then tighten the locknuts.
11 Measure the exposed length of cable inner.
12 Refill the cooling system and run the engine to normal operating temperature.
13 With the engine hot, check that the length of cable inner has increased by at least 6.0 mm, indicating that the thermostatic sensor is functioning correctly.
14 On pre January 1984 Bosch injection pumps, check that there is a gap of 1.0 mm between the cable end fitting and the adjuster. If not, adjust the ferrule.
15 Check that the engine speed increases when the fast idle lever or adjuster is pushed towards the flywheel end of the engine. On the early Bosch pump, the speed should be 200 ± 50 rpm. On other models the fast idling speed should be 950 ± 50 rpm. Turn the knurled adjuster or lever stop, as necessary.
16 Switch off the engine.

5 Fast idle thermostatic sensor (Peugeot 306 and 405) - removal, refitting and adjustment

Note: *Refer to the illustrations in Section 3 before carrying out the following procedure.*
Note: *A new sealing washer must be used when refitting the thermostatic sensor.*

Removal

1 The thermostatic sensor is located in the side of the thermostat housing cover (early 405 models), or in the side of the thermostat/fuel filter housing (later 405 and all 306 models).
2 For improved access on Turbo models, remove the intercooler. On non turbo models with the D9B engine, remove the air distribution housing. If necessary, also remove the intake duct and disconnect the breather hose from the engine oil filler tube.
3 Drain the cooling system.
4 Loosen the clamp screw or nut (as applicable) and disconnect the fast idle cable end fitting from the cable inner at the fuel injection pump fast idle lever.
5 Slide the cable from the adjustment screw located in the bracket on the fuel injection pump.
6 Using a suitable open-ended spanner, unscrew the thermostatic sensor from its housing and withdraw the sensor, complete with the cable. Recover the sealing washer, where applicable.

Refitting

7 If sealing compound was originally used to fit the sensor in place of a washer, thoroughly clean all traces of old sealing compound from the sensor and housing. Ensure that no traces of sealant are left in the internal coolant passages of the housing.
8 Fit the sensor, using suitable sealing compound or a new washer as applicable, then tighten it.
9 Insert the adjustment screw into the bracket on the fuel injection pump and screw on the locknut, finger-tight.
10 Insert the cable inner through the fast idle lever and position the end fitting on the cable. Do not tighten the clamp screw or nut (as applicable).
11 Adjust the cable as follows.

Adjustment

12 With the engine cold, push the fast idle lever fully towards the flywheel end of the engine. Tighten the clamp screw or nut, with the cable end fitting touching the lever.
13 Adjust the screw to ensure that the fast idle lever is touching its stop, then tighten the locknut.
14 Measure the exposed length of cable inner.
15 Where necessary, refit the intercooler or the air distribution housing and reconnect the breather hose to the engine oil filler tube.
16 Refill the cooling system and run the engine to its normal operating temperature.
17 Check that the fast idle cable is slack. If not, it is likely that the sensor is faulty.
18 With the engine hot, check the amount of free play in the fast idle cable. If as follows, this indicates that the thermostatic sensor is functioning correctly.

Lucas injection pump - 0.5 to 1 mm
Bosch injection pump - 5 to 6 mm

19 Check that engine speed increases when the fast idle lever is pushed towards the flywheel end of the engine. With the lever against its stop, the fast idle speed should be as specified in Part A of this Chapter.
20 Stop the engine.

6 Stop solenoid - removal and refitting

Caution: Be careful not to allow dirt into the injection pump during the following procedure.
Note: *A new sealing washer or O-ring (as applicable) will be required on refitting.*

Removal

1 Disconnect the battery negative lead.
2 On models fitted with a Bosch fuel injection pump, it may be necessary to unbolt the fast idle cable support bracket from the side of the pump, to improve access.
3 Withdraw the rubber boot (where applicable), then unscrew the terminal nut and disconnect the wire from the top of the solenoid **(see illustrations)**.
4 Carefully clean around the solenoid, then unscrew and withdraw the solenoid. Recover the sealing washer or O-ring (as applicable) **(see illustration)**.

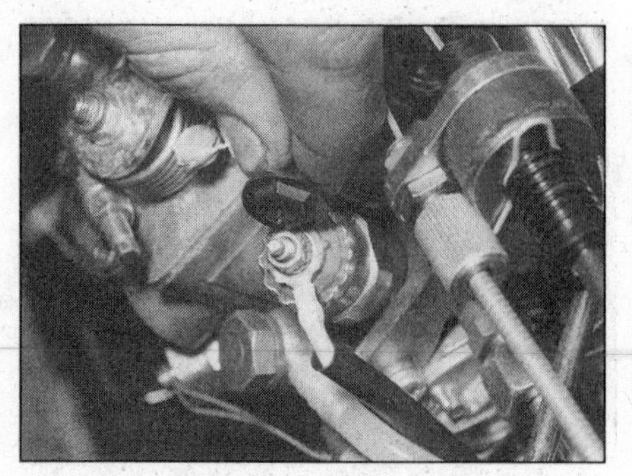

6.3a Remove rubber cover . . .

6.3b . . . then unscrew retaining nut and disconnect stop solenoid wiring connector

5 Recover the solenoid plunger and spring if they remain in the pump **(see illustration)**.

6 Operate the hand-priming pump as the solenoid is removed, to flush away any dirt.

Refitting

7 Refitting is a reversal of removal. Use a new sealing washer or O-ring and tighten the solenoid to the specified torque setting, where given.

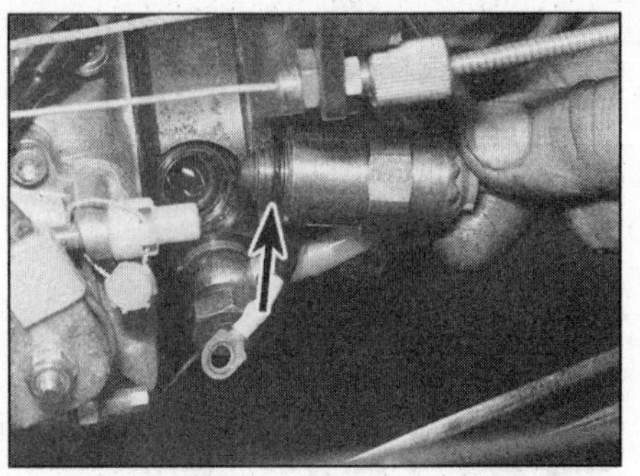

6.4 Unscrew stop solenoid from pump and recover O-ring (arrowed)

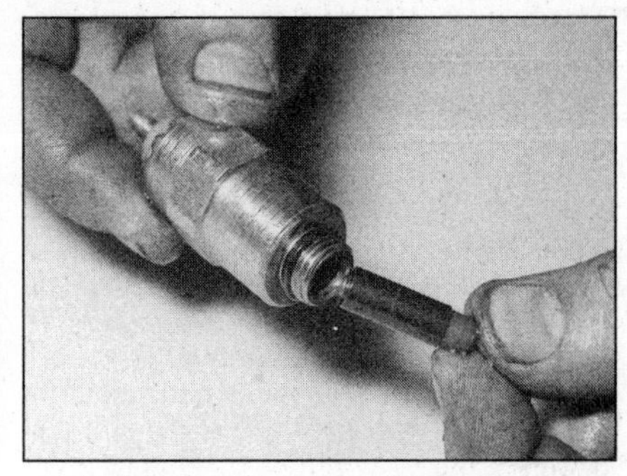

6.5 Withdrawing solenoid plunger and spring

7 Glow plugs (Peugeot 106, 306 and 405) - removal, inspection and refitting

Caution: If the preheating system has just been energised, or if the engine has been running, the glow plugs will be very hot.

Removal

Peugeot 306 and 405

1 To improve access on Turbo models, remove the intercooler. On non turbo models with the D9B engine, remove the air distribution housing. If necessary, also remove the intake duct and disconnect the breather hose from the engine oil filler tube.

All models

2 Disconnect the battery negative lead.

3 Unscrew the nut from the relevant glow plug terminal and recover the washer. Note that the main supply cable is connected to No 1 cylinder glow plug and an interconnecting wire is fitted between the four plugs **(see illustrations)**.

4 Where applicable, carefully move any obstructing pipes or wires to one side to enable access to the relevant glow plug.

5 Unscrew each glow plug and remove it from the cylinder head **(see illustration)**.

Inspection

6 Inspect each glow plug for physical damage. Burnt or eroded glow plug tips can be caused by a bad injector spray pattern. Have the injectors checked if this sort of damage is found.

7 If the glow plugs are in good physical condition, check them electrically using a 12 volt test lamp or continuity tester as described in Section 17.

8 The glow plugs can be energised by applying 12 volts to them to verify that they heat up evenly and in the required time. Observe the following precautions:

a) Support the glow plug by clamping it carefully in a vice or self-locking pliers. Remember it will become red-hot.

b) Ensure that the power supply or test lead incorporates a fuse or overload trip to protect against damage from a short-circuit.

c) After testing, allow the glow plug to cool for several minutes before attempting to handle it.

9 A glow plug in good condition will start to glow red at the tip after drawing current for 5 seconds or so. Any plug which takes much longer to start glowing, or which starts glowing in the middle instead of at the tip, is defective.

Refitting

10 Refit by reversing the removal operations. Apply a smear of copper-based anti-seize compound to the plug threads and tighten the glow plugs to the specified torque. Do not overtighten, as this can damage the glow plug element.

8 Glow plugs (Peugeot 205, 305 and 309) - removal, inspection and refitting

1 Refer to Section 7 whilst noting the following:

a) For access to the glow plugs, remove the air cleaner and ducting, as necessary.

*b) Prise any plastic clips from the glow plugs **(see illustration)**.*

7.3a Unscrew retaining nut . . .

7.3b . . . disconnect main supply cable (where necessary) . . .

7.3c . . . and interconnecting wire from glow plug

7.5 Removing glow plug from cylinder head

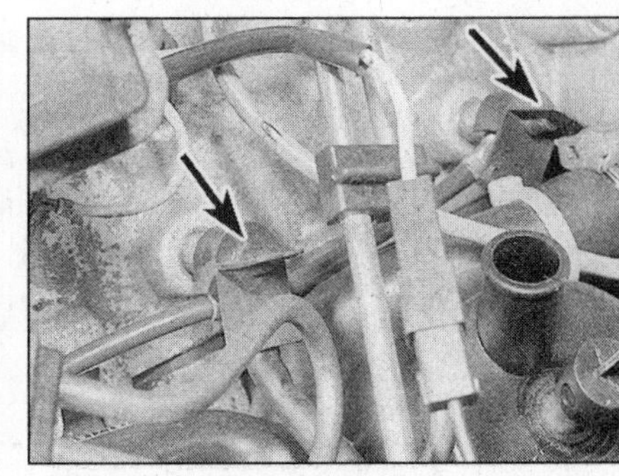

8.1 Plastic clips (arrowed) on glow plug terminals

9 Glow plug relay (Peugeot 205, 305 and 309) - removal and refitting

Removal

1 The glow plug relay is located on the left-hand side of the engine compartment near the battery **(see illustration)**.

2 To remove the relay, first disconnect the battery negative lead.

3 Unbolt the relay from the side panel and disconnect its wiring.

Refitting

4 Refitting is a reversal of removal.

9.1 Glow plug control unit - Peugeot 205

10 Injectors - testing, removal and refitting

Warning: Exercise extreme caution when working on fuel injectors. Never expose the hands or any part of the body to injector spray, as the high working pressure can cause fuel to penetrate the skin, with possibly fatal results. You are strongly advised to have any work which involves testing injectors under pressure carried out by a dealer or fuel injection specialist.

Note: *New copper washers and fire seal washers must be used on refitting.*

Testing

1 Injectors do deteriorate with prolonged use and it is reasonable to expect them to need reconditioning or renewal after 60 000 miles (90 000 km) or so. Accurate testing, overhaul and calibration of the injectors must be left to a specialist. A defective injector which is causing knocking or smoking can be located without dismantling as follows.

2 Run the engine at a fast idle. Slacken each injector union in turn, placing rag around the union to catch spilt fuel and being careful not to expose the skin to any spray. When the union on the defective injector is slackened, the knocking or smoking will stop.

Removal

Peugeot 306 and 405

3 For improved access on Turbo models, remove the intercooler. On non turbo models with the D9B engine, remove the air distribution housing. If necessary, also remove the intake duct and disconnect the breather hose from the engine oil filler tube.

All models

4 Carefully clean around the injectors and injector pipe union nuts.

5 Pull the leak-off pipes from the injectors **(see illustration)**.

6 Unscrew the union nuts securing the injector pipes to the fuel injection pump. Counterhold the unions on the pump when unscrewing the nuts. Cover open unions to keep dirt out.

7 Unscrew the union nuts and disconnect the pipes from the injectors **(see illustration)**. If necessary, the injector pipes may be completely removed. Note carefully the locations of the pipe clamps, for use when refitting. Cover the ends of the injectors, to prevent dirt ingress.

8 Unscrew the injectors using a deep socket or box spanner (27 mm across-flats) and remove them from the cylinder head **(see illustration)**.

9 Recover the copper washers and fire seal washers from the cylinder head. Also recover the sleeves if they are loose **(see illustrations)**.

Refitting

10 Obtain new copper washers and fire seal washers. Also renew the sleeves, if damaged.

11 Take care not to drop the injectors or allow the needles at their tips to become damaged. Injectors are precision-made to fine limits and must not be handled roughly. In particular, never mount them in a bench vice.

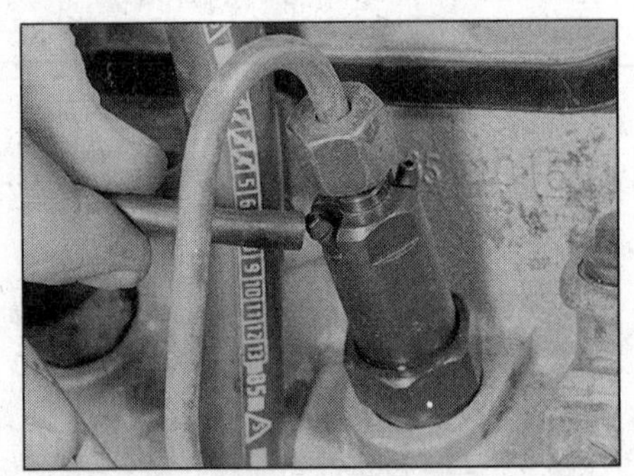

10.5 Disconnect leak off pipes from injectors

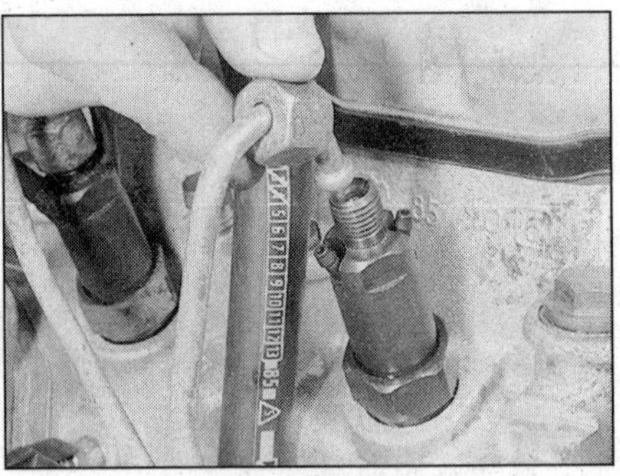

10.7 Disconnecting injector pipes

10.8 Removing an injector

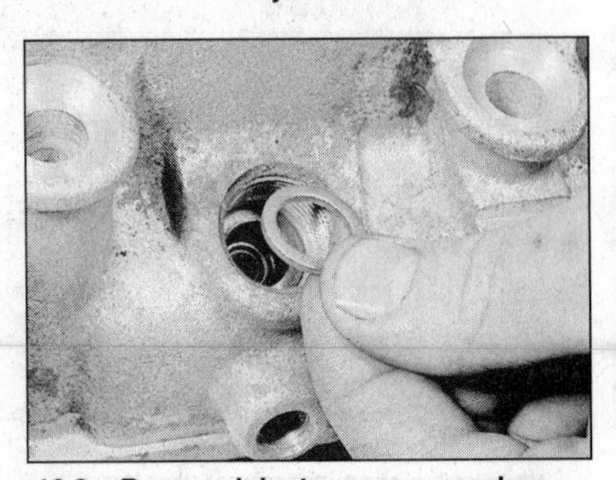

10.9a Remove injector copper washer . . .

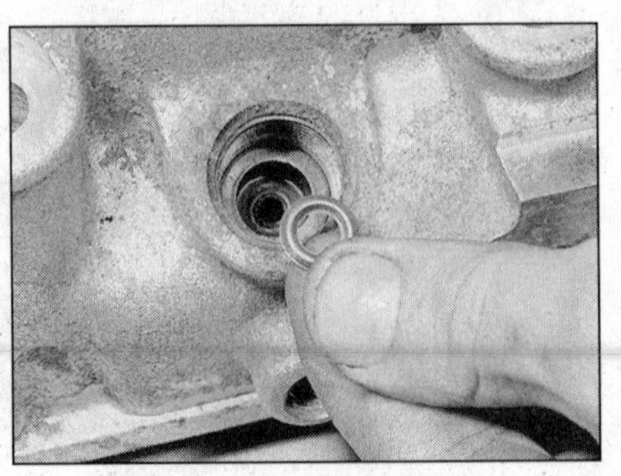

10.9b . . . fire-seal washer . . .

10.9c . . . and sleeve

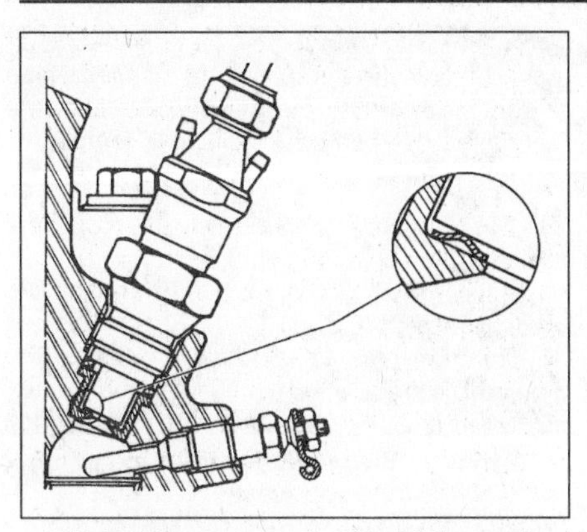

10.12 Ensure convex side of fire seal washer is facing towards injector

12 Commence refitting by inserting the sleeves (if removed) into the cylinder head, followed by the fire seal washers (convex face uppermost) and copper washers **(see illustration)**.

13 Insert the injectors and tighten them to the specified torque.

14 Refit the injector pipes and tighten the union nuts. Ensure the pipe clamps are in their previously-noted positions. If the clamps are wrongly positioned or missing, problems may be experienced with pipes breaking or splitting.

15 Reconnect the leak-off pipes.

16 Refit the intercooler or air distribution housing, where applicable.

17 Start the engine. If difficulty is experienced, bleed the fuel system as described in Part A of this Chapter.

11 Fuel injection pump (Peugeot 106) - removal and refitting

Removal

1 Disconnect the battery negative terminal.

2 Remove the right-hand headlight unit.

3 Remove the timing belt upper and centre covers, as described in Part A of this Chapter.

4 Align the engine assembly/valve timing holes as described in Part A of this Chapter (timing belt renewal), then lock the crankshaft, camshaft sprocket and injection pump sprocket in position. Do not attempt to rotate the engine whilst the pins are in position.

5 Remove the injection pump sprocket.

6 Loosen the clamp nut and slide the fast idle cable end fitting off the injection pump end of the cable inner **(see illustration)**. Free the fast idle cable from the bracket on the injection pump.

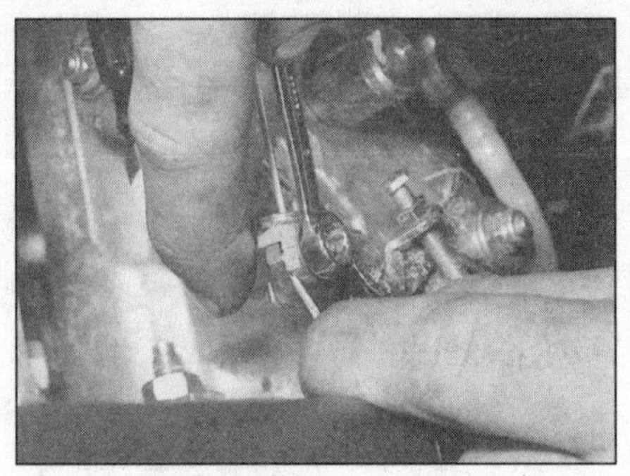

11.6 Loosen clamp nut and remove end fitting from fast idle cable

7 Free the accelerator cable inner from the pump lever, then pull the cable outer from its mounting bracket rubber grommet. Slide the flat washer off the end of the cable and remove the spring clip **(see illustrations)**.

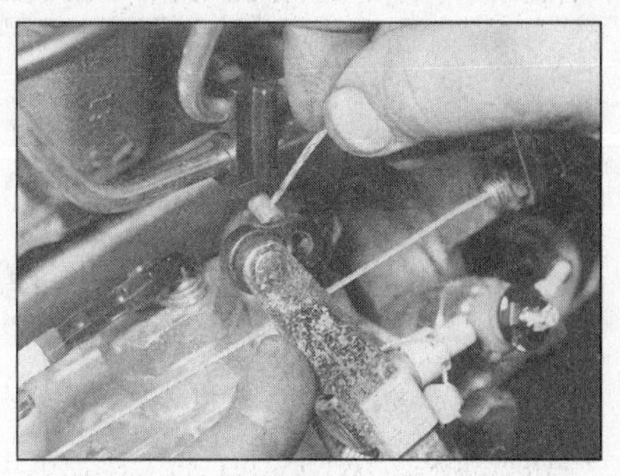

11.7a Free accelerator cable inner from pump lever . . .

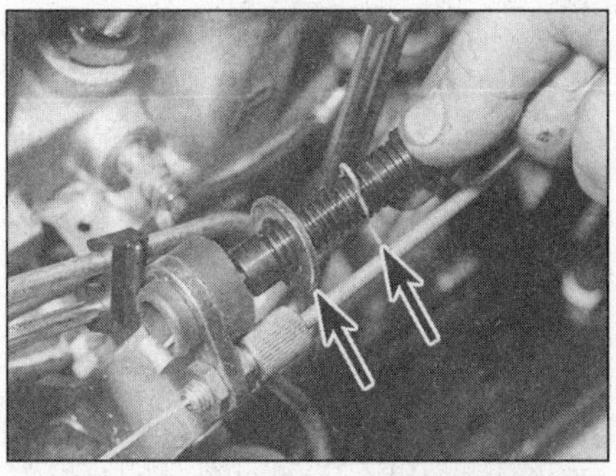

11.7b . . . then withdraw cable outer from mounting bracket and recover washer and spring clip (arrowed)

8 Wipe clean the fuel feed and return unions on the injection pump. Cover the alternator to prevent fuel being spilt onto it.

9 Slacken and remove the fuel feed hose union bolt from the injection pump. Recover the sealing washer from each side of the hose union and position the hose clear of the pump. Screw the union bolt back into position on the pump for safe-keeping and cover both the hose end and union bolt to prevent the ingress of dirt into the fuel system.

10 Detach the fuel return hose from the injection pump as described in the previous paragraph **(see illustration)**. Note that the injection pump feed and return hose union bolts are not interchangeable.

11 Wipe clean the pipe unions, then slacken the union nut securing the injector pipes to the top of each injector and the four union nuts securing the pipes to the rear of the injection pump. As each pump union nut is slackened, retain the adapter with a suitable open-ended spanner to prevent it being unscrewed from the pump. With all the union nuts undone, remove the injector pipes (in pairs) from the engine **(see illustration)**.

12 Remove the rubber cover (where fitted), then undo the retaining nut and disconnect the wiring from the injection pump stop solenoid.

13 Make alignment marks between the injection pump front flange and the front mounting bracket. These marks can then be used to ensure that the pump is correctly positioned on refitting. To improve access to the pump, undo the two screws and remove the cover panel from the right-hand side of the radiator **(see illustrations)**.

14 Unscrew the bolt securing the injection pump rear mounting bracket to the cylinder block **(see illustration)**.

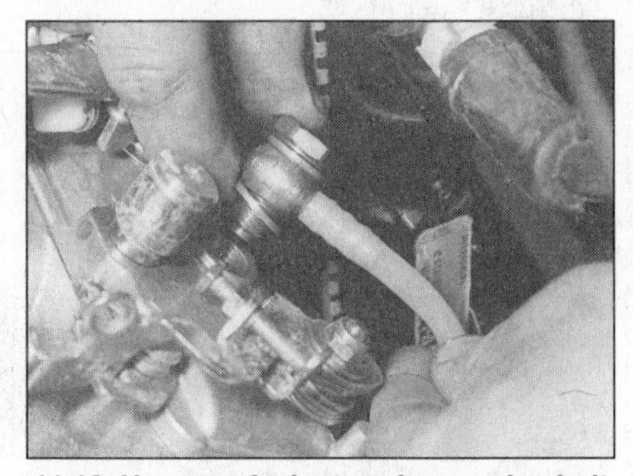

11.10 Unscrew fuel return hose union bolt and recover sealing washer from each side of hose union

11.11 Remove injector pipes in pairs

11.13a Remove cover panel from side of radiator to improve access . . .

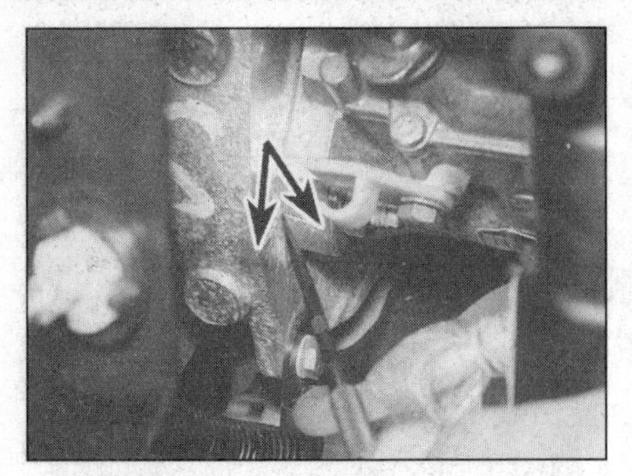
11.13b . . . then make alignment marks (arrowed) between injection pump and mounting bracket

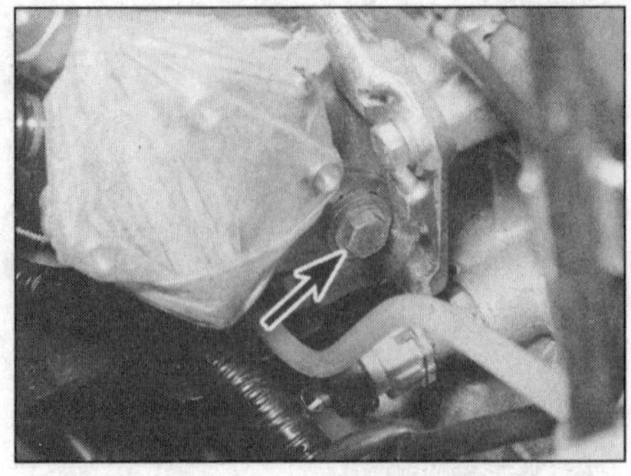
11.14 Unscrew rear mounting bracket bolt (arrowed) . . .

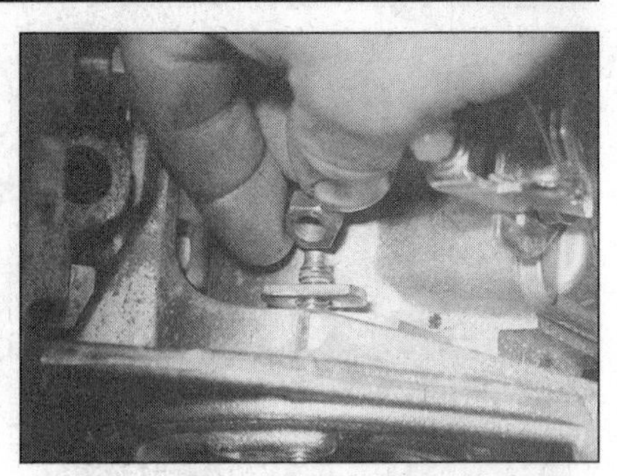
11.15a . . . then unscrew front mounting nuts and washer . . .

15 Slacken and remove the three nuts and washers securing the pump to its front mounting bracket, then manoeuvre the pump out of the engine compartment **(see illustrations)**.

Refitting

16 If a new pump is being installed, transfer the alignment mark from the original pump onto the mounting flange of the new pump.

17 Manoeuvre the pump into position and refit its three front washers and mounting nuts, then the rear mounting bolt. Align the marks made prior to removal, then securely tighten the retaining nuts and bolt.

18 Refit the injection pump sprocket. Align the sprocket timing holes with those in the mounting plate and lock the sprocket in position with the two timing bolts.

19 Check the crankshaft, camshaft and injection pump sprockets are all correctly positioned, then engage the timing belt and tension it as described in Part A of this Chapter. With the timing belt correctly fitted, remove the pins/bolts from the sprockets.

20 Set the injection pump timing as described in Section 14.

21 With the pump timing correctly set, reconnect the wiring to the stop solenoid and securely tighten its retaining nut. Refit the rubber boot.

22 Reconnect the fuel feed and return hose unions to the pump, not forgetting to fit the filter to the feed hose union. Position a new sealing washer on each side of both unions and tighten the union bolts to the specified torque setting.

23 Refit the injector pipes and tighten their union nuts to the specified torque setting.

24 Mop up any spilt fuel then uncover the alternator.

25 Reconnect and adjust the accelerator cable.

26 Reconnect and adjust the fast idle thermostatic valve cable.

27 Refit the right-hand headlight unit.

28 Reconnect the battery negative lead.

29 Bleed the fuel system as described in Part A of this Chapter.

30 On completion, start the engine and adjust the idle speed and anti-stall speed as described in Part A of this Chapter.

12 Fuel injection pump (Peugeot 205, 305 and 309) - removal and refitting

Note: *From April 1988, the Lucas CAV/Roto-Diesel pump is fitted with a dust shield to protect the front bearing seals. If an earlier-type pump is removed for any reason, the opportunity should be taken to obtain and fit a dust shield kit.*

Removal

1 Disconnect the battery negative lead.

2 Cover the alternator as a precaution against spillage of fuel.

3 Remove the air cleaner assembly, crankcase ventilation hoses and oil separator, as necessary.

4 Apply the handbrake, then jack up the front right-hand corner of the vehicle until the wheel is just clear of the ground.

5 Support the vehicle on an axle stand and engage 4th or 5th gear. This will enable the engine to be turned easily by turning the right-hand wheel.

11.15b . . . and remove injection pump from engine

6 Release the retaining clips and withdraw the front timing cover section.

7 Open the accelerator lever on the fuel injection pump and disconnect the cable by passing it through the special slot **(see illustration)**. Disconnect the cable adjustment ferrule from the bracket.

8 Note the position of the end stop on the fast idle cable then loosen the screw and disconnect the cable inner. Unscrew the adjustment locknut and remove the cable and ferrule from the bracket.

9 Loosen the clip and disconnect the fuel supply hose **(see illustration)**. On Turbo models, disconnect the boost pressure hose from the overfuelling device.

10 Disconnect the main fuel return pipe and the injector leak off return pipe from the union tube **(see illustration)**.

12.7 Accelerator cable connection (arrowed) - Peugeot 205

12.9 Fuel supply hose (A) and return pipe (B) - early Bosch pump

12.10 Disconnecting main fuel return pipe - 205 with Lucas CAV/Roto-Diesel pump

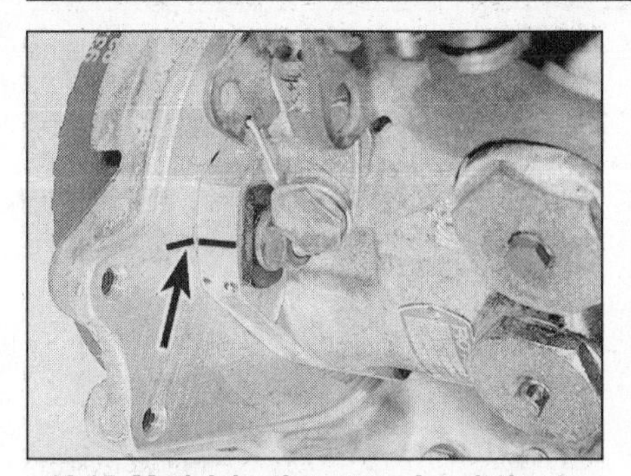

12.15 Mark injection pump in relation to mounting bracket (arrowed)

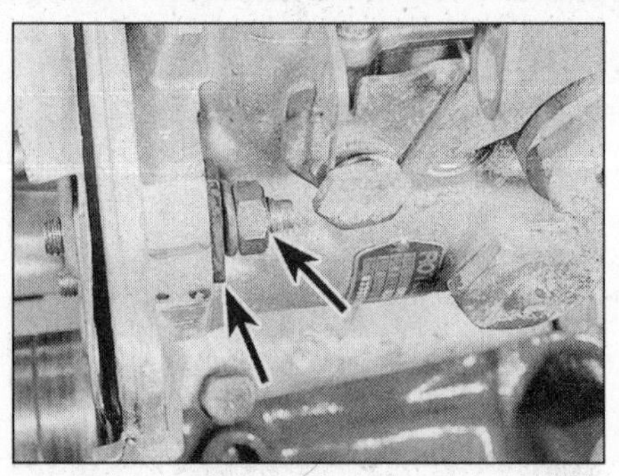

12.16a Injection pump mounting nut and plate (arrowed)

12.16b Injection pump mounting bracket (arrowed)

11 Disconnect the wire from the stop solenoid.

12 Unscrew the union nuts securing the injector pipes to the injection pump and injectors. Remove the pipes complete.

13 Turn the engine by means of the front right-hand wheel or crankshaft pulley bolt until the two bolt holes in the injection pump sprocket are aligned with the corresponding holes in the engine front plate.

14 Insert two M8 bolts through the holes and hand tighten them. The bolts must retain the sprocket while the injection pump is removed thereby making it unnecessary to remove the timing belt.

15 Mark the injection pump in relation to the mounting bracket **(see illustration)**. This will ensure correct timing when refitting. If a new pump is being fitted, transfer the mark from the old pump to give an approximate setting.

16 Unscrew the three mounting nuts and remove the plates. Unscrew and remove the rear mounting bolt and support the injection pump on a block of wood **(see illustrations)**.

17 On pre late 1992 models, unscrew the sprocket nut until the taper is released from the sprocket. The nut acts as a puller, together with the plate bolted to the sprocket. From late 1992, the fuel injection pump sprocket bolt no longer incorporates a puller. To free the sprocket from the taper on the injection pump shaft, a flange must be bolted to the sprocket before unscrewing the bolt. This flange can be obtained from an old injection pump sprocket, if available, and used to remove the new sprocket. Alternatively, a flange can be made up from steel plate. Do not be tempted to free the sprocket by hammering or levering as there is a risk of damaging the injection pump if this is done.

18 Continue to unscrew the sprocket nut and withdraw the injection pump from the mounting bracket **(see illustration)**. Recover the Woodruff key from the shaft groove, if loose.

Refitting

19 Fit the Woodruff key to the shaft groove (if removed).

20 Unbolt the puller plate from the injection pump sprocket.

21 Insert the injection pump from behind the sprocket, making sure that the shaft key enters the groove in the sprocket. Screw on the nut and hand-tighten it.

22 Fit the mounting nuts, together with their plates. Hand-tighten the nuts.

23 Tighten the sprocket nut to the specified torque then refit the puller plate and tighten the bolts.

24 Unscrew and remove the two bolts from the injection pump sprocket.

25 If the original injection pump is being refitted, align the scribed marks and tighten the mounting nuts. If fitting a new pump, the timing must be set as described in Section 15.

26 Refit the rear mounting bolt and special nut, tightening the nut slowly to allow the bush to align itself as shown **(see illustration)**.

27 Refit the injector pipes to the injection pump and tighten the union nuts.

28 Reconnect the wire to the stop solenoid.

29 Refit the fuel supply and return pipes.

30 Refit and adjust the fast idle and accelerator cables.

31 Refit the timing cover.

32 Lower the vehicle to the ground and apply the handbrake.

33 Uncover the alternator and reconnect the battery negative lead.

34 Where applicable, refit the oil separator, crankcase ventilation hoses, air cleaner and ducting.

35 Prime the fuel circuit by first switching on the ignition to energise the stop solenoid, then actuating the pump on the fuel filter until resistance is felt. On early models fitted with a Lucas CAV/Roto-Diesel filter, the pump plunger must first be unscrewed then retightened after priming.

12.18 Removing injection pump from mounting bracket

36 Turn the ignition key to position 'M' and wait for the preheating warning light to go out. Start the engine and adjust the idling speed, referring to Part A of this Chapter.

13 Fuel injection pump (Peugeot 306 and 405) - removal and refitting

Caution: Be careful not to allow dirt into the injection pump or injector pipes during this procedure. New sealing rings should be used on the fuel pipe banjo unions when refitting.

Removal

1 Disconnect the battery negative lead.

2 Cover the alternator as a precaution against fuel spillage.

3 For improved access on Turbo models, remove the intercooler. On non turbo models with the D9B engine, remove the air distribution housing. If necessary, also remove the intake duct and disconnect the breather hose from the engine oil filler tube.

4 On manual transmission models, chock the rear wheels and release the handbrake. Jack up the front right-hand corner of the vehicle until the wheel is just clear of the ground.

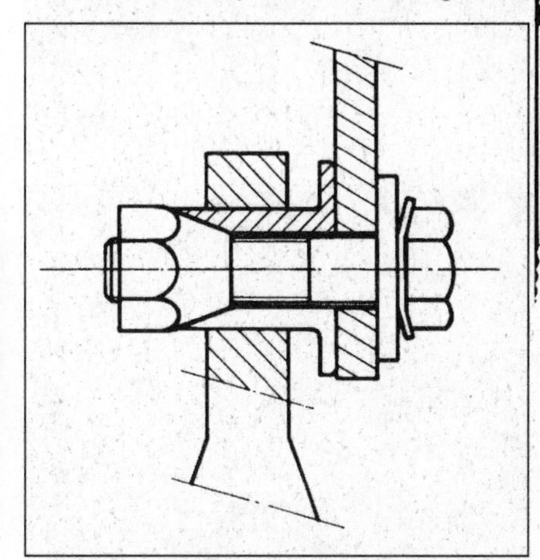

12.26 Cross-section of injection pump rear mounting

13.9a Disconnecting fuel pump supply banjo union. Note sealing washers (arrowed)

13.9b Refitting fuel supply banjo bolt with small section of fuel hose (arrowed) to prevent dirt ingress

13.10 Injection pump fuel return pipe banjo union (arrowed)

Support the vehicle on an axle stand and engage 4th or 5th gear. This will enable the engine to be turned easily by turning the roadwheel. On automatic transmission models, turn the engine using a spanner on the crankshaft pulley bolt. It will be easier to turn the engine if the glow plugs are removed.

5 Remove the upper timing belt covers, with reference to Part A of this Chapter.

6 Where necessary, disconnect the hoses from the vacuum converter on the end of the fuel injection pump.

7 Disconnect the accelerator cable from the fuel injection pump. On models with automatic transmission, also disconnect the kickdown cable.

8 Disconnect the fast idle cable from the fuel injection pump, with reference to Section 5.

9 Loosen the clip or undo the banjo union, then disconnect the fuel supply hose. Recover the sealing washers from the banjo union, where applicable. Cover the open end of the hose and refit and cover the banjo bolt to keep dirt out **(see illustrations)**.

10 Disconnect the main fuel return pipe and the injector leak-off return pipe banjo union **(see illustration)**. Recover the sealing washers from the banjo union. Again, cover the open end of the hose and the banjo bolt to keep dirt out. Take care not to get the inlet and outlet banjo unions mixed up.

11 Disconnect all relevant wiring from the pump. Note that on certain Bosch pumps, this can be achieved by simply disconnecting the wiring connectors at the brackets on the pump **(see illustration)**. On some pumps, it will be necessary to disconnect the wiring from the individual components (some connections may be protected by rubber covers).

12 Unscrew the union nuts securing the injector pipes to the injection pump and injectors. Counterhold the unions on the pump, while unscrewing the pipe-to-pump union nuts. Remove the pipes as a set. Cover open unions to keep dirt out **(see illustrations)**.

13 Turn the crankshaft until the two bolt holes in the injection pump sprocket are aligned with the corresponding holes in the engine front plate.

14 Insert two M8 bolts through the holes and hand-tighten them. Note that the bolts must retain the sprocket while the fuel injection pump is removed, thereby making it unnecessary to remove the timing belt **(see illustration)**.

15 Mark the injection pump in relation to the mounting bracket, using a scriber or felt tip pen. This will ensure the correct pump timing is retained when refitting.

13.11 Disconnecting fuel injection pump wiring plug

13.12a Unscrewing fuel pipe-to-pump union

13.12b Cover open end of each injector to prevent dirt ingress

13.14 Bolts inserted through timing holes in injection pump sprocket

13.16a Unscrewing an injection pump front mounting nut

13.16b Unscrewing an injection pump rear mounting nut (arrowed)

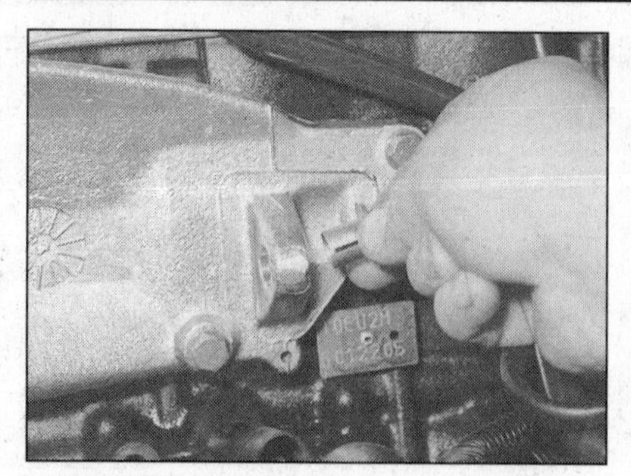

13.18 With pump removed, recover bush from rear of pump mounting bracket

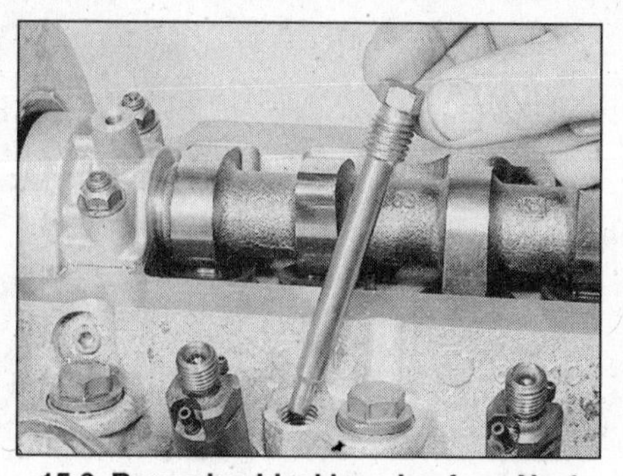

15.6 Removing blanking plug from No 4 cylinder

15.8 Setting No 4 piston timing position with dial test indicator

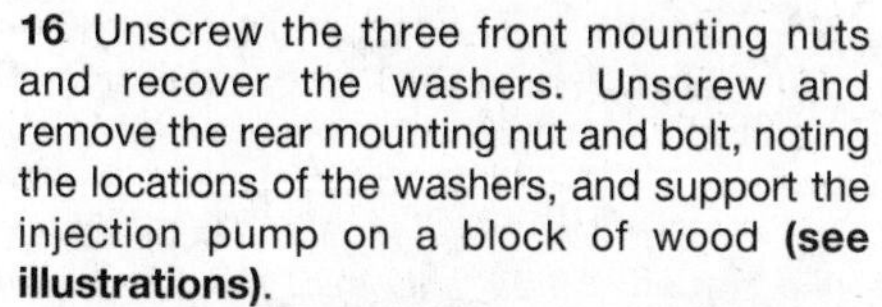

16 Unscrew the three front mounting nuts and recover the washers. Unscrew and remove the rear mounting nut and bolt, noting the locations of the washers, and support the injection pump on a block of wood **(see illustrations)**.

17 Release the injection pump sprocket from the pump shaft. Note that the sprocket can be left engaged with the timing belt as the pump is withdrawn from its mounting bracket. Refit the M8 bolts to retain the sprocket in position while the pump is removed.

18 Carefully withdraw the pump. Recover the Woodruff key from the end of the pump shaft if it is loose and recover the bush from the rear of the mounting bracket **(see illustration)**.

Refitting

19 Commence refitting the injection pump by fitting the Woodruff key to the shaft groove (if removed).

20 Offer the pump to the mounting bracket and support on a block of wood, as during removal.

21 Engage the pump shaft with the sprocket and refit the sprocket. Ensure that the Woodruff key does not fall out of the shaft as the sprocket is engaged.

22 Align the marks made on the pump and mounting bracket before removal. If a new pump is being fitted, transfer the mark from the old pump to give an approximate setting.

23 Refit and lightly tighten the pump mounting nuts and bolt.

24 Set up the injection timing, as described in Section 16.

15.10 Lucas CAV/Roto-Diesel injection pump with timing plug removed

25 Refit and reconnect the injector fuel pipes.

26 Reconnect all relevant wiring to the pump.

27 Reconnect the fuel supply and return hoses and tighten the unions, as applicable. Use new sealing washers on the banjo unions.

28 Reconnect the fast idle cable and adjust it as described in Section 5.

29 Reconnect and adjust the accelerator cable with reference to Section 1. Also reconnect the kickdown cable, where applicable.

30 Where necessary, reconnect the hoses to the vacuum converter.

31 Refit the upper timing belt covers.

32 Lower the vehicle to the ground.

33 Where applicable, refit the intercooler or the air distribution housing.

34 Uncover the alternator.

35 Reconnect the battery negative lead.

36 Bleed the fuel system, as described in Part A of this Chapter.

37 Start the engine and check the idle speed and anti-stall speed, as described in Part A of this Chapter.

14 Fuel injection pump (Peugeot 106) - timing

1 Refer to Section 16, paragraphs 1 to 21 inclusive. Pay particular attention to the Notes at the beginning of the same Section.

15 Fuel injection pump (Peugeot 205, 305 and 309) - timing

1 Refer to Section 16, paragraphs 1 to 3 inclusive. Pay particular attention to the Notes at the beginning of the same Section.

Lucas CAV/Roto-Diesel pump

Pre 1987 models

2 Disconnect the battery negative lead and cover the alternator as a precaution against fuel spillage.

3 Apply the handbrake, then jack up the front right-hand corner of the vehicle until the wheel is just clear of the ground. Support the vehicle on an axle stand and engage 4th or 5th gear. This will enable the engine to be turned easily by turning the right-hand wheel.

4 Disconnect the wire and unscrew the glow plug from No 4 cylinder (timing belt end). Note that the engine is timed with No 4 piston at TDC on compression (i.e. No 1 piston at TDC with valves rocking).

5 Two dial test indicators (DTIs) are now necessary for checking the positions of the No 4 piston and the injection pump. Magnetic type stands will be found helpful, or alternatively brackets may be made for fitting to appropriate positions on the engine.

6 Unscrew and remove the blanking plug from the cylinder head next to No 4 injector **(see illustration)**.

7 Turn the engine forwards until pressure is felt in No 4 cylinder, indicating that No 4 piston is beginning its compression stroke.

8 Position the DTI over the blanking hole and fit the probe **(see illustration)**.

9 Turn the engine forwards until the maximum lift of piston No 4 is registered on the DTI. Turn the engine slightly back and forth to determine the exact point of maximum lift then zero the indicator.

10 Loosen the lower of the two large side plugs on the side of the injection pump. Position a small container beneath the plug then remove the plug and catch any escaping fuel in the container **(see illustration)**.

11 Inside the plug aperture there is a probe guide. Insert the probe and connect it to the DTI directly over the hole **(see illustration)**. Note that the end of the probe must be

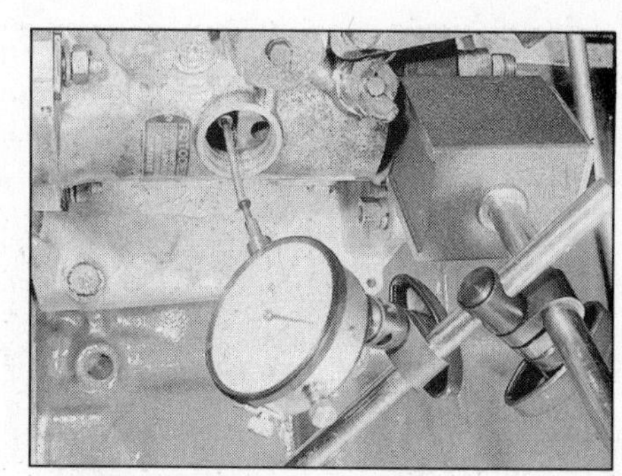

15.11a Timing Lucas CAV/Roto-Diesel injection pump with dial test indicator

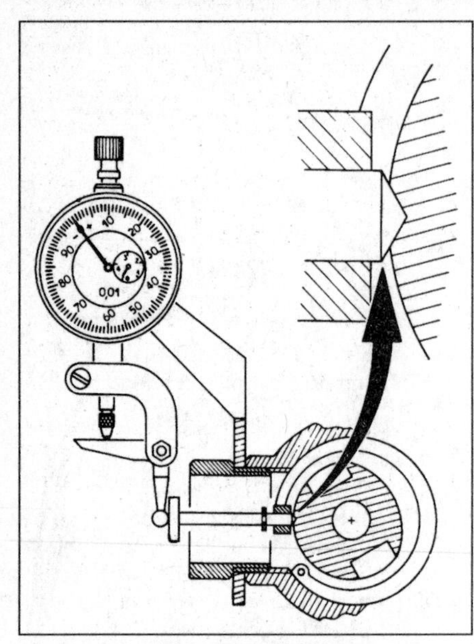

15.11b Checking timing on Lucas CAV/Roto-Diesel fuel injection pump

pointed in order to fully engage the groove in the pump rotor **(see illustration)**.

12 Turn the engine backwards approximately 1/8th of a turn or until No 4 piston has moved 4.0 mm down the cylinder. Now turn the engine slowly forwards while watching the DTI on the injection pump. After the probe has reached the bottom of the timing groove then risen by 0.01 to 0.02 mm, check that the upper DTI reads 2.26 ± 0.05 mm before TDC. If the timing is incorrect continue as follows.

13 Check the zero setting of the upper DTI by repeating the procedure given in paragraph 9.

14 Turn the engine backwards approximately 1/8th of a turn or until No 4 piston has moved 4.0 mm down the cylinder. Now turn the engine slowly forwards until No 4 piston is 2.26 ± 0.05 mm before TDC.

15 Unscrew the union nuts and disconnect the injector pipes from the injection pump. Loosen the injection pump mounting nuts and bolt.

16 Turn the pump body until the probe is at the bottom of the timing groove in the rotor. Zero the DTI. Now turn the pump clockwise (from the injector pipe end) until the probe has risen by 0.01 to 0.02 mm.

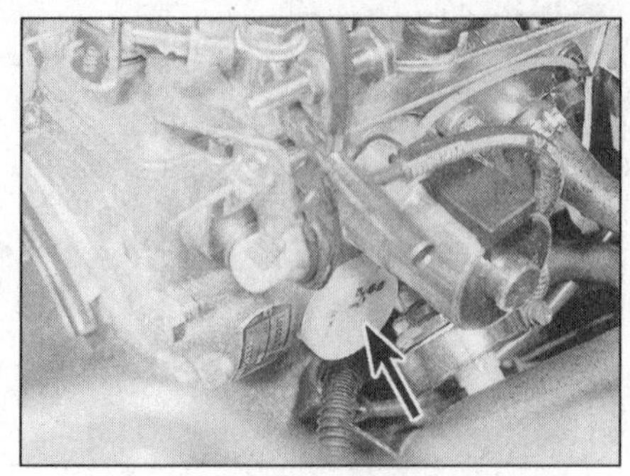

15.23 White plastic disc (arrowed) indicates static timing setting

17 Tighten the mounting nuts and bolts, making sure that there is no movement on the DTI.

18 Recheck the timing as described in paragraph 12.

19 Remove the DTIs and refit the plugs. Reconnect the injector pipes and tighten the union nuts.

20 Refit the glow plug and connect the wire.

21 Lower the vehicle to the ground and reconnect the battery negative lead. Uncover the alternator.

22 Prime the fuel system as described in Part A of this Chapter.

Post 1987 models

23 From 1987, a modified fuel injection pump was progressively introduced. This pump can be recognised by the presence of a white plastic disc on its front face. A timing value is engraved on the disc **(see illustration)**. If the disc is blue, this denotes a factory-reconditioned pump. The timing value may also be found on a plastic tag attached to the pump control lever.

24 Pump timing is now carried out at TDC. Only one dial test indicator (DTI) is needed but it will be necessary to make up a bent rod or similar tool to enter the TDC setting hole. The tool made up in the workshop consisted of an M8 bolt with the threads filed away, attached to a piece of welding rod **(see illustration)**. Alternatively, with the starter motor removed, a twist drill or straight rod can be used.

25 Prepare the engine, as described in paragraphs 2 and 3.

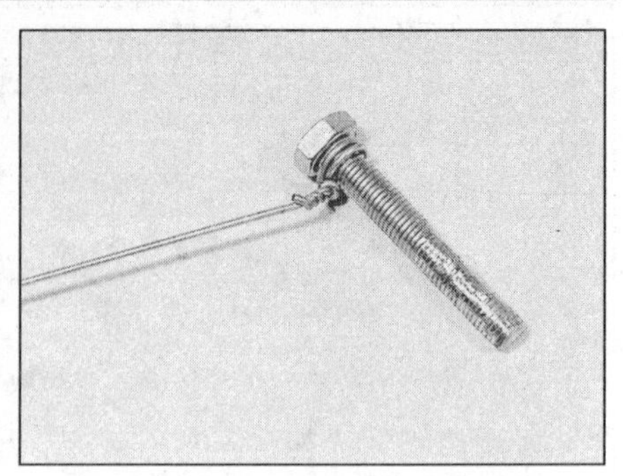

15.24 Home-made TDC setting tool

26 Turn the engine to bring No 4 cylinder (timing belt end) to TDC on compression. To establish which cylinder is on compression, remove No 4 cylinder glow plug or the TDC probe plug located near No 4 injector (see illustration 15.6) and feel for pressure. Alternatively, remove the valve cover and observe when No 1 cylinder valves are rocking (inlet opening and exhaust closing).

27 Insert the TDC setting tool into the hole at the left-hand end of the cylinder block, behind the starter motor location. Turn the engine back and forth slightly until the tool enters the hole in the flywheel. Leave the tool in position **(see illustration)**.

28 Remove the inspection plug from the top of the pump. Position the DTI so that it can read the movement of a probe inserted into the hole. If a magnetic stand is to be used, the absence of ferrous metal in the vicinity poses a problem. A piece of steel plate can be bolted to the engine mounting or valve cover to carry the stand **(see illustrations)**.

29 Make up a probe to the dimensions shown **(see illustration)**. Insert the probe into the inspection hole so that the tip of the probe rests on the rotor timing piece. Position the DTI to read the movement of the probe **(see illustration)**.

30 Remove the TDC setting tool. Turn the engine approximately a quarter-turn backwards. Zero the DTI.

31 Turn the engine forwards slowly until the TDC setting tool can be re-inserted. Read the DTI. The reading should correspond to the value engraved on the pump disc (± 0.04 mm).

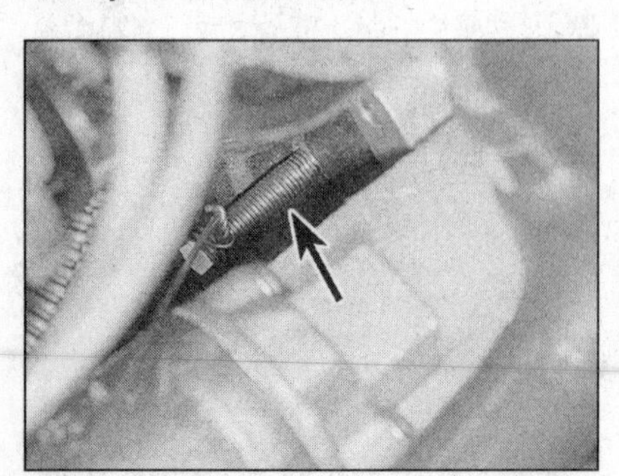

15.27 TDC setting tool (arrowed) inserted into cylinder block hole

15.28a Removing inspection plug from top of pump

15.28b Dial test indicator positioned over inspection hole

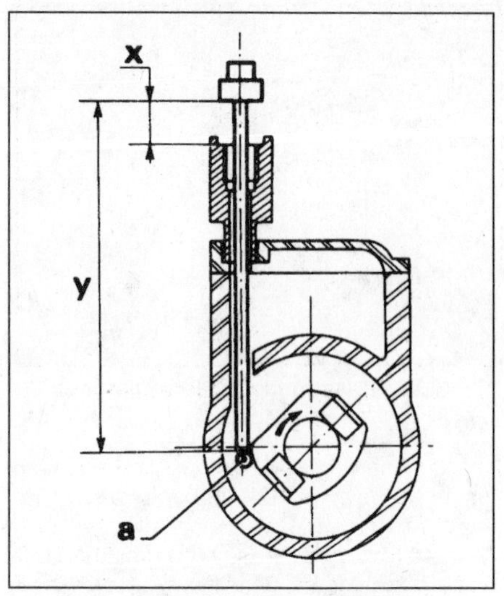

15.29a Timing probe details - later Lucas CAV/Roto-Diesel pump

a Timing piece
x Timing value (engraved on disc)
y 95.5 ± 0.01 mm
Probe diameter = 7 mm

32 If the reading is not as specified, continue as follows.
33 Disconnect the injector pipes from the pump. Slacken the pump mounting nuts and bolts, then swing the pump away from the engine. Zero the DTI.
34 With the engine still at TDC, slowly swing the pump back towards the engine until the DTI displays the value engraved on the pump disc. In this position, tighten the pump mountings. Remove the TDC setting tool and recheck the timing.
35 When the timing is correct, reconnect the injector pipes, remove the DTI and TDC setting tool, then refit the inspection plug.
36 Refit any other disturbed components, uncover the alternator and lower the vehicle to the ground.

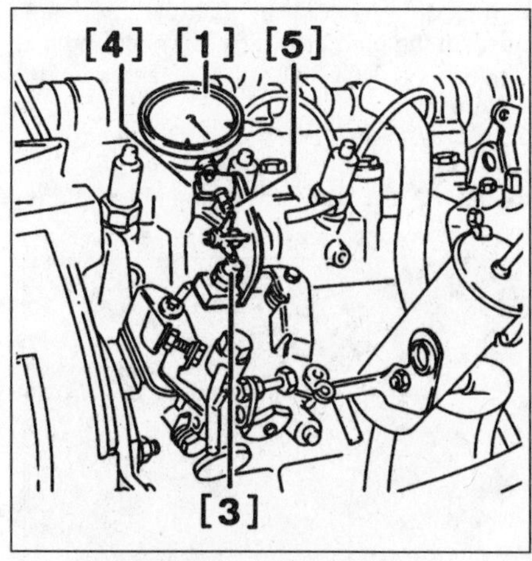

15.29b Checking static timing on Lucas injection pump

1 Dial test indicator
3 Probe
4 Fixture
5 Finger

Bosch pump

37 Proceed as described in paragraphs 2 to 9 inclusive.
38 Unscrew the union nuts and disconnect the injector pipes for cylinders 1 and 2 from the injection pump.
39 Unscrew the blanking plug from the end of the injection pump, between the injector pipe connections. Be prepared for the loss of some fuel.
40 Insert the probe and connect it to the dial test indicator (DTI) positioned directly over the hole **(see illustration).**
41 Turn the engine backwards approximately 1/8th of a turn or until the No 4 piston has moved 4.0 mm down the cylinder.
42 Zero the DTI on the injection pump.
43 Turn the engine slowly forwards until the DTI on the injection pump reads 0.30 mm. Then check that the upper DTI reads as follows:

1769 cc engine - 0.80 ± 0.03 mm BTDC
1905 cc engine - 0.50 ± 0.03 mm BTDC

If the timing is incorrect continue as follows.
44 Check the zero setting of the upper DTI by repeating the procedure given in paragraph 9.
45 Turn the engine backwards approximately 1/8th of a turn, or until No 4 piston has moved 4.0 mm down the cylinder. Now turn the engine slowly forwards until the upper DTI reads as stated in paragraph 43.
46 Unscrew the union nuts and disconnect the remaining injector pipes from the injection pump. Loosen the injection pump mounting nuts and bolt.
47 Turn the pump body anti-clockwise (from the injector pipe end) and check that the DTI is zeroed. Now turn the pump body slowly clockwise until the DTI reads 0.30 mm.
48 Proceed as described in paragraphs 17 to 22 inclusive.

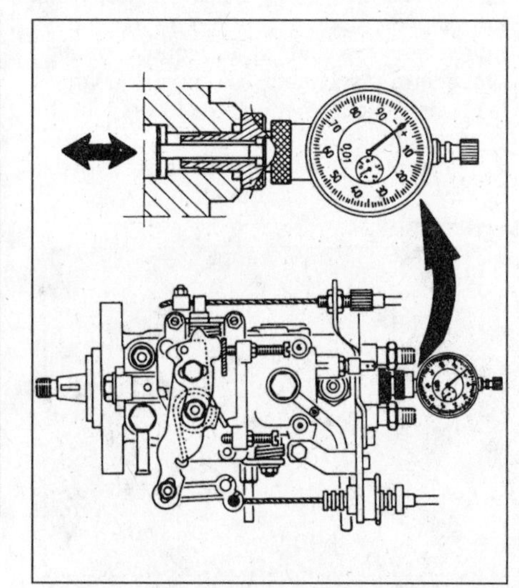

15.40 Checking timing on Bosch fuel injection pump

16 Fuel injection pump (Peugeot 306 and 405) - timing

Note: *Some fuel injection pump setting and access plugs are sealed by the manufacturer, with locking wire and lead seals. Do not disturb these seals if the vehicle is still within the warranty period, otherwise the warranty will be invalidated. Also, do not attempt the timing procedure unless accurate instrumentation is available. Suitable special tools for carrying out pump timing are available from motor factors or your Peugeot dealer.*
Note: *Turning the engine will be much easier if the glow plugs are removed.*
1 Checking the injection timing is only necessary after the fuel injection pump has been disturbed.
2 Dynamic timing equipment does exist but it is unlikely to be available to the home mechanic. If such equipment is available, use it in accordance with the manufacturer's instructions.
3 Static timing, as described in this Section, gives good results if carried out carefully. A dial test indicator (DTI) will be needed, with probes and adapters appropriate to the type of injection pump. Read through the following procedure before starting work, to find out what is involved.

Lucas pump

4 To check injection pump timing, a special timing probe and mounting bracket (Peugeot tool No. 0117AM) is required. Without access to this piece of equipment, injection pump timing should be entrusted to a Peugeot dealer or other suitably equipped specialist.
5 If injection timing is being checked with the pump in position on the engine, rather than as part of the pump refitting procedure, disconnect the battery negative lead and cover the alternator to prevent the possibility of fuel being spilt onto it. Remove the injector pipes as described in Section 13.
6 Referring to Part A of this Chapter, align the engine assembly/valve timing holes to lock the crankshaft in position. Remove the crankshaft locking tool, then turn the crankshaft backwards (anti-clockwise) approximately a quarter of a turn.
7 Unscrew the access plug from the guide on the top of the pump body and recover the sealing washer - see illustration 15.28a. Insert the special timing probe into the guide, making sure it is correctly seated against the guide sealing washer surface. The timing probe must be seated against the guide sealing washer surface and not the upper lip of the guide for the measurement to be accurate.
8 Mount the bracket on the pump guide (Peugeot tool No. 0117AM) and securely mount a dial test indicator (DTI) in the bracket

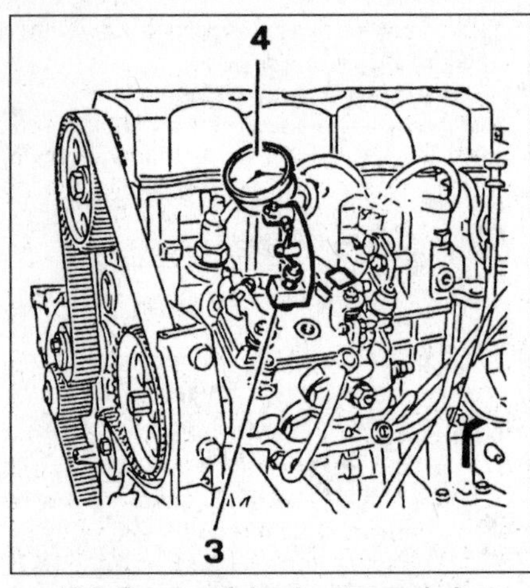

16.8 Peugeot injection pump timing gauge (4) and mounting bracket (3) in position on injection pump

so that its tip is in contact with the bracket linkage **(see illustration)**. Position the DTI so that its plunger is at the mid-point of its travel and zero the gauge.

9 Rotate the crankshaft slowly in the correct direction of rotation (clockwise) until the crankshaft locking tool can be re-inserted.

10 With the crankshaft locked in position, read the DTI. The reading should correspond to the value marked on the pump (there is a tolerance of ± 0.04 mm). The timing value may be marked on a plastic disc attached to the front of the pump or alternatively, on a tag attached to the pump control lever **(see illustration)**.

11 If adjustment is necessary, slacken the pump front mounting nuts and the rear mounting bolt, then slowly rotate the pump body until the point is found where the specified reading is obtained on the DTI. When the pump is correctly positioned, tighten its mounting nuts and bolt to the specified torque settings. Where necessary, to improve access to the pump nuts, undo the two screws and remove the cover panel from the side of the radiator.

12 Withdraw the timing probe slightly so that it is positioned clear of the pump rotor dowel, then remove the crankshaft locking pin. Rotate the crankshaft through one and three quarter rotations in the normal direction of rotation.

13 Slide the timing probe back into position, ensuring that it is correctly seated against the guide sealing washer surface, not the upper lip. Zero the DTI.

16.10 Pump timing values marked on label (1) and tag (2) - Lucas pump

14 Rotate the crankshaft slowly in the correct direction of rotation until the crankshaft locking tool can be re-inserted. Recheck the timing measurement.

15 If adjustment is necessary, slacken the pump mounting nuts and bolt and repeat the operations in paragraphs 11 to 14.

16 When the pump timing is correctly set, remove the DTI and mounting bracket and withdraw the timing probe.

17 Refit the screw and sealing washer to the guide and tighten it securely.

18 If the procedure is being carried out as part of the pump refitting sequence, proceed as described in Section 13.

19 If the procedure is being carried out with the pump fitted to the engine then refit the injector pipes, tightening their union nuts to the specified torque setting.

20 Reconnect the battery then bleed the fuel system as described in Part A of this Chapter.

21 Start the engine and adjust the idle speed and anti-stall speeds as described in Part A of this Chapter.

Bosch pump

22 If the injection timing is being checked with the injection pump in position on the engine, rather than as part of the pump refitting procedure, disconnect the battery negative lead and cover the alternator to prevent the possibility of fuel being spilt onto it.

23 Remove the injector pipes as described in Section 13 **(see illustrations)**.

16.23a Disconnect injector pipes . . .

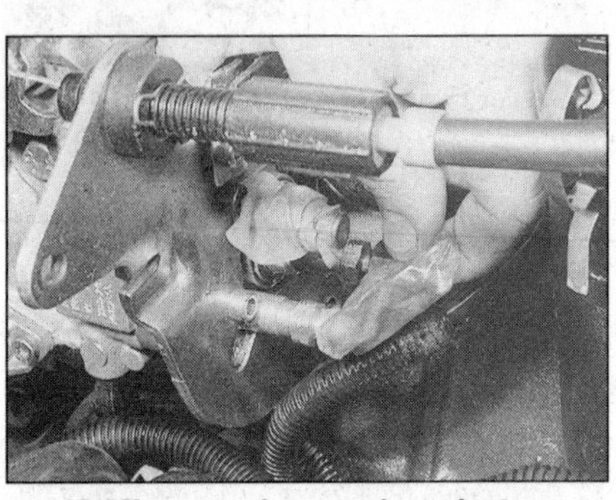
16.23b . . . and cover pipe adapters

24 If not already having done so, slacken the clamp screw and/or nut (as applicable) and slide the fast idle cable end fitting arrangement along the cable so that it is no longer in contact with the pump fast idle lever (ie. so the fast idle lever returns to its stop).

25 Referring to Part A of this Chapter, align the engine assembly/valve timing holes to lock the crankshaft in position. Remove the crankshaft locking tool, then turn the crankshaft backwards (anti-clockwise) approximately a quarter of a turn.

26 Unscrew the access screw (situated in the centre of the four injector pipe unions) from the rear of the injection pump. As the screw is removed, position a suitable container beneath the pump to catch any escaping fuel. Mop up any spilt fuel with a clean cloth **(see illustration)**.

27 Screw an adapter (Peugeot tool No. 0117F) into the rear of the pump and mount a DTI in the adapter **(see illustrations)**.

16.26 Remove blanking plug

16.27a Fit adapter . . .

16.27b . . . and dial test indicator

16.29 Inserting TDC timing rod

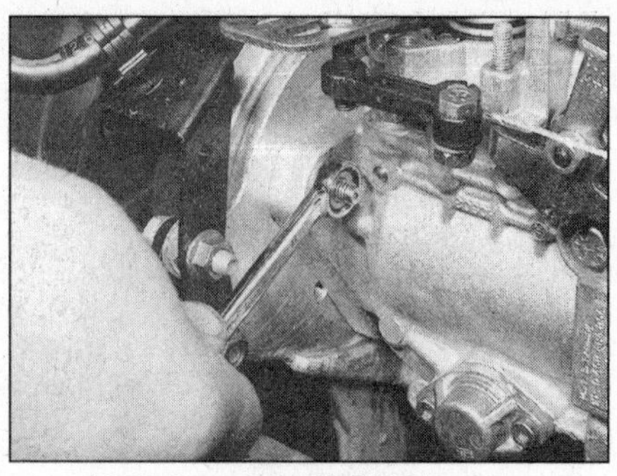

16.30 Loosening injection pump mounting bolts

An adapter can be purchased from most good motor factors. Position the DTI so that its plunger is at the mid-point of its travel and securely tighten the adapter locknut.

28 Slowly rotate the crankshaft back and forth whilst observing the DTI, to determine when the injection pump piston is at the bottom of its travel (BDC). When the piston is correctly positioned, zero the DTI.

29 Rotate the crankshaft slowly in the correct direction until the crankshaft locking tool can be re-inserted **(see illustration)**.

30 The reading obtained on the DTI should be equal to the specified pump timing measurement. If adjustment is necessary, slacken the front and rear pump mounting nuts and bolts and slowly rotate the pump body until the point is found where the specified reading is obtained. When the pump is correctly positioned, tighten both its front and rear mounting nuts and bolts securely **(see illustration)**.

31 Rotate the crankshaft through one and three quarter rotations in the normal direction of rotation. Find the injection pump piston BDC as described in paragraph 28 and zero the DTI.

32 Rotate the crankshaft slowly in the correct direction of rotation until the crankshaft locking tool can be re-inserted (bringing the engine back to TDC). Recheck the timing measurement.

33 If adjustment is necessary, slacken the pump mounting nuts and bolts and repeat the operations in paragraphs 30 to 32.

34 When the pump timing is correctly set, unscrew the adapter and remove the DTI.

35 Refit the screw and sealing washer to the pump and tighten it securely.

36 If the procedure is being carried out as part of the pump refitting sequence, proceed as described in Section 13.

37 If the procedure is being carried out with the pump fitted to the engine then refit the injector pipes, tightening their union nuts to the specified torque setting.

38 Reconnect the battery, then bleed the fuel system as described in Part A of this Chapter.

39 Start the engine and adjust the idle speed and anti-stall speeds as described in Part A of this Chapter.

40 Adjust the fast idle cable as described in Section 5.

17 Preheating system - testing, component removal and refitting

System testing

1 If the preheating system malfunctions, testing is ultimately by substitution of known good units but some preliminary checks may be made as follows.

2 Connect a voltmeter or 12-volt test lamp between the glow plug supply cable and earth (engine or vehicle metal). Ensure that the live connection is kept clear of the engine and bodywork.

3 Have an assistant switch on the ignition and check that voltage is applied to the glow plugs. Note the time for which the warning light is lit and the total time for which voltage is applied before the system cuts out. Switch off the ignition.

4 At an under-bonnet temperature of 20°C, typical times noted should be 5 or 6 seconds for warning light operation, followed by a further 10 seconds supply after the light goes out. Warning light time will increase with lower temperatures and decrease with higher temperatures.

5 If there is no supply at all, the relay or associated wiring is at fault.

6 To locate a defective glow plug, first disconnect the main supply cable and the interconnecting wire or strap from the top of the glow plugs. Be careful not to drop the nuts and washers. On Peugeot 306 and 405 Turbo models, remove the intercooler. On Peugeot 306 and 405 non turbo models with the D9B engine, remove the air distribution housing. If necessary, also remove the intake duct, and disconnect the breather hose from the engine oil filler tube.

7 Use a continuity tester, or a 12-volt test lamp connected to the battery positive terminal, to check for continuity between each glow plug terminal and earth. The resistance of a glow plug in good condition is very low (less than 1 ohm), so if the test lamp does not light or the continuity tester shows a high resistance, the glow plug is certainly defective.

8 If an ammeter is available, the current draw of each glow plug can be checked. After an initial surge of 15 to 20 amps, each plug should draw the following amperage. Any plug which draws much more or less than this is probably defective:

10 amps - Peugeot 106
12 amps - All other models

9 As a final check, the glow plugs can be removed and inspected as described in Sections 7 or 8, as applicable.

Control unit

Removal

10 The preheating system control unit is located as follows:

Peugeot 106 - On the right-hand side of the engine compartment, on the coolant expansion tank ***(see illustrations).***
Peugeot 306 - On the left-hand side of the engine compartment, on the rear of the battery box.

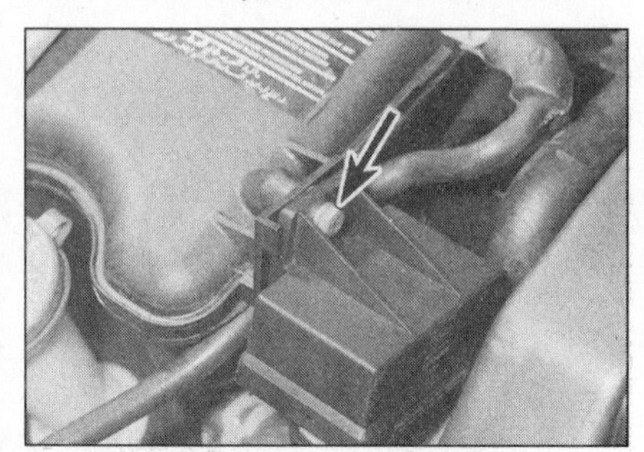

17.10a Unscrew preheating unit retaining bolt (arrowed) and free unit from expansion tank

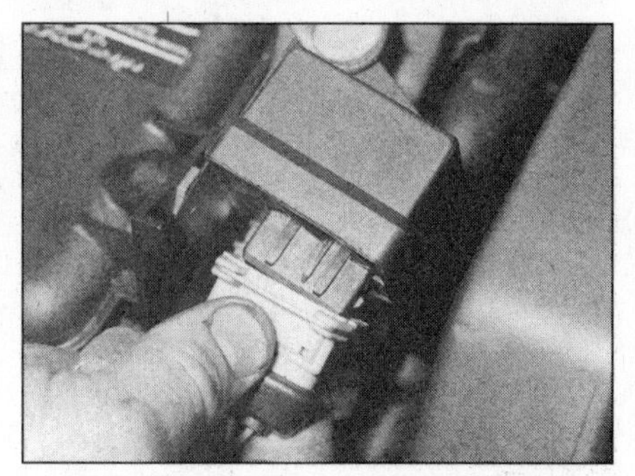

17.10b Disconnect wiring connector . . .

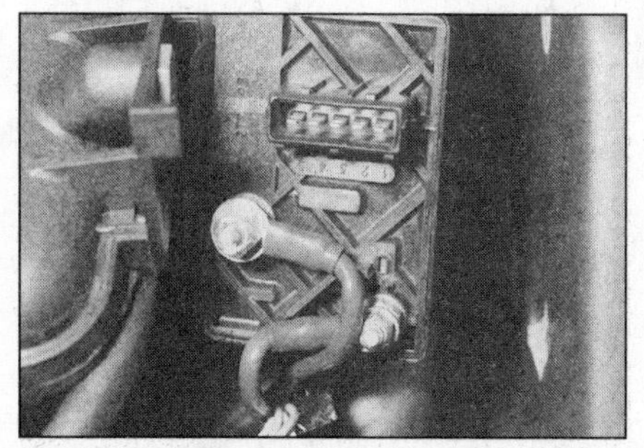

17.10c . . . then undo two nuts securing feed and supply wires to unit - Peugeot 106

17.10d Preheating system control unit location (arrowed) - Peugeot 405

Peugeot 405 - On the left-hand side of the engine compartment bulkhead, behind the battery (early models) or on the side of the battery tray (later models) ***(see illustration)****.*

All other models - Refer to Section 9.

11 Disconnect the battery negative lead.

12 Unscrew the unit retaining nut or bolt and recover the washer, where fitted.

13 Where applicable, disconnect the wiring connector from the base of the unit, then unscrew the two retaining nuts and free the main feed and supply wires from the unit. Remove the unit from the engine compartment.

Refitting

14 Refitting is a reversal of removal, ensuring that the wiring connectors are correctly connected.

18 Post heating cut-off switch (Peugeot 405) - adjustment, removal and refitting

Adjustment

1 The post heating cut-off switch is mounted on a bracket, on the top of the fuel injection pump.

2 Before proceeding, check that the accelerator cable is correctly adjusted, as described in Section 1.

3 Mark the accelerator cable inner, 1.0 mm from the point where it enters the cable sheath end fitting **(see illustration)**.

4 Move the pump control lever until the mark is against the end of the cable sheath end fitting.

5 Loosen the switch securing screws.

6 Carefully move the switch until the contacts just click open.

7 Tighten the switch securing screws.

Removal

8 Release the switch wiring from any clips.

9 Disconnect the switch wiring connector and release the connector from the bracket on the fuel injection pump.

10 Unscrew the two securing screws and withdraw the switch.

Refitting

11 Refitting is a reversal of removal. On completion, adjust the switch.

19 Exhaust gas recirculation system (Peugeot 306 and 405) - testing and component renewal

System testing

1 Testing of the exhaust gas recirculation (EGR) system should be entrusted to a Peugeot dealer.

Component renewal

2 At the time of writing, no specific information was available regarding removal and refitting of the system components.

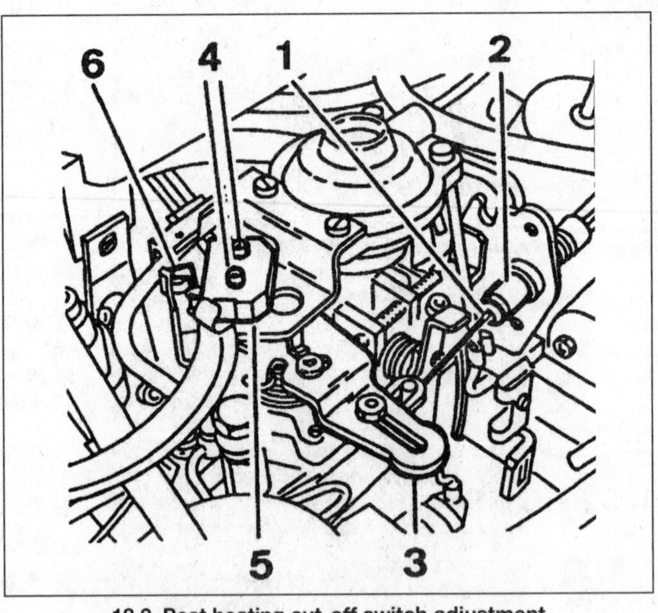

18.3 Post heating cut-off switch adjustment

1 Mark made on inner cable
2 Cable sheath end fitting
3 Pump control lever
4 Switch securing screws
5 Switch
6 Switch contacts

Chapter 9
Renault 1870cc, 2068cc & 2188cc engines

Part A: Routine maintenance and servicing

Contents

Engine application

1870cc engine . . . . Renault Clio and 19 - 1989 to 1996
2068cc engine . . . . Renault Espace - 1985 to 1996
2188cc engine . . . . Renault Laguna - 1994 to 1996

Manufacturer's engine codes

Renault 19

Non turbo . . . . F8Q 706, F8Q 764, or F8Q 742
Turbo . . . . F8Q 740 or F8Q 744

Renault Clio

Codes . . . . F8Q 714, F8Q 730 and F8Q 732

Renault Espace

Code J8S

Renault Laguna

Code G8T

Servicing specifications

Oil filter

Renault 19 and Espace . . . . Champion F105
Renault Clio . . . . Champion F121
Renault Laguna . . . . Champion listing not available at time of writing

Valve clearances (cold)

Renault 19 and Clio

Inlet . . . . 0.20 mm
Exhaust . . . . 0.40 mm

Renault Espace

Inlet . . . . 0.20 mm
Exhaust . . . . 0.25 mm

Renault Laguna

Inlet and Exhaust . . . . Hydraulic tappets. Automatic valve clearance adjustment

Timing belt

Renault 19 and Clio

Type	Toothed belt
Tension - using Renault tool Ele. 364.04	7.0 to 8.0 mm deflection under 30N load

Renault Espace

Type	Toothed belt
Tension - using Renault tool Ele. 364.04	3.0 to 5.0 mm deflection under 30N load

Renault Laguna

Type	Toothed belt
Tension - using Renault tool Mot. 1312	See text

Auxiliary drivebelt tension

Renault 19

Tension - using Renault tool:	
With power steering and air conditioning	2.0 to 3.5 mm deflection under 30N load
Without power steering and air conditioning	3.0 to 6.0 mm deflection under 30N load

Renault Clio

Tension - using Renault tool:	
Cold	2.5 to 3.5 mm deflection under 30N load
Hot	3.5 to 4.5 mm deflection under 30N load

Renault Espace

Tension - using Renault tool:	
Alternator/coolant pump	4.5 to 5.5 mm deflection under 30N load
Power steering pump	4.0 to 4.5 mm deflection under 30N load
Air conditioning compressor	3.5 to 4.5 mm deflection under 30N load

Renault Laguna

Tension - using Renault tool	No deflection figures available at time of writing

Air filter

Renault 19:	
Non turbo	Champion W212
Turbo	Champion listing not available at time of writing
Renault Clio	Champion V429
Renault Espace	Champion W132
Renault Laguna	Champion U550

Fuel filter

Renault 19	Champion L131 or L137
Renault Clio:	
Roto-Diesel/Lucas	Champion L131 or L137
Bosch	Champion L136
Renault Espace:	
Pre 1991, Lucas/CAV	Champion L132
All other types	Champion L111
Renault Laguna	Champion L115

Glow plugs

Renault 19:	
Non turbo	Champion CH88 or CH137
Turbo	Champion CH69
Renault Clio	Champion CH155
Renault Espace	Champion CH137
Renault Laguna	Champion listing not available at time of writing

Idle speed

Renault 19:	
Non turbo - except F8Q 706	825 ± 25 rpm
F8Q 706 engine	800 ± 50 rpm
Turbo	825 ± 50 rpm
Renault Clio	825 ± 25 rpm
Renault Espace	750 ± 50 rpm
Renault Laguna	775 ± 25 rpm

Fast idle speed

Renault 19, Clio and Espace:	
Bosch injection pump	1000 ± 50 rpm
Roto-Diesel/Lucas injection pump	Not adjustable (factory set)
Renault Laguna	875 ± 25 rpm

Anti-stall speed

Renault 19

Non turbo (4.0 mm shim)	1350 ± 50 rpm
Turbo (4.0 mm shim)	1250 ± 50 rpm

Renault Clio

Roto-Diesel/Lucas injection pump (5.0 mm shim)	1600 ± 100 rpm
Bosch injection pump:	
F8Q 714 and 730 engines (4.0 mm shim)	1300 ± 50 rpm
F8Q 732 engine (1.0 mm shim)	Idle speed should raise by 10 to 20 rpm

Renault Espace

With pump-mounted fast idle valve	Not adjustable
With cylinder head-mounted fast idle valve (1.0 mm shim)	Idle speed should raise by 10 to 20 rpm

Renault Laguna

With 1.0 mm shim	Idle speed should raise by 10 to 20 rpm

Torque wrench settings

	Nm	lbf ft
Renault 19 and Clio		
Sump drain plug	15 to 25	11 to 18
Timing belt tensioner roller nut	50	37
Crankshaft pulley bolt	90 to 100	66 to 74
Right-hand engine mounting plate-to-body nuts	45	33
Lower engine steady bracket nuts	45	33
Renault Espace		
Crankshaft pulley bolt	98	74
Renault Laguna		
Crankshaft pulley bolt:		
Stage 1	25	18
Stage 2	Angle-tighten through 64°	
Timing belt tensioner pulley nut	32	22
Engine/transmission right-hand mounting:		
Mounting/injection pump bracket bolts	45	33
Mounting bracket to engine bracket bolts	55	41
Mounting bracket to rubber mounting nut	35	26
Rubber mounting to body bolts	55	41

Lubricants, fluids and capacities

Component or system	Lubricant or fluid	Capacity
Renault 19		
Engine	Multigrade engine oil, viscosity range SAE 10W/30 to 15W/40, to specification CCMC-PD2 or API SG/CD	5.5 litres - with filter
Cooling system	Ethylene glycol based antifreeze. 50% volume with water	6.8 litres - non turbo 7.1 litres - turbo
Fuel system	Commercial Diesel fuel for road vehicles (DERV)	55.0 litres
Renault Clio		
Engine	Multigrade engine oil, viscosity range SAE 10W/30 to 15W/40, to specification CCMC-PD2 or API SG/CD	5.5 litres - with filter
Cooling system	Ethylene glycol based antifreeze. 50% volume with water	6.6 litres
Fuel system	Commercial Diesel fuel for road vehicles (DERV)	43.0 litres
Renault Espace		
Engine	Multigrade engine oil, viscosity range SAE 10W/40 to 15W/40, to specification API SG/CD	6.0 litres - with filter
Cooling system	Ethylene glycol based antifreeze. 50% volume with water	7.2 litres
Fuel system	Commercial Diesel fuel for road vehicles (DERV)	60.0 litres
Renault Laguna		
Engine	Multigrade engine oil, viscosity range SAE 10W/40 to 20W/50, to specification API SG/CD	6.5 litres - with filter
Cooling system	Ethylene glycol based antifreeze. 50% volume with water	9.0 litres
Fuel system	Commercial Diesel fuel for road vehicles (DERV)	66.0 litres

Renault diesel engine - maintenance schedule

The maintenance schedules which follow are basically those recommended by the manufacturer. Servicing intervals are determined by mileage or time elapsed - this is because fluids and systems deteriorate with age as well as with use. Follow the time intervals if the appropriate mileage is not covered within the specified period.

Vehicles operating under adverse conditions may need more frequent maintenance. Adverse conditions include climatic extremes, full-time towing or taxi work, driving on unmade roads, and a high proportion of short journeys. The use of inferior fuel can cause early degradation of the engine oil. Consult a Renault dealer for advice on these points.

Every 250 miles (400 km), weekly, or before a long journey - all models

- ☐ Check engine oil level and top up if necessary (Section 3)
- ☐ Check coolant level and top up if necessary (Section 4)
- ☐ Check exhaust emission (Section 5)
- ☐ Check operation of glow plug warning light (Section 6)

Every 5000 miles (8000 km) - all models

- ☐ Renew engine oil and filter (Section 7)
- ☐ Drain water from fuel filter (Section 8)
- ☐ Check engine compartment hoses for security and leaks
- ☐ Check condition and tension of auxiliary drivebelt(s)
- ☐ Check emission control system (Section 9)
- ☐ Check turbocharger components (Section 10)

Every 10 000 miles (16 000 km) - Renault 19, Clio and Laguna

- ☐ Renew fuel filter (Sections 11,12 and 13)
- ☐ Renew air filter element

Certain models are fitted with a dual-element fuel filter assembly. On these models, only the inlet (fuel tank side) filter should be renewed at the specified interval. The outlet (injection pump) side fuel filter should be renewed at every third inlet filter change.

Every 10 000 miles (16 000 km) - Renault Espace

- ☐ Renew fuel filter (Section 14)
- ☐ Check engine idle speed and anti-stall speed (Section 15)

Every 15 000 miles (24 000 km) - Renault 19, Clio and Laguna

- ☐ Check engine idle speed and anti-stall speed (Section 16)

Every 15 000 miles (24 000 km) - Renault Espace

- [ ] Renew air filter element

Every 70 000 miles (112 000 km) - Renault 19, Clio and Laguna

- [ ] Renew timing belt (Sections 17, 18 and 19)

It is strongly recommended that the timing belt renewal interval is reduced to 40 000 miles (64 000 km) on vehicles which are subjected to intensive use, ie. mainly short journeys or a lot of stop-start driving. The actual belt renewal interval is therefore very much up to the individual owner but bear in mind that severe engine damage may result if the belt breaks.

Every 80 000 miles (120 000 km) - Renault Espace

- [ ] Renew timing belt (Section 20)

It is strongly recommended that the timing belt renewal interval is halved on vehicles which are subjected to intensive use, ie. mainly short journeys or a lot of stop-start driving. The actual belt renewal interval is therefore very much up to the individual owner but bear in mind that severe engine damage will result if the belt breaks.

Every 2 years - all models

- [ ] Renew engine coolant

Underbonnet view of Turbo Diesel engine in Renault 19

1 *Washer fluid reservoir*
2 *Suspension strut top mounting*
3 *Brake fluid reservoir*
4 *Engine oil filler cap*
5 *Preheating system control unit*
6 *Brake vacuum pump*
7 *Coolant expansion tank*
8 *Auxiliary fuse/relay box*
9 *Intercooler*
10 *Air cleaner*
11 *Thermostat housing*
12 *Cooling fan*
13 *Engine oil level dipstick*
14 *Engine oil filter*
15 *Power steering fluid reservoir*
16 *Alternator*
17 *Fuel filter*
18 *Fuel system priming plunger*
19 *Right-hand engine mounting cover*
20 *Fuel injection pump*
21 *Accelerator cable*

Underbonnet view of Diesel engine in Renault Clio

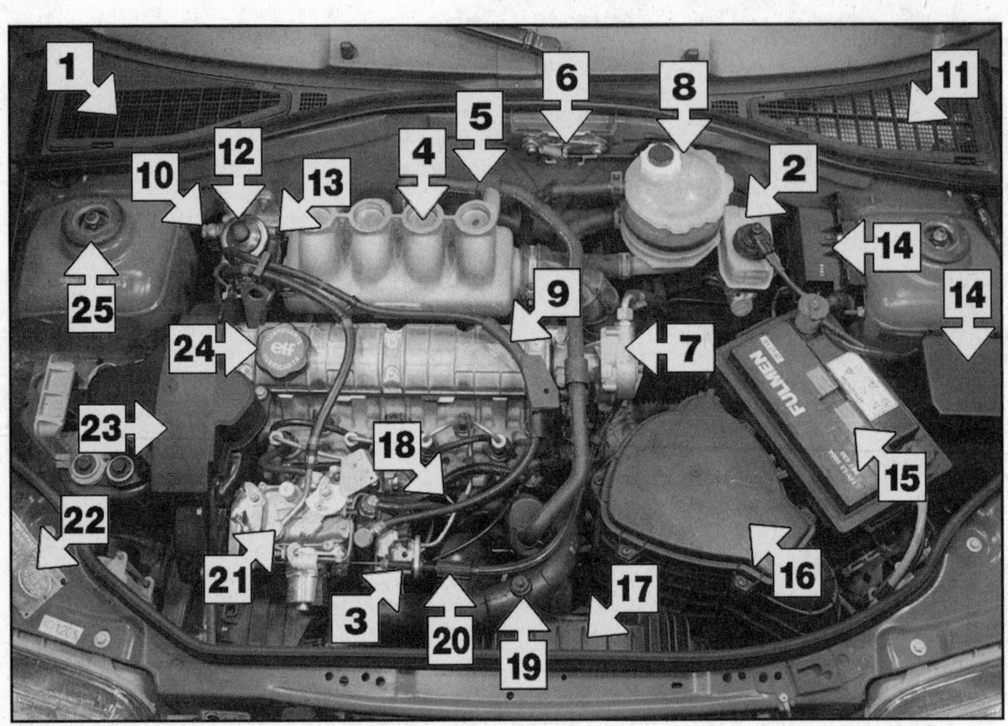

1 *Jack location*
2 *Brake fluid reservoir*
3 *Accelerator cable*
4 *Inlet manifold*
5 *Crankcase ventilation hose*
6 *Bonnet lock assembly*
7 *Brake vacuum pump*
8 *Coolant expansion tank*
9 *Fuel filter outlet hose*
10 *Fuel filter inlet union*
11 *Washer fluid reservoir location*
12 *Fuel system priming plunger*
13 *Fuel filter bleed screw*
14 *Relay box*
15 *Battery*
16 *Air cleaner assembly*
17 *Radiator cowl*
18 *Engine oil level dipstick*
19 *Bleed screw on radiator top hose*
20 *Oil filter*
21 *Fuel injection pump*
22 *VIN plate*
23 *Right-hand engine mounting cover*
24 *Engine oil filler cap*
25 *Suspension strut top mounting*

Underbonnet view of Diesel engine in Phase 3 Renault Espace

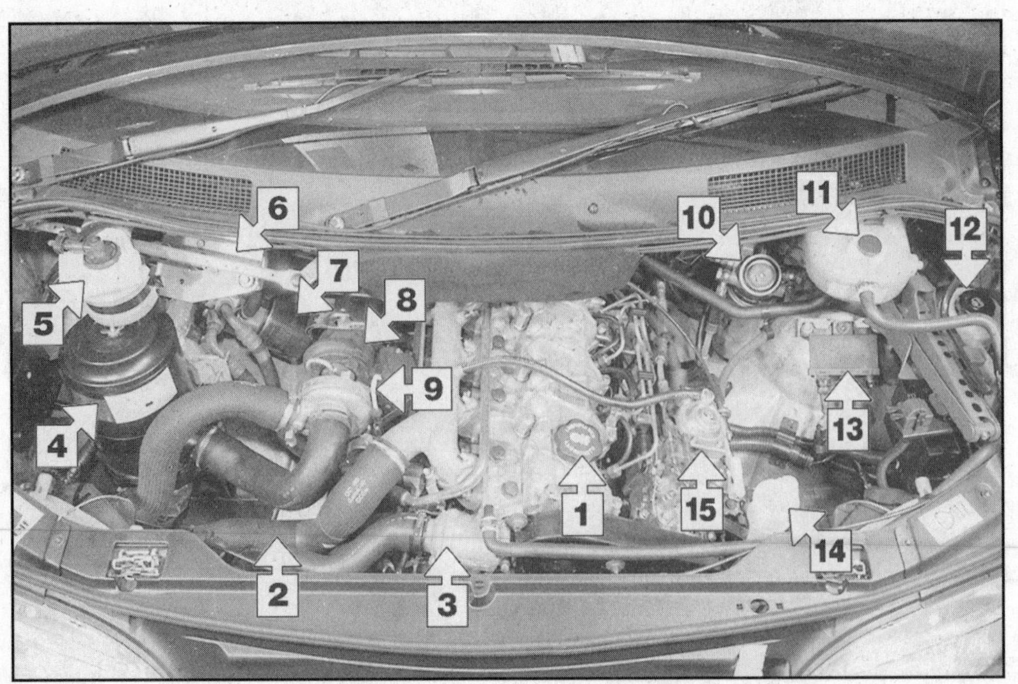

1 *Oil filler cap*
2 *Intercooler ducting*
3 *Intercooler*
4 *Air cleaner*
5 *Brake fluid reservoir*
6 *Wiper motor and linkage*
7 *Oil filter*
8 *Turbocharger*
9 *Engine oil dipstick*
10 *Fuel filter*
11 *Coolant expansion tank*
12 *Steering fluid reservoir*
13 *Preheating control unit*
14 *Washer reservoir*
15 *Injection pump*

Underbonnet view of Diesel engine in Renault Laguna

1 *Engine oil filler cap*
2 *Engine oil level dipstick*
3 *Battery*
4 *Brake fluid reservoir*
5 *Coolant expansion tank*
6 *Suspension strut upper mounting*
7 *Air filter housing*
8 *Brake vacuum pump/power steering pump drivebelt cover*
9 *Power steering fluid reservoir*
10 *Fuel injection pump*
11 *Fuel filter housing and priming button*
12 *Washer fluid reservoir*

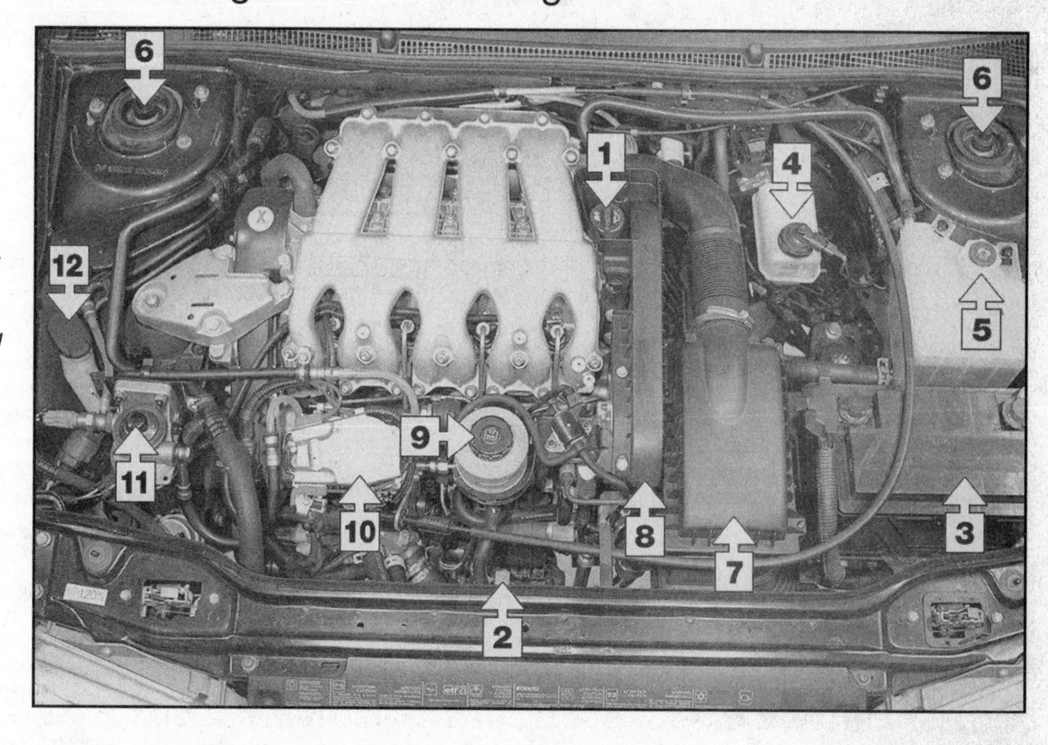

Maintenance procedures

1 Introduction

Refer to Chapter 2, Part A, Section 1.

2 Intensive maintenance

Refer to Chapter 2, Part A, Section 2.

250 mile (400 km) Service - all models

3 Engine oil level check

1 Refer to Chapter 2, Part A, Section 3 **(see illustrations)**.

4 Coolant level check

1 Refer to Chapter 2, Part A, Section 4. Note that the tank is translucent, so the coolant level can be verified without removing the cap. The level should be between the MAX (HOT) and MIN (COLD) marks embossed on the side of the tank. If the level is below the MIN mark, remove the cap and top up with coolant mixture to the MAX mark **(see illustration)**.

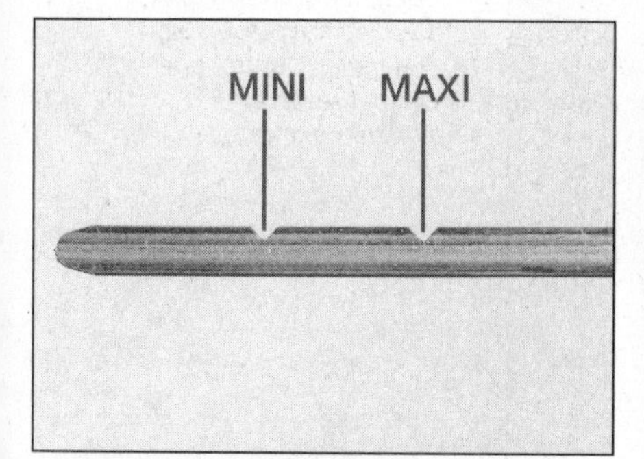

3.1a Engine oil level dipstick markings - Renault Espace shown, others similar

3.1b Topping-up engine oil - Renault 19 shown

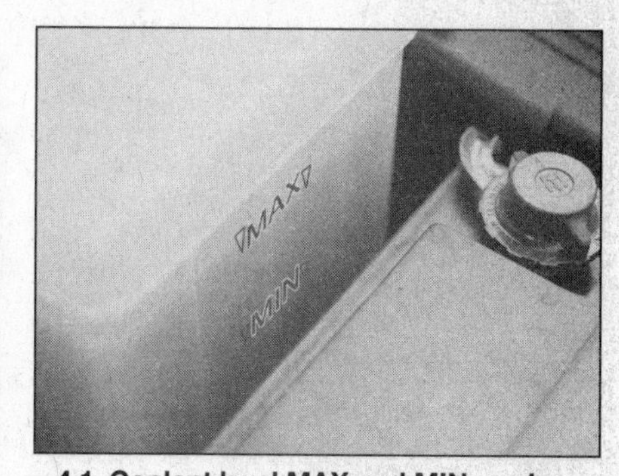

4.1 Coolant level MAX and MIN marks - Renault Laguna

5 Exhaust smoke check

1 Refer to Chapter 2, Part A, Section 5.

6 Warning light check

1 Refer to Chapter 2, Part A, Section 6.

5000 mile (8000 km) Service - all models

7 Engine oil and filter renewal

1 Refer to Chapter 2, Part A, Section 7, whilst noting the following **(see illustrations)**.

2 Whereas on non turbo engines, there will be a delay upon starting of a few seconds before the oil pressure warning light goes out, this does not apply to Turbo models, for which the following procedure should be followed before starting the engine:

a) Disconnect the wiring from the stop solenoid on the injection pump, then insulate the connector.

b) Crank the engine on the starter motor until the instrument panel oil pressure warning light goes out (this may take several seconds).

c) Reconnect the wiring to the stop solenoid, then start the engine using the normal procedure.

d) Run the engine at idle speed and check the turbocharger oil and coolant unions for leakage. Rectify any problems without delay.

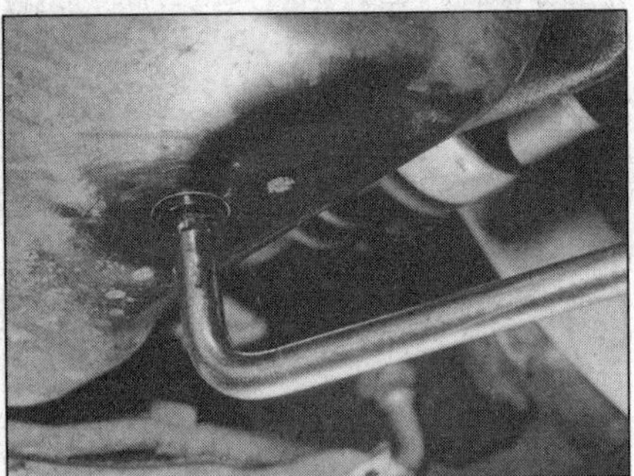

7.1a Removing engine oil drain plug

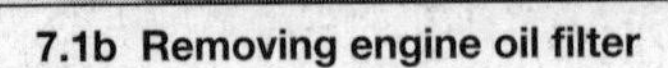

7.1b Removing engine oil filter

8 Fuel filter water draining

1 A water drain plug is provided at the base of the fuel filter housing.

2 Place a suitable container beneath the plug. To make draining easier, a suitable length of tubing can be attached to the outlet on the plug to direct the fuel flow **(see illustration)**.

3 Loosen the fuel inlet union on the filter head, then open the drain plug by turning it anti-clockwise **(see illustration)**.

4 Allow the entire contents of the filter to drain into the container, then tighten the drain plug and the fuel inlet union.

5 Dispose of the drained fuel safely.

6 Prime and bleed the fuel system as follows.

Fuel system priming and bleeding

7 All models are fitted with a hand-operated priming pump, which is operated by a plunger located on top of the fuel filter head.

8 To prime the system, loosen the bleed screw, which is located on the filter head outlet union or on the fuel pump inlet union **(see illustrations)**. If no bleed screw is fitted, loosen the outlet union itself.

9 Pump the priming plunger until fuel which is free from air emerges from the outlet union or bleed screw (as applicable) **(see illustration)**. Retighten the bleed screw or outlet union.

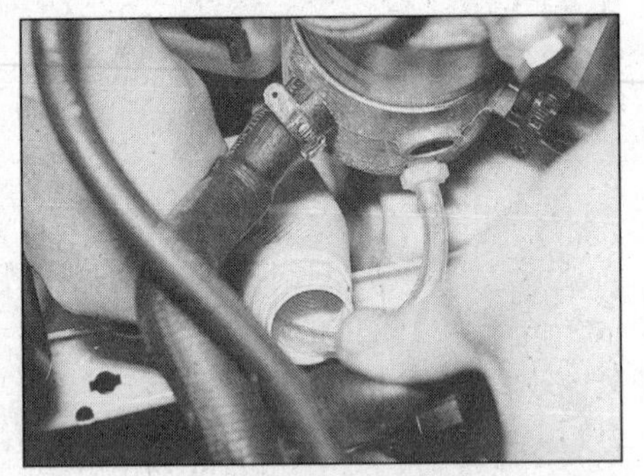

8.2 Tubing attached to drain plug at base of fuel filter housing

8.3 Loosening fuel inlet union on filter head

8.8a Fuel system bleed screw (arrowed) - Bosch filter

8.8b Loosening fuel system bleed screw (arrowed) located on fuel pump inlet union

8.9 Pumping fuel system priming plunger

10 Switch on the ignition (to activate the stop solenoid) and continue pumping the priming plunger until firm resistance is felt, then pump a few more times.

11 If a large amount of air has entered the pump, place a wad of rag around the fuel return union on the pump (to absorb spilt fuel), then slacken the union. Operate the priming plunger (with the ignition switched on to activate the stop solenoid), or crank the engine on the starter motor in 10 second bursts, until fuel which is free from air emerges from the fuel union. Tighten the union and mop up split fuel. Be prepared to stop the engine if it should fire, to avoid excessive fuel spray and spillage.

12 If air has entered the injector pipes, place wads of rag around the injector pipe unions at the injectors (to absorb spilt fuel), then slacken the unions. Crank the engine on the starter motor until fuel emerges from the unions, then stop cranking the engine and retighten the unions. Mop up any spilt fuel.

13 Start the engine with the accelerator pedal fully depressed. Additional cranking may be necessary to finally bleed the system before the engine starts.

9 Emission control system check

1 Detailed checking and testing of the exhaust emission systems should be entrusted to a Renault dealer.

10 Turbocharger component check

1 Check all turbocharger hose and pipe connections (oil, coolant and boost pressure) for security and leaks. Any deficiencies must be rectified without delay.

10 000 mile (16 000 km) Service - Renault 19, Clio & Laguna

11 Fuel filter renewal - Renault 19

1 Drain the fuel filter bowl.

2 Unscrew the through-bolt from the top of the filter head, then withdraw the bolt whilst supporting the filter bowl **(see illustration)**.

3 Lower the filter bowl, taking care not to strain the coolant hoses. Recover the lower seal and lift out the element **(see illustrations)**. If desired, the filter bowl can be removed completely after disconnecting the coolant hoses.

4 Recover the upper seals, noting their locations **(see illustrations)**.

5 Clean out the filter bowl.

6 Fit a new element with new seals (supplied with the filter) to the bowl, ensuring that the seals are correctly located.

7 Fit the element and the bowl to the filter head, with the drain plug positioned on the engine side of the bowl. Fit and tighten the through-bolt.

8 Prime and bleed the fuel system as described in Section 8.

12 Fuel filter renewal - Renault Clio

1 Drain the fuel filter bowl.

2 Position a suitable container on the engine to accept the fuel filter assembly when it is removed.

3 Unscrew the mounting nuts and move the fuel filter assembly away from the bulkhead **(see illustration)**.

4 Place some absorbent cloth beneath the inlet union on the side of the fuel filter housing, then unscrew the union bolt and

11.2 Unscrewing fuel filter through-bolt

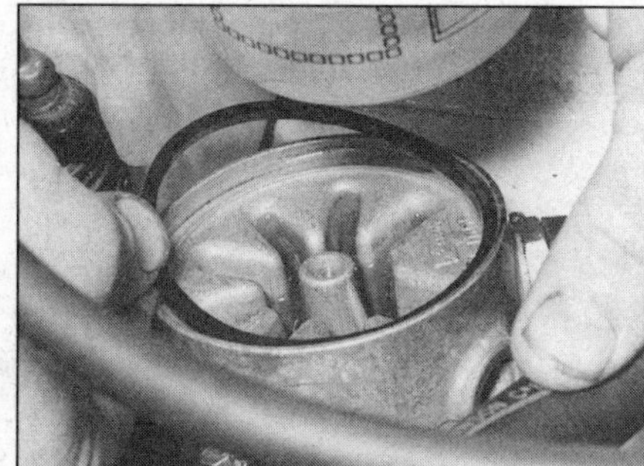

11.3a Recover lower seal . . .

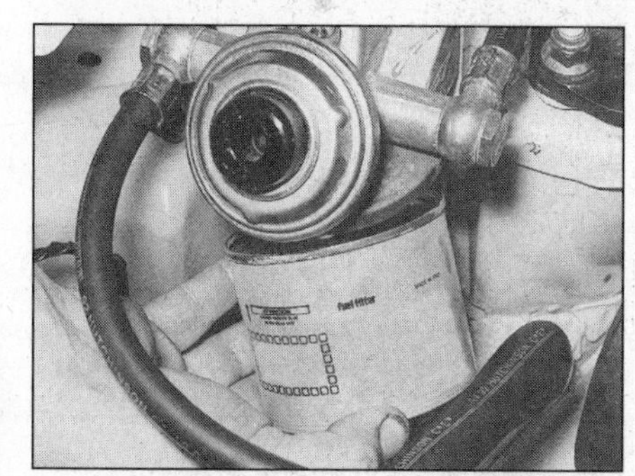

11.3b . . . and lift out filter element

11.4a Recover large . . .

11.4b . . . and smaller upper seals

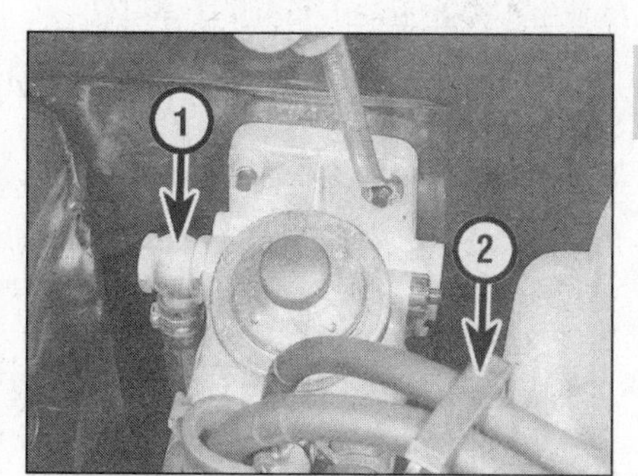

12.3 Removing fuel filter mounting nuts. Note fuel inlet union (1) and hose clip (2)

9A

disconnect the inlet hose. Recover the sealing washers.
5 Tape over the end fitting of the inlet hose to prevent entry of dust and dirt.
6 Release the outlet hose from the retaining clip.
7 Release the coolant hoses from the bulkhead and from the clips on the fuel filter chamber, then position the assembly in the container on the engine. The fuel outlet should be uppermost **(see illustration)**.
8 Using an Allen key, unscrew the through-bolt from the bottom of the fuel chamber and withdraw the chamber.
9 Recover the seals noting their locations.
10 Clean out the filter bowl.
11 Fit a new element with new seals (supplied with the filter) to the bowl, ensuring that the seals are correctly located.
12 Fit the element and the bowl to the filter head, with the drain plug positioned on the engine side of the bowl. Fit and tighten the through-bolt.
13 Refit the fuel filter assembly, making sure that the coolant hoses are correct located. Tighten the mounting nuts.
14 Locate the outlet hose in its retaining clip.

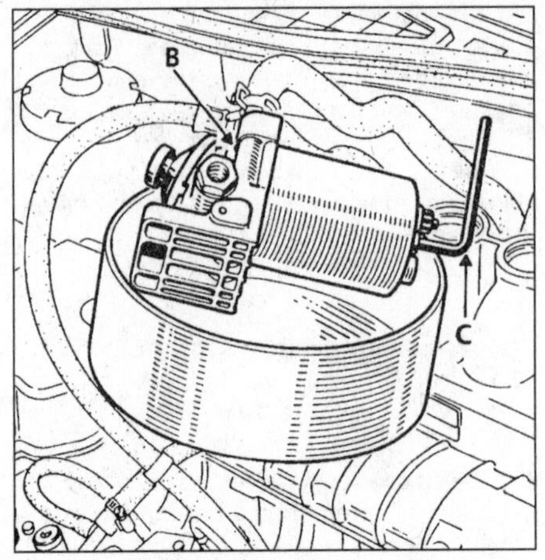

12.7 Fuel filter assembly located in container
B Fuel outlet C Allen key

15 Remove the tape, then reconnect the inlet hose together with new sealing washers. Tighten the union bolt.
16 Prime and bleed the fuel system as described in Section 8.

13 Fuel filter renewal - Renault Laguna

1 Drain the contents of the fuel filter.
2 Use a strap wrench to loosen the filter, then unscrew the filter and remove it from the base of its housing. Recover the filter sealing ring. To improve access, unscrew the retaining nuts and free the filter housing from its mounting bracket.
3 Smear the sealing ring of the new filter with fuel and screw the new filter onto the housing. Tighten the filter firmly, by hand only.
4 Refit the filter housing to its mounting bracket and securely tighten the nuts.
5 Prime and bleed the fuel system as described in Section 8.

10 000 mile (16 000 km) Service - Renault Espace

14 Fuel filter renewal

Lucas/CAV type

1 Refer to Section 11.

Bosch type

2 Drain the filter bowl.
3 Use a strap wrench to loosen the filter, then unscrew it by hand **(see illustration)**. Recover the filter sealing ring
4 Smear the sealing ring of the new filter with fuel. Ensure that the seal is in position on the new filter element then screw the element into position.
5 Tighten the element moderately tight by hand, then tighten a further quarter turn with the strap wrench.
6 Prime and bleed the fuel system as described in Section 8.

15 Idle speed and anti-stall speed check

Note: *The following procedure varies according to the type of fast idle thermostatic valve fitted. Two different types of valve may be fitted. One type of valve is screwed into the cylinder head and the other mounted on a bracket attached to the rear of the injection pump. Identify the type fitted, then proceed as described under the relevant sub-heading.*

1 The usual type of tachometer (rev counter) which works from ignition system pulses cannot be used on diesel engines. A diagnostic socket is provided for the use of Renault test equipment but this will not normally be available to the home mechanic. If it is not felt that adjusting the idle speed by ear is satisfactory, then one of the following alternatives may be used.

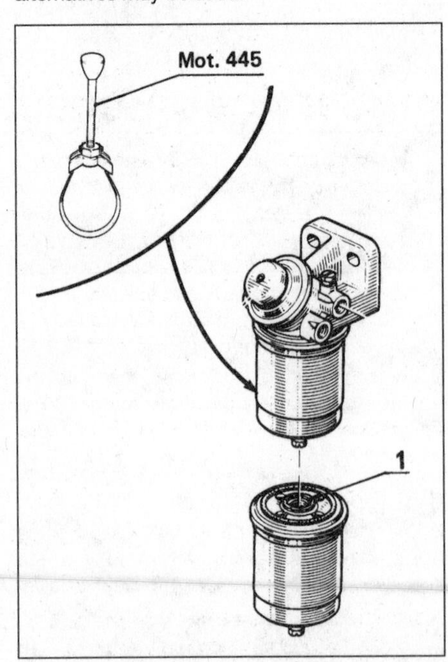

14.3 Bosch fuel filter showing removal tool and seal location (1)

a) Purchase or hire of an appropriate tachometer.
b) Delegation of the job to a Renault dealer or other specialist.
c) Timing light (strobe) operated by a petrol engine running at the desired speed. If the timing light is pointed at a mark on the camshaft or injection pump sprocket, the mark will appear stationary when the two engines are running at the same speed (or multiples of that speed). The sprocket will be rotating at half crankshaft speed but this will not affect adjustment. In practice it was found impossible to use this method on the crankshaft pulley due to the acute viewing angle.

2 Before making adjustments, warm up the engine to normal operating temperature and ensure that the accelerator cable is correctly adjusted.

Idle speed

3 With the accelerator lever resting against the idle stop, check that the engine idles at the specified speed. If necessary, adjust as follows.

Pump-mounted fast idle valve

4 Loosen the locknut on the idle speed adjustment screw. Turn the screw as required and retighten the locknut **(see illustration)**.

Cylinder head-mounted fast idle valve

5 Loosen the locknut and unscrew the anti-stall speed adjustment screw until it is clear of the pump accelerator lever.

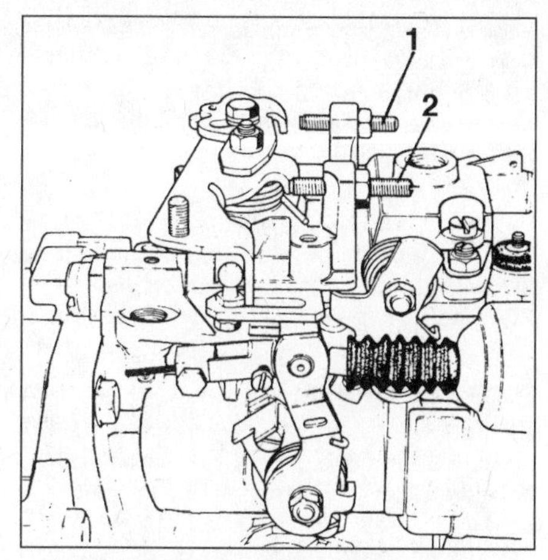

15.4 Adjustment points - pump mounted fast idle valve

1 *Idle speed adjustment screw*
2 *Maximum speed adjustment screw*

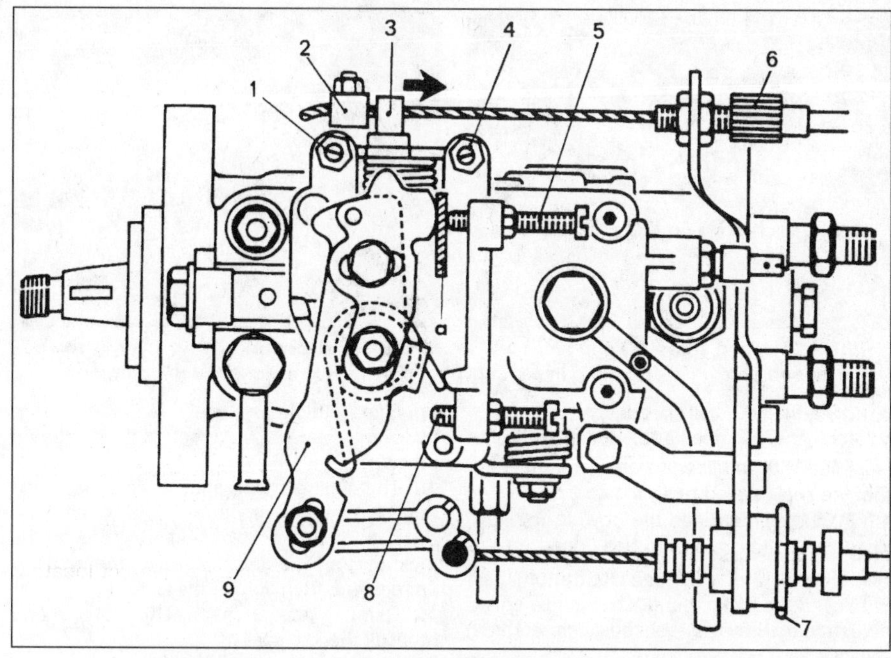

15.6 Adjustment points - cylinder head-mounted fast idle valve

1 *Fast idle adjustment screw*
2 *Cable end clamp*
3 *Fast idle lever*
4 *Idle speed adjustment screw*
5 *Anti-stall adjustment screw*
6 *Fast idle cable adjustment screw*
7 *Accelerator cable spring clip*
8 *Maximum speed adjustment screw*
9 *Accelerator lever*
a *Shim for anti-stall speed adjustment*

6 Loosen the locknut and turn the idle speed adjustment screw as required, then retighten the locknut **(see illustration)**.

7 Carry out anti-stall speed adjustment.

8 Stop the engine and disconnect the tachometer, where applicable.

Anti-stall speed

Pump-mounted fast idle valve

9 On these pumps it is not possible to adjust the anti-stall speed setting.

Cylinder head-mounted fast idle valve

10 Make sure that the engine is at operating temperature and idling at the specified speed.

11 Insert a 1.0 mm shim or feeler blade between the pump accelerator lever and the anti-stall speed adjustment screw. The idle speed should rise by about 10 to 20 rpm.

12 If adjustment is necessary, loosen the locknut and turn the anti-stall speed screw as required. Retighten the locknut.

13 Remove the shim and move the pump accelerator lever to increase the engine speed to about 3000 rpm, then quickly release the lever and check that the engine returns to the specified idle speed. Recheck the anti-stall speed setting and readjust, if necessary.

14 With the anti-stall speed correctly set, move the fast idle lever fully towards the flywheel end of the engine and check that the engine speed increases to the specified fast idle speed. If necessary, loosen the locknut and turn the fast idle adjusting screw as required, then retighten the locknut.

15 Where applicable, disconnect the tachometer on completion.

15 000 mile (24 000 km) Service - Renault 19, Clio & Laguna

16 Idle speed and anti-stall speed check

1 The usual type of tachometer (rev counter) which works from ignition system pulses, cannot be used on diesel engines. A diagnostic socket is provided for the use of Renault test equipment but this will not normally be available to the home mechanic. If it is not felt that adjusting the idle speed by ear is satisfactory, one of the following alternatives may be used:

a) Purchase or hire of an appropriate tachometer.

b) Delegation of the job to a Renault dealer or other specialist.

c) Timing light (strobe) operated by a petrol engine running at the desired speed. If the timing light is pointed at a mark on the camshaft or injection pump sprocket, the mark will appear stationary when the two engines are running at the same speed (or multiples of that speed). The sprocket will be rotating at half crankshaft speed but this will not affect adjustment. In practice it was found impossible to use this method on the crankshaft pulley due to the acute viewing angle.

2 Before making adjustments, warm up the engine to normal operating temperature. Ensure that the accelerator cable is correctly adjusted.

Idle speed

3 With the accelerator lever resting against the idle stop, check that the engine idles at the specified speed. If necessary adjust as follows.

Roto-Diesel/Lucas injection pump

4 Loosen the locknut on the idle speed adjustment screw. Turn the screw as required and retighten the locknut **(see illustration)**.

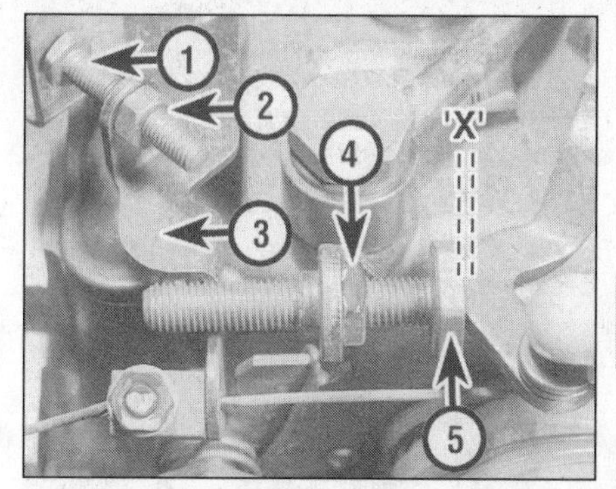

16.4 Idle speed and anti-stall speed adjustment points - Roto-Diesel/Lucas pump

1 *Idle speed adjustment screw*
2 *Locknut*
3 *Fast idle lever*
4 *Locknut*
5 *Anti-stall speed adjustment screw*
X = Clearance - accelerator lever to anti-stall speed screw

16.7 Idle speed screw (1) and anti-stall speed screw (2) - Bosch pump

16.19 Hand-operated stop lever (arrowed) - Roto-Diesel/Lucas pump

5 Check the anti-stall speed.
6 Stop the engine and disconnect the tachometer, where applicable.

Bosch injection pump

7 Loosen the locknut and unscrew the anti-stall adjustment screw until it is clear of the pump accelerator lever **(see illustration)**.
8 Loosen the locknut and turn the idle speed adjustment screw as required, then retighten the locknut.
9 Carry out anti-stall speed adjustment.
10 Stop the engine and disconnect the tachometer, where applicable.

Anti-stall speed

11 Ensure that the engine is at normal operating temperature and idling at the specified speed.

Roto-Diesel/Lucas injection pump

12 Insert a shim or feeler blade of the specified thickness between the pump accelerator lever and the anti-stall adjustment screw.
13 The engine speed should increase to the specified anti-stall speed.
14 If adjustment is necessary, loosen the locknut, turn the anti-stall adjustment screw as required, then tighten the locknut.
15 Remove the shim or feeler blade and recheck the idle speed.
16 Move the pump accelerator lever to increase engine speed to approximately 3000 rpm, then quickly release the lever. The deceleration period should be approximately 2.5 to 3.5 seconds and the engine speed should drop to approximately 50 rpm below idle.
17 If deceleration is too fast and the engine stalls, unscrew the anti-stall adjustment screw 1/4 turn towards the accelerator lever. If deceleration is too slow, resulting in poor engine braking, turn the screw 1/4 turn away from the lever.
18 Retighten the locknut after making an adjustment, then recheck the idle speed and adjust if necessary.
19 With the engine idling, check the operation of the manual stop control by turning the stop lever clockwise **(see illustration)**. The engine must stop instantly.
20 Where applicable, disconnect the tachometer on completion.

Bosch injection pump

21 Insert a shim or feeler blade of the specified thickness between the pump accelerator lever and the anti-stall adjustment screw.
22 The engine speed should be as specified for the anti-stall speed.
23 If adjustment is necessary, loosen the locknut and turn the anti-stall adjustment screw as required. Retighten the locknut.
24 Remove the shim or feeler blade and allow the engine to idle.
25 Move the fast idle lever fully towards the flywheel end of the engine and check that engine speed increases to the specified fast idle speed. If necessary, loosen the locknut and turn the fast idle adjusting screw as required, then retighten the locknut.
26 With the engine idling, check the operation of the manual stop control by turning the stop lever. The engine must stop instantly.
27 Where applicable, disconnect the tachometer on completion.

70 000 mile (112 000 km) Service - Renault 19, Clio & Laguna

17 Timing belt renewal - Renault 19

Note: *A suitable tool will be required to check the timing belt tension on completion of refitting and a suitable puller may be required to remove the crankshaft pulley.*
Note: *An 8 mm dia. rod or drill bit is needed to lock the crankshaft in the TDC position.*

Removal

1 Disconnect the battery negative lead.
2 Jack up the front right-hand corner of the vehicle and remove the roadwheel and the lower wheel arch cover, which is secured by plastic clips.
3 Further access may be gained by unbolting the strengthening bar from between the front suspension strut turrets.
4 Remove the auxiliary drivebelt.
5 Unscrew the crankshaft pulley bolt while holding the crankshaft stationary. To hold the crankshaft, from under the vehicle, remove the flywheel cover plate/engine-to-gearbox bracing bracket. Note the locations of any brackets secured by the bolts. Refit one of the cover plate-to-gearbox bolts to act as a fulcrum, and then have an assistant insert a screwdriver or similar tool in the starter ring gear teeth to prevent crankshaft rotation **(see illustrations)**.

17.5a Unscrew side . . .

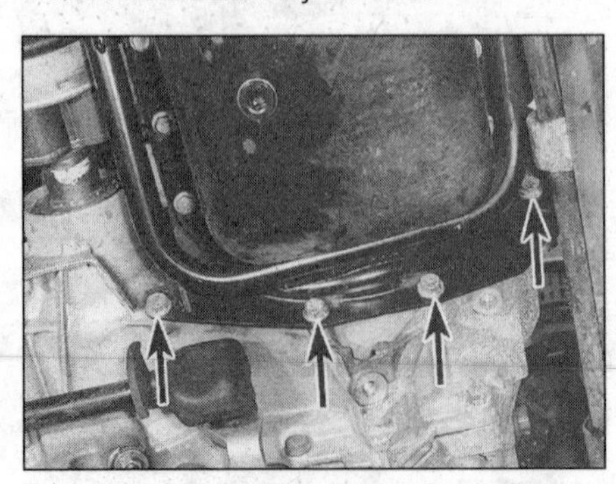
17.5b . . . and front securing bolts (arrowed) . . .

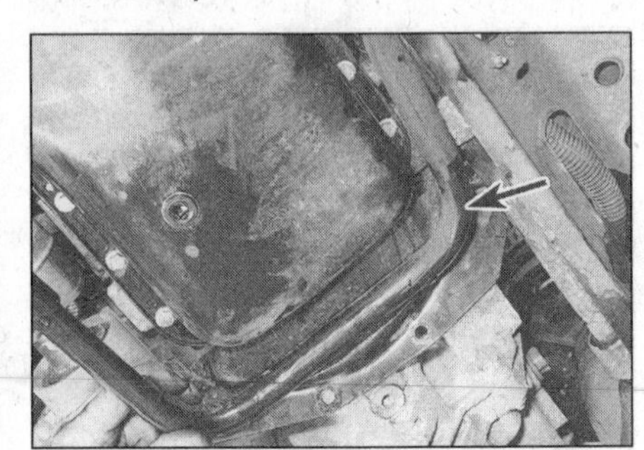
17.5c . . . and remove flywheel cover plate/engine-to-gearbox bracing bracket (arrowed)

17.6a Remove crankshaft pulley bolt . . .

17.6b . . . and pulley

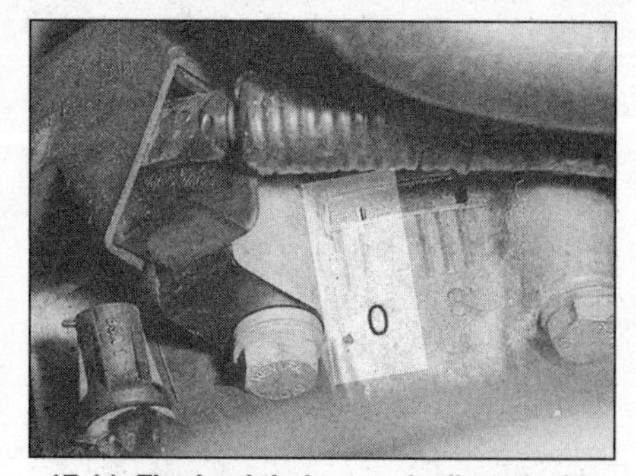
17.11 Flywheel timing mark aligned with TDC (0) mark on bellhousing

6 Remove the bolt and the pulley from the front of the crankshaft **(see illustrations)**. Use a suitable puller if the pulley is tight.

7 To improve access, unscrew the two bolts securing the fuel filter assembly to the body panel, then unclip the filter hoses from the brackets on the engine. The assembly can be moved to one side (on top of the engine) until completion of refitting.

8 Temporarily refit the crankshaft pulley bolt. Turn the crankshaft to position No 1 piston (flywheel end of engine) at TDC on the compression stoke, then lock the crankshaft in position as follows.

9 With No 1 piston at TDC, the timing mark on the camshaft sprocket should be aligned with the pointer on the outer timing belt cover. The sprocket mark can be viewed through the cut-out in the timing belt cover, below the pointer. Additionally, the timing mark on the flywheel should be aligned with the TDC mark on the gearbox bellhousing.

10 The crankshaft must be turned to align the timing marks. This should be done by using a spanner on the crankshaft pulley bolt. To enable the engine to be turned more easily, remove the glow plugs or fuel injectors.

11 Look through the timing aperture in the gearbox bellhousing and turn the crankshaft until the timing mark on the flywheel is aligned with the TDC (0°) mark on the bellhousing **(see illustration)**.

12 Unscrew the three securing bolts and remove the plastic cover from the upper right-hand engine mounting bracket **(see illustration)**. Note the location of any brackets which may be secured by the bolts.

13 Check that the timing mark on the camshaft sprocket is aligned with the pointer on the outer timing belt cover **(see illustration)**. Note that the mark may not align exactly due to the possible movement of the timing belt cover within its bolts holes.

14 Remove the plug on the lower front-facing side of the cylinder block, at the flywheel end, and obtain a metal rod which is a snug fit in the plug hole (8 mm diameter). Turn the crankshaft slightly if necessary to the TDC position, then push the rod through the hole to locate in the slot in the crankshaft web **(see illustrations)**.

15 Ensure that the crankshaft is exactly at TDC for No 1 piston by aligning the timing mark on the flywheel with the TDC (0°) mark on the gearbox bellhousing as described previously. If the crankshaft is not positioned accurately, it is possible to engage the rod with a balance hole in the crankshaft web by mistake, instead of the TDC slot **(see illustration)**.

16 The right-hand upper engine mounting

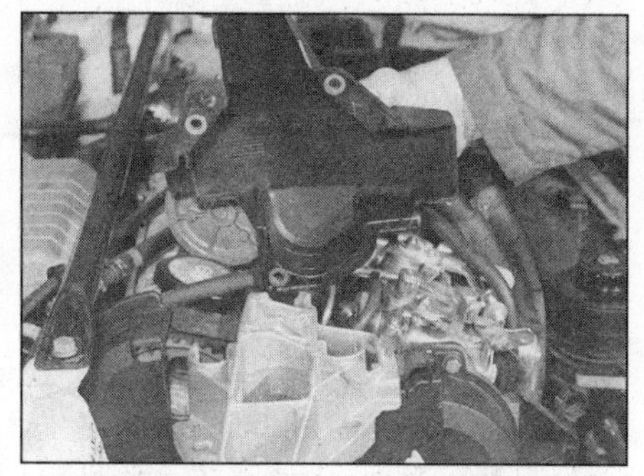
17.12 Removing cover from engine mounting bracket

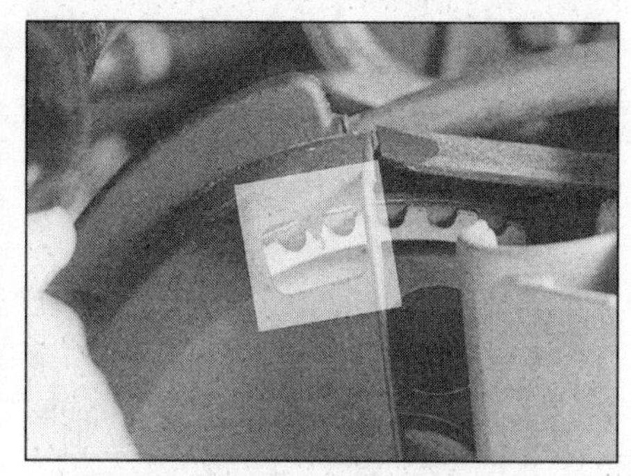
17.13 Camshaft sprocket timing mark aligned with pointer on timing belt cover

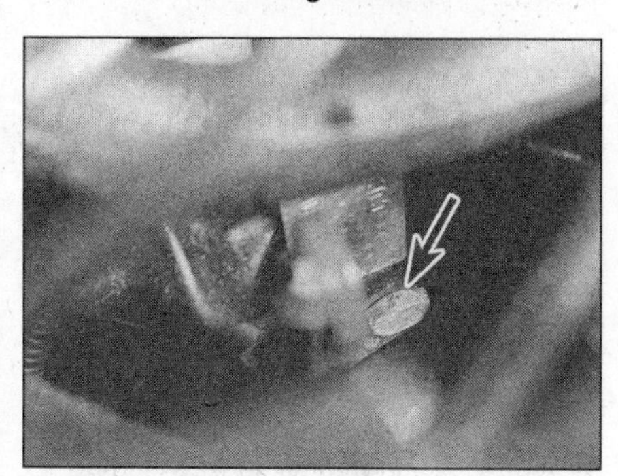
17.14a Remove plug (arrowed) from cylinder block . . .

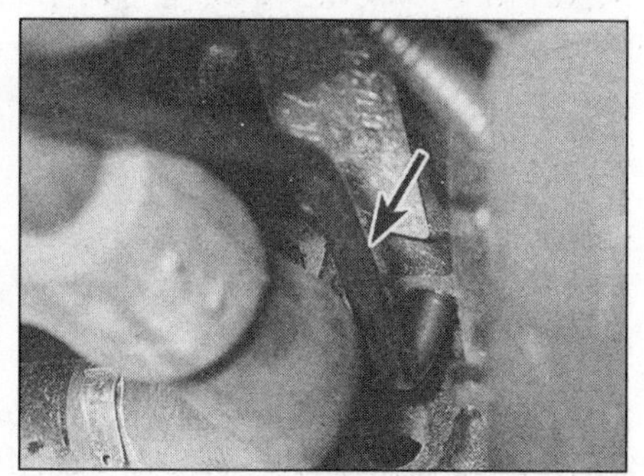
17.14b . . . and insert suitable 8 mm rod (arrowed)

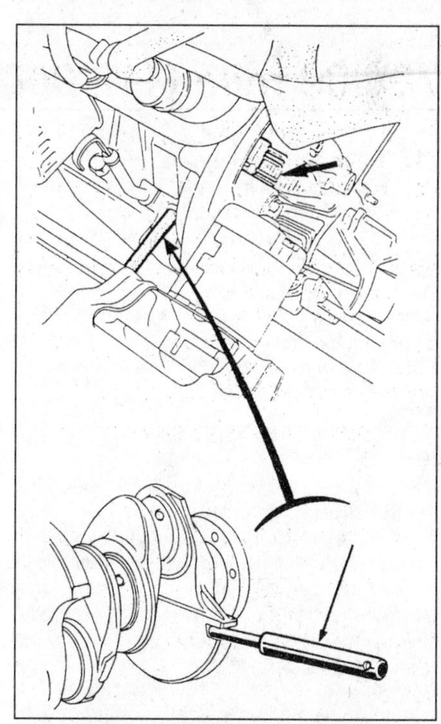
17.15 TDC mark on flywheel seen through bellhousing aperture, and TDC locking tool engaged with crankshaft (arrowed)

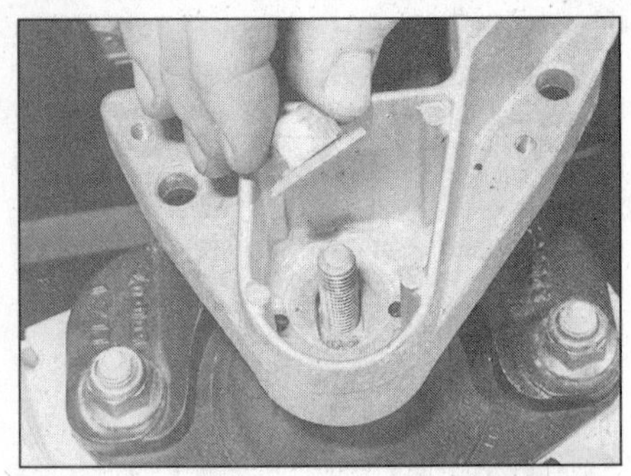

17.17 Remove upper engine mounting bracket from mounting on vehicle body

17.18a Unscrew three securing bolts (arrowed) . . .

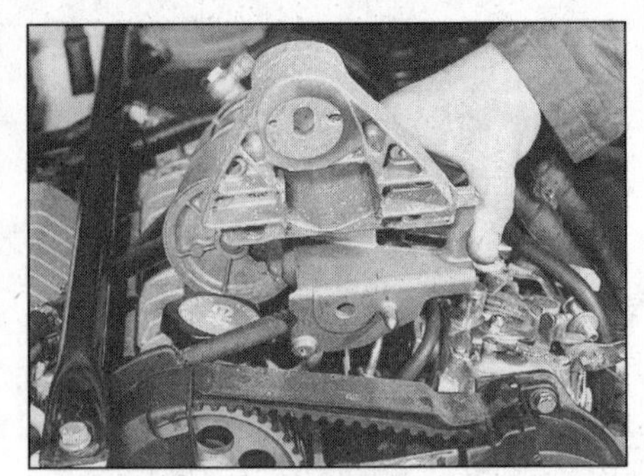

17.18b . . . and withdraw engine mounting bracket

17.19 Remove engine mounting rubber/movement limiter assembly

17.20 Removing timing belt cover from fuel injection pump sprocket

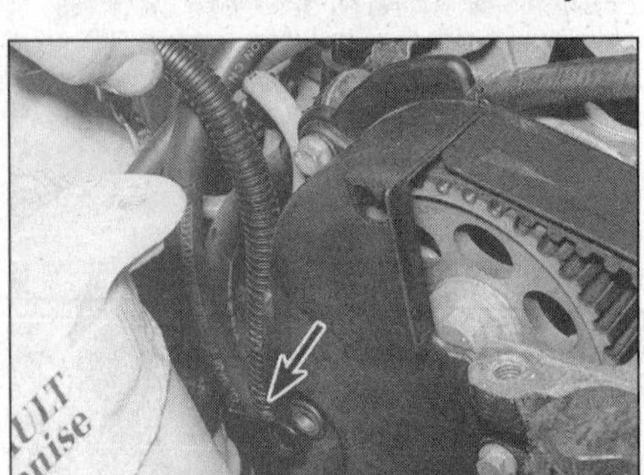

17.21a Note location of brackets (arrowed) . . .

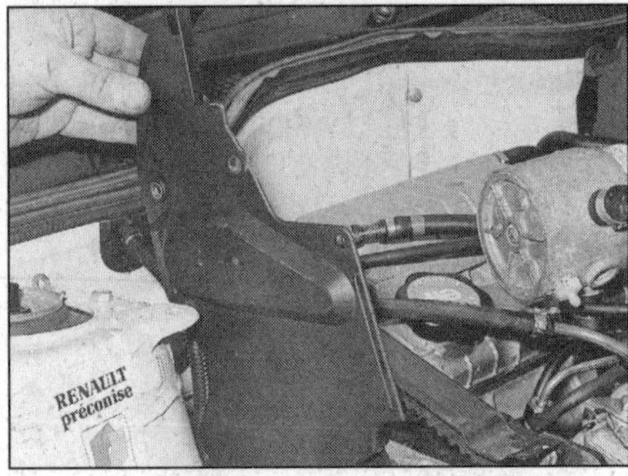

17.21b . . . and remove timing belt cover from camshaft sprocket

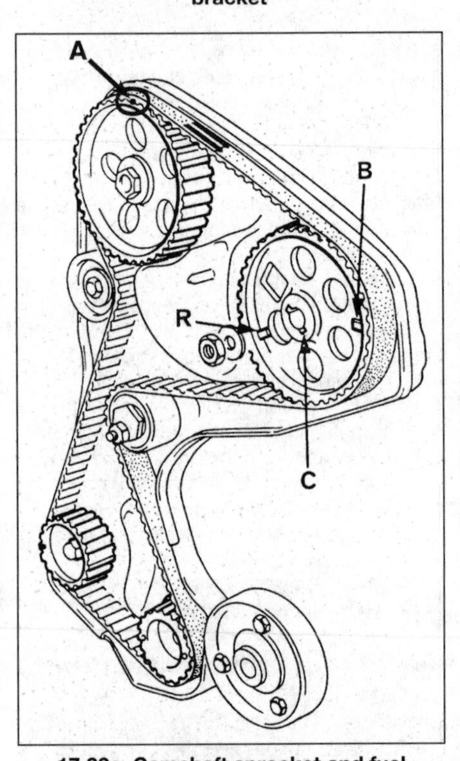

17.22a Camshaft sprocket and fuel injection pump sprocket timing mark positions with No 1 piston at TDC - Engines with 1-piece fuel injection pump sprocket and Bosch pump

A *Camshaft sprocket mark (aligned with pointer on outer timing belt cover - cover removed in this view)*
B *Injection pump sprocket mark for use with Bosch pump*
C *Woodruff key*
R *Injection pump sprocket mark for use with Lucas pump*

bracket must be removed to enable the timing belt to be removed, therefore the engine must be supported. The assembly can be supported using a jack and a suitable block of wood to spread the load under the sump (in which case, remove the engine undershield, where applicable). Alternatively, connect a hoist and suitable lifting tackle to the engine lifting brackets. In this case, the fuel return hose will have to be disconnected from the injection pump and withdrawn from the hole in the rear engine lifting bracket.

17 Ensure that the engine/gearbox assembly is adequately supported, then unscrew the nut securing the upper mounting bracket to the mounting on the body **(see illustration)**. On certain models it is necessary to counterhold the mounting threaded rod using a suitable Allen key or hexagon bit, whilst loosening the nut with an open-ended spanner.

18 Unscrew the three bolts securing the upper mounting bracket to the engine, then withdraw the bracket **(see illustrations)**.

19 Unscrew the two nuts securing the engine mounting rubber/movement limiter assembly to the body, then withdraw the assembly **(see illustration)**.

20 Unscrew the securing bolts and withdraw the timing belt cover, which covers the fuel injection pump sprocket **(see illustration)**.

21 Unscrew the securing bolts whilst noting the locations of any brackets secured by the bolts, then remove the timing belt cover which covers the camshaft sprocket **(see illustrations)**.

22 With the crankshaft locked in position with No 1 piston at TDC, note the position of the timing mark on the fuel injection pump sprocket **(see illustrations)**. On models fitted with a two-piece adjustable injection pump sprocket, the sprocket timing mark may differ from those shown for the one-piece sprocket. If this is the case, take note of the type of mark found and its location, for use when refitting. Note that on models with a single-piece sprocket, there are two timing marks on the sprocket. The mark used depends on whether a Bosch or Lucas injection pump is fitted.

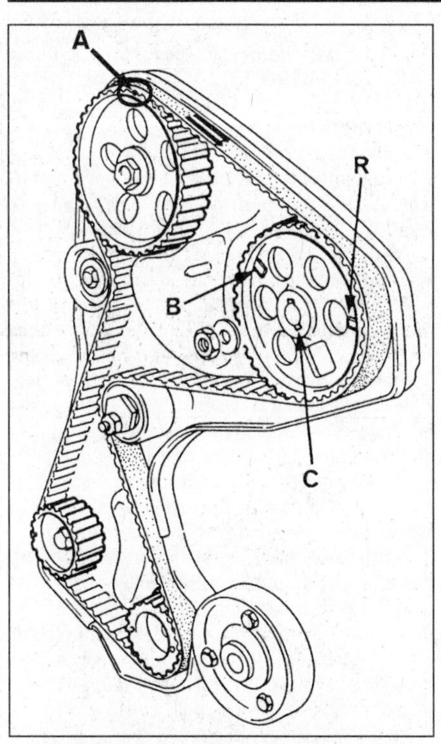

17.22b Camshaft sprocket and fuel injection pump sprocket timing mark positions with No 1 piston at TDC - Engines with 1-piece fuel injection pump sprocket and Lucas pump

A *Camshaft sprocket mark (aligned with pointer on outer timing belt cover - cover removed in this view)*
B *Injection pump sprocket mark for use with Bosch pump*
C *Woodruff key*
R *Injection pump sprocket mark for use with Lucas pump*

23 Loosen the adjuster nut and slide the timing belt tensioner back to relieve the tension from the belt **(see illustration)**. Re-tighten the nut.

24 Release the timing belt from the camshaft sprocket, fuel injection pump sprocket, idler wheel, crankshaft sprocket and auxiliary shaft sprocket, then remove it from the engine.

25 Do not turn the camshaft or the crankshaft whilst the timing belt is removed, as there is a risk of piston-to-valve contact. If it is necessary to turn the camshaft for any reason, remove the TDC locking tool from the cylinder block before doing so and turn the crankshaft anti-clockwise (viewed from the timing belt end of the engine) by a quarter turn to position all four pistons half way down their bores.

Refitting and tensioning

26 Clean the sprockets, idler wheel and tensioner and wipe them dry. Do not apply excessive amounts of solvent to the idler and tensioner wheels otherwise the bearing lubricant may be contaminated. Also clean the rear timing belt cover and the front of the cylinder head and block.

27 Check that the crankshaft is positioned with No 1 piston at TDC and is locked in position using the tool through the hole in the cylinder block as described previously. If the pistons have been positioned halfway down their bores, temporarily refit the outer timing belt cover which covers the camshaft sprocket and check that the TDC mark on the camshaft sprocket is aligned with the pointer on the timing belt cover, then turn the crankshaft clockwise (viewed from the timing belt end of the engine) until the TDC locking tool can be refitted.

28 Align the timing marks on the new belt with those on the crankshaft, camshaft and fuel injection pump sprockets, ensuring that the running direction arrows on the belt are pointing clockwise (viewed from the timing belt end of the engine) **(see illustrations)**. Fit the belt over the crankshaft sprocket first, followed by the idler wheel, fuel injection pump sprocket, camshaft sprocket, tensioner and auxiliary shaft sprocket.

29 Check that all the timing marks are still aligned.

30 The timing belt must now be tensioned as follows.

Adjustment using Renault special tool Ele. 346.04

Note: *Timing belt tension must be adjusted with the engine cold. Renault specify the use of a special gauge (tool no. Ele. 346.04) for checking timing belt tension. If access to a suitable tool cannot be obtained, it is strongly recommended that the vehicle is taken to a Renault dealer to have the belt tension checked at the earliest opportunity.*

31 Fit the gauge to the engine, as shown **(see illustration)**.

32 Screw an M6 bolt through the threaded hole in the rear timing belt cover next to the tensioner. Loosen the tensioner nut and tighten the bolt so that it pushes against the tensioner roller bracket to tension the belt.

33 Adjust the bolt pushing against the tensioner roller bracket to give the specified reading on the gauge.

34 With the correct tension applied, re-tighten the tensioner nut to the specified torque. This torque is critical, since if the nut were to come loose, considerable engine damage would result. Loosen the bolt fitted to the rear timing belt cover so that it no longer rests on the tensioner roller bracket.

17.23 Loosen timing belt tensioner adjuster nut

17.28a Running direction arrows on belt must point clockwise

17.28b Align timing marks on belt with crankshaft . . .

17.28c . . . camshaft sprocket . . .

17.28d . . . and injection pump sprocket marks - Lucas pump shown

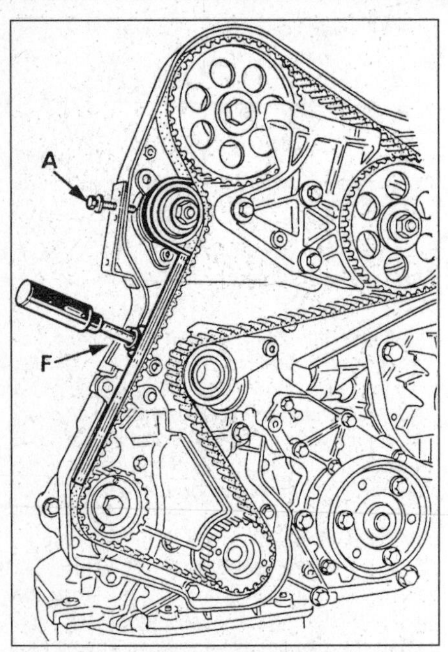

17.31 Renault tool (F) and M6 bolt (A) used to tension timing belt

35 Remove the TDC locking tool from the cylinder block, then refit the crankshaft pulley and securing bolt. Prevent the crankshaft turning using the method described previously, then tighten the bolt to the specified torque. Refit the flywheel cover plate/engine-to-gearbox bracing bracket.
36 Check that the crankshaft is still positioned with No 1 piston at TDC (by temporarily refitting the locking tool to the cylinder block), then remove the TDC locking tool and turn the crankshaft two complete turns in the normal direction of rotation, returning it to the TDC position again. Re-insert the TDC locking tool in the cylinder block.
37 Temporarily refit the timing belt cover which covers the camshaft sprocket and check that the camshaft sprocket timing mark still aligns with the pointer on the cover, as noted before removal.
38 Re-check the belt tension as described previously. If the tension is incorrect, the setting and checking procedure must be repeated until the correct tension is achieved.
39 With the belt tensioned correctly, remove the M6 bolt from the rear timing belt cover and remove the TDC locking tool from the cylinder block, if not already done. Refit the plug to the cylinder block TDC hole.
40 Check the fuel injection pump timing.
41 Refit the upper timing belt covers, ensuring that any brackets secured by the bolts are in position as noted before removal.
42 Refit the engine mounting rubber/movement limiter assembly to the body, then refit the upper mounting bracket to the engine.
43 Refit the fuel filter assembly and clip the hoses into position.

17.49 Twisting timing belt as an approximate tension check

44 Refit and tension the auxiliary drivebelt.
45 Refit the strengthening bar to the front suspension turrets.
46 Withdraw the jack or lifting tackle used to support the engine.
47 Refit the wheel arch cover and roadwheel, then lower the vehicle to the ground.
48 Reconnect the battery negative lead.

Approximate adjustment

49 If the special tensioning gauge is not available, the timing belt tension can be checked approximately by twisting the belt between the thumb and forefinger, at the centre of the run between the tensioner pulley and the auxiliary shaft pulley. It should be just possible to twist the belt through 90° by using moderate pressure **(see illustration)**.
50 The checking, adjustment and final refitting procedures are as described previously but note the following:

a) Have the belt tension checked by a Renault dealer at the earliest opportunity.
b) If in doubt, err on the tight side when adjusting belt tension. If the belt is too slack, it may jump on the sprockets, which could result in serious engine damage.

18 Timing belt renewal - Renault Clio

1 Follow the procedure given for the Renault 19 in Section 17, whilst noting the following:
2 To gain the necessary access for timing belt removal, remove the following components, as applicable:

a) The bonnet.
b) The air cleaner housing assembly.
c) The electric cooling fan.

19 Timing belt renewal - Renault Laguna

Note: *On early models with a belt-driven brake vacuum pump (driven from the camshaft), Renault recommend that the vacuum pump drivebelt is renewed with the timing belt.*

Warning: Do not refit a used timing belt.

Removal

1 Disconnect both battery leads.
2 Firmly apply the handbrake then jack up the front of the vehicle and support it on axle stands. Remove the right-hand front roadwheel.
3 Undo the retaining screws and remove the engine undercover and the front and rear protective covers from the right-hand wheelarch
4 Remove the auxiliary drivebelt. On models where the coolant pump is driven by the auxiliary drivebelt, unbolt the drivebelt pulley and remove it from the pump.
5 Position No. 1 cylinder (transmission end of engine) at TDC on its compression stroke and lock the crankshaft in position, as follows.
6 Turn the crankshaft until the index mark on the rear of the camshaft sprocket is aligned with the timing mark cast into the aperture in the end of the camshaft cover. The crankshaft can be turned by using a spanner or socket on the pulley bolt. Always turn the crankshaft in a clockwise direction (viewed from the right-hand side of vehicle). On some models, the mark on the front injection pump sprocket will also be aligned with the pointer in the timing belt cover aperture **(see illustrations)**.
7 Turn the crankshaft in the normal direction of rotation (clockwise) whilst keeping an eye

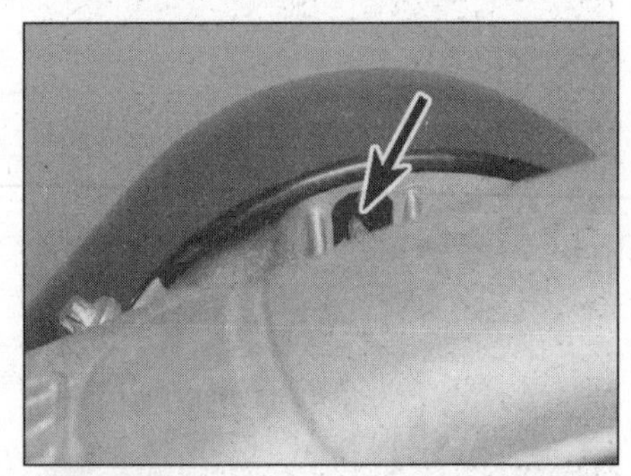
19.6a No 1 cylinder is positioned at TDC on compression stroke when timing mark on rear of camshaft sprocket is aligned with pointer on camshaft cover (arrowed)

19.6b On some engines there is also a TDC pointer on injection pump sprocket cover

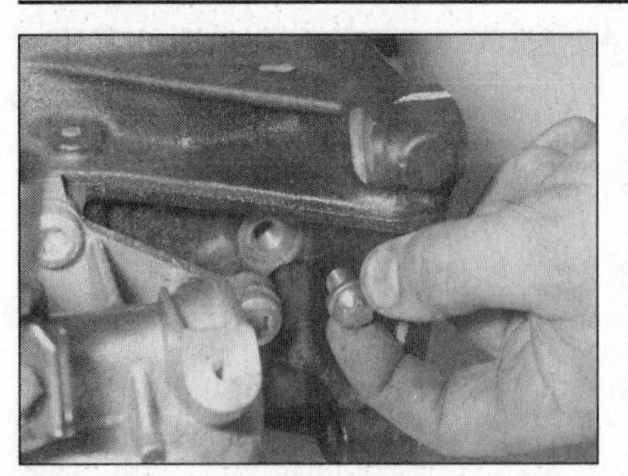

19.8a Unscrew access bolt . . .

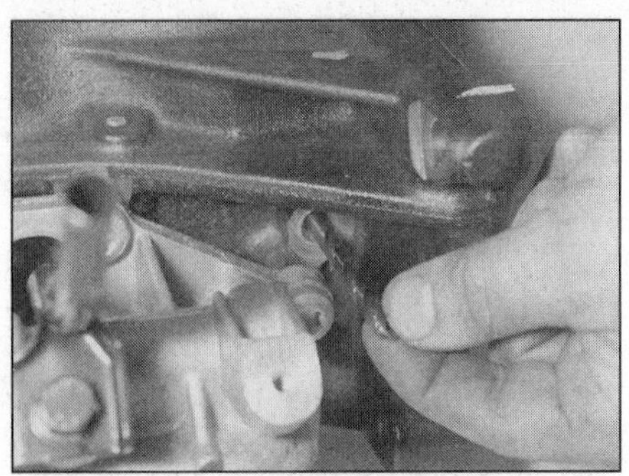

19.8b . . . and insert 7 mm diameter rod through cylinder block . . .

19.8c . . . so that it engages with timing slot in crankshaft web (arrowed)

19.11 Using fabricated tool to lock flywheel ring gear and prevent crankshaft rotation

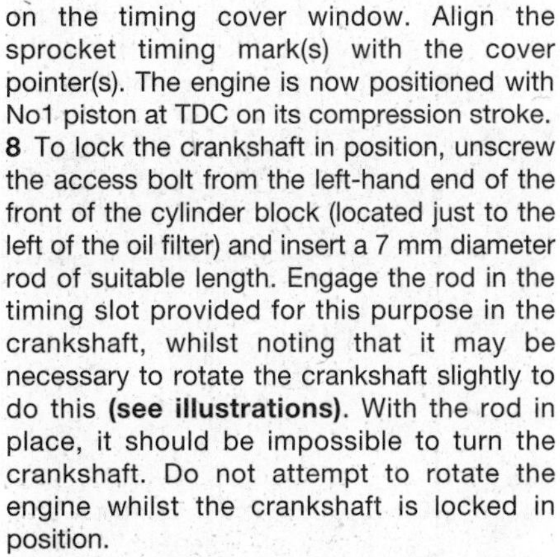

on the timing cover window. Align the sprocket timing mark(s) with the cover pointer(s). The engine is now positioned with No1 piston at TDC on its compression stroke.

8 To lock the crankshaft in position, unscrew the access bolt from the left-hand end of the front of the cylinder block (located just to the left of the oil filter) and insert a 7 mm diameter rod of suitable length. Engage the rod in the timing slot provided for this purpose in the crankshaft, whilst noting that it may be necessary to rotate the crankshaft slightly to do this **(see illustrations)**. With the rod in place, it should be impossible to turn the crankshaft. Do not attempt to rotate the engine whilst the crankshaft is locked in position.

9 Position a jack beneath the engine, with a block of wood on the jack head. Raise the jack until it is supporting the weight of the engine. Alternatively, attach and support bar to the engine and use the bar to support the weight of the engine/transmission unit.

10 Slacken and remove the retaining nut and bolts and remove the right-hand engine mounting bracket. Undo the three retaining bolts and remove the rubber mounting from the body.

11 Slacken the crankshaft pulley retaining bolt. To prevent crankshaft rotation whilst the retaining bolt is slackened, select top gear and have an assistant apply the brakes firmly. If this fails to prevent rotation, remove the lower cover plate and lock the flywheel ring gear, using an arrangement similar to that shown **(see illustration)**. Do not be tempted to use the crankshaft locking pin to prevent the crankshaft from rotating. As a precaution, when slackening the pulley retaining bolt, temporarily remove the locking rod from the crankshaft. Once the bolt is loose, slide the rod back into position.

12 Remove the retaining bolt and pulley from the end of the crankshaft, then temporarily refit the bolt. A new bolt must be used when refitting the pulley.

13 Remove the timing belt covers as follows, noting that all retaining bolts must be renewed on refitting:

14 Depending on engine type, there are two possible timing belt cover arrangements. Early models (fitted with G8T 706 and 790 engines) are fitted with a three cover arrangement - a top cover, an injection pump sprocket cover and the main cover **(see illustration)**. Later models (all engines except G8T 706 and 790) have a four cover arrangement - a top cover, an injection pump cover, the camshaft sprocket cover and the crankshaft sprocket cover.

15 Access to the timing belt covers is poor. To improve access, not only is it necessary to remove the mounting bracket from the engine mounting but also to unbolt the fuel filter housing from its mounting bracket and position it clear of the cover. Proceed as follows:

16 To remove the top cover, undo the retaining nut then free the wiring loom from its retaining clips and position it clear of the timing belt covers. Undo the retaining screws and remove the cover from the engine **(see illustration)**.

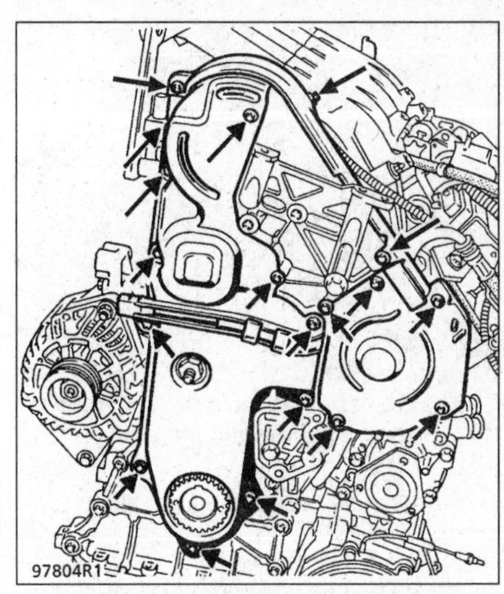

19.14 Timing belt cover bolt locations - early G8T 706 and 790 engines

17 To remove the injection pump sprocket cover, with the top cover removed, unclip the wiring loom from the side of the timing belt cover then unbolt the sprocket cover and remove it from the engine **(see illustration)**.

18 To remove the camshaft sprocket cover on later models, with the top cover removed, unclip the wiring loom from the side of the timing belt cover then unbolt the sprocket cover and remove it from the engine.

19 To remove the main cover on early models, with the top cover and injection pump sprocket cover removed, undo the retaining bolts and remove the auxiliary drivebelt

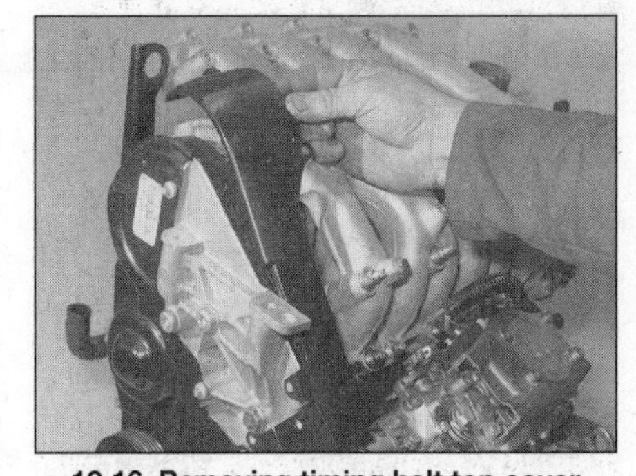

19.16 Removing timing belt top cover

19.17 Removing injection pump sprocket cover

19.19a Undo retaining bolts and remove auxiliary drivebelt tensioner

19.19b Unscrew retaining nut and remove auxiliary drivebelt idler pulley

19.19c Removing timing belt main cover - early engine shown

tensioner pulley assembly from the cylinder block **(see illustration)**. Unscrew the retaining nut and remove the auxiliary drivebelt idler pulley from the engine **(see illustration)**. As the retaining nut is unscrewed, ensure that the pulley mounting stud remains in position. If necessary, retaining the stud with an open-ended spanner as the nut is slackened. Unscrew the cover retaining bolts, noting the correct fitted location of the wiring loom holder, then remove the main cover from the engine **(see illustration)**.

20 To remove the crankshaft sprocket cover on later models, with the top cover, injection pump sprocket cover and camshaft sprocket cover removed, remove the cover as described in paragraph 19.

21 Check the crankshaft, camshaft and injection pump sprocket timing marks are positioned as shown **(see illustration)**. The injection pump sprocket mark should be aligned with the mark on the pump mounting bracket and the crankshaft sprocket Woodruff key should be uppermost with the sprocket timing mark at the bottom. The mark on the rear of the camshaft sprocket should be aligned with the pointer in the camshaft cover aperture and the mark on the front of the sprocket should be aligned with the lug on the cylinder head.

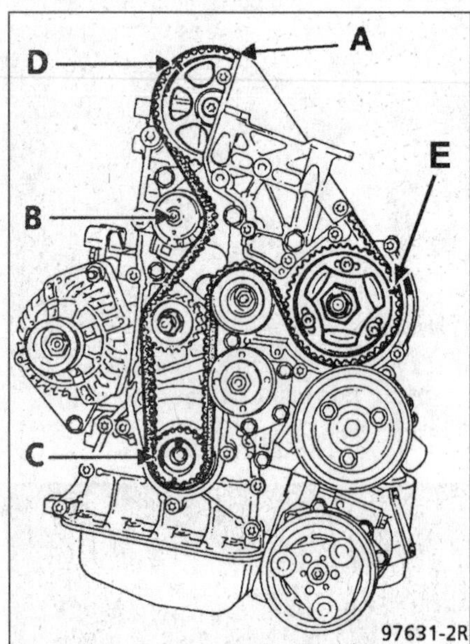
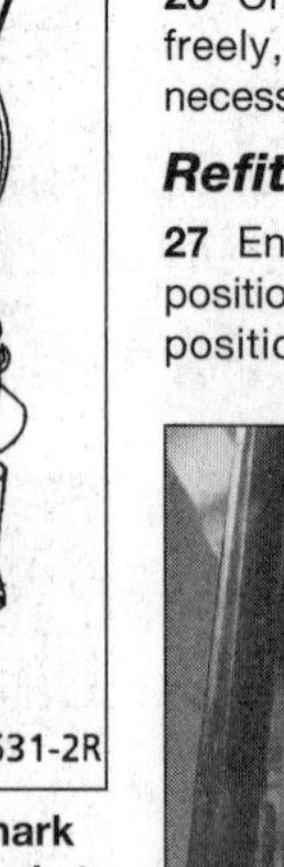

19.21 Timing belt sprocket timing mark locations with No 1 cylinder positioned at TDC on compression stroke

A Camshaft sprocket rear timing mark
B Timing belt tensioner pulley nut
C Crankshaft sprocket
D Camshaft sprocket front timing mark
E Injection pump sprocket timing mark

22 Slacken the tensioner pulley retaining nut and, where necessary, slacken the locknut and unscrew the tensioner pulley adjuster bolt.

23 Slip the timing belt off the sprockets and remove it from the engine.

24 If signs of oil contamination are found, trace the source of the oil leak and rectify it. Wash down the engine timing belt area and all related components, to remove all traces of oil.

25 Clean the sprockets and tensioner, wiping them dry. Do not apply excessive amounts of solvent to the tensioner wheels, otherwise the bearing lubricant may be contaminated. Also clean the front of the cylinder head and block.

26 Check that the tensioner pulley rotates freely, without any sign of roughness. If necessary, renew it.

Refitting and tensioning

27 Ensure that the crankshaft is at the TDC position for No 1 cylinder and is locked in this position. Check that the sprocket timing marks are correctly positioned **(see illustrations)**.

28 Offer up the new belt, ensuring that the arrows marked on it are pointing in the direction of rotation. Starting with the crankshaft sprocket, align the mark on the inside of the new belt with the sprocket mark, then route the belt around the idler pulley and over the injection pump and camshaft sprockets. Ensure that the marks on the outside of the timing belt are correctly aligned with both sprockets, then slide the belt fully into position **(see illustrations)**.

29 With the timing marks correctly aligned, ensure the tensioner pulley is correctly engaged with the upper peg then remove all slack from the timing belt by pivoting the tensioner into contact with the belt. Position the tensioner so that tensioner indicator arm

19.27a Ensure crankshaft sprocket timing mark (arrowed) is at bottom . . .

19.27b . . . camshaft sprocket marks (arrowed) are correctly positioned . . .

19.27c . . . and injection pump sprocket mark (arrowed) is aligned with mark on bracket

19.28a Ensure timing belt arrows are pointing in direction of normal rotation

19.28b Align belt inner mark with crankshaft sprocket timing mark . . .

19.28c . . . then align second mark with injection pump sprocket mark (arrowed) . . .

19.28d . . . and third mark with camshaft sprocket mark (arrowed)

contacts its backplate maximum tension stop lightly, then tighten the pulley retaining nut to the specified torque. Do not force the tensioner pulley against the stop. On early models, adjust the tensioner by levering between the tensioner and cylinder block lugs with a suitable bar. On later models, screw in the adjuster bolt **(see illustrations)**.

30 Remove the crankshaft locking rod and, using a suitable socket and extension bar on the crankshaft sprocket bolt, rotate the crankshaft through three complete rotations in a clockwise direction (viewed from the right-hand end of the engine). Do not at any time rotate the crankshaft anti-clockwise.

31 Hold the tensioner pulley in position and carefully slacken its retaining nut. Slowly release the tensioner pulley until its indicator arm is aligned with the reference mark on the backplate **(see illustration)**. Hold the tensioner pulley in position and tighten its retaining nut to the specified torque setting. On later models, tighten the adjuster bolt locknut securely.

32 Rotate the crankshaft through another complete rotation, then refit the locking rod and check that all the sprocket timing marks are correctly position.

33 Remove the locking rod and refit the access plug to the front of the cylinder block.

34 Refit the timing belt covers, using new retaining bolts. Ensure that the cover(s) are correctly seated before tightening the retaining bolts securely.

35 Remove all traces of locking compound from the crankshaft threads. Clean the threads of the new crankshaft pulley retaining bolt and apply a few drops of locking compound (Renault recommend the use of Loctite Autoform).

36 Refit the pulley to the crankshaft and screw in the retaining bolt. Tighten the bolt first to the specified stage 1 torque and then through the specified stage 2 angle **(see illustrations)**.

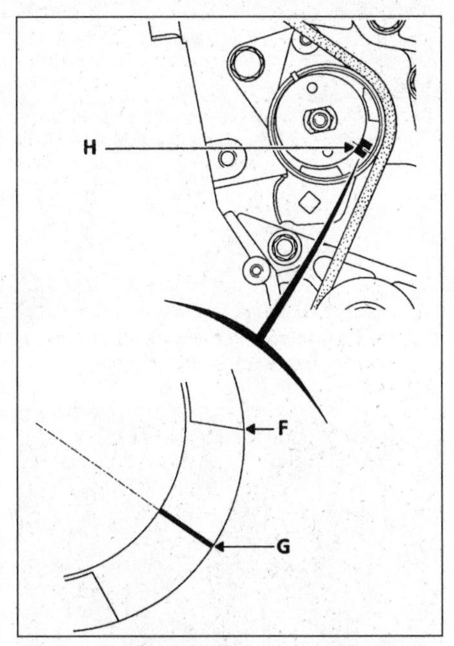

19.29a Timing belt tensioner pulley details

F Backplate maximum tension mark (used to preload belt)
G Backplate correct tension mark (used to correctly set belt tension)
H Indicator arm

19.29b Adjust tensioner using suitable lever between tensioner and cylinder block lugs - early engines

19.31 Back off tensioner and align indicator arm with correct tensioner mark on backplate (arrowed)

19.36a Tighten crankshaft pulley bolt to specified Stage 1 torque setting . . .

19.36b . . . then tighten through specified Stage 2 angle

9A

37 Refit the rubber mounting to the body and tighten its retaining bolts securely to the specified torque. Install the mounting bracket and loosely tighten its mounting nut and bolts. Ensure that the bracket is positioned centrally in relation to the rubber mounting lug then tighten its retaining nut and bolts to their specified torque wrench settings. Remove the jack/engine support bar (as applicable).

38 Refit the coolant pump pulley (where necessary) and refit the auxiliary drivebelt.

39 Refit the undercover and wheelarch covers and then the roadwheel.

40 Reconnect the battery.

80 000 mile (120 000 km) Service - Renault Espace

20 Timing belt renewal

Note: *To prevent the camshaft and injection pump sprockets rotating whilst the timing belt is removed, Renault technicians use a special tool (Mot. 854)* ***(see illustration)****. This tool slots between the two sprockets, engaging with their teeth and so locking them together. Use of this tool greatly reduces the risk of incorrectly setting the valve and/or injection pump timing when fitting a new timing belt.*

Removal

1 Disconnect the battery negative lead.

2 Position No. 1 piston (flywheel end of engine) at TDC on its compression stroke.

3 With No 1 piston at TDC, the timing mark on the camshaft and injection pump sprockets should be aligned with the pointers on the outer timing belt cover (the sprocket mark can be viewed through the cut-outs in the timing belt cover, above the pointers) **(see illustration).** Additionally, the timing mark on the flywheel should be aligned with the TDC (0°) mark on the transmission bellhousing. However, unless the engine is removed from the vehicle, it is almost impossible to see the flywheel and bellhousing marks.

4 To align the timing marks, the crankshaft must be turned. This should be done by using a spanner on the crankshaft pulley bolt.

5 Turn the crankshaft in the normal direction of rotation until the timing marks just appear in the viewing windows on the timing belt cover, then align the marks with the pointers.

6 To lock the crankshaft at TDC, remove the brass plug (located just forward of the starter motor) from the crankcase. Insert a dowel rod of 8.0 mm diameter through the hole to engage in the slot in the crankshaft counterbalance weight **(see illustrations)**. It may be necessary to move the crankshaft very slightly back and forth to check for positive engagement of the dowel rod in the crankshaft slot. Ensure that the rod is not inserted into one of the balancing holes either side of the TDC slot. Check that the crankshaft will not turn when the rod is fully engaged. Slight movement one way or the other indicates that the rod is in a balance hole.

7 Remove the crankshaft pulley as follows. To prevent the possibility of the locking pin being damaged, remove the pin temporarily as the pulley retaining bolt is slackened and refit it once the bolt is slack.

8 Access to the crankshaft pulley is very limited, necessitating removal of the radiator and power steering pump and/or alternator auxiliary drivebelt(s), as applicable.

9 To prevent crankshaft rotation whilst the pulley retaining bolt is slackened, select top gear and have an assistant apply the brakes firmly. Do not attempt to lock the crankshaft by inserting the locking pin.

10 Unscrew the retaining bolt and remove the pulley from the end of the crankshaft.

11 Remove all auxiliary drivebelts. Note that on vehicles equipped with air conditioning and having their drivebelt situated behind the timing belt, this drivebelt can be left in position.

12 Undo the nuts and free the cable guide from the front of the timing belt cover.

13 Work around the cover and remove all the nuts and bolts along with their washers.

14 Carefully withdraw the cover from the engine compartment and recover the collars from the centre of the each cover rubber mounting.

15 With the cover removed, slide the three spacers off the cover mounting studs, noting the correct location of each spacer as it is removed **(see illustration).**

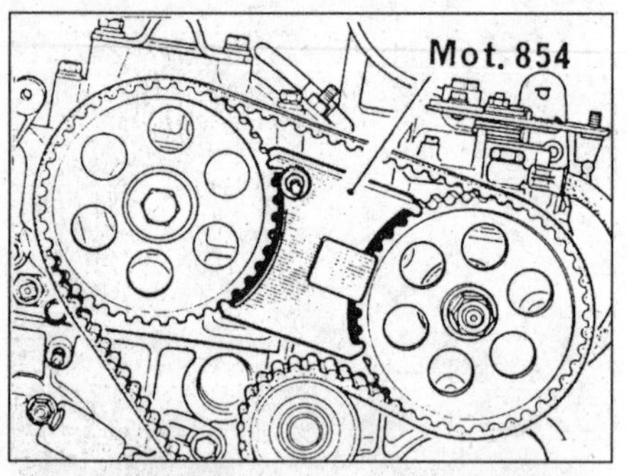

20.0 Renault tool for locking injection pump and camshaft sprockets in position

20.3 When No 1 piston is at TDC, timing mark on camshaft and injection pump sprockets should align with pointers on timing belt cover

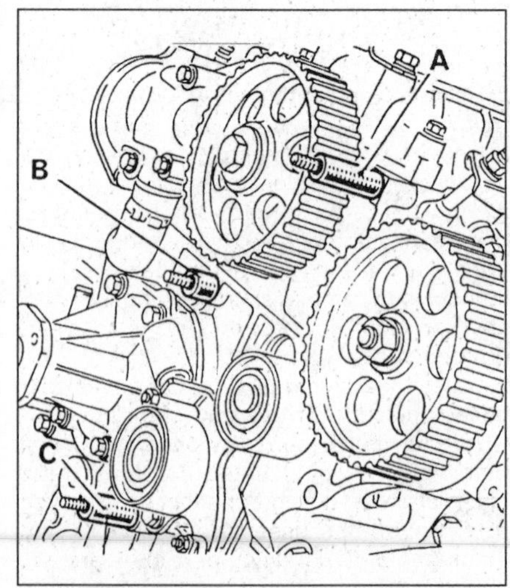

20.15 Timing belt cover spacer locations

A Long spacer
B Short spacer
C Medium spacer

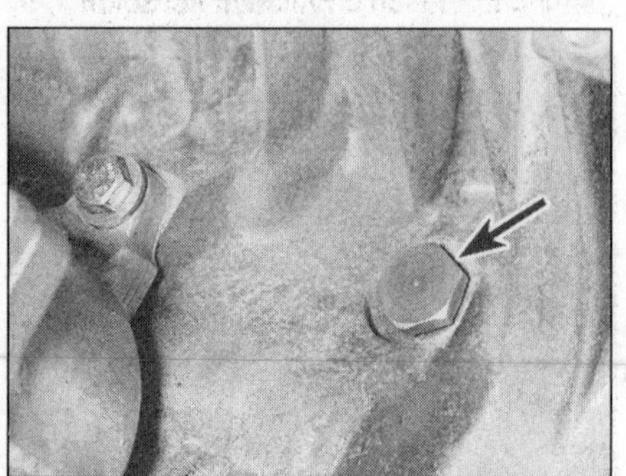

20.6a To lock crankshaft in position, unscrew plug from cylinder block . . .

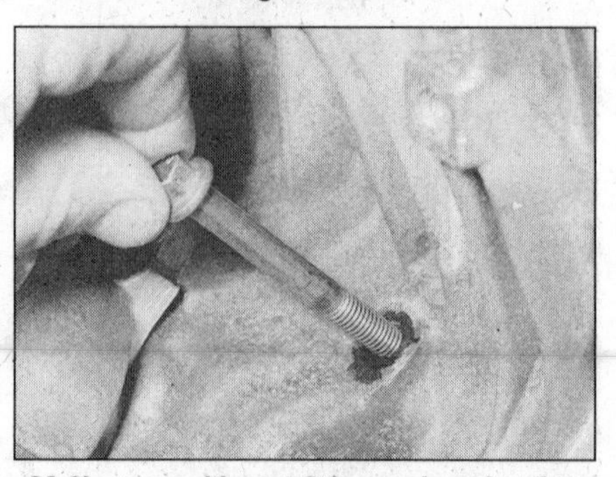

20.6b . . . and insert 8.0 mm dowel rod to lock crankshaft at TDC

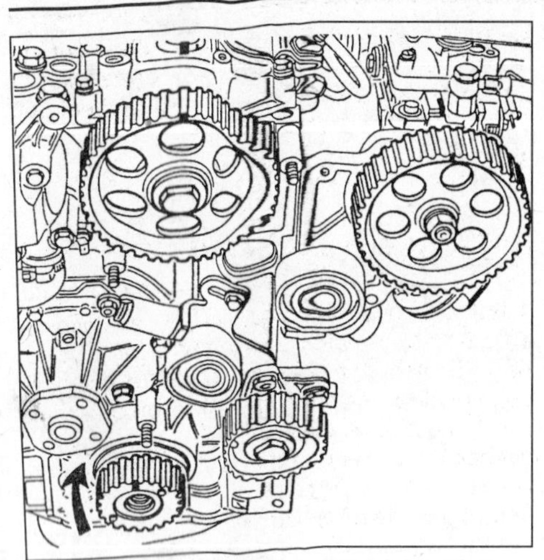

20.17a Sprocket timing mark locations

16 Examine each cover mounting rubber for signs of damage or deterioration and renew as necessary.

17 Check that the camshaft, injection pump and crankshaft sprockets are correctly positioned **(see illustration)**. The camshaft sprocket timing mark should be aligned with the boss on the centre of the cylinder head cover and the injection pump sprocket mark should be aligned with the centre of the boss on the injection pump. If alignment marks do not already exist, use white paint or similar to mark the cylinder head cover and injection pump. These marks can then be used on refitting to ensure that the valve and pump timing is correctly set **(see illustration)**.

18 Insert the sprocket locking tool between the camshaft and injection pump sprockets.

19 Slacken both the tensioner pulley retaining nut and bolt, then pivot the pulley fully away from the timing belt. Hold the tensioner in this position and securely tighten the retaining nut and bolt to retain it.

20 Slip the belt off the sprockets and remove it from the engine.

21 Due to the amount of work required to renew the air conditioning compressor drivebelt, it is recommended that it is now renewed, regardless of its apparent condition.

22 If signs of oil contamination are found, trace the source of the oil leak and rectify it. Wipe down the engine timing belt area and sprockets to remove all traces of oil. Renew any sprocket which shows signs of wear, damage or cracks.

23 Clean the timing belt idler and tensioner pulleys but do not use any strong solvent which may enter the pulley bearings. Check that each pulley rotates freely on the backplate, with no sign of stiffness or of free play. Renew the assembly if there is any doubt about its condition or if there are any obvious signs of wear or damage. It is recommended that the tensioner spring is renewed regardless of its apparent condition, since its condition is critical.

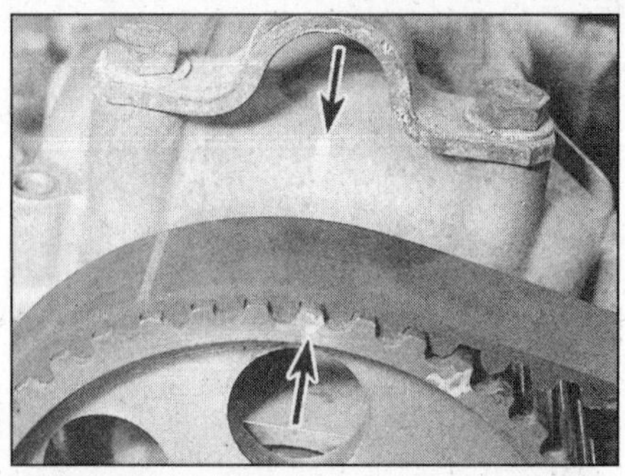

20.17b Make alignment marks on cylinder head and injection pump for sprocket timing marks prior to removing timing belt

Refitting and tensioning

24 Prior to fitting the new timing belt, check the clearance between the tensioner pulley backplate and the adjusting screw on the auxiliary shaft cover. A 0.1 mm feeler blade should be a light, sliding fit between the two components. If not, slacken the locknut and adjust the screw as required **(see illustration)**. Once the clearance is correct, hold the screw stationary and securely tighten its locknut.

25 Check that the camshaft and injection pump sprockets are correctly aligned with the marks made or noted prior to removal. If the sprockets were locked in position they should not have moved.

26 Offer up the timing belt, observing any marks indicating the direction of rotation. Starting at the crankshaft sprocket and working in an anti-clockwise direction, align the lines on the belt with the timing marks on each sprocket and engage the belt with the auxiliary shaft, injection pump and camshaft sprockets **(see illustrations)**.

27 Ensure that the belt front and top runs are taut, that is, all slack is on the tensioner pulley side of the belt. Do not twist the belt sharply and ensure that its teeth are seated centrally in the sprockets and that the timing marks remain in alignment. Note that if the belt is correctly installed, there should be a total of twenty tooth troughs between the camshaft and injection pump sprocket timing marks.

28 Remove the sprocket locking tool and slacken the tensioner pulley retaining nut and bolt. Check that the tensioner pulley is forced against the timing belt under spring pressure then securely tighten the pulley retaining nut and bolt.

29 Temporarily refit the timing belt cover and check that the camshaft sprocket and injection pump timing marks are aligned with their respective pointers. If not, the belt will have to be removed and the refitting procedure repeated.

30 Refit the crankshaft pulley, tightening its retaining bolt loosely, then remove the crankshaft locking pin. Rotate the crankshaft through two complete turns in a clockwise direction until both sprocket timing marks are realigned with their pointers. Do not under any circumstances rotate the crankshaft anti-clockwise.

31 Remove the timing belt cover then slacken the tensioner retaining nut and bolt by half a turn and retighten them securely.

20.24 Adjusting tensioner pulley backplate clearance

20.26a Align lines on timing belt with timing marks on crankshaft sprocket . . .

20.26b . . . camshaft sprocket . . .

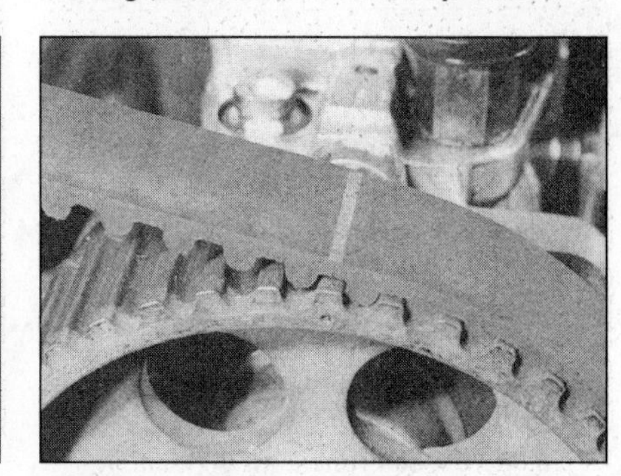

20.26c . . . and injection pump sprocket

32 Belt tension should now ideally be checked using the Renault service tool. If the tool is available, use it to check that belt deflection is 3 to 5 mm midway between the camshaft and injection pump sprockets.

33 If the special tool is not available, an approximate check of the belt tension can be made using a spring balance and steel rule. At the mid-point between the camshaft and injection pump sprockets the belt deflection should be between 3 and 5 mm under a force of 30 N **(see illustration)**. It must be stressed however that this is only an approximate check, the tension can only be accurately checked using the Renault tool.

34 With the belt correctly tensioned, refit the timing belt cover.

35 Refit the plug to the cylinder block/ crankcase locking pin hole and tighten the crankshaft pulley bolt to the specified torque.

36 Refit the radiator and refit and tension the auxiliary drivebelt(s).

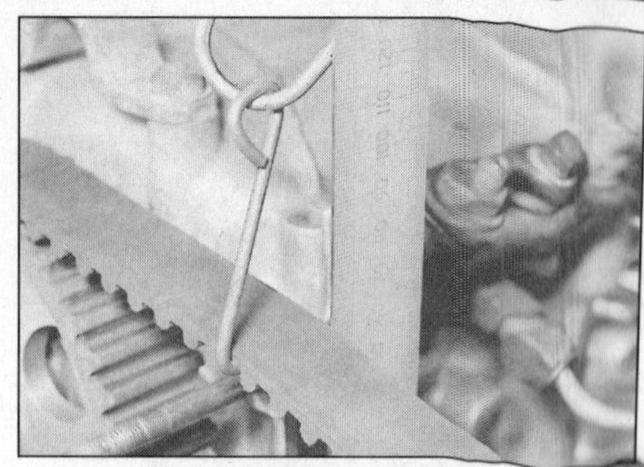

20.33 Using spring balance and ruler to check timing belt tension

Chapter 9
Renault 1870cc, 2068cc & 2188cc engines
Part B: Fuel system servicing

Contents

Specifications

Glow plugs

Renault 19:	
Non turbo	Champion CH88 or CH137
Turbo	Champion CH69
Renault Clio	Champion CH155
Renault Espace	Champion CH137
Renault Laguna	Champion listing not available at time of writing

Injectors

Type (all models)	Pintle
Opening pressure:	
Renault 19:	
F8Q 706 and F8Q 764 engines with Lucas injection pump	118 + 7 - 5 bar
All other engines	130 + 8 - 5 bar
Renault Clio:	
Bosch injection pump	130 + 8 - 5 bar
Roto-Diesel/Lucas injection pump	118 + 7 - 5 bar
Renault Espace	125 to 138 bar
Renault Laguna:	
Standard	130 ± 5 bar
Maximum difference between any two injectors	8 bar

Fuel injection pump

Renault 19 - Bosch type

Direction of rotation	Clockwise viewed from sprocket end
Static timing:	
Engine position	No 1 cylinder at TDC
Pump position:	
All engines except F8Q 706 from early 1993*	0.70 ± 0.02 mm
F8Q 706 engine from early 1993*	0.82 ± 0.02 mm
Dynamic timing	No information available at time of writing

**From early 1993, the pump on F8Q 706 engines was modified to meet revised European exhaust emissions regulations. Applicable pumps can be identified from the timing value marked on the pump accelerator lever.*

Renault 19 - Lucas CAV/Roto-Diesel type

Direction of rotation	Clockwise viewed from sprocket end
Static timing:	
Engine position	No 1 cylinder at TDC
Pump position	Value shown on pump
Dynamic timing	No information available at time of writing

Renault Clio - Bosch type

Direction of rotation	Clockwise viewed from sprocket end
Static timing:	
Engine position	No 1 cylinder at TDC
Pump position:	
F8Q 730 engine	0.82 ± 0.02 mm
F8Q 732 engine	0.70 ± 0.02 mm
Dynamic timing:	
F8Q 730 engine	No information available at time of writing
F8Q 732 engine	12.5 ± 1° BTDC at idle

Renault Clio - Roto-Diesel/Lucas/CAV type

Direction of rotation	Clockwise viewed from sprocket end
Static timing:	
Engine position	No 1 cylinder at TDC
Pump position	Value shown on pump
Dynamic timing	No information available at time of writing

Renault Espace

Type	Bosch VE4/9F2200
Direction of rotation	Clockwise, viewed from sprocket end
Static timing:	
Engine position	No 1 piston at TDC
Pump position	0.70 ± 0.02 mm
Dynamic timing at idle	13.5° ± 1°

Renault Laguna

Direction of rotation	Clockwise, viewed from sprocket end
Static timing:	
Engine position	No 1 piston at TDC
Pump position	0.80° 0.04 mm (shown on pump accelerator lever)

Maximum speed

Renault 19

Bosch injection pump:	
F8Q 706 engine	5200 to 5400 rpm
F8Q 742 engine	5100 to 5300 rpm
Lucas injection pump:	
F8Q 706 and F8Q 764 engines	5100 to 5300 rpm
F8Q 740 and F8Q 744 engines	4800 to 5000 rpm

Renault Clio

All engines	5100 to 5300 rpm

Renault Espace

2068 cc engine	4700 to 4800 rpm

Renault Laguna

No load	5300 to 5500 rpm
Load	4700 to 4900 rpm

Torque wrench settings

	Nm	lbf ft
Renault 19 and Clio		
Injectors	70	52
Fuel pipe union nuts and bolts	25	18
Injection pump:		
Timing hole blanking plug:		
Lucas	5	4
Bosch	10	7
Mounting nuts and bolts	25	18
Sprocket securing nut	50	37
Sprocket adjuster bolts (two-piece adjustable sprocket)	20	15
Fast idle thermostatic actuator	35	26
Stop solenoid	20	15
Stop solenoid terminal nut	3.5	3
Glow plugs	20	15
Renault Espace		
Injectors:		
Clamp-type:		
Clamp retaining nuts	17	13
Return hose union bolts	10	7
Screw-type	70	52
Injector pipe union nuts	25	18
Injection pump:		
Feed and return hose union bolts	25	18
Mounting nuts and bolts	25	18
Sprocket nut	50	36
Stop solenoid	20	15
Glow plugs	25	18
Renault Laguna		
Injectors	70	52
Injection pump sprocket nut	90	66
Glow plugs	15	11

1 Accelerator cable - adjustment

1 Have an assistant fully depress the accelerator pedal, then check that the accelerator lever on the injection pump is touching the maximum speed adjustment screw.

2 If adjustment is required, remove the spring clip from the adjustment ferrule **(see illustration)**, reposition the ferrule as necessary, then insert the clip in the next free groove on the ferrule.

3 With the accelerator pedal fully released, check that the accelerator lever is touching the anti-stall adjustment screw.

2 Maximum speed - checking and adjustment

Caution: The maximum speed adjustment screw is sealed by the manufacturers with paint or locking wire and a lead seal. Do not disturb the screw if the vehicle is still within the warranty period, otherwise the warranty will be invalidated. Maximum speed adjustment requires the use of a tachometer.

1 Run the engine to normal operating temperature.

2 If the vehicle does not have a tachometer (rev counter), connect a suitable instrument in accordance with its manufacturer's instructions.

3 Have an assistant fully depress the accelerator pedal and check that the maximum engine speed is as specified. Do not keep the engine at maximum speed for more than two or three seconds.

4 If adjustment is necessary, stop the engine then loosen the locknut. Turn the maximum speed adjustment screw as necessary and retighten the locknut **(see illustrations)**.

5 Repeat the procedure in paragraph 3 to check adjustment.

6 Stop the engine and disconnect the tachometer.

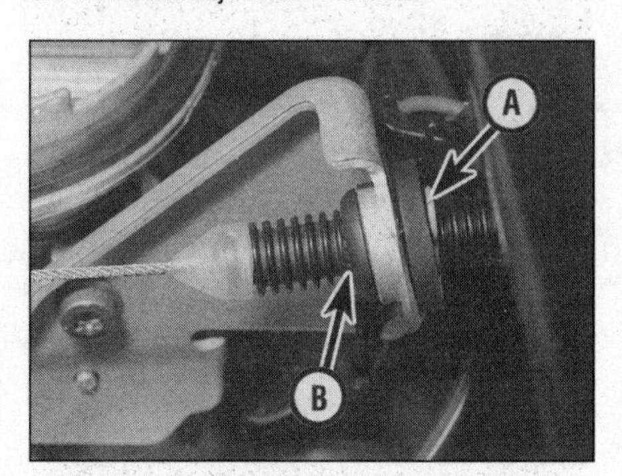

1.2 Accelerator cable spring clip (A) and outer end fitting (B)

2.4a Maximum speed adjustment screw (arrowed) - Lucas pump

2.4b Maximum speed adjustment screw (arrowed) - Bosch pump

3.3 Fast idle cable end fitting (arrowed) - Roto-Diesel/Lucas pump

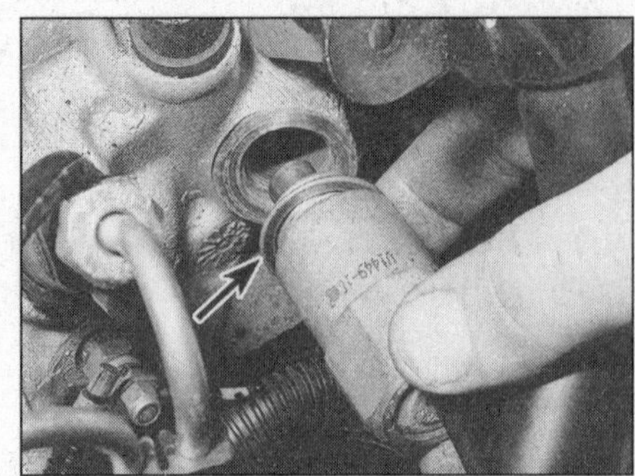

3.5 Unscrewing thermostatic actuator. Note sealing ring (arrowed)

3 Fast idle thermostatic actuator and cable - removal, refitting, testing and adjustment

Note: *This procedure only applies to the Renault 19 and Clio models.*

Note: *A new thermostatic actuator sealing ring will be required on refitting.*

Removal

1 The thermostatic actuator is located at the left-hand end of the cylinder head.

2 Disconnect the battery negative lead and partially drain the cooling system.

3 Loosen the clamp screw or nut (as applicable) and slide the fast idle cable end fitting from the cable inner at the fast idle lever on the fuel injection pump **(see illustration)**.

4 Slide the cable outer from the bracket on the injection pump.

5 Using a suitable open-ended spanner, unscrew the thermostatic actuator from the cylinder head and withdraw the actuator complete with cable. Recover the sealing ring **(see illustration)**.

Refitting

6 Fit the actuator with a new sealing ring, then tighten it.

7 Refill the cooling system.

8 Insert the cable outer through the bracket on the injection pump.

9 Insert the cable inner through the fast idle lever and position the end fitting on the cable. Do not tighten the clamp screw or nut (as applicable).

10 Adjust the cable as follows:

Testing and adjustment

Bosch pump

11 During this procedure, it is necessary to measure engine speed. The usual type of tachometer (rev counter) which works from ignition system pulses cannot be used on diesel engines. A diagnostic socket is provided for the use of Renault test equipment but this will not normally be available to the home mechanic. If it is not felt that adjusting the idle speed by ear is satisfactory, or that (where fitted) the instrument panel tachometer is not sufficiently reliable, one of the following alternatives may be used.

a) Purchase or hire of an appropriate tachometer.

b) Delegation of the job to a Renault dealer or other specialist.

c) Timing light (strobe) operated by a petrol engine running at the desired speed. If the timing light is pointed at a mark on the camshaft pump pulley, the mark will appear stationary when the two engines are running at the same speed (or multiples of that speed). The pulley will be rotating at half the crankshaft speed but this will not affect the adjustment. (In practice it was found impossible to use this method on the crankshaft pulley due to the acute viewing angle.)

12 With the engine warm (the cooling fan should have cut in and out once) and running at the correct idle speed, proceed as follows.

13 Move the fast idle lever on the injection pump towards the flywheel end of the engine so that it contacts the fast idle adjustment screw **(see illustration)**.

14 Check the fast idle speed. If necessary, loosen the locknut and turn the adjustment screw to give the specified fast idle speed. Retighten the locknut on completion.

15 Stop the engine and disconnect the tachometer, where applicable.

16 The fast idle cable should now be adjusted as follows.

17 With the engine still at normal operating temperature and the fast idle lever resting against the idle speed adjustment screw (not the fast idle adjustment screw), gently pull the fast idle cable taught.

18 Position the end fitting on the cable so that the dimension between the end of the fast idle lever and the end fitting is as shown **(see illustration)**.

19 With the end fitting correctly positioned, tighten the clamp screw.

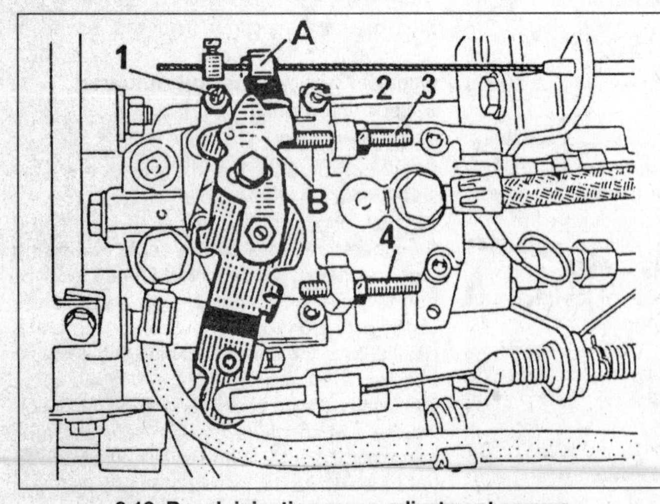

3.13 Bosch injection pump adjustment screws

A Fast idle lever
B Accelerator lever
1 Fast idle adjustment screw
2 Idle adjustment screw
3 Anti-stall adjustment screw
4 Max. speed adjustment screw

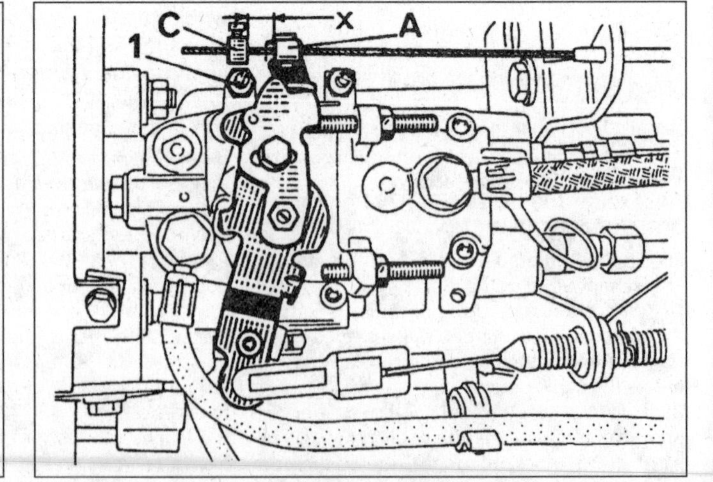

3.18 Fast idle cable adjustment (thermostatic actuator) - Bosch pump

A Fast idle lever
C Cable end fitting
1 Fast idle adjustment screw
x = 6.0 mm

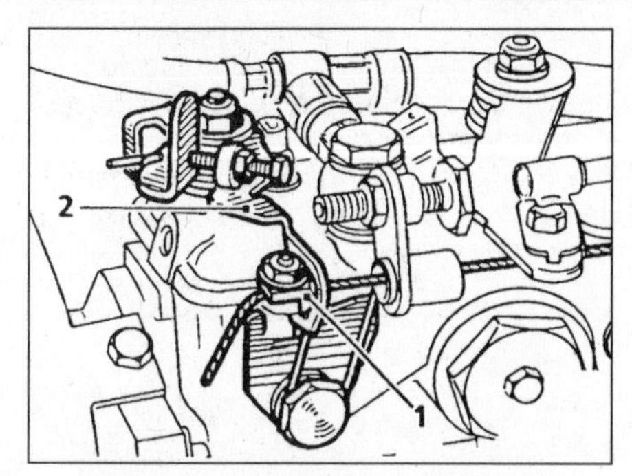

3.31 Fast idle cable adjustment (thermostatic actuator) - Lucas pump

1 Cable clamp 2 Fast idle lever

20 With the engine cool, check that the cable has pulled the fast idle lever so that it rests against the fast idle adjustment screw. Recheck that with the engine at normal operating temperature, the dimension X between the end of the fast idle lever and the cable end fitting is as specified. If not, it is likely that the thermostatic actuator is faulty.

Roto-Diesel/Lucas pump - pre early 1993 Clio (F8Q 730 engine)

21 The fast idle speed is set at the factory on a test bench and cannot be adjusted.

22 With the engine cold, loosen the cable clamp and push the fast idle lever fully away from the timing end of the engine. This is the fast idling position of the lever.

23 With the lever held in the fast idle position, pull the end of the cable so that it is moderately tensioned, then locate the clamp on the cable so that it is just in contact with the fast idle lever. Tighten the clamp onto the cable.

24 Run the engine until it is at normal operating temperature (the cooling fan should have cut in and out once), then stop the engine. The fast idle lever should now have been fully released by the thermostatic actuator.

25 Pull the end of the cable (paragraph 23) then use a feeler gauge to check that the clearance between the clamp and the fast idle lever is 2.0 to 3.0 mm. If not, adjust the position of the clamp on the inner cable.

Roto-Diesel/Lucas pump - post early 1993 Clio (F8Q 714 engine) and Renault 19

26 The fast idle speed is set at the factory and cannot be adjusted.

27 With the engine cold, note the length of the exposed fast idle cable inner, measured from the end of the cable to the point where it enters the cable outer.

28 Run the engine until it is at normal operating temperature (the cooling fan should have cut in and out once), then stop the engine.

29 Again measure the length of the exposed cable inner, which should have increased by 7.0 to 8.5 mm. If the cable travel between cold and normal operating temperature is not as stated, it is likely that the thermostatic actuator is faulty.

30 With the engine still at normal operating temperature and the fast idle lever in the rest position, gently pull the fast idle cable taught.

31 Position the fast idle cable end fitting on the cable so that the dimension between the end of the fast idle lever and the end fitting is 3.0 ± 1.0 mm **(see illustration)**.

32 With the end fitting correctly positioned, tighten the clamp nut.

4 Fast idle thermostatic actuator and cable - removal, refitting, testing and adjustment

***Note:** This procedure only applies to the Renault Espace.*

Note: *Two different types of thermostatic actuator may be encountered. One type is screwed into the cylinder head and the other mounted on a bracket attached to the rear of the injection pump.*

Note: *A new thermostatic actuator sealing ring will be required on refitting.*

Removal

Cylinder head-mounted actuator

1 Proceed as described in Section 3, paragraphs 2 to 5 inclusive.

Injection pump-mounted actuator

2 Disconnect the battery negative lead.

3 Using a hose clamp, clamp both actuator coolant hoses to minimise coolant loss during the following operation.

4 Slacken the retaining clips and disconnect both coolant hoses from the actuator. Be prepared for some coolant spillage.

5 Loosen the clamp screw and nut, then slide the fast idle cable end fitting arrangement off the cable end.

6 Slacken and remove the bolts securing the fast idle actuator mounting bracket to the rear of the injection pump. Remove the bracket and actuator assembly from the pump, freeing the cable from the fast idle lever. Remove the cable fitting (where fitted) from the pump lever and store it with the actuator for safe-keeping. If necessary, the actuator assembly can be dismantled as follows.

7 Slacken the two bolts securing the two halves of the actuator housing together. As the bolts near the ends of their threads, compress the two halves of the actuator together to relieve spring pressure on the bolts. With the bolts removed, carefully separate the actuator, gradually relieving spring pressure, removing both halves from the bracket.

8 Remove the rubber gaiter and cable guide from the front half of the actuator housing then withdraw the cable and springs.

9 Using a suitable peg spanner, unscrew the thermostatic capsule ring nut from the rear half of the actuator. Lift out the capsule and recover the sealing ring.

Refitting

Cylinder head-mounted actuator

10 Proceed as described in Section 3, paragraphs 6 to 9 inclusive.

11 Adjust the cable as described under the appropriate sub-heading.

Injection pump-mounted actuator

12 If the actuator has been dismantled, proceed as follows. If not, proceed to paragraph 16.

13 Fit a new sealing ring to the thermostatic capsule and fit the capsule to the rear half of the actuator. Refit the ring nut and tighten it securely.

14 Fit the springs to the cable and insert the cable through the front half of the actuator. Locate the cable guide in the rubber gaiter then slide the gaiter into position, ensuring it is correctly seated in the groove on the front of the actuator.

15 Position the actuator halves on either side of the mounting bracket. With the aid of an assistant, compress the two halves and refit the retaining bolts, tightening them securely.

16 Refit the cable fitting to the pump lever and manoeuvre the fast idle actuator and bracket assembly into position, passing the cable through its fitting.

17 Refit the injection pump rear mounting bracket and securely tighten both the fast idle actuator and mounting bracket retaining nuts and bolts.

18 Connect the coolant hoses to the fast idle actuator and securely tighten their retaining clips. Remove the hose clamps and top-up the cooling system.

19 Slide the cable end fitting arrangement onto the cable and lightly tighten its clamp screw and nut.

20 Adjust the cable as described under the appropriate sub-heading.

Testing and adjustment

Cylinder head-mounted actuator

21 Run the engine until it reaches normal operating temperature. Refer to Part A of this Chapter and adjust the idle speed, anti-stall speed and fast idle speed.

22 Pull the cable inner tight, then measure the clearance between the cable end fitting and the lever. There should be a gap of approximately 6.0 mm. If not, slacken the clamp screw or nut (as applicable), move the end fitting to the correct position and securely retighten the screw or nut.

23 Switch off the engine and allow it to cool. As the engine cools the fast idle actuator cable should retract and eventually pull the lever back towards the rear of the pump.

Injection pump-mounted actuator

24 Loosen the injection pump fast idle lever stop retaining screw and move the stop away from the lever.

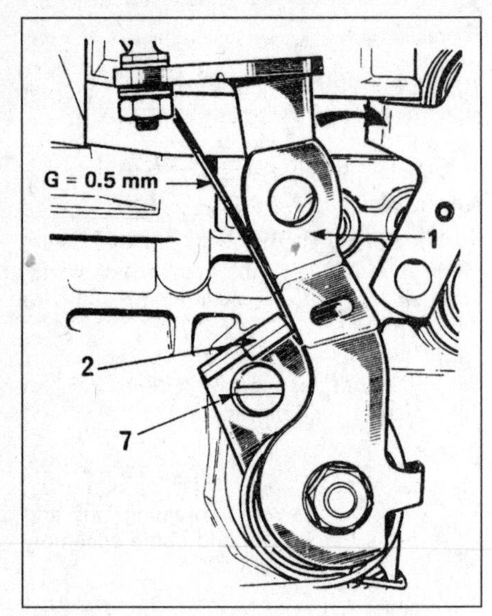

4.25 Position fast idle lever (1) and adjust gap (G) by slackening screw (7) and repositioning lever stop (2) - pump-mounted fast idle valve

25 With the cable end fitting positioned clear of the fast idle lever, move the lever towards the rear of the pump until the position is reached where resistance is felt. This is the point where the lever is starting to act on the fast idle mechanism in the pump. Hold the fast idle lever in this position and set the lever stop so that there is a gap of 0.5 mm between the stop and the lever **(see illustration)**. With the stop correctly positioned, tighten its retaining screw.

26 With the engine cold, accurately measure the temperature of the fast idle actuator thermostatic capsule located in the rear half of the actuator. Referring to the following table, obtain the relevant dimensions A and B **(see illustration)** which correspond to the temperature of the capsule.

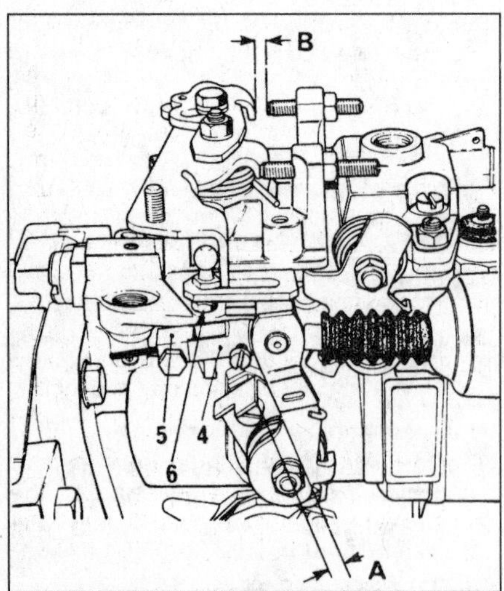

4.26 Fast idle valve adjustment details - pump-mounted valve

4 Cable end fitting front section
5 Cable end fitting rear section
6 Balljoint
A Fast idle lever-to-stop clearance
B Idle speed screw-to-accelerator lever clearance

Capsule temperature	Dimension A (mm)	Dimension B (mm)
Less than 18°C	6.5	4.5
22°C	5.9	3.5
25°C	5.5	2.7
30°C	4.75	1.5
35°C	4.0	0.2
40°C	3.25	0

27 Insert shims equal in thickness to dimension A between the pump fast idle lever and its stop. Remove all slack from the cable then slide the end fitting along the cable until it abuts the fast idle lever, then securely tighten its clamp screw and nut. Withdraw the shims and check that the clearance between the fast idle lever and stop is equal to dimension A. If not, repeat the adjustment procedure.

28 With dimension A correctly set, slacken the fast idle lever balljoint nut and slide the balljoint away from the accelerator lever.

29 Insert shims equal in thickness to dimension B between the idle speed adjusting screw and the accelerator lever. Slide the balljoint along its slot until it abuts the accelerator lever, then securely tighten its retaining nut. Withdraw the shims and check the clearance between the accelerator lever and the idle speed adjusting screw is equal to dimension B. If not, repeat the adjustment procedure.

30 Run the engine until it reaches normal operating temperature. As the engine warms up, the cable end fitting should slowly extend until the fast idle lever returns to its stop and the cable end fitting is clear of the lever. At the same time, the accelerator lever should be back against the idle speed adjusting screw.

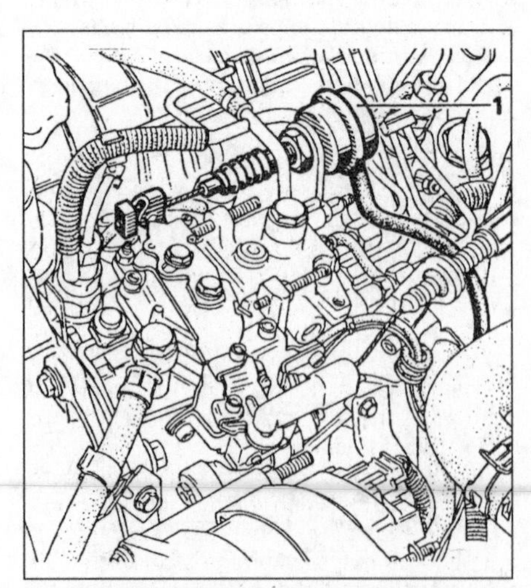

5.1a Fast idle vacuum actuator (1) - Bosch pump

5 Fast idle vacuum actuator, cable and solenoid valve - removal, refitting, testing and adjustment

Note: *This procedure only applies to the Renault 19.*

Vacuum actuator and cable

Removal

1 The vacuum actuator is attached to a bracket located on the end of the fuel injection pump **(see illustrations)**.

2 Loosen the clamp screw or nut (as applicable) and slide the fast idle cable end fitting from the cable inner at the fast idle lever on the injection pump.

3 Disconnect the vacuum hose from the actuator.

4 Unscrew the nut securing the actuator to the bracket and withdraw the actuator, passing the cable through the bracket as it is withdrawn.

Refitting

5 Refit the actuator to the bracket and tighten the securing nut.

6 Reconnect the vacuum hose.

7 Insert the cable inner through the fast idle lever and position the end fitting on the cable. Do not tighten the clamp screw or nut (as applicable).

8 Adjust the cable as follows:

Testing and adjustment - Bosch pump

9 Proceed as described in Section 3, paragraphs 11 to 19 inclusive.

10 If a faulty vacuum actuator is suspected, first test the solenoid valve.

11 The actuator can be tested using a vacuum pump. With the engine stopped, disconnect the vacuum hose from the actuator and connect the vacuum pump in its place. With a vacuum of 500 mbars applied,

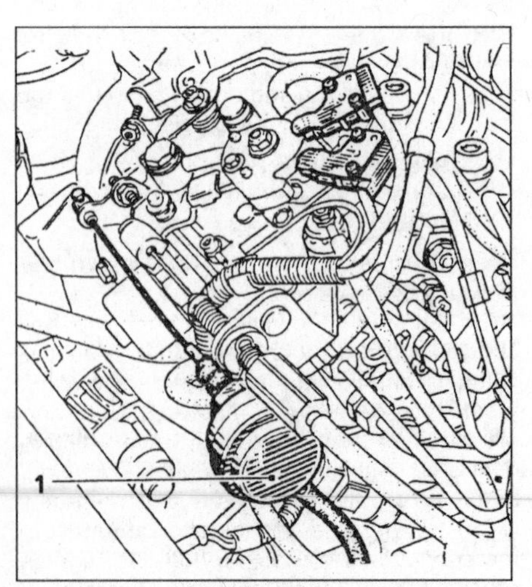

5.1b Fast idle vacuum actuator (1) - Lucas pump

the actuator should operate the cable sufficiently to pull the fast idle lever so that it rests against the fast idle adjustment screw. If not, it is likely that the vacuum actuator is faulty.

Testing and adjustment - Lucas pump

12 The fast idle speed is set at the factory and cannot be adjusted.

13 With the engine stopped and the fast idle lever in the rest position, gently pull the fast idle cable taught.

14 Position the fast idle cable end fitting on the cable so that the dimension between the end of the fast idle lever and the end fitting is 3.0 ± 1.0 mm.

15 With the end fitting correctly positioned, tighten the clamp nut.

16 The actuator can be tested with reference to paragraphs 10 and 11 but note that the fast idle lever should rest against the lever stop rather than the fast idle adjustment screw.

Solenoid valve

Removal

17 The solenoid valve is located on a bracket attached to the front body panel in the engine compartment **(see illustration)**.

18 Disconnect the wiring plug and the vacuum hoses from the valve.

19 Unscrew the two securing nuts and withdraw the valve, complete with its bracket.

Refitting

20 Refitting is a reversal of removal. Ensure that the vacuum hoses are securely reconnected.

Testing

21 Remove the solenoid valve.

22 Attempt to blow gently through one of the vacuum hose connections. No air should pass through the valve.

23 With a 12-volt supply connected across the solenoid terminals, again attempt to blow through the valve. Air should now pass through.

24 If the valve proves to be faulty, it should be renewed.

6 Fast idle system - component removal, refitting and adjustment

***Note:** This procedure only applies to the Renault Laguna models.*

1 On Laguna models equipped with air conditioning and some later models not fitted with air conditioning, the fast idle system is vacuum-operated via a diaphragm unit and electrically-operated solenoid valve which is controlled by the preheating unit. The fast idle diaphragm is also used as a load corrector (LDA) to fine tune the injection pump fuel metering under certain conditions. On all other models, the fast idle system is controlled by a thermostatic actuator which is screwed into the front of the cylinder head.

5.17 Fast idle solenoid valve (4) - vacuum fast idle actuator

Thermostatic actuator

Removal

2 To improve access to the actuator, unclip the power steering reservoir and position it clear of its mounting bracket.

3 Proceed as described in Section 3, paragraphs 2 to 5 inclusive.

Refitting

4 If sealing compound was originally used on the actuator, thoroughly clean all traces of old compound from the actuator and cylinder head. Ensure that no traces of compound are left in the internal coolant passages.

5 Fit the sensor, using suitable sealing compound or a new washer as applicable, and tighten it securely.

6 Insert the adjustment screw into the bracket on the fuel injection pump and screw on the locknut, finger-tight.

7 Insert the cable inner through the fast idle lever and position the end fitting on the cable. Do not tighten the clamp screw or nut (as applicable).

8 Clip the power steering fluid reservoir back into position.

9 Refill the cooling system and adjust the cable as follows.

Adjustment

10 With the engine cold, push the fast idle lever fully towards the rear of the injection pump, until it is in contact with the fast idle adjusting screw. Hold it in this position and slide the cable end fitting along the cable until its abuts the fast idle lever, then securely tighten its clamp nut or screw (as applicable).

11 Start the engine and run it until it reaches normal operating temperature. As the engine warms up, the fast idle cable should extend so that the fast idle lever returns to is stop.

12 Once the cooling fan has cut in, measure the clearance between the fast idle lever and the cable end fitting. There should be a gap of 6 ± 1 mm. If not, slacken the clamp screw or nut (as applicable), move the end fitting to the correct position and securely retighten the screw or nut.

13 Switch off the engine and allow it to cool. As the engine cools, the fast idle valve cable should retract and eventually pull the lever back against the fast idle adjustment screw.

Vacuum-operated system

Removal

14 To remove the system solenoid valve, disconnect the vacuum hoses and wiring connector then undo the retaining nuts and remove the valve from the front of the engine compartment.

15 To remove the vacuum diaphragm unit first disconnect the vacuum hose. Loosen the clamp screw or nut (as applicable) and disconnect the fast idle cable end fitting from the cable inner at the fuel injection pump fast idle lever Unscrew the retaining nut and remove the diaphragm and cable assembly from the pump bracket.

Refitting

16 Refit the diaphragm unit and securely tighten its retaining nut.

17 Reconnect the cable to the injection pump, making sure the cable end fitting is correctly located. Do not tighten the clamp screw/nut.

18 Reconnect the vacuum hose to the diaphragm unit.

19 Refit the solenoid valve, tightening its retaining nuts securely. Reconnect the vacuum hoses. Adjust the cable as follows.

Adjustment

20 Disconnect the vacuum hose from the diaphragm unit on the injection pump. Hold the diaphragm cable taut and position the end fitting so there is a clearance of 2 ± 1 mm between the end fitting and fast idle lever. Move the end fitting to the correct position and securely tighten its clamp screw/nut.

21 Reconnect the vacuum hose to the diaphragm and start the engine. With the engine cold, the diaphragm should pull the fast lever towards the rear of the pump until it is in contact with the fast idle adjustment screw. Once the engine is warm, the solenoid valve should cut-off the vacuum supply to the diaphragm and the cable will extend, returning the fast idle lever to its stop against the idle speed screw. Check the clearance between the fast idle cable end fitting and lever is 2 ± 1 mm, then switch off the engine.

7 Cold-start timing advance solenoid - testing, removal and refitting

Note: *This procedure only applies to the Renault 19 and Clio models.*

Note: *Do not allow dirt to enter the fuel injection pump when removing the solenoid. A new sealing washer must be used on refitting.*

Testing

1 To check system operation, start the engine from cold and listen for a knocking or harshness, disappearing after between 30

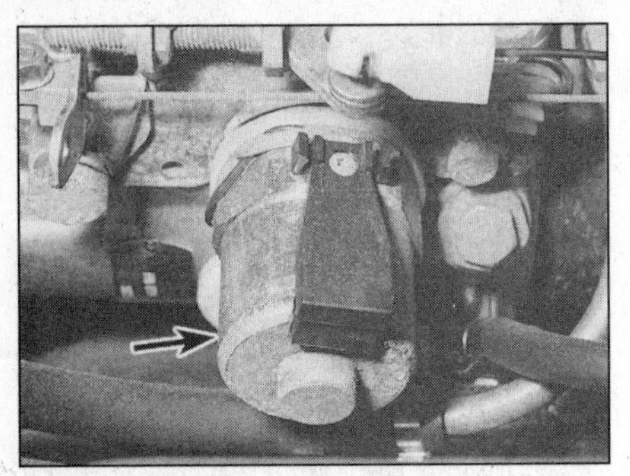

7.4a Cold start timing advance solenoid (arrowed) - Lucas pump

seconds and 2 minutes 45 seconds. This shows that the system is working correctly. If dynamic timing equipment is available, this can be used to check the advance.

2 If the system does not seem to be working, check for voltage at the solenoid feed wire with the starter motor cranking and then 5 to 6 seconds after start-up. The feed to the solenoid is controlled by the preheating system control unit.

3 If voltage is present but the system is still not working, the solenoid valve is probably faulty and should be renewed.

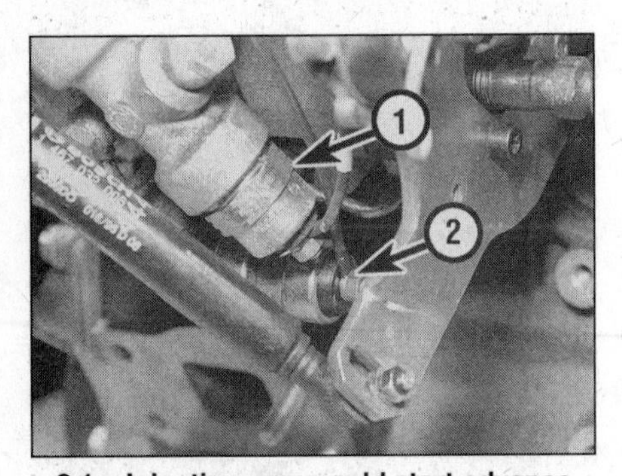

8.1a Injection pump cold start advance (KSB) solenoid (1) and hydraulic load adjustment (AFLB) solenoid (2)

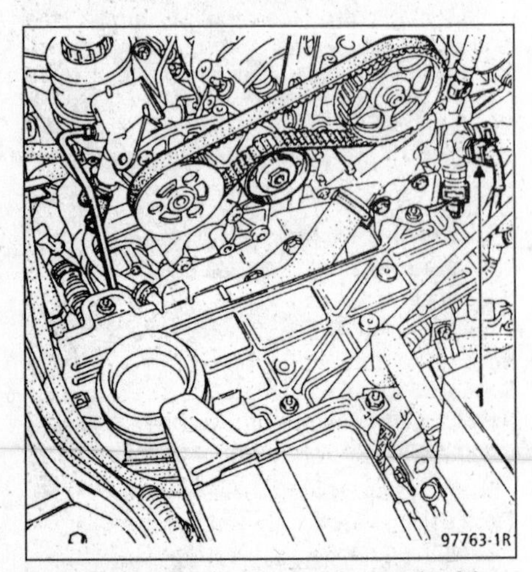

8.1b Coolant temperature sender (1) screwed into cylinder head coolant outlet

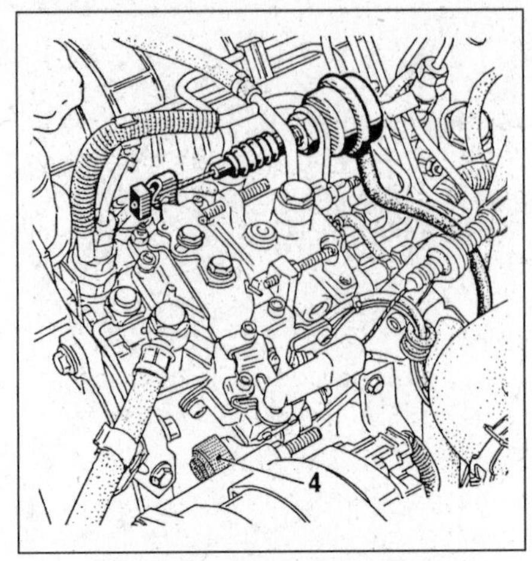

7.4b Cold start timing advance solenoid (4) - Bosch pump

Removal

4 Disconnect the battery negative lead, then disconnect the solenoid wiring connector **(see illustrations)**.

5 Unscrew the solenoid from the pump and recover the sealing washer, whilst taking care not to allow dirt to enter the pump.

Refitting

6 Refitting is a reversal of removal. Use a new sealing washer.

8 Cold start advance system (Renault Laguna) - testing

1 The fuel injection pump fitted to the Renault Laguna is equipped with a cold start advance (KSB) solenoid to advance pump timing when the engine is cold. This solenoid is the upper of two fitted to the front of the injection pump. The solenoid is controlled by the preheating unit, which has an integral air temperature sensor, and a coolant temperature sender which is screwed into the coolant outlet housing on the left-hand end of the cylinder head **(see illustrations)**. The solenoid operates when the ambient air temperature is less than 15°C and the engine coolant temperature less than 60°C.

2 If the cold start advance system develops a fault, check the electrical feed to the solenoid valve and the condition of the wiring connecting the preheating unit, the coolant temperature sender and the solenoid. Note that if the air temperature sensor is faulty, the solenoid is operated for a set time depending on the engine coolant temperature **(see illustration).** If the coolant temperature sender is faulty, the solenoid is operated for 3 minutes, regardless of air temperature. Any further testing of the system should be entrusted to a Renault dealer.

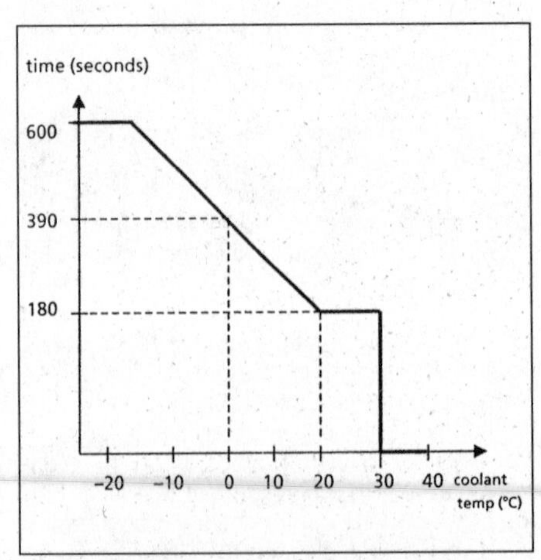

8.2 Cold start advance (KSB) solenoid operating time when air temperature sensor is faulty

9 Stop solenoid - removal and refitting

Caution: Do not allow dirt to enter the fuel injection pump during this procedure. A new sealing washer or O-ring must be used on refitting.

Removal

1 Disconnect the battery negative lead.

2 On Renault Laguna models, it will be necessary to release the retaining clip and position the power steering fluid reservoir clear of the injection pump to improve access to the solenoid

3 Withdraw the rubber boot (where applicable), then unscrew the terminal nut and disconnect the wire from the top of the solenoid **(see illustration)**.

4 Carefully clean around the solenoid, then unscrew and withdraw the solenoid and recover the sealing washer or O-ring (as applicable).

5 Operate the hand priming pump as the solenoid is removed to flush away any dirt.

6 Recover the solenoid plunger and spring if they remain in the pump.

Refitting

7 Check that the aperture in the injection pump is completely free of dust or dirt.

9.3 Disconnecting stop solenoid wiring - Roto-Diesel/Lucas pump

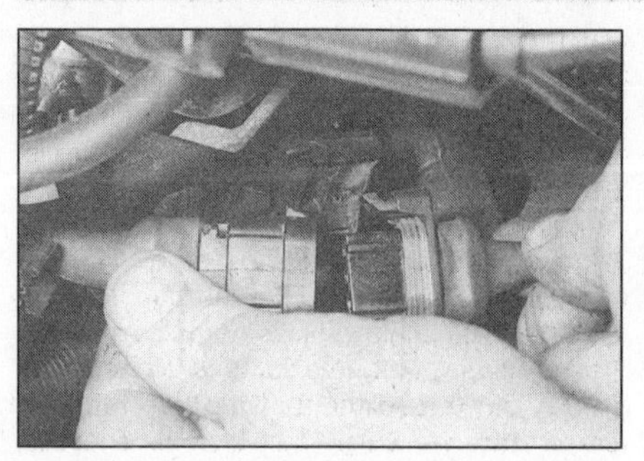

10.2 Disconnecting no-load switch wiring - Lucas pump

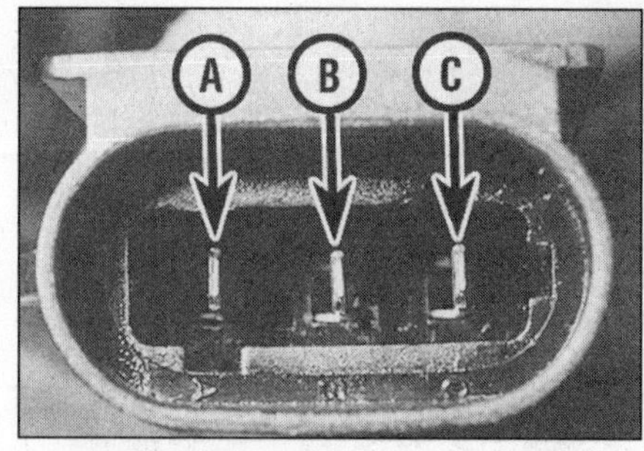

10.3 No-load switch wiring connector terminal identification - Lucas pump

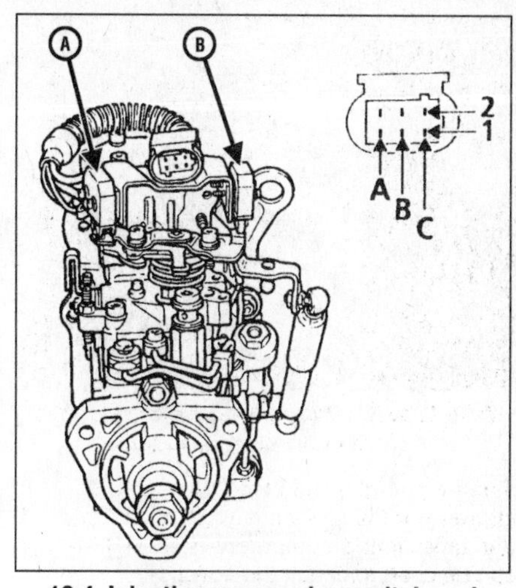

10.4 Injection pump microswitch and wiring connector details

A Rear switch used on engines not equipped with EGR
B Front switch used on engines equipped with EGR

8 On Roto-Diesel/Lucas pumps, instances have been known of a small piece of metal swarf preventing the valve from fully closing when the ignition switch is turned off. Insert a small magnet in the aperture to collect any swarf. Do not blow into the aperture otherwise swarf may enter the fuel circuit.

9 Refitting is a reversal of removal. Use a new sealing washer or O-ring.

10 When refitting the terminal wire on Roto-Diesel/Lucas injection pumps, ensure that the fan-shaped washer is located under the wire end fitting. Failure to fit the washer may cause the engine to stop while driving, or prevent the engine from being started.

10 No-load switch - testing, adjustment, removal and refitting

Note: *On the Renault Clio, the information in this Section appertains to the F8Q 714 and F8Q 730 engines.*

Note: *A continuity tester or an ohmmeter will be required for testing the no-load switch.*

Testing and adjustment

1 Ensure that the idle and anti-stall speed settings are correctly adjusted, as described in Part A of this Chapter.

2 Disconnect the switch wiring connector **(see illustration).**

3 On Renault 19, Clio and Espace models, connect a continuity tester or ohmmeter across wiring connector terminals B and C **(see illustration).**

4 On Renault Laguna models, connect a continuity tester or an ohmmeter across the switch wiring connector terminals of the injection pump connector **(see illustration).** On models not equipped with an exhaust gas recirculation (EGR) system, the rear switch is used and the tester should be connected across terminals B1 and C1. On models equipped with EGR, the front switch is used and the tester should be connected across terminals B2 and C2.

5 On all models, insert feeler gauges of different thicknesses between the fuel injection pump accelerator lever and the anti-stall adjustment screw. Note the readings on the continuity tester or ohmmeter, as applicable **(see illustrations).** The readings obtained should be as follows:

Renault 19 - Bosch pump

Spacer thickness	*Test reading*
Up to 7.0 mm	*Continuity/zero resistance*
Above 8.0 mm	*No continuity/infinite resistance*

Renault 19 - Roto-Diesel/Lucas pump

Spacer thickness	*Test reading*
Up to 9.0 mm	*Continuity/zero resistance*
Above 11.0 mm	*No continuity/infinite resistance*

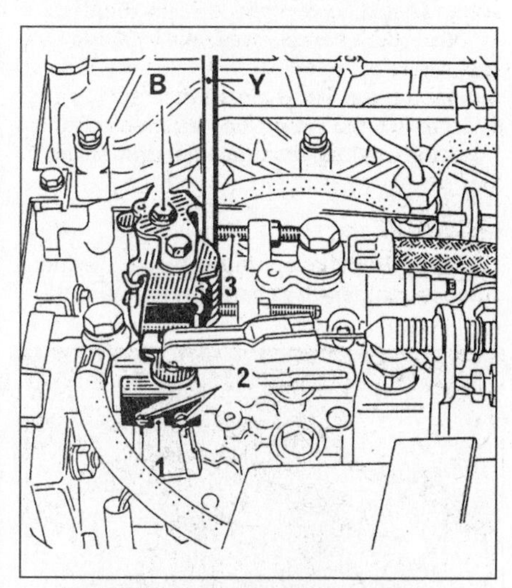

10.5a No-load adjustment details - early version

1 No-load switch
2 No-load switch securing screws
3 Anti-stall adjustment screw
B Accelerator lever
Y Feeler blades

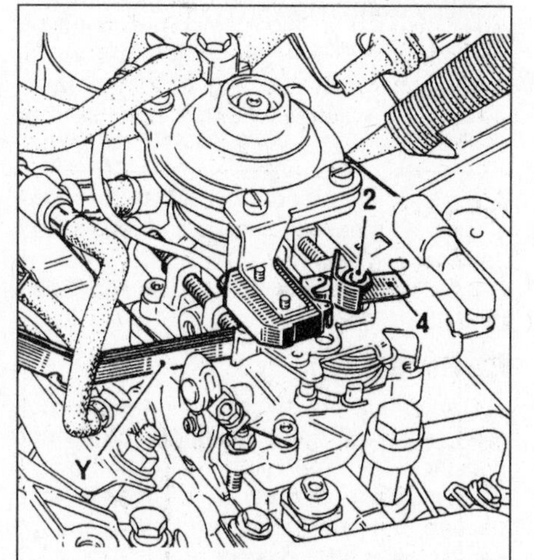

10.5b No-load adjustment details - later version

2 Retaining nut
4 Operating cam
Y Feeler blades

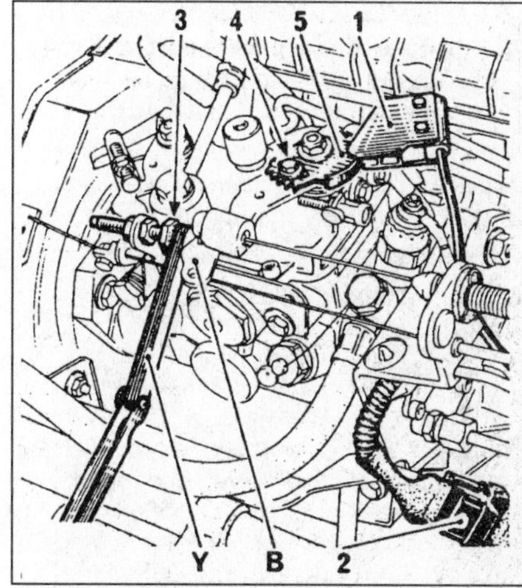

10.5c Adjusting no-load switch - Lucas pump (vehicle without air conditioning)

B Accelerator lever
Y Feeler gauges
1 No-load switch
2 Switch wiring connector
3 Anti-stall adjustment screw
4 Bolt
5 Cam

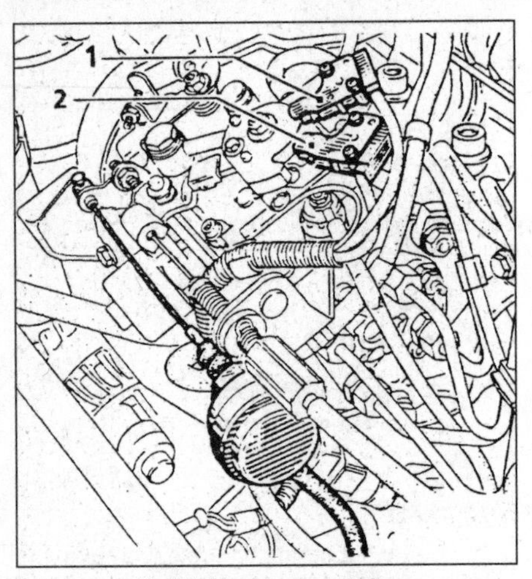

10.5d No-load switch - Turbo engines fitted with EGR

1 *No-load switch* 2 *EGR cut-off switch*

Renault Clio - Bosch pump

Spacer thickness	*Test reading*
Up to 9.7 mm	*Continuity/zero resistance*
Above 10.7 mm	*No continuity/infinite resistance*

Renault Clio - Roto-Diesel/Lucas pump

Spacer thickness	*Test reading*
Up to 8.0 mm	*Continuity/zero resistance*
Above 12.0 mm	*No continuity/infinite resistance*

Renault Espace

Spacer thickness	*Test reading*
Up to 10.2 mm	*Continuity/zero resistance*
Above 11.5 mm	*No continuity/infinite resistance*

Renault Laguna - without EGR

Spacer thickness	*Test reading*
Up to 13.1 mm	*Continuity/zero resistance*
Above 14.1 mm	*No continuity/infinite resistance*

Renault Laguna - with EGR

Spacer thickness	*Test reading*
Up to 11.7 mm	*Continuity/zero resistance*
Above 12.3 mm	*No continuity/infinite resistance*

6 If the switch does not behave as described, slacken its mounting screws and reposition it as necessary. Note that on certain Lucas fuel injection pumps, the adjustment is made by loosening the screw and adjusting the position of the cam in relation to the accelerator lever.

7 If the switch is permanently open or closed, renew it.

Removal

8 Disconnect the switch wiring connector, then remove the two securing screws and withdraw the switch from its bracket on the injection pump.

Refitting

9 Refitting is a reversal of removal. Where applicable, adjust the switch before tightening the securing screws.

11 Fuel injection pump microswitches - testing, adjustment, removal and refitting

Note: *The information in this Section appertains to the F8Q 732 engine fitted to the Renault Clio only.*

1 On F8Q 732 engines fitted to the Renault Clio, there are two microswitches on the fuel injection pump. The inner switch is the post-heating cut-out switch and the outer switch is the exhaust gas recirculation (EGR) system switch. Both switches are of the full-load type.

Testing and adjustment

2 Disconnect the relevant wiring connector.

3 Connect a continuity tester or an ohmmeter across the relevant wiring connector terminals **(see illustration)**.

4 Insert feeler gauges of different thicknesses between the injection pump accelerator lever and the anti-stall adjustment screw, then note the readings on the continuity tester or ohmmeter, as applicable. The readings obtained should be as follows:

Post-heating switch

Spacer thickness	*Test reading*
Up to 7.0 mm	*Continuity/zero resistance*
Above 8.0 mm	*No continuity/infinite resistance*

EGR system switch

Spacer thickness	*Test reading*
Up to 13.5 mm	*Continuity/zero resistance*
Above 14.5 mm	*No continuity/infinite resistance*

5 If the switch does not behave as described, slacken its mounting screws and reposition it as necessary.

6 If the switch is permanently open or closed, renew it.

Removal

7 Disconnect the switch wiring connector, then remove the two securing screws and withdraw the switch from its bracket on the injection pump. In order to remove the post-heating cut-out (inner) switch, it will be necessary to first remove the EGR system (outer) switch.

Refitting

8 Refitting is a reversal of removal. Where applicable, before tightening the securing screws, adjust the switch(es) as described previously.

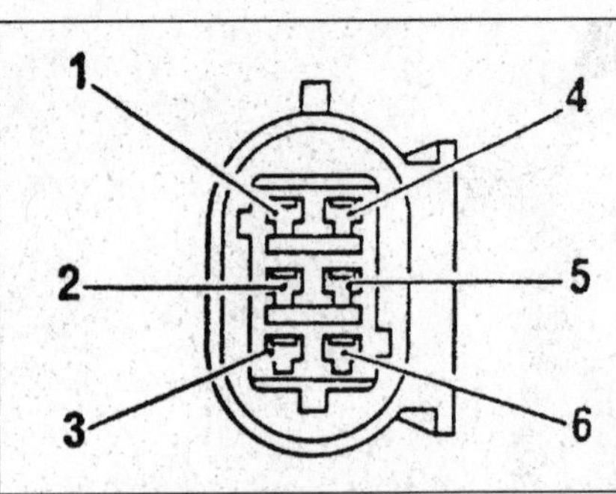

11.3 Injection pump microswitch wiring connector terminal details - F8Q 732 engines

1 *Cold start advance solenoid terminal*
2 and 3 *Post heating microswitch terminals*
4 *Not used*
5 and 6 *EGR system switch*

12 Glow plugs - removal, inspection and refitting

Caution: If the preheating system has just been energised, or if the engine has been running, the glow plugs may be very hot.

Removal

1 Disconnect the battery negative lead.

2 On Renault Laguna models, gain access to the glow plugs by removing the inlet manifold.

3 Unscrew the nuts from the glow plug terminals and recover the washers. Disconnect the wiring **(see illustration)**. Note that on Renault 19 and Clio models, the main electrical feed wiring is connected to two of the plugs. On the Espace engine, the main supply cable is connected to one plug.

4 Where applicable, carefully move any obstructing pipes or wires to one side to enable access to the glow plugs.

5 Unscrew the glow plugs and remove them from the cylinder head **(see illustration)**.

Inspection

6 Inspect the glow plugs for physical damage. Burnt or eroded glow plug tips can be caused by a bad injector spray pattern.

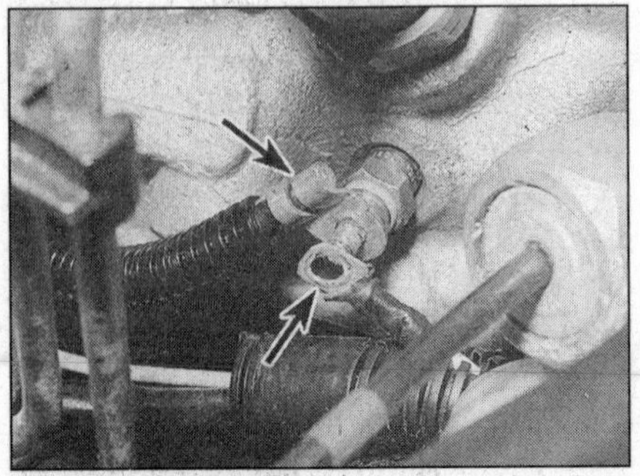

12.3 Disconnecting wiring (arrowed) from glow plug terminal

12.5 Removing glow plug from cylinder head

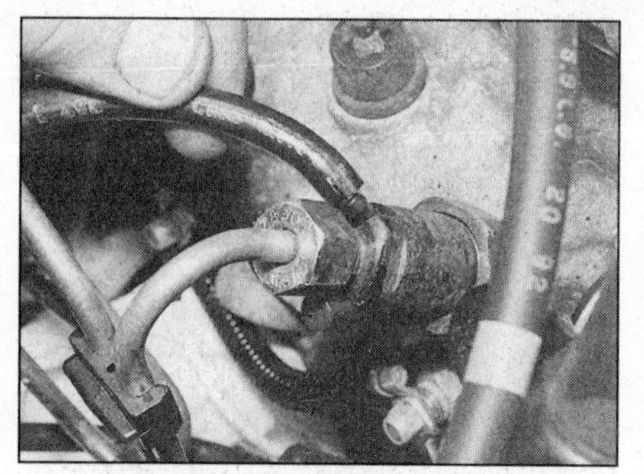
13.4 Pulling leak-off pipes from fuel injector

13.6 Disconnecting fuel pipes from injectors

Have the injectors checked if this sort of damage is found.

7 If the glow plugs are in good physical condition, check them electrically using a 12 volt test lamp or continuity tester, as described in Section 23.

8 The glow plugs can be energised by applying 12 volts to them to verify that they heat up evenly and in the required time. Observe the following precautions:

a) *Support the glow plug by clamping it carefully in a vice or self-locking pliers. Remember it will become red-hot.*

b) *Ensure that the power supply or test lead incorporates a fuse or overload trip to protect against damage from a short-circuit.*

c) *After testing, allow the glow plug to cool for several minutes before attempting to handle it.*

9 A glow plug in good condition will start to glow red at the tip after drawing current for 5 seconds or so. Any plug which takes much longer to start glowing, or which starts glowing in the middle instead of at the tip, is defective.

Refitting

10 Refit by reversing the removal operations. Apply a smear of copper-based anti-seize compound to the plug threads and tighten each glow plug to the specified torque. Do not overtighten as this can damage the glow plug element.

13 Injectors (Renault 19, Clio and Laguna) - testing, removal and refitting

Warning: Exercise extreme caution when working on fuel injectors. Never expose the hands or any part of the body to injector spray, as the high working pressure can cause fuel to penetrate the skin, with possibly fatal results. You are strongly advised to have any work which involves testing injectors under pressure carried out by a dealer or fuel injection specialist.

Note: *Do not allow dirt into the injectors or fuel pipes. New copper washers and fire seal washers must be used on refitting.*

Testing

1 Injectors do deteriorate with prolonged use and it is reasonable to expect them to need reconditioning or renewal after 60 000 miles (90 000 km) or so. Accurate testing, overhaul and calibration of injectors must be left to a specialist. A defective injector which is causing knocking or smoking can be located without dismantling as follows.

2 Run the engine at a fast idle. Slacken each injector union in turn, placing rag around the union to catch spilt fuel and being careful not to expose the skin to any spray. When the union on the defective injector is slackened, the knocking or smoking will stop.

Removal

3 On Renault Laguna models, remove the upper section of the inlet manifold to gain access to the injectors.

4 Clean around the injectors and injector pipe union nuts, then pull the leak-off pipes from the injectors **(see illustration)**.

5 Unscrew the union nuts securing the injector pipes to the fuel injection pump. Counterhold the unions on the pump when unscrewing the nuts. Cover open unions to keep dirt out.

6 Unscrew the union nuts and disconnect the pipes from the injectors **(see illustration)**. If necessary the injector pipes may be completely removed. Note the locations of any clips attached to the pipes. Cover the ends of the injectors to prevent dirt ingress.

7 Unscrew the injectors using a deep socket or box spanner (27 mm across flats) and remove them from the cylinder head **(see illustration)**.

8 Recover the copper washers and fire seal washers from the cylinder head. Also recover the sleeves if they are loose **(see illustrations)**.

Refitting

9 Obtain new copper washers and fire seal washers. Also renew the sleeves if they are damaged.

10 Take care not to drop the injectors or allow the needles at their tips to become damaged. The injectors are precision-made to fine limits and must not be handled roughly. In particular, do not mount them in a bench vice.

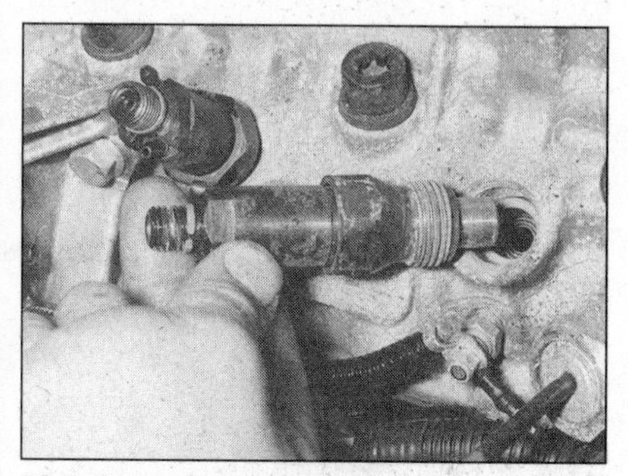
13.7 Removing injector from cylinder head

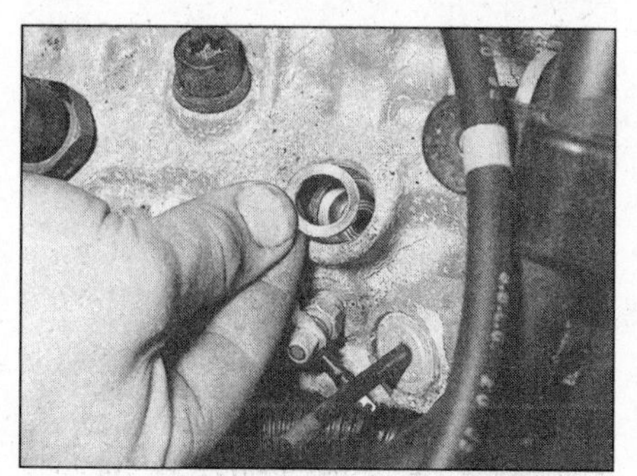
13.8a Recover copper washers . . .

13.8b . . . and fire seal washers

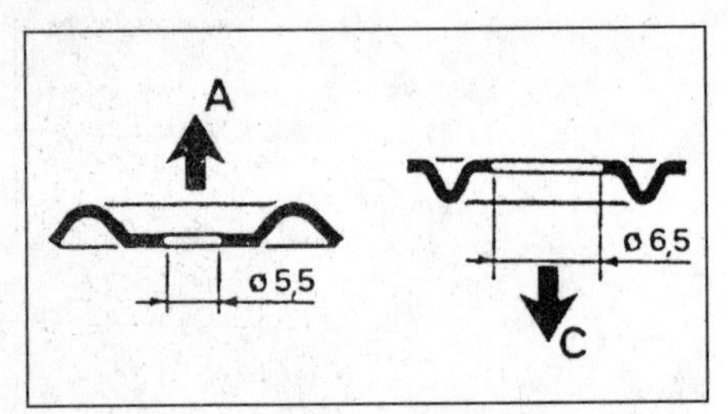

13.12 Fire seal washer fitting details

A Early type washer - fits with convex side upwards
C Later type washer - fits with convex side downwards

11 Commence refitting by inserting the sleeves (if removed) into the cylinder head.
12 Fit the new fire seal washers to the cylinder head. Note that two types of fire seal washers have been fitted to Renault engines. Ensure that the washers are fitted correctly according to type, as follows **(see illustration)**:
Early-type washer - 5.5 mm hole diameter, fitted with convex side upwards towards injector.
Later-type washer - 6.5 mm hole diameter, fitted with convex side downwards towards cylinder head.
13 Fit the copper washers to the cylinder head.
14 Insert the injectors and tighten them to the specified torque.
15 Refit the injector pipes and tighten the union nuts. Position any clips attached to the pipes as noted before removal.
16 Reconnect the leak-off pipes.
17 Start the engine. If difficulty is experienced, bleed the fuel system as described in Part A of this Chapter.

14 Injectors (Renault Espace) - testing, removal and refitting

Warning: Exercise extreme caution when working on fuel injectors. Never expose the hands or any part of the body to injector spray, as the high working pressure can cause fuel to penetrate the skin, with possibly fatal results. You are strongly advised to have any work which involves testing injectors under pressure carried out by a dealer or fuel injection specialist.

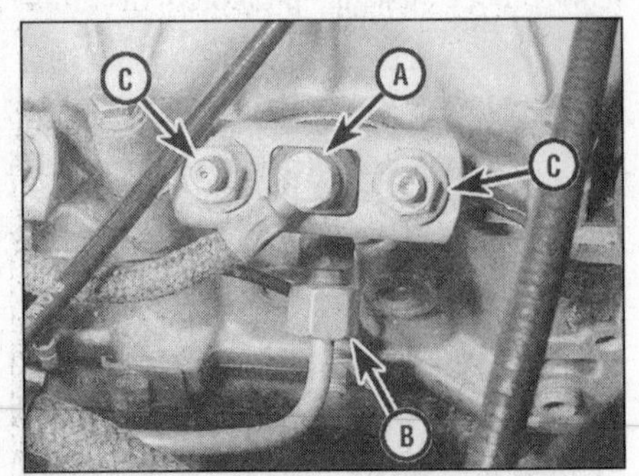

14.3 View of typical clamp-type injector

A Return hose union bolt
B Injector pipe union nut
C Retaining nuts

Note: *Do not allow dirt into the injectors or fuel pipes. New copper washers and fire seal washers must be used on refitting.*

Testing

1 Refer to Section 13, paragraphs 1 and 2.

Removal

Clamp-type injector

2 Disconnect the battery negative lead. Cover the alternator to prevent fuel being spilt onto it.
3 Wipe clean each injector then unscrew the union bolt and disconnect the return hose from the top of the injector **(see illustration)**. Recover the sealing washer positioned on each side of the hose union and cover the hose and injector union to prevent the entry of dirt into the system.
4 Slacken the union nut and free the injector pipe from the side of the injector. Cover the hose and injector union to prevent the entry of dirt into the system.
5 Slacken and remove the two retaining nuts and washers and lift off the injector retaining clamp.
6 Lift out the injector and recover the sealing and flame shield washers. Also remove the injector sleeve if it is a loose fit in the head.

Screw-type injector

7 Disconnect the battery negative lead. Cover the alternator to prevent the possibility of fuel being spilt onto it.
8 Proceed as described in Section 13, paragraphs 4 to 8 inclusive.

Refitting

Clamp-type injector

9 Obtain a new sealing washer and flame shield washer. Where removed, also renew the injector sleeve, if damaged.
10 Where necessary, refit the injector sleeve to the cylinder head.
11 Fit the new flame shield washer to the sleeve, noting that it should be fitted with its convex side downwards (facing the cylinder head).
12 Fit the new sealing washer to the top of the sleeve.
13 Slide the injector into position, ensuring that it enters the sleeve squarely.
14 Reconnect the injector pipe and tighten its union nut, by hand only at this stage.
15 Install the injector clamp and refit the washers and retaining nuts. Tighten the retaining nuts evenly and progressively to the specified torque setting.
16 Position a new sealing washer on each side of the return hose union and refit the union bolt to the top of the injector. Tighten both the union bolt and the injector pipe union nut to their specified torque settings.
17 Start the engine. If difficulty is experienced, bleed the fuel system as described in Part A of this Chapter.

Screw-type injector

18 Proceed as described in Section 13, paragraphs 9 to 17 inclusive.

15 Fuel injection pump (Renault 19) - removal and refitting

Note: *Do not allow dirt into the fuel injection pump or injector pipes during this procedure. New sealing rings should be used on the fuel pipe banjo unions when refitting.*

Removal

Non turbo models with air conditioning

1 At the time of writing, it was not possible to obtain a vehicle on which to carry out detailed work. It is therefore possible that some differences to the sequence of work described may be noted. It is recommended that notes and sketches are made during removal, where any differences to procedures are noted.
2 To gain access to the injection pump securing bolts, the alternator and its mounting bracket must be removed.
3 Disconnect the battery negative lead and remove the alternator.
4 Unscrew the securing bolts and remove the power steering pump pulley from the pump drive flange. Note that it will be necessary to counterhold the pulley in order to loosen the bolts.
5 Remove the securing bolts and withdraw the auxiliary drivebelt guide roller/bracket assembly **(see illustration)**.

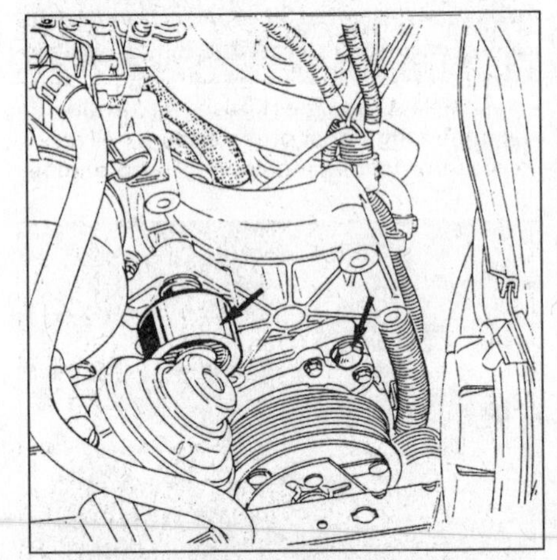

15.5 Auxiliary drivebelt guide roller/bracket assembly and one of upper air conditioning compressor-to-alternator mounting bracket securing bolts (arrowed)

6 Remove the two upper bolts securing the air conditioning compressor to the alternator mounting bracket.

7 Apply the handbrake, then jack up the front of the vehicle and support it securely on axle stands.

8 Remove the engine undershield, where applicable.

9 Remove the right-hand front roadwheel and the wheel arch liner.

10 Loosen the lower air conditioning compressor mounting nuts and bolts, then pivot the compressor downwards to enable the alternator mounting bracket to be removed from above **(see illustration)**.

11 Proceed as described in the following paragraphs.

All models

12 If not already done, disconnect the battery negative lead.

13 If not already done, remove the two bolts securing the fuel filter assembly to the body panel, unbolt the hose bracket from the fuel injection pump mounting bracket and move the fuel filter assembly to one side, leaving the hoses connected **(see illustration)**. Take care not to strain the hoses.

14 Turn the crankshaft to bring No 1 piston to TDC on the compression stroke, then fit the tool to lock the crankshaft in position, as described in Part A of this Chapter (timing belt renewal).

15 Unscrew the securing bolts and remove the timing belt cover which covers the fuel injection pump sprocket.

15.21 Disconnect hose (arrowed) connecting boost pressure fuel delivery corrector to inlet manifold - Turbo engine

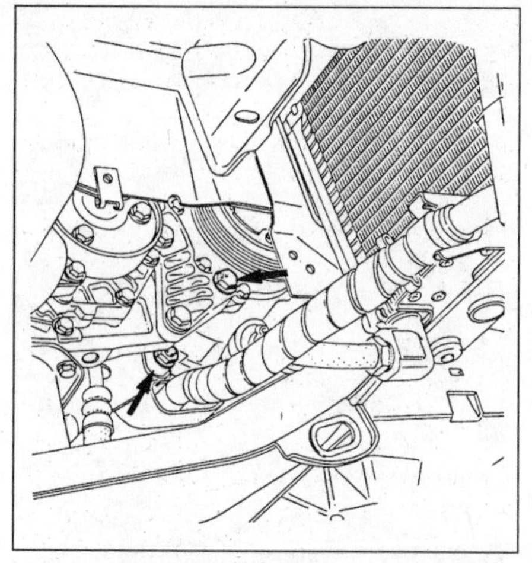

15.10 Air conditioning compressor lower mounting nuts and bolts (arrowed)

16 If an injection pump sprocket locking tool is available (Renault tool Mot.1131 for one-piece sprockets, or Mot.1200 for two-piece adjustable sprockets), remove the crankshaft locking tool, turn the engine back from TDC by one camshaft sprocket tooth and fit the injection pump sprocket locking tool. Turning the engine back by one sprocket tooth will ensure that sufficient adjustment is available to set the pump timing on refitting.

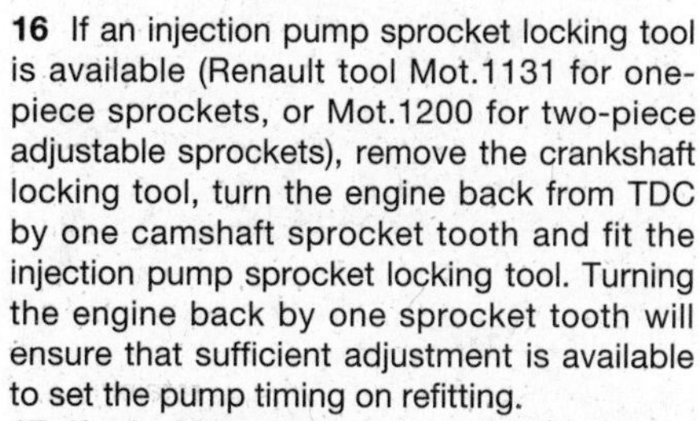

17 If a locking tool is not available, remove the timing belt as described in Part A of this Chapter.

18 Disconnect the accelerator cable from the injection pump.

19 On models with a fast idle thermostatic actuator, disconnect the fast idle cable from the injection pump.

20 On models with a fast idle vacuum actuator, disconnect the vacuum hose from the actuator.

21 On Turbo models, disconnect the hose connecting the boost pressure fuel delivery corrector to the inlet manifold **(see illustration)**.

22 Loosen the clip or undo the banjo union, as applicable, and disconnect the fuel supply hose from the injection pump. Recover the sealing washers from the banjo union, where applicable. Cover the open end of the hose or pipe and plug the opening in the injection pump to keep dirt out. On models with a banjo union, the banjo bolt can be refitted to the pump and covered.

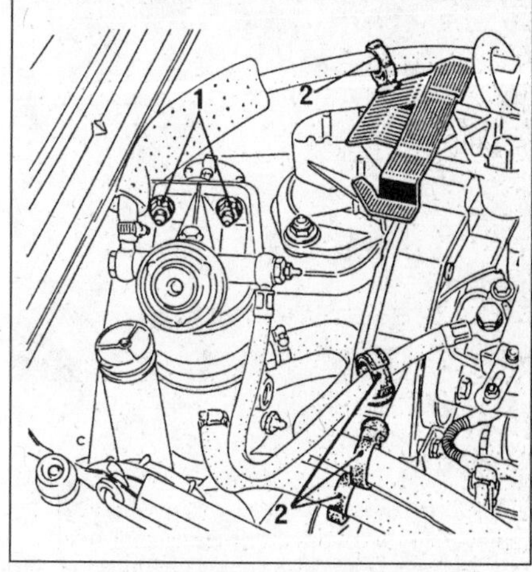

15.13 Fuel filter assembly securing bolts (1) and fuel and coolant hose securing clips (2)

23 Disconnect the main fuel leak-off return hose (connected to the main fuel return pipe) from the relevant fuel injector.

24 Where applicable, disconnect the auxiliary fuel return hose from the pump. On Turbo models, the auxiliary hose is connected to the boost pressure fuel delivery corrector on the pump. Also, unclip it from the accelerator cable bracket **(see illustration)**.

25 Disconnect the main fuel return pipe banjo union from the injection pump. Recover the sealing washers from the banjo union. Again, cover the open end of the hose and the banjo bolt to keep dirt out **(see illustration)**. Take care not to get the inlet and outlet banjo unions mixed up.

26 Disconnect all relevant wiring from the pump. Note that on certain pumps, this can be achieved by simply disconnecting the wiring connectors at the brackets on the pump **(see illustration)**. On some pumps, it will be necessary to disconnect the wiring from the individual components (some connections may be protected by rubber covers).

15.24 Disconnecting auxiliary fuel return hose - Turbo engine

15.25 Disconnecting main fuel return pipe union - Turbo engine

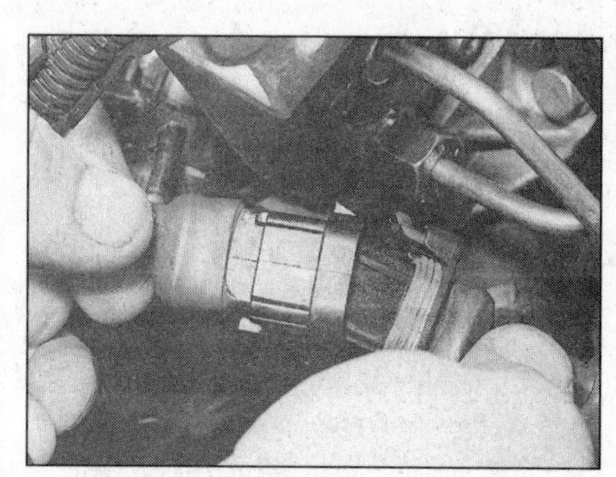

15.26 Disconnecting main fuel injection pump wiring connector - Turbo engine

15.27a Unscrewing injector pipe-to-injection pump union

15.27b Cover injectors to keep dirt out

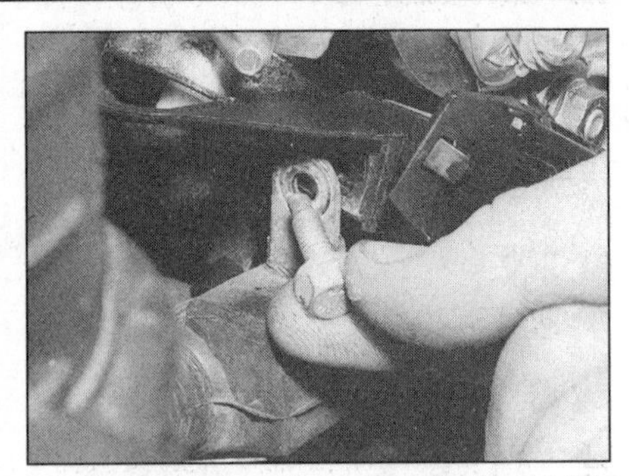
15.28 Removing alternator plastic shield securing bolt. Note location of bracket

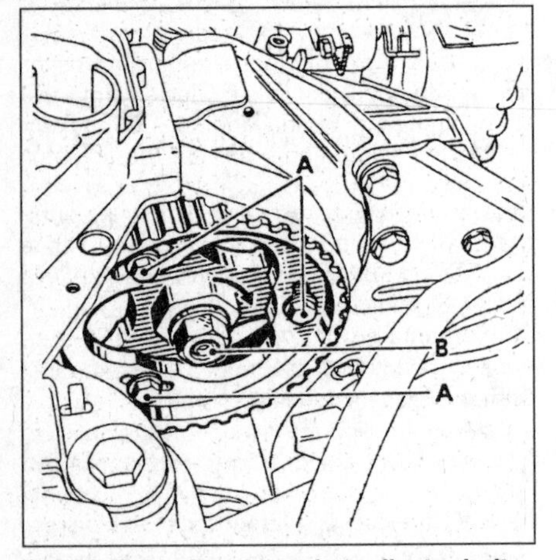

15.30 Two-piece sprocket adjuster bolts (A) and sprocket securing nut (B). Turn sprocket boss in direction arrowed before removing pump

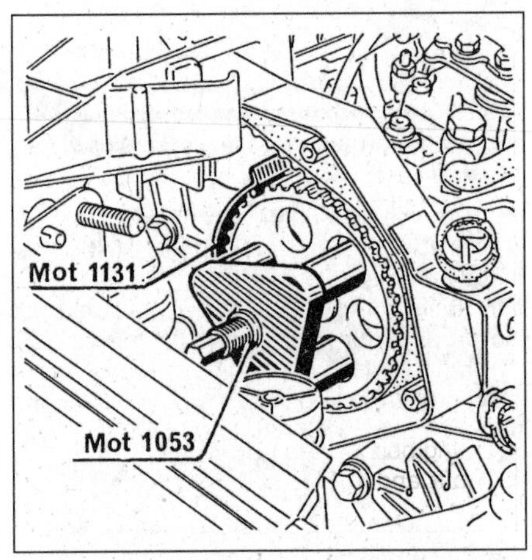

15.31a Renault sprocket locking tool and puller in position - 1-piece sprocket

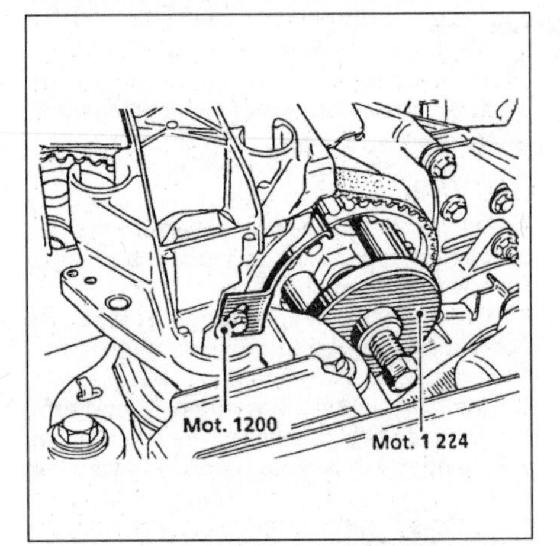

15.31b Renault sprocket locking tool and puller in position - 2-piece adjustable sprocket

27 Unscrew the union nuts securing the injector pipes to the injection pump and injectors. Counterhold the unions on the pump when unscrewing the pipe-to-pump union nuts. Remove the pipes as a set. Cover open unions to keep dirt out **(see illustrations)**. Note that the leak-off hoses will have to be removed from the fuel injectors to enable the injectors to be covered.

28 Where applicable, remove the alternator plastic shield from below the injection pump. Note the locations of any brackets secured by the shield securing nut and bolt **(see illustration)**.

29 Loosen the injection pump sprocket securing nut and unscrew it to the end of the thread on the pump shaft. Do not remove the nut at this stage. If a Renault sprocket locking tool is not available, counterhold the sprocket using an improvised tool engaged with the holes in the sprocket, not the sprocket teeth.

30 On models with a two-piece adjustable pump sprocket, loosen the three sprocket adjuster bolts **(see illustration)**. Using the centre boss, turn the sprocket rear section clockwise (viewed from the timing belt end of the engine - effectively turning the pump shaft) so that the adjuster bolts are positioned at the ends of the elongated slots. Retighten the adjuster bolts.

31 Fit a puller to the pump sprocket, acting on the sprocket nut, and free the sprocket from the taper on the pump shaft **(see illustrations)**. Note that the puller must bear on the sprocket holes (between the two sprocket halves on models with two-piece adjustable sprockets) and not on the teeth. Do not hammer on the end of the pump shaft to free it, as this will damage the internal components of the pump.

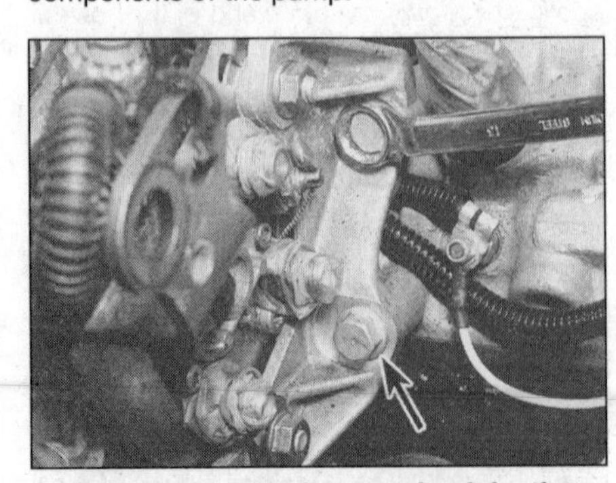
15.34 Unscrew bolts securing injection pump rear mounting bracket to cylinder head - Turbo engine shown

32 On models with a one-piece sprocket, mark the sprocket in relation to the end of the pump shaft to ensure correct refitting. This is necessary, regardless of whether the timing belt has been removed, because there are two keyways in the sprocket which are for use with different injection pump types and it is possible to refit the sprocket to the pump shaft incorrectly.

33 Remove the puller and the sprocket nut. Unless an injection pump sprocket locking tool has been fitted, remove the sprocket.

34 Unscrew the bolts securing the rear injection pump mounting bracket to the cylinder head **(see illustration)**.

35 Make a final check to ensure that all relevant pipes, hoses and wires have been disconnected to facilitate pump removal.

36 Make alignment marks between the pump and the mounting bracket. This will aid pump timing on refitting.

37 Unscrew the three pump securing bolts and withdraw the pump from its mounting bracket, leaving the sprocket engaged with the timing belt, where applicable **(see illustrations)**. Access to the lower pump mounting bolt is most easily obtained from the rear of the pump, using a deep socket and extension.

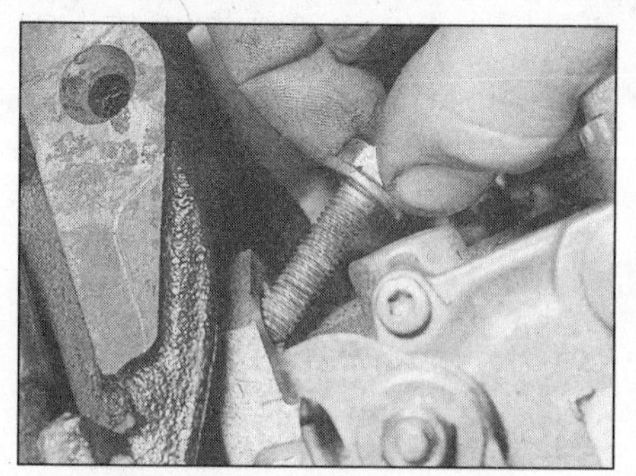

15.37a Remove securing bolts . . .

15.37b . . . and withdraw fuel injection pump - Turbo engine shown

38 Recover the Woodruff key from the end of the pump shaft if it is loose.

39 If desired, the rear pump mounting bracket and the accelerator cable bracket can be unbolted from the rear of the pump.

Refitting

40 Where applicable, refit the rear mounting bracket and the accelerator cable bracket to the rear of the pump.

41 Commence refitting by fitting the Woodruff key to the end of the pump shaft, where applicable.

42 Offer the pump to the mounting bracket. If the sprocket is still engaged with the timing belt, engage the pump shaft with the sprocket. On models with a one-piece sprocket, align the marks made on the sprocket and the pump shaft before removal. This will ensure that the key engages with the correct keyway in the sprocket **(see illustrations)**. Ensure that the Woodruff key does not fall out of the shaft as the sprocket is engaged.

43 Where applicable, align the marks made on the pump and the mounting bracket before removal. If a new pump is being fitted, transfer the mark from the old pump to give an approximate setting.

44 Refit and lightly tighten the front pump mounting bolts.

45 Refit and tighten the bolts securing the rear pump mounting bracket to the cylinder head.

46 Where applicable, refit the sprocket to the pump shaft, ensuring that the Woodruff key engages correctly. On models with a one-piece sprocket, align the marks made on the sprocket and the pump shaft before removal, to ensure that the key engages with the correct keyway in the sprocket.

47 Tighten the pump sprocket securing nut to the specified torque, counterholding the sprocket as during removal **(see illustration)**.

48 If the timing belt has been removed, refit and tension it as described in Part A of this Chapter.

49 On models with a two-piece adjustable sprocket, loosen the three sprocket adjuster bolts. Using the centre boss, turn the sprocket rear section anti-clockwise (viewed from the timing belt end of the engine - effectively turning the pump shaft) so that the adjuster bolts are positioned at the ends of the elongated slots. Lightly tighten the adjuster bolts.

50 Where applicable, remove the sprocket locking tool, then turn the crankshaft to bring No 1 piston to TDC on the compression stroke. Fit the tool to lock the crankshaft in position, as described in Part A of this Chapter.

51 Carry out injection timing as described in Section 19.

52 Refit the plastic shield under the pump, ensuring that any brackets noted during removal are in place.

53 Refit and reconnect the injector fuel pipes and tighten the unions. Counterhold the unions on the pump when tightening the pipe-to-pump union nuts.

54 Reconnect all relevant wiring to the pump.

55 Reconnect the fuel supply and return pipes and hoses, tightening the unions, as applicable. Use new sealing washers on the banjo unions. Also reconnect the leak-off hoses.

56 On Turbo models, reconnect the hose connecting the boost pressure fuel delivery corrector to the inlet manifold.

57 Reconnect and adjust the accelerator cable.

58 Refit the fuel filter assembly and tighten the securing bolts, then refit the hose bracket.

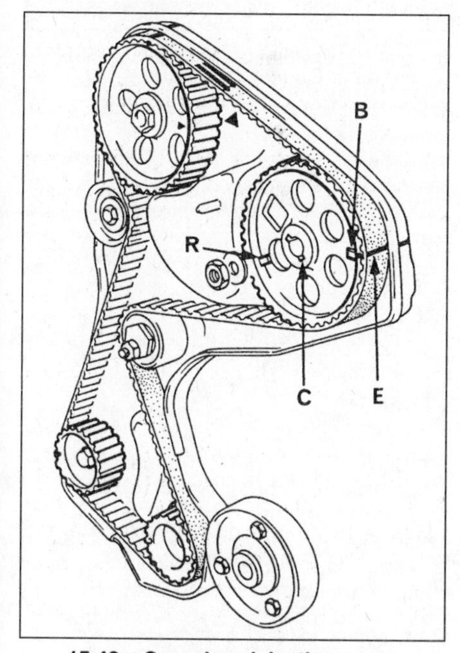

15.42a One-piece injection pump sprocket orientation - Bosch pump (No 1 piston at TDC)

B Sprocket alignment mark for Bosch injection pump
C Position of injection pump shaft Woodruff key
E Sprocket alignment mark on timing belt
R Sprocket alignment mark for Lucas injection pump

15.42b One-piece injection pump sprocket orientation - Lucas pump (No 1 cylinder at TDC)

B Sprocket alignment mark for Bosch injection pump
C Position of injection pump shaft Woodruff key
E Sprocket alignment mark on timing belt
R Sprocket alignment mark for Lucas injection pump

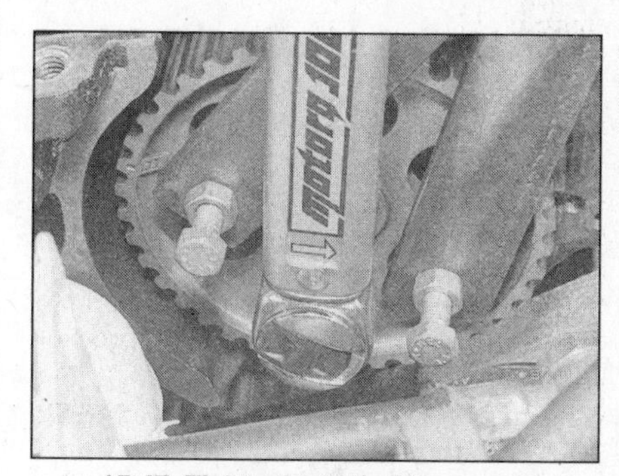

15.47 Tightening injection pump sprocket bolt

59 On non turbo models with air conditioning, reverse the operations carried out in paragraphs 1 to 10. Refit and tighten the auxiliary drivebelt.

60 On models with a fast idle thermostatic actuator, reconnect and adjust the fast idle cable, noting that final adjustment must be carried out after the engine has been started and reached normal operating temperature.

61 On models with a fast idle vacuum actuator, reconnect the hose to the actuator and check fast idle cable adjustment.

62 Check the no-load switch adjustment.

63 Reconnect the battery negative lead.

64 Prime and bleed the fuel system as described in Part A of this Chapter.

65 Start the engine and check the idle speed and anti-stall speed, as described in Part A of this Chapter.

16 Fuel injection pump (Renault Clio) - removal and refitting

Note: *Do not allow dirt into the fuel injection pump or injector pipes during this procedure. New sealing rings should be used on the fuel pipe banjo unions when refitting.*

Removal

1 Disconnect the battery negative lead.

2 Apply the handbrake, then jack up the front of the vehicle and support it securely on axle stands.

3 Remove the right-hand front roadwheel and the wheel arch liner.

4 Remove the air cleaner housing assembly.

5 Remove the electric cooling fan assembly from the rear of the radiator.

6 Remove the alternator.

7 Complete removal of the injection pump by following the procedure given in Section 15, paragraphs 14 to 39 inclusive, whilst ignoring all references to turbocharged engines. Note that the plastic cover must be removed from the front of the injection pump to facilitate disconnection of the pump wiring.

Refitting

8 Follow the procedure given in Section 15, paragraphs 40 to 53 inclusive, then proceed as follows:

9 Reconnect all relevant wiring to the injection pump, then refit the plastic cover to the front of the pump.

10 Reconnect the fuel supply and return pipes and hoses, then tighten the unions. Use new sealing washers on the banjo unions. Also reconnect the leak-off hoses.

11 Reconnect and adjust the accelerator cable.

12 Reconnect and adjust the fast idle cable as described in Section 3, noting that final adjustment must be carried out after the engine has been started and reached normal operating temperature.

13 Refit the alternator.

14 Refit the electric cooling fan assembly.

15 Refit the air cleaner housing assembly.

16 Refit the right-hand front roadwheel and the wheel arch liner.

17 Lower the vehicle to the ground.

18 Reconnect the battery negative lead.

19 Check the no-load switch adjustment as described in Section 10.

20 Prime and bleed the fuel system as described in Part A of this Chapter.

21 Start the engine and check the idle speed and anti-stall speed, as described in Part A of this Chapter.

17 Fuel injection pump (Renault Espace) - removal and refitting

Note: *Do not allow dirt into the fuel injection pump or injector pipes during this procedure. New sealing rings should be used on the fuel pipe banjo unions when refitting.*

Removal

1 Disconnect the battery negative lead.

2 Referring to Part A of this Chapter (timing belt renewal), rotate the crankshaft until No.1 cylinder is positioned on TDC at the end of its compression stroke.

3 Remove the timing belt cover.

4 Check the sprocket timing marks are positioned as described in Part A of this Chapter (timing belt renewal).

5 Rotate the crankshaft backwards slightly so that the injection pump sprocket timing mark moves back by three teeth. That is, so the tooth three in front of the timing mark is aligned with the pointer in the timing cover window.

6 Slacken both the timing belt tensioner pulley retaining nut and bolt and pivot the pulley fully away from the belt. Hold the tensioner in this position and securely tighten the retaining nut and bolt to keep it in position.

7 Remove the belt from the injection pump sprocket, taking care not to twist it too sharply. Use fingers only to handle the belt.

8 Hold the pump sprocket stationary with a suitable peg spanner which engages with the sprocket holes. A suitable home-made tool can be fabricated from two lengths of steel strip (one long, the other short) and three nuts and bolts - one nut and bolt forming the pivot of a forked tool with the remaining two nuts and bolts at the tips of the forks to engage with the sprocket spokes.

17.10 Using puller to draw sprocket off injection pump shaft taper

9 Slacken the pump sprocket retaining nut. Unscrew the nut and position it so that it is flush with the end of the pump shaft. The nut will protect shaft threads during the following operation.

10 A suitable puller will then be needed to free the sprocket from its taper on the pump shaft. The puller should be inserted through the holes in the sprocket so that its legs bear against the back of the sprocket and not positioned so that they bear against the sprocket teeth. Screw in the puller centre bolt until it contacts the pulley shaft and draw the sprocket off the pump shaft taper **(see illustration)**. Do not be tempted to strike the pump with a hammer in an attempt to free the sprocket as the pump internals will almost certainly be damaged.

11 Remove the puller then remove the sprocket retaining nut and washer and slide off the sprocket. If the Woodruff key is a loose fit in the pump shaft, remove it and store it with the sprocket for safe-keeping. Note that the crankshaft and camshaft must not be rotated whilst the sprocket is removed.

12 Cover the alternator to prevent the possibility of fuel being spilt onto it.

13 Where the fast idle thermostatic valve is screwed into the cylinder head, loosen the clamp screw or nut (as applicable) and slide the end fitting off the end of the fast idle inner cable. Where necessary, remove the cable fitting from the pump lever and store it with the valve for safe-keeping.

14 Where the fast idle thermostatic valve is mounted on the injection pump, use a hose clamp or similar to clamp both the fast idle valve coolant hoses to minimise coolant loss. Slacken the retaining clips and disconnect both coolant hoses from the valve whilst being prepared for some coolant spillage.

15 Unclip the accelerator cable end fitting from the lever balljoint and free the cable from the injection pump bracket.

16 Wipe clean the fuel feed and return unions on the injection pump.

17 Slacken and remove the fuel feed hose union bolt from the pump and recover the sealing washer from each side of the hose union. Position the hose clear of the pump and screw the union bolt back into position on the pump for safe-keeping. Cover both the hose end and union bolt to prevent any ingress of dirt into the fuel system.

18 Detach the fuel return hose from the pump as described in the previous paragraph. Note that the injection pump feed and return hose union bolts are not interchangeable. Great care must be taken to ensure that the bolts are not swapped.

19 Wipe clean the pipe unions then slacken the union nut securing the injector pipes to each injector and the four union nuts securing the pipes to the rear of the injection pump. As each pump union nut is slackened, retain the adapter with a suitable open-ended spanner to prevent it being unscrewed from the pump. With all the union nuts undone, remove the injector pipes from the engine.

20 Undo the retaining nut and disconnect the wiring from the injection pump stop solenoid. Where necessary, trace the wiring back from the pump microswitch(es) and disconnect it at the connector(s) (as applicable). Free all wiring from any relevant retaining clips.

21 Make alignment marks between the injection pump front flange and the front mounting bracket **(see illustration)**. These marks can then be used to ensure that the pump is correctly positioned on refitting.

22 Undo the retaining nuts/bolts securing the injection pump rear mounting bracket to the cylinder head.

23 Slacken and remove the three nuts securing the pump to its front mounting bracket and manoeuvre the pump away from the bracket and out of the engine compartment. Do not rotate the crankshaft or camshaft whilst the pump is removed.

Refitting

24 If a new pump is being fitted, transfer the alignment mark from the original pump onto the mounting flange of the new pump.

25 Manoeuvre the pump into position and refit its three front retaining nuts. Align the marks made prior to removal then securely tighten the retaining nuts.

26 Refit the rear bracket to the injection pump and securely tighten its retaining nuts/bolts.

27 Ensure that the pump sprocket and shaft are clean and dry. Where necessary, refit the Woodruff key to the shaft.

28 Slide the pump sprocket onto the shaft and refit the washer and retaining nut.

29 Hold the sprocket stationary by using the method employed on removal and tighten the sprocket retaining nut to the specified torque setting.

30 Referring to Part A of this Chapter, refit and tension the timing belt.

31 With the timing belt fitted, set up the injection pump timing as described in Section 20.

32 Reconnect all relevant wiring to the pump.

33 Reconnect the fuel feed and return hose unions to the pump. Position a new sealing washer on each side of both unions and tighten the union bolts to the specified torque setting.

34 Refit the injector pipes and tighten their union nuts to the specified torque setting.

35 Where the fast idle valve is mounted on the injection pump, reconnect the coolant hoses to the fast idle valve and securely tighten their retaining clips. Remove the hose clamps and top-up the cooling system.

36 Mop up any spilt fuel/coolant then uncover from the alternator.

37 Reconnect and adjust the accelerator cable.

38 Reconnect and adjust the fast idle valve cable.

17.21 Mark injection pump in relation to mounting bracket (arrowed)

39 Reconnect the battery negative lead.

40 Bleed the fuel system as described in Part A of this Chapter.

41 On completion, start the engine and adjust the idle speed and anti-stall speed, as described in Part A of this Chapter.

18 Fuel injection pump (Renault Laguna) - removal and refitting

Note: *The following procedure describes pump removal and refitting using Renault injection pump sprocket holding tool Mot 1317. This tool holds the sprocket securely in position whilst the pump is removed, keeping the timing belt correctly tensioned and so removing the need to disturb the timing belt. If the procedure is to be attempted without the special tool, great care must be taken to ensure that the pump sprocket is held firmly in position so that it does not move in relation to the timing belt. If the sprocket moves or the timing belt tension is released, it will be necessary to remove the timing belt cover and check the position of the sprocket timing marks prior to starting the engine.*

Note: *New timing belt top and sprocket cover bolts will be required on refitting.*

Note: *Do not allow dirt into the fuel injection pump or injector pipes during this procedure. New sealing rings should be used on the fuel pipe banjo unions when refitting.*

Removal

1 Disconnect the battery negative lead.

2 Position No 1 cylinder at TDC on its compression stroke, then lock the crankshaft in position as described in Part A of this Chapter (timing belt renewal). Do not attempt to rotate the engine once the crankshaft is locked in position.

3 Undo the retaining nut and disconnect the wiring connector from the injection pump stop solenoid terminal on the pump rear bracket.

4 On models with a thermostatic fast idle valve, disconnect the cable from the injection pump.

5 On models with a vacuum-operated fast idle system, disconnect the vacuum hose from the pump diaphragm unit.

6 Unclip the accelerator cable inner end fitting from the injection pump lever then free the cable outer from mounting bracket and position it clear of the pump.

7 Disconnect the pump microswitch wiring connector and free the connector from its retaining clip.

8 Wipe clean the fuel feed and return unions on the injection pump. To improve access to the rear of the pump, unclip the power steering fluid reservoir and position it clear of the pump. Unbolt the reservoir bracket and remove it from the engine.

9 Slacken and remove the fuel feed hose union bolt from the pump. Recover the sealing washer from each side of the hose union and position the hose clear of the pump. Screw the union bolt back into position on the pump for safe-keeping and cover both the hose end and union bolt to prevent the ingress of dirt into the fuel system.

10 Detach the fuel return hose from the pump as described in the previous paragraph. Note that the injection pump feed and return hose union bolts are not interchangeable. Great care must be taken to ensure that the bolts are not swapped.

11 Wipe clean the pipe unions then slacken the union nuts securing the injector pipes to the top of each injector and the four union nuts securing the pipes to the rear of the injection pump. As each pump union nut is slackened, retain the adapter with a suitable open-ended spanner to prevent it being unscrewed from the pump. With all the union nuts undone, remove the injector pipe assembly from the engine and mop up any spilt fuel **(see illustration)**.

12 Undo the retaining nuts securing the fuel filter housing to its mounting bracket and position the filter clear of the timing belt cover. Undo the retaining bolts and remove the timing belt top cover and injection pump sprocket cover. Discard the cover retaining bolts as they must be renewed whenever they are disturbed.

13 With the cover removed, bolt the pump sprocket retaining tool (Renault tool Mot 1317) in position on the engine mounting. In the absence of the Renault tool, a suitable alternative can be fabricated out of a piece of angled-metal, or alternately the sprocket can

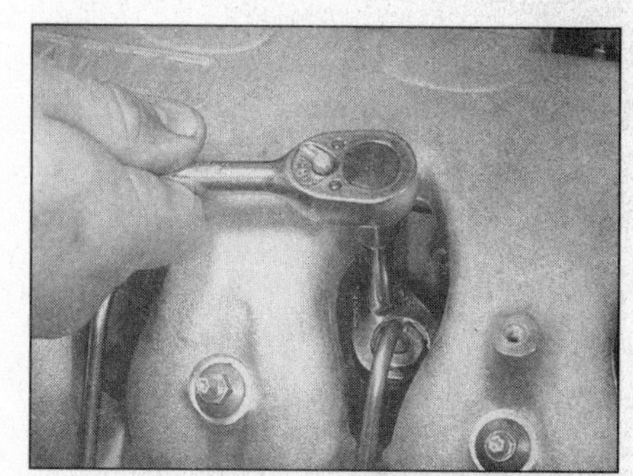

18.11 Unscrewing an injector - Renault Laguna

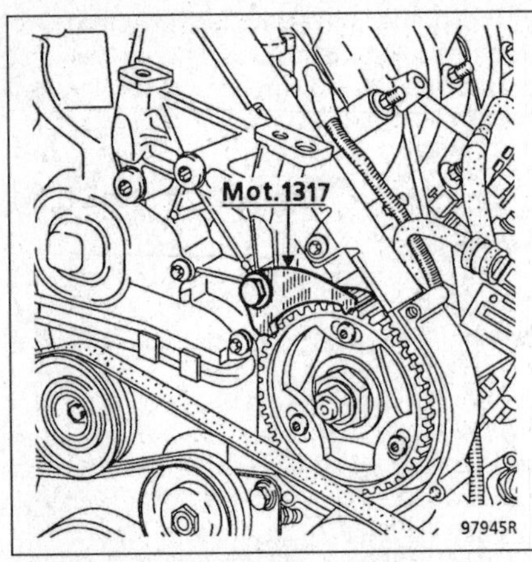

18.13a Renault special tool (Mot. 1317) for holding injection pump sprocket stationary during pump removal

be held in position by firmly inserting two wooden wedges between the sprocket and bracket **(see illustrations).**

14 With the sprocket locked in position, check the sprocket alignment mark is correctly aligned with the mark on the injection pump bracket, then slacken and remove the sprocket retaining nut. If the Renault tool is being used, the sprocket will be held in position. If the tool is not being used, prevent rotation by holding the sprocket with a large open-ended spanner on the hub flats **(see illustration).**

15 Slacken and remove the retaining nuts/bolts and remove the pump rear mounting bracket **(see illustration).**

16 Loosen the front retaining nuts/bolts (as applicable). Note that on early G8T 706 and 790 engined models, access to the lower pump nut/bolt can be improved by removing the coolant pump.

17 Attach a suitable puller to the injection pump sprocket hub and carefully free the hub from the pump shaft taper. The Renault puller is attached to the sprocket hub using three 8 mm bolts once the sprocket rim bolts have been removed. Make alignment marks

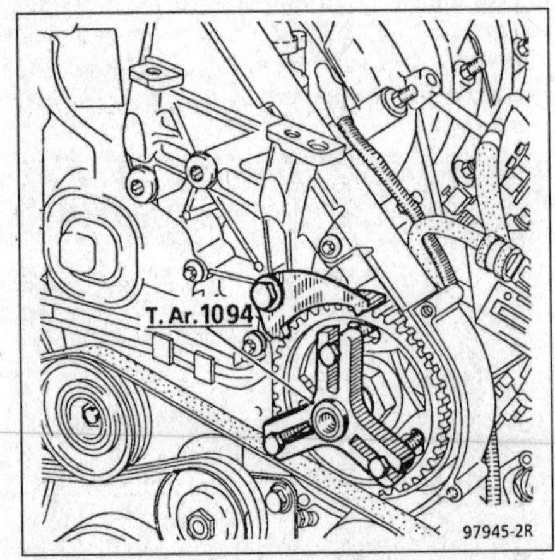

18.17b Renault special puller (T. Ar. 1094) for releasing pump sprocket

18.13b If care is taken, sprocket can be held in position using wooden wedges (arrowed)

between the bolts and sprocket before unscrewing them **(see illustrations).**

18 Once the sprocket is free from the pump, remove the front mounting nuts/bolts and remove the pump assembly **(see illustrations).** As the pump is removed, take care to ensure that the sprocket Woodruff key is not lost. Remove the key for safekeeping if it is a loose fit in the pump shaft.

Refitting

19 Ensure that the Woodruff key is securely fitted to the pump shaft and position the shaft so the key will engage with the sprocket hub slot as the pump is refitted. If the key is a loose fit, hold it in position using a smear of grease.

20 Manoeuvre the pump into position. Ensure the Woodruff key engages with the sprocket groove, then loosely refit the pump front mounting nuts/bolts.

18.14 Retain pump sprocket with large open-ended spanner as retaining nut is slackened

21 Refit the injection pump sprocket nut and draw the sprocket fully onto the pump. Ensure that the Woodruff key does not fall out of the shaft as the sprocket is pulled onto the shaft.

22 Once the sprocket is correctly seated, securely tighten the pump front mounting nuts/bolts.

23 Refit the pump rear mounting bracket and securely tighten its mounting nuts/bolts.

24 With the pump in position, tighten the sprocket retaining nut to the specified torque setting. Where necessary, prevent rotation using the tool used on removal.

25 Set up the injection timing as described in Section 20.

26 Ensure that the unions are clean and dry then refit the injector pipes and securely tighten their unions nuts.

27 Remove the injection pump sprocket locking tool(s) (as applicable). Refit the timing

18.15 Unbolt injection pump rear mounting bracket

18.17a Using a legged puller to free sprocket from injection pump shaft

18.18a With sprocket freed, undo front mounting bolts . . .

18.18b . . . and remove injection pump from the engine

belt covers, tightening the new retaining bolts securely. Refit the wiring loom clip to the cover and refit the fuel filter to its mounting bracket.

28 Reconnect all relevant wiring to the pump.

29 Reconnect the fuel feed and return hose unions to the pump, positioning a new sealing washer on each side of both unions. Securely tighten the union bolts. Refit the mounting bracket and clip the power steering fluid reservoir into position.

30 Reconnect and adjust the accelerator cable.

31 On models with a thermostatic fast idle valve, reconnect and adjust the fast idle cable.

32 On models with a vacuum-operated fast idle system, reconnect the vacuum hose to the diaphragm.

33 Reconnect the battery negative lead and bleed the fuel system as described in Part A of this Chapter.

34 On completion, start the engine and adjust the idle speed and anti-stall speed, as described in Part A of this Chapter.

19 Fuel injection pump (Renault 19 and Clio) - timing

Caution: Some fuel injection pump settings and access plugs may be sealed by the manufacturer, with paint or locking wire and lead seals. Do not disturb these seals if the vehicle is still within the warranty period, otherwise the warranty will be invalidated. Also, do not attempt the timing procedure unless accurate instrumentation is available. Suitable special tools for carrying out pump timing are available from motor factors. A dial test indicator (DTI) will be required regardless of the method used.

Note: *Turning the engine will be much easier if the glow plugs are removed.*

1 Checking the injection timing is only necessary after the injection pump has been disturbed.

2 Dynamic timing equipment does exist but it is unlikely to be available to the home mechanic. If such equipment is available, use it in accordance with the manufacturer's instructions.

3 Static timing, as described in this Section, gives good results if carried out carefully. A dial test indicator (DTI) will be needed, with probes and adapters appropriate to the type of injection pump **(see illustration)**. Read through the procedures before starting work, to find out what is involved.

Lucas pump

4 Disconnect the battery negative lead.

5 Apply the handbrake, then jack up the front right-hand corner of the vehicle until the wheel is just clear of the ground. Support the vehicle on an axle stand and engage 4th or 5th gear. This will enable the crankshaft to be turned easily by turning the right-hand wheel.

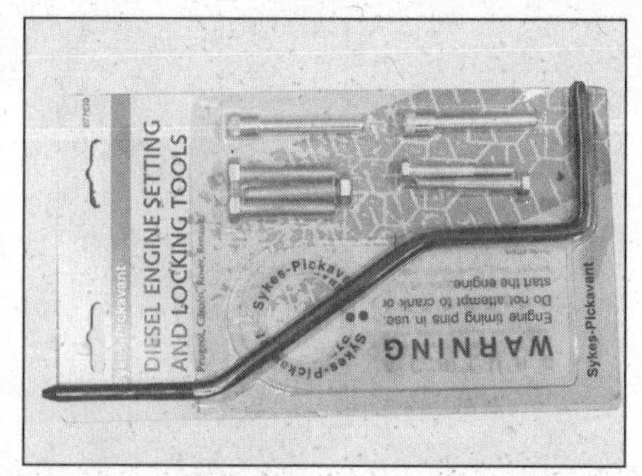

19.3 TDC locking tools for setting injection timing on Renault diesel engines

Alternatively, the engine can be turned using an open-ended spanner on the crankshaft pulley bolt.

6 Turn the crankshaft to bring No 1 piston to TDC on the compression stroke. Fit the tool to lock the crankshaft in position, as described in Part A of this Chapter (timing belt renewal).

7 A DTI will now be required, along with a suitable probe (Renault tool Mot.1079, or an alternative available from motor factors). Note that the probe must seat on the sealing washer surface in the timing aperture and not on the top surface of the timing aperture. The probe is waisted to allow it to clear the pump rotor **(see illustration)**.

8 Remove the inspection plug from the top of the pump **(see illustration)** and recover the sealing washer. Position the timing probe in the aperture so that the tip of the probe rests on the rotor timing piece.

9 Position the DTI securely on the injection pump body, so that it can read the movement of the timing probe. Ensure that the gauge is positioned directly in line with the probe, with the gauge plunger at the mid-point of its travel.

One-piece fixed pump sprocket

10 Remove the crankshaft locking tool, then turn the crankshaft approximately a quarter-turn anti-clockwise (viewed from the timing belt end of the engine). Zero the DTI. Check that the timing probe is seated against the sealing washer surface of the timing aperture.

11 Turn the crankshaft clockwise slowly until the crankshaft locking tool can be re-inserted, bringing the engine back to TDC.

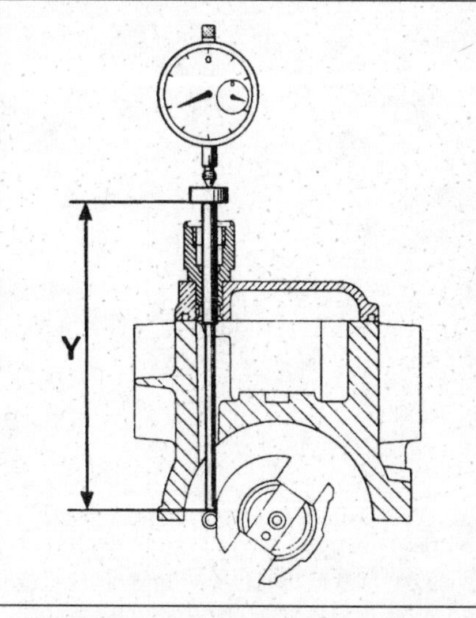

19.7 Timing probe details (Renault tool Mot.1079) - Lucas injection pump

Y = 95.5 ± 0.1 mm

12 Read the DTI. The reading should correspond to the timing value marked on the pump. The timing value may be marked on a plastic disc on the front of the pump, or alternatively, may appear on a label attached to the top of the pump or a tag attached to the accelerator pump lever **(see illustration)**.

13 If the reading is not as specified, proceed as follows.

14 Cover the alternator as a precaution against fuel spillage.

15 Unscrew the union nuts securing the injector pipes to the fuel injection pump and the fuel injectors. Counterhold the unions on the pump when unscrewing the nuts. Cover open unions to keep dirt out.

16 Slacken the three front pump mounting bolts and the two rear pump mounting nuts. Slowly rotate the pump body until the point is found where the specified reading is obtained on the DTI. When the pump is correctly positioned, tighten the mounting nuts and bolts, ensuring that the reading on the DTI does not change as the fixings are tightened.

17 Withdraw the timing probe slightly so that it is positioned clear of the pump rotor.

19.8 Unscrewing timing inspection plug from top of Lucas injection pump

19.12 Injection pump timing value marked on accelerator lever tag (arrowed) - Lucas pump

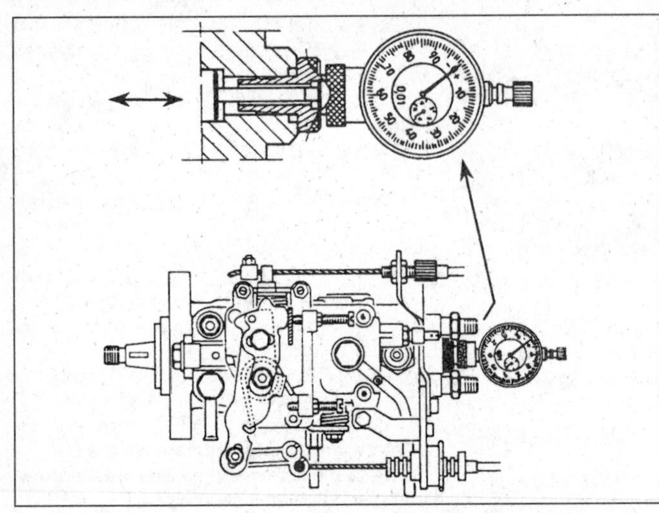

19.41 Dial test indicator and timing probe for use with Bosch injection pump

Pump cable linkages may differ from that shown

19.64 Three adjuster bolts (arrowed) on 2-piece adjustable injection pump sprocket

Remove the crankshaft locking tool. Rotate the crankshaft through one and three quarter turns clockwise.

18 Slide the timing probe back into position, ensuring that it is correctly seated against the sealing washer surface. Zero the DTI.

19 Rotate the crankshaft slowly clockwise until the crankshaft locking tool can be reinserted, bringing No 1 piston back to TDC. Recheck the timing measurement.

20 If adjustment is necessary, slacken the pump mounting nuts and bolts, then repeat the operations described in paragraphs 16 to 19.

21 When the timing is correct, reconnect the fuel injector pipes to the pump and the injectors, then remove the DTI. Remove the probe from the inspection hole and refit the inspection plug, ensuring that the sealing washer is in place.

22 Where applicable, uncover the alternator.

23 Remove the crankshaft locking tool.

24 Lower the vehicle to the ground and reconnect the battery negative lead.

25 Bleed the fuel system as described in Part A of this Chapter.

26 Check and if necessary, adjust the idle speed and anti-stall speed as described in Part A of this Chapter.

Two-piece adjustable pump sprocket

27 Remove the crankshaft locking tool, then turn the crankshaft approximately a quarter-turn anti-clockwise (viewed from the timing belt end of the engine). Zero the DTI. Check that the timing probe is seated against the sealing washer surface of the timing aperture.

28 Turn the crankshaft clockwise slowly until the crankshaft locking tool can be re-inserted, bringing the engine back to TDC.

29 Read the DTI. The reading should correspond to the timing value marked on the pump. The timing value may be marked on a plastic disc on the front of the pump, or alternatively, may appear on a label attached to the top of the pump or a tag attached to the accelerator pump lever.

30 If the reading is not as specified, proceed as follows.

31 Loosen the three sprocket adjuster bolts. Using the centre boss, turn the sprocket rear section anti-clockwise (viewed from the timing belt end of the engine - effectively turning the pump shaft) so that the adjuster bolts are positioned at the ends of the elongated slots. Tighten the adjuster bolts.

32 Zero the DTI. Check that the timing probe is seated against the sealing washer surface of the timing aperture.

33 Remove the crankshaft locking tool, then turn the crankshaft through two complete turns clockwise. Refit the locking tool and check that the DTI is still zeroed.

34 Loosen the sprocket adjuster bolts and using the centre boss, turn the sprocket rear section clockwise (viewed from the timing belt end of the engine - effectively turning the pump shaft) until the DTI displays the appropriate timing value marked on the pump. In this position, tighten the sprocket adjuster bolts. The reading on the DTI should not change as the bolts are tightened.

35 Remove the crankshaft locking tool, then turn the crankshaft through two complete turns clockwise. Refit the locking tool and recheck the timing value.

36 If adjustment is necessary, slacken the sprocket adjuster bolts and repeat the operations described in paragraphs 34 and 35.

37 When the timing is correct, remove the DTI. Remove the probe from the inspection hole and refit the inspection plug, ensuring that the sealing washer is in place.

38 Proceed as described in paragraphs 23 to 26.

Bosch pump

39 Proceed as described in paragraphs 4 to 6.

40 Cover the alternator as a precaution against fuel spillage.

41 A DTI will now be required, along with a special probe and adapter to screw into the hole in the rear of the pump (designed specifically for the Bosch pump and available from motor factors) **(see illustration)**.

42 Unscrew the union nuts securing the injector pipes to the fuel injection pump. Counterhold the unions on the pump when unscrewing the nuts. Cover open unions to keep dirt out.

43 Unscrew the blanking plug from the end of the injection pump, between the injector pipe connections. Be prepared for the loss of some fuel.

44 Insert the probe and connect it to the DTI, positioned directly over the inspection hole.

One-piece fixed pump sprocket

45 Remove the locking tool from the flywheel and turn the engine approximately a quarter-turn anti-clockwise, viewed from the timing belt end of the engine. Zero the DTI.

46 Turn the crankshaft clockwise slowly, until the crankshaft locking tool can be re-inserted, bringing the engine back to TDC.

47 Read the DTI. The reading should correspond to the specified value. Note that on later pumps, the timing value is marked on the pump accelerator lever.

48 If the reading is not as specified, proceed as follows.

49 Slacken the three front pump mounting bolts and the rear pump mounting nuts, then slowly rotate the pump body until the point is found where the specified reading is obtained on the DTI. When the pump is correctly positioned, tighten the mounting nuts and bolts, ensuring that the reading on the DTI does not change as the fixings are tightened.

50 Remove the crankshaft locking tool and rotate the crankshaft through one and three quarter turns clockwise. Check that the DTI is reading zero.

51 Rotate the crankshaft slowly clockwise until the crankshaft locking tool can be reinserted, bringing No 1 piston back to TDC. Recheck the timing measurement.
52 If adjustment is necessary, slacken the pump mounting nuts and bolts and repeat the operations described in paragraphs 49 to 51.
53 When the timing is correct, remove the DTI, remove the probe from the inspection hole and refit the blanking plug.
54 Reconnect the fuel injector pipes to the pump.
55 Where applicable, uncover the alternator.
56 Remove the crankshaft locking tool.
57 Lower the vehicle to the ground and reconnect the battery negative lead.
58 Bleed the fuel system, as described in Part A of this Chapter.
59 Check and if necessary adjust the idle speed and anti-stall speed, as described in Part A of this Chapter.

Two-piece adjustable pump sprocket

60 Remove the locking tool from the flywheel and turn the engine approximately a quarter-turn anti-clockwise (viewed from the timing belt end of the engine). Zero the DTI.
61 Turn the crankshaft clockwise slowly until the crankshaft locking tool can be re-inserted, bringing the engine back to TDC.
62 Read the DTI. The reading should correspond to the specified value. Note that on later pumps, the timing value is marked on the pump accelerator lever.
63 If the reading is not as specified, proceed as follows:
64 Loosen the three sprocket adjuster bolts **(see illustration)**. Using the centre boss, turn the sprocket rear section anti-clockwise (viewed from the timing belt end of the engine - effectively turning the pump shaft) so that the adjuster bolts are positioned at the ends of the elongated slots. Tighten the adjuster bolts.
65 Zero the DTI.
66 Remove the crankshaft locking tool, then turn the crankshaft through two complete turns. Refit the locking tool and check that the DTI is still zeroed.
67 Loosen the sprocket adjuster bolts and using the centre boss, turn the sprocket rear section clockwise (viewed from the timing belt end of the engine - effectively turning the pump shaft) until the DTI displays the appropriate specified timing. In this position, tighten the sprocket adjuster bolts. The reading on the DTI should not change as the bolts are tightened. Remove the crankshaft locking tool.
68 Turn the crankshaft through two complete turns clockwise. Refit the locking tool and recheck the timing value.
69 If adjustment is necessary, slacken the sprocket adjuster bolts and repeat the operations described in paragraphs 67 and 68.
70 When the timing is correct, proceed as described in paragraphs 53 to 59.

20 Fuel injection pump (Renault Espace and Laguna) - timing

1 Refer to Section 19, paragraphs 1 to 3 inclusive. Pay particular attention to the Notes at the beginning of the same Section.
2 Disconnect the battery negative lead.
3 Where necessary, cover the alternator to prevent the possibility of fuel being spilt onto it.
4 On Renault Espace models, wipe clean the injector pipe unions. Slacken the union nut securing the injector pipes to each injector and the four union nuts securing the pipes to the rear of the pump. As each pump union nut is slackened, retain the adapter with a suitable open-ended spanner to prevent it being unscrewed from the pump. With all the union nuts undone, remove the injector pipes from the engine.
5 Slacken the clamp screw and/or nut (as applicable) and slide the fast idle cable end fitting arrangement along the cable so that its no longer in contact with the pump fast idle lever (ie, so the fast idle lever returns to its stop).
6 Rotate the crankshaft until No.1 cylinder is positioned on TDC at the end of its compression stroke, then turn the crankshaft backwards (anti-clockwise) approximately a quarter-turn.
7 Remove the access screw, situated in the centre of the four injector pipe unions, from the rear of the injection pump. As the screw is removed, position a suitable container beneath the pump to catch any escaping fuel.
8 Screw an adapter (Part of Renault tool kit Mot. 856) into the rear of the pump and mount a dial test indicator (DTI) in the adapter. Position the DTI so that its plunger is at the mid-point of its travel, then securely tighten the adapter locknut - see illustration 19.41.
9 Slowly rotate the crankshaft back and forth whilst observing the DTI, to determine when the injection pump piston is at the bottom of its travel (BDC). When the piston is correctly positioned, zero the DTI.
10 Rotate the crankshaft slowly in the correct direction of rotation to bring No.1 piston to TDC. Referring to Part A of this Chapter (timing belt renewal), unscrew the plug from the cylinder block/crankcase and lock the crankshaft in position by inserting a suitable locking pin.
11 The reading obtained on the DTI should be equal to the specified pump timing measurement. If adjustment is necessary, proceed as follows:
12 On Renault Espace models, slacken the front and rear pump mounting nuts and bolts and slowly rotate the pump body until the point is found where the specified reading is obtained. When the pump is correctly positioned, tighten both its front and rear mounting nuts and bolts securely.
13 On Renault Laguna models, remove the timing belt top cover and injection pump sprocket cover (if not already done). Slacken the three bolts securing the sprocket rim to the hub and slowly rotate the hub until the point is found where the specified reading is obtained. When the sprocket hub is correctly positioned, tighten the three rim retaining bolts securely.
14 On all models, remove the locking pin and rotate the crankshaft through one and three quarter rotations in the normal direction of rotation. Find the injection pump piston BDC position and zero the DTI.
15 Rotate the crankshaft slowly in the correct direction of rotation until the crankshaft locking tool can be re-inserted (bringing the engine back to TDC). Recheck the timing measurement.
16 If adjustment is necessary, repeat the operations in paragraphs 11 to 15.
17 When pump timing is correctly set, unscrew the adapter and remove the DTI.
18 Refit the screw and sealing washer to the pump and tighten it securely.
19 On Renault Espace models, refit the injector pipes, tightening their union nuts to the specified torque setting.
20 On Renault Laguna models, refit the timing belt covers, tightening the new retaining bolts securely. Refit the wiring loom clip to the cover and refit the fuel filter to its mounting bracket.
21 Reconnect the battery then bleed the fuel system as described in Part A of this Chapter.
22 Start the engine and adjust the idle and anti-stall speeds as described in Part A of this Chapter. Also adjust the fast idle cable.

21 Hydraulic load adjustment system (Renault Laguna) - testing

1 The hydraulic load adjustment (ALFB) solenoid reduces fuel injection pump transfer pressure during low engine speeds in order to reduce the pump timing advance. The solenoid is controlled by the preheating unit and coolant temperature sender and also by the atmospheric pressure sensor and relay, which are mounted on the right-hand side of the engine compartment, behind the headlight **(see illustration)**.

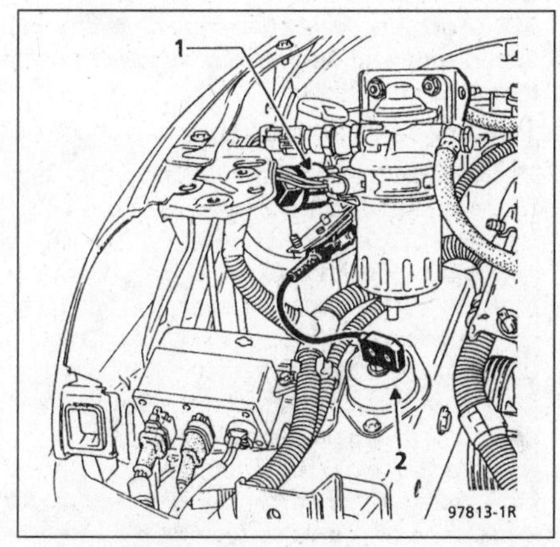

21.1 Hydraulic load adjustment relay (1) and atmospheric pressure sensor (2)

2 The hydraulic load adjustment solenoid is the lower of the two solenoids fitted to the front of the injection pump and operates under the following conditions:

a) When the air temperature is less than 15° and the engine coolant temperature is less than 70°C.

b) When the atmospheric pressure is less than 890 ± mb.

3 If the system develops a fault, check the electrical feed to the solenoid valve and the condition of the wiring connecting the preheating unit, the coolant temperature sender and the solenoid. Note that if the air temperature sensor is faulty, the solenoid is operated when the engine coolant temperature is less than 70°C. If the coolant temperature sender is faulty, the solenoid is operated for 10 minutes, regardless of the air temperature. More detailed testing of the system should be entrusted to a Renault dealer.

22 Fuel filter heating system (Renault Laguna) - component renewal

Caution: Do not to allow dirt into the fuel system during component renewal.

Fuel filter heating element

1 Disconnect the battery negative terminal.

2 Remove the fuel filter as described in Part A of this Chapter. If the filter is damaged during removal then it must be renewed.

3 Disconnect the wiring connector then unscrew the centre bolt and remove the heating element from the base of the fuel filter housing. Discard the sealing ring, which is fitted between the element and filter housing. A new seal must be used on refitting.

4 On refitting, fit the new sealing ring to the groove in the heating element and refit the element to the filter housing, tightening the centre bolt securely.

5 Reconnect the wiring connector and fit the fuel filter.

Temperature switch

6 Disconnect the battery negative terminal then disconnect the wiring connector from the temperature switch.

7 Wipe clean the area around the temperature switch and fuel filter housing. Position a container to catch any spilt fuel then slacken and remove the switch from the fuel filter housing. Discard the sealing washers, which are fitted on each side of the fuel hose union. New washers must be used on refitting.

8 Refitting is the reverse of removal. Position a new sealing washer on each side of the fuel hose union.

23 Preheating system - testing, component removal and refitting

System testing

1 If the preheating system malfunctions, testing is ultimately by substitution of known good units but some preliminary checks may be made as follows.

2 Connect a voltmeter or 12 volt test lamp between the glow plug supply cable and earth (engine or vehicle metal). Ensure that the live connection is kept clear of the engine and bodywork.

3 Have an assistant switch on the ignition and check that voltage is applied to the glow plugs. Note the time for which the warning light is lit and the total time for which voltage is applied before the system cuts out. Switch off the ignition.

4 At an under-bonnet temperature of 20°C, typical times noted for Renault 19, Clio and Espace models should be 5 or 6 seconds for warning light operation, followed by a further 4 to 5 seconds supply after the light goes out, provided the starter motor is not operated. On Renault Laguna models, at an under-bonnet temperature of 20°C, the warning light should operate for approximately 2 seconds, followed by a further 8 seconds supply after the light goes out. On all models, warning light time will increase with lower temperatures and decrease with higher temperatures.

5 If there is no supply at all, the relay or associated wiring is at fault.

6 To locate a defective glow plug, disconnect the main supply cable and the interconnecting wire or strap from the top of the glow plugs. Be careful not to drop the nuts and washers. On Renault Laguna models, access to the glow plugs is poor and it will be necessary to remove the inlet manifold to improve access.

7 Use a continuity tester, or a 12 volt test lamp connected to the battery positive terminal, to check for continuity between each glow plug terminal and earth. The resistance of a glow plug in good condition is very low (less than 1 ohm), so if the test lamp does not light or the continuity tester shows a high resistance, the glow plug is certainly defective.

8 If an ammeter is available, the current draw of each glow plug can be checked. After an initial surge of around 15 to 20 amps, each plug should draw around 10 amps. Any plug which draws much more or less than this is probably defective.

9 As a final check, the glow plugs can be removed and inspected as described in Section 12.

Control unit

Removal

10 The preheating system control unit is located as follows:

*Renault 19 - On the engine compartment bulkhead **(see illustration)**.*
*Renault Clio - On the left-hand suspension tower, to the rear of the battery **(see illustration)**.*
Renault Espace - On the left-hand side of the engine compartment, behind the battery.
*Renault Laguna - On the right-hand side of the engine compartment, behind the headlight **(see illustration)**.*

11 Disconnect the battery negative lead. On Renault Laguna models, improve access to the control unit by freeing the fuel filter housing from its mounting bracket.

12 Unscrew the securing nut and withdraw the unit from its mounting bracket.

13 Disconnect the wiring from the base of the unit, noting the connector locations.

Refitting

14 Refitting is a reversal of removal. Ensure that the wiring connectors are correctly connected.

23.10a Unscrewing preheating system control unit securing nut - Renault 19

23.10b Withdrawing preheating system control unit - Renault Clio

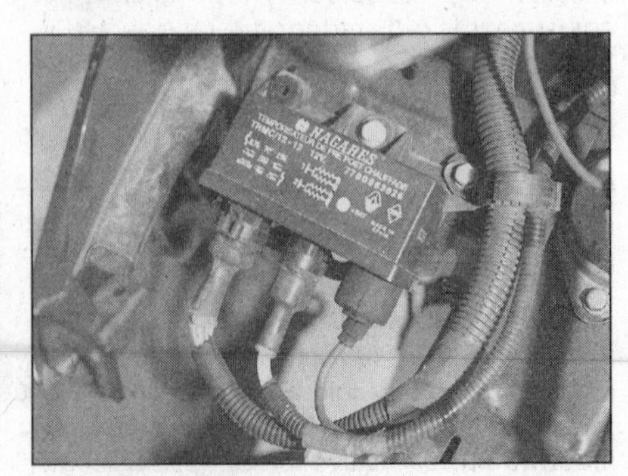

23.10c Preheating control unit (shown with headlight removed) - Renault Laguna

24 Exhaust gas recirculation system (Renault 19) - testing and component renewal

Note: *On Renault 19 models, this system is fitted to vehicles equipped with the F8Q 742 and F8Q 744 engines.*

System testing

1 Start the engine and run it until it reaches normal operating temperature, the cooling fan should have cut in and out at least once.

2 With the engine idling, disconnect the vacuum hose from the recirculation valve. As the hose is disconnected it should be possible to hear the valve click shut. If no click is heard, proceed as follows.

3 Check that vacuum is present at the recirculation valve end of the vacuum hose. If a vacuum gauge is available, check that the vacuum is at least 500 mbars. If vacuum is present, it is likely that the recirculation valve is faulty (ie. a jammed or pierced diaphragm). If no vacuum is present, carry out the following checks.

4 Check the security of all vacuum hose connections.

5 Check the electrical feed to the solenoid valve.

6 Check the operation of the temperature valve. This can be done by checking that vacuum will pass through the valve with the engine at normal operating temperature. Stop the engine and disconnect the temperature valve vacuum hoses at the recirculation valve and the solenoid valve. Check that it is possible to blow through the hoses. If not, it is likely that the temperature valve is faulty or the hoses are obstructed.

7 Check the operation of the micro-switch on the injection pump, using a continuity tester or an ohmmeter. With the pump accelerator lever in the idle position, the switch should be open (no continuity/infinite resistance). As the accelerator lever is moved from the idle position, the switch should close (continuity/zero resistance), until the lever reaches a predetermined position towards the end of its travel, when the switch should open again. Note that adjustment of the switch should not be attempted. If it is suspected that adjustment is required, or if a new switch is fitted, consult a Renault dealer who will have access to the specialist calibration equipment required to carry out accurate adjustment.

Component renewal

Note: *Where applicable, new gaskets should be used on refitting.*

Recirculation valve

8 This valve is located at the rear of the engine, on the exhaust manifold (F8Q 742 engines) or the inlet manifold (F8Q 744 engines) **(see illustration)**. The valve is connected to the remaining manifold via a metal pipe bolted between the valve and the manifold.

24.8 Exhaust gas recirculation (EGR) system components - F8Q 744 engine

1 *Solenoid valve*
2 *Recirculation valve*
3 *Vacuum take-off*
4 *Temperature valve*
5 *Recirculation pipe*

9 To remove the valve, first disconnect the vacuum hose from the valve.

10 Remove the securing bolts and disconnect the valve pipe from the appropriate manifold. Recover the gasket.

11 Unbolt the valve body from the manifold and recover the gasket, where applicable. Remove the valve, complete with pipe.

12 If a new valve is to be fitted, unscrew the securing bolts and transfer the pipe to the new valve, using a new gasket.

13 Refitting is a reversal of removal. Use new gaskets, where applicable.

Solenoid valve

14 This valve is located on a bracket attached to the engine compartment bulkhead.

15 Disconnect the wiring plug and the vacuum hoses from the valve.

16 Unscrew the securing nut(s) and withdraw the valve complete with its bracket.

17 Refitting is a reversal of removal, ensuring that the vacuum hoses are securely reconnected.

Temperature valve

18 This valve is located in the coolant hose, at the left-hand front corner of the cylinder block.

19 To remove the valve, simply disconnect the wiring plug and unscrew the valve from the hose. Be prepared for coolant spillage.

20 Refitting is reversal of removal. Check for coolant leaks on completion and if necessary, top up the coolant level.

Altimetric capsule

21 This capsule is located on the crossmember, at the front of the engine compartment **(see illustration)**.

22 Disconnect the wiring plug from the capsule, then unscrew the securing nut(s) and withdraw the capsule.

23 Refitting is a reversal of removal.

Injection pump micro-switch (EGR cut-off switch)

24 This switch is located on a bracket on the fuel injection pump.

25 Removal and refitting of the switch is self-explanatory but note that on completion, the switch must be adjusted by a Renault dealer using specialist calibration equipment.

25 Exhaust gas recirculation system (Renault Clio) - testing and component renewal

Note: *On Renault Clio models, this system is fitted to vehicles equipped with the F8Q 732 engine.*

System testing

1 Commence testing of the exhaust gas recirculation (EGR) system by following the procedure given in Section 24, paragraphs 1 to 6.

2 Check operation of the EGR microswitch on the injection pump as described in Section 11. If it proves impossible to adjust the switch, it is faulty and must be renewed.

Component renewal

Note: *Where applicable, new gaskets should be used on refitting.*

Recirculation valve

3 This valve is located at the rear of the engine. It is bolted to the exhaust manifold and connected to the inlet manifold via a metal pipe bolted between the valve and the manifold. To improve access to the valve, unbolt the oil separator from the rear of the inlet manifold.

4 To renew the valve, follow the procedure given in Section 24, paragraphs 9 to 13.

Solenoid valve

5 This valve is mounted on the engine compartment bulkhead, directly behind the inlet manifold.

6 To renew the valve, follow the procedure given in Section 24, paragraphs 15 to 17.

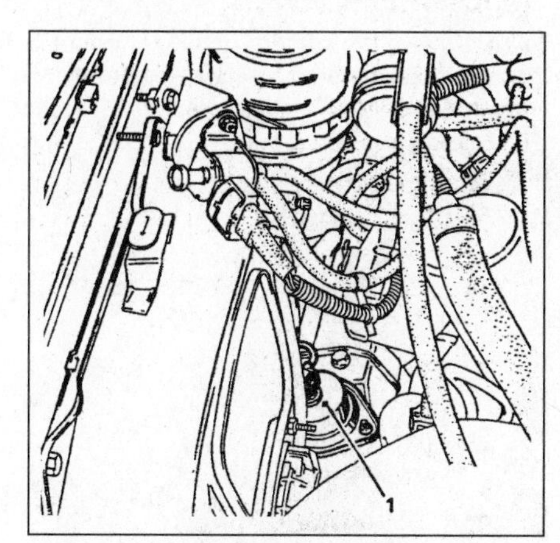

24.21 Exhaust gas recirculation system altimetric capsule (1)

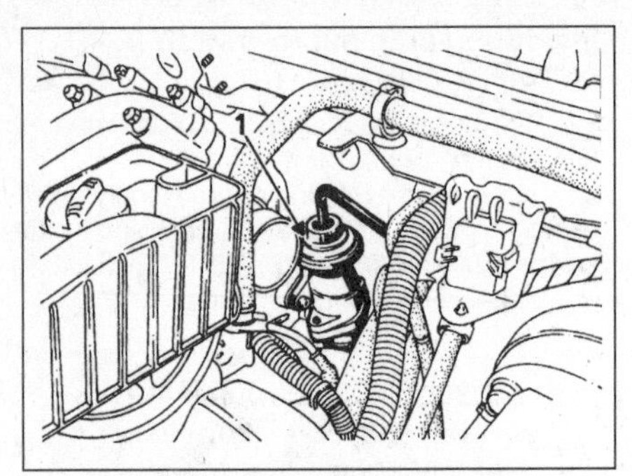

26.3 EGR recirculation valve (1) - Renault Laguna

Temperature valve

7 This valve is screwed into one of the cooling system hoses, near the left-hand end of the cylinder head. To locate the valve, trace the vacuum pipe back from the solenoid valve and then onto the valve.

8 To renew the valve, follow the procedure given in Section 24, paragraphs 19 and 20.

Injection pump micro-switch (EGR cut-off switch)

9 To renew this switch, follow the procedure given in Section 24.

26 Exhaust gas recirculation system (Renault Laguna) - testing and component renewal

System testing

1 Testing of the exhaust gas recirculation (EGR) system fitted to Renault Laguna models should be entrusted to a Renault dealer.

Component renewal

Recirculation valve

2 Slacken the retaining clips and remove the duct connecting the air cleaner housing to the manifold inlet chamber.

3 Disconnect the vacuum hose from the EGR recirculation valve which is mounted on the left-hand end of the inlet chamber **(see illustration).**

4 Slacken and remove the retaining bolts and free the valve from the inlet chamber. Recover the gasket and discard it. A new gasket must be used on refitting.

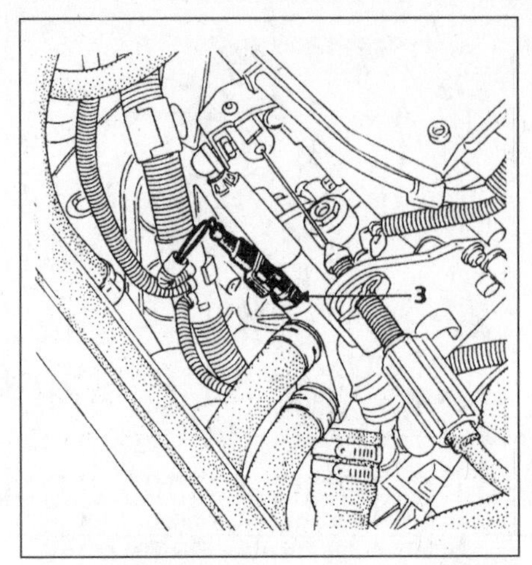

26.11 EGR system temperature sender (3)

5 Either undo the bolts securing the valve to the pipe or undo the bolts securing the pipe to the exhaust manifold (as applicable). Recover the gasket and remove the recirculation valve/valve and pipe assembly from the engine compartment.

6 Refitting is the reverse of removal, using new gaskets and ensuring that the bolts are securely tightened.

Solenoid valve

7 The EGR solenoid valve is located in the left-hand rear corner of the engine compartment.

8 To remove the solenoid, unscrew the retaining nuts and free the valve from its mounting bracket.

9 Disconnect the wiring connector and vacuum hoses from the valve and remove it from the engine compartment.

10 Refitting is the reverse of removal, ensuring that the vacuum hoses are securely reconnected.

Temperature sender

11 The EGR system temperature sender is situated directly beneath the fuel injection pump **(see illustration).** Access to the sender is poor, and surrounding components may need to be moved to one side before the sender can be reached.

12 To remove the sender, first disconnect the battery negative lead.

13 Partially drain the cooling system to just below the level of the sender.

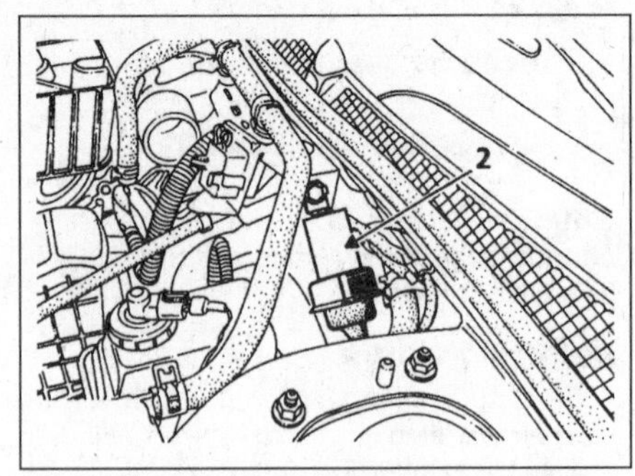

26.22 EGR system clutch pedal switch time delay relay (2)

14 Disconnect the wiring plug from the sender.

15 Carefully unscrew the sender from its housing and recover the sealing ring, where applicable.

16 If the sender was originally fitted using sealing compound, clean its threads thoroughly and coat them with fresh sealing compound

17 If the sender was originally fitted using a sealing ring, use a new sealing ring on refitting.

18 Refitting is a reversal of removal. Tighten the sender and replenish the cooling system.

Clutch pedal switch

19 Access to the clutch pedal switch can be gained from underneath the facia. To improve access, unclip the facia fusebox lid. Undo the retaining screws situated along the lower edge of the fusebox lid cover panel and unclip the panel assembly from the facia.

20 Reach up behind the facia and disconnect the wiring connector from the switch which is mounted onto the clutch pedal bracket. Twist the switch and carefully ease it out of its retaining clip.

21 Refitting is the reverse of removal, pushing the switch into position until it contacts the clutch pedal stop.

Clutch pedal switch time delay relay

22 Disconnect the wiring connector from the relay, which is located in the left-hand rear corner of the engine compartment **(see illustration).**

23 Undo the retaining bolt and remove the relay from the engine compartment.

24 Refitting is the reverse of removal.

Chapter 10
Vauxhall/Opel 1488cc, 1598cc,1686cc & 1699cc engines

Part A: Routine maintenance and servicing

Contents

16D and 16DA engines

Schedule A - 1982/83 model years

Schedule B - 1984/85/86 model years

Schedule C - 1987 model year on

15D, 15DT,17D, 17DR, 17DTL and 17DT engines

Section contents apply to all engine types unless otherwise stated

Engine application

1488cc (15D & 15DT) engine	Vauxhall/Opel Nova, Corsa and Combi van - 1982 to 1996
1598cc (16D & 16DA) engine	Vauxhall/Opel Astra, Belmont, Cavalier and Bedford equivalents - 1982 to 1996
1686cc (17DT) engine	Vauxhall/Opel Astra and Cavalier - 1982 to 1996
1699cc (17D, 17DR & 17DTL) engine	Vauxhall/Opel Astra, Belmont and Cavalier - 1982 to 1996

Servicing specifications

Oil filter types

15D and 15DT engines	Champion F126
16D and 16DA engines, 17D and 17DR engines	Champion G105
17DTL engine, 17DT engine	Champion F208

Valve clearances (cold)

15D, 15DT and 17DT engines:	
Inlet	0.15 mm
Exhaust	0.25 mm
16D, 16DA, 17D, 17DR and 17DTL engines:	
Inlet	Automatically adjusted
Exhaust	Automatically adjusted

Camshaft drivebelt tension

15D and 15DT engines	Automatic tensioner
16D and 16DA engines (using tension gauge):	
New belt, warm	9.0
New belt, cold	6.5
Run-in belt, warm	8.0
Run-in belt, cold	4.0
17D engine (using tension gauge):	
New belt, warm	7.5
New belt, cold	9.5
Run-in belt, warm	5.0
Run-in belt, cold	9.0
17DR and 17DTL engines	Automatic tensioner
17DT engine	Automatic tensioner

Auxiliary drivebelts

15D, 15DT and 17DT engines (V-belt)

Tension (using gauge):	
Alternator:	
New	440 to 540 N
Used	320 to 390 N
Power steering pump:	
New	450 N
Used	250 to 300 N

16D, 16DA, 17D, 17DR and 17DTL engines (V-belt)

Tension (using gauge):	
Alternator:	
New	450 N
Used	250 to 400 N
Power steering pump:	
New	450 N
Used	250 to 300 N

Air filter types

15D and 15DT engines	Champion U641
16D and 16DA engines	Champion U503
17D and 17DR engines:	
Astra 1988 to 1991, and Astramax	Champion U558
Astra from 1991	Champion U599
Cavalier from 1988	Champion U554
17DTL engine	Champion U548
17DT engine	Champion U548

Fuel filter types

15D and 15DT engines	Champion L111
16D and 16DA engines	Champion L113
17D and 17DR engines:	
Cavalier from 1988, and Astra to 1991	Champion L113
Astra from 1991, and Astramax	Champion L111
17DTL engine	Champion L111
17DT engine	Champion L111

Glow plug types

15D engine:	
5 volt system	Champion CH-110, or equivalent
11 volt system	Champion CH-157, or equivalent
15DT engine	Champion CH-158, or equivalent
16D and 16DA engines	Champion CH-68, or equivalent
17D and 17DR engines	Champion CH-68, or equivalent
17DTL engine	Champion CH-158, or equivalent
17DT engine	Champion CH-158, or equivalent

Injection pump adjustment

Idle speed	
15D and 15DT engines	830 to 930 rpm
16D and 16DA engines	825 to 875 rpm
17D engine	820 to 920 rpm
17DR and 17DTL engines:	
Below 20°C	1200 rpm
Above 20°C	850 rpm
17DT engine	780 to 880 rpm
Maximum speed	
15D engine	5800 rpm
15DT engine	5600 rpm
16D and 16DA engines	5600 rpm
17D, 17DR and 17DTL engines	5500 to 5600 rpm
17DT engine	5100 to 5300 rpm

Torque wrench settings

	Nm	lbf ft
Camshaft - 15D and 15DT engines		
Bearing cap to cylinder head nuts	25	18
Drivebelt sprocket bolts	10	7
Drivebelt cover to cylinder block	8	6
Drivebelt guide roller to cylinder block	80	60
Drivebelt tension roller bolt and nut	19	15
Camshaft - 17DT engine		
Bearing cap to cylinder head nuts	19	15
Drivebelt sprocket bolts	10	7
Drivebelt cover to cylinder block	8	6
Drivebelt guide roller to cylinder block	76	55
Drivebelt tension roller to cylinder block	19	15
Crankshaft - 15D and 15DT engines		
Pulley-to-sprocket bolts	20	15
Drivebelt sprocket centre bolt	133 to 161	98 to 118
Crankshaft - 17DT engine		
Pulley-to-sprocket bolts	20	15
Drivebelt sprocket centre bolt	196	144
Engine mounting - 15D and 15DT engines		
Right-hand mounting bracket:		
To cylinder block	45	33
To damping block	45	33
Engine mounting - 17DT engine		
Right-hand mounting bracket:		
To cylinder block	40	30
To mounting	45	33
Coolant pump - 17DR and 17DTL engines		
Pump to cylinder block	25	18
Glow plugs		
15D and 15DT engines	20	15
16D and 16DA engines	40	30
17D and 17DR engines	20	15
17DT engine	20	15

Lubricants, fluids and capacities

Component or system	Lubricant or fluid	Capacity
Engine - 15D, 15DT	Multigrade engine oil, viscosity range SAE 5W/50 to 20W/50, to specification API SF/CD, SG/CD or CD	3.75 litres - With filter
Engine - 16D, 16DA	Multigrade engine oil, viscosity range SAE 10W/40 to 20W/50, to specification API SG/CD or better	3.75 litres - With filter - Pre 1984 5.0 litres - With filter - 1985 on
Engine - 17D	Multigrade engine oil, viscosity range SAE 10W/40 to 20W/50, to specification API SG/CD or better	4.75 litres - With filter
Engine - 17DR, 17DTL	Multigrade engine oil, viscosity range SAE 5W/50 to 20W/50, to specification API SG/CD, SH/CD or CD	5.0 litres - With filter
Engine - 17DT	Multigrade engine oil, viscosity range SAE 5W/50 to 20W/50, to specification API SF/CD, SG/CD or CD	5.0 litres - With filter
Cooling system	Ethylene glycol based antifreeze to GME specification 13368	6.0 litres - 15D 6.3 litres - 15TD 7.7 litres - 16D, 16DA 9.1 litres - 17D, 17DR 6.8 litres - 17DTL 6.8 litres - 17DT
Fuel system	Commercial Diesel fuel for road vehicles (DERV)	Dependent on model type

Vauxhall/Opel diesel engine - maintenance schedule

The maintenance schedules which follow are basically those recommended by the manufacturer. Servicing intervals are determined by mileage or time elapsed - this is because fluids and systems deteriorate with age as well as with use. Follow the time intervals if the appropriate mileage is not covered within the specified period.

Vehicles operating under adverse conditions may need more frequent maintenance. Adverse conditions include climatic extremes, full-time towing or taxi work, driving on unmade roads, and a high proportion of short journeys. The use of inferior fuel can cause early degradation of the engine oil. Consult a Vauxhall/Opel dealer for advice on these points.

16D and 16DA engines

All models

Every 250 miles (400 km), weekly, or before a long journey

- ☐ Check engine oil level and top up if necessary (Section 3)
- ☐ Check coolant level and top up if necessary (Section 4)
- ☐ Check battery electrolyte level (if applicable)
- ☐ Check exhaust emission (Section 5)
- ☐ Check operation of glow plug warning light (Section 6)

Every 6000 miles (10 000 km) or 6 months

- ☐ Check idle speed; adjust if necessary (Section 11)
- ☐ Renew fuel filter element (Section 12)
- ☐ Renew air filter element
- ☐ Check auxiliary drivebelts for condition and tension
- ☐ Check coolant strength
- ☐ Check cooling system hose condition and security

Every 18 000 miles (30 000 km) or 2 years

- ☐ Check condition and tension of camshaft drivebelt (Section 17)
- ☐ Renew engine coolant (regardless of mileage)

Every 36 000 miles (60 000 km) or 4 years

- ☐ Renew camshaft drivebelt (Section 24)

Every 60 000 miles (100 000 km) or 5 years

- ☐ Renew glow plugs (Section 26)

Schedule A - 1982/83 model years

Every 3000 miles (5000 km) or 6 months, whichever comes first

- ☐ Renew engine oil and oil filter (Section 7)
- ☐ Drain fuel filter (Section 8)

Schedule B - 1984/85/86 model years

Every 3000 miles (5000 km) or 6 months, whichever comes first - 1984 only

- ☐ Renew engine oil and oil filter (Section 7)
- ☐ Drain fuel filter (Section 8)

Every 4500 miles (7500 km) or 6 months - 1985/86

- ☐ Renew engine oil and oil filter (Section 9)
- ☐ Drain fuel filter (Section 10)

Every 9000 miles (15 000 km) or 12 months

- ☐ Check idle speed and adjust if necessary (Section 13)
- ☐ Check auxiliary drivebelts for condition and tension
- ☐ Lubricate throttle linkage
- ☐ Check coolant strength
- ☐ Check cooling system hoses for condition and security

Every 18 000 miles (30 000 km) or 2 years

- ☐ Renew fuel filter element (Section 18)
- ☐ Renew air filter element
- ☐ Check condition and tension of camshaft drivebelt (Section 17)

Every 36 000 miles (60 000 km) or 4 years

- ☐ Renew camshaft drivebelt (Section 24)

Every 63 000 miles (105 000 km) or 7 years

- ☐ Renew glow plugs (Section 27)

Every 2 years, regardless of mileage

- ☐ Renew engine coolant

Schedule C - 1987 model year on

Every 4500 miles (7500 km) or 6 months, whichever comes first

- ☐ Renew engine oil and filter (Section 9)
- ☐ Drain fuel filter (Section 10)

Every 9000 miles (15 000 km) or 12 months

- ☐ As for Schedule B

Every 18 000 miles (30 000 km) or 2 years

- ☐ As for Schedule B but without inspecting the camshaft drivebelt

Every 27 000 miles (45 000 km) or 3 years

- ☐ If operating in adverse driving conditions, check condition and tension of camshaft drivebelt (Section 21)

Every 36 000 miles (60 000 km) or 4 years

- ☐ When operating in normal driving conditions, check condition and tension of camshaft drivebelt (Section 22)

Every 54 000 miles (90 000 km) or 6 years

- ☐ If operating in adverse driving conditions, renew camshaft drivebelt (Section 25)

Every 63 000 miles (105 000 km) or 7 years

- ☐ Renew glow plugs (Section 27)
- ☐ When operating in normal driving conditions, renew camshaft drivebelt (Section 28)

Every 2 years, regardless of mileage

- ☐ Renew engine coolant

15D, 15DT,17D, 17DR, 17DTL and 17DT engines

1992 model year on

Note: *The following maintenance schedule is based on the vehicle being driven for 9000 miles per year. Should the vehicle be driven for an appreciably lesser or greater mileage than this, then the Schedule must be modified to suit. Ask advice from your Vauxhall/Opel dealer.*
Section contents apply to all engine types unless otherwise stated.

Every 250 miles (400 km), weekly, or before a long journey

- ☐ Check engine oil level and top up if necessary (Section 3)
- ☐ Check coolant level and top up if necessary (Section 4)
- ☐ Check battery electrolyte level (if applicable)
- ☐ Check exhaust smoke (Section 5)
- ☐ Check operation of glow plug warning light (Section 6)

Every 4500 miles (7500 km) or 12 months, whichever comes first

- ☐ Renew engine oil and oil filter (Section 9)

Every 9000 miles (15 000 km) or 12 months

- ☐ Check the engine and gearbox for leaks
- ☐ Drain any accumulation of water from the fuel filter (Section 16)
- ☐ Renew air filter element
- ☐ Check engine idle speed (Section 13)
- ☐ Check maximum speed (Section 14)
- ☐ Check exhaust emissions (Section 15)
- ☐ Check condition and tension (where applicable) of the auxiliary drivebelts

Every 18 000 miles (30 000 km) or 2 years

- ☐ Renew fuel filter (Section 19)
- ☐ Check condition of camshaft drivebelt - 17DR and 17DTL engines (Section 17)
- ☐ Check valve clearances - 15D, 15DT and 17DT engines (Section 20)
- ☐ Renew engine coolant - every 2 years, regardless of mileage

Every 36 000 miles (60 000 km) or 4 years

- ☐ Check condition and tension of camshaft drivebelt - 17D engine (Section 22)
- ☐ Check condition of camshaft drivebelt - 15D, 15DT and 17DT engines (Section 23)
- ☐ Renew camshaft drivebelt regardless of condition - 17DR and 17DTL engines (Section 24)

Every 63 000 miles (105 000 km) or 7 years

- ☐ Renew glow plugs (Section 27)

Every 72 000 miles (120 000 km) or 8 years

- ☐ Renew camshaft drivebelt regardless of condition - 15D, 15DT, 17D and 17DT engines (Section 29)

Underbonnet view of 15D engine in Vauxhall Combi Van

1 *Cooling system filler/pressure cap*
2 *Brake fluid reservoir cap*
3 *Brake servo line*
4 *Fuel filter*
5 *Screen washer reservoir*
6 *Suspension turret*
7 *Air cleaner housing*
8 *Battery*
9 *Radiator fan*
10 *Engine oil dipstick*
11 *Engine oil filler cap*
12 *Fuel injector*
13 *Thermostat housing*
14 *Engine breather*
15 *Camshaft drivebelt cover*
16 *Inlet manifold*
17 *Plenum chamber*
18 *Air resonator box*
19 *EGR valve*
20 *Exhaust manifold*
21 *VIN plate*
22 *Coolant pump*
23 *Relay box*

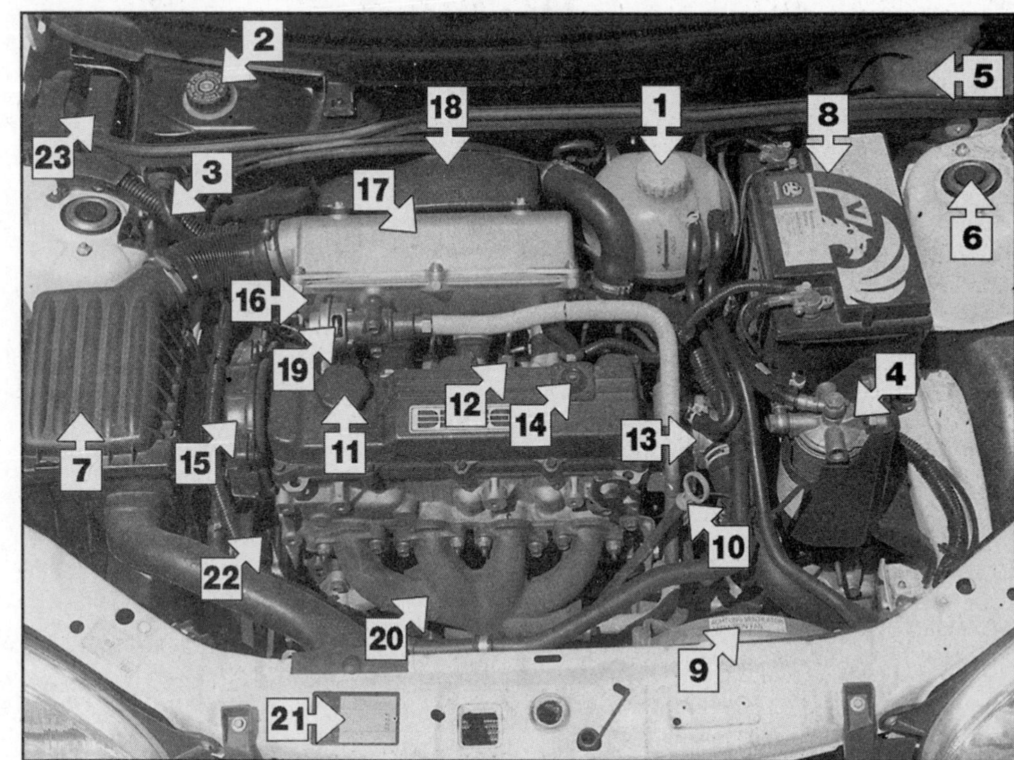

Underbonnet view of 15DT engine in Vauxhall Corsa

1 *Cooling system filler/pressure cap*
2 *Brake fluid reservoir cap*
3 *Brake servo line*
4 *Fuel filter*
5 *Fuel heater*
6 *Screen washer reservoir*
7 *Suspension turret*
8 *Air cleaner housing*
9 *Battery*
10 *Radiator fan*
11 *Engine oil dipstick*
12 *Engine oil filler cap*
13 *Fuel injector*
14 *Thermostat housing (beneath hose)*
15 *Engine breather*
16 *Camshaft drivebelt cover*
17 *Inlet manifold*
18 *Plenum chamber*
19 *Charge air safety valve*
20 *Turbocharger*
21 *Exhaust manifold heat shield*
22 *VIN plate*
23 *Coolant pump*
24 *Relay box*

Underbonnet view of 16D engine in Vauxhall Cavalier

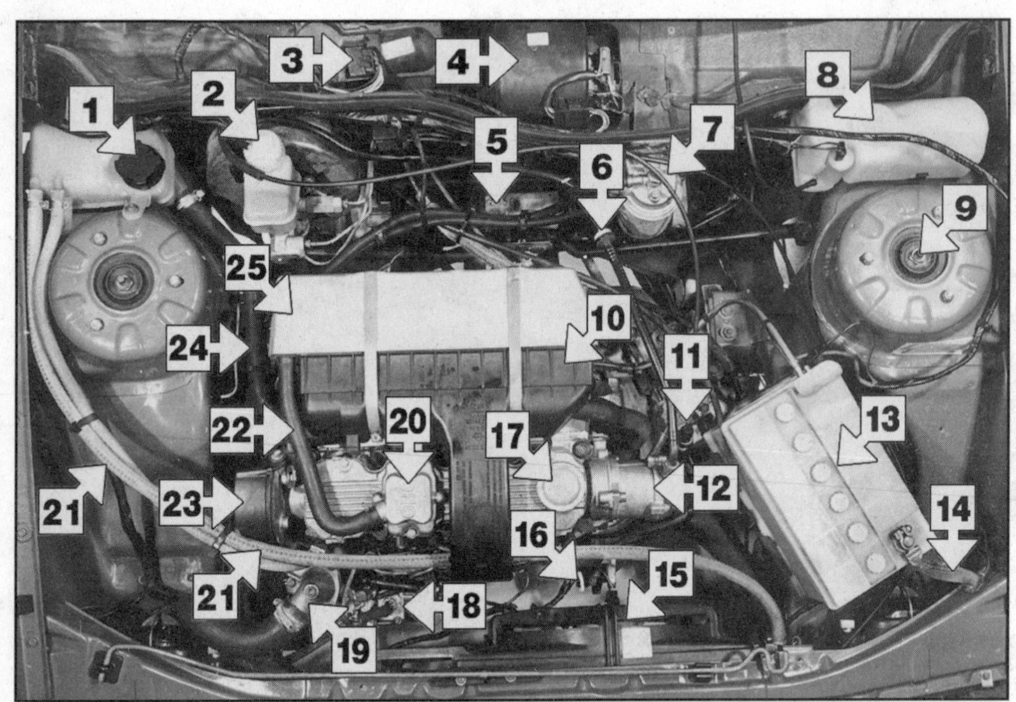

1 *Cooling system filler/pressure cap*
2 *Brake fluid reservoir cap*
3 *Windscreen wiper motor*
4 *Heater blower motor*
5 *Fuel hoses*
6 *Brake servo non-return valve*
7 *Fuel filter*
8 *Screen washer reservoir*
9 *Suspension turret*
10 *Air cleaner housing*
11 *Gearbox breather*
12 *Vacuum pump*
13 *Battery*
14 *Earth strap*
15 *Radiator fan*
16 *Engine oil dipstick*
17 *Engine oil filler*
18 *Fuel injection pump*
19 *Thermostat elbow*
20 *Engine breather*
21 *Cooling system vent hoses*
22 *Crankcase ventilation hose*
23 *Camshaft drivebelt cover*
24 *Coolant hose (to expansion tank)*
25 *Inlet manifold*

Underbonnet view of 17D engine in Vauxhall Cavalier

1 *Cooling system filler/pressure cap*
2 *Brake fluid reservoir cap*
3 *Electrical ancillary box*
4 *Fuel filter*
5 *Fuel filter heater unit*
6 *Fuel filter temperature sensor*
7 *Fuel hoses*
8 *Brake servo non-return valve*
9 *Suspension turret*
10 *Air cleaner housing*
11 *Gearbox breather*
12 *Vacuum pump*
13 *Battery*
14 *Battery earth strap*
15 *Radiator fan*
16 *Engine oil dipstick*
17 *Engine oil filler*
18 *Fuel injection pump*
19 *Thermostat elbow*
20 *Engine breather*
21 *Cooling system vent hoses*
22 *Crankcase ventilation hose*
23 *Camshaft drivebelt cover*
24 *Coolant hose (to expansion tank)*
25 *Inlet manifold*
26 *Clutch cable*
27 *Screen washer reservoir*
28 *VIN plate*

Underbonnet view of 17DR engine in Vauxhall Astra

1 Cooling system filler/pressure cap
2 Brake fluid reservoir cap
3 Relay box
4 Fuel filter
5 EGR valve
6 Screen washer reservoir
7 Suspension turret
8 Air cleaner housing
9 Battery
10 Radiator fan
11 Engine oil dipstick
12 Engine oil filler cap
13 Fuel injector
14 Fuel injection pump
15 Cold start device
16 Thermostat elbow
17 Engine breather
18 Camshaft drivebelt cover
19 Inlet manifold
20 Vacuum pump
21 Relay box
22 Clutch lever

Underbonnet view of 17DTL engine in Vauxhall Astra

1 Cooling system filler/pressure cap
2 Brake fluid reservoir cap
3 Relay box
4 Fuel filter
5 Fuel heater
6 Screen washer reservoir
7 Suspension turret
8 Air cleaner housing
9 Battery
10 Radiator fan
11 Engine oil dipstick
12 Engine oil filler cap
13 Fuel injector
14 Thermostat elbow
15 Engine breather hose
16 Camshaft drivebelt cover
17 Inlet manifold
18 EGR valve
19 Relay box
20 Vacuum pump
21 Fuel injection pump
22 VIN plate
23 Power steering fluid reservoir

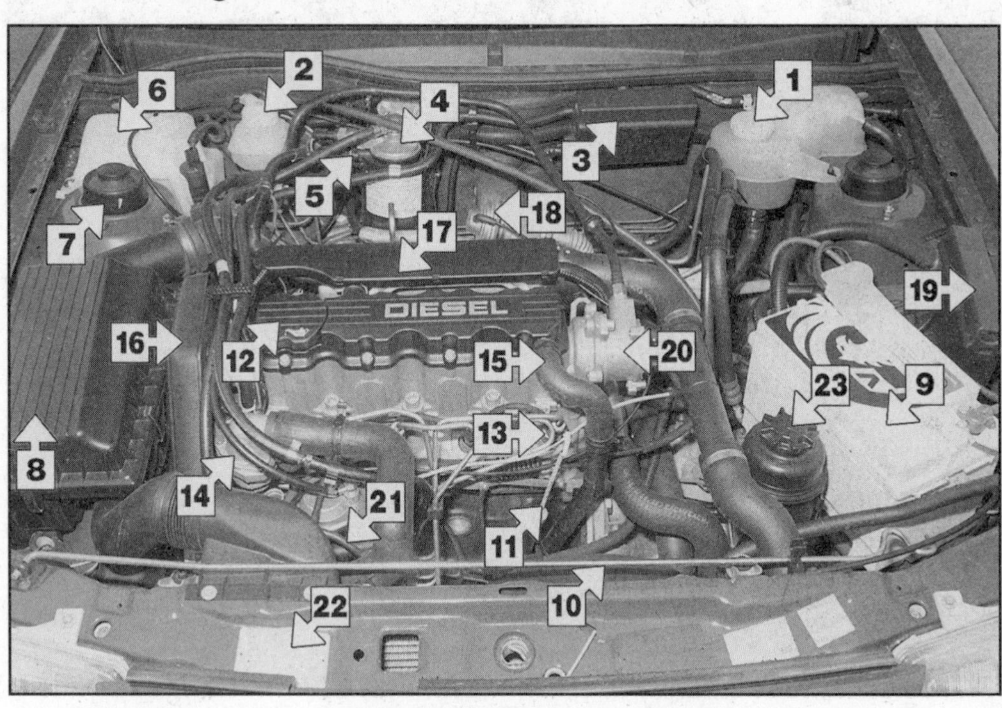

Underbonnet view of 17DT engine in Vauxhall Astra

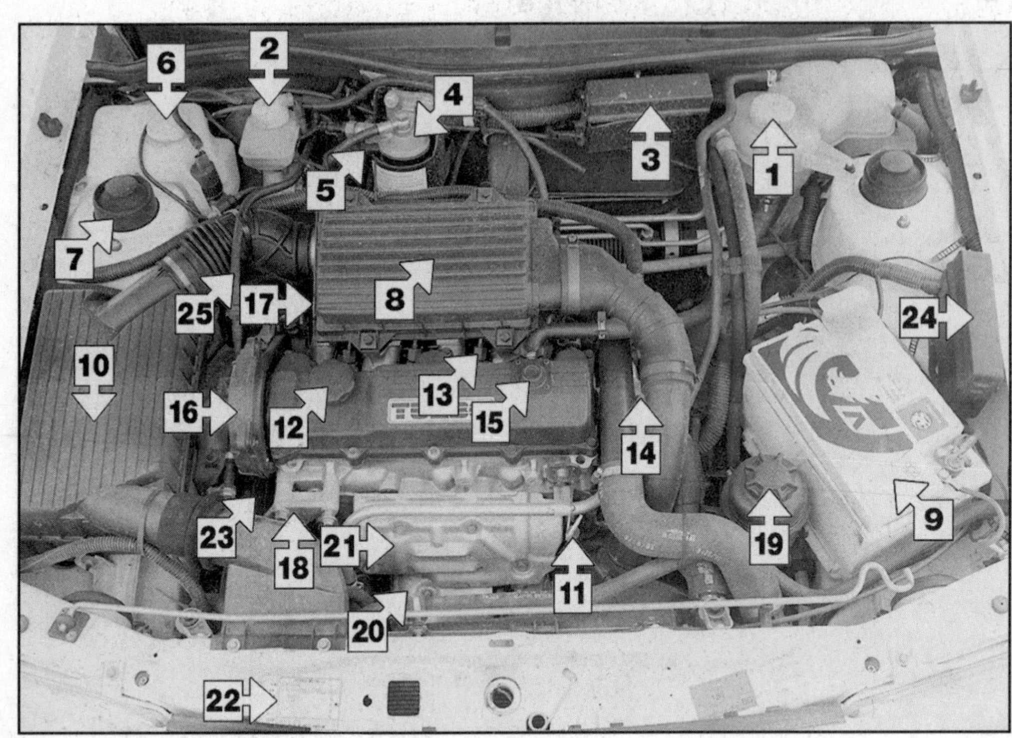

1 Cooling system filler/pressure cap
2 Brake fluid reservoir cap
3 Relay box
4 Fuel filter
5 Fuel heater
6 Screen washer reservoir
7 Suspension turret
8 Air cleaner housing
9 Battery
10 Air collector box
11 Engine oil dipstick
12 Engine oil filler cap
13 Fuel injector
14 Thermostat housing (beneath hose)
15 Engine breather
16 Camshaft drivebelt cover
17 Inlet manifold
18 Power steering pump bracket
19 Power steering fluid reservoir
20 Turbocharger heat shield
21 Exhaust manifold heat shield
22 VIN plate
23 Coolant pump
24 Relay box
25 Brake servo line

Underbonnet view of 17DT engine in Vauxhall Cavalier

1 Cooling system filler/pressure cap
2 Brake fluid reservoir cap
3 Electrical ancillary box
4 Fuel filter
5 Fuel heater
6 Screen washer reservoir
7 Suspension turret
8 Air cleaner housing
9 Battery
10 Air collector box
11 Engine oil dipstick
12 Engine oil filler cap
13 Fuel injector
14 Thermostat housing (beneath hose)
15 Engine breather
16 Camshaft drivebelt cover
17 Inlet manifold
18 Power steering pump
19 Power steering fluid reservoir
20 Turbocharger heat shield
21 Exhaust manifold heat shield
22 VIN plate
23 Coolant pump
24 Brake servo line

Maintenance procedures

1 Introduction

Refer to Chapter 2, Part A, Section 1.

2 Intensive maintenance

Refer to Chapter 2, Part A, Section 2.

250 mile (400 km) Service

3 Engine oil level check

1 Refer to Chapter 2, Part A, Section 3 **(see illustrations)**.

4 Coolant level check

1 Refer to Chapter 2, Part A, Section 4. Note that the tank is translucent, so the coolant level can be verified without removing the cap. The level should be between the MAX (HOT) and MIN (COLD) marks embossed on the side of the tank. If it is below the MIN mark, remove the cap and top up with coolant to the MAX mark **(see illustration)**.

5 Exhaust smoke check

1 Refer to Chapter 2, Part A, Section 5.

6 Warning light check

1 Refer to Chapter 2, Part A, Section 6.

3.1a Engine oil level dipstick markings

3.1b Topping up engine oil

4.1 Coolant level MIN and MAX marks (arrowed)

3000 mile (5000 km) Service

7 Engine oil and filter renewal

16D and 16DA engines, schedules A and B

1 Refer to Chapter 2, Part A, Section 7 **(see illustrations)**.

7.1a Engine oil drain plug - 16D engine shown, others similar

7.1b Removing engine oil filter - 16D engine shown, others similar

8 Fuel filter water drainage

16D and 16DA engines, schedules A and B

Unheated filter

1 The fuel filter should be drained to remove any water which may have accumulated.

2 Position a container underneath the filter drain plug. Loosen the vent plug on top of the filter carrier by one turn **(see illustration)**.

3 Loosen the drain plug at the filter base by one turn and allow the water layer to drain from the filter **(see illustration)**.

4 When clean fuel emerges, tighten both screws and remove the container.

5 Dispose of the water/fuel safely.

Heated filter

6 For most purposes, this filter type can be dealt with as described for the unheated type. It is easier to release the assembly from the bulkhead to carry out the periodic draining operation, as access below the filter is restricted while it is in place, making the operation potentially messy. The main reason for the poor access problem is the adoption of the heat shield around the filter head **(see illustrations)**.

8.2 Loosening fuel filter vent plug - 16D engine

8.3 Fuel filter drain plug (arrowed) - 16D engine

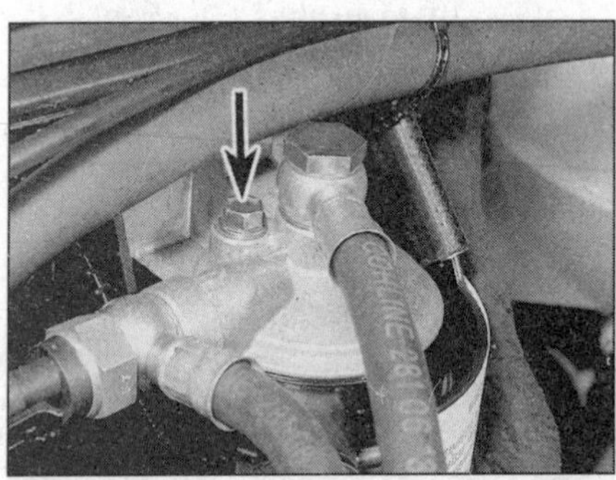

8.6a Top of heated filter unit, showing vent plug location (arrowed) - later 16DA engine

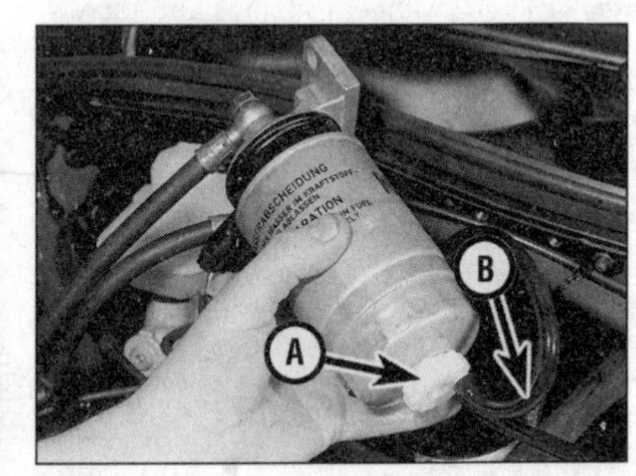

8.6b Fuel filter drain plug (A) and hose (B) - later 16DA engine

4500 mile (7500 km) Service

9 Engine oil and filter renewal

16D and 16DA engines, schedule C. 15D, 15DT, 17D 17DR, 17DTL and 17DT engines

1 Refer to Section 7.

10 Fuel filter water drainage

16D and 16DA engines, schedule C

Refer to Section 8.

6000 mile (10 000 km) Service

11 Idle speed check and adjustment

16D and 16DA engines, schedule A

Caution: Keep clear of the cooling fan when making adjustments.

16D and early 16DA engines

1 The main difficulty in making engine speed adjustments is the measurement of the speed. Conventional tachometers cannot be used because they are triggered by ignition system pulses. Proprietary instruments are available which operate by sensing the passage of a mark on the crankshaft pulley, but they are expensive.

2 If the relationship of road speed to engine rpm is known for any gear, the vehicle can be positioned with its front wheels off the ground and the speedometer reading converted to rpm. Apply the handbrake and chock the rear wheels securely if this method is adopted. The accuracy of the speedometer may not be great, especially at the low speeds at idle.

3 A third possibility is the use of a dynamic timing light (stroboscope) connected to the ignition system of a petrol-engined vehicle. Make a chalk or paint mark on the crankshaft pulley of the Diesel engine and shine the stroboscope at it. Run the petrol engine at the desired speed. When the Diesel engine is running at the same speed, the pulley chalk mark will appear stationary. The same applies at half or twice the speed, so some common sense must be used.

4 If adjustment is necessary, remove the air cleaner snorkel to improve access. Slacken the locknut on the idle speed adjusting screw

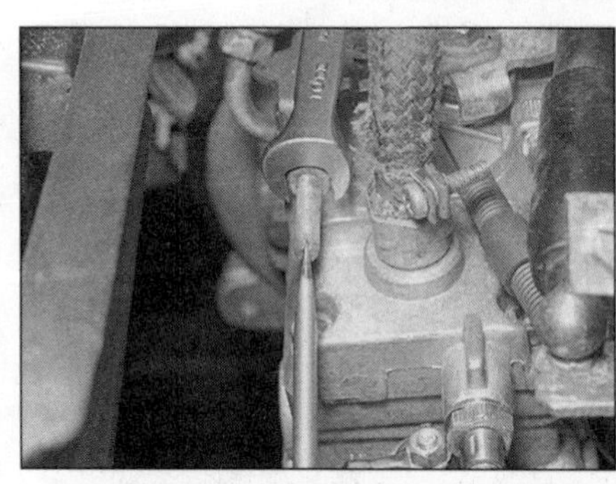
11.4 Adjusting idle speed - 16D engine

and turn the screw clockwise to increase the speed, anti-clockwise to decrease it. Tighten the locknut, without altering the screw position, when adjustment is correct **(see illustration)**. Refit the snorkel.

Later 16DA engine

Bosch VE fuel injection pump

Caution: The manufacturer warns that injection pumps which have had the stop screw tampered with cannot be re-adjusted by a dealer, which suggests that the pump will have to be set up by a Bosch specialist

5 Later versions of the Bosch VE injection pump require a revised idle speed adjustment procedure to that described above. The later pump can be identified by the vertical idle speed adjustment screw located on the front face of the pump. Where this type of pump is fitted, it is essential that the engine speed control lever stop screw is not disturbed. The positions of the adjustment screws are as shown **(see illustration)**.

6 Refer to paragraphs 1 to 4 for details of various methods of measuring the engine speed. It is recommended that the methods described in paragraph 1 or 3 be adopted for the following adjustments.

7 To adjust the idle speed, slacken the locknut on the idle speed adjustment screw and turn the screw as necessary to obtain the specified speed. Tighten the locknut, without disturbing the screw position, on completion.

Lucas/CAV fuel injection pump

8 The idle speed on engines fitted with the Lucas/CAV injection pump is adjusted using the stop screw shown **(see illustration)**. The engine speed control lever stop screw must not be disturbed and is covered with a plastic anti-tamper cap.

9 Refer to paragraphs 1 to 4 for details of various methods of measuring the engine speed. It is recommended that the methods described in paragraph 1 or 3 of that Section be adopted for the following adjustments.

10 To adjust the idle speed, slacken the locknut on the idle speed stop screw and turn

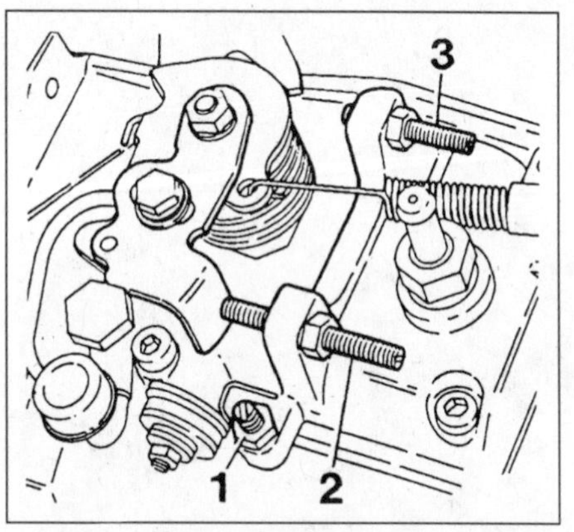

11.5 Bosch VE injection pump adjustment points - later 16DA and 17D engines

1 *Idle speed adjustment screw*
2 *Engine speed control lever stop screw - do not disturb*
3 *Maximum speed adjustment screw*

the screw as necessary to obtain the specified speed. Tighten the locknut, without disturbing the screw position, on completion.

12 Fuel filter element renewal

16D and 16DA engines, schedule A

1 Thoroughly clean the filter element and carrier, especially around the joint between the two.

2 Drain the fuel from the filter by opening the vent and drain plugs. Catch the fuel in a container and dispose of it safely. Tighten the vent plugs.

3 Unscrew the filter element with the aid of a chain or strap wrench similar to that used for oil filter removal **(see illustration)**. Discard the

12.3 Removing fuel filter element - 16D engine

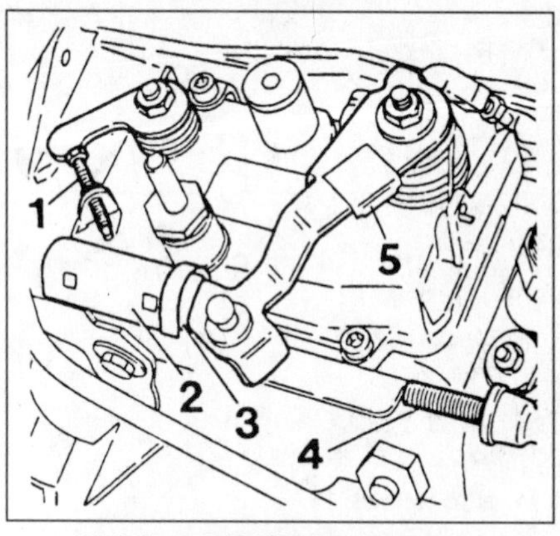

11.8 Lucas/CAV injection pump adjustment points - later 16DA and 17D engines

1 *Idle speed stop screw*
2 *Plastic anti-tamper cap*
3 *Engine speed control lever stop screw - do not disturb*
4 *Cut-off speed stop screw*
5 *Timing value for individual pump (marked on plate)*

old element and make sure that no sealing rings have been left behind on the filter carrier.

4 Place the sealing ring supplied with the new filter over the centre hole in the filter and clip it into place with the retainer **(see illustration)**.

5 Lubricate the outer sealing ring with a smear of clean fuel. Offer the filter to the carrier and tighten it with firm hand pressure or as directed by the filter manufacturer. Tighten the drain plug.

6 Start the engine and run it at a fast idle for a minute or so to vent the system. Check around the filter seal for leaks, tightening a little further if necessary.

12.4 Fuel filter inner sealing ring (A) retainer (B) and outer sealing ring (C) - 16D engine

9000 mile (15 000 km) Service

13 Idle speed check and adjustment

16D and 16DA engines, schedules B and C

1 Refer to Section 11.

17D engine

Bosch VE fuel injection pump

2 Refer to the information given for the later 16DA engine in Section 11.

Lucas/CAV fuel injection pump

3 Refer to the information given for the later 16DA engine in Section 11.

17DR and 17DTL engines

Bosch VE fuel injection pump

4 The Bosch injection pump fitted to these engines is equipped with a vacuum-operated cold start device which allows the engine idle speed to increase when the temperature is below 20°C **(see illustration)**. Two idle speed adjustments are therefore necessary, one for a cold engine and one for a hot engine.

5 Refer to paragraphs 1 to 4 of Section 11 for details of various methods of measuring the engine speed. It is recommended that the methods described in paragraph 1 or 3 of that Section be adopted for the following adjustments.

6 With the engine cold (ie. below 20°C), check that there is approximately 2 to 3 mm of free play between the clamping sleeve on the end of the cold start device operating cable and the actuating lever **(see illustration)**. Alter the position of the clamping sleeve if necessary.

13.4 Bosch VE injection pump cold start device (arrowed) - 17DR and 17DTL engines

7 Start the engine and check that the cold idling speed is as specified. If adjustment is necessary, turn the cold idling speed adjustment screw as required to achieve the desired speed **(see illustration)**.

8 Warm the engine up by taking the vehicle on a short test drive. With the engine temperature above 20°C, check that the cold start device operating cable has retracted and moved the actuating lever into contact with the hot idling speed adjustment screw. The engine should now be idling at the (lower) hot engine idling speed specified. If adjustment is necessary, turn the hot idling adjustment screw as necessary.

Lucas/CAV fuel injection pump

9 As with the Bosch pump described earlier, the Lucas/CAV injection pump is also equipped with a vacuum operated cold start device which allows the engine idle speed to increase when the temperature is below 20°C. Two idle speed adjustments are therefore necessary, one for a cold engine and one for a hot engine.

10 Refer to paragraphs 1 to 4 of Section 11 for details of various methods of measuring the engine speed. It is recommended that the methods described in paragraph 1 or 3 of that Section be adopted for the following adjustments.

11 With the engine cold (ie. below 20°C), check that the cold idling speed is as specified. If adjustment is necessary, slacken the locknut on the vacuum unit thrust-rod and turn the thrust-rod as required to achieve the desired speed **(see illustration)**. Tighten the locknut when the setting is correct.

12 Warm the engine up by taking the vehicle on a short test drive. With the engine temperature above 20°C, the engine should now be idling at the (lower) hot engine idling speed specified. If adjustment is necessary, slacken the locknut and turn the hot idling speed adjustment screw as necessary. Tighten the locknut when the setting is correct.

15D and 15DT engines

Checking

13 Measure the engine speed by using the following method. Do not vary from this procedure, since there is a grave risk of injury or damage should anything go wrong.

14 Clean the outer rim of the crankshaft pulley and mark it by using a 1 to 2 cm wide piece of aluminium foil as shown **(see illustration)**.

15 Set up an optical or pulse-sensitive tachometer to read the engine speed.

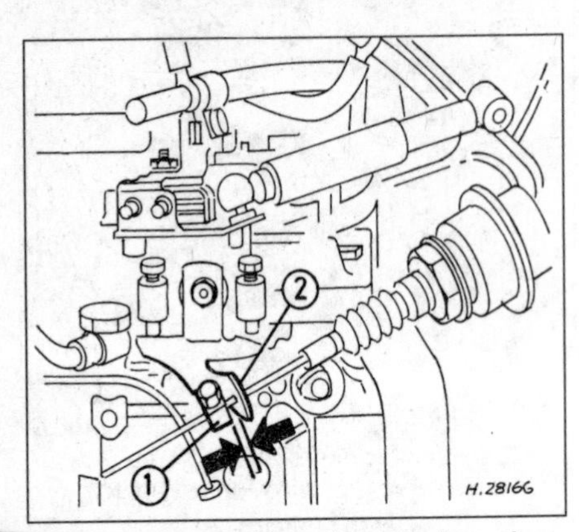

13.6 Checking cold start device free play - Bosch VE injection pump, 17DR and 17DTL engines

1 Clamping sleeve 2 Actuating lever
Arrows indicate free play checking point - engine cold

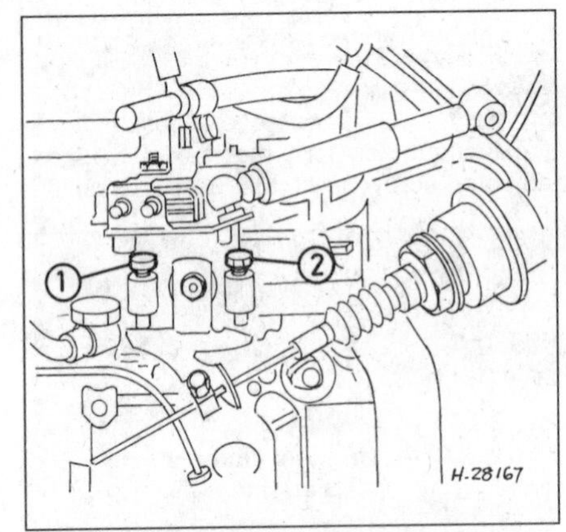

13.7 Bosch VE injection pump idle speed adjustment screws - 17DR and 17DTL engines

1 Cold idling speed adjustment screw
2 Hot idling speed adjustment screw

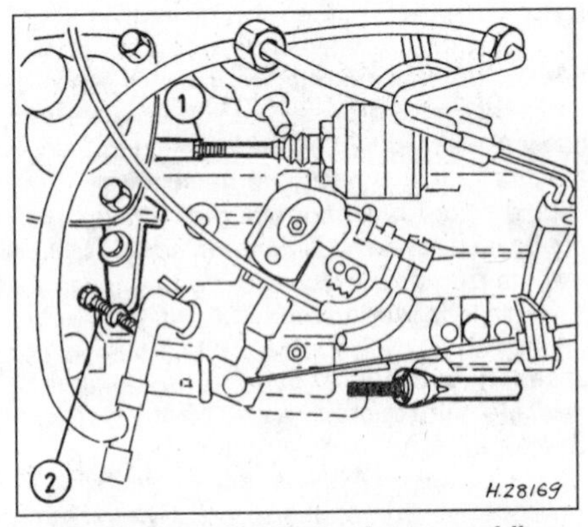

13.11 Lucas/CAV injection pump idle speed adjustment screws - 17DR and 17DTL engines

1 Vacuum unit thrust-rod locknut (cold idle adjustment)
2 Hot idling speed adjustment screw

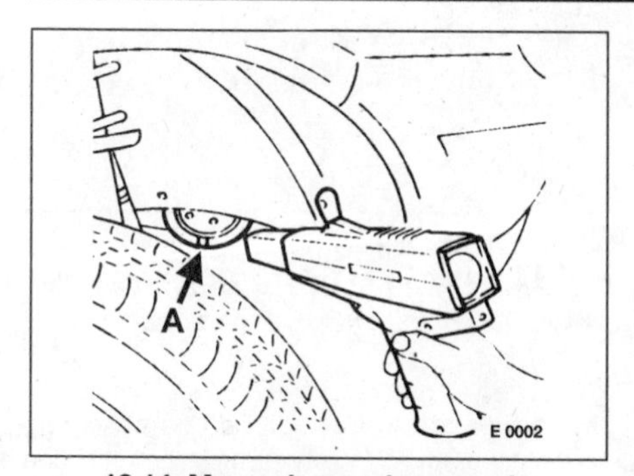

13.14 Measuring engine speed - 15D and 15DT engines
A 1 to 2 cm wide aluminium foil strip

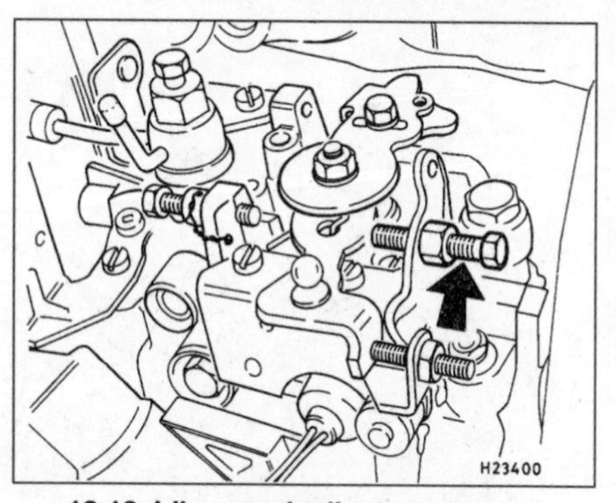

13.18 Idle speed adjustment screw (arrowed) - 15D and 15DT engines

13.21 Adjusting idle speed - 17DT engine

16 Start the engine and run it until it reaches normal operating temperature.
17 With the engine at idle speed, observe the tachometer reading and compare it with the figure specified. If the idle speed is incorrect, adjust it as follows.

Adjustment

18 If adjustment is necessary, slacken the idle speed adjustment screw locknut and turn the screw until the desired result is obtained **(see illustration)**.
19 On completion, tighten the locknut without moving the screw.

17DT engine

Checking

20 Proceed as detailed for the 15D and 15DT engines, noting the idle speed figure specified for the 17DT engine.

Adjustment

21 If adjustment is necessary, slacken the idle speed adjustment screw locknut and turn the screw until the desired result is obtained **(see illustration)**.
22 On completion, tighten the locknut without moving the screw.

14 Maximum speed check and adjustment

Note: *Fuel injection pumps have their maximum speed adjustment screw locked with a lead seal which must be removed for adjustment. As the screw should ideally be resealed after adjustment, it may be beneficial to leave this operation to a Bosch or Lucas/CAV specialist.*

15D, 15DT and 17DT engines

1 Measure the engine speed by using the following method. Do not vary from this procedure, since there is a grave risk of injury or damage should anything go wrong.
2 Clean the outer rim of the crankshaft pulley and mark it by using a 1 to 2 cm wide piece of aluminium foil, as shown in illustration 13.14.
3 Set up an optical or pulse-sensitive tachometer to read the engine speed.
4 Start the engine and run it until it reaches normal operating temperature.
5 Gradually increase the engine speed, observing the tachometer reading until the maximum speed is reached. Do not accelerate the engine much beyond the specified maximum, should maladjustment make this possible.
6 If adjustment is necessary, remove the lead seal from the maximum speed adjustment screw, slacken its locknut and turn the screw until the desired result is obtained. On completion, tighten the locknut without moving the screw.

17D engine

Bosch VE fuel injection pump

7 Refer to Section 11 for ways of measuring engine speed. It is unwise to use the speedometer method, since there is a grave risk of injury or damage should anything go wrong.
8 Start the engine and gradually increase its speed, observing the tachometer or its equivalent until the governed maximum speed is reached. Do not accelerate the engine much beyond the specified maximum, should maladjustment make this possible.
9 If adjustment is necessary, remove the air cleaner snorkel to improve access. Slacken the locknut and turn the maximum speed adjuster screw until the desired result is obtained, then tighten the locknut without moving the screw **(see illustration)**. Refit the snorkel.

14.9 Adjusting maximum speed - 17D engine

Lucas/CAV fuel injection pump

10 Maximum (cut-off) speed is set in production, using the cut-off speed stop screw **(see illustration)**. The screw is sealed with lead after adjustment has been made. As with all injection pumps it is not normally necessary to disturb the cut-off speed setting in normal circumstances, but if adjustment is necessary, it is recommended that this be carried out by a Lucas/CAV injection specialist.

17DR and 17DTL engines

Bosch VE fuel injection pump

11 The procedure for adjustment of the maximum speed is the same as described for the 17D engine. The location of the adjustment screw is as shown **(see illustration)**.

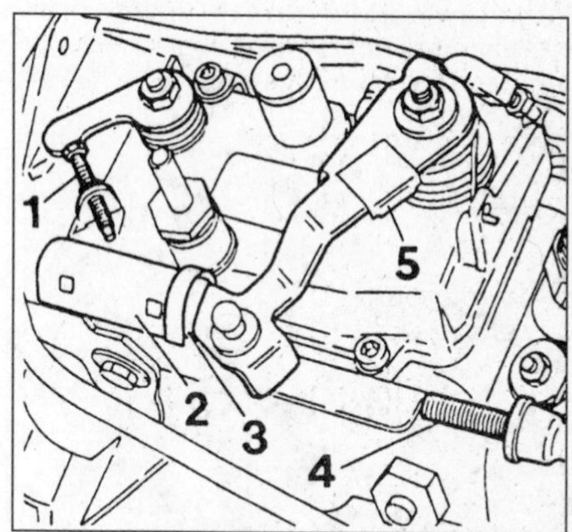

14.10 Adjustment points - Lucas/CAV injection pump

1. *Idle speed stop screw*
2. *Plastic anti-tamper cap*
3. *Engine speed control lever stop screw - do not disturb*
4. *Cut-off speed stop screw*
5. *Timing value for individual pump (marked on plate)*

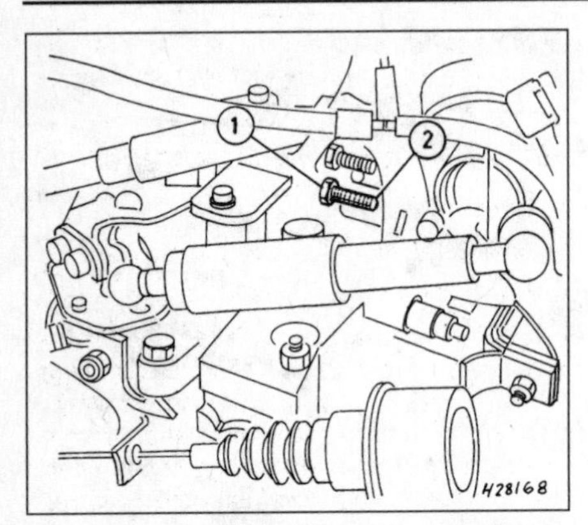

14.11 Bosch VE injection pump maximum speed adjustment screw location - 17DR and 17DTL engines
1 Locknut 2 Adjustment screw

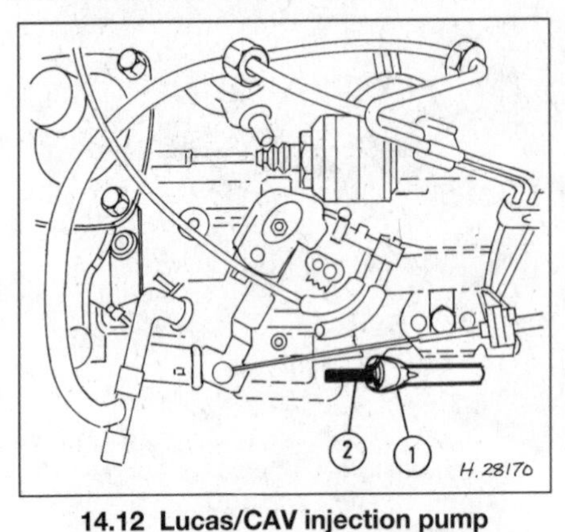

14.12 Lucas/CAV injection pump maximum speed adjustment screw location - 17DR and 17DTL engines
1 Lead seal 2 Cut-off speed stop screw

Lucas/CAV fuel injection pump

12 The procedure for adjustment of the maximum speed is the same as described for the 17D engine. The location of the adjustment screw is as shown **(see illustration)**.

15 Exhaust emission check

15D, 15DT, 17D, 17DR, 17DTL and 17DT engines

Refer to Chapter 2, Part A, Section 10.

16 Fuel filter water drainage

15D, 15DT, 17D, 17DR, 17DTL and 17DT engines

Refer to Section 8.

18 000 mile (30 000 km) Service

17 Camshaft drivebelt condition and tension check

16D and 16DA engines, schedules A and B

Inspection

1 Remove the alternator drivebelt.

2 Remove the camshaft drivebelt covers. The large cover is secured by four screws - note the fuel pipe clip under one of them. The injection pump sprocket cover is secured by three screws **(see illustration)**. On 1987 models, the covers completely enclose the drivebelt and additional clamps and gaskets are fitted.

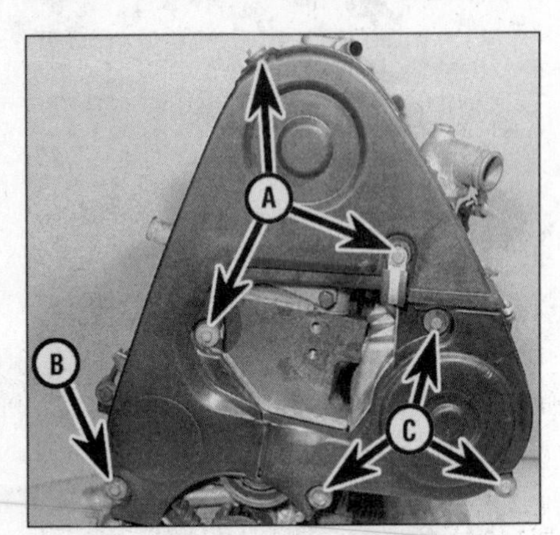

17.2 Camshaft drivebelt cover screw location - 16D engine
A Large cover - short screws
B Large cover - long screw
C Pump sprocket cover screws

3 Turn the engine using a spanner on the crankshaft pulley bolt, removing the right-hand front wheel for access if necessary. Inspect the belt for damage or contamination. Pay particular attention to the roots of the teeth where cracking may occur. Renew the belt if it is damaged or contaminated. If necessary, attend to the source of contamination.

Tensioning

4 Belt tension can only be adjusted accurately using tension gauge KM-510-A or equivalent **(see illustration)**. If this gauge is not available, an approximation to the correct tension can be achieved by tensioning the belt so that it can just be twisted through 90° by thumb and forefinger in the middle of its longest run. A belt which is too tight will usually hum when running and a belt which is too slack will wear rapidly and may jump teeth. Use of a proper tension gauge is strongly recommended.

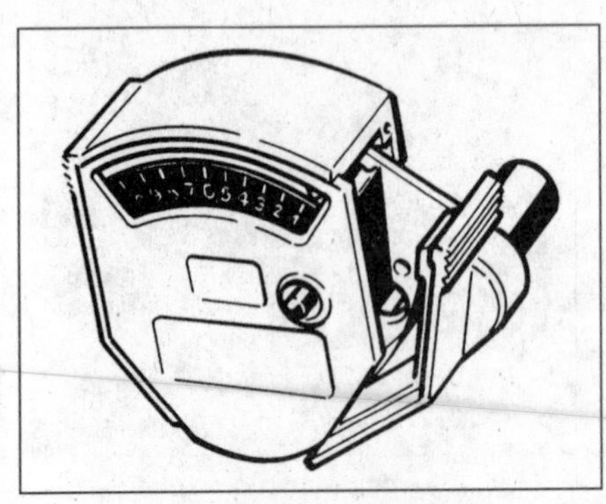

17.4 Camshaft drivebelt tension gauge

5 Settle the belt by rotating the crankshaft through half a turn in the normal direction of rotation. Fit the tension gauge to the slack side of the belt (the alternator side) and read the tension. Desired values are given in the Specifications.

6 If adjustment is necessary, slacken the coolant pump bolts and pivot the pump to increase or decrease the tension. Nip up the coolant pump bolts.

7 Turn the crankshaft through one full turn, then recheck the tension. Keep adjusting the belt tension until a stable value is obtained.

8 Tighten the coolant pump bolts to the specified torque.

9 If the drivebelt has been re-tensioned or renewed, check the injection pump timing.

10 Refit the belt covers, clutch/flywheel cover and other disturbed components.

11 Refit the roadwheel, lower the vehicle and tighten the wheel bolts.

17DR and 17DTL engines

Inspection

12 The camshaft drivebelt cover is a two-piece assembly, it being necessary to remove the upper part prior to removal of the lower part.

13 Remove the auxiliary drivebelt(s) and the air cleaner assembly for access to the drivebelt cover. Where applicable, remove the power steering drivebelt.

14 To remove the upper part of the cover, undo the five securing bolts and lift it off the engine **(see illustration)**.

17.14 Removing camshaft drivebelt upper cover - 17DR engine

17.16 Removing camshaft drivebelt lower cover (crankshaft pulley removed) - 17DR engine

15 From under the front wheel arch, undo the four crankshaft pulley retaining bolts and withdraw the pulley from the drivebelt sprocket.
16 Undo the remaining three bolts and remove the lower part of the cover from the engine **(see illustration)**.
17 Turn the engine using a spanner on the crankshaft pulley bolt, removing the right-hand front wheel for access if necessary. Inspect the belt for damage or contamination. Pay particular attention to the roots of the teeth, where cracking may occur. Renew the belt if it is damaged or contaminated. If necessary, attend to the source of contamination.

Tensioning

18 A spring-loaded automatic camshaft drivebelt tensioner is fitted to this engine. The tensioner automatically sets the drivebelt to the correct tension on assembly and maintains that tension for the life of the drivebelt.

18 Fuel filter element renewal

16D and 16DA engines, schedules B and C

Refer to Section 12.

19 Fuel filter element renewal

15D and 15DT engines

Removal

1 Because of its location in the engine bay and the fitting of a heat shield around it, access to the fuel filter element is extremely restricted **(see illustration)**. To facilitate removal of the filter element, it is therefore necessary to withdraw the filter assembly from its heat shield.
2 Commence by disconnecting the battery earth (negative) lead.
3 Where fitted, unplug the wiring connectors from the heating element and temperature sensor.
4 Clean around the pipe unions and disconnect both fuel pipes from the filter element carrier. Renew the union sealing washers.
5 Blank off the exposed pipe connections to prevent any ingress of dirt and moisture.
6 Undo the filter assembly retaining nuts and withdraw the assembly from its heat shield.
7 Drain all water/fuel from the filter and dispose of it safely, whilst observing the usual safety precautions.
8 Grip the filter head carefully between the padded jaws of a vice and unscrew the element by using a chain or strap wrench.

Fitting

9 Fitting a filter element is a reversal of the removal procedure. Lightly smear the sealing ring of the new element with clean Diesel fuel before fitting.
10 Offer the element to its carrier and tighten it with firm hand pressure or as directed by the manufacturer.
11 Refit the filter assembly to its heat shield.
12 Remove all blanking materials and reconnect both fuel pipes to the filter element carrier, using new sealing washers.
13 Reconnect all electrical connections.

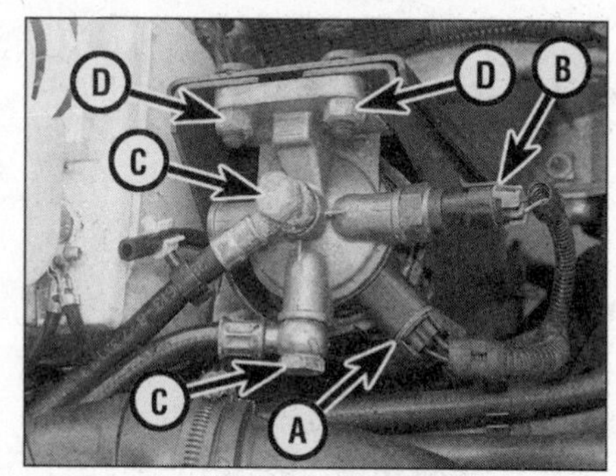

19.1 Fuel filter assembly - 15D and 15DT engines

A Heating element connector
B Temperature sensor connector
C Fuel pipe unions
D Retaining nuts

14 Start the engine and run it at a fast idle for a minute or so to vent the fuel system. Check the filter seal for leaks.

17D, 17DR and 17DTL engines

Unheated filter

15 Refer to Section 12.

Heated filter

16 This filter type can be dealt with as described for the unheated type. Depending on accessibility, it may be easier to withdraw the assembly from its heat shield and place it in a vice to facilitate unscrewing of the filter element. Refer to the procedure given for the 15D and 15DT engines.

17DT engine

Removal

17 Drain all water/fuel from the filter and dispose of it safely, whilst observing the usual safety precautions.
18 Unscrew the filter element with the aid of a chain or strap wrench. Discard the old element, making sure that no sealing ring has been left behind on the filter carrier.

Fitting

19 Lightly smear the sealing ring of the new filter element with clean fuel before fitting.
20 Offer the element to its carrier **(see illustration)** and tighten it with firm hand pressure or as directed by the manufacturer.
21 Start the engine and run it at a fast idle for a minute or so to vent the system. Check around the filter seal for leaks, tightening a little further if necessary.

20 Valve clearance check

15D, 15DT and 17DT engines

Note: *Never attempt to carry out valve clearance adjustment with the pistons at TDC as there is a possibility of the valves striking the piston crown.*

Checking

1 The engine must be cold when checking the valve clearances.

19.20 Refitting fuel filter element - 17DT engine

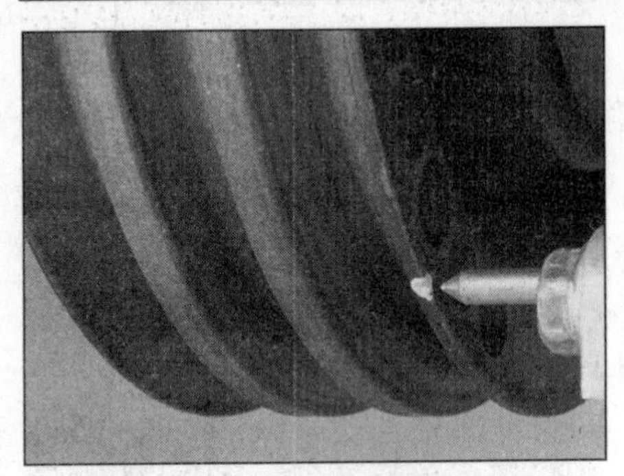

20.6 Crankshaft pulley timing mark aligned with engine block reference pointer - 17DT engine

20.7 Using a feeler blade to measure valve clearance - 17DT engine

20.11 Use flat of a large screwdriver to depress valve lifter and then remove shim

20.12 Shim thickness marking

2 The engine can be turned over by placing the engine in gear and rocking the vehicle back and forth. It will be easier to turn if the fuel injectors or glow plugs are removed.

3 The following procedure is for the valves of No 1 cylinder and should be repeated for the valves of the other three cylinders in the firing order of 1-3-4-2.

4 Remove the cylinder head cover (with attached baffle plate) to expose the camshaft. Obtain a new cover gasket.

5 The Manufacturers recommend that the camshaft bearing cap retaining nuts are now checked for tightness to the specified torque setting.

6 Turn the crankshaft in the normal direction of rotation until the timing mark on its pulley aligns with the reference pointer on the engine block **(see illustration)**. In this position No 1 piston is at TDC on the firing stroke and the two cams of that cylinder are positioned with both valves closed.

7 Using feeler blades, measure the clearances between the Inlet and Exhaust cams and their respective shims **(see illustration)**. The blade should be a stiff sliding fit in the gap. The valve sequence from the timing side of the engine is:

In - Ex - In - Ex - In - Ex - In - Ex

8 Each clearance should be equal to that specified. Should a clearance be incorrect, adjust as follows:

Adjustment

9 Turn the crankshaft until the tip of the cam of the valve to be adjusted is pointing upwards.

10 Rotate the valve lifter so that its groove points towards the front of the engine.

11 Depress the lifter by using GM tool KM - 650 or alternatively, the flat of a large screwdriver placed carefully between the edge of the lifter and the camshaft. With the lifter depressed, use the flat of a small screwdriver to flip the shim out of the lifter (a magnetic pick-up tool is particularly useful for this task) **(see illustration)**.

12 Use the following formulae for determining the thickness of the replacement shim **(see illustration)**:

Thickness of original fitted shim:	*3.25 mm*
Plus measured valve clearance of:	*0.25 mm*
Equalling:	*3.50 mm*
Minus specified valve clearance of:	*0.15 mm*
Equals thickness of new shim:	*3.35 mm*

13 Once selected, the replacement shim should be coated in clean engine oil and fitted in the depressed lifter with its size mark facing downwards.

14 With the valve clearances of all four cylinders checked and if necessary, adjusted, turn the engine over and recheck the adjusted clearances

15 On completion, refit the cylinder head cover with a new gasket.

27 000 mile (45 000 km) Service

21 Camshaft drivebelt condition and tension check

16D and 16DA engines, schedule C for adverse operating conditions

Refer to Section 17.

36 000 mile (60 000 km) Service

22 Camshaft drivebelt condition and tension check

16D and 16DA engines, schedule C for normal operating conditions

1 Refer to Section 17.

17D engine

2 The camshaft drivebelt arrangement employed on this engine is largely unchanged from its predecessors and as such can be dealt with as described in Section 17 for the 16D and 16DA engines. Note however, that revisions to the belt covers and air filter assembly dictate some changes of approach.

3 Both the Cavalier and the Astra/Belmont models have a new air filter system, with a remote filter housing attached to the inner wing area at the right-hand side of the engine bay. To gain access to the drivebelt covers, it will be necessary to remove the filter housing.

4 Two versions of the moulded plastic drivebelt covers have been used since the introduction of this engine, the later version being identified by the squared-off top surface of the outer belt cover. On the earlier version, a screwdriver blade can be used to release the outer cover retaining clips and the cover sections can then be removed as required to gain access to the drivebelt. On the later version, the method of retention is by bolts instead of clips. This arrangement is, in fact, the same as used on the 17DR engine.

23 Camshaft drivebelt condition check

15D and 15DT engines

1 The drivebelt cover is a two-piece assembly, it being necessary to remove the upper part for drivebelt inspection.

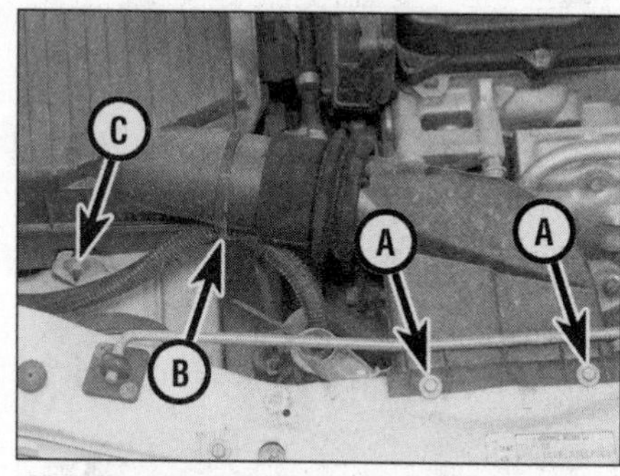

23.9 Remove air intake collector box inlet scoop securing screws (A) unclip cable loom (B) and release box front mounting nut (C) - 17DT engine in Astra

2 Gain access to the drivebelt cover by first removing the air cleaner housing from its mounting on the right-hand side of the engine bay. Do this by first detaching the outlet tube retaining clamp at the engine manifold. Release the housing inlet scoop from the vehicle front crossmember and manoeuvre it clear of the housing. Disconnect the front retainer at the housing base and pull the housing forward to release it from its rear retainer.

3 Where necessary, release the brake servo vacuum line retaining clamp from the cover and pull the line from the servo unit, moving it to one side. Move any electrical cables clear of the drivebelt cover after having released their respective retaining clamps.

4 Remove the upper part of the drivebelt cover by undoing its securing bolts (noting their respective lengths) and lifting it from position.

5 With the drivebelt thus exposed, turn the engine and inspect the belt for damage or contamination. Pay particular attention to the roots of the teeth, where cracking may occur. Renew the belt if it is damaged or contaminated. If necessary, attend to the source of contamination.

17DT engine

6 The drivebelt cover is a two-piece assembly, it being necessary to remove the upper part for drivebelt inspection.

7 Gain access to the drivebelt cover by first removing the air intake collector box from its mounting on the right-hand side of the engine bay. Proceed as follows:

Cavalier

8 Remove the box lid retaining screws and clips and the outlet tube retaining clamp at the engine air filter box. With the lid removed, remove the box retaining nuts and release the box inlet tube to allow the box to be lifted from position, unclipping the alternator cable ties if necessary. Note that the inlet tube may be a very tight fit on the box stub, ensure that the retaining tangs are fully depressed before attempting to release the tube **(see illustrations)**.

Astra

9 Release the box inlet scoop from the vehicle front crossmember by removing its two securing screws and then pull it clear of the box inlet stub. Unclip the cable loom from the inlet stub **(see illustration)**. Release the outlet tube retaining clamp at the engine air filter box. Release the box mounting nuts at its base and lift the box from the vehicle.

Both models

10 Release the brake servo vacuum line retaining clamp and pull the line from the servo unit **(see illustrations)**.

11 Remove the upper part of the drivebelt cover by undoing its nine securing bolts

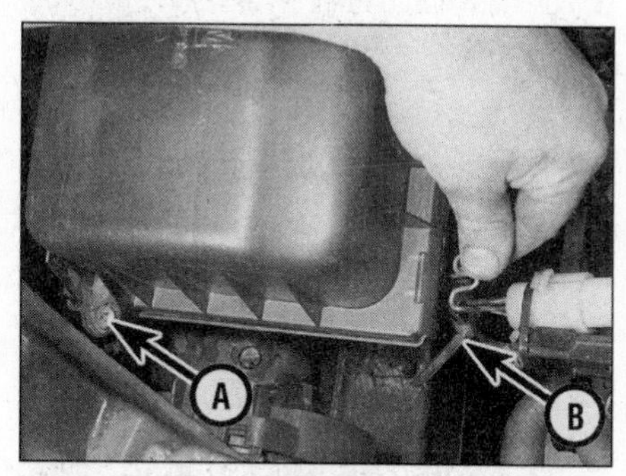

23.8a Release air intake collector box lid retaining clips, screws (A) and alternator cable ties (B) . . .

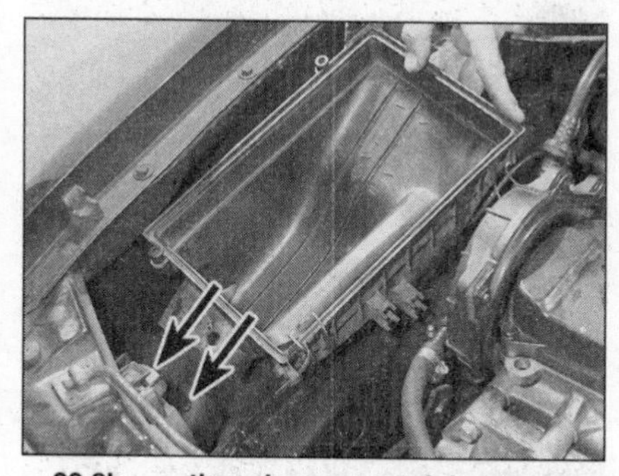

23.8b . . . then depress retaining tangs (arrowed) before releasing collector box - 17DT engine in Cavalier

23.10a Release brake servo vacuum line retaining clamp (arrowed) . . .

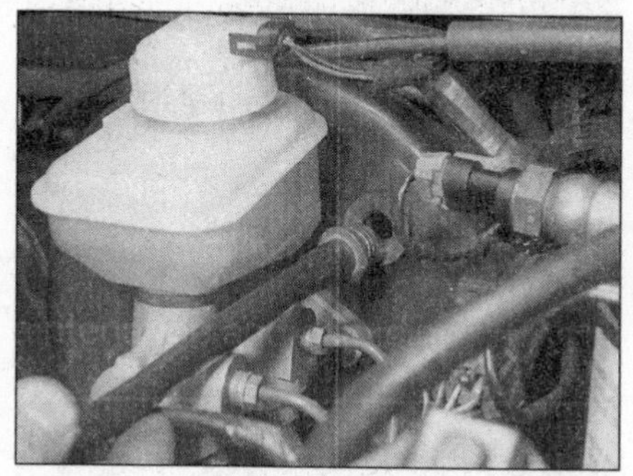

23.10b . . . and pull line from servo unit - 17DT engine

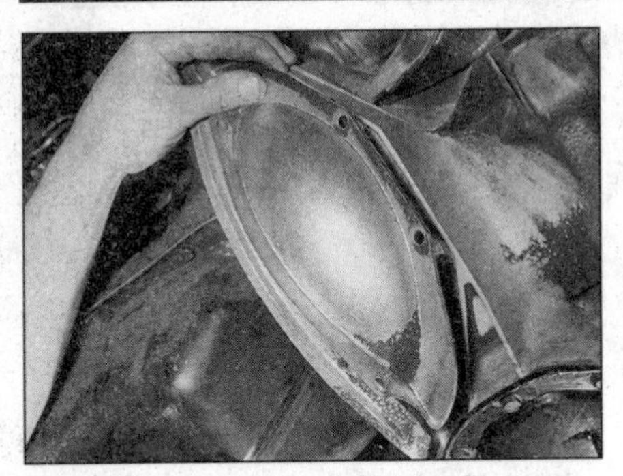

24.3 Removing clutch/flywheel access cover - 16D engine

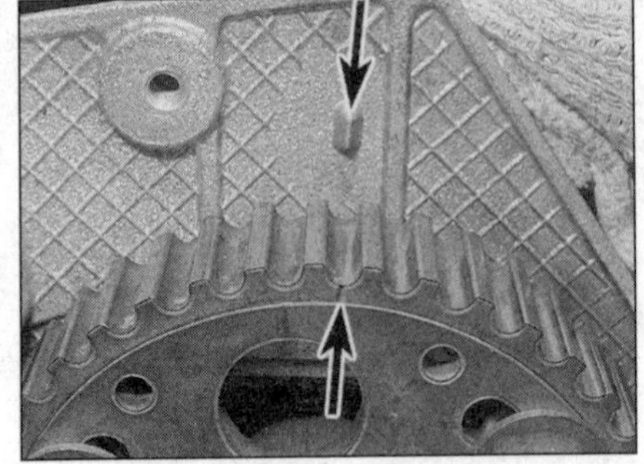

24.4 Injection pump sprocket timing mark aligned with mark on pump bracket - 16D engine

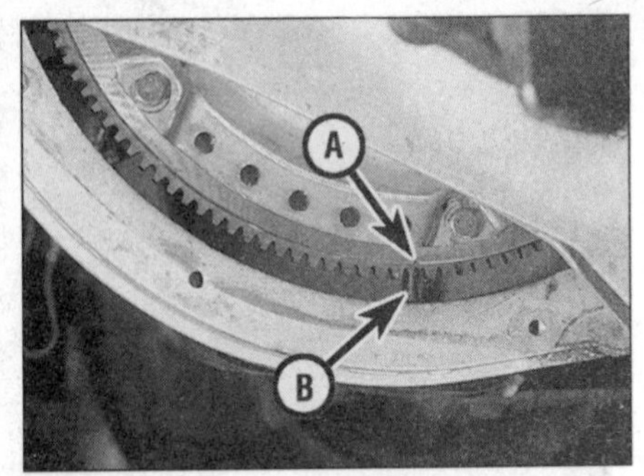

24.5 TDC mark on flywheel (A) and pointer on clutch housing (B) - 16D engine

(noting their respective lengths) and lifting it from position.

12 With the drivebelt thus exposed, turn the engine and inspect the belt for damage or contamination. Pay particular attention to the roots of the teeth, where cracking may occur. Renew the belt if it is damaged or contaminated. If necessary, attend to the source of contamination.

24 Camshaft drivebelt renewal

16D and 16DA engines, schedules A and B

Removal

1 With the drivebelt covers removed (see Section 17), remove the crankshaft pulley. It is secured to the sprocket by four Allen screws.

2 Disconnect the battery earth lead.

3 Remove the clutch/flywheel access cover from the bottom of the gearbox bellhousing **(see illustration)**.

4 Turn the crankshaft in the normal direction of rotation, using a spanner on the sprocket bolt, until the timing mark on the injection pump sprocket aligns with the reference mark on the pump bracket. In this position No 1 piston is at TDC on the firing stroke **(see illustration)**.

5 Check that the TDC mark on the flywheel and the pointer on the clutch housing are aligned **(see illustration)**.

6 If tool KM-537 or equivalent is available, remove the vacuum pump and lock the camshaft in position by fitting the tool. If the tool is not available or cannot be fitted, make alignment marks between the camshaft sprocket and its backplate for use when refitting.

7 Slacken the three bolts which secure the coolant pump to the block **(see illustration)**. Using a large open-ended spanner on the flats of the pump, pivot it to release the tension on the belt.

8 Separate the right-hand front engine mounting by undoing the two bolts which are accessible from the top.

24.7 Undoing coolant pump bolt - other two arrowed (engine removed) - 16D engine

9 Slip the belt off the sprockets and jockey wheel. Remove the belt by feeding it through the engine mounting.

Fitting

10 Commence fitting by threading the belt through the engine mounting. Refit and tighten the engine mounting bolts.

11 Place the belt over the sprockets and the jockey wheel **(see illustration)**. Make sure that No 1 piston is still at TDC, the injection pump sprocket mark is aligned and the camshaft position is still correct.

12 Move the coolant pump so as to put some tension on the drivebelt. Nip up the pump securing bolts but do not tighten them fully yet.

13 Remove the camshaft locking tool, if used, and refit and secure the crankshaft pulley.

Tensioning

14 Refer to Section 17.

17DR and 17DTL engines

Removal

15 This procedure is essentially the same as described for the 16D and 16DA engines, except that it is not necessary to remove the engine mounting, nor to slacken the coolant pump mounting bolts and move the pump to adjust the belt tension. Instead, belt adjustment is catered for by means of the automatic tensioner, as follows.

24.11 Camshaft drivebelt correctly fitted - 16D engine

16 Remove the drivebelt covers **(see illustrations)**.

17 To release the belt tension prior to removal, unscrew the drivebelt tensioner securing bolt slightly then, with a suitable Allen key inserted in the slot on the tensioner arm, turn the tensioner arm until the timing belt is slack **(see illustration)**. Tighten the securing bolt slightly to hold the tensioner in this position. The drivebelt can now be removed.

Fitting

18 Prior to fitting the drivebelt, first ensure that the coolant pump is correctly positioned by checking that the lug on the pump flange is aligned with the corresponding lug on the

24.16a Remove five retaining bolts to release camshaft drivebelt upper cover - 17DR engine

24.16b Remove crankshaft pulley (viewed through front wheel arch) . . .

24.16c . . . and remove retaining bolts (arrowed) to release camshaft drivebelt lower cover - 17DR engine

24.17 Release drivebelt tensioner securing bolt, then turn tensioner arm until belt is slack - 17DR engine

cylinder block. If this is not the case, slacken the pump mounting bolts slightly and move the pump accordingly. Tighten the bolts to the specified torque on completion.

19 Fit the drivebelt, ensuring that No 1 piston is still at TDC, that the injection pump sprocket mark is still aligned and the camshaft position is still correct **(see illustration)**. On 17DTL engines, flywheel position for TDC must be determined by the use of a setting tool (Adjuster KM-851) fitted next to the flywheel as shown **(see illustration)**.

Tensioning

20 Tension the belt by first slackening the automatic tensioner securing bolt and moving the tensioner arm anti-clockwise until the tensioner pointer is at its stop. Tighten the tensioner securing bolt to hold the tensioner in this position.

21 Turn the crankshaft through two complete revolutions in the normal direction of rotation until No 1 piston is once again at the TDC

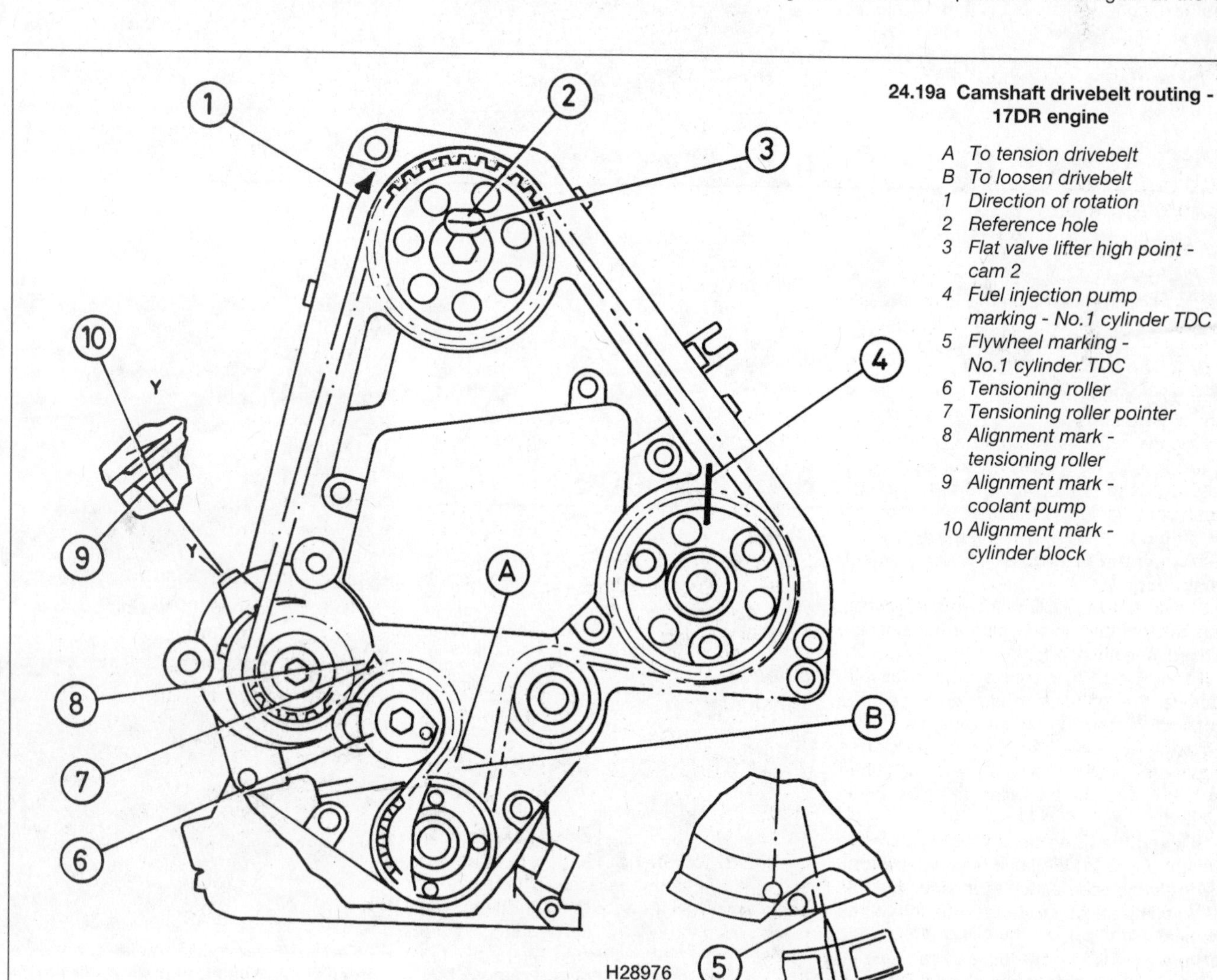

24.19a Camshaft drivebelt routing - 17DR engine

A To tension drivebelt
B To loosen drivebelt
1 Direction of rotation
2 Reference hole
3 Flat valve lifter high point - cam 2
4 Fuel injection pump marking - No.1 cylinder TDC
5 Flywheel marking - No.1 cylinder TDC
6 Tensioning roller
7 Tensioning roller pointer
8 Alignment mark - tensioning roller
9 Alignment mark - coolant pump
10 Alignment mark - cylinder block

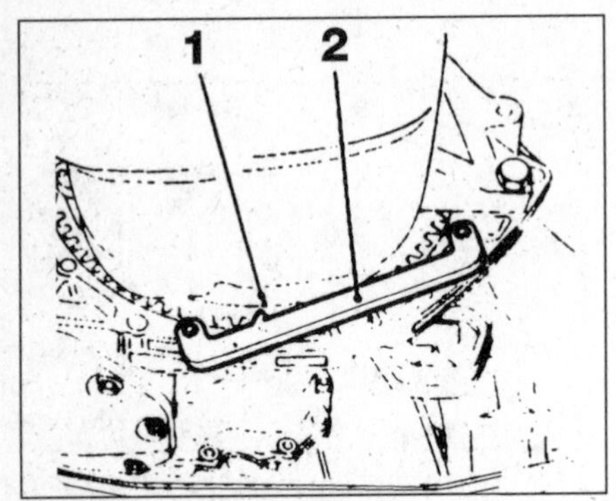

24.19b Determine flywheel position for TDC by use of setting tool KM-851 - 17DTL engine

1 Flywheel marking - No.1 cylinder TDC
2 Setting tool

position. Check that the injection pump sprocket and camshaft sprocket positions are still correct.

22 Slacken the automatic tensioner securing bolt once again and move the tensioner arm until the tensioner pointer and tensioner bracket notch coincide **(see illustration)**. Tighten the tensioner securing bolt securely.

23 Check the valve timing and injection pump timing.

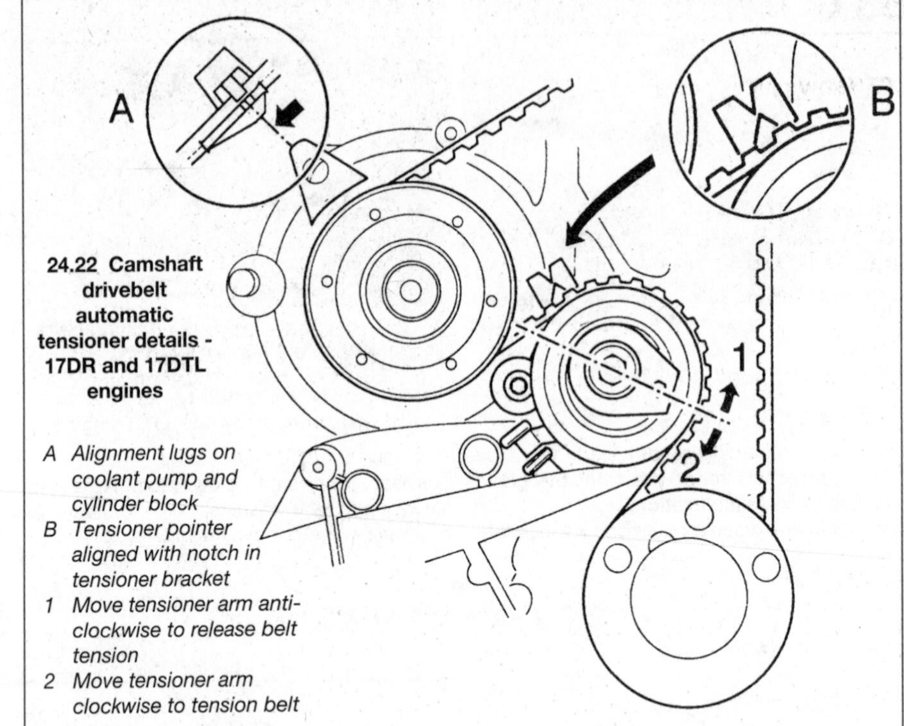

24.22 Camshaft drivebelt automatic tensioner details - 17DR and 17DTL engines

A Alignment lugs on coolant pump and cylinder block
B Tensioner pointer aligned with notch in tensioner bracket
1 Move tensioner arm anti-clockwise to release belt tension
2 Move tensioner arm clockwise to tension belt

54 000 mile (90 000 km) Service

25 Camshaft drivebelt renewal

16D and 16DA engines, schedule C for adverse operating conditions

Refer to Section 24.

60 000 mile (100 000 km) Service

26 Glow plug renewal

16D and 16DA engines, schedule A

Removal

1 Disconnect the battery earth lead.

2 Remove the air cleaner snorkel.

3 Disconnect the feed wire from the glow plug bus bar **(see illustration)**.

4 Unscrew the retaining nuts and remove the bus bar and link wire from each glow plug **(see illustration)**. Note the disposition of the washers.

5 Unscrew and remove the glow plugs **(see illustration)**.

Fitting

6 Refit in the reverse order of removal. Tighten the glow plugs to the specified torque and make sure that the electrical connections are clean and tight.

26.3 Disconnect glow plug bus bar feed wire . . .

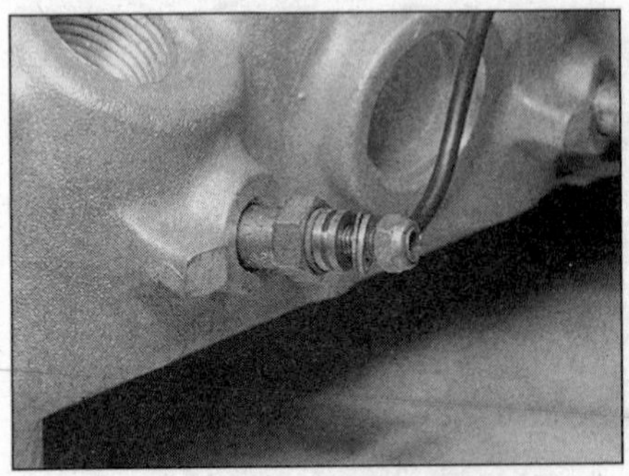

26.4 . . . unscrew the nuts and remove bus bar and link wire from each glow plug . . .

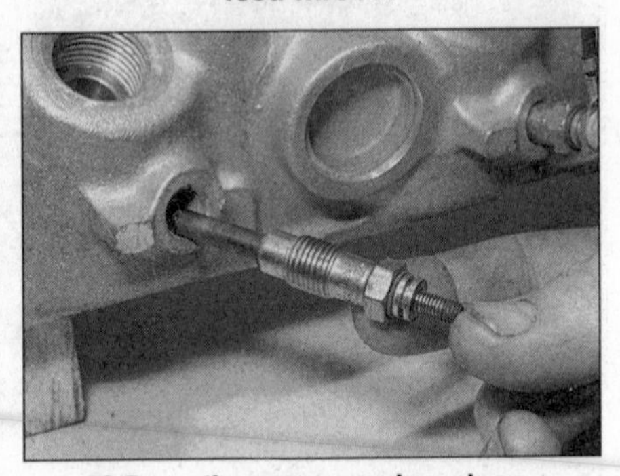

26.5 . . . then remove glow plugs - 16D engine

63 000 mile (105 000 km) Service

27 Glow plug renewal

16D and 16DA engines, schedules B and C, 17D, 17DR and 17DTL engines

1 Refer to Section 26.

15D, 15DT and 17DT engines

Removal

2 Disconnect the battery earth lead.
3 Disconnect the feed wire from the glow plug bus bar **(see illustration)**.
4 Unscrew the retaining nuts and remove the bus bar from each glow plug. Note the disposition of the washers.
5 Unscrew and remove the glow plugs.

27.3 Disconnecting glow plug bus bar feed wire. Plug arrowed - 17DT engine

Fitting

6 Refit in the reverse order of removal. Tighten the glow plugs to the specified torque and make sure that the electrical connections are clean and tight.

28 Camshaft drivebelt renewal

16D and 16DA engines, schedule C for normal operating conditions

Refer to Section 24.

72 000 mile (120 000 km) Service

29 Camshaft drivebelt renewal

17D engine

1 The camshaft drivebelt arrangement employed on this engine is largely unchanged from its predecessors and as such can be dealt with as described in Section 24 for 16D and 16DA engines. Note, however, that revisions to the belt covers and air filter assembly dictate some changes of approach when working on the drivebelt components.
2 Both the Cavalier and the Astra/Belmont models have a new air filter system, with a remote filter housing attached to the inner wing area at the right-hand side of the engine bay. To gain access to the drivebelt covers, it will be necessary to remove the filter housing.
3 Two versions of the moulded plastic drivebelt covers have been used since the introduction of this engine, the later version being identified by the squared-off top surface of the outer belt cover. On the earlier version, a screwdriver blade can be used to release the outer cover retaining clips and the cover sections can then be removed as required to gain access to the drivebelt. On the later version, the method of retention is by bolts instead of clips. This arrangement is, in fact, the same as used on the 17DR engine.

15D and 15DT engines

Removal

4 Disconnect the battery earth lead and remove the drivebelt upper cover.
5 Gain access to the side of the engine through the right-hand wheel arch.
6 Support the engine by positioning a jack beneath its sump and raising it slightly. Protect the sump by placing a piece of thick wood between it and the jack.
7 Remove the engine right-hand mounting assembly.
8 Where applicable, slacken the power steering pump upper and lower retaining bolts to allow the pump to be moved towards the engine. With the V-belt slackened, detach it from the crankshaft, coolant pump and power steering pump pulleys.
9 Slacken the alternator pivot and retaining bolts and move it towards the engine. With the V-belt slackened, detach it from the crankshaft, coolant pump and alternator pulleys.
10 Turn the crankshaft in the normal direction of rotation until the timing mark on its pulley aligns with the reference pointer on the engine block **(see illustration)**. In this position No 1 piston is at TDC on the firing stroke.
11 Now check that the locking bolt holes in the camshaft and fuel injection pump sprockets are aligned with their respective threaded holes in the engine casing before inserting the locking bolts (bolt sizes M6 x 1.00 for camshaft and M8 x 1.25 for injection pump) **(see illustrations)**.
12 Mark the fitted position of the crankshaft pulley. Remove the pulley retaining bolts and detach the pulley, gently tapping its rim to free it if necessary.

29.10 Align timing mark on crankshaft pulley with reference pointer on engine block to bring No 1 piston to TDC on firing stroke - 15DT engine

29.11a Insert locking bolt (arrowed) through camshaft sprocket . . .

29.11b . . . and insert locking bolt through injection pump sprocket - 15DT engine

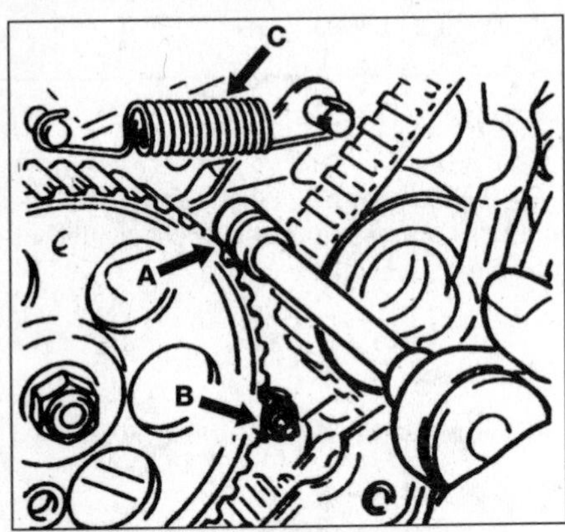

29.14 Release camshaft drivebelt tensioner pulley securing bolts (A and B) and remove spring (C) - 15DT engine

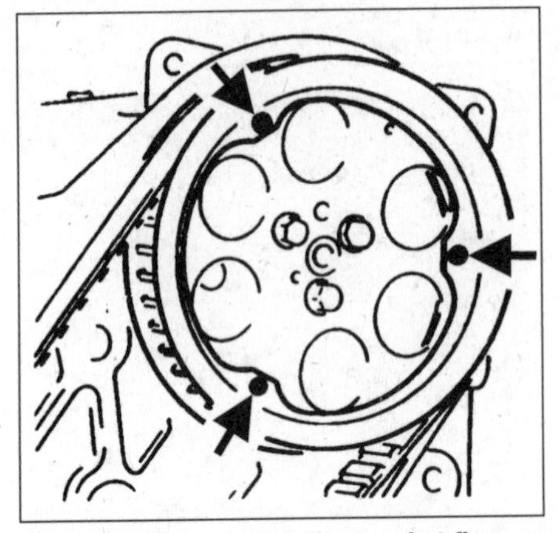
29.15 Remove camshaft sprocket flange securing screws (arrowed) - 15DT engine

13 Remove the lower part of the drivebelt cover to fully expose the belt.
14 Release the drivebelt tensioner pulley and remove the spring **(see illustration)**.
15 Unbolt the flange from the camshaft sprocket **(see illustration)**. Slip the belt off the sprocket and then the remaining sprockets to remove it from the engine.

Fitting and tensioning

16 Place the drivebelt over the camshaft sprocket and then the injection pump sprocket etc., until it is correctly routed **(see illustration)**. The crankshaft must not be disturbed and the camshaft and fuel injection pump sprockets should still be locked in alignment. Refit the flange to the camshaft sprocket
17 Remove the camshaft and fuel injection pump sprocket alignment bolts.
18 Refit the drivebelt tensioner spring and check that the tensioner assembly moves freely before tightening the tensioner securing bolts to the specified torque setting **(see illustration)**.

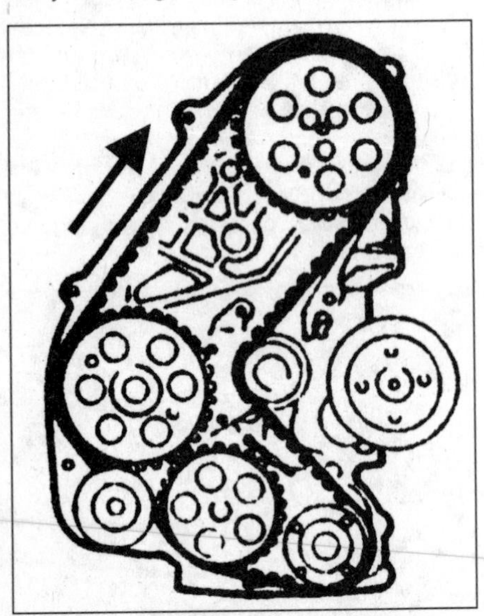
29.16 Ensure camshaft drivebelt is correctly routed - 15DT engine
Arrow denotes direction of belt travel

19 Refit the lower part of the drivebelt cover to the engine, renewing any damaged sealing strips and tightening the retaining bolts to the specified torque setting.
20 Refit the crankshaft pulley in its previously noted position, tightening its retaining bolts to the specified torque setting.
21 Refit and tension each auxiliary drivebelt.
22 Refit the engine right-hand mounting in the reverse sequence to removal, tightening all retaining bolts to the specified torque settings.
23 Refit the upper part of the drivebelt cover, renewing any damaged sealing strips and tightening the retaining bolts to the specified torque setting.
24 Refit all other removed components.
25 Remove the jack from beneath the engine and reconnect the battery earth lead.

17DT engine

Note: *The procedure described in this Section relates to one particular vehicle, therefore allowances must be made for individual model and year variations. Reference to the under-bonnet views will show detail differences of hose and cable routing etc.*

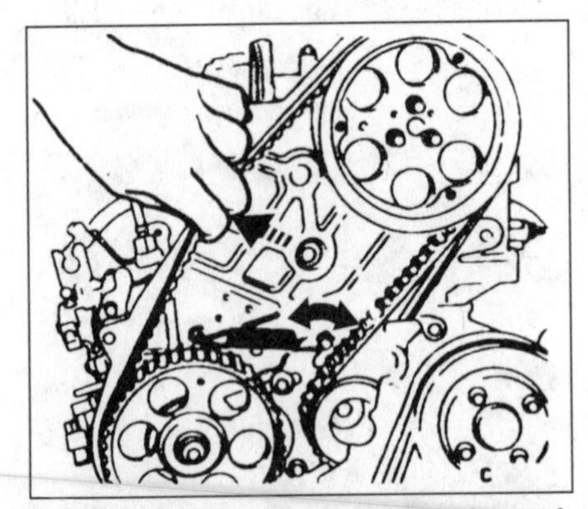
29.18 Refit drivebelt tensioner spring and check tensioner assembly moves freely before tightening tensioner securing bolts - 15DT engine

Removal

26 Disconnect the battery earth lead.
27 Remove the drivebelt upper cover.
28 Turn the steering wheel so that access to the side of the engine can be gained through the right-hand wheel arch, in front of the roadwheel.
29 Support the engine by positioning a jack beneath its sump and raising it slightly. Protect the sump by placing a piece of thick wood between it and the jack.
30 Remove the engine right-hand mounting by first removing its two centre bolts. Remove the two mounting to vehicle body retaining bolts and then the three mounting to engine bolts to allow the complete mounting assembly to be withdrawn.
31 Slacken the power steering pump upper and lower retaining bolts to allow the pump to be moved towards the engine. With the V-belt slackened, detach it from the crankshaft, coolant pump and power steering pump pulleys.
32 Slacken the alternator pivot and retaining bolts and move it towards the engine. With the V-belt slackened, detach it from the crankshaft, coolant pump and alternator pulleys.
33 Turn the crankshaft in the normal direction of rotation until the timing mark on its pulley aligns with the reference pointer on the engine block - see illustration 29.10. In this position No 1 piston is at TDC on the firing stroke.
34 Now check that the locking bolt holes in the camshaft and fuel injection pump sprockets are aligned with their respective threaded holes in the engine casing before inserting the locking bolts (bolt sizes M6 x 1.00 for camshaft and M8 x 1.25 for injection pump) - see illustrations 29.11a and 29.11b.
35 Mark the fitted position of the crankshaft pulley. Remove the four pulley retaining bolts and detach the pulley, gently tapping its rim to free it if necessary.
36 Undo the three retaining bolts and remove the lower part of the drivebelt cover from the engine.
37 Release the drivebelt tensioner by loosening the pulley centre bolt, the upper spring bracket securing bolt and the lower pivot securing nut. Push the tensioner spring towards the front of the engine to release belt tension and then nip tight the bracket securing bolt.
38 Slip the belt off the injection pump sprocket first and then the remaining sprockets to remove it from the engine .

Refitting and tensioning

39 Commence refitting by first placing the drivebelt over the camshaft sprocket and then the injection pump sprocket etc. until it is correctly routed - see illustration 29.16. The crankshaft must not be disturbed and the camshaft and fuel injection pump sprockets should still be locked in alignment.
40 Remove the camshaft and fuel injection pump sprocket alignment bolts.

41 Release the tensioner spring bracket securing bolt to allow the tensioner to act upon the drivebelt. Turn the crankshaft against the normal direction of rotation by approximately 60 degrees to automatically tension the drivebelt and then tighten the tensioner pulley centre bolt, the upper spring bracket securing bolt and the lower pivot securing nut to the specified torque settings (where given).

42 Refit the lower part of the drivebelt cover to the engine, renewing any damaged sealing strips and tightening the retaining bolts to the specified torque wrench setting **(see illustration)**.

43 Refit the crankshaft pulley in its previously noted position, tightening the retaining bolts to the specified torque setting.

44 Refit and tension both auxiliary drivebelts.

45 Refit the engine right-hand mounting in the reverse sequence to removal, tightening all retaining bolts to the specified torque settings.

46 Refit the upper part of the drivebelt cover, renewing any damaged sealing strips and tightening the retaining bolts to the specified torque setting.

47 Refit all other removed components.

48 Remove the jack from beneath the engine and reconnect the battery earth lead.

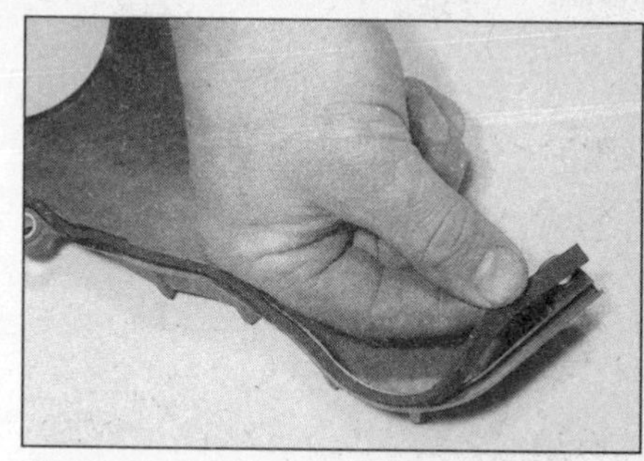

29.42 Checking sealing strip in lower front section of camshaft drivebelt cover - 15DT engine

Chapter 10
Vauxhall/Opel 1488cc, 1598cc,1686cc & 1699cc engines

Part B: Fuel system servicing

Contents

Specifications

Glow plug types

15D engine:	
5 volt system	Champion CH-110, or equivalent
11 volt system	Champion CH-157, or equivalent
15DT engine	Champion CH-158, or equivalent
16D and 16DA engines	Champion CH-68, or equivalent
17D and 17DR engines	Champion CH-68, or equivalent
17DTL engine	Champion CH-158, or equivalent
17DT engine	Champion CH-158, or equivalent

Injectors

15D and 15DT engines	
Type	2 jet - Pintaux
Identification	NP - DN OPD N 108
Opening pressure	142 to 162 bar
16D and 16DA engines	
Identification:	
16D engine (early models)	DN 05D 193
16D engine (later models)	DN 5D 193
16DA engine	Flat pintle type
Opening pressure:	
16D engine (new)	140 to 148 bar
16D engine (used)	135 bar
16DA engine	135 bar
17DT engine	
Type	2 jet - Pintaux
Identification	NP - DN OPD N 122
Opening pressure	142 to 162 bar

Injectors (continued)

17D, 17DR and 17DTL engines

Identification:	
Bosch	DN OSD 309
Lucas/CAV	BDN OSD C 6751 D or RDN OSD C 6751 D
Opening pressure (Bosch and Lucas/CAV):	
New	135 to 143 bar
Used	130 to 138 bar

Fuel injection pump

15D and 15DT engines

Bosch identification:	
15D engine	8 970 786 380 VE R 284
15DT engine	8 970 786 390 VE R 305
Timing:	
15D engine	0.85 to 0.95 mm
15DT engine	0.63 to 0.73 mm

16D and 16DA engines

Identification:	
16D engine (early)	VE 2300 R 82
16D engine (late)	VE 4/9 F 2400 RTV 8253
16DA engine	VE 4/9 F 2300 R 215
Identification of No 1 cylinder union	D
Injection commencement at idle	3 to 5° BTDC
Timing:	
16D engine	1.0 ± 0.05 mm
16DA engine	0.9 ± 0.05 mm

17DT engine

Identification:	
Bosch	9 460 620 007 VE R 365 - 1
Zexel	NP - VE 4/10 F 2200 R 365 - 1
Timing	0.50 to 0.60 mm

17D, 17DR and 17DTL engines

Identification:	
Bosch:	
1989 model year	VE 4/9F 2300 R 313 MT or VE 4/9F 2300 R 313 - 1 AT
1991/ 1992 model year	VE 4/9F 2300 R 443
1993 model year	VE 4/9F 2300 R 487
Lucas/CAV:	
1989 model year	OP 02 DPC R8443 B55 OA
1991/ 1992 model year	OP 02 DPC R8443 B55 OA
1993 model year	OP 03 DPC R8443 B85 OC
Identification of No 1 cylinder union	D
Injection commencement at idle	2° to 4° BTDC
Timing:	
Bosch	0.80 + 0.05 mm
Lucas/CAV	X - 0.15 mm *(where X = manufacturer's calibration marked on pump)*

Idle speed

15D and 15DT engines	830 to 930 rpm
16D and 16DA engines	825 to 875 rpm
17DT engine	780 to 880 rpm
17D engine	820 to 920 rpm
17DR and 17DTL engines:	
Below 20°C	1200 rpm
Above 20°C	850 rpm

Maximum speed

15D engine	5800 rpm
15DT engine	5600 rpm
16D and 16DA engines	5600 rpm
17DT engine	5100 to 5300 rpm
17D, 17DR and 17DTL engines	5500 to 5600 rpm

Torque wrench settings

	Nm	lbf ft
15D and 15DT engines		
Fuel injection pump:		
Pump to cylinder block/flange	25	18
Sprocket to pump	64	47
Injectors:		
Injector nozzle union nut to nozzle	50	38
16D and 16DA engines		
Fuel injection pump:		
Main bracket to block	25	18
Subsidiary brackets - M6 bolts	14	10
Subsidiary brackets - M8 bolts	25	18
Pump sprocket bolts	25	18
Glow plugs	40	30
Injectors to head	70	52
17DT engine		
Fuel injection pump:		
Pump to cylinder block/flange	23	17
Sprocket to pump	70	51
15D, 15DT and 17DT engines		
Fuel injection pump:		
Central vent bolt	20	15
Fuel lines to pump	25	18
Pump to bracket	40	30
Injectors:		
Fuel line to nozzle	25	18
Injector holder to cylinder head	50	38
Injector nozzle to holder	45	33
Return line to injector nozzle holder	30	22
Glow plugs	20	15
17D, 17DR and 17DTL engines		
EGR system:		
Corrugated pipe clamp	4.8	3
Corrugated pipe to exhaust manifold	8	6
Valve to inlet manifold	20	15
Fuel filter:		
Filter to support bracket	25	18
Fuel line to filter	30	22
Thermoswitch to filter	15	11
Fuel injection pump:		
Fuel lines to pump	25	18
Hub to pump	25	18
Pump to bracket(s)	25	18
Pump to support - M6 bolts	12	9
Sprocket to hub	25	18
Vent bolt to pump	25	18
Glow plugs	20	15
Injectors:		
Injector holder to cylinder head	70	52
Injector holder assembly	80	60

1 Accelerator cable - adjustment

1 With the accelerator pedal released, there should be a small amount of slack in the cable inner. If not, move the clip on the pump end of the cable outer until adjustment is correct.

2 Cold start cable (16D, 16DA, 17D, 17DR and 17DTL engines) - adjustment

1 There is no provision for adjustment of the cold start cable.

3 Cold start acceleration (15D, 15DT and 17DT engines) - checking and adjustment

Note: *To carry out this operation, it is necessary to obtain a means of accurately measuring the engine coolant temperature. Because of the expense involved in purchasing the necessary instrument and the dangers of possibly exposing oneself to hot coolant, it may be beneficial to leave this operation to a Vauxhall/Opel dealer.*

Checking

1 Refer to Part A of this Chapter and check the engine idle speed.

3.3 Using feeler gauge to measure gap between idle speed stop bolt and engine speed adjuster lever - throttle cable removed for clarity

3.4 Adjusting idle speed stop bolt to engine speed adjuster lever gap

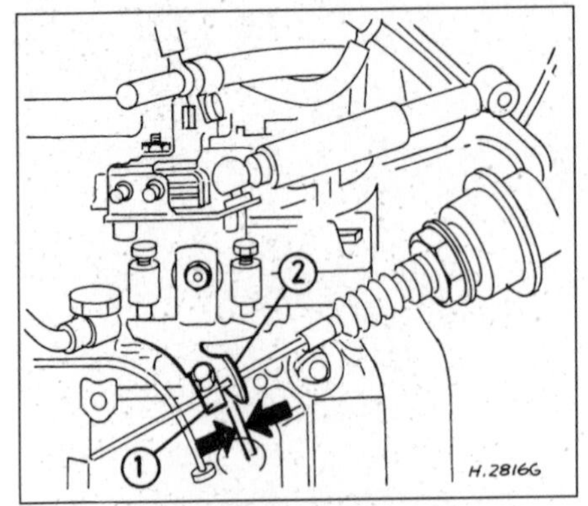

4.1 Cold start device components - Bosch VE injection pump

1 Clamping sleeve 2 Actuating lever
Arrows indicate free play checking point - engine cold

2 Run the engine until it reaches normal operating temperature.

3 Allow the engine to cool and use a feeler gauge to measure the gap between the idle speed stop bolt and the engine speed adjuster lever **(see illustration)**. The gap should be as follows:

Coolant temperature	Gap
- 20°C	1.7 ± 1.0 mm
+20°C	0.8 ± 0.3 mm

Adjustment

4 If adjustment is necessary, loosen the stop bolt locknut and turn the bolt until the correct gap is obtained **(see illustration)**. On completion, retighten the locknut.

4 Vacuum-operated cold start device (17DR and 17DTL engines) - removal and refitting

Bosch fuel injection pump

1 Slacken the lockbolt and remove the clamping sleeve from the end of the cold start device operating cable **(see illustration)**.

2 Disconnect the vacuum hose, undo the clamping nut and remove the cold start device from its mounting bracket.

3 Refitting is a reversal of removal. On completion, adjust the idle speed.

Lucas/CAV injection pump

4 Undo the two bolts securing the cold start device mounting bracket to the injection pump **(see illustration)**. Note the position of the end of the speed control lever return spring.

5 Release the mounting bracket, then detach the vacuum hoses from the cold start device, noting their locations.

6 Disconnect the cold start device thrust rod and remove the unit complete with mounting bracket. Separate the device from the mounting bracket if necessary, after removal.

7 Refitting is a reversal of removal. On completion, adjust the idle speed.

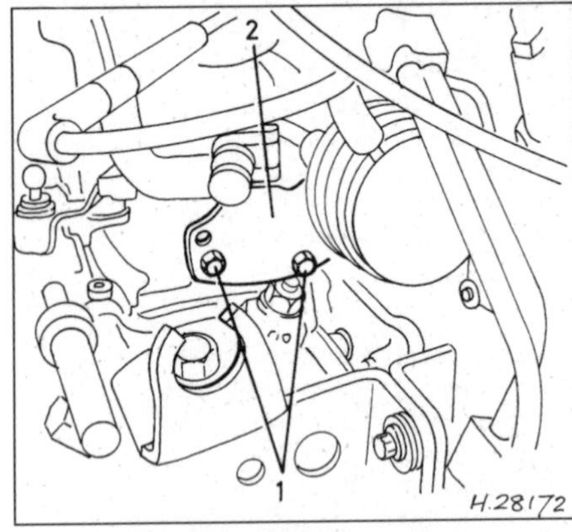

4.4 Cold start device attachments - Lucas/CAV injection pump

1 Mounting bracket securing bolts
2 Mounting bracket

5 Maximum speed (16D and 16DA engines) - checking and adjustment

Caution: Keep clear of the cooling fan when making adjustments.

16D and early 16DA engines

Checking

1 There should not normally be any need to adjust the maximum speed, except after major component renewal.

2 Refer to Part A of this Chapter (idle speed check) for ways of measuring engine speed. It is unwise to use the speedometer method, since there is a grave risk of injury or damage should anything go wrong.

3 Start the engine and gradually increase its speed, observing the tachometer or its equivalent until the governed maximum speed is reached. Do not accelerate the engine much beyond the specified maximum, should maladjustment make this possible.

Adjustment

4 If adjustment is necessary, remove the air cleaner snorkel to improve access. Slacken the locknut and turn the maximum speed adjuster screw until the desired result is obtained, then tighten the locknut without moving the screw **(see illustration)**. Refit the snorkel.

5.4 Adjusting maximum speed

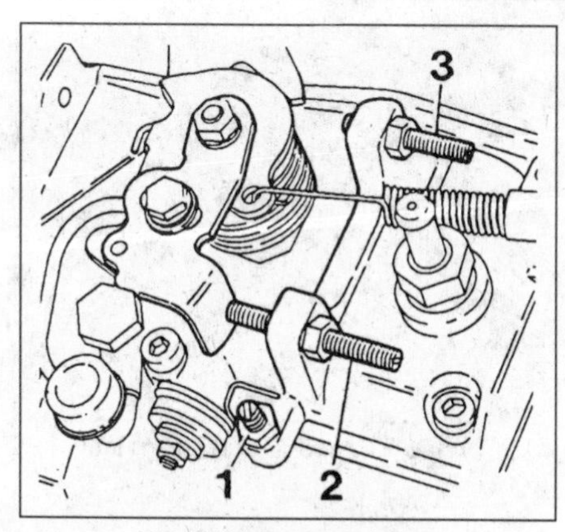

5.5 Adjustment points - Bosch VE injection pump

1 *Idle speed adjustment screw*
2 *Engine speed control lever stop screw - do not disturb*
3 *Maximum speed adjustment screw*

Later 16DA engines

Bosch VE fuel injection pump

5 The procedure for adjustment of the maximum speed is the same as described above. Note, however, that these later injection pumps have their maximum speed adjustment screws locked with a lead seal which must be removed for adjustment. As the screw should ideally be resealed after adjustment, it may be beneficial to leave this operation to a Bosch injection specialist **(see illustration)**.

Lucas/CAV fuel injection pump

6 Maximum (cut-off) speed is set in production, using the cut-off speed stop screw **(see illustration)**. The screw is sealed with lead after adjustment has been made. As with all injection pumps it is not normally necessary to disturb the cut-off speed setting in normal circumstances but if adjustment is necessary, it is recommended that this be carried out by a Lucas/CAV injection specialist.

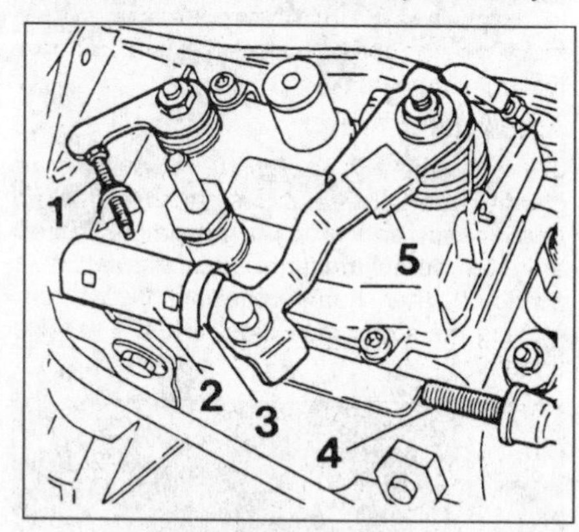

5.6 Adjustment points - Lucas/CAV injection pump

1 *Idle speed stop screw*
2 *Plastic anti-tamper cap*
3 *Engine speed control lever stop screw - do not disturb*
4 *Cut-off speed stop screw*
5 *Timing value for individual pump (marked on plate)*

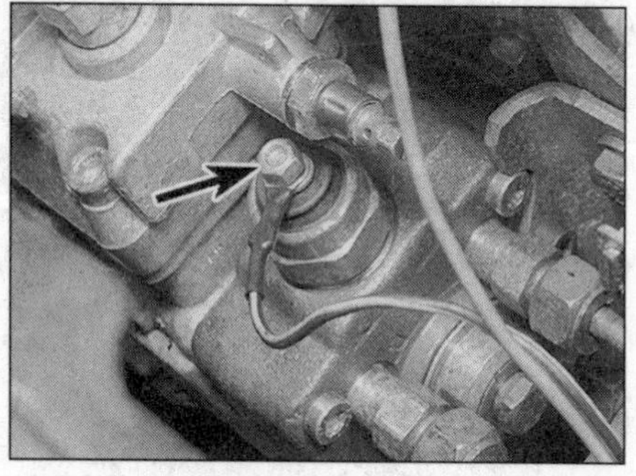

6.5 Idle stop solenoid terminal (arrowed)

6 Stop solenoid - removal and refitting

Removal

1 Disconnect the battery earth lead.
2 Where necessary, remove the inlet manifold assembly for access.
3 Where necessary, gain access to the solenoid by first cleaning around the pipe unions and then disconnecting the necessary fuel feed and return pipes from the pump.
4 Blank off all exposed pipe connections to prevent the ingress of dirt and moisture.
5 Disconnect the electrical lead from the screw terminal on top of the solenoid **(see illustration)**.
6 Clean around the solenoid, then unscrew it from the pump.
7 Recover the O-ring, spring and plunger **(see illustration)**. Cover the pump orifice to keep dirt out.

Refitting

8 Commence refitting by inserting the plunger and spring into the pump orifice.
9 Fit and tighten the solenoid, using a new O-ring. Do not overtighten.
10 Reconnect the solenoid electrical lead.
11 Remove any blanking materials and reconnect all injection pipe unions, working in the reverse sequence to removal and tightening them to the specified torque settings.
12 Refit any other disturbed components, start the engine and check for fuel leaks.

6.7 Idle stop solenoid, O-ring, spring and plunger

7 Injectors - removal, overhaul and refitting

Warning: Exercise extreme caution when working on fuel injectors. Never expose the hands or any part of the body to injector spray, as working pressure can cause fuel to penetrate the skin with possibly fatal results. You are strongly advised to have any work which involves testing injectors under pressure carried out by a Vauxhall/Opel dealer or fuel injection specialist.

15D, 15DT and 17DT engines

Removal

1 Remove the inlet manifold assembly.
2 Clean around the injection pipe unions, then remove the pipes from the injectors and pump. Be prepared for fuel spillage.
3 Blank off all exposed pipe connections to prevent the ingress of dirt and moisture.
4 Remove the fuel return line and sealing washer from each injector. Obtain new washers for reassembly.
5 Clean around the base of each injector and unscrew it.
6 Recover the copper sealing ring, corrugated washer and heat sleeve from each injector and obtain new items for reassembly.

Overhaul

7 Injectors can be overhauled but this is not a DIY job. Consult a Vauxhall/Opel dealer or other reputable specialist.

Refitting

8 Commence refitting by inserting the heat sleeves, corrugated washers and sealing rings into the cylinder head. They must be fitted the right way up, as shown **(see illustration)**.

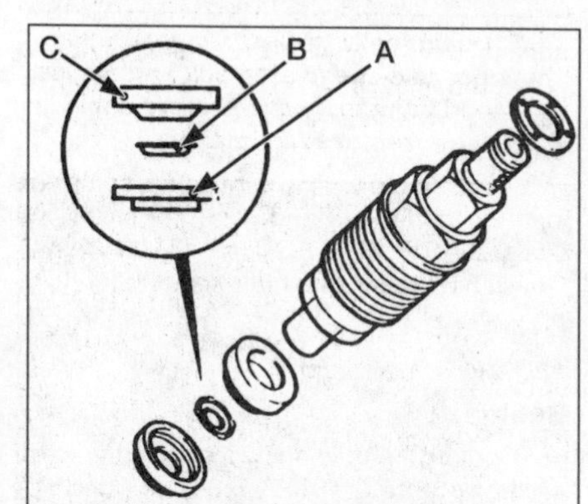

7.8 Correct fitted positions of fuel injector components

A Heat sleeve *B Corrugated washer*
C Sealing ring

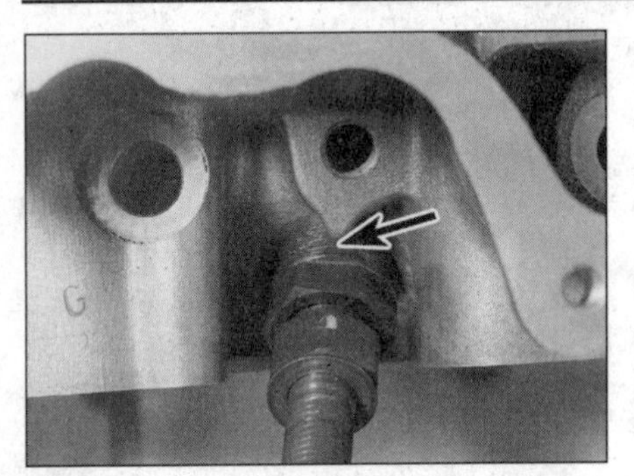

7.9 Coloured dot on injector must align with projection on cylinder head (arrowed)

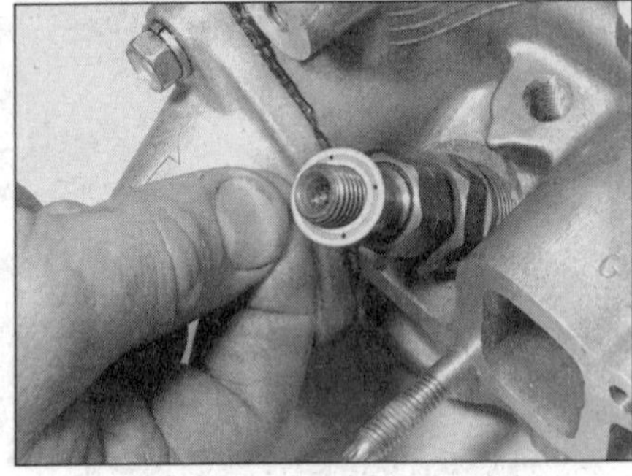

7.10a Place a new sealing washer over each injector . . .

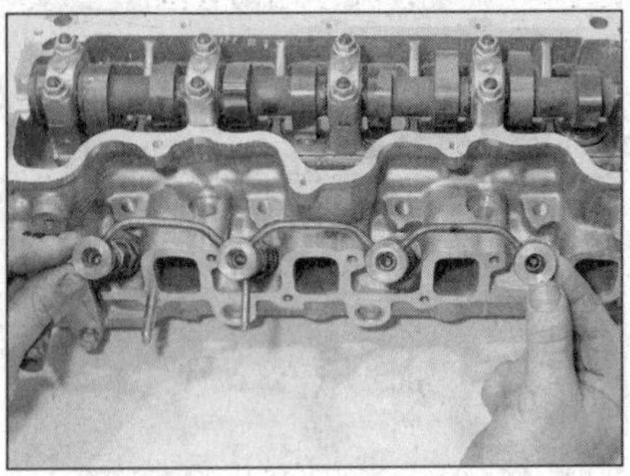

7.10b . . . and fit fuel return line

9 Screw in the injectors, tightening them to the specified torque setting. Note that the coloured dot or stamp mark on each injector must align with the projection on the cylinder head **(see illustration)**.

10 Place a new sealing washer over each injector and fit the fuel return line, tightening each of its securing nuts to the specified torque setting whilst preventing the injector from turning **(see illustrations)**.

11 Remove any blanking materials and reconnect all injection pipe unions, tightening them to the specified torque settings.

12 Refit any other disturbed components, start the engine and check for fuel leaks.

16D, 16 DA, 17D, 17DR and 17DTL engines

Removal

13 Where necessary, remove the air cleaner snorkel.

14 Clean around the unions, then remove the injection pipes from the injectors and fuel pump. Plug or cap the open unions on the pump. Also remove the fuel return hoses from the injectors. Be prepared for fuel spillage.

15 Clean around the bases of the injectors, then unscrew and remove them **(see illustration)**. A deep socket 27mm spanner is the best tool to use. On later models (January 1987 on), due to the alteration of the location of the crankcase vent hose connection, access to No 2 cylinder fuel injector is restricted. If a socket wrench is used, its diameter may require reducing by grinding.

16 Recover the injector washers. There are two per injector - the large one seals the injector carrier-to-head joint, the small one seals the injector tip **(see illustrations)**. Obtain new washers for reassembly.

Overhaul

17 Refer to paragraph 7.

Refitting

18 Commence refitting by inserting the small washers. Note that they must be fitted the right way up, as shown **(see illustration)**.

19 Fit the large washers, either way up, then screw in the injectors. Tighten the injectors to the specified torque.

20 Refit the return hoses and injection pipes.

21 Run the engine and check that there are no leaks at the pipe unions. Check again with the engine stopped.

8 Fuel injection pump - removal and refitting

Note: *Where the injection pump is equipped with an EGR system vacuum regulator valve, then the valve setting must be checked and, if necessary, adjusted whenever the pump is disturbed. The same instructions apply if a new valve has been fitted.*

Note: *Checking and adjustment of the vacuum regulator valve (where fitted) is only possible if a hand-operated vacuum pump/gauge is available. At the time of writing, no information was available for valve adjustment. It is therefore recommended that before carrying out any work on the injection pump, advice is sought from a Vauxhall/Opel dealer.*

Warning: Many tamperproof seals and Torx screws will be observed around the pump, which are intended to discourage or detect unauthorised dismantling. Do not break any seals if the pump is under warranty or if it is hoped to obtain an exchange unit.

15D, 15DT and 17DT engines

Removal

1 Disconnect the battery earth lead.

2 Remove the inlet manifold assembly.

3 Refer to Part A of this Chapter and remove the camshaft drivebelt from the injection pump sprocket.

7.15 Removing a fuel injector

7.16a Removing large plain washer . . .

7.16b . . . and small corrugated washer

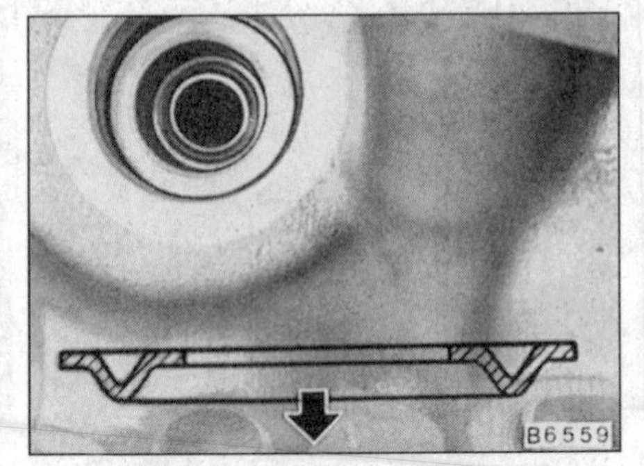

7.18 Correct installation of injector small washer - arrow points to cylinder head

8.4 Removing fuel injection pump sprocket securing nut . . .

8.5a . . . and using puller to remove sprocket from pump shaft

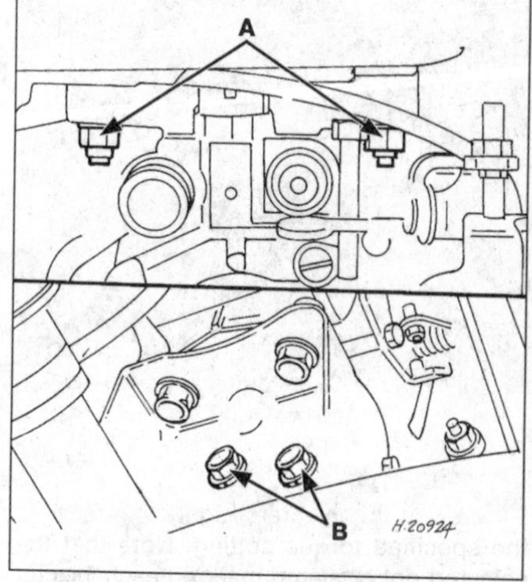

8.13 Fuel injection pump securing nuts (A) and pump bracket bolts (B)

8.5b Recovering Woodruff key from pump shaft

8.11 Cold start accelerator (arrowed)

4 Using a locking tool similar to that shown, prevent the pump sprocket from turning and remove its securing nut **(see illustration)**.

5 Use a puller to remove the sprocket from the pump shaft and recover the Woodruff key from the shaft **(see illustrations)**.

6 Unscrew the oil filter, catching any escaping oil in a drip tray.

7 Clean around the pipe unions and disconnect the fuel feed and return pipes from the pump.

8 Blank off all exposed pipe connections to prevent the ingress of dirt and moisture.

9 Disconnect the accelerator cable from the pump.

10 Drain the cooling system, recovering the coolant if it is fit for re-use.

11 Disconnect the two coolant hoses from the cold start accelerator **(see illustration)**.

12 Disconnect the lead from the idle stop solenoid.

13 Support the pump and remove the two nuts which secure it and the two bolts which secure the pump bracket **(see illustration)**. Remove the pump from the engine.

Refitting

14 Refit in the reverse order of removal, noting the following points:

a) *With the pump fitted, check its timing.*
b) *Tighten all fastenings to the specified torque settings.*
c) *Replenish the coolant and engine oil.*
d) *Check for coolant, oil and fuel leaks when the engine is running and again when stopped.*

15 Note that a good deal of cranking on the starter motor will be required to prime the pump before the engine will run. Do not operate the starter for more than 10 seconds at a time, then pause for a 5 second period to allow the battery and starter motor to recover.

16D, 16 DA, 17D, 17DR and 17DTL engines

Removal

16 Slacken the camshaft drivebelt and slip it off the pump sprocket.

17 If not already done, remove the air cleaner snorkel.

18 Disconnect the fuel feed and return hoses from the pump. Also disconnect the fuel return hose from the T-piece **(see illustrations)**. Be prepared for fuel spillage. Plug or cap the open unions to keep fuel in and dirt out.

19 Clean around the unions, then remove the injection pipes. Do not separate the pipes from their brackets. Again, plug the open unions.

20 Disconnect the lead from the idle stop solenoid.

21 Disconnect the throttle and cold start cables from the pump.

22 Restrain the pump sprocket from turning and remove the central securing nut **(see illustration)**.

23 Remove the sprocket from the pump shaft. The use of a puller is recommended **(see illustration)**. If a "face" puller is used, it

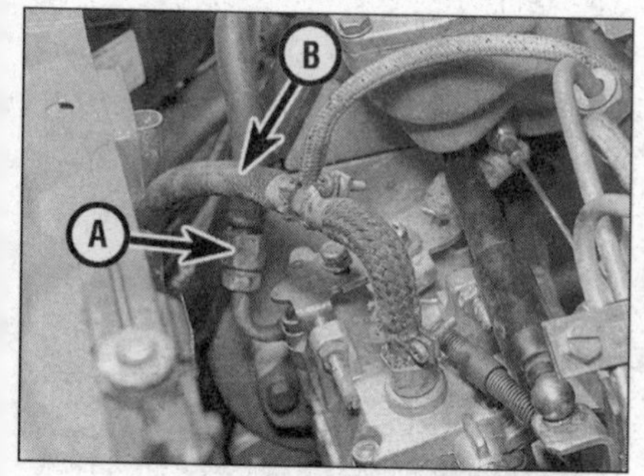

8.18a Fuel pump feed hose (A) and return hose (B) connections

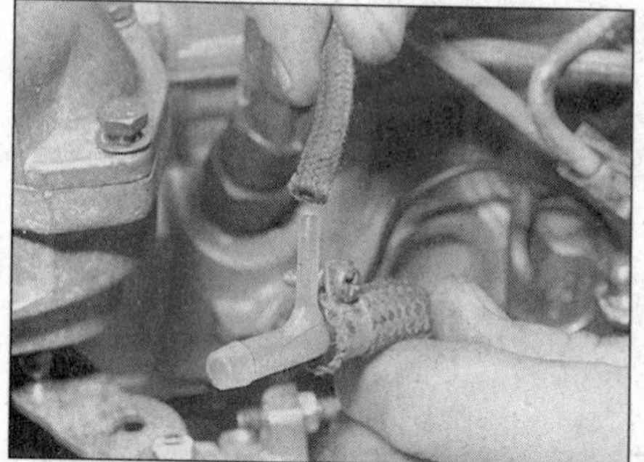
8.18b Disconnecting injector fuel return hose

8.22 Remove injection pump sprocket nut . . .

8.23 . . . and use puller to remove sprocket . . .

8.25 Removing an injection pump securing bolt

will have to be secured with the bolts which clamp the two parts of the sprocket together. If these bolts have been disturbed, the pump timing will have to be reset after refitting. Make alignment marks between the parts of the sprocket if wished.

24 Recover the Woodruff key from the shaft if it is loose **(see illustration)**.

25 Remove the two bolts which secure the sprocket end of the pump to the bracket. Access to the bolt on the engine side is achieved with a socket and a long extension **(see illustration)**.

26 Remove the two bolts which secure the spring/damper bracket to the fuel pump

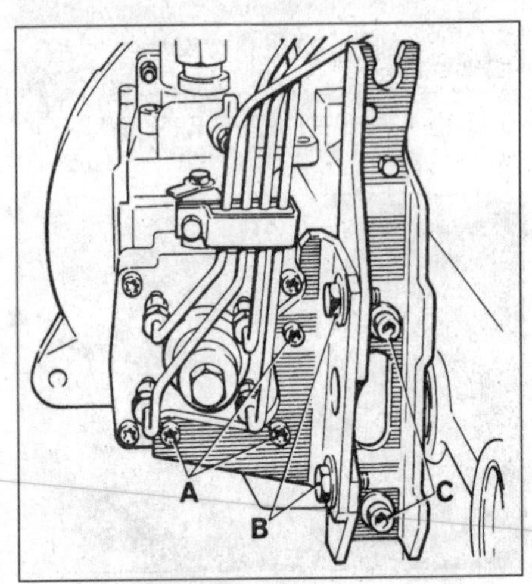

8.28 Injection pump bracket bolts - tighten in sequence A - B - C

8.24 . . . taking care to retain Woodruff key (arrowed)

bracket. Remove the pump complete with subsidiary brackets.

Refitting

27 If a new pump is being fitted, transfer the brackets and other necessary components to it. Do not tighten the bracket bolts yet.

28 Refit in the reverse order of removal, noting the following points:

*a) Slacken the subsidiary bracket bolts, then tighten in the sequence shown **(see illustration)**.*

b) Tighten all fastenings to the specified torque, when known.

c) Check the valve timing.

d) Check the injection timing if the sprocket was separated, or if a new pump has been fitted.

29 A good deal of cranking on the starter motor will be required to prime the pump before the engine will run. Do not operate the starter for more than 10 seconds at a time, then pause for a 5 second period to allow the battery and starter motor to recover.

30 Check all fuel unions for leaks when the engine is running, and again when it has been stopped.

9 Fuel injection pump (15D, 15DT and 17DT engines) - timing

Note: *The following procedure was carried out with the engine removed from the vehicle. Should the engine be in the vehicle, then access to the injection pump will be restricted. Depending on vehicle type, remove the inlet manifold and/or the starter motor for access to the pump.*

Note: *Valve timing must be correct before checking fuel injection pump timing.*

1 Timing of the injection pump should only be necessary in the following circumstances:

a) When fitting a new or overhauled pump.

b) If the timing is suspected of being wrong.

c) If the timing belt has been re-tensioned or renewed.

2 Obtain a dial test indicator (DTI) and adapter **(see illustration)**. The manufacturer specifies the use of an adapter which screws into, and seals, the plug hole.

3 Disconnect the battery earth lead.

4 Clean around the injection pipe unions to the pump and cylinder head.

5 Disconnect Nos 1 and 2 injection pipes from the injectors and the pump and remove them from the engine. Be prepared for fuel spillage during subsequent operations.

6 Blank off all exposed pipe connections to prevent the ingress of dirt and moisture.

7 Remove the central plug from the injection pump **(see illustration)**.

8 Turn the crankshaft in the normal direction of rotation until the timing mark on its pulley aligns with the reference pointer on the engine block **(see illustration)**. In this position No 1 piston is at TDC on the firing stroke.

9 Deactivate the cold start lever by using a screwdriver as shown **(see illustration)**.

10 Fit the adapter and dial test indicator with the indicator probe entering the central plug

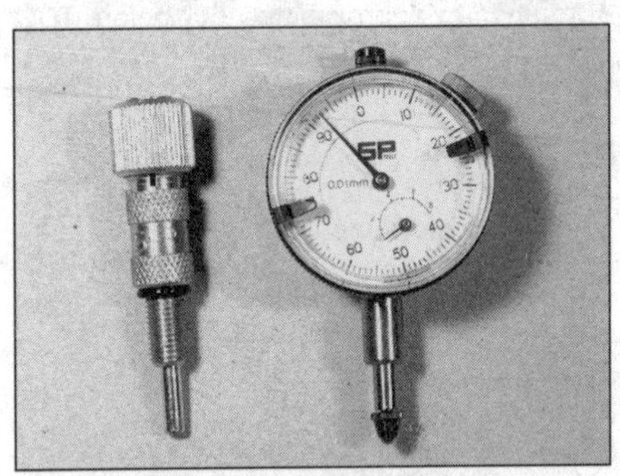

9.2 Dial test indicator and adapter required to set fuel injection pump timing

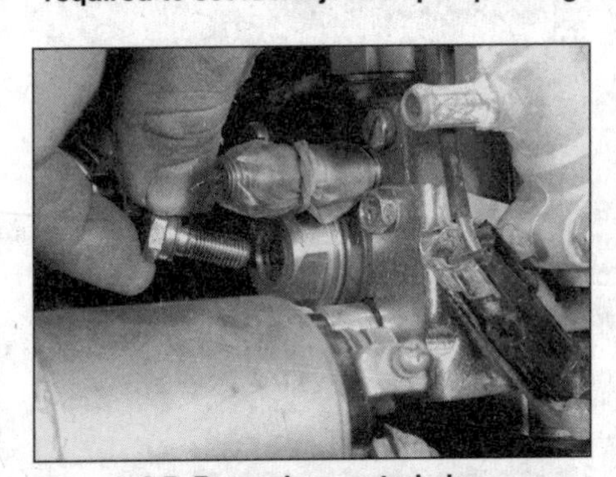

9.7 Removing central plug from injection pump

9.8 Timing mark on crankshaft pulley aligned with reference pointer on block

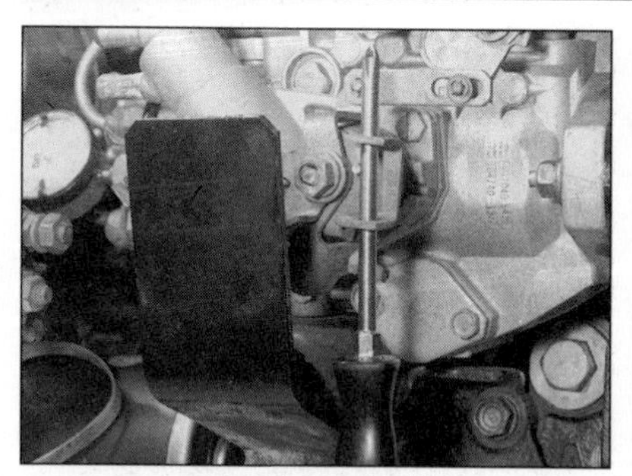

9.9 Deactivating cold start lever with screwdriver

9.10 Adapter and dial test indicator fitted to injection pump

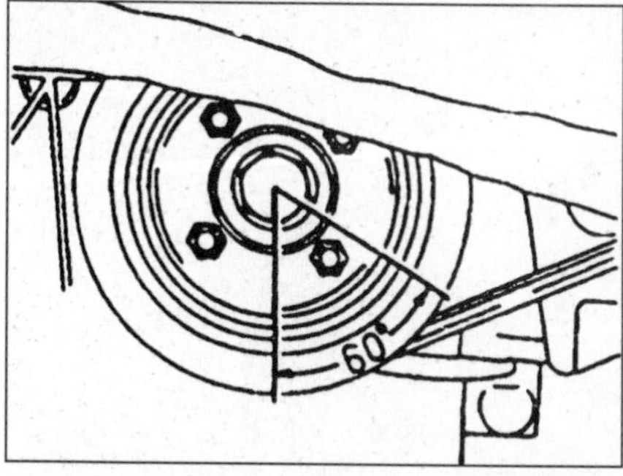

9.11 Turn crankshaft in normal direction of rotation to approximately 60° before TDC (No 1 firing)

hole and contacting the pump piston **(see illustration)**.

11 Turn the crankshaft in the normal direction of rotation to approximately 60° before TDC (No 1 firing) **(see illustration)**. At this point, the injection pump piston will be at bottom dead centre (BDC).

12 Zero the indicator, checking its adjustment by rotating the crankshaft slightly in either direction to ensure BDC.

13 Bring the engine back to TDC (No 1 firing). When the timing mark on the pulley is aligned with the reference pointer, the dial test indicator should show a lift corresponding to the specified timing setting.

14 If adjustment is necessary, loosen the two nuts which secure the injection pump and the two bolts which secure the pump bracket - see illustration 8.13.

15 Loosen Nos 3 and 4 injection pipes at the injectors and pump.

16 Rotate the pump until the dial test indicator shows the desired lift, then tighten the loosened nuts and bolts to the specified torque settings. Rotating the top of the pump towards the engine will lower the lift value, whereas rotating the pump in the opposite direction will raise the lift value.

17 Repeat the checking procedure.

18 With the pump timing correct, remove the DTI and adapter then refit the plug to the pump.

19 Remove any blanking materials and reconnect all injection pipe unions, working in the reverse sequence to removal and tightening them to the specified torque settings.

20 Refit any other disturbed components, start the engine and check for fuel leaks.

10 Fuel injection pump (16D and 16DA engines) - timing

Note: *The following procedure was carried out during engine rebuilding. With the engine in the vehicle, it will be necessary to remove the drivebelt covers, the air cleaner snorkel and the clutch/flywheel cover. A dial test indicator with a long probe and a suitable support will be needed for timing the pump.*

1 Timing of the injection pump should only be necessary in the following circumstances:

a) When fitting a new or overhauled pump
b) If the timing is suspected of being incorrect
c) If the timing belt has been re-tensioned or renewed

2 Check the valve timing.

3 Bring the engine to TDC, No 1 firing. The timing mark on the pump sprocket must be aligned with the pip on the pump bracket **(see illustration)**.

4 Turn the engine against the normal direction of rotation so that the flywheel TDC mark is approximately 5.0 cm away from the TDC pointer.

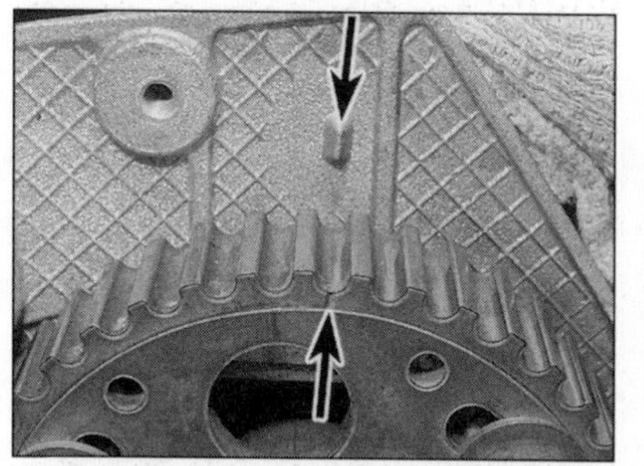

10.3 Injection pump sprocket timing mark aligned with mark on pump bracket

10.6 Dial test indicator mounted with probe in plug hole

5 Remove the central plug from the rear of the injection pump **(see illustration)**.

6 Mount the dial test indicator with its probe entering the central plug hole. Zero the indicator **(see illustration)**.

7 Be prepared for fuel spillage during subsequent operations. The manufacturers specify the use of a probe which screws into, and presumably seals, the plug hole.

8 Bring the engine back to TDC, No 1 firing. When the timing marks are aligned, the dial test indicator should show a lift corresponding to the specified timing setting.

9 If adjustment is necessary, slacken the three bolts which clamp together the two halves of the pump sprocket **(see illustration)**. Turn the inner part of the sprocket anti-clockwise (against the normal direction of rotation) as far

10.5 Removing plug from rear of injection pump

10.9a Slacken injection pump sprocket clamping bolts . . .

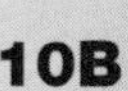

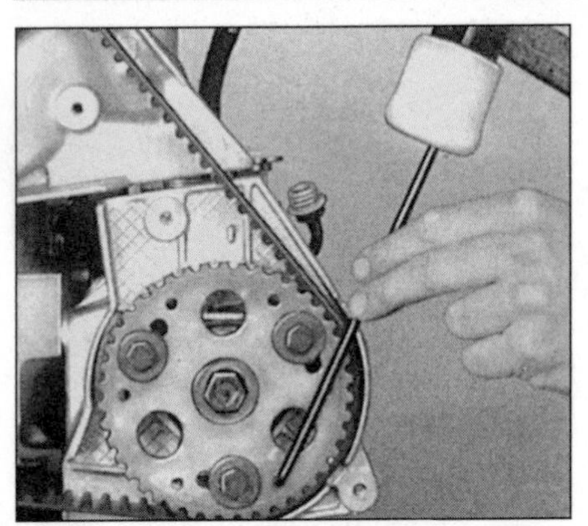

10.9b . . . and use rod and mallet to move inner part of sprocket

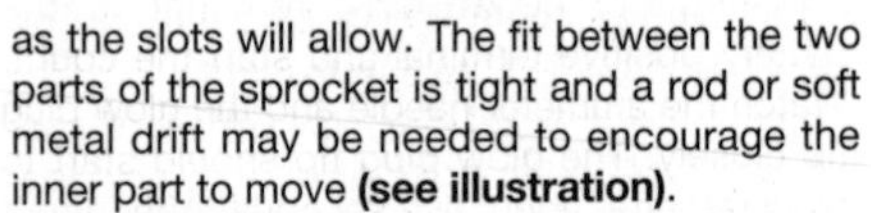

as the slots will allow. The fit between the two parts of the sprocket is tight and a rod or soft metal drift may be needed to encourage the inner part to move **(see illustration)**.

10 With the sprocket positioned as just described and the engine still at TDC, No 1 firing, the dial test indicator should again read zero. Reset it if necessary.

11 Turn the inner part of the sprocket clockwise until the dial test indicator shows the desired lift, then tighten the sprocket clamp bolts.

12 Repeat the checking procedure from paragraph 4.

13 When the injection timing is correct, remove the test gear and refit the plug to the rear of the pump.

14 Refit the drivebelt covers and other disturbed components.

11.5 Fuel injection pump sprocket timing mark aligned with moulded mark on drivebelt inner cover

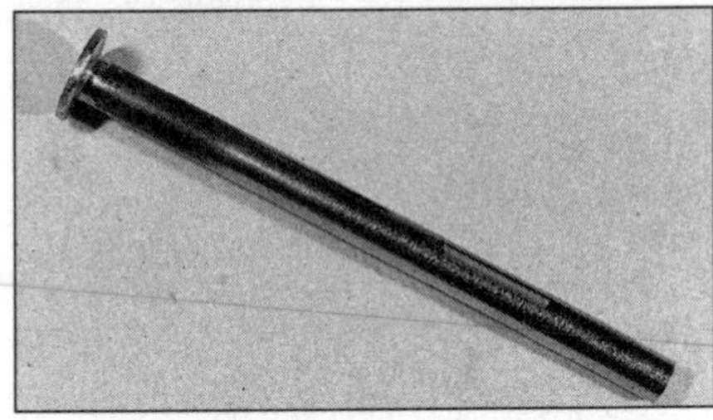

11.7a Home-made probe used for checking Lucas/CAV pump timing

11.3 Flywheel timing marks visible through clutch housing inspection cover

11 Fuel injection pump (17D, 17DR and 17DTL engines) - timing

Bosch and Lucas/CAV pumps

1 The pump timing procedure is generally similar to that given in Section 10 for the 16D and 16DA engines, whilst noting the following.

2 With the introduction of the revised camshaft drivebelt inner and outer covers, the timing mark for the injection pump sprocket is now located on the drivebelt inner cover.

3 On 17D and 17DR engines, remove the clutch housing cover plate. With No 1 piston set to TDC on the firing stroke, the TDC mark on the flywheel and the pointer on the clutch housing will be aligned **(see illustration)**.

4 On 17DTL engines, remove the flywheel cover plate. Flywheel position for TDC must be determined by the use of a setting tool (Adjuster KM-851) fitted next to the flywheel as shown **(see illustration)**. With No 1 piston set to TDC on the firing stroke, the TDC mark on the flywheel and the pointer on the setting tool will be aligned.

5 On all engines, the timing mark on the injection pump sprocket will be aligned with the moulded mark on the drivebelt inner cover **(see illustration)**.

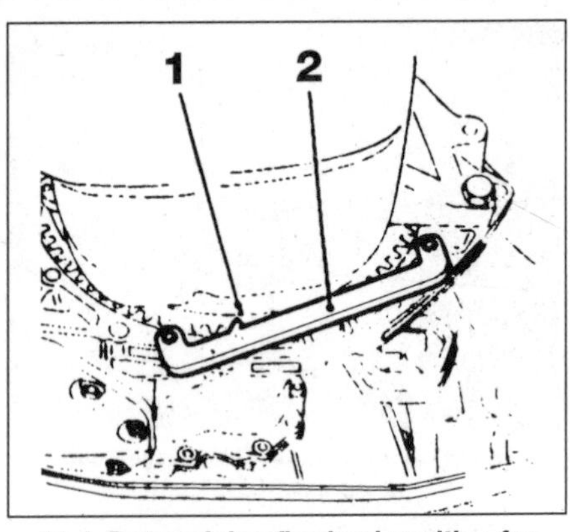

11.4 Determining flywheel position for TDC by use of setting tool KM-851

1 Flywheel TDC mark 2 Setting tool

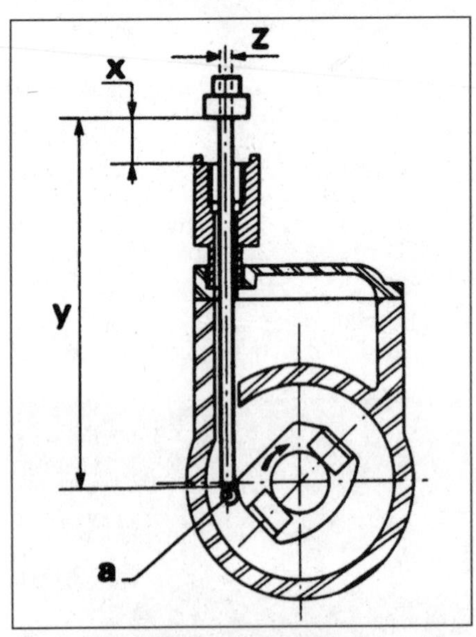

11.7b Special DTI probe shown in position during pump timing check - Lucas/CAV injection pump

a Timing piece
x Timing value (as shown on plate)
Y 95.5 ± 0.01 mm z 7.00 mm dia. shank

Lucas/CAV pump

6 There are also some slight changes to the timing procedure when dealing with the Lucas/CAV injection pump as detailed below.

7 Note that the closing plug is located on the upper surface of the pump rather than at the end of the pump casing as on the Bosch pump. In the absence of the measuring tool KM-690-A and the dial test indicator KM-571-B, you will need a standard dial test indicator (DTI), together with some method of mounting it above the timing hole at the appropriate height. Also required is a headed probe made to the dimensions shown, this being placed in the timing hole before the DTI is mounted in position **(see illustrations)**.

8 Check the amount of lift indicated on the DTI when the crankshaft timing marks are brought into alignment. There is no standard specified lift figure for Lucas/CAV pumps. Each pump is calibrated during manufacture and the lift figure marked on a plate which is fitted to the pump lever **(see illustration)**. If the lift figure shown

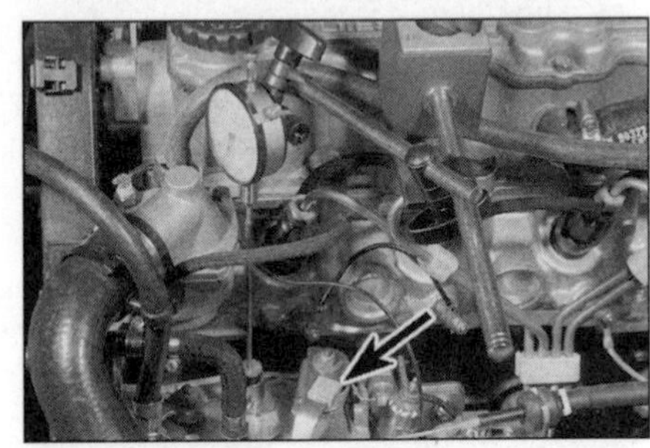

11.8 Lucas/CAV pump showing DTI set up for timing check. Individual value for each pump is stamped on plate (arrowed)

12.2 Fuel filter heating element wiring connector (arrowed)

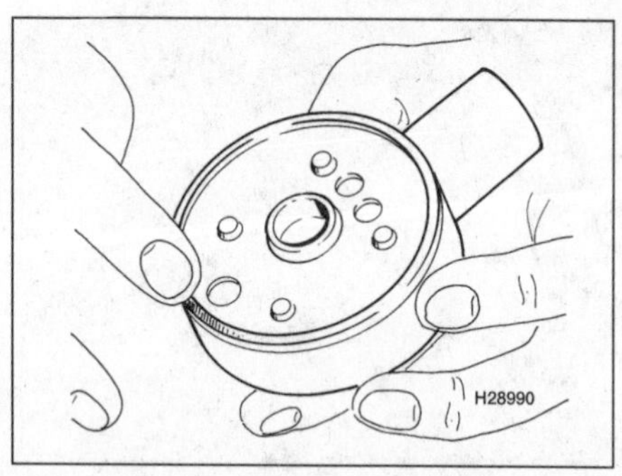

12.3 Lightly smear sealing ring of fuel filter heating element with clean Diesel fuel before fitting

on the DTI does not correspond with that given on the plate, adjust the pump sprocket as described in Section 10. Once adjustment is complete, remove the DTI with probe and refit the closing plug.

12 Fuel filter heating element - renewal

1 Where fitted, the fuel filter heating element is located between the filter housing and bowl. A sensor monitors the fuel temperature passing through the filter and if this falls to a point where fuel waxing is likely to occur, the heater is switched on to warm the fuel.
2 To remove the heating element, unplug its wiring connector then remove the filter element followed by the heating element **(see illustration)**.
3 Fitting the heating element is a reversal of the removal procedure. Lightly smear the sealing ring of the element with clean Diesel fuel before fitting **(see illustration)**.

13 Preheating system - testing

Caution: Take care to avoid burns. Glow plug tips become very hot during testing.

15D, 17DR and later 17D engines - 5 volt system

1 These engines have a 5-volt preheating system which cannot be tested without specialist equipment. Refer to a Vauxhall/Opel dealer or Diesel specialist.

15D, 15DT, 16D, 16DA, 17DT and early 17D engines - 11 volt system

2 If malfunction of the system is suspected, check first that battery voltage appears at the glow plug bus bar for a few seconds when the ignition key is first turned to the ON position. If not, there is a fault in the wiring or the relay. Testing of the relay is by substitution.
3 If battery voltage is present at the bus bar but one or more glow plugs do not seem to be working, it is possible to identify a defective plug with the aid of a high range ammeter (say 0 to 50A). An ohmmeter is unlikely to be able to distinguish between the resistance of a good plug (less than 1 ohm) and a short circuit.
4 Connect the ammeter between the bus bar and the feed wire. Have an assistant turn the key. Each plug will draw between 8 and 9 amps after an initial surge, so if the reading is much above or below 32 to 36 amps, there is a defect in one or more plugs. Disconnect each plug in turn to isolate the culprit.
5 In the absence of an ammeter, a 12 volt test lamp can be used. Remove the bus bar and connect the lamp between the battery live (+) terminal and each glow plug in turn. If the lamp lights, either the glow plug is OK or there is a short-circuit. If the lamp does not light, then the glow plug is defective.
6 In addition to the above tests, it is possible to carry out a visual operational check of a suspect glow plug. Proceed as follows:
7 There are commercially-produced glow plug testers available which comprise a casing in which the plug is clamped, an ammeter, 12-volt connection leads and a simple timing circuit which illuminates successive LEDs in five-second intervals. With the glow plug in place and the leads connected to a 12-volt battery, note the time taken before the tip of the plug begins to glow and the current drops.
8 Whilst such equipment is available in a commercial workshop, it is too infrequently needed by most owners to justify the purchase price. However, an equivalent test rig can be made up at home at little cost.

13.10 Glow plug test rig in use. Glow plug clamped to a sound earth point (arrowed)

9 Using an ammeter with a range of at least 30A, connect a lead to each terminal, fitting a crocodile clip at each end. In the interests of safety, fit an in-line fuseholder to one of the leads, using a 30A fuse.
10 With the suspect glow plug removed from the cylinder head, clamp it with self-locking pliers against its metal body to a sound earth point on the engine. Connect the lead from the positive (+) terminal on the ammeter to the glow plug terminal **(see illustration)**. Have an assistant ready with a watch so that a running count of seconds elapsed can be made while you watch the glow plug tip.
11 Connect the remaining crocodile clip from the ammeter negative (-) terminal to the battery positive terminal and start the count. Watch the ammeter needle and the glow plug tip closely. The glow plug tip should start to glow red after about five seconds. After about fifteen seconds, the current reading should drop from around 25A to about 12A.
12 Note that the above timings and current figures are not precise. If the glow plug under test performs reasonably closely to the above sequence, it is likely to be in serviceable condition. An abnormally high or low current reading (or a blown fuse) indicates the need for renewal, as does a failure of the tip to glow at all.

14 Exhaust gas recirculation system (15D, 17DR and 17DTL engines) - maintenance

15D engine

1 At the time of writing, no service information was available for the exhaust gas recirculation (EGR) system fitted to certain 15D engines, although it can safely be assumed that component location and function is as described for the 17DR and 17DTL engines

17DR and 17DTL engines

2 The EGR system comprises the following components:

a) *The Thermal-Operated Vacuum Switch - fitted to the thermostat housing **(see illustrations)**. This is closed until the coolant reaches a certain temperature, thus preventing the system from operating while the engine is warming up.*
b) *The Vacuum Regulator Valve - mounted on the top of the fuel injection pump. This regulates according to throttle opening the amount of vacuum applied to the EGR valve.*
c) *The Vacuum Delay Valve - fitted in the vacuum line to control the rate at which vacuum is applied to the EGR valve **(see illustration)**.*
d) *The EGR valve - mounted on the inlet manifold and connected by a supply pipe to the exhaust manifold **(see illustration)**.*

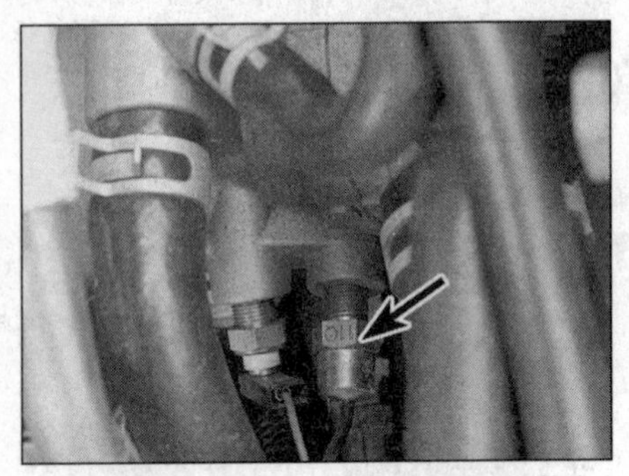

14.2a Thermal-operated vacuum switch (arrowed) - 15D engine shown

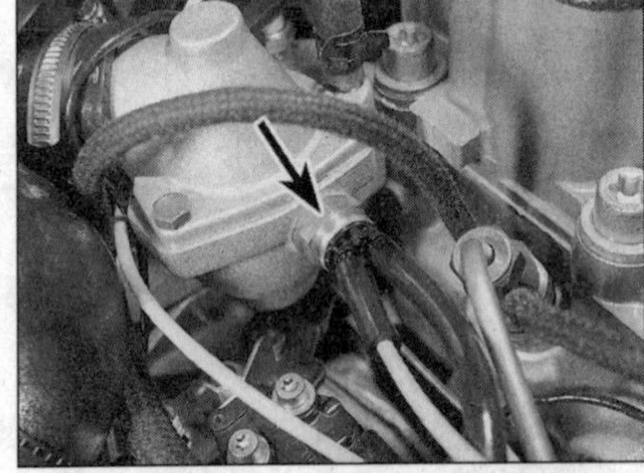

14.2b Thermal-operated vacuum switch (arrowed) - 17DR engine shown

14.2c Vacuum delay valve - 15D engine shown

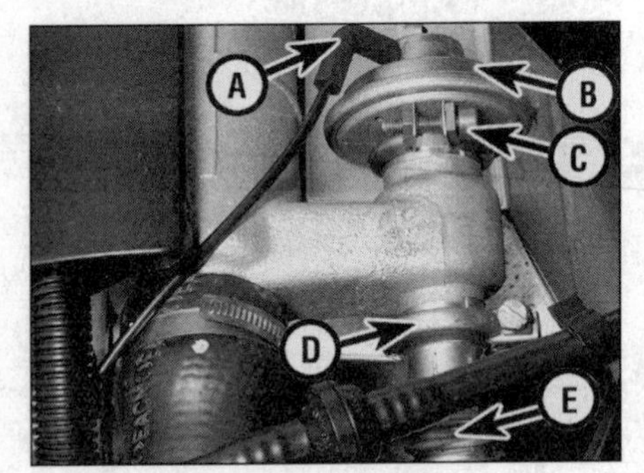

14.2d EGR valve and pipe connections - 17DTL engine shown

A Vacuum hose
B EGR valve
C Valve clamp
D Pipe clamp
E Corrugated pipe

14.8 EGR system vacuum take-off (arrowed) on vacuum pump - 17DR engine shown

14.25 EGR system corrugated pipe (arrowed) inlet manifold connection - 17DR engine shown

This opens under the control of the vacuum switch, regulator and delay valves, using the depression created by the vacuum pump which allows a proportion of the exhaust gases to flow up into the inlet manifold and into the combustion chamber.

System checking

3 This system is virtually maintenance-free, the only routine operations necessary are checks for condition and security of the component parts.

4 Whenever the fuel injection pump is removed, the vacuum regulator valve setting must be checked and if necessary, adjusted. Refer to Section 8.

5 To check system operation, warm the engine up to normal operating temperature and allow it to idle. Disconnect and reconnect several times the vacuum pipe from the top of the EGR valve. The valve should be heard to operate each time.

6 If the EGR valve does not operate and vacuum can be felt at the pipe end, first check the setting of the vacuum regulator valve.

7 If the vacuum regulator valve is functioning correctly, the fault must be in the EGR valve, which must then be renewed. If the valve is to be renewed, it is always worth first trying the effect of cleaning any carbon build-up from its passages to check whether this is the reason for the failure. If the valve diaphragm has failed, on the other hand, there is no alternative to the renewal of the complete valve unit.

8 If no vacuum can be felt, check back through the system until the leak or blockage is found and rectified. Vacuum supply is provided by an additional take-off from the vacuum pump **(see illustration)**.

Thermal-operated vacuum switch - removal and refitting

9 Drain the cooling system, either completely or down as far as the thermostat.

10 Disconnect the vacuum pipes from the switch, having noted their fitted positions.

11 Unscrew the vacuum switch.

12 On fitting the new switch, ensure that a new sealing washer is used. Tighten the switch securely.

13 Refill the cooling system.

Vacuum regulator valve - removal and refitting

14 Note the fitted position of each valve pipe for reference when refitting.

15 Disconnect each pipe.

16 Unbolt and remove the regulator valve.

17 Refitting is a reversal of removal but if a new valve is being fitted, then it must be adjusted. See Section 8.

Vacuum delay valve - removal and refitting

18 At the time of writing, no information was available concerning the precise location of this unit, or whether it is available separately from the vacuum pipes. Consult your local Vauxhall/Opel dealer for details.

19 Note that valves of this type are usually clearly marked to show which way round they are to be fitted. Note any such markings before removing the valve.

20 Refitting is a reversal of removal. Check that all pipe connections are secure.

EGR valve - removal and refitting

21 Disconnect the battery earth (negative) terminal.

22 Disconnect the vacuum pipe from the top of the valve.

23 Release the valve retaining clamp and withdraw the valve from the inlet manifold, tapping it lightly on either side with a soft-faced hammer if it proves difficult to remove.

24 Refitting is a reversal of removal. Do not use undue force when relocating the valve in the inlet manifold .

Supply pipe - removal and refitting

25 Disconnect the corrugated supply pipe by removing its flange securing bolts (17DR engine) **(see illustration)** or retaining clamp (17DTL engine) from the inlet manifold and its flange securing bolts from the exhaust manifold. Discard the flange gasket(s).

26 Refitting is a reversal of removal. Fit new flange gaskets and tighten the pipe securing bolts to the specified torque settings.

Chapter 11
Volkswagen 1896cc engine

Part A: Routine maintenance and servicing

Contents

Engine application

1896cc engine .... Volkswagen Golf and Vento - 1992 to 1996

Servicing specifications

Oil filter

Type .... Champion C150

Timing belt

Type .... Toothed belt
Tension .... See text

Auxiliary drivebelt

Type .... Ribbed or V-belt
Deflection .... 5.0 mm at midpoint of longest run

Air filter

Type .... Champion U583

Fuel filter

Type .... Champion L114

Glow plugs

Type CH160

Idle speed

Engine codes AAZ and 1Y .... 900 ± 30 rpm

Torque wrench settings

Torque wrench settings	Nm	lbf ft
Camshaft sprocket bolt	45	33
Coolant pump pulley bolts	25	18
Crankshaft auxiliary belt pulley screws	25	18
Glow plugs:		
Engine code 1Z	15	11
Engine codes 1Y, AAZ	25	18
Sump drain plug	30	22
Timing belt tensioner locknut	20	15

Lubricants, fluids and capacities

Component or system	Lubricant or fluid	Capacity
Engine	Multigrade engine oil, viscosity range SAE 10W/40 to 20W/50, to specification API SG/CD	4.3 litres - with filter
Cooling system	Ethylene glycol based antifreeze. 50% volume with water	6.3 litres
Fuel system	Commercial Diesel fuel for road vehicles (DERV)	62 litres

Volkswagen diesel engine - maintenance schedule

The maintenance schedules which follow are basically those recommended by the manufacturer. Servicing intervals are determined by mileage or time elapsed - this is because fluids and systems deteriorate with age as well as with use. Follow the time intervals if the appropriate mileage is not covered within the specified period.

Vehicles operating under adverse conditions may need more frequent maintenance. Adverse conditions include climatic extremes, full-time towing or taxi work, driving on unmade roads, and a high proportion of short journeys. The use of inferior fuel can cause early degradation of the engine oil. Consult a Volkswagen dealer for advice on these points.

All VW Golf/Vento models are equipped with a service interval display indicator in the instrument panel. Every time the engine is started the panel will illuminate for a few seconds, displaying either of the following. This provides a handy reminder of when the next service is required:

Display shows IN 00 - no service required

Display shows OEL - 5000 mile (7500 km) service required on non Turbo models

Display shows OEL - 10 000 mile (15 000 km) service required on Turbo models

Display shows IN 01 - 12 monthly service required

Display shows IN 02 - 20 000 mile (30 000 km) service required

Every 250 miles (400 km), weekly, or before a long journey

- ☐ Check engine oil level and top up if necessary (Section 3)
- ☐ Check coolant level and top up if necessary (Section 4)
- ☐ Check exhaust smoke (Section 5)
- ☐ Check operation of glow plug warning light (Section 6)

Every 5000 miles (7500 km) - non Turbo models (OEL on interval display)

- ☐ Renew engine oil and filter (Section 7)
- ☐ Drain water from fuel filter (Section 8)
- ☐ Reset service interval display (Section 9)

Every 10 000 miles (15 000 km) - Turbo models (OEL on interval display)

- ☐ Renew engine oil and filter (Section 10)
- ☐ Drain water from fuel filter (Section 11)
- ☐ Reset service interval display (Section 12)

Every 12 months - IN 01 on interval display

If the vehicle is a non Turbo model travelling less 5000 miles (7500 km) or a Turbo model travelling less than 10 000 miles (15 000 km) a year, also carry out the tasks listed above

- ☐ Check engine idle speed (Section 13)
- ☐ Check all underbonnet components for fluid leaks
- ☐ Check condition of exhaust system and mountings
- ☐ Reset service interval display (Section 14)

Every 20 000 miles (30 000 km) - IN 02 on interval display

If the vehicle is travelling more than 20 000 miles (30 000 km) a year, also carry out all the operations described above

- ☐ Renew fuel filter (Section 15)
- ☐ Renew air filter element
- ☐ Check condition of timing belt and adjust if necessary (Section 16)
- ☐ Check condition of auxiliary drivebelt(s) and renew if necessary
- ☐ Reset service interval display (Section 17)

Every 60 000 miles (90 000 km)

- ☐ Renew timing belt (Section 18)

Every 2 years (regardless of mileage)

- ☐ Renew engine coolant
- ☐ Check exhaust emissions (Section 19)

Underbonnet view of early VW Golf and Vento Turbo Diesel engine

1 *Engine oil filler cap*
2 *Engine oil dipstick*
3 *Oil filter housing*
4 *Master cylinder brake fluid reservoir*
5 *Air cleaner housing*
6 *Alternator*
7 *Coolant expansion tank*
8 *Windscreen/tailgate washer fluid reservoir*
9 *Suspension strut upper mounting*
10 *Fuel filter*
11 *Injection pump*
12 *Battery*
13 *Turbocharger*
14 *Power steering fluid reservoir*

Maintenance procedures

1 Introduction

Refer to Chapter 2, Part A, Section 1.

2 Intensive maintenance

Refer to Chapter 2, Part A, Section 2.

250 mile (400 km) Service

3 Engine oil level check

1 Refer to Chapter 2, Part A, Section 3 **(see illustration)**.

4 Coolant level check

1 Refer to Chapter 2, Part A, Section 4. Note that the tank is translucent, so the coolant level can be verified without removing the cap. The level should be between the MAX (HOT) and MIN (COLD) marks embossed on the side of the tank. If it is below the MIN mark, remove the cap and top up with coolant to the MAX mark **(see illustration)**.

5 Exhaust smoke check

1 Refer to Chapter 2, Part A, Section 5.

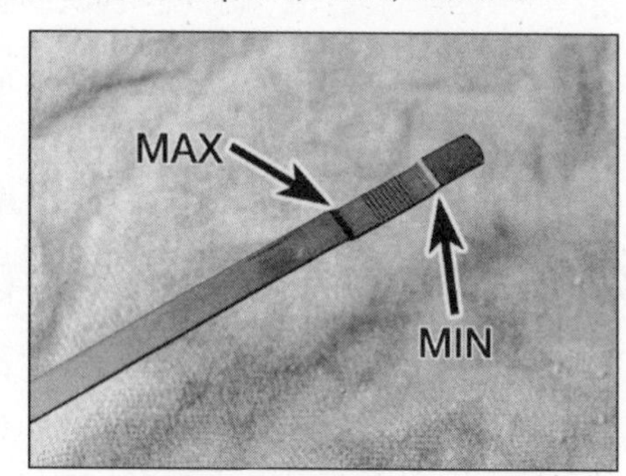

3.1 Engine oil level dipstick markings

6 Warning light check

1 Refer to Chapter 2, Part A, Section 6.

4.1 Coolant level MIN and MAX marks

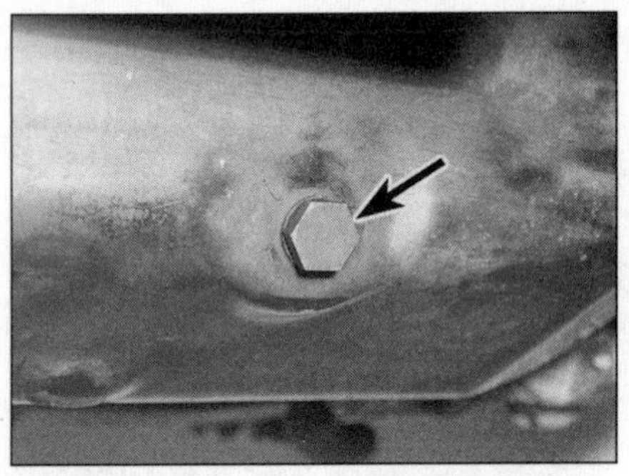
7.1a Engine oil drain plug (arrowed)

7.1b Removing engine oil filter

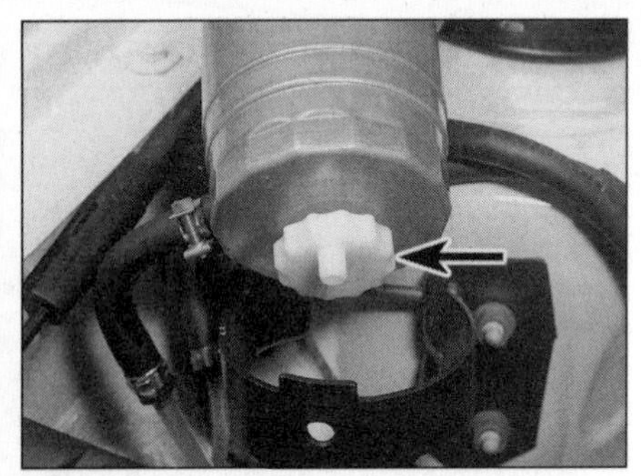
8.5 Unscrew drain valve (arrowed) at base of fuel filter

5000 mile (7500 km) Service - OEL on interval display

7 Engine oil and filter renewal - non-Turbo

1 Refer to Chapter 2, Part A, Section 7 **(see illustrations)**.

8 Fuel filter draining - non-Turbo

1 Water, collected from the fuel supply by the filter, must be drained from the unit.
2 The fuel filter is mounted on the inner wing, above the right hand wheel arch. At the top of the filter unit, release the clip and lift out the control valve, leaving the fuel hoses attached.
3 Slacken the screw and raise the filter in its retaining bracket
4 Position a container below the filter unit and pad the surrounding area with rags to absorb any fuel that may be spilt.
5 Unscrew the drain valve at the base of the filter unit until fuel starts to run out into the container **(see illustration)**. Keep the valve open until about 100 cc of fuel has been collected.
6 Refit the control valve to the top of the filter and insert the retaining clip. Close the drain valve and wipe off any surplus fuel from the nozzle.
7 Remove the collecting container and rags, then push the filter unit back into the retaining bracket and tighten the bracket securing screw.
8 Run the engine at idle and check around the fuel filter for fuel leaks.
9 Raise the engine speed to about 2000 rpm several times, then allow the engine to idle again. Observe the fuel flow through the transparent hose leading to the fuel injection pump and check that it is free of air bubbles.

9 Service interval display resetting - non-Turbo

1 After all necessary maintenance work has been completed, the relevant service interval display code must be reset. If more than one service schedule is carried out, then the relevant display intervals must be reset individually.
2 The display is reset using the reset button on the left-hand side of the instrument panel (below the speedometer) and the clock setting button on the right-hand side of the panel (below the clock/tachometer). On models with a digital clock, the lower (minute) button is used. Resetting is carried out as follows:

a) Turn the ignition switch and check that the speedometer mileage indicator is set to the mileage setting and not the trip meter setting.
b) Press and hold in the button on the left of the instrument panel.
c) Keeping the button depressed, switch off the ignition and release the button.
d) The word OEL should be shown on the display.
e) By depressing the left-hand button again, the display will change to IN 01, followed by IN 02.
f) Set the display to the relevant service which has just been performed, then depress the clock adjustment button briefly until "-----" is displayed. This indicates that the service interval display has been reset.
g) Repeat the reset procedure for all the relevant service display intervals.

3 On completion, switch on the ignition and check that IN 00 is shown in the display.

10 000 mile (15 000 km) Service - OEL on interval display

10 Engine oil and filter renewal - Turbo

Refer to Section 7.

11 Fuel filter draining - Turbo

Refer to Section 8.

12 Service interval display resetting - Turbo

Refer to Section 9.

Yearly Service - IN 01 on interval display

13 Idle speed check and adjustment

Engine codes AAZ and 1Y

1 Start the engine and run it until it reaches its normal operating temperature. With the handbrake applied and the transmission in neutral, allow the engine to idle. Check that the cold start knob is pushed in to the fully off position.

2 Using a diesel tachometer, check that the engine idle speed is as specified.

3 If necessary, adjust the idle speed by rotating the adjustment knob at the fuel injection pump **(see illustration)**.

Engine code 1Z

4 The engine idle speed must be checked and adjusted by a VAG dealer using dedicated electronic test equipment.

13.3 Idle speed adjustment knob (arrowed)

14 Service interval display resetting

Refer to Section 9.

20 000 mile (30 000 km) Service - IN 02 on interval display

15 Fuel filter renewal

1 The fuel filter is mounted on the inner wing, above the right hand wheel arch. Position a container underneath the filter unit and pad the surrounding area with rags to absorb any fuel that may be spilt.

2 At the top of the filter unit, release the clip and lift out the control valve, leaving the fuel hoses attached to it **(see illustrations)**.

3 Slacken the hose clips and pull the fuel supply and delivery hoses from the ports on the of the filter unit. If crimp type clips are fitted, cut them off using snips and use equivalent size worm drive clips on refitting. Note the fitted position of each hose, to aid correct refitting later. Be prepared for fuel loss.

4 Slacken the securing screw and raise the filter out its retaining bracket **(see illustrations)**.

5 Fit a new fuel filter into the retaining bracket and tighten the securing screw.

6 Refit the control valve to the top of the filter and insert the retaining clip.

7 Reconnect the fuel supply and delivery hoses **(see illustration)**. Note the fuel flow arrow markings next to each port.

8 Start and run the engine at idle, then check around the fuel filter for fuel leaks. It may take a few seconds of cranking before the engine starts.

9 Raise the engine speed to about 2000 rpm several times, then allow the engine to idle again. Observe the fuel flow through the transparent hose leading to the fuel injection pump and check that it is free of air bubbles.

15.2a Release clip . . .

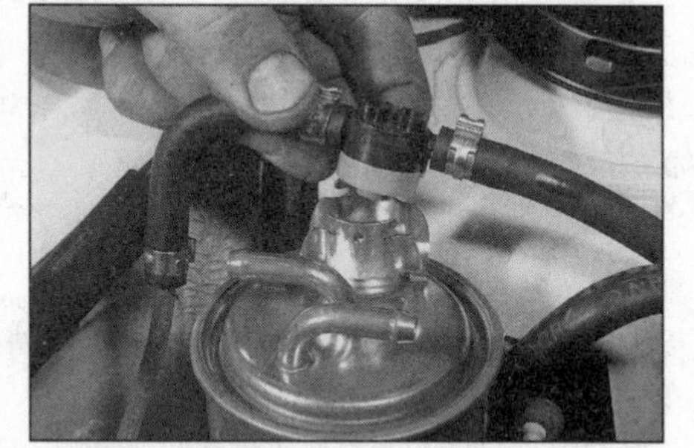

15.2b . . . and lift out control valve, leaving fuel hoses attached

15.4a Slacken securing screw . . .

15.4b . . . and lift filter out of retaining bracket

15.7 Reconnecting fuel supply and delivery hoses

16 Timing belt check and adjustment

1 Refer to Section 18, remove the timing belt cover and inspect the timing belt for signs of damage or deterioration.

2 Check the timing belt carefully for any signs of uneven wear, splitting or oil contamination. Pay particular attention to the roots of the teeth. Renew the belt if there is the slightest doubt about its condition.

3 If signs of oil contamination are found, trace the source of the oil leak and rectify it. Wash down the engine timing belt area and all related components to remove all traces of oil.

4 Check and if necessary adjust the belt tension, as described in Section 18. On completion, refit the belt cover.

17 Service interval display resetting

Refer to Section 9.

18.1 Fuel cut-off valve connector (arrowed)

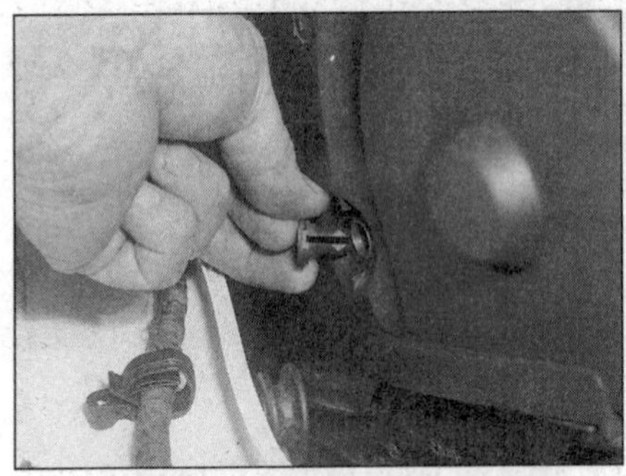
18.3 Removing a press-stud fixings from timing belt upper cover

18.6a Disconnect crankcase breather regulator valve . . .

60 000 mile (90 000 km) Service

18 Timing belt renewal

Note: *To lock the engine in the TDC position, it is necessary to either borrow or hire a kit of locking tools.*

Removal

1 Immobilise the engine by disconnecting the fuel cut-off solenoid cable **(see illustration)**. Prevent any vehicle movement by applying the handbrake and chocking the rear wheels.

2 Access to the timing belt covers can be improved by removing the air cleaner housing.

3 Release the uppermost part of the timing belt outer cover by prising open the metal spring clips and where applicable, removing the press-stud fixings **(see illustration)**. Lift the cover away from the engine

4 Remove the auxiliary drivebelt(s). Slacken and withdraw the screws and lift off the coolant pump pulley.

5 Set the engine to TDC on No 1 cylinder, as follows.

6 Remove the camshaft cover **(see illustrations)**.

7 Remove the inspection bung from the transmission bellhousing. Rotate the crankshaft clockwise until the timing mark machined onto the edge of the flywheel lines up with the pointer on the bellhousing casting **(see illustration)**.

8 To lock the engine in the TDC position, the camshaft (not the sprocket) and fuel injection pump sprocket must be secured in a reference position, using special locking tools. Improvised tools may be fabricated but due to the exact measurements and machining involved, it is strongly recommended that a kit of locking tools is either borrowed or hired from a VAG dealer, or purchased from a reputable tool manufacturer. Sykes Pickavant produce a kit of camshaft and fuel injection pump sprocket locking tools specifically for the range of engines covered in this Chapter **(see illustration)**.

9 Engage the edge of the locking bar with the slot in the end of the camshaft **(see illustration)**.

10 With the locking bar still inserted, turn the camshaft slightly (by turning the crankshaft clockwise, as before), so that the locking bar

18.6b . . . remove camshaft cover retaining nuts . . .

18.6c . . . lift camshaft cover away from cylinder head . . .

18.6d . . . and recover camshaft cover gasket

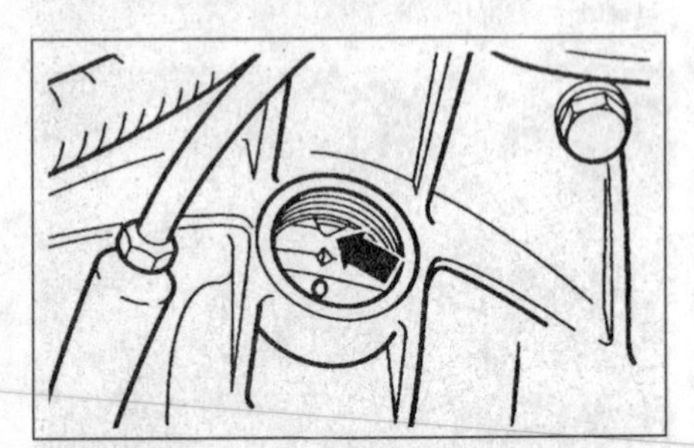
18.7 Remove inspection bung from transmission bellhousing to reveal timing mark on flywheel edge (arrowed) aligned with pointer on bellhousing casting

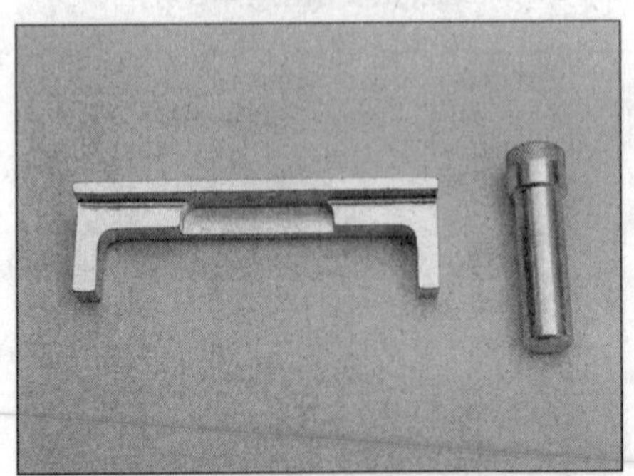
18.8 Engine locking tools

18.9 Engaging locking bar with camshaft slot

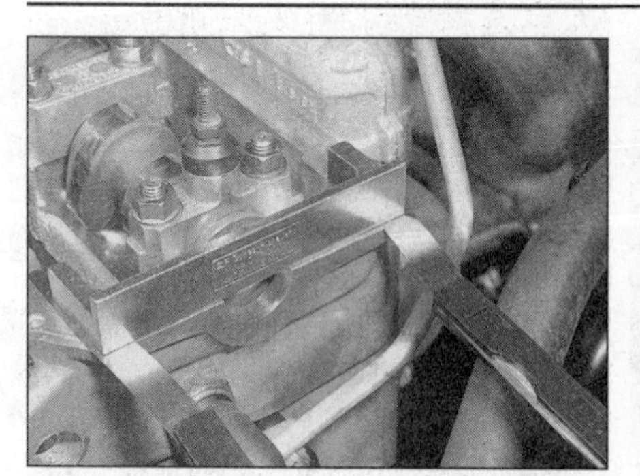
18.11 Camshaft centred and locked using locking bar and feeler blades

18.12 Fuel injection pump sprocket locked with locking pin (arrowed) - Engine code AAZ shown

18.14 Removing crankshaft auxiliary belt pulleys

rocks to one side, allowing one end of the bar to contact the cylinder head surface. At the other side of the locking bar, measure the gap between the end of the bar and the cylinder head using a feeler blade.

11 Turn the camshaft back slightly, then pull out the feeler blade. The idea now is to level the locking bar by inserting two feeler blades (each with a thickness equal to half the originally measured gap) on either side of the camshaft between each end of the locking bar and the cylinder head. This centres the camshaft and sets the valve timing in reference condition **(see illustration)**.

12 Insert the locking pin through the fuel injection pump sprocket alignment hole and thread it into the support bracket behind the sprocket. This locks the fuel injection pump in a reference condition **(see illustration)**.

13 The engine is now set to TDC on No 1 cylinder.

14 Slacken and withdraw the retaining screws, then remove the pulley for the ribbed auxiliary belt (together with the V-belt pulley, where fitted) from the crankshaft sprocket **(see illustration)**. To prevent the auxiliary belt pulley from rotating whilst the mounting bolts are being slackened, select top gear (manual transmission) or PARK (automatic transmission) and get an assistant to apply the footbrake firmly. Failing this, grip the sprocket by wrapping a length of old rubber hose or inner tube around it. On completion, check that the engine is still set to TDC.

15 Remove the retaining screws and clips, then lift off the timing belt lower cover.

16 On engines with a two-part fuel injection pump sprocket, ensure that the sprocket locking pin is firmly in position, then loosen the outer sprocket securing bolts by half a turn. Do not loosen the sprocket centre bolt, as this will alter the fuel injection pump's basic timing setting.

17 Relieve the tension on the timing belt by slackening the tensioner mounting nut slightly, allowing it to pivot away from the belt.

18 On engine code 1Z, slacken and withdraw the bolt and remove the idler roller from the timing belt inner cover.

19 Slide the belt off the sprockets.

20 Examine the belt for evidence of contamination by coolant or lubricant. If this is the case, identify and rectify the source of the contamination before progressing any further.

Refitting and tensioning

21 Ensure that the crankshaft is still set to TDC on No 1 cylinder.

22 Slacken the camshaft sprocket bolt by half a turn. Release the sprocket from the camshaft taper mounting by carefully tapping it with a pin punch inserted through the hole provided in the timing belt inner cover **(see illustration)**.

23 Loop the timing belt loosely under the crankshaft sprocket whilst observing the direction of rotation markings on the belt.

24 Engage the timing belt teeth with the crankshaft sprocket, then manoeuvre it into position over the camshaft and fuel injection pump sprockets. Ensure that the belt teeth seat correctly on the sprockets. Note that slight adjustments to the position of the camshaft sprocket (and where applicable, fuel injection pump sprocket) may be necessary to achieve this.

25 Pass the flat side of the belt over the intermediate shaft pulley and tensioner roller. Avoid bending the belt back on itself or twisting it excessively as you do this.

26 On engine code 1Z only, refit the idler roller to the timing belt inner cover and tighten the retaining bolt to the specified torque.

27 On engines with a single-part fuel injection pump sprocket, remove the locking pin from the fuel injection pump sprocket.

28 Ensure that the front run of the belt is taut. That is, all the slack should be in the section of the belt that passes over the tensioner roller.

29 Tension the belt by turning the eccentrically-mounted tensioner clockwise. Two holes are provided in the side of the tensioner hub for this purpose. A pair of sturdy right-angled circlip pliers is a suitable substitute for the correct VAG tool **(see illustrations)**.

30 On engines with a semi-automatic belt tensioner, turn the tensioner clockwise until the alignment markings on the pulley and hub are aligned **(see illustration)**.

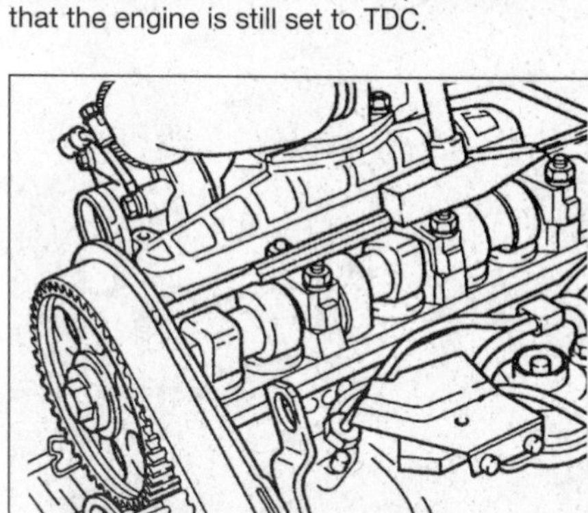
18.22 Releasing camshaft sprocket from taper by using pin punch

18.29a Tensioning timing belt with pair of circlip pliers in tensioner

18.29b Timing belt correctly fitted

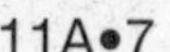

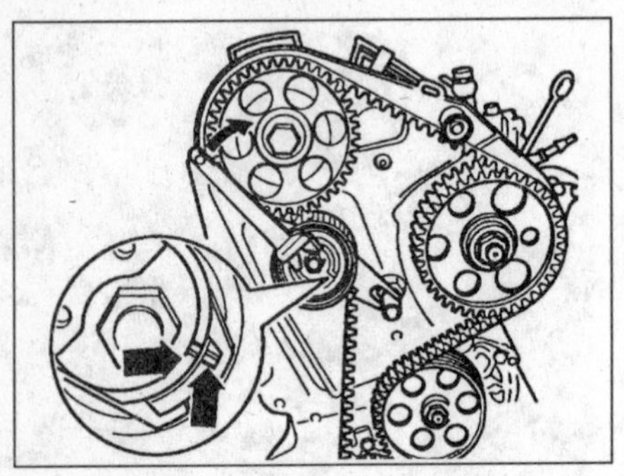

18.30 Alignment markings on pulley and hub - Engines with semi-automatic belt tensioner

31 Test the timing belt tension by grasping it between the fingers at a point mid-way between the intermediate shaft and camshaft sprockets, then twisting it. Belt tension is correct when it can just be twisted through 90° (quarter of a turn) and no further.

32 When the correct belt tension has been achieved, tighten the tensioner locknut to the specified torque.

33 On engines without a semi-automatic tensioner, belt tension must be accurately checked and if necessary, adjusted. This involves the use of a dedicated belt tension measuring device (Volkswagen tool No VW 210) and it is advisable to have this operation carried out by a VAG dealer.

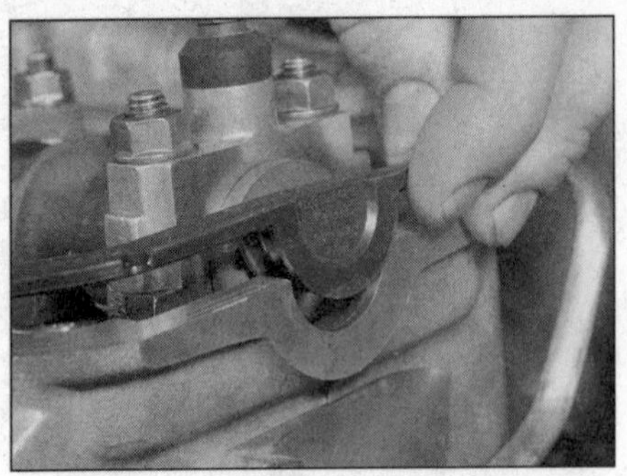

18.39 Ensure camshaft cover gasket is correctly seated on cylinder head

34 At this point, check that the crankshaft is still set to TDC on No 1 cylinder.

35 Tighten the camshaft sprocket bolt to the specified torque.

36 On engines with a two-part fuel injection pump sprocket, tighten the outer sprocket bolts then remove the sprocket locking pin.

37 Remove the camshaft locking bar.

38 Using a spanner or wrench and socket on the crankshaft pulley centre bolt, rotate the crankshaft through two complete revolutions. Reset the engine to TDC on No 1 cylinder and check that the fuel injection pump sprocket locking pin can be inserted. Re-check the timing belt tension and adjust it, if necessary.

39 Refit the upper and lower sections of the timing belt outer cover, tightening the retaining screws securely. Refit the camshaft cover **(see illustration)**.

40 Where applicable, refit the coolant pump pulley and tighten the retaining screws to the specified torque.

41 Refit the crankshaft auxiliary belt pulley and tighten the retaining screws to the specified torque, using the method employed during removal. Note that the offset of the pulley mounting holes allows only one fitting position.

42 Refit and tension the auxiliary drivebelt(s).

43 Restore the fuelling system by reconnecting the fuel cut-off solenoid wiring.

44 On completion, check the fuel injection pump timing.

Every 2 years, regardless of mileage

19 Exhaust emission check

1 This task should be entrusted to a VW dealer or suitable specialist equipped with the necessary gas analyser needed to check diesel exhaust gas emissions.

Chapter 11
Volkswagen 1896cc engine

Part B: Fuel system servicing

Contents

Specifications

Glow plugs

Type	CH160
Electrical resistance:	
Engine codes AAZ, 1Y	1.5 ohms (approx)
Engine code 1Z	N/A
Current consumption:	
Engine codes AAZ, 1Y	8 amps (per glow plug)
Engine code 1Z	N/A

Fuel injection pump

Timing - DTI reading (engine codes AAZ and 1Y):	
Test	0.83 - 0.97 mm
Setting	0.90 ± 0.02 mm

Idle speed

Engine codes AAZ and 1Y	900 ± 30 rpm

Fast idle speed

Engine codes AAZ and 1Y	1050 ± 50 rpm

Maximum speed

Engine codes AAZ and 1Y	5200 ± 100 rpm

Torque wrench settings

	Nm	lbf ft
Glow plugs:		
Engine code 1Z	15	11
Engine codes 1Y, AAZ	25	18
Injection pump fuel supply and return banjo bolts	25	18
Injection pump fuel union lock nuts	20	15
Injection pump head fuel unions	25	18
Injection pump timing plug	15	11
Injection pump to front support bracket bolts	25	18
Injection pump to rear support bracket bolts	25	18
Injection pump top cover screws (engine code 1Z)	10	7
Injector fuel pipe unions	25	18
Injectors	70	52

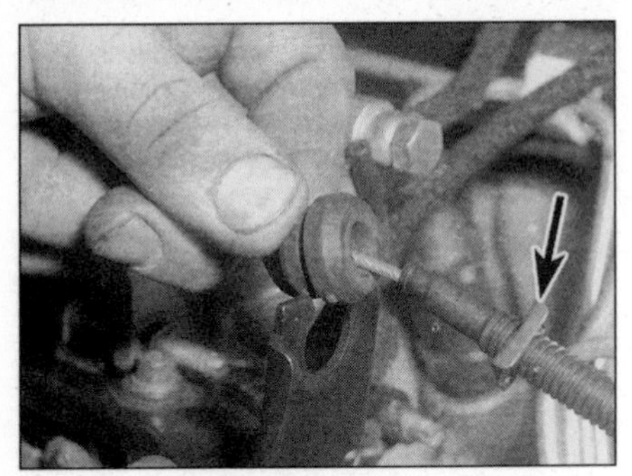
1.2 Accelerator cable adjuster clip (arrowed)

1 Accelerator cable - adjustment

Note: *This Section applies only to engine codes 1Y and AAZ. Engine code 1Z is fitted with an electronic accelerator position sensor, see Section 11.*

1 With the accelerator pedal fully depressed, the throttle lever of the fuel injection pump must be held wide open to its end stop.

2 If necessary, to achieve correct adjustment, remove the metal clip from its locating groove in the cable outer end and adjust the position of the cable outer in its mounting bracket before reinserting the clip **(see illustration)**.

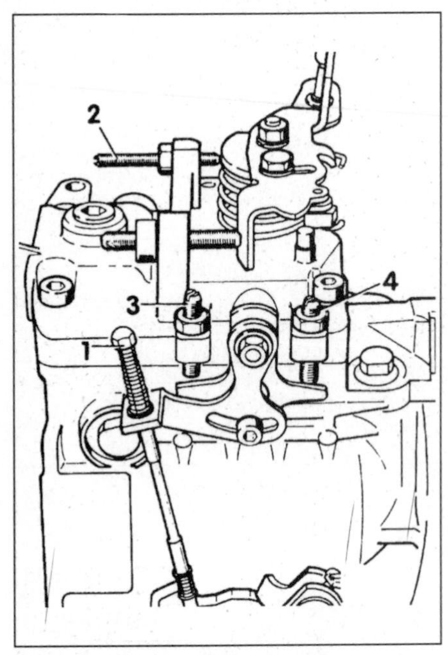

4.3 Fuel injection pump adjustment points - Engine codes AAZ and 1Y

1 *Idling speed adjustment screw*
2 *Maximum engine speed adjustment screw*
3 *Minimum idling speed stop screw*
4 *Maximum idling speed stop screw*

2 Cold Start Accelerator (CSA) cable - adjustment

1 Push the cold start knob into the "fully off" position.

2 Thread the CSA cable inner through the drilling in the lever on the injection pump. Hold the injection pump cold start lever in the closed position, then pull the cable inner taught to take up the slack and tighten the locking screw.

3 Operate the cold start knob and check that it is possible to move the injection pump lever through its full range of travel.

4 Push the cold start knob in to its "fully off" position, then start the engine and check the idle speed.

5 Pull the cold start knob fully out and check that the idle speed rises to approximately 1050 rpm. Readjust the cable if necessary.

3 Fast idle speed - checking and adjustment

Note: *This Section does not apply to engine code 1Z.*

1 With reference to Part A of this Chapter, check and if necessary adjust the engine idling speed.

2 Pull the facia cold start knob fully out and using a diesel tachometer, check that the idle speed rises to that specified.

3 If necessary, adjust the setting by slackening the lock nut and rotating the adjusting screw - refer to illustration 4.3.

4 On completion, tighten the lock nut.

4 Maximum speed - checking and adjustment

Note: *This Section does not apply to engine code 1Z.*

Warning: Do not maintain maximum engine speed for more than 2 or 3 seconds.

1 Start the engine and with the handbrake applied and the transmission in neutral, have an assistant depress the accelerator fully.

2 Using a diesel tachometer, check that the maximum engine speed is as specified.

3 If necessary, adjust the maximum engine speed by slackening the lock nut and rotating the adjusting screw **(see illustration)**.

4 On completion, tighten the lock nut.

5.2 Fuel cut-off valve connector (arrowed)

5 Fuel cut-off solenoid - removal and refitting

Removal

1 The fuel cut-off solenoid is located at the rear of the fuel injection pump.

2 Disconnect the battery negative cable and position it away from the terminal. Unplug the harness from the connector at the top of the valve **(see illustration)**.

3 Slacken and withdraw the valve body from the injection pump. Recover the sealing washer, O-ring and plunger.

Refitting

4 Refitting is a reversal of removal. Use a new sealing washer and O-ring.

6 Glow plugs - testing, removal and refitting

Testing

1 Connect a voltmeter or 12 volt test lamp between the glow plug supply cable and a good earth point on the engine, whilst ensuring that the live connection is kept well clear of the engine and bodywork.

2 Have an assistant activate the pre-heating system (either using the ignition key, or opening the drivers door as applicable) and check that a battery voltage is applied to the glow plug electrical connection. Note that the voltage will drop to zero when the pre-heating period ends.

3 If no supply voltage can be detected at the glow plug, then either the glow plug relay (where applicable) or the supply cabling must be faulty.

4 To locate a faulty glow plug, first disconnect the battery negative cable and position it away from the terminal.

5 Remove the supply cabling from the glow plug terminal. Measure the electrical resistance between the glow plug terminal and the engine earth. A reading of anything more than a few Ohms indicates that the plug is defective.

6 If a suitable ammeter is available, connect it between the glow plug and its supply cable and measure the steady state current consumption. Ignore the initial current surge which will be about 50% higher. Compare the result with that specified. High current consumption (or no current draw at all) indicates a faulty glow plug.

7 As a final check, remove each glow plug and inspect it visually, as follows.

Removal

8 Disconnect the battery negative cable and position it away from the terminal.

9 Remove the nuts and washers from the glow plug terminal. Lift off the bus bar **(see illustration)**.

10 Slacken and withdraw the glow plug **(see illustration)**.

11 Inspect the glow plug probe for signs of damage. A badly burned or charred probe is usually an indication of a faulty fuel injector.

Refitting

12 Refitting is a reversal of removal. Tighten the glow plug to the specified torque.

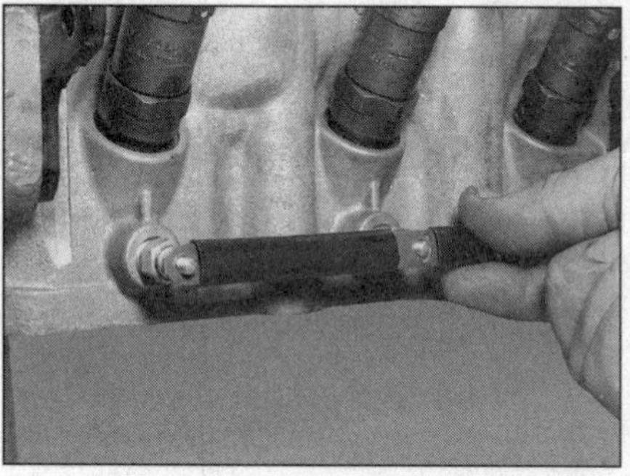

6.9 Detaching glow plug bus bar

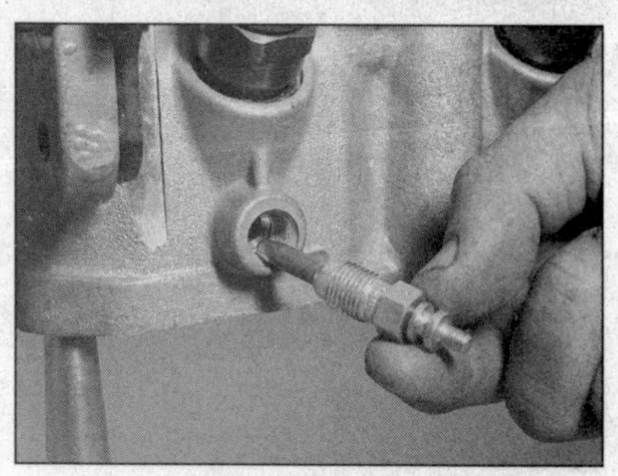

6.10 Removing a glow plug

7 Injectors - removal and refitting

Warning: Exercise extreme caution when working on fuel injectors. Never expose the hands or any part of the body to injector spray, as the high working pressure can cause the fuel to penetrate the skin, with possibly fatal results. You are strongly advised to have any work which involves testing the injectors under pressure carried out by a dealer or fuel injection specialist.

Note: *Take care not to allow dirt into the injectors or fuel pipes. Do not drop the injectors or allow the needles at their tips to become damaged. The injectors are precision-made to fine limits and must not be handled roughly.*

1 Injectors deteriorate with prolonged use and it is reasonable to expect them to need reconditioning or renewal after 60 000 miles (90 000 km) or so. Accurate testing, overhaul and calibration of the injectors must be left to a specialist. A defective injector which is causing knocking or smoking can be located without dismantling as follows.

2 Run the engine at a fast idle. Slacken each injector union in turn, placing rag around the union to catch spilt fuel and being careful not to expose the skin to any spray. When the union on the defective injector is slackened, the knocking or smoking will stop.

Removal

3 Disconnect the battery negative lead and cover the alternator with a clean cloth or plastic bag to prevent the possibility of fuel being spilt onto it.

4 Carefully clean around the injectors and pipe union nuts and disconnect the return pipe from the injector.

5 Wipe clean the pipe unions then slacken the union nut securing the relevant injector pipes to each injector and the relevant union nuts securing the pipes to the rear of the fuel injection pump (pipes are removed as one assembly). As each pump union nut is slackened, retain the adapter with a suitable open-ended spanner to prevent it being unscrewed from the pump. With the union nuts undone, remove the injector pipes from the engine. Cover the injector and pipe unions to prevent the entry of dirt into the system.

6 Unscrew the injector, using a deep socket or box spanner and remove it from the cylinder head **(see illustration)**.

7 Recover the heat shield washer **(see illustration)**.

Refitting

8 Fit a new heat shield washer to the cylinder head, noting that it must be fitted with its convex side facing downwards, towards the cylinder head **(see illustration)**.

9 Screw the injector into position and tighten it to the specified torque.

10 Refit the injector pipes and tighten the union nuts to the specified torque setting. Position any clips attached to the pipes as noted before removal.

11 Reconnect the return pipe securely to the injector.

12 Restore the battery connection and check the running of the engine.

8 Fuel injection pump - removal and refitting

Note: *On engine code 1Z, the injection pump commencement of injection setting must be checked and if necessary adjusted after refitting. The commencement of injection is controlled by the fuel injection ECU and is influenced by several other engine parameters, including coolant temperature and engine speed and position. Although the adjustment is a mechanical operation, checking can only be carried out by a VAG dealer, as dedicated electronic test equipment is needed to interface with the fuel injection ECU.*

Removal

1 Disconnect the battery negative cable and position it away from the terminal.

2 Carry out the following:

a) Remove the air cleaner (and air flow meter on engine code 1Z) and associated ducting.

7.6 Removing an injector

7.7 Recovering a heat shield washer

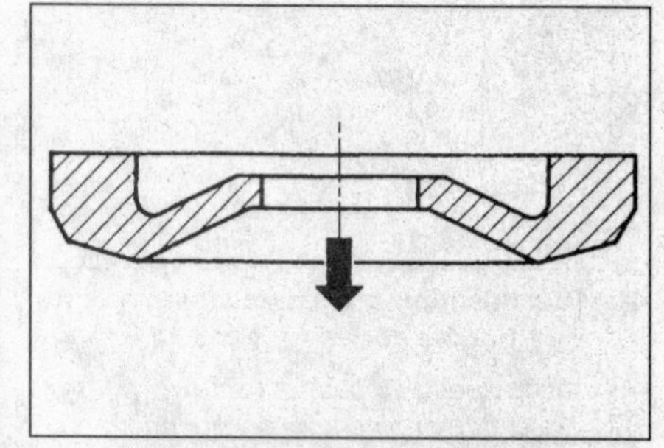

7.8 Heat shield washers must be fitted with convex side downwards (arrow faces cylinder head)

8.3 Loosening fuel injection pump sprocket retaining nut

8.4 Pull off injection pump sprocket . . .

8.5 . . . and recover Woodruff key

b) Remove the cylinder head cover and timing belt outer cover, see Part A of this Chapter (timing belt renewal).
c) Set the engine to TDC on No.1 cylinder, see Part A of this Chapter (timing belt renewal).
d) Remove the timing belt from the camshaft and fuel injection pump sprockets, see Part A of this Chapter.

3 Loosen the nut or bolts (as applicable) that secure the timing belt sprocket to the injection pump shaft. The sprocket must be braced whilst its fixings are loosened. A home made tool can easily be fabricated for this purpose **(see illustration)**. On engine codes AAZ and 1Y from Oct. 1994, the sprocket is a two-piece assembly which is secured with three bolts. On no account should the shaft centre nut be slackened, as this will alter the basic injection timing .

4 Attach a two-legged puller to the injection pump sprocket, then gradually tighten the puller until the sprocket is under firm tension **(see illustration)**. To prevent damage to the injection pump shaft, insert a piece of scrap metal between the end of the shaft and the puller centre bolt.

5 Tap sharply on the puller centre bolt with a hammer. This will free the sprocket from the tapered shaft. Detach the puller, then fully slacken and remove the sprocket fixings, lift off the sprocket and recover the Woodruff key **(see illustration)**.

6 Using a pair of spanners, slacken the rigid fuel pipe unions at the rear of the injection pump and at each end of the injectors, then lift the fuel pipe assembly away from the engine **(see illustrations)**. Be prepared for an amount of fuel leakage during this operation. Position a small container under the union to be slackened and pad the area with old rags, to catch any spilt diesel. Take great care to avoid stressing the rigid fuel pipes as they are removed.

7 Cover the open pipes and ports to prevent the ingress of dirt and excess fuel leakage.

8 Slacken the fuel supply and return banjo bolts at the injection pump ports, again taking precautions to minimise fuel spillage. Cover the open pipes and ports to prevent the ingress of dirt and excess fuel leakage.

9 Disconnect the injector bleed hose from the port on the fuel return union **(see illustration)**.

10 Disconnect the cabling from the stop control valve.

Engine codes except 1Z

11 Disconnect the cold start accelerator cable and accelerator cable from the injection pump.

Engine code 1Z only

12 Unplug the electrical wiring from the fuel cut-off valve/commencement of injection valve and the quantity adjuster module at the connectors, labelling the cables to aid refitting later.

Engine codes except post Oct 1994 AAZ and 1Y

13 If the existing injection pump is to be refitted later, mark the relationship between the injection pump body and the front mounting bracket. This will allow an approximate injection timing setting to be achieved when the pump is refitted.

Engine codes post Oct 1994 AAZ and 1Y

14 Unplug the electrical wiring from the following components, labelling the connectors to aid refitting later:

a) Commencement of injection valve.
b) Injection period sensor.
c) Engine code AAZ: The boost pressure enrichment cut-off valve.
d) Engine code 1Y: Full throttle stop valve.
e) Vehicles air conditioning: Idle speed boost actuator.

15 On later models, where the fuel injection pump wiring is not provided with individual connectors, free the engine harness multiway connector from its retaining bracket and unbolt the earth connection. Note that new injection pumps are not supplied with harness multiway connector housings. If the pump is to be renewed, then the relevant spade terminal pins must be pushed out of the existing connector housing, to allow those from the new pump to be inserted.

16 On vehicles with air conditioning, disconnect the vacuum hose from the idle speed boost actuator.

All engines

17 Slacken and withdraw the bolt that secures the fuel injection pump to the rear mounting bracket **(see illustration)**. Do not slacken the pump distributor head bolts, as this could cause serious internal damage to the pump.

8.6a Slackening rigid fuel pipe unions at rear of injection pump

8.6b Lifting fuel pipe assembly from engine

8.9 Disconnect injector bleed hose from port on fuel return union (arrowed)

8.17 Withdrawing injection pump rear mounting bolt

18 Slacken and withdraw the three nuts/bolts that secure the injection pump to the front mounting bracket. Note that where fixing bolts are used, the two outer bolts are held captive with metal brackets. Support the pump body as the last fixing is removed.

19 Check that nothing remains connected to the injection pump, then lift it away from the engine.

Refitting

20 Offer up the fuel injection pump to the engine, then insert the pump-to-rear support bracket bolt and tighten it to the specified torque.

21 Insert the injection pump-to-front support bracket bolts and tighten them to the specified torque. Note that on engine code 1Z and pre Oct 1994 engine codes AAZ and 1Y, the mounting holes are elongated to allow adjustment. If a new pump is being fitted, then mount it so that the bolts are initially at the centre of the holes to allow the maximum range of pump timing adjustment. Alternatively, if the existing pump is being refitted, use the markings made during removal for alignment.

22 On engine code 1Z and post Oct 1994 engine codes AAZ and 1Y where a new injection pump is being fitted, prime the pump by fitting a small funnel to the fuel return pipe union and filling the cavity with clean diesel. Pad the area around the union with clean dry rags to absorb any spillage.

23 Reconnect the fuel injector delivery pipes to the injectors and injection pump head, then tighten the unions to the correct torque.

24 Reconnect the fuel supply and return pipes to the FIP and tighten the banjo bolts to the specified torque, use new sealing washers. Note that the inside diameter of the banjo bolt for the fuel return pipe is smaller than that of the fuel supply line and is marked OUT.

25 Push the injector bleed hose onto the port on the return hose union.

26 Fit the timing belt sprocket to the injection pump shaft, ensuring that the Woodruff key is correctly seated. Fit the washer and retaining nut/bolts (as applicable), hand tightening them only at this stage.

27 Lock the injection pump sprocket in position by inserting a bar or bolt through its alignment hole and into the drilling in the pump front mounting bracket. Ensure that there is minimal play in the sprocket once it has been locked in position.

28 With reference to Part A of this Chapter, refit the timing belt, then check and adjust the injection pump to camshaft timing. On completion, tension the timing belt and tighten the fuel injection pump sprocket to the specified torque. Refit the timing belt outer cover and cylinder head cover, using a new gasket where necessary.

29 The remainder of the refitting procedure is a direct reversal of removal, noting the following points:

a) Reconnect all electrical connections to the pump, using the labels made during removal. When fitting a new injection pump to post Oct 1994 engine codes AAZ and 1Y, push the pump wiring terminal pins into their respective locations in the existing engine harness multiway connector.
b) All engine codes except 1Z: Reconnect the accelerator and cold start accelerator cables to the pump and adjust them as necessary.
c) Refit the air cleaner (and air flow meter on engine code 1Z) and its associated ducting.
d) Reconnect the battery negative cable.

Engine code 1Z

30 The commencement of injection must now be dynamically checked and if necessary adjusted by a VAG dealer.

Engine code AAZ and 1Y

31 Carry out the following:

a) Pre Oct 1994 engine codes AAZ and 1Y only: Check and if necessary adjust the injection pump static timing.
b) Check and if necessary adjust the engine idling speed.
c) Check and if necessary adjust the maximum no-load engine speed.
d) Post Oct 1994 models only: Check and if necessary adjust the engine fast idle speed.

9 Fuel injection pump - timing

Note: *On engine code 1Z, the fuel injection pump timing can only be tested and adjusted using dedicated test equipment. Refer to a VAG dealer for advice.*

1 Disconnect the battery negative cable and position it away from the terminal.

2 With reference to Part A of this Chapter, set the engine to TDC on No.1 cylinder then check the valve timing, adjusting it if necessary. On completion, reset the engine to TDC on No.1 cylinder.

3 At the rear of the injection pump, unscrew the plug from the pump head and recover the seal **(see illustration)**.

4 Using a suitably threaded adapter, screw a DTI gauge into the pump head **(see illustration)**. Pre-load the gauge by a reading of approximately 2.5 mm.

5 Using a socket and wrench on the crankshaft bolt, slowly rotate the crankshaft anti-clockwise. The DTI gauge will indicate movement. Keep turning the crankshaft until the movement just ceases.

6 Zero the DTI gauge, with a pre-load of approximately 1.0 mm.

7 Now rotate the crankshaft clockwise to bring the engine back up to TDC on cylinder No 1. Observe the reading indicated by the DTI gauge and compare it with that specified.

8 If the reading is within the specified test tolerance, remove the DTI gauge and refit the pump head plug. Use a new seal and tighten the plug to the specified torque.

9 If the reading is out of tolerance, proceed as follows.

10 Slacken the pump securing bolts at the front and rear brackets.

11 Rotate the injection pump body until the "Setting " reading specified is indicated on the DTI gauge.

12 On completion, tighten the pump securing bolts to the specified torque.

13 Remove the DTI gauge and refit the pump head plug. Use a new seal and tighten the plug to the specified torque.

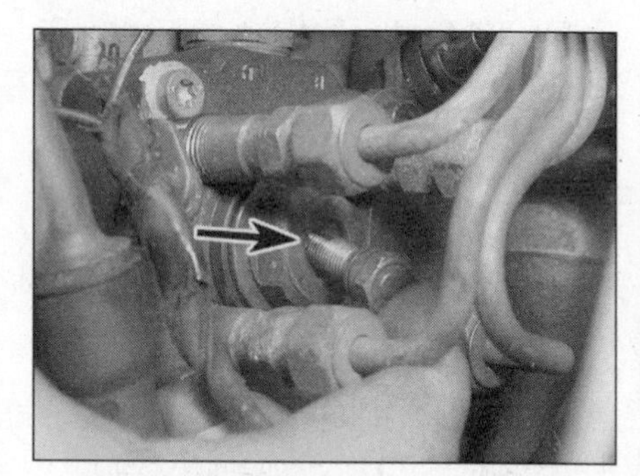

9.3 Unscrewing plug (arrowed) from pump head

9.4 Screw DTI gauge with adapter into pump head

10 Glow plug control unit - removal and refitting

Note: *On engine code 1Z, the pre-heating system is controlled by the diesel engine management system ECU.*

Removal

1 The glow plug control unit is located behind the facia, above the main relay box. Remove the relevant sections of trim to gain access.
2 Disconnect the battery negative cable and position it away from the terminal.
3 Unplug the wiring harness from the control unit at the connector.
4 Remove the retaining screws and lift the control unit from its mounting bracket.

Refitting

5 Refitting is a reversal of removal.

11 Engine management system - component removal and refitting

Note: *This Section refers to engine code 1Z only.*

Accelerator position sensor

Removal

1 Disconnect the battery negative cable and position it away from the terminal.
2 Remove the trim panels from under the steering column area of the facia, to gain access to the pedal cluster.
3 Prise the clip from the end of the accelerator pedal spindle, then withdraw the spindle and recover the bush and spring.
4 Lift the accelerator pedal clear of the pedal bracket, disengaging it from the position sensor cable cam plate.

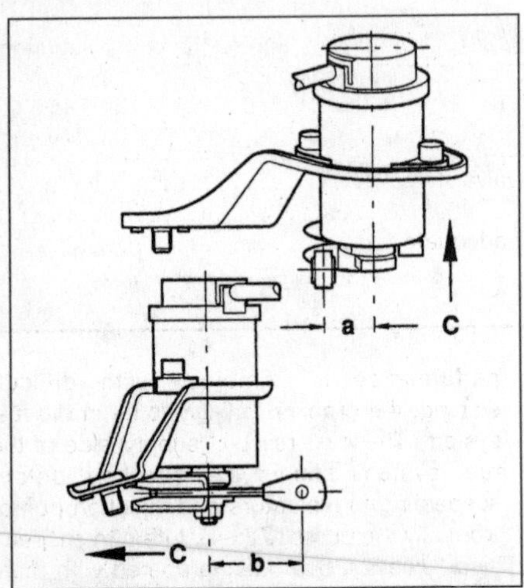

11.9 Mounting arrangement of accelerator position sensor cable cam plate

a 22 ± 0.5 mm
b 41± 0.5 mm
C Towards front of vehicle

5 Unplug the position sensor from the wiring harness at the connector.
6 Remove the screw that secures the position sensor bracket to the pedal bracket.
7 Remove the sensor from the pedal bracket, then remove the fixings and release it from the mounting bracket.
8 Slacken and remove the spindle nut, then pull the cable cam plate off the spindle.

Refitting

9 Refitting is a reversal of removal, noting the following points:

*a) The cable cam plate must be fitted to the position sensor spindle, according to the dimensions shown **(see illustration)**.*
b) On completion, the adjustment of the position sensor must be verified electronically, using dedicated test equipment. Refer to a VAG dealer for advice.

Coolant temperature sensor

Removal

10 Disconnect the battery negative cable and position it away from the terminal, then drain approximately one quarter of the coolant from the engine.
11 The sensor is mounted at the top coolant outlet elbow, at the front of the cylinder head. Unplug the wiring harness from it at the connector.
12 Remove the securing clip and extract the sensor from its housing, recovering the O-ring. Be prepared for an amount of coolant loss.

Refitting

13 Refit the coolant temperature sensor by reversing the removal procedure, using a new O-ring. Replenish the cooling system.

Fuel temperature sensor

Removal

14 Disconnect the battery negative cable and position it away from the terminal.
15 Slacken and withdraw the retaining screws and lift the top cover from the injection pump. Recover the gasket.
16 Remove the screws and lift out the fuel temperature sensor.

Refitting

17 Refitting is a reversal of removal. Tighten the pump top cover screws to the specified torque.

Inlet air temperature sensor

Removal

18 Disconnect the battery negative cable and position it away from the terminal.
19 The sensor is mounted in the air duct between the intercooler and the inlet manifold. Unplug the wiring harness from it at the connector.
20 Remove the securing clip and extract the sensor from its housing, recovering the O-ring.

Refitting

21 Refit the inlet air temperature sensor by reversing the removal procedure, using a new O-ring. Replenish the cooling system.

Engine speed signal sensor

Removal

22 The engine speed sensor is mounted on the front cylinder block, adjacent to the mating surface of the block and transmission bellhousing.
23 Disconnect the battery negative cable and position it away from the terminal, then unplug the harness connector from the sensor.
24 Remove the retaining screw and withdraw the sensor from the cylinder block.

Refitting

25 Refitting is a reversal of removal.

Air flow meter

Removal

26 Disconnect the battery negative cable and position it away from the terminal.
27 Slacken the clips and disconnect the air ducting from the air flow meter, at the rear of the air cleaner housing.
28 Unplug the harness connector from the air flow meter.
29 Remove the retaining screws and extract the meter from the air cleaner housing. Recover the O-ring. Handle the air flow meter carefully as its internal components are easily damaged.

Refitting

30 Refitting is a reversal of removal. Renew the O-ring if damaged.

Manifold pressure sensor

31 The manifold pressure sensor is an integral part of the Electronic Control Unit and hence cannot be renewed separately.

Absolute pressure sensor

Vehicles up to Aug 1994

32 The sensor is mounted behind the facia, above the relay board. Remove the relevant sections of the facia to gain access.
33 Disconnect the battery negative cable and position it away from the terminal. Unclip the sensor from its bracket and unplug it from the wiring harness at the connector.

Vehicles from Aug 1994

34 The absolute pressure sensor is an integral part of the Electronic Control Unit and hence cannot be renewed separately.

Boost pressure valve

Removal

35 The boost pressure valve is mounted on the inner wing, to the rear of the air cleaner housing.
36 Disconnect the battery negative cable and position it away from the terminal. Unplug the wiring harness from it at the connector.
37 Remove the vacuum hoses from the ports on the boost control valve, noting their order of connection carefully to aid correct refitting later.
38 Remove the retaining screw and lift the valve away from the inner wing.

Refitting

39 Refitting is a reversal of removal.

Chapter 12
Fault diagnosis

Contents

1 Introduction

The majority of starting problems on small Diesel engines are electrical in origin. The mechanic who is familiar with petrol engines but less so with Diesel may be inclined to view the Diesel's injectors and pump in the same light as the spark plugs and distributor but this is generally a mistake.

When investigating complaints of difficult starting for someone else, ensure that the correct starting procedure is understood and is being followed. Some drivers are unaware of the significance of the preheating warning light - many modern engines are sufficiently forgiving for this not to matter in mild weather but with the onset of winter, problems begin.

As a rule of thumb, if the engine is difficult to start but runs well when it has finally got going, the problem is electrical (battery, starter motor or preheating system). If poor performance is combined with difficult starting, the problem is likely to be in the fuel system. The low pressure (supply) side of the fuel system should be checked before suspecting the injectors and injection pump. Normally the pump is the last item to suspect, since unless it has been tampered with there is no reason for it to be at fault.

The following table lists various possible causes of faults:

2 Fault diagnosis - symptoms and reasons

Engine turns but will not start (cold)

- ☐ Incorrect use of preheating system
- ☐ Preheating system fault
- ☐ Fuel waxing (in very cold weather)
- ☐ Overfuelling or cold start advance mechanism defective

Engine turns but will not start (hot or cold)

- ☐ Low cranking speed (see below)
- ☐ Poor compression (Section 3)
- ☐ No fuel in tank
- ☐ Air in fuel system (Section 4)
- ☐ Fuel feed restriction (Section 5)
- ☐ Fuel contaminated
- ☐ Stop solenoid defective (Section 17)
- ☐ Major mechanical failure
- ☐ Injection pump internal fault

Low cranking speed

- ☐ Inadequate battery capacity
- ☐ Incorrect grade of oil
- ☐ High resistance in starter motor circuit
- ☐ Starter motor internal fault

Engine is difficult to start

- ☐ Incorrect starting procedure
- ☐ Battery or starter motor fault
- ☐ Preheating system fault
- ☐ Air in fuel system (Section 4)
- ☐ Fuel feed restriction (Section 5)
- ☐ Poor compression (Section 3)
- ☐ Valve clearances incorrect
- ☐ Valves sticking
- ☐ Blockage in exhaust system
- ☐ Valve timing incorrect
- ☐ Injector(s) faulty
- ☐ Injection pump timing incorrect
- ☐ Injection pump internal fault

Engine starts but stops again

- ☐ Fuel very low in tank
- ☐ Air in fuel system (Section 4)
- ☐ Idle adjustment incorrect
- ☐ Fuel feed restriction (Section 5)
- ☐ Fuel return restriction
- ☐ Air cleaner dirty
- ☐ Blockage in induction system
- ☐ Blockage in exhaust system
- ☐ Injector(s) faulty

Engine will not stop when switched off

- ☐ Stop solenoid defective (Section 17)

Misfiring/rough idle

- ☐ Air cleaner dirty
- ☐ Blockage in induction system
- ☐ Air in fuel system (Section 4)
- ☐ Fuel feed restriction (Section 5)
- ☐ Valve clearances incorrect
- ☐ Valve(s) sticking
- ☐ Valve spring(s) weak or broken
- ☐ Poor compression (Section 3)
- ☐ Overheating (Section 15)
- ☐ Injector pipe(s) wrongly connected or wrong type
- ☐ Valve timing incorrect
- ☐ Injector(s) faulty or wrong type
- ☐ Injection pump timing incorrect
- ☐ Injection pump faulty or wrong type

Lack of power (Section 6)

- ☐ Accelerator linkage not moving through full travel (cable slack or pedal obstructed)
- ☐ Injection pump control linkages sticking or maladjusted
- ☐ Air cleaner dirty
- ☐ Blockage in induction system
- ☐ Air in fuel system (Section 4)
- ☐ Fuel feed restriction (Section 5)
- ☐ Valve timing incorrect
- ☐ Injection pump timing incorrect
- ☐ Blockage in exhaust system
- ☐ Turbo boost pressure inadequate, when applicable (Section 7)
- ☐ Valve clearances incorrect
- ☐ Poor compression (Section 3)
- ☐ Injector(s) faulty or wrong type
- ☐ Injection pump faulty

Fuel consumption excessive (Section 8)

- ☐ External leakage
- ☐ Fuel passing into sump (Section 9)
- ☐ Air cleaner dirty
- ☐ Blockage in induction system
- ☐ Valve clearances incorrect
- ☐ Valve(s) sticking
- ☐ Valve spring(s) weak
- ☐ Poor compression (Section 3)
- ☐ Valve timing incorrect
- ☐ Injection pump timing incorrect
- ☐ Injector(s) faulty or wrong type
- ☐ Injection pump faulty

Engine knocks (Section 10)

- ☐ Air in fuel system (Section 4)
- ☐ Fuel grade incorrect or quality poor
- ☐ Injector(s) faulty or wrong type (Section 10)
- ☐ Valve spring(s) weak or broken
- ☐ Valve(s) sticking
- ☐ Valve clearances incorrect
- ☐ Valve timing incorrect
- ☐ Injection pump timing incorrect
- ☐ Piston protrusion excessive/head gasket thickness inadequate (after repair)
- ☐ Valve recess incorrect (after repair)
- ☐ Piston rings broken or worn
- ☐ Pistons and/or bores worn
- ☐ Crankshaft bearings worn or damaged
- ☐ Small-end bearings worn
- ☐ Camshaft worn

Black smoke in exhaust (Section 11)

- ☐ Air cleaner dirty
- ☐ Blockage in induction system
- ☐ Valve clearances incorrect
- ☐ Poor compression (Section 3)
- ☐ Turbo boost pressure inadequate, when applicable (Section 7)
- ☐ Blockage in exhaust system
- ☐ Valve timing incorrect
- ☐ Injector(s) faulty or wrong type
- ☐ Injection pump timing incorrect
- ☐ Injection pump faulty

Blue or white smoke in exhaust (Section 11)

- ☐ Engine oil incorrect grade or poor quality
- ☐ Glow plug(s) defective, or controller faulty (smoke at start-up only)
- ☐ Air cleaner dirty
- ☐ Blockage in induction system
- ☐ Valve timing incorrect
- ☐ Injection pump timing incorrect
- ☐ Injector(s) defective, or heat shields damaged or missing
- ☐ Engine running too cool
- ☐ Oil entering via valve stems (Section 12)
- ☐ Poor compression (Section 3)
- ☐ Head gasket blown
- ☐ Piston rings broken or worn
- ☐ Pistons and/or bores worn

Oil consumption excessive (Section 13)

- ☐ External leakage (standing or running)
- ☐ New engine not yet run-in
- ☐ Engine oil incorrect grade or poor quality
- ☐ Oil level too high
- ☐ Crankcase ventilation system obstructed
- ☐ Oil leaking from oil feed pipe into fuel feed pipe
- ☐ Oil leakage from ancillary component (vacuum pump etc.)
- ☐ Oil leaking into coolant
- ☐ Oil leaking into injection pump
- ☐ Air cleaner dirty
- ☐ Blockage in induction system
- ☐ Cylinder bores glazed (Section 14)
- ☐ Piston rings broken or worn
- ☐ Pistons and/or bores worn
- ☐ Valve stems or guides worn
- ☐ Valve stem oil seals worn

Overheating (Section 15)

- ☐ Coolant leakage
- ☐ Engine oil level too high
- ☐ Electric cooling fan malfunctioning
- ☐ Coolant pump defective
- ☐ Radiator clogged externally
- ☐ Radiator clogged internally
- ☐ Coolant hoses blocked or collapsed
- ☐ Coolant reservior pressure cap defective or incorrect
- ☐ Coolant thermostat defective or incorrect
- ☐ Thermostat missing
- ☐ Air cleaner dirty
- ☐ Blockage in induction system
- ☐ Blockage in exhaust system
- ☐ Head gasket blown
- ☐ Cylinder head cracked or warped
- ☐ Valve timing incorrect
- ☐ Injection pump timing incorrect (over-advanced)
- ☐ Injector(s) faulty or wrong type
- ☐ Injection pump faulty
- ☐ Imminent seizure (piston pick-up)

Crankcase pressure excessive (oil being blown out)

- ☐ Blockage in crankcase ventilation system
- ☐ Leakage in vacuum pump or exhauster
- ☐ Piston rings broken or sticking
- ☐ Pistons or bores worn
- ☐ Head gasket blown

Erratic running

- ☐ Operating temperature incorrect
- ☐ Accelerator linkage maladjusted or sticking
- ☐ Air cleaner dirty
- ☐ Blockage in induction system
- ☐ Air in fuel system (Section 4)
- ☐ Injector pipe(s) wrongly connected or wrong type
- ☐ Fuel feed restriction (Section 5)
- ☐ Fuel return restriction
- ☐ Valve clearances incorrect
- ☐ Valve(s) sticking
- ☐ Valve spring(s) broken or weak
- ☐ Valve timing incorrect
- ☐ Poor compression (Section 3)
- ☐ Injector(s) faulty or wrong type
- ☐ Injection pump mountings loose
- ☐ Injection pump timing incorrect
- ☐ Injection pump faulty

Vibration

- ☐ Accelerator linkage sticking
- ☐ Engine mountings loose or worn
- ☐ Cooling fan damaged or loose
- ☐ Crankshaft pulley/damper damaged or loose
- ☐ Injector pipe(s) wrongly connected or wrong type
- ☐ Valve(s) sticking
- ☐ Flywheel or (when applicable) flywheel housing loose
- ☐ Poor (uneven) compression (Section 3)

Low oil pressure

- ☐ Oil level low
- ☐ Oil grade or quality incorrect
- ☐ Oil filter clogged
- ☐ Overheating (Section 15)
- ☐ Oil contaminated (Section 16)
- ☐ Gauge or warning light sender inaccurate
- ☐ Oil pump pick-up strainer clogged
- ☐ Oil pump suction pipe loose or cracked
- ☐ Oil pressure relief valve defective or stuck open
- ☐ Oil pump worn
- ☐ Crankshaft bearings worn

High oil pressure

- ☐ Oil grade or quality incorrect
- ☐ Gauge inaccurate
- ☐ Oil pressure relief valve stuck shut

Injector pipe(s) break or split repeatedly

- ☐ Missing or wrongly located clamps
- ☐ Wrong type or length of pipe
- ☐ Faulty injector
- ☐ Faulty delivery valve

3.14a Leakdown test adaptor being fitted to a glow plug hole

3.14b Whistle fitted to adaptor to find TDC

3 Poor compression

1 Poor compression may give rise to a number of faults, including difficult starting, loss of power, misfiring or uneven running and smoke in the exhaust.

2 Before looking for mechanical reasons for compression loss, check that the problem is not on the induction side. A dirty air cleaner or some other blockage in the induction system can restrict air intake to the point where compression suffers.

3 Mechanical reasons for low compression include :

a) Incorrect valve clearances
b) Sticking valves
c) Weak or broken valve springs
d) Incorrect valve timing
e) Worn or burnt valve heads and seats
f) Worn valve stems and guides
g) Head gasket blown
h) Piston rings broken or sticking
i) Pistons or bores worn
j) Head gasket thickness incorrect (after rebuild)

4 Compression loss on one cylinder alone can be due to a defective or badly seated glow plug, or a leaking injector sealing washer. Some engines also have a cylinder head plug for the insertion of a dial test indicator probe when determining TDC and this should not be overlooked.

5 Compression loss on two adjacent cylinders is almost certainly due to the head gasket blowing between them. Sometimes the fault will be corrected by renewing the gasket but a blown gasket can also be an indication that the cylinder head itself is warped. Always check the head mating face for distortion when renewing the gasket. On wet liner engines also check liner protrusion.

Compression test

6 A compression tester specifically intended for Diesel engines must be used, because of the higher pressures involved. The tester is connected to an adaptor which screws into the glow plug or injector hole. Normally sealing washers must be used on both sides of the adaptor.

7 Unless specific instructions to the contrary are supplied with the tester, observe the following points :

a) The battery must be in a good state of charge, the air cleaner element must be clean and the engine should be at normal operating temperature
b) All the injectors or glow plugs should be removed before starting the test. If removing the injectors, also remove their heat shields (when fitted), otherwise they may be blown out
c) The stop control lever on the injection pump must be operated, or the stop solenoid disconnected, to prevent the engine from running or fuel from being discharged

8 There is no need to hold the accelerator pedal down during the test because the Diesel engine air inlet is not throttled. There are rare exceptions to this case, when a throttle valve is used to produce vacuum for servo or governor operation.

9 The actual compression pressures measured are not so important as the balance between cylinders. Typical values at cranking speed are:

Good condition - 25 to 30 bar (363 to 435 lbf/in²)
Minimum - 18 bar (261 lbf/in²)
Maximum difference between cylinders - 5 bar (73 lbf/in²)

10 The cause of poor compression is less easy to establish on a Diesel engine than on a petrol one. The effect of introducing oil into the cylinders (wet testing) is not conclusive, because there is a risk that the oil will sit in the bowl in the piston crown (direct injection engines) or in the swirl chamber (indirect) instead of passing to the rings.

3.15 Leakdown tester in use

Leakdown test

11 A leakdown test measures the rate at which compressed air fed into the cylinder is lost. It is an alternative to a compression test and in many ways it is better, since it provides easy identification of where pressure loss is occurring (piston rings, valves or head gasket). However, it does require a source of compressed air.

12 Before beginning the test, remove the cooling system pressure cap. This is necessary because if there is a leak into the cooling system, the introduction of compressed air may damage the radiator. Similarly, it is advisable to remove the dipstick or the oil filler cap to prevent excessive crankcase pressurisation.

13 Connect the tester to a compressed air line and adjust the reading to 100% as instructed by the manufacturer.

14 Remove the glow plugs or injectors and screw the appropriate adaptor into a glow plug or injector hole. Fit the whistle to the adaptor and turn the crankshaft. When the whistle begins to sound, the piston in question is rising on compression. When the whistle stops, TDC has been reached **(see illustrations)**.

15 Engage a gear and apply the handbrake to stop the engine turning. Remove the whistle and connect the tester to the adaptor. Note the tester reading, which indicates the rate at which the air escapes. Repeat the test on the other cylinders **(see illustration)**.

16 The tester reading is in the form of a percentage, where 100% is perfect. Readings of 80% or better are to be expected from an engine in good condition. The actual reading is less important than the balance between cylinders, which should be within 5%.

17 The areas from which escaping air emerges show where a fault lies, as follows :

Air escaping from	Probable cause
Oil filler cap or dipstick tube	*Worn piston rings or cylinder bores*
Exhaust pipe	*Worn or burnt exhaust valve*
Air cleaner/inlet manifold	*Worn or burnt inlet valve*
Cooling system	*Blown head gasket or cracked cylinder head*

18 Bear in mind that if the head gasket is blown between two adjacent cylinders, air escaping from the cylinder under test may emerge via an open valve in the cylinder adjacent.

4 Air in fuel system

1 The Diesel engine will not run at all, or at best will run erratically, if there is air in the fuel lines. If the fuel tank has been allowed to run dry, or after operations in which the fuel supply lines have been opened, the fuel system must be bled before the engine will run.
2 Unlike some older systems, manual bleeding or venting of the fuel system fitted to the engines covered in this Manual is not necessary, even if the fuel tank is run dry. Provided that the battery is in good condition, simply cranking the engine on the starter motor will eventually bleed the system. Note that the starter motor should not be operated for more than ten seconds at a time whilst allowing five seconds between periods of operation.
3 Air will also enter the fuel lines through any leaking joint or seal, since the supply side is under negative pressure all the time that the engine is running.

5 Fuel feed restricted

1 Restriction in the fuel feed from the tank to the pump may be caused by any of the following faults :
a) Fuel filter blocked
b) Tank vent blocked
c) Feed pipe blocked or collapsed
d) Fuel waxing (in very cold weather)

Fuel waxing

2 In the case of fuel waxing, the wax normally builds up first in the filter. If the filter can be warmed this will often allow the engine to run. ***Caution : Do not use a naked flame for this.*** Only in exceptionally severe weather will waxing prevent winter grade fuel from being pumped out of the tank.

Microbiological contamination

3 Under certain conditions it is possible for micro-organisms to colonise the fuel tank and supply lines. These micro-organisms produce a black sludge or slime which can block the filter and cause corrosion of metal parts. The problem normally shows up first as an unexpected blockage of the filter.
4 If such contamination is found, drain the fuel tank and discard the drained fuel. Flush the tank and fuel lines with clean fuel and renew the fuel filter - in bad cases steam clean the tank as well. If there is evidence that the contamination has passed the fuel filter, have the injection pump cleaned by a specialist.
5 Further trouble may be avoided by only using fuel from reputable outlets with a high turnover. Proprietary additives are also available to inhibit the growth of micro-organisms in storage tanks or in the vehicle fuel tank.

6 Lack of power

1 Complaints of lack of power are not always justified. If necessary, perform a road or dynamometer test to verify the condition. Even if power is definitely down, the complaint is not necessarily due to an engine or injection system fault.
2 Before commencing detailed investigation, check that the accelerator linkage is moving through its full travel. Also make sure that an apparent power loss is not caused by items such as binding brakes, under-inflated tyres, overloading of the vehicle, or some particular feature of operation.

7 Turbo boost pressure inadequate

1 If boost pressure is low, power will be down and too much fuel may be delivered at high engine speeds (depending on the method of pump control). Possible reasons for low boost pressure include :
a) Air cleaner dirty
b) Leaks in induction system
c) Blockage in exhaust system
d) Turbo control fault (wastegate or actuator)
e) Turbo mechanical fault

8 Fuel consumption excessive

1 Complaints of excessive fuel consumption, as with lack of power, may not mean that a fault exists. If the complaint is justified and there are no obvious fuel leaks, check the same external factors as for lack of power before turning to the engine and injection system.

9 Fuel in sump

1 If fuel oil is found to be diluting the oil in the sump, this can only have arrived by passing down the cylinder bores. Assuming that the problem is not one of excessive fuel delivery, piston and bore wear is indicated.
2 Fuel contamination of the oil can be detected by smell, and in bad cases by an obvious reduction in viscosity.

10 Knocking caused by injector fault

1 A faulty injector which is causing knocking noises can be identified as follows.
2 Clean around the injector fuel pipe unions. Run the engine at a fast idle so that the knock can be heard. Using for preference a split ring spanner, slacken and retighten each injector union in turn.

Warning: Protect yourself against contact with Diesel fuel by covering each union with a piece of rag to absorb the fuel which will spray out.

3 When the union supplying the defective injector is slackened, the knock will disappear. Stop the engine and remove the injector for inspection.

11 Excessive exhaust smoke

1 Check first that the smoke is still excessive when the engine has reached normal operating temperature. A cold engine may produce some blue or white smoke until it has warmed up; this is not necessarily a fault.

Black smoke

2 This is produced by incomplete combustion of the fuel in such a way that carbon particles (soot) are formed. Incomplete combustion shows that there is a lack of oxygen, either because too much fuel is being delivered or because not enough air is being drawn into the cylinders. A dirty air cleaner is an obvious cause of air starvation; incorrect valve clearances should also be considered. Combustion may also be incomplete because the injection timing is incorrect (too far retarded) or because the injector spray pattern is poor.

Blue smoke

3 This is produced either by incomplete combustion of the fuel or by burning lubricating oil. This type of incomplete combustion may be caused by incorrect injection timing (too far advanced), by defective injectors or by damaged or missing injector heat shields.
4 All engines burn a certain amount of oil, especially when cold, but if enough is being burnt to cause excessive exhaust smoke this suggests that there is a significant degree of wear or some other problem.

White smoke

5 Not to be confused with steam, this is produced by unburnt or partially burnt fuel appearing in the exhaust gases. Some white smoke is normal during and immediately after start-up, especially in cold conditions. Excessive amounts of white smoke can be caused by a preheating system fault, by incorrect injection pump timing, or by too much fuel being delivered by the injection pump (overfuelling device malfunctioning). The use of poor quality fuel with a low cetane number, and thus a long ignition delay, can also increase emissions of white smoke.
6 Accurate measurement of exhaust smoke requires the use of a smoke meter. This is not a DIY job, but any garage which carries out Diesel MoT tests will have such a meter.

12 Oil entering engine via valve stems

1 Excessive oil consumption due to oil passing down the valve stems can have three causes :

a) Valve stem wear
b) Valve guide wear
c) Valve stem oil seal wear

2 In the first two cases the cylinder head must be removed and dismantled so that the valves and guides can be inspected and measured for wear.

13 Oil consumption excessive

1 When investigating complaints of excessive oil consumption, make sure that the correct level checking procedure is being followed. If insufficient time is allowed for the oil to drain down after stopping the engine, or if the level is checked while the vehicle is standing on a slope, a false low reading may result. The unnecessary topping-up which follows may of itself cause increased oil consumption as a result of the level being too high.

14 Cylinder bore glazing

1 Engines which spend long periods idling can suffer from glazing of the cylinder bores, leading to high oil consumption even though no significant wear has taken place. The same effect can be produced by incorrect running-in procedures, or by the use of the incorrect grade of oil during running-in. The remedy is to remove the pistons, deglaze the bores with a hone or 'glaze buster' tool and to fit new piston rings.

15 Overheating

1 Any modern engine will certainly suffer serious damage if overheating is allowed to occur. The importance of regular and conscientious cooling system maintenance cannot be overstressed. Always use a good quality antifreeze and renew it regularly. When refilling the cooling sytem, follow the specified procedures carefully in order to eliminate any airlocks.

2 If overheating does occur, do not continue to drive. Stop at once and do not proceed until the problem is fixed.

17.3 Stop solenoid wire secured by nut (arrowed)

16 Oil contamination

1 Oil contamination falls into three categories - dirt, sludge and dilution.

Dirt

2 Dirt or soot builds up in the oil in normal operation. It is not a problem if regular oil and filter changes are carried out. If it gets to the stage where it is causing low oil pressure, change the oil and filter immediately.

Sludge

3 This occurs when inferior oils are used, or when regular oil changes have been neglected. It is more likely to occur on engines which rarely reach operating temperature. If sludge is found when draining, a flushing oil may be used if the engine manufacturer allows it. The engine should then be refilled with fresh oil of the correct grade and a new oil filter be fitted.

Caution : Some engine manufacturers forbid the use of flushing oil, because it cannot all be drained afterwards. If in doubt, consult a dealer or specialist.

Dilution

4 This is of two kinds - fuel and coolant. In either case if the dilution is bad enough the engine oil level will appear to rise with use.

5 Coolant dilution of the oil is indicated by the 'mayonnaise' appearance of the oil and water mixture. Sometimes oil will also appear in the coolant. Possible reasons are :

a) Blown head gasket
b) Cracked or porous cylinder head or block
c) Cylinder liner seal failure (on wet liner engines)
d) Leaking oil-to-coolant oil cooler (when fitted)

6 With either type of dilution, the cause must be dealt with and the oil and filter changed.

17 Engine stop (fuel cut-off) solenoid - emergency repair

1 The solenoid valve cuts off the supply of fuel to the high pressure side of the injection pump when the ignition is switched off. If the solenoid fails electrically or mechanically so that its plunger is in the shut position, the engine will not run. One possible reason for such a failure is that the ignition has been switched off while engine speed is still high. In such a case the plunger will be sucked onto its seat with considerable force, and perhaps jam.

2 Should the valve fail on the road and a spare not be immediately available, the following procedure will serve to get the engine running again.

Caution : It is important that no dirt is allowed to enter the injection pump via the solenoid hole.

3 With the ignition off, disconnect the wire from the solenoid. Thoroughly clean around the solenoid where it screws into the pump **(see illustration)**.

4 Unscrew the solenoid and remove it. If a hand priming pump is fitted, operate the pump a few times while lifting out the solenoid to wash away any particles of dirt. Do not lose the sealing washer.

5 Remove the plunger from the solenoid (or from the recess in the pump, if it is stuck inside) **(see illustrations)**. Refit the solenoid body, making sure the sealing washer is in place, again operating the priming pump at the same time to flush away dirt.

6 Tape up the end of the solenoid wire so that it cannot touch bare metal.

7 The engine will now start and run as usual, but it will not stop when the ignition is switched off. It will be necessary to use the manual stop lever (if fitted) on the injection pump, or to stall the engine in gear.

8 Fit a new solenoid and sealing washer at the earliest opportunity.

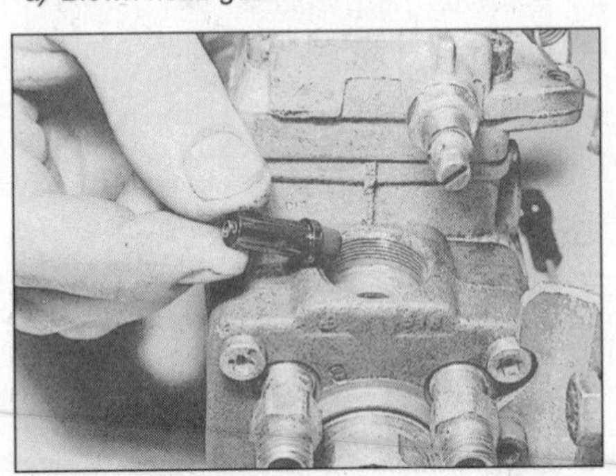

17.5a Removing stop solenoid plunger from pump

17.5b Stop solenoid components

Chapter 13
Tools and equipment

Contents

1 Normal workshop tools

1 The decision as to what range of tools is necessary will depend on the work to be done, the range of vehicles which it is expected to encounter, and not least the financial resources available. The tools in the following list, with additions as necessary from the various categories of Diesel-specific tools described later, should be sufficient for carrying out most routine maintenance and repair operations.

Combination spanners (see below)
Socket spanners (see below)
Ratchet, extension piece and universal joint (for use with sockets)
Torque wrench
Angle tightening indicator (see below)
Adjustable spanner
Set of sump drain plug keys
Strap or chain wrench (for fuel and oil filters)
Oil drain tray
Feeler gauges
Combination pliers
Long-nosed pliers
Self-locking pliers (Mole wrench)
Screwdrivers (large and small, flat blade and cross blade)
Set of Allen keys
Set of splined and Torx keys and sockets (see below)
Ball pein hammer
Soft-faced hammer
Puller (universal type, with interchangeable jaws)
Cold chisel
Scriber
Scraper
Centre punch
Hacksaw
File
Steel rule/straight-edge
Axle stands and/or ramps
Trolley jack
Inspection light
Inspection mirror
Telescopic magnet/pick-up tool

Socket and spanner sizes

2 A good range of open-ended, ring and socket spanners will be required. Most vehicles use metric size fastenings throughout but some earlier UK-built machines will have Imperial fastenings - or a mixture of both.
3 Split ring spanners (also known as flare nut spanners) are particularly useful for dealing with fuel pipe unions, on which a conventional ring or socket cannot be used because the pipe is in the way. The most common sizes are 17 mm and 19 mm on metric systems, and 5/8 in and 3/4 in on Imperial.
4 Sockets are available in various drive sizes. The half inch square drive size is most widely used and accepts most torque wrenches. Smaller drive sizes (3/8 or 1/4 in) are useful for working in confined spaces, while for large high-torque fastenings (driveshaft or hub nuts, crankshaft pulley bolts) 3/4 inch drive is most satisfactory.
5 The humble box spanner should not be overlooked. Box spanners are cheap and will sometimes serve as a substitute for a deep socket, though they cannot be used with a torque wrench and are easily deformed.

Angle tightening

6 For fastenings such as cylinder head bolts, many manufacturers now specify tightening in terms of angular rotation rather than an absolute torque. After an initial 'snug' torque wrench setting, subsequent tightening stages are specified as angles through which each bolt must be turned. Variations in tightening torque which could be caused by the presence or absence of dirt, oil etc. on the bolt threads thus have no effect. A further benefit is that there is no need for a high-range torque wrench.

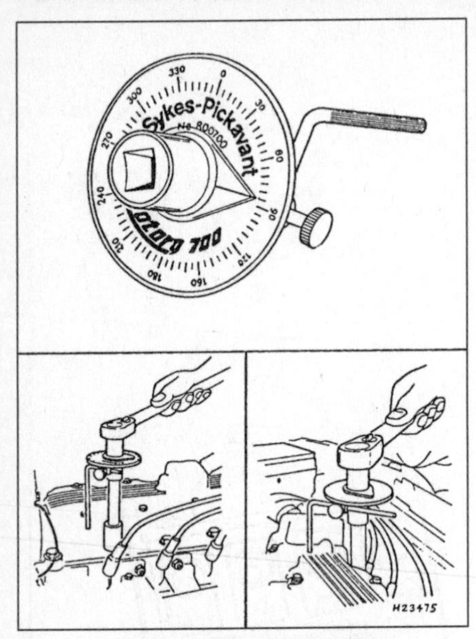

1.7 Sykes-Pickavant 800700 angle tightening gear

7 The owner-mechanic who expects to use this method of tightening only once or twice in the life of the vehicle may be content to make up a cardboard template, or mark the bolt heads with paint spots, to indicate the angle required. Greater speed and accuracy will result from using one of the many angle tightening indicators commercially available. Most of them are intended for use with 1/2 in drive sockets or keys **(see illustration)**.

Splined bolt heads

8 The conventional hexagon head bolt is being replaced in many areas by the splined or 'Torx' head bolt. This type of bolt has multiple splines in place of the hexagon. A set of splined or Torx keys will be needed to deal with female splined heads. Torx bolts with male heads also exist, and for these Torx sockets will be needed. Both keys and sockets are available to accept 1/2 in square drives.

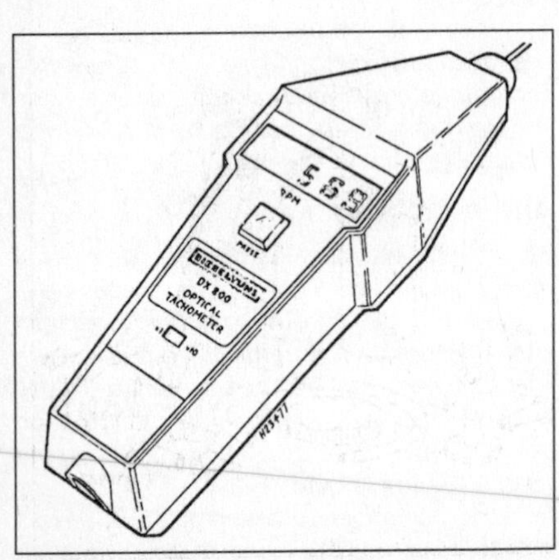

2.5 Dieseltune DX.800 optical tachometer

2 Diesel-specific tools

Basic tune-up and service

1 Besides the normal range of spanners, screwdrivers and so on, the following tools and equipment will be needed for basic tune-up and service operations on most models :

Deep socket for removing and tightening screw-in injectors
Injector puller for removing clamp type injectors
Optical or pulse-sensitive tachometer
Electrical multi-meter, or dedicated glow plug tester
Compression or leakdown tester
Vacuum pump and/or gauge

Injector socket

2 The size most commonly required is 27 mm/ 1$\frac{1}{16}$ in AF. Some Japanese injectors require 22 mm / $\frac{7}{8}$ in AF. The socket needs to be deep in order not to foul the injector body. On some engines it also needs to be thin-walled. Suitable sockets are sold by Dieseltune, Sykes-Pickavant and Snap-On, among others.

Tachometer

3 The type of tachometer which senses ignition system HT pulses via an inductive pick-up cannot be used on Diesel engines, unless a device such as the Sykes-Pickavant timing light adaptor is available.

4 If an engine is fitted with a TDC sensor and a diagnostic socket, an electronic tachometer which reads the signals from the TDC sensor can be used.

5 Not all engines have TDC sensors. On those which do not, the use of an optical or pulse-sensitive tachometer is necessary **(see illustration)**.

6 The optical tachometer registers the passage of a paint mark or (more usually) a strip of reflective foil placed on the crankshaft pulley. It is not so convenient to use as the electronic or pulse-sensitive types, since it has to be held so that it can 'see' the pulley, but it has the advantage that it can be used on any engine, petrol or Diesel, with or without a diagnostic socket.

7 The pulse-sensitive tachometer uses a transducer similar to that needed for a timing light. The transducer converts hydraulic or mechanical impulses in an injector pipe into electrical signals, which are displayed on the tachometer as engine speed.

8 Some dynamic timing equipment for Diesel engines incorporates a means of displaying engine speed. If this equipment is available, a separate tachometer will not be required.

9 Both optical and pulse-sensitive tachometers are sold by A. M. Test Systems and Kent-Moore. Optical tachometers are sold by (inter alia) Dieseltune, and pulse-sensitive by Souriau and Bosch.

DIY alternative tachometer

10 The owner-mechanic who only wishes to check the idle speed of one engine occasionally may well feel that the purchase of a special tachometer is not justified. Assuming that mains electric light is available, the use of a stroboscopic disc is a cheap alternative. The principle will be familiar to anyone who has used such a disc to check the speed of a record-player turntable.

11 A disc must be constructed of stiff paper or card to fit onto the crankshaft pulley (or camshaft pulley, if appropriate - but remember that this rotates at half speed). The disc should be white or light-coloured, and divided using a protractor into regular segments with heavy black lines **(see illustration)**. The number of segments required will depend on the desired idle speed and the frequency of the alternating current supply. For the 50 Hz supply used in the UK and most of Europe the figures are as follows:

Speed (rpm	*No of segments*	*Angle per segment*
706	*17*	*21° 11'*
750	*16*	*22° 30'*
800	*15*	*24°*
857	*14*	*25° 43'*
923	*13*	*27° 42'*

12 Attach the disc to the crankshaft pulley and position the car so that the disc can be viewed using only artificial light.

13 A fluorescent tube is best. Failing this a low-wattage incandescent bulb will give better results than a high-wattage one. Run the engine at idle and observe the disc.

Warning : Do not run the engine in a confined space without some means of extracting the exhaust fumes.

14 If the engine speed corresponds to the calculated disc speed, the disc segments will appear to be stationary. If the speed is different, the segments will appear to drift in the direction of engine rotation (too fast) or against it (too slow). The segments will also appear to be stationary at multiples or sub-multiples of the calculated speed - twice or half the speed, and so on - so some common sense must be used.

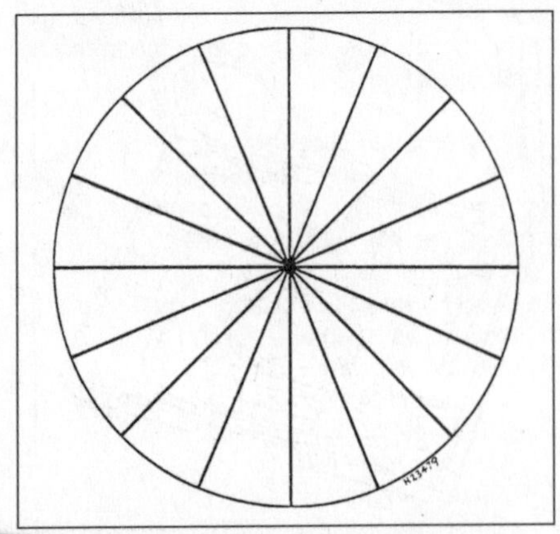

2.11 Home-made tachometer disc

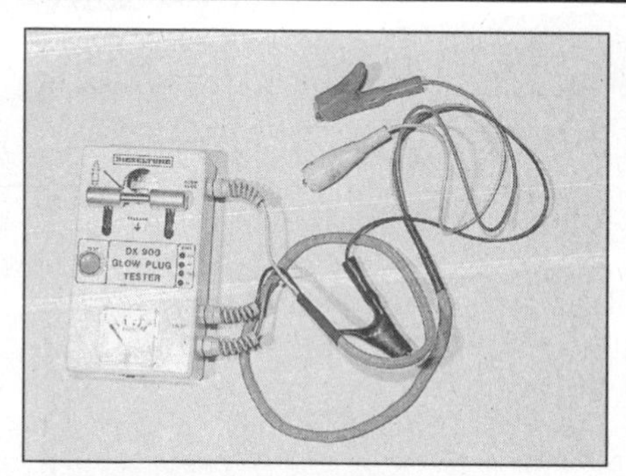

2.15 Dieseltune DX.900 glow plug tester

Electrical multi-meter or glow plug tester

15 It is possible to test glow plugs and their control circuitry with a multi-meter, or even (to a limited extent) with a 12 volt test lamp. A purpose-made glow plug tester will do the job faster and is much easier to use, but on the other hand it will not do anything else **(see illustration)**.

16 If it is decided to purchase a multi-meter, make sure that it has a high current range - ideally 0 to 100 amps - for checking glow plug current draw. Some meters require an external shunt to be fitted for this. An inductive clamp connection is preferred for high current measurement since it can be used without breaking into the circuit. Other ranges required are dc voltage (0 to 20 or 30 volts is suitable for most applications) and resistance. Some meters have a continuity buzzer in addition to a resistance scale ; the buzzer is particularly useful when working single-handed **(see illustration)**.

17 Glow plug testers are available from makers such as Beru, Dieseltune and Kent-Moore. Some incorporate a 'hot test chamber' in which the heating of individual plugs can be observed.

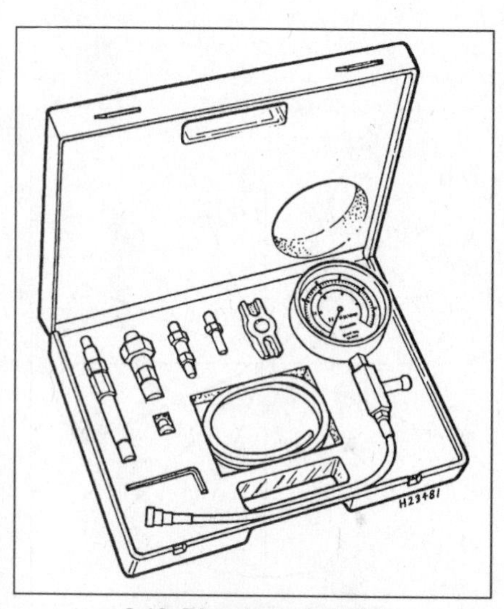

2.18 Dieseltune DX.511 compression tester

Compression tester

18 A tester specifically intended for Diesel engines must be used **(see illustration)**. The push-in connectors used with some petrol engine compression testers cannot be used for Diesel engines because of the higher pressures involved. Instead, the Diesel engine compression tester screws into an injector or glow plug hole, using one of the adaptors supplied with the tester.

19 Most compression testers are used while cranking the engine on the starter motor. A few, such as the Dieseltune DX 511, can be used with the engine idling. This gives more reliable results, since it is hard to guarantee that cranking speed will not fall in the course of testing all four cylinders, whereas idle speed will remain constant.

20 Recording testers, which produce a pen-and-ink trace for each cylinder, are available from A. M. Test Systems and Kent-Moore. Non-recording testers are more common and are available from Dieseltune and Sykes-Pickavant as well as the makers previously mentioned.

Leak-down tester

21 The leak-down tester measures the rate at which air pressure is lost from each cylinder, and can also be used to pinpoint the source of pressure loss (valves, head gasket or bores). It depends on the availability of a supply of compressed air, typically at 5 to 10 bar (73 to 145 lbf/in²). The same tester (with different adaptors) can be used on both petrol and Diesel engines **(see illustration)**.

22 In use, the tester is connected to an air line and to an adaptor screwed into the injector or glow plug hole, with the piston concerned at TDC on the compression stroke. Leak-down testers are offered by Dieseltune, Sykes-Pickavant and others.

Vacuum pump and/or gauge

23 A vacuum gauge, with suitable adaptors, is useful for locating blockages or air leaks in the supply side of the fuel system. A simple gauge is used with the engine running to create vacuum in the supply lines. A hand-held vacuum pump with its own gauge can be used without running the engine, and is also useful for bleeding the fuel system when a hand priming pump is not fitted **(see illustration)**.

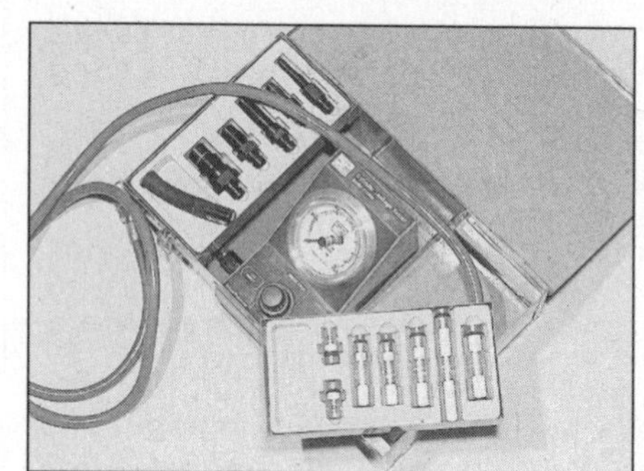

2.21 Sykes-Pickavant 013800 leak-down tester

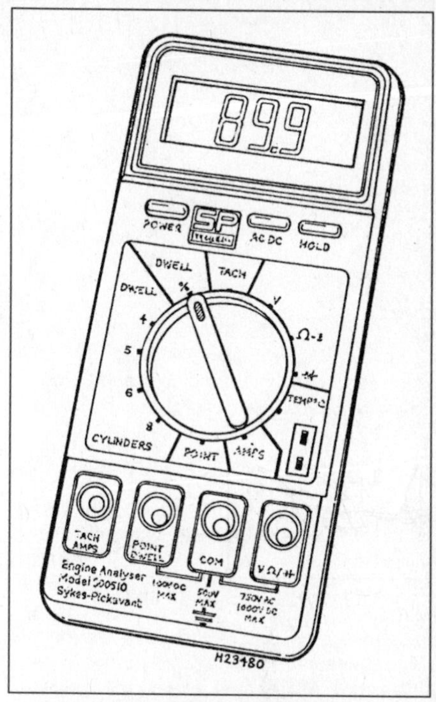

2.16 Sykes-Pickavant 300510 engine analyser / multi-meter

3 Injection pump timing tools

1 If work is undertaken which disturbs the position of the fuel injection pump, certain tools will be needed to check the injection timing on reassembly. This also applies if the pump drive is disturbed - including renewal of the timing belt on some models. Checking of the timing is also a necessary part of fault diagnosis when investigating complaints such as power loss, knock and smoke.

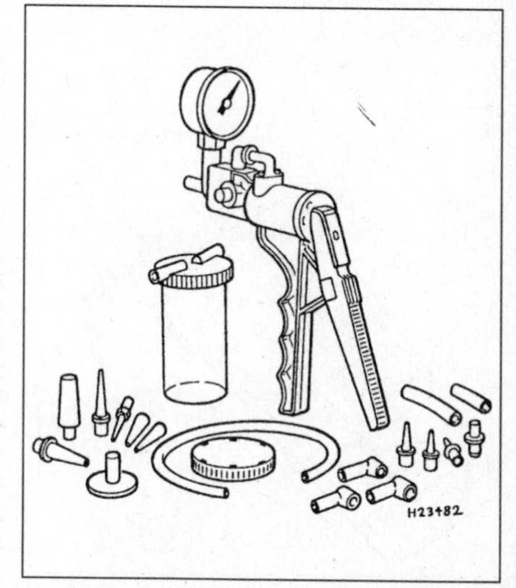

2.23 Dieseltune DX 760 'Mityvac' test kit

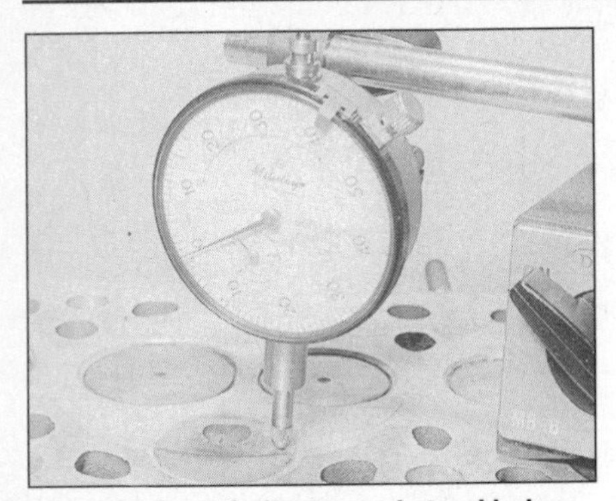

3.4 Dial test indicator and stand being used to check swirl chamber protrusion

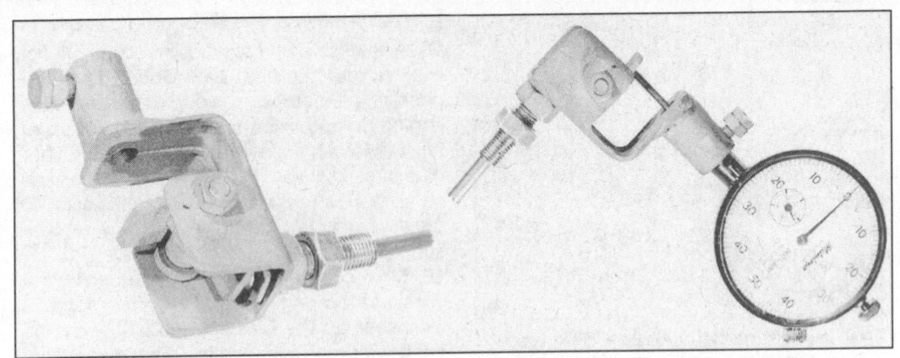

3.6a DTI and locally-made bellcrank adaptor for timing a Bosch VE pump

Static timing tools

2 Static timing is still the most widely-used method of setting Diesel injection pumps. It is time-consuming and sometimes messy. Precision measuring instruments are often needed for dealing with distributor pumps. Good results depend on the skill and patience of the operator.

3 The owner-mechanic who will only be dealing with one engine should refer to the appropriate text to find out what tools will be required. The Diesel tune-up specialist will typically need the following :

Dial test indicators (DTIs) with magnetic stands
DTI adaptors and probes for Bosch and CAV distributor pumps
Spill tube for in-line pumps
Timing gear pins or pegs
Crankshaft or flywheel locking pins

Dial test indicator and magnetic stand

4 This is a useful workshop tool for many operations besides timing. It is the most accurate means of checking the protrusion or recession of swirl chambers, pistons and liners when renewing cylinder head gaskets. If major overhauls are undertaken it can also be used for measuring values such as crankshaft endfloat **(see illustration)**.

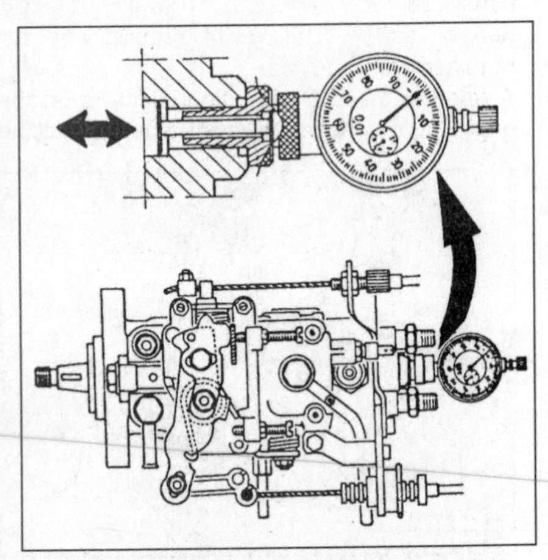

3.6b DTI and in-line adaptor used for timing a Bosch VE pump

5 Two DTIs may be needed for setting the timing on some engines - one to measure the pump plunger or rotor movement and one to measure engine piston position.

DTI adaptors

6 Adaptors and probes for fitting the DTI to the distributor pump are of various patterns, due partly to the need to be able to use them in conditions of poor access on the vehicle **(see illustrations)**. This means that the same adaptor cannot necessarily be used on the same type of pump and engine if the under-bonnet layout is different. On the bench it is often possible to use simpler equipment.

7 A spring-loaded probe is used on some CAV/RotoDiesel pumps to find the timing groove in the pump rotor **(see illustration)**.

Timing gear pins or pegs

8 Pins or pegs are used on some engines to lock the pump and/or the camshaft in a particular position. They are generally specific to a particular engine or manufacturer. It is sometimes possible to use suitably sized dowel rods, drill shanks or bolts instead.

Crankshaft or flywheel locking pins

9 These are used for locking the crankshaft at TDC (or at the injection point on some models).

10 The crankshaft locking pin is inserted through a hole in the side of the crankcase after removal of a plug, and enters a slot in a crankshaft counterweight or web. The flywheel pin passes through a hole in the flywheel end of the crankcase and enters a hole in the flywheel. Again, suitably sized rods or bolts can sometimes be used instead.

Dynamic timing tools

11 Dynamic timing on Diesel engines has not yet become widespread, due no doubt in part to the relatively expensive equipment required. Additionally, not all vehicle manufacturers provide dynamic timing values. In principle it makes possible much faster and more accurate checking of the injection timing, just as on petrol engines. It can also be used to verify the operation of cold start advance systems.

12 Most dynamic timing equipment depends on converting mechanical or hydraulic impulses in the injection system into electrical signals. An alternative approach is adopted by one or two manufacturers who use an optical-to-electrical conversion, with a sensor which screws into a glow plug hole and 'sees' the light of combustion. The electrical signals are used to trigger a timing light, or as part of the information fed into a diagnostic analyser.

13 Not all Diesel engines have ready-made timing marks. If the engine has a TDC sensor (or provision for fitting one) and the timing equipment can read the sensor output, this is not a problem. Some engines have neither timing marks nor TDC sensors. In such cases there is no choice but to establish TDC accurately and make marks on the flywheel or crankshaft pulley.

Timing lights

14 The simplest dynamic timing equipment uses a transducer to convert the pressure

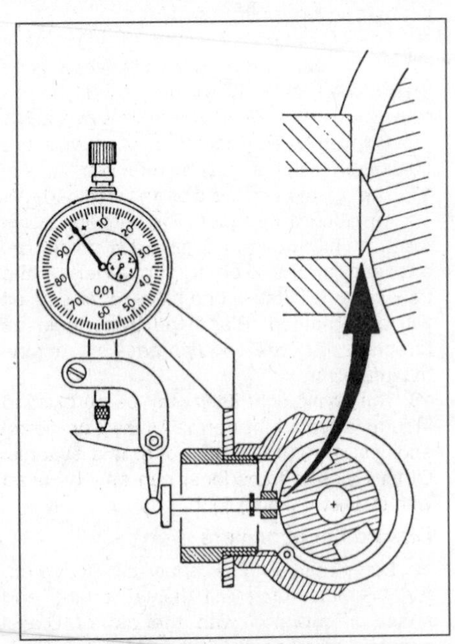

3.7 DTI and adaptor used for timing Lucas / CAV pump

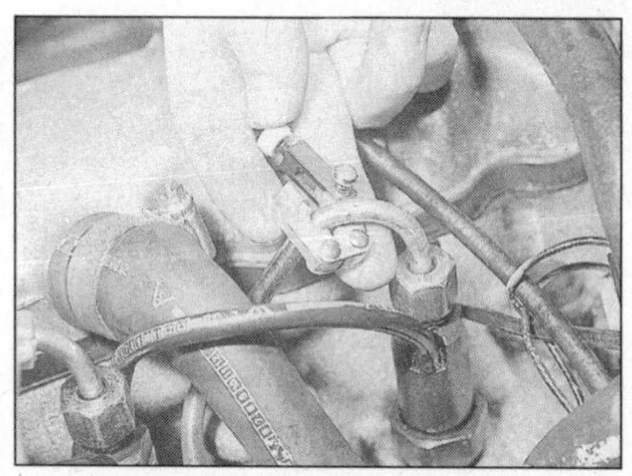

3.14 Clamping a timing light transducer onto an injector pipe

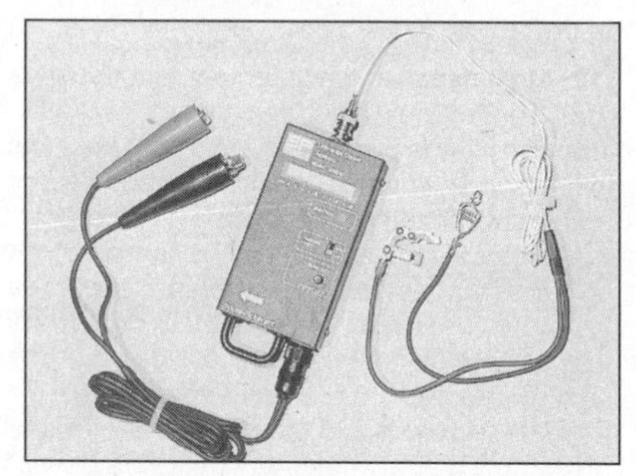

3.22a Sykes-Pickavant 300540 diesel timing light adaptor

pulse in the injector pipe into an electrical signal which triggers a timing light. Such transducers are of two types - in-line and clamp-on **(see illustration)**.

15 The in-line transducer is connected into No 1 injector pipe using adaptors to suit the fuel pipe unions. The electrical connection from the transducer goes to the timing light, which will also require a 12 volt or mains supply to energise its tube.

16 The clamp-on transducer is used in a similar way but instead of actually tapping into the injector pipe it clamps onto it. The transducer must be of the right size for the pipe concerned and any dirt, rust or protective coating on the pipe must be removed.

17 The position of the clamp-on transducer on the pipe is important. The injection pulse takes a finite amount of time to travel from one end of the pipe to the other. If the transducer is in the wrong place, a false result will be obtained. Place the transducer as directed by the equipment or engine manufacturer.

18 The timing light itself may be an existing inductive type light normally used on petrol engines, if the transducer output is suitable. Other types of transducer can only be used with their own timing light.

Diagnostic analysers

19 Diagnostic engine analysers (Crypton, AVL, Souriau etc.) will display timing and speed information with the aid of Diesel adaptors or interface units. These will normally be specific to the equipment concerned; consult the manufacturers for details.

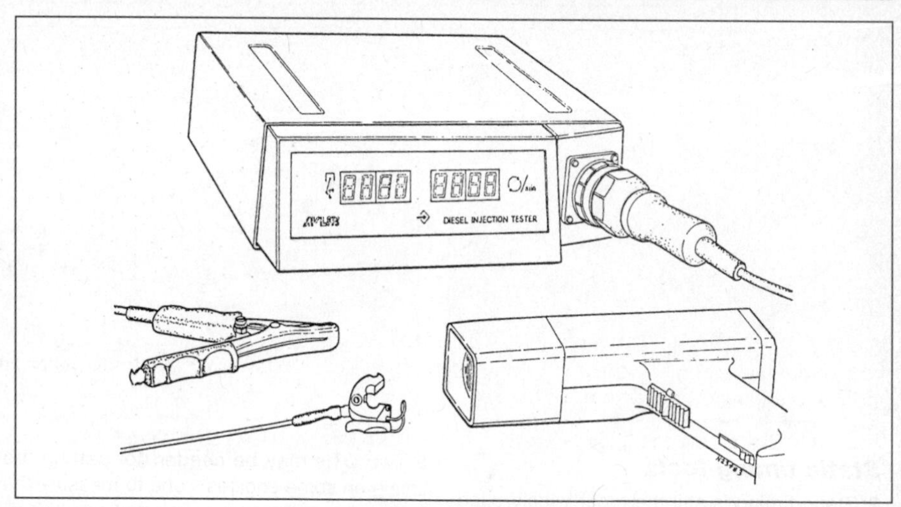

3.22b AVL Diesel Injection Tester 873

20 The output from the Sykes-Pickavant Diesel adaptor can be used to drive the inductive HT pick-up on a diagnostic analyser.

Injection testers

21 Injection testers are halfway between simple timing light/tachometer combinations and full-blown diagnostic analysers. They interpret the transducer output to provide a 'start-of-injection' signal, enabling comparison to be made between all the injectors on an engine, so that defective injectors can be identified.

22 The Diesel adaptor sold by Sykes-Pickavant for use with a conventional inductive timing light has an injection testing facility **(see illustration)**. More sophisticated equipment, such as the AVL Diesel Injection Tester 873 **(see illustration)**, accepts an input from the engine's TDC sensor (if fitted) as well, giving a digital read-out of injection timing without the need for a stroboscope.

4 Injector testing equipment

Warning : Never expose the hands, face or any other part of the body to injector spray. The high working pressure can penetrate the skin, with potentially fatal results. When possible use injector test oil rather than fuel for testing. Take precautions to avoid inhaling the vaporised fuel or injector test fluid. Remember that even Diesel fuel is inflammable when vapourised.

1 Some kind of injector tester will be needed if it is wished to identify defective injectors, or to test them after cleaning or prolonged storage. Various makes and models are available, but the essential components of all of them are a high pressure hand-operated pump and a pressure gauge.

2 For safety reasons, injector test or calibration fluid should be used for bench testing rather than Diesel fuel or paraffin. Use the fluid specified by the maker of the test equipment if possible.

3 One of the simplest testers currently available is Dieseltune's DX 710 **(see illustrations)**. This has the advantage that (access permitting) it can be used to test opening pressure and back leakage without removing the injectors from the engine. Its small reservoir makes it of limited use for bench testing, but good results can be obtained with practice.

4 Another method of testing injectors on the engine is to connect a pressure gauge into the

4.3a Dieseltune DX 710 tester in use on bench . . .

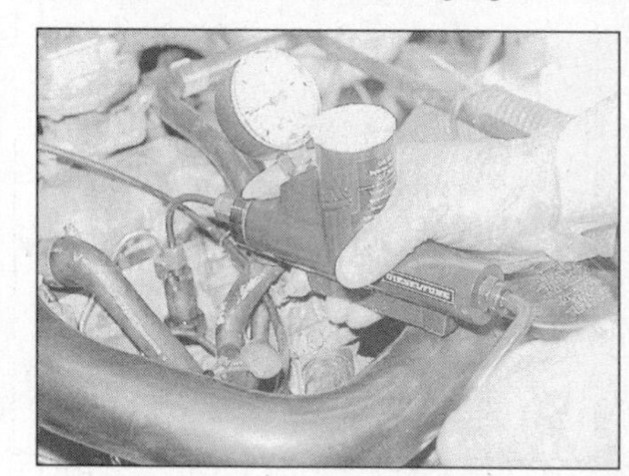

4.3b . . . and on engine

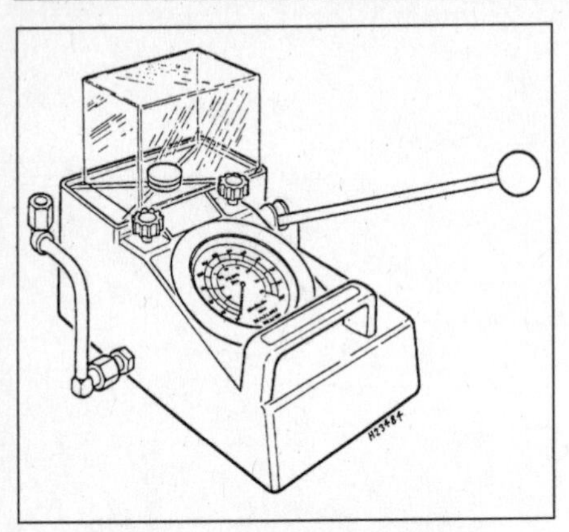
4.5 Dieseltune 111 injector tester

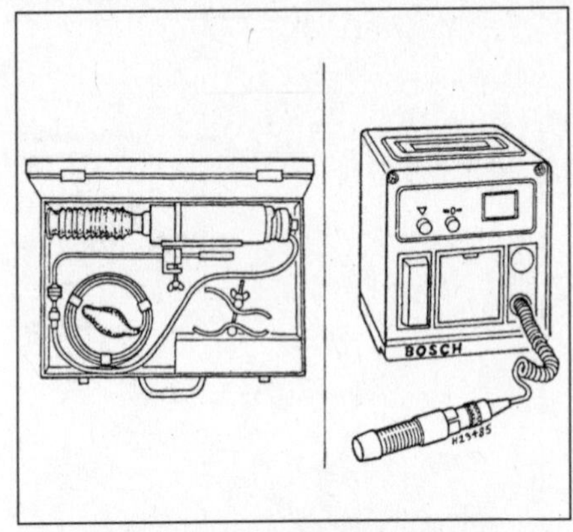

6.3a Bosch smoke sampling kit (left) and measuring unit

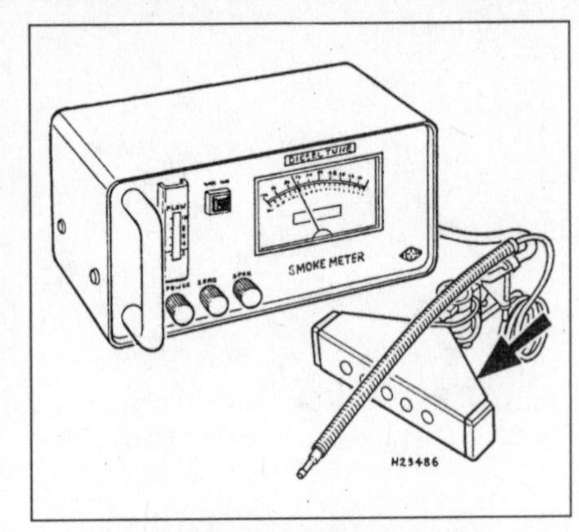

6.3b Dieseltune Smokemeter

line between the injection pump and the injector. This test can also detect faults caused by the injection pump high pressure piston or delivery valve.

5 The workshop which tests or calibrates injectors regularly will need a bench-mounted tester. These testers have a lever-operated pump, and a larger fluid reservoir than the hand-held tester. The best models also incorporate a transparent chamber for safe viewing of the injector spray pattern and perhaps a test fluid recirculation system **(see illustration)**.

6 Some means of extracting the vapour produced when testing, such as a hood connected to the workshop's fume extraction system, is desirable. Although injector test fluid is relatively non-toxic, its vapour is not particularly pleasant to inhale.

5 Injection pump testing and calibration equipment

1 The equipment needed for testing and calibration of injection pumps is beyond the scope of this Book. Any such work should be entrusted to the pump manufacturer's agent - though the opportunity is taken to say yet again that the injection pump is often blamed for faults when in fact the trouble lies elsewhere.

6 Smoke testing equipment

1 Smoke emission testing is already mandatory for heavy goods vehicles and is likely to become so, probably as part of the MoT test, for cars and light commercial vehicles.

2 Smoke testing equipment falls into two categories - indirect and direct reading. With the indirect systems, a sample of exhaust gas is passed over a filter paper and the change in opacity of the paper is measured using a separate machine. With the direct systems, an optically sensitive probe measures the opacity of the exhaust gas and an immediate read-out is available.

3 The smoke sampling kit from Bosch is an example of the indirect reading system and is used in conjunction with a photoelectric measuring unit. Dieseltune's Smokemeter is an example of the direct reading machine **(see illustrations)**.